TECHNIQUE OF ORGANIC CHEMISTRY

ARNOLD WEISSBERGER, *Editor*

Volume III

Second Completely Revised and Augmented Edition

PART I. *SEPARATION AND PURIFICATION*

D1482582

TECHNIQUE OF ORGANIC CHEMISTRY

ARNOLD WEISSBERGER, *Editor*

TECHNIQUE OF ORGANIC CHEMISTRY
Volume III
Second Completely Revised and Augmented Edition

PART I
SEPARATION AND PURIFICATION

Editor: ARNOLD WEISSBERGER

Authors: Charles M. Ambler   A. Letcher Jones
Geoffrey Broughton   K. Kammermeyer
David Craig   Frederick W. Keith, Jr.
Lyman C. Craig   E. MacWilliam
A. B. Cummins   Edward G. Scheibel
F. B. Hutto, Jr.   R. Eliot Stauffer
R. Stuart Tipson

INTERSCIENCE PUBLISHERS, INC.
a Division of John Wiley & Sons, Inc.   New York • London • Sydney

SECOND PRINTING, DECEMBER, 1966

PRINTED IN THE UNITED STATES OF AMERICA

TECHNIQUE OF ORGANIC CHEMISTRY

INTRODUCTION

Organic chemistry, from its very beginning, has used specific tools and techniques for the synthesis, isolation, and purification of compounds, and physical methods for the determination of their properties. Much of the success of the organic chemist depends upon a wise selection and a skillful application of these methods, tools, and techniques, which, with the progress of the science, have become numerous and often intricate.

The present series is devoted to a comprehensive presentation of the techniques which are used in the organic laboratory and which are available for the investigation of organic compounds. The authors give the theoretical background for an understanding of the various methods and operations and describe the techniques and tools, their modifications, their merits and limitations, and their handling. It is hoped that the series will contribute to a better understanding and a more rational and effective application of the respective techniques.

The field is broad and some of it is difficult to survey. Authors and editor hope that the volumes will be found useful and that many of the readers will let them have the benefit of their criticism and of suggestions for improvements.

A. W.

Research Laboratories
Eastman Kodak Company
Rochester, New York

TECHNIQUE OF ORGANIC CHEMISTRY

Editor: ARNOLD WEISSBERGER

GENERAL PLAN

Volume I (Second Edition—in three parts). Physical Methods of Organic Chemistry. J. R. Anderson, E. D. Bailey, W. F. Bale, N. Bauer, E. R. Blout, J. F. Bonner, Jr., L. O. Brockway, L. Corliss, B. P. Dailey, J. D. H. Donnay, K. Fajans, I. Fankuchen, A. L. Geddes, F. A. Hamm, D. Harker, W. D. Harkins, J. M. Hastings, W. Heller, E. E. Jelley, T. E. McGoury, H. Mark, L. Michaelis, D. H. Moore, O. H. Müller, J. B. Nichols, M. A. Peacock, J. G. Powles, P. W. Selwood, T. Shedlovsky, R. Signer, E. L. Skau, C. P. Smyth, D. W. Stewart, J. M. Sturtevant, W. Swietoslawski, G. W. Thomson, M. J. Vold, R. D. Vold, R. H. Wagner, H. Wakeham, and W. West

Volume II (Second Edition). Catalytic Reactions, V. I. Komarewsky, C. H. Riesz, and F. L. Morritz; **Photochemical Reactions,** C. R. Masson, V. Boekelheide, and W. A. Noyes, Jr.; **Electrolytic Reactions,** S. Swann, Jr.

Volume III (Second Edition).

Part I. **Separation and Purification: Diffusion Methods,** A. Letcher Jones, K. Kammermeyer, R. E. Stauffer, and E. MacWilliam; **Laboratory Extraction and Countercurrent Distribution,** L. C. Craig, D. Craig, and E. G. Scheibel; **Crystallization and Recrystallization,** R. S. Tipson; **Centrifuging,** C. M. Ambler and F. W. Keith, Jr.; **Filtration,** A. B. Cummins and F. B. Hutto, Jr.; **Solvent Removal, Evaporation, and Drying,** G. Broughton.

Part II. **Laboratory Engineering: Selection of Materials for the Construction of Equipment,** R. F. Eisenberg and R. R. Kraybill; **Heating and Cooling,** R. S. Egly; **Grinding, Screening, and Classifying,** J. W. Axelson and W. C. Streib; **Mixing,** J. H. Rushton and M. P. Hofmann; **Operations with Gases,** G. H. Miller

Volume IV. Distillation. J. R. Bowman, C. S. Carlson, A. L. Glasebrook, J. C. Hecker, E. S. Perry, Arthur Rose, E. Rose, R. S. Tipson, and F. E. Williams

Volume V. Adsorption and Chromatography. H. G. Cassidy

Volume VI. Micro and Semimicro Methods. N. D. Cheronis. With contributions by A. R. Ronzio and T. S. Ma.

Volume VII. Organic Solvents. A. Weissberger and E. S. Proskauer. *Second Edition* by J. A. Riddick and E. E. Toops, Jr.

Volume VIII. Investigation of Rates and Mechanisms of Reactions. *Editors:* S. L. Friess and A. Weissberger. *Authors:* G. M. Burnett, B. Chance, E. Grunwald, S. L. Friess, F. M. Huennekens, T. H. James, T. S. Lee, J. E. Leffler, R. Livingston, H. W. Melville, B. K. Mores, P. R. O'Connor, W. J. Priest, F. J. W. Roughton, and W. D. Walters

Volume IX. Chemical Applications of Spectroscopy. *Editor:* W. West. *Authors:* A. B. F. Duncan, W. Gordy, R. Norman Jones, F. A. Matsen, C. Sandorfy, and W. West

PREFACE TO THE SECOND EDITION

The first edition of this volume contained, in a rather loose arrangement, chapters dealing with general methods and operations used in preparative organic chemistry. Distillation, Adsorption and Chromatography were omitted because Volumes IV and V, respectively, are devoted to these techniques, and these methods are for the same reasons not included in the new edition of Volume III.

In this edition, methods of *Separation and Purification* used in preparative organic chemistry have been collected in a special *Part I*. The older chapters were revised or rewritten, and new sections were added to deal with Thermal Diffusion, Barrier Separation, Zone Electrophoresis, Liquid-Liquid Extraction for Increased Quantities, Inclusion Complexes, and other topics not treated in the first edition.

The chapters on Heating and Cooling and on Mixing, in the first edition, dealt with techniques long recognized in their importance for pilot plant operation and large-scale production but often handled haphazardly in the laboratory. These presentations have been found useful in the design and the operation of laboratory equipment, particularly on a larger scale. Both chapters were brought up to date for the new edition and the chapter on Heating and Cooling was in part rewritten and expanded, emphasizing practical applications to supplement the chapters by J. M. Sturtevant in Volume I of this series. The success of these two chapters has encouraged the addition of new chapters of a similar nature dealing with Choice of Materials for Equipment, with Diminution and Classifying, and with Operations with Gases, and to collect these chapters in a special *Part II* on *Laboratory Engineering*.

We deeply regret the death of two of the authors of the first edition, Mr. H. Golding and Dr. G. Broughton. Dr. C. M. Ambler has taken over the authorship of the chapter on Centrifuging which was written for the first edition by the late H. Golding. I am grateful to Dr. S. Miller, successor to the late Dr. G. Broughton, and to Miss S. Stamm for reading the proof of the chapter on Solvent Removal, Evaporation, and Drying which Dr. Broughton completed in manuscript form. To

Mr. J. W. Axelson and Drs. G. Beyer, C. Duboc, F. Kottler, E. A. MacWilliam, E. Perry, R. E. Stauffer, and F. Urbach, I owe thanks for advice and assistance in various phases of the editorial work.

A. W.

Research Laboratories
Eastman Kodak Company
Rochester, New York

TECHNIQUE OF ORGANIC CHEMISTRY

Volume III

CONTENTS

Part I: Separation and Purification

DIFFUSION METHODS

CONTENTS (*Continued*)

Part 1. THERMAL DIFFUSION OF ORGANIC LIQUIDS

I. GENERAL CONSIDERATIONS

It has been only within the last decade that any serious consideration has
been given to the possibility of using the phenomenon of thermal diffusion
in the liquid phase for the practical separation of the components of organic
liquid mixtures.   The thermal diffusion effect, however, has been known
for about a century.   The first recorded observation of it was made by
Ludwig[1] in 1856.   From that time until 1916, the principle received very

[1] C. Ludwig, *Wien. Acad. Ber.*, **20**, 539 (1856).

little attention either experimentally or theoretically. Consequently, it remained in the category of a laboratory curiosity.

In 1916, S. Chapman,[2] an English mathematician, using the kinetic theory of gases as a basis, calculated that a transport effect should exist when a mixture of two gases is subjected to a temperature gradient. This transport effect depends upon the relative masses of the molecules of the mixture and their degree of molecular interaction. Stimulated by Chapman's calculations, several independent investigators experimentally confirmed his predictions with very good agreement. Perhaps the first practical application of thermal diffusion was made by Clusius and Dickel[3] when, in 1938, they successfully separated the isotopes of chlorine in the gaseous phase. In the case of gases, Chapman's theory holds reasonably well and successful isotope separations have been accomplished by many different investigators. To a limited extent, the mass difference principle also applies to the separation of isotopes in liquid aqueous media. The isotopes of zinc and other metals have been effectively concentrated by thermal diffusion in water solutions with the use of very simple apparatus.[4-7]

As a result of the extreme complexity of the liquid state of matter, the kinetic theory treatments of thermal diffusion as applied to gases cannot be extended to liquids to any useful degree. In 1940 Korsching, Wirtz and Masch[8] reported that the thermal diffusion separation of water from 95.6% ethyl alcohol concentrated the components in a direction opposite to that which might be expected from a consideration of gaseous separations. In gases, the higher molecular weight components would be expected to concentrate toward the cold wall of the apparatus and the lower molecular weight ones toward the hot wall. In the liquid separation of alcohol and water, the alcohol concentrated toward the hot wall and, hence, upward in the Clusius and Dickel[9] type of apparatus used. The water concentrated downward. They also studied the separation of ordinary water and heavy water (D_2O) in the same apparatus. In this case, the higher molecular weight component concentrated toward the cold wall and downward, as the gas theory would predict. A mixture of C_6H_6 and C_6D_6 also gave molecular-weight concentrations in a direction contrary to that which they observed for alcohol and water. They were not able to propose a satisfactory explanation for this anomaly.

[2] S. Chapman, *Phil. Mag.*, **38**, 182 (1919).

[3] K. Clusius and G. Dickel, *Naturwissenschaften*, **26**, 546 (1938).

[4] R. C. Jones and W. H. Furry, *Revs. Modern Phys.*, **18**, No. 2, 151–224 (1946).

[5] H. Korsching, *Naturwissenschaften*, **31**, 348 (1943).

[6] H. Korsching, and K. Wirtz, *Naturwissenschaften*, **27**, 367 (1939).

[7] A. N. Murin, *Uspekhi Khim.*, **10**, 671 (1941).

[8] H. Korsching, K. Wirtz, and L. W. Masch, *Ber.*, *B***73**, 249 (1940).

[9] K. Clusius and G. Dickel, *Naturwissenschaften*, **26**, 546 (1938).

Clusius and Dickel[10] suggested that the degree of polymerization of water in the liquid phase might be such that the aggregate particles of water being diffused were of higher molecular weight than the alcohol molecules. This explanation would make the observed direction of separation consistent with the kinetic-theory explanation of Chapman. DeGroot[11] did not agree with the polymerization explanation and proposed a different one based upon density changes in the convection streams.

Niyogi[12] reported that a 1:1 mixture of n-heptane and n-butyl alcohol is separated by thermal diffusion, with the latter lower molecular weight component concentrating at the "heavy" end of the column. He demonstrated by dielectric-constant and molar-polarization measurements that n-butyl alcohol is not in a polymerized or associated state in the n-heptane mixture. He concludes that "it is the density and not the molecular weight which determines the increase in concentration of a liquid at the bottom of the column."

Wirtz[13] proposed that the separation of isotopes in the liquid phase appears to be more a function of the volume of the diffusing particles than it is of their relative masses. Those with smaller volume concentrate at the cold wall. This explanation is not sufficient in that the differences in volume of isotopes, other than those of hydrogen, are extremely small. Thermal diffusion has been successfully applied to the separation of light and heavy uranium hexafluorides in the liquid phase. The difference in volume between these isotopes is quite small. Reference to these separations in the Smyth report[14] illustrates the complexity of the phenomenon: "The theory of thermal diffusion in gases is intricate enough; that of thermal diffusion in liquids is practically impossible."

Schafer and Corte[15] have shown that ortho- and parahydrogen may be separated from each other in the gaseous phase by thermal diffusion. They suggest that the separation may be based upon the difference in entropy between the two forms of hydrogen. The molecules will concentrate in such a manner as to produce maximum entropy. Parahydrogen has the higher entropy of the two types and concentrates at the cold wall. Attempts to extend the entropy explanation to the thermal diffusion separations of liquids have not been successful.

Kramers and Broeder[16] have studied the phenomenon with respect to

[10] K. Clusius and G. Dickel, *Naturwissenschaften*, **26**, 546 (1938).

[11] S. R. DeGroot, *L'Effet Soret.* North-Holland, Amsterdam, 1945.

[12] K. C. Niyogi, *Science and Culture*, **7**, 567 (1942).

[13] K. Wirtz, *Naturwissenschaften*, **31**, 349 (1943).

[14] H. D. Smyth, *Atomic Energy for Military Purposes.* Princeton Univ. Press, Princeton, 1945, p. 162.

[15] K. Schafer and H. Corte, *Naturwissenschaften*, **33**, 92 (1946).

[16] H. Kramers and J. J. Broeder, *Anal. Chim. Acta*, **2**, 687 (1948).

the separation of mixtures of hydrocarbon liquids and have considered the experimental results in terms of the cage model theory of liquids. They conclude that in hydrocarbon-type liquids, molecular mass is less important in determining the separation effect than the energy required for a molecule to escape from its "hole" in the liquid. Their experiments show that the sequence of separation of hydrocarbon types in a multicomponent mixture from top to bottom in a Clusius-Dickel type of column is: light normal paraffins, heavy normal paraffins, branched paraffins, cyclic paraffins and monocyclic aromatics, and bicyclic aromatics.

Drickamer and co-workers[17-20] have studied many aspects of both gaseous and liquid thermal diffusion. They also have interpreted the separations of hydrocarbon mixtures in the liquid phase in terms of the cage model theory of liquids. Their experimental results are consistent with the assumption that the mobility of a molecule in a given system is inversely proportional to the product of the molecular mass and molecular cross section in the direction of flow.

Debye and co-workers[21] investigated the possibility of using liquid thermal diffusion for separating different molecular-weight fractions of rubber polymers from each other in xylene solution. During the course of this investigation the observation was made that thermal diffusion produced differences in the refractive index of the xylene solvent even when no rubber polymer was present. This suggested that the xylene solvent either contained an unidentified impurity which was being fractionated from the xylene, or the isomers of xylene itself were being separated. On the basis of theories which had been proposed up to this time, a separation of molecules of identical masses would not be expected to occur. In order to determine the explanation for observed results, the author prepared mixtures of xylene isomers of known purity and subjected them to thermal diffusion. It was shown that the isomers were being separated from each other unmistakably. Other isomeric mixtures were prepared and separated with equally conclusive results.[22]

In the absence of adequate theory, it has been necessary for investigators to determine the range of applicability of the phenomenon by direct experiment. Thermal diffusion has now been applied to the separation of the components of a wide variety of organic liquids of both hydrocarbon and

[17] D. J. Trevoy and H. G. Drickamer, *J. Chem. Phys.*, **17**, 1120 (1949).

[18] Lu-Ho Tung and H. G. Drickamer, *J. Chem. Phys.*, **18**, 1031 (1950).

[19] H. G. Drickamer, E. W. Mellow, and L. H. Tung, *J. Chem. Phys.*, **18**, 945 (1950).

[20] F. E. Caskey and H. G. Drickamer, *J. Chem. Phys.*, **21**, 153 (1953).

[21] P. Debye and A. M. Bueche, *High Polymer Physics*. Chemical Publ., Brooklyn, 1948, pp. 497-527. *Collected Papers of Peter J. W. Debye*. Interscience, New York-London, 1954.

[22] A. L. Jones, *Petroleum Processing*, **6**, 132 (1951).

nonhydrocarbon types.[23-27] These studies have shown that the phenomenon depends upon molecular properties different from those by which any other known separation processes are governed. Mixtures which are very difficult or impossible to separate by conventional techniques have been successfully fractionated by liquid thermal diffusion.

Relatively simple and inexpensive apparatus has been developed for laboratory-scale fractionations of organic liquids. Once assembled, the apparatus is much easier to operate than a simple distillation or adsorption column. Small samples (25 ml.) may be separated into almost any desired number of fractions with complete recovery of the total sample.

II. APPARATUS

The apparatus necessary to produce liquid thermal diffusion separations is basically simple. Essentially, it consists of two smooth parallel surfaces arranged vertically and separated by a narrow and uniform spacing, as

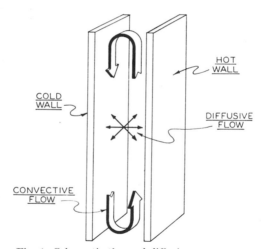

Fig. 1. Schematic thermal diffusion apparatus.

shown diagrammatically in Figure 1. This type of apparatus may be assembled from either flat plates or concentric tubes. The space between the surfaces is filled with the liquid to be processed. One surface is heated, the other cooled. A sharp temperature gradient is thereby produced

[23] A. L. Jones and R. W. Foreman, *Ind. Eng. Chem.*, **44**, 2249 (1952).
[24] A. L. Jones and E. C. Milberger, *Ind. Eng. Chem.*, **45**, 2689 (1953).
[25] A. L. Jones and E. C. Hughes, U. S. Pat. 2,541,069 (Feb. 13, 1951).
[26] A. L. Jones and E. C. Hughes, U. S. Pat. 2,541,070 (Feb. 13, 1951).
[27] A. L. Jones and E. C. Hughes, U. S. Pat. 2,541,071 (Feb. 13, 1951).

across the thin column of liquid located between the hot and cold walls. It is this temperature gradient which is responsible for the thermal diffusion separation. After a short period of time, a concentration gradient is produced between the hot and cold walls.

Convective flow, upward along the hot wall and downward along the cold wall, results from the density difference produced by the temperature gradient. This convection of the liquid occurs whether any thermal diffusion separation is obtained or not. It is caused by the liquid becoming less dense as a result of thermal expansion near the hot wall and the opposite effect near the cold wall. This density difference in the liquid films adjacent to the two walls can be influenced by the concentration gradient produced by thermal diffusion. If the more dense components are concentrated in the direction of the hot wall, the convection tends to be retarded and sometimes very queer effects are observed. This latter situation will be discussed in more detail later in the chapter.

The concentration gradient produced by the temperature gradient is a result of a difference in mobility of various molecular types in the liquid medium when subjected to a condition of more thermal agitation of the molecules from one direction than another. The degree of thermal agitation is higher near the hot wall than it is near the cold wall. Under these conditions, certain molecular types tend to be displaced away from the hot wall to a greater extent than other types. Those which move away in greater proportion also enter the downward moving convective stream in greater proportion and thus concentrate toward the bottom of the column. Conversely, the molecular types which do not diffuse away from the hot wall so readily remain in the upward moving convective stream and concentrate toward the top of the column. This countercurrency reduces the probability of a given molecule getting back to its original location, by ordinary diffusion, and therefore produces a vertical concentration gradient in the apparatus. After a period of time, the composition of a liquid mixture in the upper part of the apparatus is quite different from that in the lower part.

The apparatus used in most of the investigations of liquid thermal diffusion was designed for batchwise operation. Until quite recently, the most common design of apparatus consisted primarily of a thermal diffusion section made from either parallel plates or concentric tubes with reservoirs attached at the upper and lower extremities. The volume of the reservoirs is large relative to the volume of the space between the walls where the separation is produced. Apparatus of this type is shown diagrammatically in Figure 2. The reservoir design of apparatus has two principal disadvantages: (1) only two fractions are produced, and (2) the time required to reach a steady state is very long. The principal reason for the long time requirement is that the liquid in the reservoirs is subjected to purification or concentration change by displacement. For example, the liquid entering a reservoir from the rectifying section may be quite different in composition from that in the reservoir. After entering, it is mixed with the contents and that which leaves is a mixture of the two. At best, this is an extremely slow process of purification.

A more practical design of apparatus, which many research workers with separation problems are beginning to use, is one which has no reservoirs and which separates the charge material into a large number of fractions (Fig. 3). This apparatus is fabricated from a pair of metal concentric tubes 5 or

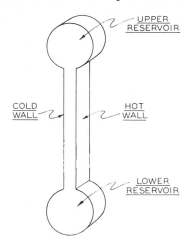

Fig. 2. Reservoir-type apparatus.

6 feet long. The diameter of the outer tube is approximately 0.75 inch with an annular spacing between the tubes of about 0.011 to 0.012 inch. This spacing is the most critical dimension involved in thermal diffusion apparatus. (An excellent discussion of the relationship of this and other apparatus dimensions to separation performance has been presented by Debye and Bueche.[21]) The total volume of the annular space is 22–30 ml. The column is usually equipped with ten or more withdrawal ports located at uniform intervals along its length in order that the contents may be withdrawn in ten or more separate fractions after a concentration gradient has been established between the ends of the apparatus. This is accomplished by draining the uppermost fraction first and successively removing the remaining fractions, proceeding from the top to the bottom of the apparatus.

The outer tube of the concentric pair is heated by a uniform spiral winding of electrical resistance wire. Heating control is maintained by means of a variable transformer. The inner tube is cooled by circulating cold water or other liquid coolants entering at the bottom of the column. The rate of coolant flow should be such that the temperature rise in passing through the column is not more than about 10°C.

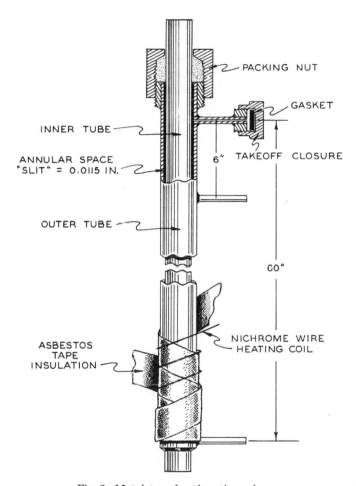

PACKING NUT

GASKET

INNER TUBE

ANNULAR SPACE
"SLIT" = 0.0115 IN.

6" TAKEOFF CLOSURE

OUTER TUBE

60"

NICHROME WIRE
HEATING COIL

ASBESTOS
TAPE
INSULATION

Fig. 3. Metal-type fractionating column.

The most convenient way of measuring hot-wall temperatures is by means of thermocouples attached to the outer tube at intervals along the length. It is usually sufficient to have three of these, located at the top, middle, and bottom of the apparatus. The cold-wall temperature can be determined sufficiently accurately by measurements of the inlet and outlet coolant fluid temperatures.

Apparatus of this type may be fabricated from commercially available metal tubing if careful selection is made to ensure the proper dimensions for the annulus between them when arranged concentrically. Uniformity of the annulus is maintained by means of small spacers attached to the inner tube at intervals along the length of the column. Reasonably good mechanical shop facilities are usually necessary to fabricate satisfactory apparatus of this type. A patent covering this type of apparatus has been applied for by The Standard Oil Company of Ohio.

Very effective thermal diffusion apparatus suitable for fractionating small samples (25–50 ml.) is now commercially available. It is recommended that investigators wishing to apply thermal diffusion to their particular separation problems give careful consideration to the availability of commercially assembled equipment rather than attempt to fabricate it themselves.

Another type of apparatus which is useful in some research operations is one which is fabricated entirely from glass and which can be operated on a continuous flow basis. This type of apparatus has the advantage of being capable of producing larger quantities of separated products than can be obtained from the conventional type of batch apparatus. The number of fractions produced is limited to two per pass through the apparatus. Additional fractions can be obtained, however, by reprocessing given fractions.

This type of apparatus may be fabricated from the ordinary borosilicate type of glass tubing, provided that individual pieces of tubing are carefully selected for uniformity of diameter and roundness. A column of handy dimensions for ordinary laboratory work may be fabricated from two 5-foot lengths of standard glass tubing. The annular space in which the total separation occurs is made by selecting a pair of tubes so that when they are arranged concentrically, an annular space of approximately 14-mm. diameter results. The spacing between the tubes should not be greater than approximately 1 mm. (0.043 inch). In order to maintain uniform spacing between the inner and outer tube of the concentric pair, small spacers approximately 1 mm. high are fused to the inner tube at intervals as often as necessary to maintain uniformity. The spacers are arranged in triplets at equidistant points around the circumference of the tube in a plane perpendicular to the axis of the tube. It is desirable to check the uniformity of spacing before continuing with the fabrication of the apparatus. This may be done by filling the annulus with a liquid, such as water, and then observing the meniscus as the water is slowly drained from the bottom of the annulus. If the two tubes are uniformly spaced, the meniscus will remain nearly horizontal. If the annulus is not uniform, the meniscus will tilt and indicate the area of nonuniformity very distinctly. When such areas are found they can usually be made uniform by attaching additional spacers to the inner tube in the vicinity of the region of nonuniformity.

After a uniform annulus has been fabricated the concentric pair of tubes

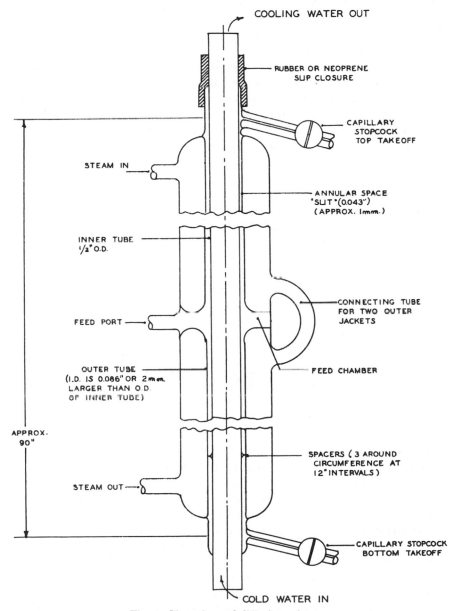

Fig. 4. Glass thermal diffusion column.

may be assembled into a thermal diffusion column in some manner such as that illustrated in Figure 4.   This apparatus is designed to permit heating by either circulating hot liquids or condensing vapors.   It is cooled by circulating liquids, usually water.   The general appearance of such a thermal diffusion column is quite similar to that of a long laboratory condenser of ordinary design.   The principal difference is the narrow annular space in which the separation occurs.

When such a column is to be operated on a continuous-flow basis the material to be separated is introduced at a point intermediate to the ends of the column, usually near the center.   The products are withdrawn from the top and bottom extremities of the annular space.   The liquid to be separated can be caused to flow through the apparatus either from gravity feed or pressure-feed reservoirs.   The rate of throughput is usually controlled by the adjustment of capillary stopcocks located at both ends of the apparatus.

For a column of the dimensions described, operating at hot-wall temperatures produced by condensing steam at atmospheric pressure and utilizing tap water to cool the cold wall, the rate of throughput is relatively slow. This varies somewhat with respect to the viscosity of the liquid being processed; but even with very thin liquids, not more than 5 to 10 ml. per hour may be withdrawn from each end of the apparatus if any appreciable separation is to be expected.   In general, it is not possible to select glass tubing of sufficient uniformity to be able to fabricate apparatus having the separating power of the previously described metal apparatus.   The glass apparatus has the desirable characteristic of being resistant to corrosion by many liquids.   But in most cases this advantage is outweighed by the much greater separating power that can be obtained from metal apparatus of greater uniformity.   Actually, the material of construction has no appreciable influence on the separating ability of a particular piece of apparatus.   The separating power is strictly a function of the uniformity of spacing and other geometric aspects of the parts of the apparatus.

The separation obtained from the ends of apparatus operated continuously is always less than that obtained from noncontinuous or batch apparatus of the same dimensions.   At very slow feed rates the degree of separation produced by continuous apparatus approaches that of the batch; but as feed rates are increased, separation declines.

The effect of apparatus dimensions on the performance of continuous-flow, thermal diffusion equipment is somewhat different from that described for batch-type operations.   At this time no publication has appeared which treats the subject of the effect of apparatus variables on continuous-flow, thermal diffusion operations in complete detail.   Limited discussion of the effects of apparatus variables on performance have been published by

Jones and co-workers.[28] More recently, Powers,[29] of the Chemical Engineering Department of the University of California has written a Ph.D. thesis on the general subject of continuous-flow, thermal diffusion operations. It is expected that this work will be published at some later date.

III. APPLICATION

1. Binary Systems

As an example of a pair of liquids that would be very difficult to separate by conventional techniques, Figure 5 illustrates the separation pattern when

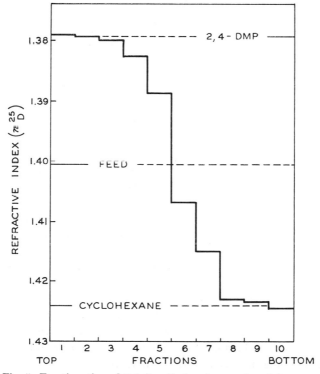

Fig. 5. Fractionation of 2,4-dimethylpentane and cyclohexane.

2,4-dimethylpentane and cyclohexane are thermally diffused. This pair of liquids would be difficult to separate by present-day distillation equipment

[28] A. L. Jones, *Petroleum Processing*, **6**, 132 (1951).
[29] J. E. Powers, Ph.D. Dissertation, University of California, August, 1954.

because of the closeness of the boiling points of the two liquids—80.50° and 80.74°C. for the 2,4-dimethylpentane and cyclohexane, respectively. The apparatus used to perform this separation is the metal type described previously, which is approximately 5 feet long and produces ten separate fractions. The horizontal axis of Figure 5 represents the fractions, and the vertical axis the refractive-index values. The fractions are numbered progressively from the top to the bottom of the apparatus and represent

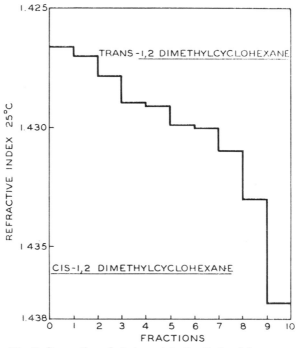

Fig. 6. Separation of *cis-trans*-1,2-dimethylcyclohexane.

its entire contents. The liquid charged was a 50:50 volume per cent mixture of the two components. The refractive indexes of the relatively pure (99.9%) components and the mixture charged are shown by the broken lines in the figure. The solid line shows the refractive indexes of the ten fractions after being subjected to thermal diffusion.

These data demonstrate that this mixture is easily separated by thermal diffusion. Although the relative boiling points of the components are very close to each other, the high degree of separation shows that the thermal diffusion separation is not dependent on the vapor-pressure properties of the components. The degree of purity of the materials in the fractions at each end of the apparatus is greater than that of the starting materials before mixing.   The average composition of the upper 30% of the column contents is approximately the equivalent of the 2,4-dimethylpentane used in preparing the mixture.   The bottom fraction contains cyclohexane of slightly greater purity than the starting material and the next two lower fractions approach that degree of purity.   It is also of interest to note that this separation does not depend on the molecular-weight difference of the components because the component with the higher molecular weight

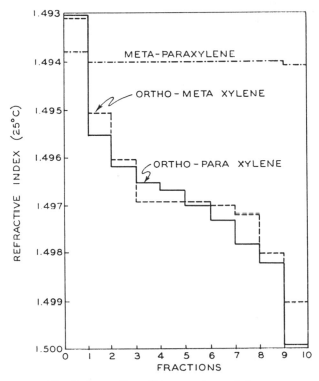

Fig. 7. Separation of binary xylene mixtures.

(2,4-dimethylpentane) concentrates at the top of the column instead of the bottom.

The separation of the *cis* and *trans* isomers of 1,2-dimethylcyclohexane is an illustration of the separation of a pair of liquids of identical molecular weights.   Using the same apparatus as in the previous illustration, the data for this separation are shown in Figure 6.   The mixture was obtained from API Hydrocarbon Research Project 45 at Ohio State University. The *cis* isomer concentrates at the bottom of the column, the *trans* at the top.   The values shown in the figure for the refractive indexes of the pure components are the best values available at the time of the experiment. Since that time, API Project 6 has separated these same isomers by distillation, obtaining products of excellent purity. Although the data illustrated here indicate that thermal diffusion produces fractions of greater purity than those presented by API 45, the end fractions do not attain a degree of purity quite as high as that obtained by API Project 6. There is no question, however, about the susceptibility of this pair of isomers to separation by thermal diffusion.

Figure 7 illustrates the separation patterns for the three isomeric pairs of xylene. 50:50 volume per cent mixtures of the isomers were used in all three cases. Two of the pair of isomers are easily separated from each other, while the third pair does not separate at all. The o-m and o-p pairs separate easily, while the m-p mixture does not separate. In the two binary mixtures involving o-xylene, the o-isomer concentrates toward the bottom of the apparatus. The m- and p-isomers concentrate toward the top of the apparatus with apparently about the same ease of separation. Since both the m- and p-isomers behave so similarly, relative to the o-isomer, it is not surprising that they prove to be difficult to separate from each other.

Table I contains separation data for seven different binary mixtures of isomers. The components of each pair are listed with respect to the direction of separation if a separation is observed. For example, n-heptane is listed above triptane in the first pair. This means that n-heptane con-

TABLE I

GEOMETRIC ISOMERS

Components, volume per cent	Mol. wt.	Density	Final volume per cent		Per cent separation
			Top	Bottom	
50 n-heptane	100	0.6837	95	10	75
50 triptane	100	0.6900	5	90	
50 isooctane	114	0.6919	58	40	11.4
50 n-octane	114	0.7029	42	60	
50 β-methylnaphthalene	142	0.9905	55.5	42.5	13.1
50 α-methylnaphthalene	142	1.0163	44.5	57.5	
40 trans-1,2-dimethylcyclohexane	112	0.7756	100	0	100
60 cis-1,2-dimethylcyclohexane	112	0.7963	0	100	
50 p-xylene	106	0.8609	92	0	92
50 o-xylene[a]	106	0.8799	8	100	
50 m-xylene	106	0.8639	100	19	80
50 o-xylene[a]	106	0.8799	0	81	
50 p-xylene	106	0.8609	50	50	0
50 m-xylene	106	0.8639	50	50	

[a] o-Xylene contains paraffinic impurity (see Fig. 15).

centrates upward and triptane downward in the apparatus. The top and bottom concentrations are those existing in the upper and lower tenths of the total volume of the apparatus. The percentage separation is a relative value obtained by dividing the refractive index difference between the upper and lower fractions by the refractive index difference between pure components:

$$\Delta n_D \frac{\text{(between top and bottom fractions)} \times 100}{\Delta n_D \text{ (between pure compounds)}} = \% \text{ separation}$$

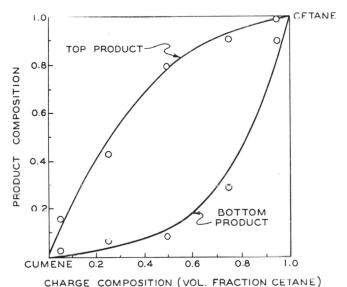

Fig. 8. Effect of relative concentrations.

All of these mixtures were processed for 48 hours under essentially the same hot- and cold-wall temperatures. The separations do not represent steady-state conditions in any case. A run of 48 hours' duration does not represent the same fraction of a steady-state separation for the mixtures involved. The relative separations listed should be considered qualitatively in all cases. Debye and Bueche[30] and DeGroot[31] have suggested that studies of the effects of the relative concentrations of components would be of importance in interpreting the significance of separations produced by thermal diffusion.

[30] P. Debye and A. M. Bueche, *High Polymer Physics*. Chemical Publ., Brooklyn, 1948, pp. 497–527. *Collected Papers of Peter J. W. Debye*. Interscience, New York-London, 1954.

[31] S. R. DeGroot, *L'Effet Soret*. North-Holland, Amsterdam, 1945.

Figure 8 is an illustration of the effect of relative concentrations on a typical pair of liquids. The composition of the liquid charged to the column is shown on the horizontal axis and the composition produced in each end of the apparatus after 48 hours is shown on the vertical axis. The experimental points represent the compositions of the upper and lower tenths of the total volume of the liquid mixture. The mixture used in this case was a blend of different ratios of hexadecane and isopropylbenzene. This binary system may be considered a normal one and the separation pattern obtained is typical of many different pairs of liquid hydrocarbons. Although

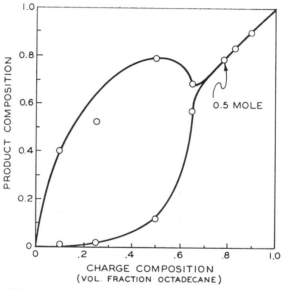

Fig. 9. Effect of relative concentrations of octadecane and benzene.

a number of different systems have been studied, the maximum separation has always been obtained at 50:50 volume composition. It is interesting that this occurs with respect to volume rather than with respect to the number of molecules involved.

Some binary systems apparently exhibit a normal separation behavior pattern at some relative concentrations and an abnormal one at others. A good example of this behavior may be illustrated by the octadecane–benzene system. Trevoy and Drickamer[32] reported that a 50:50 mole mixture of benzene and octadecane yields essentially no separation. On the other hand, the author observed that benzene and hexadecane at 50:50 volume per cent concentrations separated quite easily. The failure of one

[32] D. J. Trevoy and H. G. Drickamer, *J. Chem. Phys.*, **17**, 1120 (1949).

system to separate and the other similar one to separate easily was hard to rationalize. Since the apparatus used by Trevoy and Drickamer was somewhat different from that used to separate the benzene and hexadecane, it was, therefore, decided to check the experiment of Trevoy and Drickamer in this apparatus using the same concentrations as they utilized. Exactly the same results as reported by Trevoy and Drickamer were obtained.

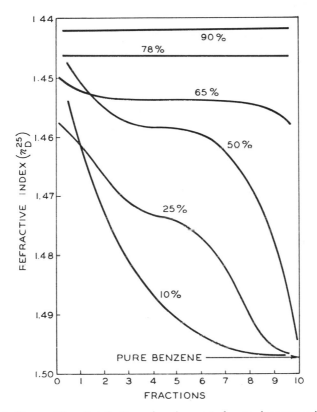

Fig. 10. Composition distribution of various octadecane–benzene mixtures.

When a 50:50 volume per cent mixture of benzene and octadecane was used rather than a 50:50 mole per cent mixture, pronounced separations were obtained. Nearly pure benzene concentrated at the bottom of the column. A mixture of benzene and octadecane concentrated at the top of the column. A number of different compositions of these two were then processed in the apparatus. The results of these studies are shown in Figure 9; the data are plotted in the same way as in Figure 8. This figure shows that whenever there is an excess of moles of ben-

zene, normal separation occurs.   Maximum separation is obtained from
50 volume per cent mixtures.   At equimolar concentrations there is no
separation and there continues to be no separation at any excess molar
concentration of octadecane.   Figure 10 is an illustration of the composition
distribution of the entire contents of the column, using six different concentrations of octadecane and benzene as charge material.   The 10, 25,
and 50 volume per cent octadecane mixtures yielded nearly pure benzene at

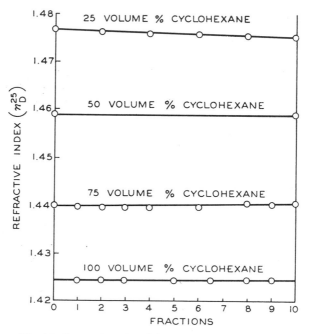

Fig. 11. Separation of cyclohexane–benzene mixtures.

the bottom of the column.   When the 50:50 mole per cent composition was
reached (78 volume per cent octadecane) no concentration difference could
be found between any fractions along the entire length of the column.
When octadecane was in larger excess (90 volume per cent) there was also
no separation anywhere in the apparatus.   This shows that the failure to
get separations when a concentration of octadecane is in excess of 50 mole
per cent cannot be attributed to an equimolar compound of octadecane and
benzene.   Measurements of density, refractive index, and molar polarization over the entire concentration range do not show any abnormalities
for these two components.   The reason for the failure of the mixtures
containing excess molar concentrations of octadecane to produce separations
is not understood.

There are some systems which fail to be separated by thermal diffusion at any relative concentration. A number of different investigators have reported the failure of benzene and cyclohexane to separate. A study of a large number of different relative concentrations for this pair of components shows that they do not separate at any relative concentrations; Figure 11 shows the results of this study. The reason for the failure of benzene and cyclohexane to separate may not be the same as that for the octadecane–benzene mixture when the octadecane is in molar excess. Cyclohexane and benzene mixtures have been reported to be nonideal. A volume increase occurs upon mixing.[33] The freezing-point lowering of benzene by cyclohexane is not ideal.[34] A straight-line relationship between index of refraction and volume per cent composition is not obtained.[35] An azeotrope is formed by the components[36] and x-ray studies of liquid mixtures of the two components indicate highly organized groups containing both types of molecules.[37]

TABLE II

SEPARATION OF BINARY LIQUID MIXTURES BY THERMAL DIFFUSION

Components, volume per cent	Mol. wt.	Density	Final volume per cent		Per cent separation
			Top	Bottom	
50 cetane........	226	0.7734	72.4	37.5	35
50 benzene......	78	0.8789	27.6	62.5	
50 cetane........	226	0.7734	60.0	44.5	14.5
50 toluene.......	92	0.8652	40.0	54.5	
50 cetane........	226	0.7734	60.0	42.0	17.5
50 m-xylene.....	106	0.8639	40.0	58.0	
50 cetane........	226	0.7734	61.0	35.8	24.9
50 mesitylene....	120	0.8653	39.0	64.2	

The relative separation tendencies of benzene, toluene, m-xylene, and mesitylene (1 3,5-trimethylbenzene) with respect to hexadecane as the other component are shown in Table II. These various substituted benzenes show no obvious correlation between the degree of separation and the number of substituted methyl groups. The two symmetrical components, benzene and mesitylene, give a larger separation from hexadecane than do the unsymmetrical components, toluene and m-xylene. The symmetry of these molecules may play some part in their diffusional movement through the liquid media of these particular systems.

[33] S. E. Wood and A. E. Austin, J. Am. Chem. Soc., 67, 480 (1945).
[34] R. Negisi, Rev. Phys. Chem. Japan, 15, 98 (1941).
[35] I. G. S. Pavlov, J. Russ. Phys.-Chem. Soc., 58, 1302 (1926).
[36] R. F. Marschner and W. P. Cropper, Ind. Eng. Chem., 38, 262 (1946).
[37] P. H. Bell and W. P. Davey, J. Chem. Phys., 9, 441 (1941).

In Table III are listed several pairs of paraffins, cycloparaffins, and aromatics, with respect to their separation tendencies. The cyclic compounds, benzene and methylcyclohexane, appear to separate from *n*-heptane with about the same degree of ease. The cyclic compounds are cold-wall or bottom products in both cases. Although benzene and methylcyclohexane behave very much alike with respect to *n*-heptane, they can also be separated from each other when they are paired. Three pairs are listed in Table III which failed to separate by thermal diffusion in the apparatus used. Toluene does not separate from methylcyclohexane, benzene from cyclohexane, and cetane from cyclohexane. The failure to obtain separation by thermal diffusion is usually restricted to binary systems. Mixtures containing more than two components generally yield to separation.

TABLE III

PARAFFINS, CYCLOPARAFFINS, AND AROMATICS

Components, volume per cent	Mol. wt.	Density	Final volume per cent		Per cent separation
			Top	Bottom	
50 *n*-heptane............	100.2	0.6837	95.0	3.0	84.0
50 benzene..............	78.0	0.8789	5.0	97.0	
50 *n*-heptane............	100.2	0.6837	94.5	9.0	85.4
50 methylcyclohexane....	98	0.7689	5.5	91.0	
50 methylcyclohexane....	98	0.7689	53.2	27.5	19.3
50 benzene..............	78	0.8789	46.8	72.5	
50 methylcyclohexane....	98	0.7689	50	50	0
50 toluene..............	92	0.8652	50	50	
50 cyclohexane..........	94	0.7783	50	50	0
50 benzene..............	78	0.8789	50	50	
50 cetane..............	226	0.7734	50	50	0
50 cyclohexane..........	84	0.7783	50	50	
50 isooctane............	114	0.6919	52.8	37.5	14.9
50 methylcyclohexane....	98	0.7689	47.2	62.5	

Molecular configuration appears to be the principal factor involved in liquid thermal diffusion separations. Several different pairs of liquids which have the same or very nearly the same molecular symmetry have been studied. Table IV lists three different pairs of liquid components which fall into this category. In all three of these pairs the component with the higher molecular weight concentrates toward the bottom of the column. If a shape or symmetry difference exists among the molecules to be separated, this effect usually predominates over the influence of mass differences. If, on the other hand, there is no significant difference in shape, mass differences determine the amount of separation that may be obtained.

TABLE IV

PAIRS OF THE SAME MOLECULAR SYMMETRY

Components, volume per cent	Mol. wt.	Density	Final volume per cent		Per cent separation
			Top	Bottom	
50 n-octane.............	114	0.7029	60	27.5	30.5
50 n-decane.............	142.3	0.7299	40	72.5	
50 n-heptane............	100.2	0.6837	74.0	22.0	52.5
50 cetane...............	226	0.7734	26.0	78.0	
50 toluene..............	92	0.8652	65.0	38.0	23.2
50 chlorobenzene........	112.6	1.070	35.0	62.0	

Thermal diffusion in organic liquids differs from that in aqueous liquids or in gases primarily with respect to the influence of molecular configuration on the movement of individual molecules in the media. In gases the molecules are sufficiently far apart so that their configuration does not materially influence their movement between collisions. In such cases mass differences play an important part in the degree of separation to be expected. In aqueous liquids the molecules are close enough together so that configuration differences could influence the movement of individual particles, but, in general, the ions are solvated to the extent that most of the particles have essentially the same symmetry. The shape of the particles is approximately spherical and the principal differences between individual aggregates are size and weight. Thermal diffusion separations of aqueous systems, therefore, occur primarily according to size and weight, with the same general principle applying, as in the case of gaseous thermal diffusion separations. In nonassociating organic liquid mixtures the situation is quite different. Here, the configuration of individual molecules has a great influence on the ability of the molecules to move in the liquid medium. The molecules are sufficiently close together for small configuration differences to have an influence on their individual movements. It is for this reason that the theoretical treatments which have proved helpful in interpreting gaseous separations and some aqueous separations are not particularly applicable to organic liquids. In many cases components of different configuration separate, with the components of higher mass going in just the opposite direction from what might be expected if gas theories were applicable.

At this time, there is no satisfactory theoretical explanation of thermal diffusion separations in organic-liquid media. Drickamer and co-workers at the University of Illinois are making good progress toward explaining the behavior in such media. Drickamer has related the separation tendencies to the activation energies required for a given species of molecule to move from one position to another in the liquid media. This activation energy may be computed from measurable properties such as viscosities of the pure components at two different temperatures and their molar volumes.   This approach shows great promise of yielding a much better explanation of the observed phenomena.   The property of specific heat per unit volume has been found useful in predicting the direction in which two components will go when the mixture is subjected to a temperature gradient.   In general, the component with the higher specific heat per unit volume tends to concentrate near the hot wall, while the one with the lower specific heat concentrates in the opposite direction toward the cold wall.   No method has been devised for using this in a quantitative manner. There are some apparent exceptions to the principle.

Another approach has been to consider that the molecular types arrange themselves between the walls so as to conduct the maximum quantity of heat.   By this criterion the components having the higher thermal conductivity may be expected to concentrate near the cold wall, while those having the lower thermal conductivity are hot-wall products.   Again, this treatment has not proved useful on a quantitative basis.

Table V shows the separation of four pairs of liquids: a monocyclic from a bicyclic aromatic, a very compact molecular compound, CCl_4, from a ring and also from a straight-chain component, and finally an azeotropic mixture of two alcohols.   The azeotropic mixture of alcohols was prepared by distillation, with the constant-boiling distillate being charged to the thermal diffusion column.   This mixture was separated relatively easily and demonstrates that thermal diffusion is not dependent upon vapor-pressure properties for the separations obtained.

TABLE V

SEPARATION OF BINARY LIQUID MIXTURES BY THERMAL DIFFUSION

Components, volume per cent	Mol. wt.	Density	Final composition		Per cent separation
			Top	Bottom	
50 cumene.	120	0.8633	66.0	31.0	34.9
50 methylnaphthalene. . .	142	1.010	34.0	69.0	
50 benzene.	78	0.8789	90.0	2.0	88
50 CCl_4.	154	1.595	10.0	98.0	
50 cetane.	226	0.7734	100	0	100
50 CCl_4.	154	1.595	0	100	
44 benzyl alcohol.	108	1.040	59.0	30.3	29
56 ethylene glycol.	62	1.113	41.0	69.7	

One factor that has made the interpretation of thermal diffusion separations difficult is the fact that the more dense of two components does not always concentrate near the cold wall or toward the bottom of the column.

In some cases the opposite is true. The less dense of the two components tends to concentrate toward the cold wall and hence is carried downward by the thermal convective stream. This tends to create a condition of instability with the heavier component concentrating upward and the less dense component concentrating downward. There is a strong tendency for the liquids to overturn and remix, depending upon the degree of separation produced between the walls. DeGroot,[38] Prigogine,[39] and van Velden, van der Voort, and Gorter[40] recognized and discussed systems in which the di-

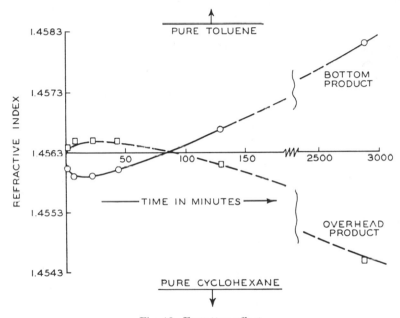

Fig. 12. Forgotten effect.

rection of concentration of components produced a density gradient in the apparatus opposed to that produced by the temperature difference alone. This phenomenon has been termed the "forgotten effect," probably because it was not taken into account by many previous investigators.

As an illustration of the "forgotten effect," Figure 12 shows the composition at the ends of a column when cyclohexane and toluene are thermally diffused. In this case the lighter cyclohexane tends to concentrate near the cold wall and the more dense toluene near the hot wall. Thermal convection carries these concentrated products to the bottom and top of the

[38] S. R. DeGroot, *L'Effet Soret*. North-Holland, Amsterdam, 1945.
[39] I. Prigogine, L. de Brouckere, and R. Amand, *Physica*, **16**, 577 (1950).
[40] P. F. van Velden, H. G. P. van der Voort, and C. J. Gorter, *Physica*, **12**, 151 (1946).

column, respectively. Inspection of the figure shows that in the early stages of the separation toluene increases in concentration at the top of the column and cyclohexane at the bottom until a sufficient degree of instability is produced to cause a reversal in the direction of separation in the apparatus. After about 80 minutes, in this case, a reversal occurs and toluene descends near the hot wall. Near the cold wall, the cyclohexane-enriched layer creeps upward and thus concentrates at the top of the column. "Forgotten effect" pairs can be predicted reasonably well from Drickamer's activation energy theory as well as by the criterion of relative specific heat per unit volume. The component with the lower specific heat would be expected to go toward the cold wall via thermal diffusion. If this component happens to be the less dense of two under consideration, a "forgotten effect" pair results. The result obtained with "forgotten effect" pairs are usually quite erratic, sometimes separating in one direction in one apparatus and in a different direction in another. This inconsistency is usually a result of the differences in the degree of instability that can be tolerated before remixing occurs. Columns of really uniform dimensions can sometimes build up a relatively high concentration of low-density material at the bottom of a column before it finally overturns and changes position with the more dense material at the top of the column.

2. Ternary Liquids

A few three-component systems have been investigated to determine their relative distribution in the apparatus as a result of thermal diffusion. The distribution resulting when a mixture of equal volumes of a normal paraffin, a cycloparaffin, and an aromatic of comparable molecular weights is subjected to thermal diffusion is shown in Figure 13. The normal paraffin concentrates toward the top of the column, while both the cyclic paraffin and the aromatic tend to concentrate toward the bottom of the apparatus. The lower 30% of the apparatus contains essentially no normal paraffin, and in this portion of the apparatus the aromatic is concentrated a little more strongly toward the bottom than is the cyclic paraffin. In the upper 70% of the column the two cyclic components behave very much alike with respect to the normal paraffin. In this region the cyclic paraffin tends to concentrate more strongly downward than does the aromatic. The upper 10% of the column contains essentially no aromatic, 3% cycloparaffin and about 97% normal paraffin.

In binary mixtures, m- and p-xylene failed to separate from each other. Figure 14 shows what happened when an equivolume mixture of the three xylene isomers was thermally diffused. The p-isomers concentrate toward the top of the column, the o- toward the bottom, and the m- increases in

concentration near the middle of the apparatus.   Although all three of
these isomers change with respect to their relative concentrations along
the entire length of the apparatus, the separation of m- from p-xylene is
still a difficult problem in spite of the fact that the relative concentrations
are changed in this case.

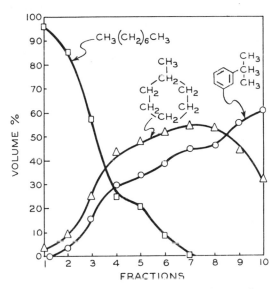

Fig. 13. Distribution of mixture of equal volumes of a normal paraffin, a cycloparaffin, and an aromatic.

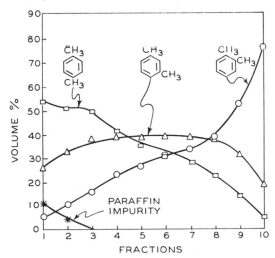

Fig. 14. Separation of a ternary xylene isomer mixture.

A paraffinic impurity is indicated on Figure 14 in the uppermost fractions. Although the isomers used to prepare this equivolume mixture were expected to be of a high degree of purity, this fractionation indicated that at least one of the isomers contained a certain amount of paraffinic impurity. Table VI shows the refractive-index values of the isomers used and the best literature values for pure isomers. The greatest deviation from the literature values was exhibited by the *o*-isomer. The column was

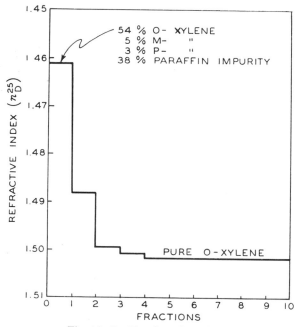

Fig. 15. Purification of *o*-xylene.

filled with *o*-xylene as obtained from the supplier. Figure 15 shows the refractive-index values obtained from the ten individual fractions and the infrared analysis of the uppermost fraction after subjecting the *o*-xylene to thermal diffusion. These data show that the *o*-xylene contained approximately 4% of a paraffinic impurity which concentrated toward the top of the apparatus. The material in the lower 60% of the column was *o*-xylene of excellent purity. This illustrates how thermal diffusion is useful as a means of detecting impurities and also as a tool of purification. There is no guarantee that failure to get a difference among fractions is proof of purity. But if differences in properties between fractions are found, it is certain that the material in question cannot be pure. Thermal diffusion is particularly useful in obtaining further separations after other techniques depending on different principles have been taken to their practical limits. It is suggested that thermal diffusion should not necessarily be considered as a substitute for other separation techniques but should be considered for use in conjunction with them to supplement and extend the separations which they now produce.

TABLE VI

REFRACTIVE INDICES (n_D^{25}) OF XYLENE ISOMERS AT 25°C.

Isomers used	Literature values (API-44)
o-Xylene 1.5000	1.5029
m-Xylene 1.4948	1.4946
p-Xylene 1.4925	1.4933

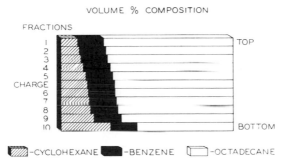

Fig. 16. Separation of mixture of octadecane, benzene, and cyclohexane.

Among the binary mixtures studied it was observed that benzene and cyclohexane failed to separate as a pair. Benzene and octadecane did not separate when octadecane was in molar excess and cyclohexane and octadecane were also found inseparable as a binary mixture. A ternary mixture of these three inseparable pairs was prepared. Octadecane was in molar excess with respect to benzene, and cyclohexane and benzene were approximately equal molar quantities. Figure 16 shows the relative concentrations of these three components when the ternary mixture was subjected to thermal diffusion. A change in relative concentrations occurred along the entire length of the column in this ternary mixture. Cyclohexane concentrated downward, octadecane concentrated upward, and the benzene content remained essentially constant in all fractions. It is believed that this is a result of benzene being intermediate in its diffusional tendencies between cyclohexane and octadecane. This is another illustration of how separations may be obtained even when they are not observed in binary mixtures of certain components.

Much of the recent experimental investigation concerning applications of liquid thermal diffusion was concerned with the separation of hydrocarbon mixtures. Enough studies, however, were carried out with other types of organic liquids to demonstrate a wide range of applicability. The thermal diffusion separation of tall oil was demonstrated and the type of separations obtained showed that this material is particularly susceptible to separation by thermal diffusion.

Tall oil is a vegetable oil which has its origin in the tissues of resinous woods used in the manufacture of paper. Tall oil is obtained as a result of the treatment of the wood fibers with alkaline sulfates. When the alkaline extracts are acidified, the oil, which is a mixture of fatty acids, resin acids, and small amounts of sterols and higher alcohols, separates from the aqueous phase. The results of the analyses of tall oil and tall oil thermal diffusion fractions are presented in Table VII. The apparatus used for the thermal

TABLE VII

ANALYSES OF TALL OIL AND TALL OIL FRACTIONS

Sample	Sample, vol. per cent	n_D^{20}	Iodine number	Rosin acids number	Total acids number	Fatty acids,[a] %	Fatty acids,[b] %	Non-acids, %
Original tall oil	100	1.4938	141.5	57.8	179	31.1	60.9	8.0
First pass top..	67	1.4807	149.6	31.7	185	17.1	76.5	6.4
First pass bottom........	33	1.5100	126.3	85.0	164	45.8	39.8	14.4
Second pass top	40	1.4676	122.9	5.2	188	2.8	92.0	5.2
Second pass bottom.....	27	1.5000	159.7	62.7	167	33.8	52.5	13.7

[a] Calculated as abietic acid of M.W. = 302.
[b] Calculated as fatty acid of M.W. = 282.

diffusion fractionation was the glass type discussed earlier in the chapter and illustrated in Figure 4. This material was processed by continuously passing two-thirds overhead while one-third was withdrawn as a bottom product. Sufficient quantity of the first-pass overhead fraction was collected to permit it to be passed through the apparatus a second time. The ratio of top to bottom products on the second pass was approximately 4:3. The analyses of the fractions showed that fatty acids tended to concentrate toward the top of the column and rosin acids toward the bottom. The iodine numbers of the fractions collected from top and bottom showed that the components of greater unsaturation concentrated toward the top of the column during the first pass of tall oil through the apparatus. The refractionation of the first-pass top fraction produced additional separation, the degree of which was about the same as during the first pass.

The more unsaturated components in this case reversed their direction of concentration and, on the second pass, the bottom fraction increased in the degree of unsaturation. This illustrates that the direction in which a given type of component concentrates depends upon the nature of the other components which may be present in the liquid. In the presence of rosin acids the unsaturated fatty acids concentrate at the top of the column but, when the concentration of rosin acids is decreased, as in the second fractionation,

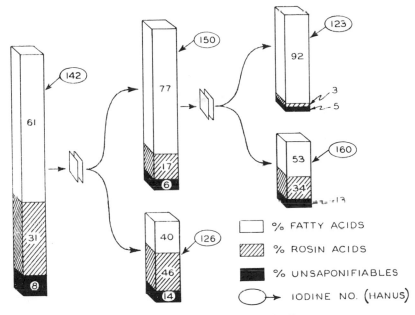

Fig. 17. Fractionation of tall oil.

the direction of concentration of the unsaturated components is the opposite of that observed when the material was fractionated the first time. This illustrates the possibility of utilizing thermal diffusion to fractionate complex mixtures of organic liquid components into many fractions of different chemical composition. The entire fractionation of tall oil is illustrated in Figure 17.[41]

Of the various petroleum liquids which have been subjected to liquid thermal diffusion, perhaps the most striking separations are observed in the case of lubricating oil stocks. Large changes in the viscosities of lubricants are usually produced when they are thermally diffused. The overhead, or hot-wall, fractions are generally increased with respect to viscosity index.

[41] A. L. Jones and R. W. Foreman, *Ind. Eng. Chem.*, **44**, 2249 (1952).

The kinematic viscosity, on the other hand, is reduced for top fractions and increased for bottom fractions. The viscosity properties of the ten fractions produced from a Mid-Continent paraffin distillate stock are shown in Table VIII. This material was processed in the same type of apparatus

TABLE VIII

VISCOSITY DATA FOR PARAFFIN DISTILLATE

Thermal diffusion fraction	Viscosity (S.U.S.)		Viscosity index
	100°F.	210°F.	
Feed..........	163.8	43.18	77.4
1............	Solid	34.86	—
2............	Solid	37.48	—
3............	74.46	38.22	159
4............	88.00	38.50	120
5............	115.7	40.40	88.6
6............	180.0	43.76	69.0
7............	330.2	47.97	16.4
8............	1,398.0	63.70	−103
9............	5,850.0	95.72	−265
10............	15,680.0	165.6	−196

as was used in the fractionation of the binary and ternary mixtures described in this chapter. The uppermost two fractions contained so much wax that their viscosities could not be measured at 100°F. The eight fractions below these two in the apparatus were completely liquid at ordinary temperatures and it may be observed that their viscosities increased substantially from the upper to the lower parts of the apparatus.

The first liquid fraction, No. 3, has a viscosity index of 159, while the bottom three fractions, 8, 9, and 10, all have negative values. Although these fractions have such different properties with respect to viscosities, measurements of their average molecular weights indicate no difference at all among them. This observation is in agreement with that shown by Mair and Rossini.[42] They have shown that mass-spectrographic examination of thermal diffusion fractions from lubricating oil reveals no detectable separation between individual fractions with respect to their average molecular weight. This means that the large viscosity differences produced among the individual fractions is a result of the sorting out of different molecular shapes or configurations by the thermal diffusion process. The volatility of each fraction is essentially the same. The bottom fraction, which has a viscosity of 15,000 S.U.S. at 100°F., distils just as readily as the much thinner No. 3 fraction, which has a viscosity of 75 S.U.S. at 100°F.

[42] B. J. Mair and F. D. Rossini, *Ind. Eng. Chem.*, **47**, 1062 (1955).

Measurements of the densities of these fractions show that the upper fractions are less dense than those occurring at the bottom.   Calculations of the number of different types of rings present in these fractions by any of several different methods of calculation show that the lowest fractions have a total ring number of around four, while the upper fractions (1, 2, 3, and 4) have, on the average, less than one ring per molecule.   These observations are typical of those that may be generally expected from the thermal diffusion of petroleum lubricant fractions.   Table IX lists the

TABLE IX

LIQUID THERMAL DIFFUSION SEPARATION OF A LUBRICATING OIL STOCK
FOR A FRACTION CUT FROM A PRESSED MID-CONTINENT PARAFFIN DISTILLATE

Property	Overhead (50 vol. %)	Feed	Bottoms (50 vol. %)
Density at 20°C	0.8448	0.9065	0.9806
Refractive index, n_D^{20}	1.4690	1.5055	1.5500
Viscosity, c.s.			
at 100°F	22.47	72.5	1750.6
at 210°F	4.74	7.6	23.3
Optical density	50	350	1600
Pour point, °F	+55	+40	−15
Boiling range,[a] °F.			
IBP	386	—	378
2%	754	—	451
5%	768	—	764
10%	785	—	779
20%	803	—	793
30%	817	—	806
40%	831	—	823
50%	840	—	831
60%	849	—	842
70%	860	—	864
80%	873	—	869
90%	909	—	891
95%	941	—	914
EP	965	—	949
Viscosity index	147.2	65	−247

[a] A.S.T.M. vacuum distillation corrected to atmospheric pressure.

properties of the two fractions produced by the continuous fractionation of a Mid-Continent lubricating oil stock.   This material was split into equal-volume top and bottom fractions.   The distillation properties of these two fractions, shown in the table, illustrate the similar volatility characteristics of thermal diffusion fractions produced from the same stock, which have widely different viscosity and density properties.

TABLE X

LIQUID THERMAL DIFFUSION SEPARATIONS OF VARIOUS PETROLEUM STOCKS

Property	Overhead (50 vol. %)	Feed	Bottoms (50 vol. %)
Kerosene			
Sp. gr. at 68°F....................	0.7941	0.8076	0.8203
Refractive index, n_D^{20}...............	1.4420	1.4489	1.4548
Viscosity, c.s.			
at 100°F.......................	1.48	1.51	1.59
at 210°F.......................	0.747	0.768	0.784
Freezing point, °F................	−39	−42	−51
Light virgin gas oil			
Sp. gr. at 68°F....................	0.8285	0.8534	0.8827
Refractive index, n_D^{20}...............	1.4603	1.4748	1.4891
Viscosity, c.s.			
at 100°F.......................	4.20	5.66	5.87
at 210°F.......................	1.51	1.63	1.82
Aniline point.....................	184.6	168.1	150.1
Light, catalytic gas oil			
Sp. gr. at 68°F....................	0.8383	0.8718	0.9036
Refractive index, n_D^{20}...............	1.4720	1.4918	1.5125
Viscosity, c.s.			
at 100°F.......................	3.58	3.76	4.05
at 210°F.......................	1.35	1.37	1.40
Aniline point.....................	165	148	118
Heavy catalytic gas oil			
Sp. gr. at 68°F....................	0.8383	0.9059	0.9792
Refractive index, n_D^{20}...............	1.4617	1.5110	1.5605
Viscosity, c.s.			
at 100°F.......................	9.93	15.4	35.9
at 210°F.......................	2.58	3.25	4.46
Viscosity index....................	99	78	−33
Aniline point.....................	221	184	—
Solvent-extracted oil			
Sp. gr. at 68°F....................	0.8408	0.8676	0.8883
Refractive index, n_D^{20}...............	1.4670	1.4760	1.4838
Viscosity, c.s.			
at 100°F.......................	18.5	25.0	39.3
at 210°F.......................	3.86	4.40	5.49
Viscosity index....................	114	89	65
Pour point, °F....................	+20	+10	−25
Optical density...................	1.6	—	10.0
Cylinder stock			
Sp. gr. at 68°F....................	0.8978	0.9371	0.9986
Viscosity, c.s.			
at 210°F.......................	24.5	53.4	415
Slack wax			
Sp. gr. at 68°F....................	0.8137	0.8408	0.8756
Refractive index, n_D^{20}...............	1.4380	1.4538	1.4747

TABLE X (*Continued*)

Property	Overhead (50 vol. %)	Feed	Bottoms (50 vol. %)
Viscosity, c.s.			
at 100°F.	9.75	12.6	18.1
at 210°F.	2.95	3.26	3.93
Viscosity index	172	145	130
Oil content, weight %	19.3	45.8	74.8
Isoparaffin-naphthene fraction[a]			
Refractive index, n_D^{25}	1.4147	1.4218	1.4249
Naphthenes, %	27.4	48.5	74.3

[a] Distillation fraction from virgin naphtha (264–404°F.). Dearomatized by silica gel chromatography (O Kattwinkel No.). Normal paraffins removed by urea adduction.

The changes in properties produced by the continuous fractionation of a variety of multicomponent petroleum fractions are presented in Table X. There is a similarity in the general pattern of all of these multicomponent petroleum separations. In general, it may be stated that the most paraffinic materials concentrate toward the top of the apparatus, while the compounds containing the largest number of rings, usually of a condensed type, concentrate toward the bottom of the apparatus. Thermal diffusion does not sharply separate aromatic from nonaromatic compounds in multicomponent mixtures. Molecules containing the same number of either unsaturated or aromatic rings behave very much alike and generally concentrate toward the bottom in the presence of isoparaffins and normal paraffins.

Data now available from many different investigators of liquid thermal diffusion indicate that the potential application of the principle is very broad. It may be applied successfully to both petroleum and nonpetroleum liquids, and since it does not depend upon the same physical principles as other separation processes, it is not limited by the same factors that restrict the applicability of other processes. In cases where separations are difficult or sometimes impossible by conventional techniques, thermal diffusion may serve as a very useful tool in simplifying or making possible such separations.

A variety of apparatus modifications is resulting from studies being conducted by different investigators. Sullivan, Ruppel, and Willingham show how equipment may be modified and improved through the utilization of packing between the hot and cold walls and also by rotating one of a pair of concentric tubes.[43] Begeman and Cramer describe several different continuous- and batch-type thermal diffusion columns.[44] All of

[43] L. J. Sullivan, T. C. Ruppel, and C. B. Willingham, *Ind. Eng. Chem.*, **47**, 208 (1955).
[44] C. R. Begeman and P. L. Cramer, *Ind. Eng. Chem.*, **47**, 202 (1955).

these studies indicate that there is considerable room for improvement of apparatus and that specific applications may require special types of apparatus.

One of the problems which many investigators are faced with is the separation of two dissimilar components, of low concentration, dissolved in a solvent. It is possible to accomplish separations of this kind by thermal diffusion, but the selection of the proper solvent is very critical. If the solvent is much different, with respect to molecular configuration, from the solutes to be separated, thermal diffusion may only separate the solutes from the solvent. It is possible, however, to choose a solvent which permits dissimilar types of solute to distribute themselves in a thermal diffusion column. This type of problem has been studied by Korsching and Wirtz[45] and they describe the techniques for accomplishing such separations. In general, it is desirable to attempt to separate different components without the addition of a solvent, if possible. Thermal diffusion separations of liquids may be carried out at any temperature level as long as the material does not decompose, vaporize, or solidify. It is possible to separate materials which are normally mixtures of solids at room temperatures by processing a melt of the materials. In such cases the "cold" wall should be at a temperature higher than the melting point of the highest melting component when it is isolated. The hot-wall temperature should not exceed the decomposition temperatures of any of the components. Liquids may be processed at temperatures above their normal boiling points by pressurizing the apparatus. In general, separations may be obtained in the shortest time by applying a temperature gradient as great as the nature of the material being processed can tolerate and still remain liquid. It is possible, however, to obtain good separations of some materials while using a small temperature gradient. In these cases a longer time is required. This technique may be useful in separating certain temperature-sensitive liquids of biological origin. As illustrated by Begeman and Cramer,[46] it is possible to obtain slightly larger separations with small temperature differences between walls than it is with large temperature differences, but the time required to obtain the separation is longer.

As yet there are relatively few outstanding patents covering liquid thermal diffusion. Beams[47] has proposed a continuous countercurrent apparatus utilizing a single, endless belt, narrowly spaced in the middle to form the separation slit. Jones[48−50] covers the vertical countercurrent flow

[45] H. Korsching and K. Wirtz, *Naturwissenschaften*, **27**, 367 (1939).

[46] C. R. Begeman and P. L. Cramer, *Ind. Eng. Chem.*, **47**, 202 (1955).

[47] J. W. Beams, U. S. Pat. 2,521,112 (1950, to U. S. A.).

[48] A. L. Jones and E. C. Hughes, U. S. Pat. 2,541,069 (1951, to The Standard Oil Company of Ohio).

pattern, and the continuous thermal diffusion separation of both petroleum and nonpetroleum liquids. Debye[51] uses thermal diffusion to separate high polymeric liquids. Hanson[52] interposes a screen in the separation chamber to aid in separating the product streams. In the field of process applications, a British patent to Barnitz[53] describes the separation of constituents of natural fats and oils by imposing a temperature gradient across a body of the material.

It is not possible at this time to outline specifically all of the areas where thermal diffusion is or is not applicable, but enough is known to indicate that investigators should give it serious consideration as a powerful separating tool when they have separations involving mixtures of components in the liquid state of matter.

Part 2. BARRIER SEPARATIONS

I. INTRODUCTION

The separation of isotopic uranium hexafluorides, necessitated by the Atomic Energy program, brought about a rapid development in the field of separations by solid barriers. The process is in operation on a vast scale, while general knowledge is quite limited. There are, however, many indications of other uses of barrier separations including those in organic chemistry.

Barrier separations are basically distributive in nature; a complete separation in one step has not been achieved and the principles involved preclude the possibility of such a separation. The principles which govern barrier separation are most easily demonstrated for mixtures of gases. Therefore, the theoretical background is presented on this basis, followed by the treatment of vapor systems with the necessary modifications. The type and extent of separation is illustrated by experimental results. Although the organic chemist is more interested in the separation of organic

[49] A. L. Jones and E. C. Hughes, U. S. Pat. 2,541,070 (1951, to The Standard Oil Company of Ohio).

[50] A. L. Jones and E. C. Hughes, U. S. Pat. 2,541,071 (1951, to The Standard Oil Company of Ohio).

[51] P. J. W. Debye, U. S. Pat. 2,567,765 (1951).

[52] O. M. Hanson, U. S. Pat. 2,585,244 (1952, to Universal Oil Products Company).

[53] E. S. Barnitz, Brit. Pat. 606,230 (1948, to Distillation Products Industries).

vapors, the separation of gases can be of importance in technological problems, for instance, in the case of plastic films used for packaging. Finally, separation in the liquid phase with a solid barrier is discussed; the meager data are qualitative in nature and a theoretical explanation of this phenomenon has not been worked out.

II. BASIC PRINCIPLES

A barrier separation proceeds as follows: a mixture of components is brought in contact with a solid barrier in such a manner that a fraction of the mixture passes through the barrier and a residual fraction remains, having passed over but not through the barrier. The process can be carried out batchwise, or in a continuous-flow system. In either case, a material balance must be satisfied so that:

$$N_f = N_o + N_p \text{ (total material balance)} \tag{1}$$

and:

$$N_f X_f^A = N_o X_o^A + N_p X_p^A \quad \text{(component material balance)} \tag{2}$$

There are as many component material balances as there are components. The fraction which passes through (or permeates) the barrier is defined as:

$$F = N_p/N_f = (N_f - N_o)/N_f \tag{3a}$$

and also:

$$F = (X_f - X_o)/(X_p - X_o) \tag{3b}$$

When $F = 1$, all of the original mixture will have passed through the barrier, and of course no change in composition—and, therefore, no enrichment in any component—will have occurred. It is a specific property of a barrier that some constituents will pass through it at greater rates than others. Consequently, whenever F is less than one, changes in composition of the permeated and unpermeated streams will occur, so that the faster permeating component or components will become enriched in the permeated stream and correspondingly depleted in the unpermeated stream. As F approaches zero, the degree of enrichment will rise to a maximum in the permeated stream when only an infinitesimally small quantity of mixture has passed through the barrier.

The fact that a solid possesses a structure which permits ready penetration by fluids (gases, vapors, and liquids) is no indication that the solid will behave as a barrier. For a solid to act as a molecular sieve, the molecular size of the components of the fluid mixture and the size of the pores of the solid must have a specific relation to each other.

III. SEPARATION OF GASES

The separation of gases by means of a barrier presents the simplest, or at any rate the least complicated, case.

1. Molecular Flow

In a mixture of gases, all molecules possess statistically the same average kinetic energy, $1/2\ mv^2$, for a given temperature and pressure. When the molecular masses (m) differ, then the velocities (v) of different molecular species also differ, so that the lighter molecules possess greater velocities than the heavier ones. If it were possible to eliminate intermolecular collisions and thus limit collisions to the striking of the solid surface, the molecules having a greater velocity would tend to separate from the slower molecules. Within the confines of a tube or a pore, a certain portion of the molecules would become separated more and more in the direction of the axis, giving rise to a "molecular flow" through the pore with resultant separation. Molecular flow occurs when the mean free path of the molecules becomes appreciably greater than the diameter of the pore. This can be accomplished with a vacuum which causes an increase in the mean free path until it exceeds the largest pore diameter of the barrier, or with barriers which possess pores of a diameter less than the mean free path of the gases at atmospheric pressure or at higher pressures. As manipulation is difficult under vacuum, particularly high vacuum, attention will be centered on barriers which can be used at or above atmospheric pressure.

The mean free paths of gases and vapors at atmospheric temperature and pressure are in the range of 500 to 3000 Å.[1] Knudsen[2] recommended that the pore diameter should be less than about 0.4 times the mean free path in order to assure essentially all molecular flow in the system. Although this value is questionable, it serves as a satisfactory guide. Consequently, the pore diameters of barriers for pressure operation should be less than about 200 Å. For a more detailed treatment of molecular flow, the pioneer work of Graham[3] and Knudsen,[4] and the comprehensive book, *Diffusion in and through Solids*, by Barrer[5] should be consulted.

2. Equations for Separation

Equations for predicting of the degree of separation in binary mixtures,

[1] *Handbook of Chemistry and Physics.* Chemical Rubber Publ., Cleveland, Ohio.

[2] M. Knudsen, *Ann. Physik*, **28**, 75 (1909).

[3] T. Graham, *Phil. Mag.*, **32**, 401 (1866).

[4] M. Knudsen, *Ann. Physik*, **28**, 75 (1909).

[5] R. M. Barrer, *Diffusion in and through Solids.* Cambridge Press, London, 1951.

when the rates of permeation of the individual components are known, were derived by Weller and Steiner[6,7] from the Fick's law equation and the material balances given in equations (1) and (2).   If the ratio of the rates of permeation is calculated from Fick's law, equation (6) is obtained;   this equation also represents a form of Graham's law.   As the derivation has been adequately covered in a number of publications,[6-8] it is not presented in detail here.

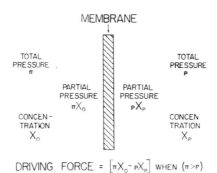

DRIVING FORCE $= \left[\pi X_o - p X_p\right]$ WHEN $(\pi > p)$

Fig. 1. Relationships for barrier flow and driving force.

Figure 1 presents the basic concept and the expression for the driving force existing across the barrier for the individual components.   Graham's law, which was developed on the basis of zero pressure on the downstream side, *i.e.*, the low-pressure side of the membrane, can be expressed for a binary system as follows:

$$X_p^A/X_p^B = (X_o^A/X_o^B) (M_B/M_A)^{1/2} \tag{4}$$

where: $X^B = 1 - X^A$

If the downstream pressure is not zero, but has a finite value p (which is almost always the case), the equation becomes:

$$\frac{X_p^A}{1 - X_p^A} = \left(\frac{M_B}{M_A}\right)^{1/2} \left[\frac{\pi X_o^A - p X_p^A}{\pi (1 - X_o^A) - p(1 - X_p^A)}\right] \tag{5}$$

Usually, not all the pores of a microporous barrier are sufficiently small to give molecular flow exclusively, and some Poiseuille or viscous flow may take place.   As flow through plastic films does not follow the $(1/M)^{1/2}$ law, it is customary to use the "permeability" ratios and equation (5) becomes:

[6] S. Weller and W. A. Steiner, *Chem. Eng. Progress*, **46**, 585 (1950).

[7] S. Weller and W. A. Steiner, *J. Appl. Phys.*, **21**, 279 (1950).

[8] H. E. Huckins, Jr., and K. Kammermeyer, *Chem. Eng. Progress*, **49**, 180, 294 (1953).

$$\frac{X_p^A}{1 - X_p^A} = \frac{P_A}{P_B}\left[\frac{\pi X_o^A - pX_p^A}{\pi(1 - X_o^A) - p(1 - X_p^A)}\right] \tag{6}$$

The significance of the preceding statement and the meaning of the permeability P will be treated in Section IV.

The Weller-Steiner equations were developed for two cases, representing different degrees of mixing of the gas mixtures on the high- and low-pressure sides of the barrier. The actual conditions of mixing depend on the geometry of the separation cell and can vary from complete mixing on both sides of the barrier (case I) to essentially no mixing as represented by laminar flow (case II). For practical purposes case I can be considered as representing an ordinary cell and a convenient solution of the equation for product composition X_p^A in a binary system is as follows:[8]

$$X_p^A = \frac{-b \pm (b^2 - 4ac)^{1/2}}{2a} \tag{7}$$

where:

$$a = (\alpha - 1)[\pi F + p(1 - F)]$$
$$b = -[\pi(1 - X_f^A) + a + c]$$
$$c = \alpha\pi X_f^A$$
$$\alpha = (M_B/M_A)^{1/2}$$

or

$$P_A/P_B,$$

and

$$1 \geqslant X_p^A > 0.$$

Although the equation was originally developed by means of Fick's law for plastic film barriers, it is applicable to microporous membranes.[9] As the permeation of each component is independent of the other components, the total flow is the sum of the individual component flows.

IV. BARRIER TYPES

The use of the two terms, microporous barrier and plastic film barrier, in the preceding discussion does not imply that plastic films are without microporous structure, but the micropores in plastic films are for the most part small in diameter (perhaps in the 10 Å. unit range) and relatively few in number. It is advantageous to differentiate between microporous and plastic barriers because the former act as molecular sieves due to the presence of pores, while separation by the latter depends on the solubility relations between the film and the components of the fluid mixture. Therefore, for microporous barriers the molecular-weight relationship expressed by Graham's law holds when all flow is molecular flow. But for plastic films, it is necessary to determine actual permeability values for each system. The determination of permeabilities is covered in some detail because a knowledge of permeability, especially of gases, permits selection of the most suitable film barrier for the separation of any particular system.

1. Permeabilities

Permeabilities of barriers for gases or vapors are relatively easy to determine. Two types of apparatus have been used for gases; in one a volume measurement is made directly, and in the other a pressure change is observed in an evacuated system.[9-14]

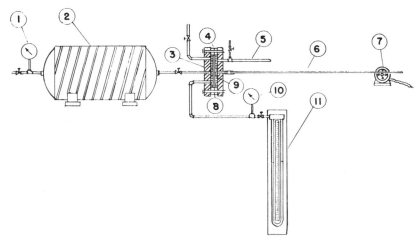

1. 600-lb. pressure gage.	7. Motor-driven vibrator.
2. Gas storage tank.	8. Plastic film.
3. 11-in. steel flange.	9. Filter paper film support.
4. Rubber gasket.	10. 100-lb. pressure gage, in
5. Thermometer.	1-lb. graduations.
6. Glass capillary tube.	11. 50-in. manometer.

Fig. 2. Testing apparatus for barriers in sheet form.[27]

A rather simple apparatus for determining **gas permeabilities** is shown in Figure 2.[27] This apparatus can be used with any kind of sheetlike barrier

[9] R. M. Barrer, *Trans. Faraday Soc.*, **43**, 3 (1947).

[10] L. C. Cartwright, *Anal. Chem.*, **19**, 393 (1947).

[11] T. W. Sarge, *Anal. Chem.*, **19**, 396 (1947).

[12] A. C. Shuman, *Ind. Eng. Chem., Anal. Ed.*, **16**, 58 (1944).

[13] V. L. Simril and A. Hershberger, *Modern Plastics*, **27**, 95 (July, 1950).

[14] H. R. Todd, *Modern Packaging*, **18**, 124 (1944).

for both permeability measurements and for gas-separation experiments. In operation, the volume of gas which permeates the membrane is measured by timing a short column of mercury which travels in a glass capillary between two fixed marks. Such equipment can be used at temperatures above the freezing point of mercury. At lower temperatures the pressure-rise method can be used. For separation experiments the glass capillary is replaced by a gas-sampling device.[15]

The measurement of **vapor permeabilities** requires a different type of apparatus. Simril and Hershberger[16] have reported a comprehensive list of organic vapor permeabilities of polymeric films obtained with a cup-type arrangement similar to one used extensively in water vapor transmission tests.[17] The equipment consists essentially of a cup with a convenient arrangement for clamping the film, or sheet material, over the cup opening. Rates of vapor permeation are then measured by observing the loss in weight of the liquid material which has been placed in the cup. A number of other methods including flow methods were reviewed by Stout, Geisman, and Mozley.[18]

The extensive work which has been done on **water-vapor permeation** through film materials of all types has been summarized through 1947[19]; most of the well-known types of apparatus are listed in this review. For more recent modifications, the bulletins of the American Society for Testing Materials (A.S.T.M.) and the publications of the Technical Association of the Pulp and Paper Industry (T.A.P.P.I.) should be consulted.

For microporous barriers, the equipment must be fitted more or less to the shape of the barrier. If the barrier is a disc, a flange-type arrangement can be used directly in the equipment shown in Figure 2. Of course, any other type of barrier holder can be installed in place of the flange type. Instead of the capillary with a traveling mercury slug, burets can be used to measure the volume in separation experiments.[20]

The results for a CO_2–H_2–O_2 mixture shown[21] in Figure 3 illustrate the difference in separating behavior of a plastic film and a strictly microporous barrier. On the basis of the molecular-weight difference H_2 and CO_2 separate as shown for the porous glass barrier, that is, enrichment in H_2 and depletion in CO_2. (Porous glass is obtained as an intermediate product in

[15] D. W. Brubaker and K. Kammermeyer, *Ind. Eng. Chem.*, **44**, 1465 (1952).

[16] V. L. Simril and A. Hershberger, *Modern Plastics*, **27**, 97 (June, 1950).

[17] W. H. Charch and A. G. Scroggie, *Paper Trade J.*, **101**, No. 14, 31 (1935).

[18] L. E. Stout, R. Geisman, and J. M. Mozley, Jr., *Chem. Eng. Progress*, **44**, 219 (1948).

[19] C. J. West, W. B. Kunz, and G. R. Sears, *Permeability of Organic Materials to Gases*, Parts I and II. Bibliographic Series No. 169. The Institute of Paper Chemistry, Appleton, Wis., June, 1948.

[20] H. E. Huckins, Jr., and K. Kammermeyer, *Chem. Eng. Progress*, **49**, 180, 294 (1953).

[21] K. Kammermeyer and D. W. Brubaker, *Chem. Eng. Progress*, **50**, 560 (1954).

the manufacture of Corning's Vycor brand glass.   It is characterized by a
rather uniform pore size with an average pore diameter of 40 to 60 Å.,[22–24]

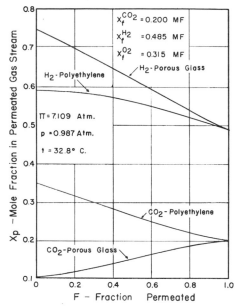

Fig. 3. A comparison of separation for the system CO_2–H_2–O_2.[21]

a surface of about 120 sq. m./g.,[25] and approximately 1.34×10^{12} pores
per sq. cm.[26]) The behavior of the third component, O_2, which is not shown,
can be calculated by difference for any F factor; it has no bearing on the
separation of CO_2 and H_2 as the gas flows are additive.   The separation
with the polyethylene barrier shows that both CO_2 and H_2 become enriched.
H_2 diffuses rapidly because of its low molecular weight and its rather high
solubility in polyethylene; CO_2 also diffuses rapidly, as its solubility in the
plastic is very high.

2. Variables Affecting Permeability

The most convenient way of dealing with permeability is by use of the
permeability constant P (often referred to simply as permeability). This
constant appears in the flow equation:

[22] P. H. Emmett and M. Cines, *J. Phys. & Colloid Chem.*, **51**, 1248 (1947).

[23] H. P. Hood and M. E. Nordberg, U. S. Pat. 2,106,744 (1938).

[24] M. E. Nordberg, *J. Am. Ceram. Soc.*, **27**, No. 10, 299 (1944).

[25] P. H. Emmett and T. D. DeWitt, *J. Am. Chem. Soc.*, **65**, 1253 (1943).

[26] F. A. Schwertz, *J. Am. Ceram. Soc.*, **32**, 390 (1949).

$$q = PA\theta(\pi - p)/d \qquad (8a)$$

and is therefore defined as:

$$P = qd/A\theta(\pi - p) \qquad (8b)$$

Any consistent set of units can be used, for instance

$$P = \frac{\text{(cc. S.T.P.) (cm. thickness)}}{\text{(sq. cm. area) (sec.) (cm. Hg partial pressure difference)}}$$

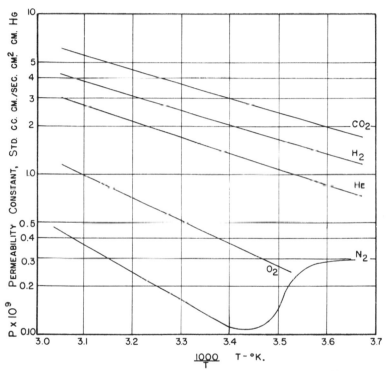

Fig. 4. Gas permeability through cellulose acetate butyrate film.[28]

The variables entering into the permeability constant are temperature, pressure, thickness, and character of the barrier. The effect of thickness is usually linear,[27] *i.e.*, the flow decreases with increasing thickness of the barrier.

For **gases** the permeability is independent of the average pressure, *i.e.*, the mean of high and low pressure, as long as the barrier behaves like a perfect molecular sieve. When the barrier, however, possesses some large

[27] D. W. Brubaker and K. Kammermeyer, *Ind. Eng. Chem.*, **45**, 1148 (1953).

pores which permit viscous flow, that portion of the flow varies with pressure according to Poiseuille's law. Permeability usually increases with temperature and often log P *vs.* $1/T$ gives a straight line over a considerable range of temperature. However, since there are cases which have a negative temperature coefficient of permeability or in which the variation of permeability with temperature is unpredictable, P values should be determined for at least three temperatures in the range of operation. In Figure 4,[28] which shows gas permeabilities for a cellulose acetate–butyrate

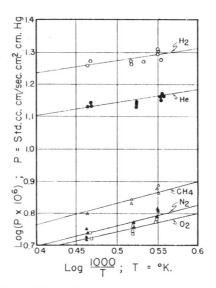

Fig. 5. Effect of temperature on gas permeability through porous glass membrane.[30]

film, the behavior of nitrogen is anomalous; neither dilatometric measurements nor x-ray diffraction pictures gave any clue to the reason for this behavior. The oxygen curve beyond the last point plotted is similar. Othmer and Frohlich[29] have prepared a nomogram for some 150 normal systems of gases and polymeric films, in which the permeability is related to temperature; only systems which have a positive temperature coefficient are covered. With the porous glass the permeability curves would be straight lines varying essentially with $T^{1/2}$ as shown in Figure 5.[30]

For **vapors** the permeability is a function of pressure, because of adsorp-

[28] D. W. Brubaker and K. Kammermeyer, *Ind. Eng. Chem.*, **46**, 733 (1954).

[29] D. F. Othmer and G. J. Frohlich, *Ind. Eng. Chem.*, **47**, 1034 (1955).

[30] D. W. Brubaker and K. Kammermeyer, *Proceedings Conference on Nuclear Engineering 1953*, F9-F28, University of California, Berkeley, Sept. 9–11, 1953.

tion. As barriers, by their very nature, are capillary systems, they adsorb fluids. A vapor or a gas, at a sufficiently high temperature or pressure, is adsorbed and a "condensed" phase is formed. Experience has shown that there is mobility in the condensed phase so that the rate of flow is greater than in the vapor phase. The occurrence of this phenomenon, sometimes called "surface flow," has been established by Volmer.[31] The permeability values increase with pressure up to about the saturation pressure and then begin to decrease, presumably because all of the pores are then filled with

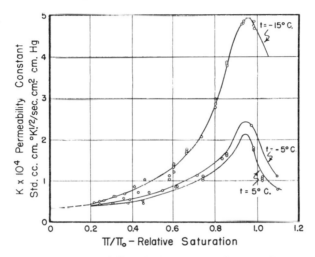

Fig. 6. NH$_3$ permeability through porous glass membrane.[30]

liquid. Temperature exerts the same effect on permeability as on adsorption. Figure 6[30] shows the permeability behavior of ammonia with porous glass. Here, the value $K = PT^{1/2}$ is used, as this value is essentially independent of T.

The permeability of vapors through plastic films and rubbers[32,33] were for the most part measured for only one temperature. Simril and Hershberger[32] presented some information for organic vapor permeation through polyethylene in the temperature range of 10–35°C. All of their results show that the permeability of the saturated vapors increased with increasing temperature. This is in line with water-vapor permeation through plastic film.[34]

[31] M. Volmer, *The Adsorption of Gases by Solids. A General Discussion.* The Faraday Society, Jan., 1932, p. 359.
[32] V. L. Simril and A. Hershberger, *Modern Plastics*, **27**, 97 (June, 1950).
[33] L. E. Stout, R. Geisman, and J. M. Mozley, Jr., *Chem. Eng. Progress*, **44**, 219 (1948).
[34] P. M. Doty, W. H. Aiken, and H. Mark, *Ind. Eng. Chem., Anal. Ed.*, **16**, 686 (1944).

3. Structural Factors

The mathematical relations, of course, are based on the concept of an ideal barrier, that is, one which permits only molecular flow. As a barrier is not likely to be perfect, factors which depend on the structure of the respective barrier types must be taken into account.

With **plastic barriers** the problem of porosity arises. Porosity implies the presence of holes which are large in comparison to those which give molecular flow. Permeability through a porous barrier is out of line with well-established values for the particular type or the general class of the film. References[35]–[42] give permeability data for many plastic materials. If the porosity is appreciable or the film has a hole or tear which may not be visible, the permeability value for a test gas will be too high or, more likely, it will not be possible to take readings. If, however, only a very minute pinhole is present, the permeability will be on the high side. In that event a selenium sulfide print should be made.[43] In this method the film is placed between a SeS coated paper and an amalgamized metal plate. Mercury vapor passes rapidly through pinholes and prints black dots where there are defective areas.

In the case of **microporous barriers** a permeability determination for a gas, such as nitrogen, at different upstream pressures shows if the flow is all molecular, or if some viscous flow is present. Molecular flow is independent of average pressure and a plot of the permeability constant P against the pressure is a line parallel to the absissa. If viscous flow is present, the line has a positive slope, and the greater the slope, the larger the amount of viscous flow. Even in the range of molecular flow, there may be a small portion of the flow which is nonseparative in nature. Present and de Bethune[44] have developed a mathematical treatment for this situation. The holes of a porous barrier vary considerably in size; the pore diameter of some is essentially of the same magnitude as the mean free path. As the pore size increases from values much smaller than the mean free path to values approaching the mean free path, the number of intermolecular collisions increases from practically zero to an appreciable fraction of the

[35] R. M. Barrer, *Diffusion in and through Solids*. Cambridge Press, London, 1951.

[36] D. W. Brubaker and K. Kammermeyer, *Ind. Eng. Chem.*, **44**, 1465 (1952).

[37] D. W. Brubaker and K. Kammermeyer, *Ind. Eng. Chem.*, **45**, 1148 (1953).

[38] D. W. Brubaker and K. Kammermeyer, *Ind. Eng. Chem.*, **46**, 733 (1954).

[39] D. F. Othmer and G. J. Frohlich, *Ind. Eng. Chem.*, **47**, 1034 (1955).

[40] V. L. Simril and A. Hershberger, *Modern Plastics*, **27**, 97 (June, 1950).

[41] V. L. Simril and A. Hershberger, *Modern Plastics*, **27**, 95 (July, 1950).

[42] L. E. Stout, R. Geisman, and J. M. Mozley, Jr., *Chem. Eng. Progress*, **44**, 219 (1948).

[43] B. W. Nordlander, *Ind. Eng. Chem.*, **19**, 518 (1927); U. S. Pat. 2,310,111.

[44] R. D. Present and A. J. de Bethune, *Phys. Rev.*, **75**, 1050 (1949).

collisions. While still in the molecular-flow range, these collisions tend to set up some kind of molecular drift in the direction of lower pressure, and this drift includes all types of molecules without separating them in accordance with molecular weights. Figure 7 is a simplified diagram which pictures schematically just what distribution of flow types may be expected in a porous barrier. An adsorption procedure, *e.g.*, the Brunauer-Emmett-Teller method[45] may be used to give an idea of the size and distribution of the pores.

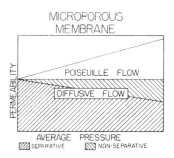

Fig. 7. Schematic diagram of flow types encountered with porous barrier.

A given barrier, therefore, gives a certain amount of molecular flow and a correction factor for barrier efficiency can thus be applied. In general, the nonseparative portion of the diffusive flow is not large in comparison to the viscous flow, and its effect can be included in the barrier efficiency. When the barrier is used in a cell, a cell efficiency must be applied in addition to the barrier efficiency. It is probably simpler to use an over-all cell efficiency, which corrects for inefficiencies due to barrier structure and cell design.

Although metal foils and glass can act as separating media, their permeabilities are in general so low that they are not suitable barrier materials unless they are modified to give a microporous structure. Permeabilities of unmodified glass and metals are presented by Barrer[46] and Jost.[47] Gas permeation through metals may involve some dissociation of gas molecules so that at least part of the gas is diffusing in its atomic state.

The time required to reach equilibrium under flow conditions may be rather long, sometimes 48 hours or more.[48] This period can be shortened to a few hours or less if the barrier is first operated at a pressure higher than

[45] S. Brunauer, P. H. Emmett, and E. Teller, *J. Am. Chem. Soc.*, **60**, 309 (1938).

[46] R. M. Barrer, *Diffusion in and through Solids*. Cambridge Press, London, 1951.

[47] W. Jost, *Diffusion in Solids, Liquids, Gases*. Academic Press, New York, 1952.

[48] D. H. Hagerbaumer and K. Kammermeyer, *Am. Inst. Chem. Engrs. J.*, **1**, No. 2, 152 (1955).

the normal operating pressure.   In this way adsorption equilibrium is established more quickly.   Probably the barrier should be subjected to a vacuum before use, to effect as much desorption of adsorbed gas or vapor as possible.   This procedure should speed up the attainment of flow equilibrium.   Of course, equilibrium can be established by exposure of the barrier to the gases or vapors for an adequate period of time; a continuous flow of the gaseous phase mixture over the barrier is unnecessary.

V. SEPARATION OF VAPORS

Whenever the mixture which is to be separated contains a vapor, adsorption comes into the picture, as vapors are readily condensed under the conditions of operation by the capillary action of the barrier.   In general, this implies that the component will be below its critical temperature.

1. Gas–Vapor Systems

The information on the separation of gaseous phase systems which contain a vapor is rather limited, except for the case of water vapor.   The interest in plastic films and coated papers[49] for packaging has given rise to numerous studies with these materials.   Separation with solid barriers is discussed in the following section.   The work on adsorptive powder, e.g., analcite crystals[50] and crystalline zeolites,[51] is not covered.

In **separations with plastic films,** data are available for binary and multicomponent mixtures of a gas, or gases, and a vapor; the vapors include CO_2, NH_3, and SO_2.[52]   The permeability behavior of vapors over the range of temperatures covered is analogous to that of gases.   Figure 8 shows P values for some gases, as well as the vapors CO_2 and NH_3, obtained with a monochlorotrifluoroethylene polymer film (Trithene).   Separation of a multicomponent mixture with this film is shown in Figure 9.   The experimental data fall on the calculated curves, indicating that prediction of separation by means of equation (7) is possible.   There are no data as yet on mixtures of gases and organic vapors and this fact should be kept in mind when equation (7) is applied.

The information on separation of gas–vapor systems by **microporous barriers** is almost as limited as that for plastic films.   Data on the separa-

[49] C. J. West, W. B. Kunz, and G. R. Sears, *Permeability of Organic Materials to Gases.* Parts I and II.   Bibliographic Series No. 169.   The Institute of Paper Chemistry, Appleton, Wis., June, 1948.

[50] R. M. Barrer and D. M. Grove, *Trans. Faraday Soc.*, **47**, No. 344, 826, 837 (1951).

[51] *Molecular Sieves for Selective Adsorption*, Linde Air Products Co., Tonawanda Research Laboratory Bulletin.

[52] D. W. Brubaker and K. Kammermeyer, *Ind. Eng. Chem.*, **46**, 733 (1954).

tion of gaseous phase mixtures, containing CO_2 and NH_3 with a porous glass barrier, have been published.[53,54]

The separation of an H_2–NH_3 mixture with porous glass is illustrated in Figure 10.[53] The deviation of the experimental curve from the curve calculated from P values at the corresponding π/π_0 values (see Fig. 6) which is appreciable at 55°C., becomes more pronounced at 5°C. Deviation is

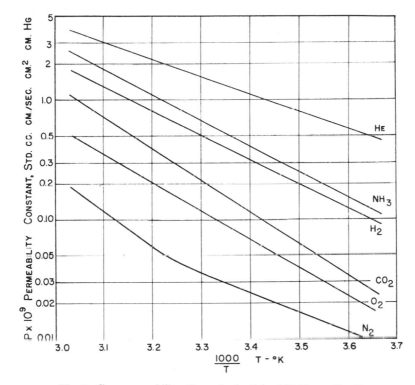

Fig. 8. Gas permeability through plasticized Trithene film.[28]

caused by the fact that NH_3 is more readily adsorbed and condensed than H_2 in the pores of the barrier. As the rate of flow in the "condensed" phase is greater than in the vapor phase,[55] more NH_3 passes through the membrane than would be the case if only vapor flow were to take place. The conditions are pictured schematically in Figure 11. Molecules of all kinds in the

[53] D. W. Brubaker and K. Kammermeyer, *Proceedings, 1953 Conference on Nuclear Engineering*, F9-F28, University of California, Berkeley, Sept. 9–11, 1953.

[54] K. Kammermeyer and D. W. Brubaker, *Chem. Eng. Progress*, **50**, 560 (1954).

[55] M. Volmer, *The Adsorption of Gases by Solids. A General Discussion*. The Faraday Society, Jan., 1932, p. 359.

feed mixture diffuse to the barrier wall and enter at conditions of surface
concentration. The more readily adsorbed molecules form a layer (probably multiple layers) of a condensed phase which covers a good deal of active surface. As a result, the concentration of the less readily adsorbed
molecules increases in the vapor phase, possibly above the concentration
existing on the entrance side of the barrier. Such conditions could cause a
reversal in driving force, so that back-diffusion may occur. The net result is a vastly increased rate of permeation of the more readily condensable
molecules through the barrier, and consequent enrichment in the permeated stream.

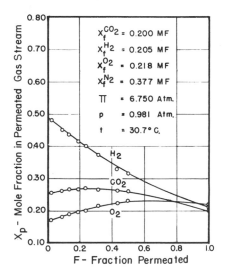

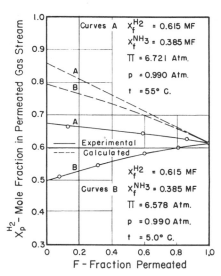

Fig. 9. Separation of system CO_2–H_2–   Fig. 10. H_2–NH_3 separation with porous
O_2–N_2 with Trithene film.[52]   glass membrane.[53]

A quantitative interpretation of the flow of a gas–vapor mixture was
attempted by Vollmer[56] for the transport of gases and vapors through paper
films. While other investigators suggested that the problem might be
solved by the use of adsorption isotherms (or isobars), Vollmer's was the
first quantitative approach. Using the isotherm to calculate a concentration gradient, he proposed a method in which the total transport is split
into that due to gas and to vapor by permeation through pores only; the
amount of the vapor transport is calculated from adsorption data. Only
the flow of water vapor and air has been treated in this way; curves for
transmission through a polyvinyl chloride film are presented. This approach, which looks promising, requires adequate testing.

[56] W. Vollmer, *Chem. Ing. Tech.*, **26**, 90 (1954).

2. Vapor–Vapor Systems

No information has been published on the separation of vapor–vapor systems by plastic membranes. However, separation by microporous membranes (porous glass) has been described for a CO_2–C_3H_8 mixture and for a number of organic vapors of azeotropic composition.[57]

Although a rather large difference in adsorbability is likely for a vapor–gas mixture, one would expect the difference in degree of adsorption for vapor–vapor mixtures to be much less. Nevertheless, it appears that adsorption from such mixtures can be highly selective, so that the mechanism illustrated in Figure 11 may take place. Adsorption from mixed vapors is reviewed in a number of texts.[58] The data reported by Tryhorn and Wyatt,[59] and by Rao[60] definitely establish the occurrence of selective adsorption from

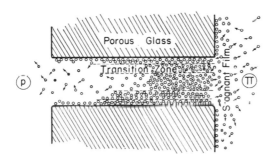

Fig. 11. Schematic diagram of vapor flow through microporous membrane.

mixed vapors, but a quantitative interpretation of vapor vapor separation data is not possible at present.

The separation of azeotropic vapors was studied in two different pressure ranges. For essentially atmospheric pressures, a vacuum was used on the low-pressure side of the porous glass barrier, and the permeated product was collected by condensation at low temperatures. The equipment for atmospheric pressure work is pictured in Figure 12. A detailed diagram for superatmospheric pressure studies has been published.[57] Pressures up to

[57] D. H. Hagerbaumer and K. Kammermeyer, *Chem. Eng. Progress Symposium*, Series No. 10, *Collected Research Papers*, **50**, 25 (1954).

[58] S. Brunauer, *The Adsorption of Gases and Vapors*, Vol. I, *Physical Adsorption*, Princeton Univ. Press, Princeton, 1943. S. J. Gregg, *The Surface Chemistry of Solids*, Reinhold, New York, 1951. E. Ledoux, *Vapor Adsorption*, Chemical Publ., Brooklyn, 1945. C. L. Mantell, *Adsorption*, McGraw-Hill, New York, 1951.

[59] F. G. Tryhorn and W. F. Wyatt, *Trans. Faraday Soc.*, **22**, 139 (1926); **24**, 36 (1928).

[60] B. S. Rao, *J. Phys. Chem.*, **36**, 616 (1932).

about 5 atmospheres upstream pressure were employed, with vacuum or atmospheric pressure on the downstream side of the barrier. The use of azeotropic compositions permitted vaporization from liquid mixtures at constant pressure for long periods without changes in vapor composition, even when the vapors were superheated.

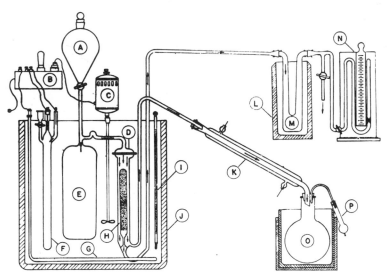

A. 500-ml. separatory funnel.
B. Relay.
C. Stirring motor.
D. 2-cm. I.D. × 16-cm. glass housing for porous glass membrane, ball-and-socket upper connection.
E. 1-liter glass still pot.
F. Mercury thermoregulator.
G. Heating coil.

H. 1.72-cm. O.D. × 8.18-cm. porous glass membrane.
I. Thermometer.
J. 5-gal. insulated constant-temperature bath.
K. Glass condenser.
L. Dewar flask.
M. U-tube collection flask for permeated vapor.
N. Manometer.
O. 500-ml. flask for unpermeated vapor.
P. Drying tube.

Fig. 12. Apparatus for vapor–vapor separation at atmospheric pressure.[57]

Separation data with porous glass are available for the following systems of minimum-boiling-point azeotropes:

Systems A	Systems B
$(CH_3)_2CO - CH_3OH$	$H_2O - iso\text{-}C_3H_7OH$
$C_6H_{12} - C_2H_5OH$	$CCl_4 - CH_3COOC_2H_5$
$C_6H_6 - iso\text{-}C_3H_7OH$	$C_6H_{12} - C_6H_6$
$C_6H_6 - n\text{-}C_3H_7OH$	$CS_2 - (CH_3)_2CO$
$C_6H_6 - CH_3OH$	
$C_6H_6 - C_2H_5OH$	
$C_2H_5OH - H_2O$	

One side of the barrier was at atmospheric pressure and the other side at about 4 mm. Hg absolute pressure, so that the pressure drop was essentially one atmosphere. With different conditions of pressure on the two sides of the barrier, it is necessary to take into account the effect of pressure upon the composition of the azeotrope, because of the possibility of vapor condensation at the higher pressure and reevaporation at the lower. If this should take place, the evaporation at the lower pressure would give a vapor

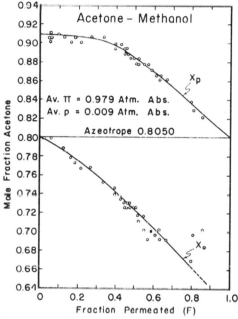

Fig. 13. Vapor separation of acetone–methanol with porous glass.[57]

composition approaching the azeotropic composition which corresponds to the lower pressure. The change in composition of systems A was in the same direction at that which results from boiling the liquid mixture at lower pressures. However, the change in composition of systems B was in the opposite direction. The mechanism of mixed vapor flow is not established completely. Two phenomena may occur: (1) adsorption from vapor mixtures is selective, and therefore one of the components exhibits greater condensed flow; and (2) it is possible that evaporation of the condensed phase at the lower pressure results in a vapor composition corresponding to the lower pressure. The two effects may enhance or oppose each other. On the other hand, one could probably explain the enrichment entirely on the basis of preferential adsorption.

Compositions obtained in vapor-phase separation at the boiling temperature of the acetone–methanol system are shown in Figure 13.[57]   The curves of the stream composition versus the fraction permeated (F) of all the other systems exhibit essentially similar shapes; they also illustrate the separation attainable.   The slight enrichment obtained with the system C_2H_5OH–H_2O is exceptional.

Benzene–methanol and benzene–ethanol were also investigated at upstream pressures up to 5 atmospheres absolute and at different degrees of

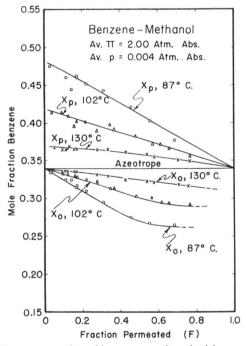

Fig. 14. Vapor separation of benzene–methanol with porous glass.[57]

superheating.   The results for benzene–methanol at 2.0 atm. absolute pressure are shown in Figure 14[57]; the behavior of both systems, at all pressures used, is similar.   The effect of temperature is as expected; as higher temperatures give less condensed flow, the effect of preferential adsorption becomes less pronounced.   If superheating had been carried to still higher temperatures, condensed flow would have been eliminated, and separation would then take place so that the lower molecular weight component—methanol—would be the one to become enriched in permeation through the barrier.   A trend in this direction is indicated in Figure 14.

Separations can be carried out more conveniently if the lower pressure side of the membrane is kept at atmospheric pressure. This can be done readily. Furthermore, it is, of course, not necessary to restrict such separations to azeotropic mixtures. If mixtures are easily separated by distillation or solvent extraction, these methods are preferable, because barrier separations are slow processes. However, when components of a mixture have very low relative volatilities, or unfavorable distribution coefficients, then barrier separation should be considered. If adsorption isobars or isotherms are available, it may be possible to predict the direction of separation, insofar as the more highly adsorbed component would be expected to permeate at a faster rate. Prediction of the degree of separation is not possible with our present knowledge, and preferential adsorption from mixed vapors is largely an unexplored field.

VI. LABORATORY EQUIPMENT

Equipment for the determination of permeabilities is discussed in Section IV. Such equipment is relatively simple when it is to be used for gases. The apparatus shown in Figure 2 is designed primarily for use with sheet-like barriers, in particular, plastic films. An apparatus which permits rapid opening and closing and easy exchange of film barriers has been described.[61] Such equipment is justified if many determinations are to be made. Microporous barriers in the form of sheets or discs can be readily used in this flange-type apparatus with appropriate sealing devices for the barriers.

The auxiliary equipment necessary to measure flow quantities and to analyze the various stream samples is arranged to fit individual requirements. A semiautomatic assembly with pneumatic flow control and an electrical timing system suitable for contact or photoelectric timing has been described[62] for use with any type of separation cell. An apparatus specifically designed for separations with plastic films uses a length of plastic film tubing closed at both ends, and one end connected by means of matching holes to an inner tube made of rigid material.[63] Porous sheet material is placed both inside and outside of the plastic, the closed plastic tubing and the porous sheets are then rolled on to the rigid tube, and the assembled core is inserted into a jacket. The portion of the mixture which diffuses through the plastic barrier is thus made to flow in a spiral path to the inner tube and leaves from one end as enriched product.

The types of apparatus mentioned so far are for the most part suitable only for work with gases. Although a flange-type apparatus with a micro-

[61] D. W. Brubaker and K. Kammermeyer, *Anal. Chem.*, **25**, 424 (1953).
[62] C. W. Hancher and K. Kammermeyer, *Anal. Chem.*, **27**, 83 (1955).
[63] J. O. Osburn and K. Kammermeyer, *Ind. Eng. Chem.*, **46**, 739 (1954).

porous disc could be used with vapors, there remains the problem of condensation, especially if the apparatus is to be operated under pressure. Consequently, equipment for vapor separation should be designed specifically for the conditions to be encountered. Most plastic films are not satisfactory for work with vapors, especially organic vapors, which may attack the plastic. Therefore, relatively inert microporous barriers are usually employed for vapor separation. The shape of the barrier determines the design of the cell itself. The auxiliary equipment normally includes a boiler to vaporize a liquid mixture and condensers for the product streams.

Of course, if the liquid mixture is not azeotropic, the composition of the vapor flowing to the barrier changes with progressive vaporization. However, as mentioned previously, if distillation is an adequate means of separation, barrier separation should not be used. Therefore, any change in the vapor due to continuous evaporation of the liquid mixture is not significant. Furthermore, the fact that the composition of the vapor feed to the barrier might not be constant is not of particular significance. It becomes important only for the calculation of separation.

The methods described for vapor permeabilities of plastic materials[64-66] might be used for separation work, particularly if enrichment in a confined liquid phase is to be accomplished. In such a case, the liquid mixture would be placed in a cup and the open end of the cup closed with a plastic film. If the plastic film is selected so that it acts as a retaining barrier for a particular component, a considerable degree of concentration in the liquid phase could be attained.

Equipment for the recovery of the vapor which permeated the plastic could be built, although it might be somewhat complicated. If the liquid in the cup is heated after the film closure is applied, the film will bulge, especially as the thinnest possible film would be used. As this could cause pinholes and tears, or even ruptures of the film, a porous rigid backing for the film should be provided. It should be emphasized again that there is no published material on vapor separations with plastic films as barriers.

VII. SEPARATION IN THE LIQUID PHASE*

Solutions can be separated in the liquid phase by means of barriers with processes utilizing osmosis, ion-exchange resins incorporated in the barrier

* An up-to-date treatise on ultrafiltration is in the chapter, "Filtration," Chapter V, this volume.

[64] W. H. Charch and A. G. Scroggie, *Paper Trade J.*, **101**, No. 14, 31 (1935).

[65] V. L. Simril and A. Hershberger, *Modern Plastics*, **27**, 97 (June, 1950).

[66] L. E. Stout, R. Geisman, and J. M. Mozley, Jr., *Chem. Eng. Progress*, **44**, 219 (1948).

(or membrane), electric potentials across barriers, and ultrafiltration. The ultrafiltration of electrolytes and nonelectrolytes from aqueous solutions is discussed by Erschler,[67] and some interesting findings on solute retention are reported by McBain and Stuewer.[68] All this material is concerned with aqueous solutions; it has been stated that other polar solvents should behave in the same way.

There is no literature on the separation of homogeneous liquid mixtures of organic compounds by means of permeation through plastic or microporous barriers, except for a recent study.[69] In the work five binary organic mixtures (see Table I) were passed through porous glass in a manner

TABLE I

SEPARATION OF ORGANIC LIQUID MIXTURES BY MEANS OF A POROUS GLASS BARRIER

System	Weight per cent of feed	Component enriched	Increase in weight per cent at pressure across barrier		
			60 p.s.i.	120 p.s.i.	200 p.s.i.
Carbon tetrachloride	56.3				
Ethyl acetate	43.7	EtAc	1.01	1.72	2.11
Cyclohexane	69.0				
Ethyl alcohol	31.0	EtOH	5.84	6.76	6.6
Ethyl alcohol	93.5				
Water	6.5	H_2O^a	Change less than 0.3		
Benzene	60.4				
Methyl alcohol	39.6	MeOH	1.15	2.61	3.83
Benzene	67.4				
Ethyl alcohol	32.6	EtOH	0.5	0.4	0.8

[a] The change in concentration was so small that it could have been due to experimental errors.

which corresponds to a straightforward pressure permeation. This "fractional filtration" resulted in changes in composition, a fact of basic importance. Earlier Manegold and Hofmann[70] suggested that a filter which is suitable for ultrafiltration should act not only as a barrier on a "go or no-go" basis for molecules of different sizes, but should also exhibit partial inhibition of the movement of the larger molecules. The barrier separation differs from ultrafiltration only in the pore size used; in general, pore diameters suitable for ultrafiltration are in the range of 10^{-4} cm. (micron); the pore diameters of the barriers, however, are in the 10^{-8} cm. (Angstrom unit) range.

[67] B. Erschler, *Kolloid-Z.*, **68**, 289 (1934).
[68] J. W. McBain and R. F. Stuewer, *J. Phys. Chem.*, **40**, 1157 (1936).
[69] K. Kammermeyer and D. H. Hagerbaumer, *Am. Inst. Chem. Engrs. J.*, **1**, No. 2, 215 (1955).
[70] E. Manegold and R. Hofmann, *Kolloid-Z.*, **51**, 220, 308 (1930).

The enrichment obtained in these experiments was at most about 6.5% with one mixture, and in several instances it was almost negligible. The permeation rates were very slow, and the amount of product taken off was small in proportion to the amount of feed used. Therefore, the enrichments observed correspond to essentially zero fraction permeated. As the work was a pioneering study to determine if separation in the liquid phase

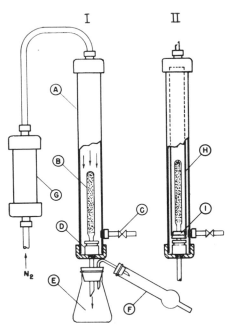

A. Metal shell of cell.	F. Drying tube (vent).
B. Porous glass membrane.	G. Silica gel drying tube.
C. Needle valve for sampling.	H. Glass liner.
D. Brass packing gland assembly.	I. Rubber stopper.
E. Sample collecting flask.	

Fig. 15. Schematic diagram of liquid–phase separation apparatus.[69]

was possible, the apparatus was constructed in the simplest manner. A continuous-flow system, which would be required to investigate the effect of variation in fraction permeated, was not used. Figure 15 shows a diagram of the separation equipment. The liquid was placed in the cylinder surrounding the porous glass barrier and compressed nitrogen was applied. Two types of cells are shown: in cell I the liquid was in direct contact with the metal wall, and in cell II a floating glass liner was inserted to avoid liquid-to-metal contact. With the mixtures investigated, it was found that

contact with the metal wall had no effect. Cell II would be suitable for use
with corrosive liquids.

Separation experiments were carried out at gage pressures of 60, 120, and
200 p.s.i. The liquid mixtures used were some of those which had been

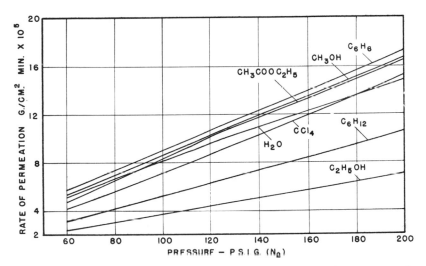

Fig. 16. Liquid rates of permeation through porous glass at various pressures.[69]

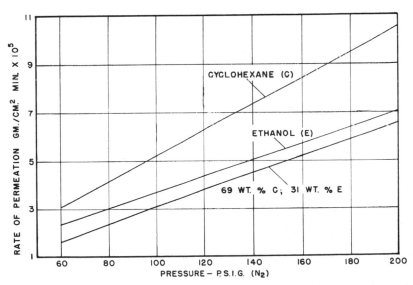

Fig. 17. Cyclohexane–ethanol rates of permeation through porous glass at
various pressures.[69]

studied in vapor-phase separation of azeotropic mixtures.[71]   The analyses of the feed and product samples were made by means of refractive-index measurements.   A summary of separations obtained is presented in Table II. Although the operations, particularly the analyses, were carried out with great care, these data should be considered as semiquantitative in nature. The rates of permeation which were determined for all components are plotted in Figure 16 against the pressure on the upstream side of the barrier. The low-pressure side was at atmospheric pressure.   Most of the mixtures permeated more slowly than either one of the components;   one permeated at an intermediate rate, and one at the rate of the faster component.   Figure 17 shows permeation rates for the system cyclohexane–ethanol.

TABLE II

SEPARATION IN LIQUID PHASE AND RELATED PROPERTIES

System	Component enriched		Component having					
	In liquid phase	In vapor phase	Lower mol. wt.	Higher dipole moment	Lower viscosity	Smaller collision diam.	Greater surface tension	Lower crit. temp.
CCl_4 – EtAc	*EtAc*	EtAc	EtAc	EtAc	EtAc	CCl_4	CCl_4	EtAc
C_6H_{12} – EtOH	*EtOH*	C_6H_{12}	EtOH	EtOH	C_6H_{12}	EtOH	C_6H_{12}	EtOH
EtOH – H_2O	*H_2O*	EtOH	H_2O	H_2O	H_2O	H_2O	H_2O	EtOH
C_6H_6 – MeOH	*MeOH*	C_6H_6	MeOH	MeOH	MeOH	MeOH	C_6H_6	MeOH
C_6H_6 – EtOH	*EtOH*	C_6H_6	EtOH	EtOH	C_6H_6	EtOH	C_6H_6	EtOH
Me_2CO – MeOH[a]	*Me_2CO*	Me_2CO	MeOH	Me_2CO	Me_2CO	MeOH	Me_2CO	Me_2CO

[a] Qualitative separation results only.

A completely satisfactory explanation of the separation process has yet to be developed.   Table II contains a summary of the separation results together with some physical properties of the components which might have a bearing on the process.   The only two properties which bear a consistent relationship to the direction of enrichment are molecular weight and dipole moment.   However, all of the binary systems which were investigated thoroughly contained a more polar component which also had the lower molecular weight.   If the qualitative separation results for acetone–methyl alcohol are taken into consideration, the only property which is correlated with the direction of separation is the dipole moment; in this system the component of higher molecular weight also possesses the greater dipole moment.

In liquid–solid interface systems, there may be competition between the solvent and the solute molecules for the surface of the adsorbent; the relative extent of adsorption may depend on a number of variables, including

[71] D. H. Hagerbaumer and K. Kammermeyer, *Chem. Eng. Progress Symposium*, Series No. 10, *Collected Research Papers*, **50**, 25 (1954).

polarity and hydrogen bonding ability, and solubility as well as many other physical properties of either the adsorbent or the adsorptive can have a major effect.[72]   If one considers the relative complexity of a permeation process, in which a liquid mixture passes over and in part through an active capillary system, and in which the components of the mixture may differ radically in their properties, it is not surprising that a satisfactory explanation of the mechanism has not been advanced.   A promising attack of the problem, by way of the thermodynamic pressure effect, has been suggested by Drickamer.[73]   This phenomenon has received little attention because a pressure gradient is normally dissipated into turbulence.   In the small pores of the porous glass barrier, however, this may not be the case, and the pressure effect, through the pressure gradient, may be the cause of the observed separation.

Very little can be said about the use of *plastic barriers* for liquid-phase separation.   The work with plastic films of the Saline Water Conversion program of the United States Department of the Interior is concerned with aqueous salt solutions and there is no information at present on the separation of organic liquids.   One of the major difficulties is that high pressures are required to force liquids through almost all plastic films.   Films in the 1-mil thickness range require a minimum pressure of approximately 150 p.s.i., and pressures above about 400 p.s.i. are needed to get reasonable flow rates.   In addition, many plastic films are subject to attack by organic liquids.   In view of these limitations it is likely that microporous barriers, which operate on a continuous basis, or so-called molecular sieves,[74,75] which operate on an adsorption-desorption cycle basis, will be the most useful devices for liquid-phase separation.

VIII.   SYMBOLS

$a = (\alpha - 1) [\pi F + p (1 - F)]$

A = area

$b = -[\pi(1 - X_f^A) + a + c]$

$c = \alpha\pi X_f^A$

d = thickness of barrier

F = fraction permeated $= N_p/N_f$

$K = PT^{1/2}$

[72] H. G. Cassidy, *Adsorption and Chromatography* (Vol. V. of *Technique of Organic Chemistry.* A. Weissberger, ed.). Interscience, New York-London, 1951.

[73] H. G. Drickamer, University of Illinois, private communication.

[74] R. M. Barrer and D. M. Grove, *Trans. Faraday Soc.*, **47**, No. 344, 826, 837 (1951).

[75] *Molecular Sieves for Selective Adsorption*, Linde Air Products Co., Tonawanda Research Laboratory Bulletin.

m = molecular mass
M = molecular weight
N = total flow, mole units
p = low pressure, downstream pressure
P = permeability constant = $qd/A\theta(\pi - p)$
q = total flow
t = temperature
T = absolute temperature
v = velocity
X = component; mole fraction

SUBSCRIPTS

f = feed
o = high-pressure side, also unpermeated side
p = low-pressure side, also permeated side

SUPERSCRIPTS

A = component A
B = component B

GREEK LETTERS

α = ratio of permeability constants: P_A/P_B or: ratio $(M_B)^{1/2}(M_A)^{1/2}$
π = high pressure; upstream pressure
π_0 = saturation pressure of a vapor
θ = time

General References

R. M. Barrer, *Diffusion in and Through Solids.* Cambridge Press, London, 1951.

M. Benedict and C. Williams, ed., *Engineering Developments in the Gaseous Diffusion Process.* McGraw-Hill, New York, 1949.

K. Cohen (George M. Murphy, ed.). *The Theory of Isotope Separation as Applied to The Large-Scale Production of U^{235}.* McGraw-Hill, New York, 1951.

W. Jost. *Diffusion in Solids, Liquids, Gases.* Academic Press, New York, 1952.

R. E. Treybal, *Mass-Transfer Operations.* McGraw-Hill, New York, 1955.

C. J. West, W. B. Kunz, and G. R. Sears, *Permeability of Organic Materials to Gases.* Parts I and II. Bibliographic Series No. 169. The Institute of Paper Chemistry, Appleton. Wisc., June, 1948.

Part 3. *DIALYSIS AND ELECTRODIALYSIS*

I. INTRODUCTION

The purpose of this chapter is to describe the apparatus and techniques available for performing the operations of dialysis and electrodialysis in the laboratory, and to indicate the usage of these procedures in various phases of organic chemistry.   Since the emphasis of the chapter is placed on laboratory practice, the various theoretical portions of the subject such as diffusion kinetics, and the theory and structure of artificial and natural semipermeable membranes are treated only to that extent necessary for intelligent application of the methods described.   References to more detailed theoretical treatments of portions of the field are given under appropriate headings throughout the chapter or in the special annotated bibliography placed at the end of the chapter.

Nature of Colloidal Solutions

The process of dialysis was first described and characterized by Thomas Graham[1] in his paper on liquid diffusion.   Dialysis was the term he applied to the fractionation of solutes by means of their differential rates of diffusion through mechanical septa or membranes.   Such septa have come to be known in the subsequent literature as semipermeable membranes. In his original treatise Graham suggested that dialysis affords for systems of solutions a method of purification and analysis similar in some degree to the processes of evaporation and distillation for volatile liquids.   In one of his experiments a sheet of "very thin well sized letter paper" was wetted thoroughly with water and formed into a pouch or cavity, partially filled with a solution containing 5% each of sucrose and gum arabic, and suspended in a larger vessel filled with pure water.   After 24 hours the water in the outer vessel contained 75% of the sucrose so purified of gum arabic that it gave only the slightest test for the latter with basic lead acetate, and could be crystallized readily after evaporation on the water bath. Graham stated that the properties of the paper membrane exhibited by the foregoing experiment arose from the starch size applied during its manufacture.

As a result of his experiments Graham recognized a class of substances which he denoted by the word "colloid," whose physical and chemical properties were different in degree, if not in kind, from "ordinary" chemical matter, which he called "crystalloid."   Substances of the first type were so named by him from the Greek for glue since he felt that "glue" or "gela-

---

[1] T. Graham, *Trans. Roy. Soc. London,* **151,** 183 (1861).

tin" was typical of the class, to which also belonged substances such as gum arabic, starch, pectin, fibrin, casein, albumin, vegetable tannins, and many other materials. Colloids are distinguished by their *low rate of diffusion through membranes* when in solution, their tendency to assume a gelatinous or pectic condition, and their apparent lack of crystallinity in the solid state. Graham recognized further that the distinction between colloids and crystalloids arises from "the peculiar form of aggregation" of the former, the difference being "no doubt one of intimate molecular constitution." Later experience has supported Graham's views, since colloidal solutions are characterized by the size of the dispersed particles, the linear dimensions of which are between 1×10^{-7} and 1×10^{-5} centimeter. Such particles can be formed by molecular solutions of high polymers, that is, by macromolecules (*e.g.*, glue), by aggregates of low-molecular substances which are insoluble in the solvent (colloidal gold), or finally by micellar association of soluble substances (dyes, soaps).

At the present time it may be held that no sharp distinction exists between the colloidal and crystalloidal conditions of matter, there being a steady progression from dispersions of small molecular species (*i.e.*, true solutions) upward through larger and larger aggregates until colloidal and eventually microscopic dispersions are reached. Some idea of the orders of magnitude of dimensions involved can be gained from the compilation of estimated particle diameters for various biological or chemical species

TABLE I

DIAMETERS OF DISPERSED PARTICLES

Dispersoid	Microns
Hydrogen molecule	0.00025
Egg albumin	0.004
Edestin	0.008
Hemocyanin (*Helix*)	0.02
Tobacco mosaic	0.03
Influenza	0.10
Serratia marcescens	0.75
Silver halide grains in photographic film ....up to	1.5

in Table I. Of comparable importance to mere particle size of colloidal or macromolecular systems are additional factors such as particle shape, surface–volume ratio, polarity and magnitude of electrostatic charges, chemical and adsorption forces, and nature of the dispersing medium whose microstructure must be considered when dealing accurately with dispersoids on a molecular size plane.

II. DESCRIPTION AND THEORY OF THE PROCESSES

1. Dialysis

Graham's sized-paper pouch suspended in pure water contains all the essentials of an operable apparatus for dialysis. A dialyzer consists of the essential components which are shown in Figure 1, in which A is an inner vessel fitted with a floor composed of the semipermeable membrane, S, and filled with the solution to be dialyzed. Vessel B is filled with a solvent such as water into which, over a period of time, the more diffusible components of the solution in A pass. A common use of dialysis is to free a colloidal solute in A from crystalloidal impurities, as, for example, in the purification of biochemical serums or proteins. In these cases it is advantageous to provide for a continuous renewal of the solvent in the outer vessel so as to reduce the concentration of crystalloids in A to a minimum. The apparatus shown in Figure 1 has been changed by different investigators for accomplishing its purposes more rapidly, more efficiently, and, in some cases, as a continuous rather than batch operation. In the laboratory, continuous operation is rarely important but in industrial procedures it may be very desirable and the more elaborate equipment may be justified.

Brintzinger *et al.*[2] have used a modification of the dialysis process, termed by them *diasolysis*, in which a membrane is used in which the substance it is desired to purify is more or less soluble than contaminating solutes. This membrane, instead of being used to separate solution which is to be purified from pure solvent, is used to separate a solution in one solvent from a different solvent, *e.g.*, nitrophenols were diffused through a rubber membrane from an aqueous solution into methanol as a second solvent. Diasolysis is considered to differ from dialysis in that the membrane is not a pore or sieve membrane. The method has value in that simple molecular species can be separated and purified from contaminating higher molecular species or colloidal substances.

2. Electrodialysis

A more rapid method of dialytic purification when it is desired to remove electrolytic solutes is the method now known as electrodialysis. According to Prausnitz and Reitstötter[3] a patent was issued in 1889 to Maigrot and Sabates[4] for a three-celled apparatus to purify sugar sirup with the aid of an electric current. Electrolytic cells containing porous diaphragms

[2] H. Brintzinger and H. Beier, *Kolloid-Z.*, **79**, 324 (1937). H. Brintzinger and M. Götze, *Ber.*, **81**, 293 (1948).

[3] P. H. Prausnitz and J. Reitstötter, *Elektrophorese, Elektro-osmose, Elektrodialyse.* Steinkopff, Dresden and Leipzig, 1931, pp. 114, 204.

[4] E. Maigrot and J. Sabates, Ger. Pat: 50,443 (1889).

are quite common in the present electrochemical industry. The special process for separation of electrolytically dissociated crystalloids from nondissociated crystalloids or colloids in multicelled apparatus containing semipermeable membranes was called "electrodialysis" by Kollrepp and Wohl.[3,5] Following pioneer work on the removal of ash constituents from gelatin in a three-celled apparatus by Morse and Pierce,[6] using parchment-paper membranes and an operating potential of 500 v., the method was further developed and applied by Dhéré[7] to the purification of gelatin and horse serum, and by Pauli, Bechhold, Reitstötter, and numerous other investigators to similar colloidal systems. Numerous patents on apparatus and applications of electrodialysis and electro-osmosis have been issued to Graf Botho Schwerin and Elektro-Osmose A.G.

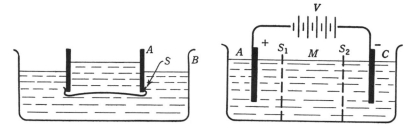

Fig. 1. Apparatus for dialysis.   Fig. 2. Apparatus for electrodialysis.

The effectiveness of electrodialysis rests upon the use of the increased rate of transport of ionic impurities through semipermeable membranes under the influence of an applied electric potential. Thus it combines electrolysis with ordinary dialytic diffusion. In its simplest form the apparatus consists (Fig. 2) of three chambers, A, M, and C, separated by semipermeable membranes S_1 and S_2, electrodes $(+)$ and $(-)$ of some corrosion-resistant conducting material, and a source of direct current, V, of suitable voltage to allow a reasonable rate of electrolysis. The latter is determined of necessity by the geometry of the apparatus, the nature of the solutions to be purified, and the rate and degree to which it is desired to carry the purification. Chamber M contains the solution or substance to be electrodialyzed, and the anodic compartment, A, and cathodic compartment, C, contain a solvent such as water, which it is desirable to renew continuously or at intervals, in order to reduce the effects of back diffusion of ions accumulating in these chambers.

[5] A. Kollrepp and A. Wohl, Ger. Pat. 136,670 (1901).
[6] H. W. Morse and G. W. Pierce, *Z. physik. Chem.*, **45**, 589 (1903).
[7] Ch. Dhéré and M. Gorgolewski, *Compt. rend.*, **150**, 934, 993 (1910).

3. Electro-ultrafiltration

A further method of fractionating solutes of various particle sizes is the technique called ultrafiltration (see Chapter V), which was introduced by Martin,[8-10] who filtered toxin solutions at pressures of 30 to 100 atmospheres through special filters impregnated with gelatin or silicic acid jellies. This was an extension of filtering procedures to fine-sieve membranes created by layers of colloidal jellies of suitable porosities. Later developments were made by Malfitano, Duclaux, Henri, and others. However, some of the most successful methods and apparatus were described by Bechhold[11] and by Zsigmondy and Bachmann.[12] Ultrafiltration has been applied as a valuable tool in bacteriological and virus studies, and in the study of high-molecular materials such as nitrocellulose. Since ultrafiltration is fundamentally a special phase of filtration, only the combined operation of electrodialysis and ultrafiltration invented by Bechhold and others[13] and called by them "electro-ultrafiltration" is discussed in this chapter.

Electro-ultrafiltration provides simultaneous removal of ionic species by electrodialysis, and pressure-filtration removal of suitable chemical species by means of the sieve membranes.

Electrodialysis, as will be explained more fully in Sect. II.5, suffers certain marked disadvantages in practical operation. One of these is the electrophoretic movement of water from the electrode compartments, usually from the anode toward the cathode, depending on the character of the membrane material, which carries electrolytic products into the intermediate cell, thus counteracting the purification of the dialyzate in the middle compartment and tending to dilute it. Another phenomenon which affords much trouble goes under the name of the Bethe-Toropoff effect and causes an alkaline reaction at the cathode membrane surface in the middle cell, and an acid reaction at the anode membrane surface. These effects provide serious difficulties in the handling of many biocolloids which may be coagulated, precipitated, or denatured.

Figure 3 represents schematically the essential components for electro-ultrafiltration. S_1 and S_2 are sieve membranes. Electrodes $(+)$ and $(-)$ are provided near the membranes, and suction is applied at points A and B

[8] C. J. Martin, *J. Physiol.*, **20**, 364 (1896).

[9] C. J. Martin, *Brit. Med. J.*, **4**, 300 (1900).

[10] C. J. Martin and Th. Cherry, *Proc. Roy. Soc. London*, **63**, 420 (1898).

[11] H. Bechhold, "Ultrafiltration and Electro-ultrafiltration," in Alexander, ed., *Colloid Chemistry.* Vol. I, Chemical Catalog Co., New York, 1926, pp. 820–837.

[12] H. Bechhold, *loc. cit.*, p. 825. R. Zsigmondy and W. Bachmann, *Z. angew. Chem.*, **35**, 449 (1922).

[13] H. Bechhold and A. Rosenberg, *Biochem. Z.*, **157**, 85 (1925).

in order to pull the solvent and low-molecular species through the membranes. The membranes must be supported on or in a rigid material such as porous clay or alumina, and the electrodes are often in the form of grids of platinum applied to the reverse side of the membrane supports.

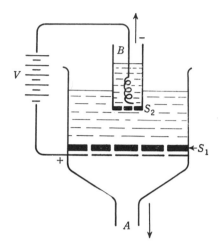

Fig. 3. Scheme for electro-ultrafiltration.

Heymann[14] published comparative data concerning the efficiency of removal of crystalloids by various dialyzing and filtering systems. Manegold[15] has discussed this subject in considerable detail and has also given data for seven purification processes: electro-filtration-dialysis (E.F.D.), electrofiltration (E.F.), electrodialysis (E.D.), filtration-dialysis (F.D.), filtration (F.), dialysis (D.), and electrolysis (E.). His data, of which Table

TABLE II[15]

RELATIVE PURIFICATION RATES OF VARIOUS PROCESSES[a]

Initial concentration	10^{-3}	10^{-3}	10^{-6} g. equiv./ml.
Final concentration	10^{-6}	10^{-6}	10^{-8} g. equiv./ml.
E.F.D.	5.24	3.26	20.6
E.F.	3.76	2.28	15.9
F.D.	3.22	3.22	3.22
F.	2.22	2.22	2.22
E.D.	1.92	1.05	13.60
D.	1.00	1.00	1.00
E.	0.028	0.014	12.30

[a] Purification rates for dialysis taken as 1. $i = 0.01$ amp., $p_e - p_a = 10^3$ g./cm.^{2}

[14] E. Heymann, Z. physik. Chem., **118**, 65 (1925).
[15] E. Manegold, Trans. Faraday Soc., **33**, 1088 (1937).

II is a portion, are based on experiments conducted at constant current as contrasted to Heymann's data, which were obtained at constant potential. Both investigators conclude that the combined methods of electro-ultra-filtration or electro-filtration-dialysis are much the most rapid for removing crystalloids of electrolytic or nonelectrolytic nature from colloidal solutions.

4. Electrodecantation

Recent years have seen the development of techniques which combine the processes of electrodialysis and electrophoresis (see Part 4). These combined processes have been variously termed *electrodecantation* or *electroconvection*. They have been especially successful as preparative methods. Electroconvection is a method for the fractionation of colloid mixtures by a combination of horizontal electrodialytic and electrophoretic

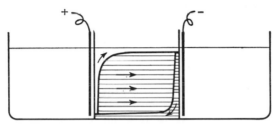

Fig. 1. Diagram of electrolytic, hydrodynamic effects observed in horizontal electrodialyzer.[18]

migration with vertical convective transport. Fractionation takes place in a vertical column carrying ascending and descending convection currents. Under the influence of a transverse electric field, interchange of molecules takes place between these currents, leading to accumulation of some components of the solution in a reservoir at the bottom of the column, while others accumulate in a reservoir at the top of the column. The convection currents themselves are the result of differences in density at the walls of the column caused by horizontal electrophoretic migration of the colloid components.

Figure 4 illustrates the electrolytic and convection effects which Pauli,[16] Pauli and Valkó,[17] and Blank and Valkó[18] found in a horizontal electrodialyzer and on which they based their design of an apparatus for purifying colloids by the process which they named electrodecantation.

They observed that colloids such as albumin, hemoglobin, agar-agar,

[16] W. Pauli, *Helv. Chim. Acta*, **25**, 137 (1942).

[17] W. Pauli and E. Valkó, *Elektrochemie der Kolloide*. Springer, Vienna, 1929.

[18] F. Blank and E. Valkó, *Biochem. Z.*, **195**, 220 (1928).

gelatin, and starch and silicic acid sols, when electrolyzed in a three-chamber Pauli electrodialyzer, are differentiated into sharply defined density layers. Similar behavior was also observed during the electrolysis of such colloidal solutions in a cell without semipermeable membranes. This layering action arises from the movement of electrically charged colloidal particles toward one membrane or electrode where they accumulate as a deposit of higher or lower density than the medium in which they are dispersed and thus sink to the bottom or rise to the top of the chamber along the membrane surface. At the opposite membrane or electrode there is depletion of the colloid ions, accumulation of the dispersing medium or solvent, which results either in a decrease or increase of the specific gravity, and consequently there results a stratification of the colloidal solution.

5. Theory and Kinetics of Dialysis and Allied Processes

In order to consider the effect of the design of apparatus on the rates of dialysis, electrodialysis, and allied processes, some general treatment of the diffusion of solutes is included at this point. For clarity, brief definitions of the various processes involved are included. *Dialysis* may be described as the fractional diffusion of solutes through a semipermeable membrane under a concentration gradient. *Electrolysis* is the process of local and spatial separation of the ions of an electrolyte and the transfer of their respective charges, *i.e.*, the decomposition of a compound by an electric current.[19] *Electrodialysis* is the combined process of dialysis and electrolysis using semipermeable membranes to confine the solution under treatment. *Electrophoresis* is the phenomenon of motion of colloidal particles or macromolecules through a fluid under the influence of an electrical potential gradient, and conversely, *electro-osmosis* or *electro-endomosis* is the movement of a liquid phase through capillary orifices or along the walls of a solid phase under a potential gradient. The last two processes depend on electrical double layers produced by ions adsorbed at phase boundaries, or charges induced by ionization of large molecules and are not considered in detail in this chapter, although preparative methods based on electrophoretic transport have been applied to proteins and other compounds.

The factors controlling the rate of dialysis of a solute can be examined by reference to Fick's general law of diffusion, which states that diffusion across a given cross section of a diffusion element is proportional to the concentration gradient. If it is assumed for dialysis that the only concentration gradient which is significant is that across the semipermeable membrane, the general law is as follows:

$$\partial S/\partial t = -D(\partial c/\partial x) \tag{1}$$

[19] J. Grant, *Hackh's Chemical Dictionary*. 3rd ed., Blakiston, New York, 1944.

where S represents the amount of substance diffused, c the concentration of the diffusing solute, t the time of diffusion, and x the diffusion path. D is a constant defined by the amount of substance diffusing across unit area in square centimeters per unit time when $\partial c/\partial x = 1$. More specifically, this equation can be rearranged as follows:

$$dS/dt = kA(C_o - C_i)/dx \tag{2}$$

and integrated for a constant thickness of membrane to give:

$$k^* = S/At(C_o - C_i) \tag{3}$$

where A is the area of the membrane, C_o and C_i the concentrations of the solute on either side of the membrane, dx the membrane thickness, and k or k^* the permeability constant characteristic of the membrane for a given solute. It is readily apparent that the amount of solute transferred in unit time will be proportional to the membrane area, inversely proportional to the membrane thickness, and will be increased by keeping the concentration of the diffusing solute as low as possible on the solvent side of the dialyzer. The permeability coefficient, k or k^*, although considered to be a constant for a given membrane–solute combination, is often variable with the concentration of the solute. Bethe, Bethe, and Terada[20] found that k was reasonably constant for nonelectrolytes such as dextrose, sucrose, and urea, but for electrolytes k was in general variable. These authors studied the temperature coefficient of k for electrolytes and non-electrolytes and concluded that in either case a quadratic function as follows expressed the trend reasonably well:

$$k_{\theta'} = k_\theta[1 + B(\theta' - \theta)]^2 \tag{4}$$

where θ' and θ are temperatures. It is obvious that the speed of dialytic purification will be increased by raising the temperature at which dialysis is carried out, although frequently this cannot be done because of other practical considerations.

The effectiveness of filtration, dialysis, electrolysis, and their intercombinations has been discussed from the viewpoint of rates by Manegold,[21] who gives the following general differential equation:

$$-dc_e = \frac{1}{v_e^0}\left[\frac{i}{96,500} - \{k^* - D(p_e - p_a)\}\,c_e A\right] dt \tag{5}$$

$$\uparrow \qquad\qquad \uparrow \qquad\qquad\qquad \uparrow$$

electrolysis   dialysis   filtration

[20] A. Bethe, H. Bethe, and Y. Terada, Z. physik. Chem., 112, 250 (1924).
[21] F. Manegold, Trans. Faraday Soc., 33, 1088 (1937).

where c_e is the concentration of electrolyte, v_e^0 the initial volume of the dialyzate, i the current in amperes flowing through the apparatus, k^* the permeability coefficient of dialysis, D a factor known as the water transmissivity of a sieve membrane, $p_e - p_a$ the pressure differential of the filtration, and A and t have the same significance as in equation (3). This equation assumes that the volume of the dialyzate is kept constant, and that special membrane effects such as osmosis, electro-osmosis, etc. can be neglected. Examination of the above differential equation shows that the rate of electrodialysis can be increased by (1) increasing the membrane area, and (2) increasing the electric current. The rate of filtration is of course increased by increasing the porosity of the filter, by filtering with a higher pressure head, and also by use of a greater area of filtering membrane. Each factor should be adjusted to the optimum consistent with mechanical and other requirements of operation.

In electrodialysis two membrane effects, which are usually spoken of under the name of the "Bethe-Toropoff effect," are of practical importance. The first is the electro-osmotic transport of water through the membranes, which tends to dilute the dialyzate. The second is the tendency of any membrane placed in a solution between electrodes to assume a charged condition on the two faces of the membrane such that the surface nearest the anode becomes negatively charged, and the face nearest the cathode positively charged. This results in an accumulation of hydroxyl ions (alkaline reaction) at the anode face, and an acid reaction at the cathode face. Bethe and Toropoff[22,23] attribute this behavior to a change in the relative transport numbers of the ions between the electrolyte and membrane phases. The magnitude and direction of the effect was found to be dependent on the acidity of the solution, the nature of the membrane, and the composition of the electrolyte. The second factor is used practically for overcoming some of the troubles in electrodialysis arising as a result of these phenomena (see Sect. III.2.B).

Table III illustrates some typical data obtained by Manegold and Kalauch[24] of the magnitude of the Bethe-Toropoff effect for certain membrane–electrolyte arrangements. These authors have treated the problem of the electrokinetic phenomena exhibited by membranes immersed in electrolytes in an electric field from the theoretical point of view for a large number of limiting cases. In addition they have related their theoretical

[22] A. Bethe and Th. Toropoff, *Z. physik. Chem.*, **88**, 686 (1914).

[23] A. Bethe and Th. Toropoff, *Z. physik. Chem.*, **89**, 597 (1915).

[24] E. Manegold and K. Kalauch, *Kolloid-Z.*, **86**, 313 (1939). See also E. Manegold and F. A. Schneider, *Z. physik. Chem.*, **158A**, 197(1932); C. Stüber, *ibid.*, **172A**, 401 (1935); E. Manegold and C. Stüber, *ibid.*, **173A**, 321 (1935)—"Concerning electricity transport through phase boundaries."

TABLE III[25]

No.	Pt Anode, H₂O	Middle chamber stirred				Pt cathode, H₂O
	Anode membrane	Contents, potential	Time, min.	Amp., $\times 10^3$	Reaction, pH	Cathode membrane
1	Parchment paper (Schleicher & Schuell) ⊖	50 ml. 0.5% NaCl, 12 v.	0 5 15 25	12 23 22 23	— 3.26 3.00 2.79	Parchment paper ⊖
2	Wool cloth impregnated with bichromated gelatin ⊕ 10 g. gelatin 3 g. (NH₄)₂Cr₂O₇ 5 g. glycerine 100 g. water	50 ml. 0.5% NaCl, 60 v.	0 5 10 15 20 25	12 120 270 318 138 78	— 3.80 — 2.39 — 3.20	Wool cloth impregnated with bichromated gelatin ⊕
7a	Chrome-gelatin membrane acc. to Ruppel ⊕	50 ml. 0.5% KCl, 60 v.	0 3 6 10	34 70 132 240	— 8.11 10.33 11.13	Parchment ⊖
8	Chrome–gelatin membrane acc. to Ruppel ⊕	50 ml. 0.5% ammonium acetate, 120 v., acidified	0 1 5 15 23	48 24 37 37 36	4.77 — 4.81 4.77 4.74	Parchment ⊖
11b	Parchment paper ⊖	50 ml. serum, 120 v.	0 5 15 20	24 30 29 24	7.34 6.51 4.81 4.01	Parchment paper ⊖

conclusions to the cell balances for three-chamber and five-chamber electrodialytic arrangements. The ideal condition for three-celled dialysis consists of a perfectly anion-permeable anode membrane (positively charged) and the opposite for the cathode membrane. With such membranes exchanged in position, the coefficient of purification by electrodialysis will be zero. Any other pairs of membrane combinations will be intermediate in effectiveness to the foregoing extreme cases. So-called "bipolar" permeable membranes are observed to assume the character of "unipolar" permeable membranes at reduced electrolyte concentrations, and this is responsible for changes observed in the dialysis coefficient with decreasing electrolyte concentration.

6. Properties of Semipermeable Membranes

It is beyond the scope of this chapter to treat in detail the theory and phenomena of membrane processes, and their many aspects in biological

[25] E. Manegold and K. Kalauch, *Kolloid-Z.*, **86**, 328 (1939).

and chemical science. For such information the reader is referred to the bibliography. The following treatment should serve as an introduction to the field and as a basis for the understanding of the methods described in the present chapter.

Semipermeable membranes are materials which permit one or more constituents of a solution to pass through, but offer high resistance to the passage of other molecular species which may be present in the solutions. Such membranes are typified by the natural plasma membranes of living cells which play such essential roles in life processes. Artificial semipermeable membranes of numerous types have been known for many years, one example being the semipermeable system formed by a gelatinous precipitate such as copper ferrocyanide. The copper ferrocyanide membrane has been extensively used in studies of the mode of action of such membranes.

Numerous theories of membrane permeability have been devised to explain the action of natural and artificial semipermeable systems. No one theory is adequate to account for all the observed data. Natural membranes show such complex permeability characteristics that some students of them have considered that they possess a mosaic structure involving lipide and nonlipide elements.[26,27] Others reject the mosaic hypothesis, and it is likely that newer investigations of the chemical and physical properties of surface films will throw fresh light on these problems. Among the theories which have been advanced for explaining semipermeability are: (a) the molecular-sieve theory, (b) the solution or phase-distribution theory, and (c) the adsorption theory.

The molecular-sieve theory merely postulates that semipermeable membranes contain pores of such a diameter as to allow only molecules of sufficiently small cross section to pass, whereas larger molecules are held back. That this theory is inadequate and only partially correct was readily seen from the conflicting data which were accumulated particularly by Tammann,[28] Traube,[29] Walden,[30] Barlow,[31] and Kahlenberg,[32] who found that substances which were unable to penetrate one type of membrane might pass another membrane with ease, whereas still other solutes to which the first membrane was permeable might be unable to diffuse through the second membrane. Such behavior is exemplified by rubber membranes, which are permeable to benzene or pyridine but not to water in solutions. Similarly, such membranes are impermeable to trichloroacetic acid in aqueous solution but allow it to pass when dissolved in benzene.

[26] A. Nathansohn, *Jahrb. wiss. Botan.*, **39**, 607 (1904).
[27] R. Höber, *Physiol. Revs.*, **16**, 52 (1936).
[28] G. Tammann, *Z. physik. Chem.*, **10**, 255 (1892).
[29] I. Traube, *Phil. Mag.*, **8** (6), 704 (1904).
[30] P. Walden, *Z. physik. Chem.*, **10**, 699 (1892).
[31] P. S. Barlow, *Phil. Mag.*, **10** (6), 1 (1905).
[32] L. Kahlenberg, *J. Phys. Chem.*, **10**, 169 (1906).

As early as 1855, l'Hermite[33] carried out some experiments designed to test the solution or partition theory of semipermeability. This theory was based on the principle that increased permeability of a given solute is associated with increased solubility of the solute species in the membrane material. L'Hermite performed several experiments such as placing in a test tube a layer of water, over it a layer of castor oil or turpentine, and above the second layer a stratum of alcohol. After a few days only two layers were present, an upper layer of oil or turpentine and a layer of an alcohol–water mixture. A similar experiment was performed placing chloroform at the bottom of the test tube with an intermediate stratum of water and an upper layer of ethyl ether. In this case, the ether was observed to diffuse through the water to mingle with the chloroform. L'Hermite considered that his observations supported the conclusion that substances which diffuse through membranes first dissolve in the membrane material.

The insufficiency of the solution theory for explaining all the data of semipermeability was shown by observations such as those of Bigelow,[34] and Bartell,[35] who found that the osmotic behavior of semipermeable membranes could be simulated by clogging the pores of unglazed porcelain cups with finely divided materials such as barium sulfate, silica, carbon, and metallic silver or gold. Furthermore, the dimensions of the upper limit of pore size for exhibiting these osmotic phenomena were found to be about one micron, which is much larger than the molecular diameter of true crystalloidal solutes. The behavior of clogged porous diaphragms was ascribed to negative adsorption by Mathieu,[36] and the significance of this for the theory of semipermeable membranes was emphasized by Bancroft.[37] Weiser[38] sums up the conditions allowing for osmosis with porous or clogged diaphragms as follows: Osmotic phenomena will be observed only when negative adsorption is so marked that the pore walls adsorb practically one component of a solution, e.g., only the solvent, and when the pore diameter is sufficiently small that the film of adsorbate fills the pores completely. However, it is essential that the adsorption of a component be reversible, or the membrane will not allow the diffusing substance to pass.[39]

Michaelis[40] has classified molecular-sieve membranes in two categories: (1) permeability membranes in which solvents or solutes are more or less soluble, and (2) sieve membranes which act as inert structures with various pore-size classes. Both categories coexist in the same membrane, as the preceding paragraphs have shown. Membranes of the first type are typified by the experimental membranes of l'Her-

[33] M. l'Hermite, *Ann. chim. phys.*, **43** (3), 420 (1855).

[34] S. L. Bigelow, *J. Am. Chem. Soc.*, **29**, 1576, 1675 (1907); **31**, 1194 (1909); *J. Phys. Chem.*, **22**, 99, 153 (1918).

[35] F. E. Bartell, *J. Phys. Chem.*, **15**, 659 (1911); **16**, 318 (1912); *J. Am. Chem. Soc.*, **36**, 646 (1914); **38**, 1029, 1086 (1916).

[36] M. Mathieu, *Ann. Physik*, **9** (4), 340 (1902).

[37] W. D. Bancroft, *J. Phys. Chem.*, **21**, 441 (1917).

[38] H. B. Weiser, *The Colloidal Salts.* 1st ed., McGraw-Hill, New York, 1928, p. 265.

[39] H. B. Weiser, *loc. cit.*, pp. 283–284.

[40] L. Michaelis, in *Colloid Symposium Monograph.* Vol. V, Chemical Catalog Co., New York, 1928, pp. 135–148.

mite,[33] and the artificial homogeneous membranes of Osterhout and others[41-43] consisting of mixtures of guaiacol and p-cresol.   The sieve membranes are graded into four classes according to their porosity as follows: (a) open-pore membranes such as filter paper retaining only large particles, (b) cell filters of less porous materials such as the finest types of filter papers able to retain cells such as blood corpuscles but allowing bacteria and viruses to pass, (c) fine-pored clay, silica, or glass filters retaining bacteria but permeable to colloidal and crystalloidal solutions, and (d) colloid filters of parchment, collodion, or other materials which are permeable only to low-molecular substances.

Michaelis[44] investigated the effect of electric charges on the permeability of low-porosity membranes, e.g., dried collodion skins.   He observed that such membranes showed differential permeability for cations and anions.   When used to separate solutions of varying concentrations of salts such as potassium chloride containing nonpolarizable reference electrodes, they gave rise to potential differences approaching the maximum value of 59 mv. for a ratio of 1:10 in salt concentration at 25°C. Sollner and co-workers[45] were unable to obtain such differential permeability with the purer grades of collodion on the market.   However, after oxidation of the membrane with sodium hypobromite solution, they were able to prepare membranes showing the behavior observed by Michaelis, and they concluded that the oxidation treatment had given rise to carboxyl groups in the nitrocellulose.   These anionic membrane groups attract cationic solute molecules and allow them to pass through the membrane provided they are not too tightly bound to the membrane charged groups.   The anionic solute molecules tend to be repelled and are less able to diffuse through the membrane.   Such differential ion permeability gives rise to the phenomenon of anomalous osmosis.   Under certain conditions, water is found to flow through such membranes from a region of high concentration of salt to a low concentration (negative anomalous osmosis), or at other times in the reverse direction (positive anomalous osmosis).

The charge on various membranes as a function of the composition of the membrane and the solution surrounding it has been investigated by many workers. Some membranes such as porous alumina showed a reversal of charge on passing from acid to alkaline solutions, whereas others such as collodion were negative even in hydrochloric acid or aluminum chloride solutions.   Only in the presence of tetravalent thorium salts was a positive charge observed on pure collodion membranes.   However, collodion membranes when impregnated or coated with gelatin assume the charge behavior of gelatin itself[46] and show a reversal or zero potential

[41] W. J. V. Osterhout and W. M. Stanley, J. Gen. Physiol., 15, 667 (1932).

[42] W. J. V. Osterhout and J. W. Murray, Science, 87, 430 (1938).

[43] H. E. Bent, Science, 88, 525 (1938).

[44] L. Michaelis, J. Gen. Physiol., 8, 33 (1925); 10, 575, 671, 685 (1927); 11, 147 (1928); 12, 55, 221, 473, 487 (1929).

[45] K. Sollner and co-workers, J. Gen. Physiol., 24, 467 (1941); 25, 7 (1941); 25, 411 (1942); 26, 17 (1942); 26, 309, 369 (1943); 27, 77, 433 (1943); 27, 451 (1944); 28, 1, 119 (1944); 28, 179 (1945); J. Phys. Chem., 50, 54, 88, 470 (1946); 49, 47, 171, 265 (1945); Z. Elektrochem., 35, 789 (1929); 36, 36, 234 (1930); 38, 274 (1932); Kolloid-Z., 62, 31 (1933).

[46] A. Gyemant, Kolloid-Z., 28, 103 (1921).

at the isoelectric point of the gelatin. This property has been utilized in preparing dialyzing membranes particularly for electrodialysis.[47,48] The properties of membranes and the zero-charge condition are discussed by Bethe and Toropoff.[49]

A somewhat different model of membrane activity has been postulated. Instead of representing the membrane as a body traversed by pores, the walls of which are charged either positively or negatively, the model was conceived as a network of primary valence chains with both lyophilic and hydrophilic groups in lateral positions, notably ionizable acid or base groups. Such a model may contain fixed anions and mobile cations, or the reverse. The mobile ions will be displaced provided a supply is available at one side or the other. The actual membrane behaves like a solution bounded by two ideal Donnan membranes through which the fixed ions cannot pass. A quantitative theory on this basis was developed by Meyer[50] and Teorell.[51] Meyer investigated the theory in relation to the following synthetic membranes: acetyl cellulose, viscose or cellophane, oxidized or dyed viscose, Glyptal, Glyptal–acetyl cellulose mixed, acetyl cellulose–polyacrylic acid mixed, dried nitrocellulose, polymer from condensation of phthalic anhydride and triethanolamine, and gelatin.

III. APPARATUS

1. Apparatus for Dialysis

A. MATERIALS AND METHODS OF CONSTRUCTION AND OPERATION

Many arrangements of equipment for dialysis have been described in the literature, but none is more simple nor more generally useful than a dialysis bag made from material such as viscose or collodion into which the material to be dialyzed is placed. This bag may be suspended by a thread in a jar or beaker of water equipped with a tube to provide for the steady influx of a slow stream of fresh solvent. For most systems the solvent supplied is distilled water, but in many applications tap water or some other solution may be used.

Simple dialyzers based on the original scheme of Graham can be made from crystallizing dishes and bell jars or wide-mouth bottles with the bottom cut off in the manner of Figure 5. In these cases membranes of collodion, cellophane, or parchment paper sheeting can be used. The membrane is fastened securely to the flange of the bottle or bell jar with cord or thread. For safety against mechanical leaks, the joint between the glass and membrane may be sealed with a pyroxylin type of cement. It is

[47] G. Ettisch and co-workers, *Biochem. Z.*, 266, 422, 436, 441 (1933); 216, 401, 430 (1929).
[48] P. Grabar, *Cold Spring Harbor Symposium Quant. Biol.*, 6, 252 (1938).
[49] A. Bethe and Th. Toropoff, *Z. physik. Chem.*, 88, 686 (1914); 89, 597 (1915).
[50] K. H. Meyer, *Trans. Faraday Soc.*, 33, 1073 (1937).
[51] H. Teorell, *Proc. Soc. Exptl. Biol. Med.*, 33, 282 (1935).

advantageous to provide stirring of the dialyzate either by a slow stream of air or, preferably, by the use of an electrical or air-driven stirrer.

The rate of dialysis (see Sect. II.5) of a given sample of liquid is increased by providing for a maximum surface of the dialyzing membrane relative to the volume of the dialyzate, and a minimum thickness of the membrane consistent with sufficient mechanical strength to prevent leaks and tears. In addition it is desirable to reduce the concentration of the solutes being removed by dialysis on the efflux side of the apparatus in order to reduce the rate of back-diffusion to a minimum. This should be accomplished

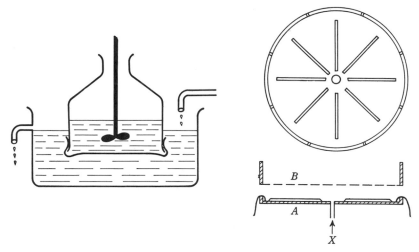

Fig. 5. Bell-jar type of dialyzer.   Fig. 6. Zsigmondy "star" dialyzer.[52-54]

with a minimum of solvent such as distilled water for economical operation. A particularly successful dialyzer fulfilling these conditions is the "star" dialyzer of Zsigmondy and Heyer,[52-54] so named from the geometry of its design. This apparatus is shown in Figure 6, and as originally described consisted of an ebonite ring, B, to which a collodion membrane was attached by means of a collodion solution. Portion A of the dialyzer is a circular plate with a tube and aperture X for introducing a slow current of distilled water which is distributed through a series of radial channels 3–4 mm. high to provide as efficient laving of the lower surface of the membrane as possible. The efflux of spent dialyzing water at the rim of the plate is

[52] R. Zsigmondy and R. Heyer, *Z. anorg. Chem.*, **68**, 169 (1910).

[53] E. Abderhalden, *Handbuch der biochemischen Arbeitsmethoden.* Urban & Schwarzenberg, Berlin and Vienna, 1912, Vol. VI, pp. 478–480.

[54] H. Bechhold, *Die Kolloide in Biologie und Medizin.* 5th ed., Steinkopff, Dresden and Leipzig, 1929, p. 109, Fig. 20.

provided by clamping strips of blotting or filter paper, P, between the ring with the membrane and plate B. This apparatus can of course be used with any semipermeable sheet material such as parchment paper, isinglass, cellophane, or sized filter paper. It can be built readily in a laboratory workshop from plastics like Lucite, Plexiglas, or Tenite II, and

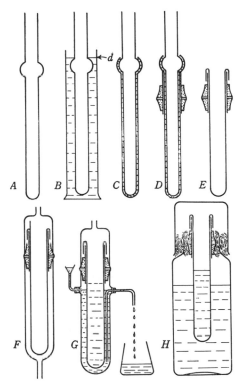

Fig. 7. Aseptic dialyzer of Malfitano.[53,55]

without excessive difficulty it could also be constructed of glass, which would provide a very suitable material for preparing highly purified solutions.

Figure 7 depicts an apparatus suitable for dialysis under aseptic conditions. A dialyzing bag with a special collar (see page 89) is prepared and supported on a glass tube bushing which passes through a double rubber stopper. Glass wool or cotton wadding is used as a closure from the air of the laboratory, and aseptic conditions are obtained by autoclaving.

A continuous dialyzer permitting the use of a limited quantity of dialyzing water and retention of the materials diffused from the dialyzate in a

[55] G. Malfitano, Z. physik. Chem., **68**, 232 (1910); Compt rend., **139**, 1223 (1904).

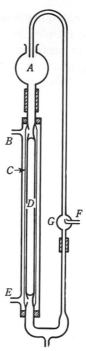

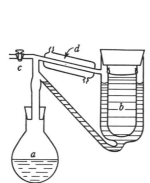

Fig. 8. Continuous dia-
lyzer of Mann.[56,57]

Fig. 9. Circulating dialyzer of Taylor *et al.*: *B*, *E*, ports for introduction
and removal of dialyzing solvent; *C*,
tubular dialyzing membrane; *D*, spacing mandrel; *G*, *F*, gas lift pump;
A, reservoir.[59]

restricted volume of solvent has been described by Mann[56] and von
Hahn.[57,58] This is a modification of the continuous Soxhlet extractor (see
Chap. II). For convenience the extractor vessel is placed at the side of the
boiling flask (see Figure 8) in order to avoid heating the dialyzate.
For substances subject to change or deterioration on heating, *e.g.*, proteins
or enzymes, it may be desirable to operate at low temperatures and pressures by first evacuating the apparatus through the side tube with stopcock *c*. A similar apparatus is described by Bechhold[54] from data by
Kopaczewski.

[56] H. Mann, *J. Biol. Chem.*, **44**, 207 (1920).

[57] F. V. Von Hahn, *Kolloid-Z.*, **31**, 200 (1912).

[58] F. V. Von Hahn, "Dispersoidanalyse," in *Handbuch der Kolloidwissenschaft.*
Vol. 3, Steinkopff, Dresden and Leipzig, 1928, pp. 249–250.

[59] A. R. Taylor, A. K. Parpart, and R. Ballentine, *Ind. Eng. Chem., Anal. Ed.*, **11**,
659 (1939).

In Figure 9 there is illustrated a circulating dialyzer designed by Taylor *et al.*[59] which utilizes a gas lift pump, *G*, to circulate the dialyzate in a thin cylindrical film between the membrane, *C*, of 19 mm. cellophane tubing, and a glass-tube spacer, *D*. Dialyzing water or other solvent is passed through the outer Liebig-type condenser jacket. This dialyzer according to its originators is capable of removing 90% of the salt from a 50%-saturated ammonium sulfate solution in 5 hours; 98% was removed in 9 hours. The apparatus is compact and can be placed in a refrigerator or other thermostat for operation at low or high temperatures. This equipment is useful for desalting proteins except in cases in which foaming may cause denaturation.

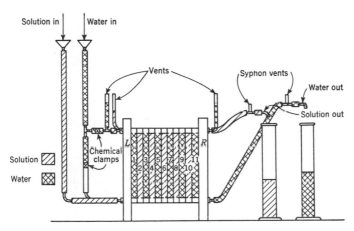

Fig. 10. Webcell continuous laboratory dialyzer. (Courtesy Brosites Machine Co.)

A micro or macro apparatus for accomplishing the same ends was built in a glass U-tube by Stegemann and Toennies,[59a] but used a magnetic stirring bar inserted in the dialyzate to agitate the fluid instead of a gas lift pump.

Several models of dialyzers or electrodialyzers are available from commercial laboratory supply houses in North America. One of these is based on descriptions published by Mattson,[60] and consists of a three-cell arrangement using U-shaped cell spacers of thick, soft rubber. These are clamped together by means of a metal frame with pressure plates and turn bolts. This apparatus, which was primarily designed for electrodialysis of clays and soils, is of rather large volume in proportion to the membrane

[59a] H. Stegemann and G. Toennies, *Nature*, **177**, 440 (1956).

[60] S. Mattson, *J. Agr. Research*, **33**, 553 (1926). American Instrument Co., Silver Spring, Maryland, Catalog No. 5–160.

surface.   Because of the flexibility of the soft rubber spacers, thin cellophane membranes may tend to sag appreciably during an experiment with
this apparatus.   Brosites Machine Co.,[61] New York, produces and mar-
kets a laboratory-scale continuous dialyzer having several distinctive features under the name of Webcell continuous dialyzer, laboratory model.
This apparatus is made of transparent Lucite and has eleven Lucite rings
with membranes clamped between them.   Figure 10 is a diagrammatic
layout for using this continuous dialyzer.   The water chambers 1, 3, 5,
7, 9, and 11 are fed from a manifold at the top of the apparatus, while
dialyzate chambers 2, 4, 6, 8, and 10 are fed from a manifold at the bottom

Fig. 11. Commercial dialysis installation.   (Courtesy Brosites Machine Co.)

of the dialyzer.   Counterflow principle is maintained through the units,
which gives the maximum diffusion potential across the membranes at all
times.   The solution cells have an approximate total volume of 930 ml. and
the water cells have an approximate total volume of 1060 milliliters.   The
dialyzing area is computed to be about 1450 square centimeters.   This
volume:area ratio is the same as that found in Webcell Production Dialys-
ers in use in plant- and semiplant-scale operations.   Therefore data obtained on the laboratory model can be translated easily to the larger production equipment.   Figure 11 shows an installation of such Webcell multi-

[61] Brosites Machine Co., Inc., 30–50 Church St., New York, N. Y.

frame dialyzers in use in a rayon plant for recovery of caustic soda. Among additional advantages of the Webcell laboratory model dialyzer of Lucite are the provision for the use of any sheet membrane material desired, small sagging tendency of the membranes, and ease of watching the course of the dialysis because of the transparent construction.

A laboratory electrodialyzer similar to the laboratory model Webcell continuous dialyzer is sold by the Brosites Machine Company. This electrodialyzer, which is shown in Figure 12, has 13 working cells with 2

Fig. 12. Laboratory electrodialyzer. (Courtesy Brosites Machine Company.)

electrode cells; the manufacturers provide a pair of carbon electrodes and a set of equal numbers of cation- and anion-type Rohm and Haas Amberplex Ion Selective Membranes which are placed in the dialyzer alternately. Although not sold with the apparatus, the electrodialyzer is so designed that platinum electrodes can be used in place of the carbon electrodes. A variable direct-current supply up to 90 volts and 12 amperes is needed to operate the dialyzer. The manufacturers recommended operating the electrodialyzer similarly to the Webcell continuous dialyzer for industrial solutions or wastes except for the use of ion-permeable membranes and an electric current. For desalting sea or brackish water, it is recommended, however, that the sea water be run into all cells, in which case alternate cells are desalted during operation and the water is concentrated to brine in the others.

A rapid laboratory dialyzer was described by Brintzinger, Rothhaar, and Beier.[62] This was modified by Heilmeyer and Sundermann[63] and by Kratz[64] by combining dialysis with electrolysis. This apparatus, which has been manufactured commercially,[65,66] is described in more detail in the section on electrodialytic apparatus (Sect. III.2.A).

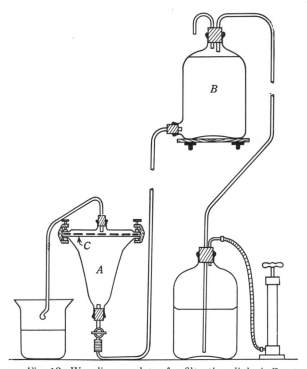

Fig. 13. Wegelin percolator for filtration dialysis.[67]

Wegelin[67] invented a type of dialyzer which he called a percolator. Strictly speaking his apparatus combines the operations of dialysis and ultrafiltration, "filtration-dialysis" (F.D. of Manegold, see Sect.II.3). A special percolator, A (Fig. 13), is arranged with a head, clamp, gasket,

[62] H. Brintzinger, A. Rothhaar, and H. G. Beier, *Kolloid-Z.*, **66**, 183 (1934).

[63] L. Heilmeyer and A. Sundermann, *Deut. Arch. klin. Med.*, **178**, 397 (1936).

[64] L. Kratz, *Kolloid-Z.*, **80**, 33–43 (1937).

[65] Jenaer Glaswerk Schott and Gen., Heidenheim, Germany, Trade Circular 5638.

[66] A. Gutbier, J. Huber, and W. Schieber, *Ber.*, **55**, 1518.

[67] G. Wegelin, *Kolloid-Z.*, **18**, 225 (1916).

and semipermeable membrane C. The dialyzate in A is washed by supplying distilled water under a sufficient hydrostatic head from reservoir B. The crystalloidal material is diffused and ultrafiltered through the membrane leaving the washed colloidal substances in the percolator. This apparatus can be constructed from Pyrex, industrial, flanged pipe fittings, which can be obtained in a variety of sizes and shapes from the Corning Glass Works, Corning, N. Y. These fittings are admirably suited to the construction of dialyzing and low-pressure ultrafiltration and electrodialyzing equipment.

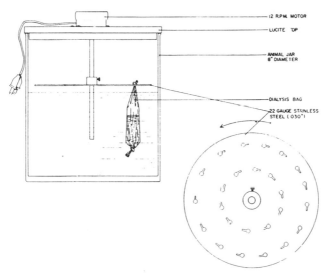

Fig. 14. Multiple-sample dialyzer.[63]

Durrum, Smith, and Jetton[68] have described a simple mechanical dialyzer capable of handling as many as twenty-five samples simultaneously. The apparatus, which is shown in Figure 14, is arranged so that the various dialyzing bags containing the samples can be hung from a rotating plate in the dialyzing fluid.

By pulling a cellulosic tube such as a sausage casing back through itself, Wentzel and Sterne[69] formed a double-walled seamless tube which could be used as an efficient double-surface dialyzer.

Methods and apparatus for separating substances dialytically have been described by Signer and co-workers,[70] who have utilized dialysis for frac-

[68] E. L. Durrum, E. R. B. Smith, and M. R. Jetton, *Science*, **120**, 956 (1954).

[69] L. M. Wentzel and M. Sterne, *Science*, **110**, 259 (1949).

[70] R. Signer *et al.*, *Helv. Chim. Acta*, **29**, 1984 (1946); **30**, 334 (1947); U.S. Pat. 2,405,456 (Aug. 6, 1946).

tionating two or more diffusible components in a solution, rather than for separating low-molecular solutes from colloidal or macromolecular solutes. If two kinds of diffusible particles are subjected to dialysis, there is an enrichment of the more readily dialyzable component in the dialyzing solvent, which is approximately inversely proportional to the square root of the ratio of the particle masses (assuming special membrane forces to be absent or negligible). This enrichment factor in a given dialysis cell will decrease with the length of time of the dialysis, although the total solutes dialyzed constantly increase.

The methods and apparatus designed by Signer allow the enriching factor to be utilized in a practical manner. For a complete understanding of the manner of operation of the fractionating dialyzers the original patent specifications and literature should be studied; the method in brief is as follows:

Apparatus is arranged to conduct a solution containing two solutes of differing coefficients of dialysis through an evaporator to concentrate the solution and provide pure solvent, which are then passed countercurrent to one another through a dialytic cell. This results in a slight enrichment of the more diffusible component in the solvent and of the less diffusible component in the residual dialyzate, which passes toward the reservoir. The enriched solvent is passed thence to a second evaporator or concentrating device, separated to an enriched concentrate and a solvent, and passed through a second dialyzer. From this cell the residuum is passed back through the first cell, and the further enriched solution from the second cell is again evaporated and passed to a third stage, and so on. At the end of the chain of dialyzers and evaporators, enriched solution of one solute (the more diffusible) is collected, and at the other end in the original solution reservoir is accumulated an enriched solution of the less diffusible solute.

This method has been used by its inventors to separate amino acids, for enriching compounds of radium or radioactive substances, preparation of hormones, vitamins, etc. For heat-labile substances, operation under reduced pressure can be used.

Efficient dialyzers have been prepared for use as artificial kidneys; these would prove equally useful in many laboratory dialysis problems. One described by Skeggs and Leonards[71] consists of a variable number of dialyzing units connected in parallel. Each unit is formed from a sheet of dialyzing Cellophane sandwiched between two rubber pads $12 \times 18 \times 0.25$ in. The inner surfaces of the rubber pads are finely grooved. Blood or other fluid to be dialyzed is pumped through the grooves on one side of the membrane, and the dialyzing solution is pumped through countercurrent on the other side. The apparatus has 840 cm.^{2} of dialyzing area per unit, contains 45 ml. of fluid to be dialyzed per unit, and is capable of re-

---

[71] L. T. Skeggs, Jr., and J. R. Leonards. *Science*, **108**, 212 (1948).

moving 0.5 g. of urea nitrogen per hour from blood containing 0.15 g. of urea nitrogen per 100 ml.

Other forms of dialyzers for use as artificial kidneys have been made and described. These include the type described by Kolff and Berk[72] which consist of long lengths of narrow Cellophane tubing wound on a drum which rotates in the dialyzing bath.

Kober,[73] and more recently Farber,[74] have concentrated colloidal solutions by evaporating the solvent from them through the dialyzing membrane or bag. Farber called the technique "pervaporation."

B. PREPARATION OF DIALYZING MEMBRANES

Collodion dialysis bags are readily prepared after some practice by filling a large, clean, dry test tube with a collodion solution which contains 3–4 grams of nitrocellulose (pyroxylin) in 100 milliliters of a 1:3 absolute ethanol–ether mixture. The pyroxylin should first be soaked with the alcohol, after which the ether is added. Solution uniformity can be obtained most rapidly by slowly tumbling a stoppered bottle of the collodion solution on a laboratory tumbling wheel. After filling the test tube with collodion, the major portion is returned to the container and the tube is inverted and allowed to drain while it is slowly rotated in the hand until the odor of ether has disappeared. The tube is now filled with lukewarm water and the collodion skin is loosened by cutting it free at the mouth of the test tube with a sharp knife or scalpel. The separation of the collodion bag from the walls of the tube can be aided by flowing water between the collodion and the glass. After removal from the mandrel the dialysis bag should be filled with water and checked for any pinhole leaks or tears. Thicker-walled dialyzing thimbles can be prepared by repeatedly flowing collodion over the walls of the test tube and drying off the ether after each coating cycle. These collodion dialyzing tubes should be washed in distilled water and should then be kept immersed in water until ready to be used in order to keep them from drying out and becoming too dense for effective dialysis. Collodion solutions can be purchased from commercial chemical supply houses; however, the iodized solutions for use in preparing photographic wet plates should be avoided. Other shapes of dialyzing bags can be made by using the interior surfaces of Erlenmeyer or balloon flasks as coating mandrels in a similar manner as described for the test tube.

Malfitano[75] has described the preparation of collodion tubes for dialyzers by forming these on the outer walls of special test-tube mandrels like

[72] W. J. Kolff and H. T. J. Berk, *Arch. néerland. physiol.*, **28**, 166 (1946).

[73] P. A. Kober, *J. Am. Chem. Soc.*, **39**, 944 (1917).

[74] L. Farber, *Science*, **82**, 158 (1935).

[75] G. Malfitano, *Z. physik. Chem.*, **68**, 232 (1909).

the one in Figure 7A–E. This consists of a tube on which a small bulb
is blown about one-third of the distance from the lip. This mandrel is
dipped to depth d in a cylinder containing collodion solution, removed from
the solution, and twirled in the hand until the collodion has set to a jelly.
Repeated dippings after short periods of drying give thicker diffusion
thimbles. When a thick enough dialysis thimble has been formed, the
coated mandrel is dried until no ether vapor is noted, and the thimble is
then removed by dipping the coated mandrel in warm water and rolling
back the collar formed at the bulb on the mandrel after cutting with a
knife at point d.

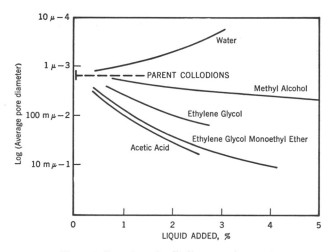

Fig. 15. Porosity of collodion membranes.[77]

Sheets for dialyzing membranes can be prepared by flowing a solution of
collodion onto a large quiet mercury surface.[76] After the proper degree of
drying, the sheet can be removed to a dish of water where it is kept until
needed. Collodion sheets can also be prepared by flowing collodion solutions over the surface of a leveled clean sheet of good-quality plate glass,
and stripping the sheet when sufficiently dried.

There are various methods of regulating the porosity of collodion or
cellophane membranes. The porosity of collodion has been regulated by
controlling the degree and rate of drying of the collodion solution after
coating. At the proper point of drying, which is determined in an empirical manner, the collodion skin is submerged in water to leach out the

[76] R. Wagner, in A. Weissberger, ed., *Physical Methods of Organic Chemistry*. 2nd ed.,
Part I, Interscience, New York-London, 1949.
[77] W. Elford, *Trans. Faraday Soc.*, **33**, 1094 (1937).

remaining solvents to give an open-pore texture of the sieve-membrane type. However, it is also possible to regulate the porosity of such membranes by introducing into the nitrocellulose solutions higher alcohols such as butanol, or other solvents such as glacial acetic acid. Elford[77] has described the conditions and principles governing the preparation of graded-porosity "gradocol" membranes of nitrocellulose. Figure 15 shows the influence of various solvents on the average pore diameter of collodion membranes. The porosity of cellophane membranes can be increased by treating commercial nonwaterproofed sheet material with sodium hydroxide or 63% zinc chloride solution according to the method of McBain and Stuewer. Such membranes lost their enhanced porosity upon drying, but when soaked first in 50% glycerol before drying, they retained up to 90% of their porosity.[78]

The conditions for preparing uniform and reproducible graded-porosity membranes of collodion, gelatin, agar, etc. were carefully studied by Brown,[79] who adopted as a general method for the preparation of such membranes the following procedure:

In a system consisting of two liquids, A and B, and a membrane substance, C such that the membrane substance imbibes only a negligible amount of A but imbibes B strongly and A and B are freely miscible, the permeability of the membranes prepared may be controlled by casting the membranes, drying them under controlled conditions, and swelling in graded mixtures of A and B. For example, collodion membranes cast from alcohol–ether solutions are dried and then immersed in various ethanol–water mixtures to grade them.

Brown found that the earlier methods of casting collodion membranes and controlling permeability by evaporation time[80] were difficult to reproduce. By the general techniques described above, he was able to prepare collodion membranes which had low permeability for night blue but allowed passage of starch through the membrane. On the other hand, reverse-acting formolized gelatin membranes were made. He suggested that some of the gelatin-in-water membranes prepared offered useful potentialities for purification of enzymes such as diastase or cytase.

Among the other materials suitable for dialyzing membranes may be mentioned viscose tubing, parchment paper, filter paper, or glass filter cloth sized with gelatin or other colloidal jellies. Parchment paper may be prepared in the form of thimbles or sheets by treating filter or extractor thimbles or sheets of filter paper with cold 50% sulfuric acid for short intervals (15 seconds to 1 minute) and washing thoroughly in running cold

[78] J. W. McBain and R. F. Stuewer, in *Colloid Symposium Monograph*, Williams & Wilkins, Baltimore, 1937, pp. 217–228; *J. Phys. Chem.*, **40**, 1157 (1936).

[79] W. Brown, *Biochem. J.*, **9**, 591 (1915); **11**, 40 (1917).

[80] S. L. Bigelow and A. Gemberling, *J. Am. Chem. Soc.*, **29**, 1585 (1907).

water.   Ettisch and Hellriegel prepared regenerated cellulose membranes by the cuprammonium process.[81]

One of the difficulties encountered in practice with semipermeable membranes of the foregoing types is their poor mechanical strength, especially if thin-walled membranes are prepared.   Biltz and von Vegesack[82] supported collodion membranes by forming them on a basket of fine platinum-wire cloth, which was dipped in collodion solutions, drained carefully, and dried to the desired degree before placing in water.   This method can be usefully applied for forming dialyzing tubes of cylindrical shape for concentric-tube, continuous-dialyzer arrangements, since such dialyzers have been difficult to build with efficient designs because of the flabbiness of the membranes available.   For many purposes, less expensive stainless-steel, nickel, or glass cloth can be used in place of platinum.   The wire-cloth support can be rolled into open-end cylinders and welded along the seam.

2. Apparatus for Electrodialysis

A. MATERIALS AND METHODS OF CONSTRUCTION AND OPERATION

Two principal types of electrodialyzers have enjoyed the major share of popularity in scientific laboratories.   The first is a simple rectangular vessel divided into three chambers by an anodic and a cathodic membrane in the manner shown diagrammatically in Figure 2.   This type of apparatus in its many forms has the advantage of ease of construction and has been used largely by Pauli and his school.   It can be set up by using old hard-rubber battery cases, glass battery jars, and similar rectangular vessels of insulating and corrosion-resistant materials.   Among the obvious disadvantages of such apparatus are the low ratio of membrane area to dialyzate volume, the large interelectrode distances, and the consequent high operating voltages or low currents resulting because of the high internal resistances of these types of equipment.   This is particularly troublesome if purification is carried to low levels of residual electrolytes in the dialyzate.

Although corrosion-resistant conductors such as platinum or graphite have usually been employed in electrodialyzers as electrodes, some experimentalists have used anodes or cathodes of mercury to advantage,[83] and Ikeda and Suzuki[84] made use of oxidizable anodes of zinc, iron, etc. to minimize undesirable electrokinetic effects.

[81] G. Ettisch and E. Hellriegel, *Biochem. Z.*, **248**, 65 (1932).

[82] W. Biltz and A. von Vegesack, *Z. physik. Chem.*, **68**, 357 (1909).

[83] H. B. Collier, *Can. J. Research*, **18B**, 252 (1940).   N. R. Joseph, *J. Biol. Chem.*, **126**, 403 (1938).   E. J. King, *Ind. Eng. Chem., Anal. Ed.*, **4**, 201 (1932).

[84] K. Ikeda and S. Suzuki, U. S. Pat. 1,015,891 (1909); Brit. Pat., 9440/09 (1912).

The horizontal electrodialyzer designed and used by Pauli[85] and co-workers is particularly suited to laboratory experiments. More recently various Pauli-type electrodialyzers have been described using Pyrex, industrial, flanged piping units.[86–91]

Such an apparatus[87] is shown in Figure 16. The middle compartment, B, for the dialyzate is a 1.5-in. Pyrex T-fitting to which was sealed a glass stopcock of 3-mm. bore for draining the compartment. Two alternate styles of electrode compartments were made and used in various experiments. Type A was made from a right-angle, 1.5-in. L-fitting to which was attached a drain-off stopcock. Electrode compartment C follows the design of Pauli and is made from a similar right-angle, 1.5-in. L-fitting to which was sealed a male 29/26 standard-taper ground joint.

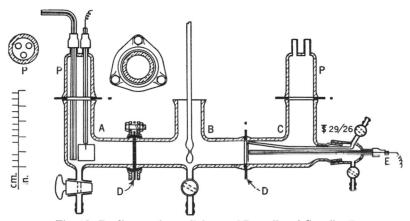

Fig. 16. Pauli-type electrodialyzer of Russell and Stauffer.[87]

The female portion of this ground joint was worked in the blast lamp to the form of a cap with an inlet jet and stopcock for the dialyzing water, and a second outlet port fitted with a similar stopcock. The electrodes, which were discs or squares of platinum sheet or gauze about 1 in. in diameter, were welded to a platinum lead wire and sealed through a length of soft-glass tubing which passed through a slip joint made water-tight with pure gum-rubber tubing at E. Caps P were provided by drawing down a 6-in. length of 1.5-in. flanged Pyrex pipe. All units were fastened with the iron flange clamps supplied as standard accessories with this piping, and membranes of collodion, parchmentized paper, Cellophane, or glass filter cloth

[85] W. Pauli, *Biochem. Z.*, **152**, 355 (1924).
[86] S. Redfern *Cereal Chem.*, **15**, 712 (1938).
[87] J. Russell and R. E. Stauffer, *Ind. Eng. Chem., Anal. Ed.*, **11**, 459 (1939).
[88] A. W. Marsden, *J. Soc. Chem. Ind. London*, **59**, 60 (1949).
[89] P. E. Lovering and M. L. Smith, *Chemistry & Industry*, **1946**, 298.
[90] T. D. Smith, *Chemistry & Industry*, **1946**, 334.
[91] Progress Report No. 41, June 29, 1945, Northern Coke Research Committee (British Coke Research Association).

impregnated with hardened gelatin were clamped at positions D. Gaskets of paraffined paper, gum rubber, Koroseal, or thin Eastman Tenite I sheet were used. The middle compartment is large enough to admit a mechanical stirrer and the electrodes of a laboratory-model Beckmann pH meter if desired. Voltages applied to such cells ranged from 50 to 1000 v. according to the material being electrodialyzed. Voltages up to 220 v. d.c. were available from laboratory mains, and for higher voltages an arrangement of step-up transformers and thermionic rectifiers was available. Some laboratories have also used a.c.–d.c. motor generator sets.

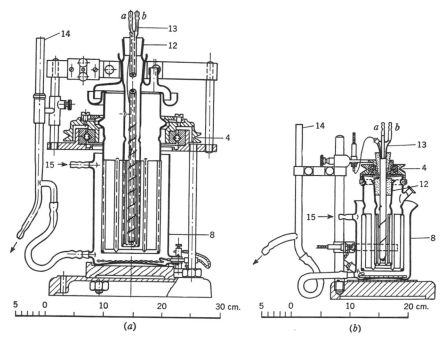

Fig. 17. Jena models of Brintzinger rapid electrodialyzer.

The middle compartment of the dialyzer using 1.5-in. flanged fittings has a capacity of 225 to 275 ml., but larger scale equipment has been constructed using larger sizes of flanged pipe fittings.

Other electrodialyzers using flanged pipe units have been described by Redfern,[86] Lovering and Smith,[89] and T. D. Smith,[90] some of which are operated in a vertical position, or are simplified by eliminating the glass blowing in the design of Figure 16 and using rubber stoppers and plastic fittings.

Russell and Stauffer (unpublished work) used the Pauli apparatus shown in Figure 16 for separating amino acids in protein hydrolyzates, for demonstrating the electrolytic separation of anionic, cationic, and aggregated dye ions, and for de-ashing gelatins and other proteids.

A second type of electrodialyzer is based on a modification of the "rapid dialyzer" of Gutbier *et al.*[92] manufactured by the Jenaer Glaswerk, Schott and Gen., Heidenheim, Germany.[93,94] Among the chief advantages claimed for these models are their high dialyzing speed as a result of their large surface:volume ratio, their convenience in aseptic manipulations, which is of paramount value in many biochemical problems, and their short electrical path, which allows larger currents to flow at low potentials. Finally, the same apparatus is suitable for pure dialysis when only non-electrolytic crystalloids are being removed from a dialyzate.

Figure 17 presents cross-sectional diagrams in the vertical plane of Jena models 5400 and 5401 of the Brintzinger electrodialyzer.* Model 5400 (Fig. 17a) is designed to handle a maximum dialyzate volume of 1000 ml., and model 5401 (Fig. 17b) will handle a maximum volume of 200 ml; both pieces of apparatus are mounted on a base plate carrying a binding post for the electrode made of platinum-wire gauze located in the outer electrode chamber 8. This chamber has inlet and outlet tubes for the dialyzing water indicated by 14 and 15. The first membrane is supported on a cage of glass rod so arranged with respect to a solid glass cylinder in its upper portion as to be free to rotate when the bearing mounted pulley, 4, is driven by a motor. The third chamber is established by a membrane similarly mounted on the glass member indicated by the number 12, within which is a double glass tube, 13, carrying a spirally wound platinum wire for the second electrode and arranged to allow the ingress and egress of the dialyzing water of the inner electrode chamber at a and b. Thin sheet membranes of collodion or Cellophane are best attached to the glass cagelike supports by moistening the sheet with water and placing the middle of the dry side over the base of the cage, and drawing the sides upward with folding in the manner of an umbrella to the solid cylindrical portion of the cage where it is fastened with a tight rubber band. When working with tubular membrane material, e. g., viscose sausage casings, the one end is drawn shut with a thread and sealed with a cellulose lacquer, after which the membrane is drawn over the cage and fastened in the same manner as before. Collodion membranes can be cast in test tubes or tall beakers of the proper diameter according to the techniques described earlier in this chapter (Sect. III.1.B). Linen thread or rubber bands are placed along the cage to ensure a minimum of sagging of thin membranes.

In operation, the inner spiral-wire electrode is made the anode and the outer wire-mesh electrode the cathode. Operating potentials are governed by the contents of the dialyzer and the degree of removal of electrolytes which is achieved.

At the beginning only a few volts will suffice to give an appreciable current through the cell and a reasonable rate of dialysis. Later on, potentials up to 220 v. or

[92] A. Gutbier, J. Huber, and W. Schieber, *Ber.*, **55**, 1518.

[93] H. Brintzinger, A. Rothhaar, and H. G. Beier, *Kolloid-Z.*, **66**, 183 (1934).

[94] Fish-Schurman Corp., New York, American representatives.

* Since World War II the Jena Brintzinger type dialyzers and electrodialyzers have not been produced by the Schott factory.

more may be needed.   During the early part of a dialysis, it is desirable to lower
the voltage in order to keep the current flow below that point at which temperature rises take place which may injure the dialyzate.   This may also be regulated
by cooling the dialyzing water before passing it into the apparatus.

Figure 18 is a graphic comparison of the rate of electrodialysis in the
Brintzinger and Pauli type electrodialyzers.[95]   The chloride ion concentration (ml. 0.1 N chloride/100 ml. dialyzate) is plotted against hours of electrodialysis for 150 ml. (*3*) or 750 ml. (*2*) of dialyzate.   The comparison
curve (*1*) for a Pauli dialyzer is based on data for a 150-ml. sample of solution; cellophane No. 300 membranes were used, and the dialyzate consisted
of 1% gum arabic solution containing 0.1 N hydrochloric acid.   Dialysis
was carried out at 40°C. with a current of 0.25 ampere.

Apparatus similar to the above-mentioned electrodialyzer of Brintzinger
was described earlier by Reiner,[96] and an especially neat and elegant micro-
electrodialyzer of glass using similar principles was described by Baer[97]
and Toth.[98]   The microdialyzer of Baer (Fig. 19) is particularly easy to

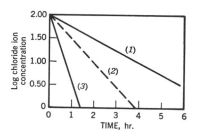

Fig. 18. Comparison of rate of
electrodialysis in Pauli and Brintzinger
electrodialyzers.[9]

construct in any laboratory.   Three glass tubes, 1, 2, and 3, of appropriate
diameters to fit loosely inside one another leaving annular spaces of 3–4
mm. are chosen.   In the original apparatus of Baer, the outer tube is a
condenser jacket about 34.5 mm. in diameter and 120 mm. in over-all
length.   Tube 1 is fitted at the bottom with a rubber stopper carrying a
spiral platinum-wire electrode sealed through a glass lead-in tube.   The
condenser side arms serve for the flow of the dialyzing water through the
outer tube, which is made the anode compartment.   The cathode compartment is the innermost tube also fitted with a three-hole rubber stopper

[95] H. Brintzinger *et al.*, *Kolloid-Z.*, **66**, 187 (1934).
[96] L. Reiner, *Kolloid-Z.*, **40**, 123 (1926).
[97] E. Baer, *Kolloid-Z.*, **46**, 176 (1928).
[98] A. Toth, *Biochem. Z.*, **189**, 270 (1927).

through which passes a spiral platinum cathode, an inlet port for water through a small-bore tube extending nearly to the cathode membrane, and an exit port placed at the top. The middle chamber for the dialyzate is set off in tube 2 by a membrane M_1 which is cut from a suitable sheet of material, fastened tightly around tube 2 with a rubber band, and sealed with a cellulose lacquer. M_2, the cathode membrane, was similarly

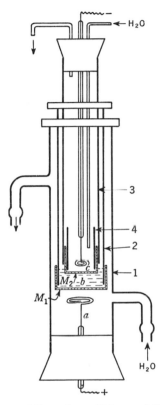

Fig. 19. Micro-electrodialyzer of Baer.[97]

mounted on the end of tube 3, except that in this case the membrane was held by slipping in an inner ring of glass, 4, which served to hold the membrane material by friction. A leak-free seal was ensured by sealing the edge with a suitable lacquer. The dialyzate was placed in position b in the apparatus, and amounts from 2 to 15 ml. could be purified.

De Bruyn and Troelstra[99] have devised an electrodialyzer (Fig. 20) of the Pauli type which contains, besides the normal three compartments,

[99] H. De Bruyn and S. A. Troelstra, *Kolloid-Z.*, **84**, 192 (1938).

two additional intermediate compartments placed between the electrode chambers and the dialyzate compartment. They have achieved a compact design with short interelectrode distances, and have used very few specially constructed parts. For the electrode chambers they have utilized vacuum–desiccator covers, and the intermediate compartments are made from ebonite rings. Dialyzing fluid is first fed through the extra intermediate compartments, thence through the electrode cells, and finally to waste.

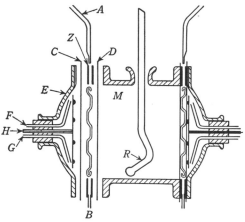

Fig. 20. Modified Pauli-type electrodialyzer of de Bruyn and Troelstra:[99] *E*, electrode chamber; *M*, middle chamber; *Z*, intermediate chamber; *C* and *D*, membranes; *R*, stirrer; *A*, *B*, *F*, and *G*, water inlets and outlets; *H*, electrode.

Modified Pauli dialyzers have been built by the author (*cf.*, Fig. 21) from Lucite chambers similar to those of the Webcell laboratory continuous dialyzer (see page 84) manufactured by the Brosites Machine Company. These chambers were cut from 0.5-in. thick sheets of Lucite, which were drilled and tapped on the edges for 0.25-in. Saran compression fittings for tubing. Slabs of graphite or retort coke,[100] nickel, stainless steel, silver or platinum backed with sheets of insulating Lucite were clamped against the outer surfaces of the first and third chambers. Gaskets and sheet dialyzing membranes were clamped in the proper locations to separate the three chambers. Multiple three-cell units could readily be assembled and operated in series.

An electrodialyzer which can be assembled from ordinary laboratory apparatus is described by Bernhardt, Arnow, and Bratton.[101] This equip-

[100] Obtainable from the National Carbon Co., New York.
[101] F. W. Bernhardt, L. E. Arnow and A. C. Bratton, *Ind. Eng. Chem., Anal. Ed.*, **9**, 387 (1937).

ment consists of a beaker or other wide-mouth vessel containing the dialyzate and a cover or other support carrying two dialyzing thimbles of test-tube shape containing electrodes and tubes for the circulation of dialyzing water. These thimbles serve as electrode compartments. In the same paper the authors describe a continuous dialyzer of the general type designed by Taylor et al.[102] (see page 83).

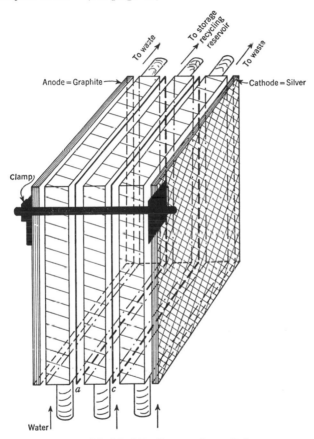

Fig. 21. Modified Pauli-type electrodialyzer.

For desalting small quantities of solutions for use in chromatography or in radio-isotope tracer studies, micro and semimicro electrodialyzers have proven of special value. An apparatus offered by the Research Equipment Corporation[103] with capacities of 3–5 ml. or 5–10 ml. has only one

[102] A. R. Taylor et al., Ind. Eng. Chem., Anal. Ed., 11, 659 (1939).
[103] Reco Electric Desalter, Research Equipment Corporation, 1135 Third Street, Oakland, California.

membrane, which is used to separate the anode chamber from the dialyzate. The anode is made of platinum, but the cathode consists of liquid mercury. Cations of inorganic salts form an amalgam with the mercury of the cathode when they are discharged to their respective metals during electrolysis; this amalgam is decomposed by hydrolysis in a separate chamber. The anions are removed, of course, by straightforward electrodialysis. The apparatus, which is constructed of glass and methyl methacrylate resin, desalts solutions in from 5 to 20 minutes. A suitable power source for providing direct current at an output from 0–40 volts and 0–3 amperes is supplied by the manufacturer for use with the equipment.

B. SPECIAL MEMBRANES

Because of the Bethe-Toropoff effect (Sect. II.5) special membranes have been devised for improving the efficiency of electrodialysis. Such membranes must, in general, be prepared in the laboratory, since they are not commercially available. Collodion and parchment membranes are spoken of as negative membranes (cf. page 74), because on immersion in solutions of electrolytes they assume a negative charge. At no concentration or pH is a positive charge exhibited. Most proteid membranes show a positive charge below the isoelectric point of the protein and a negative charge above it because of the amphoteric character of their component molecules. Thus, membranes of collodion, parchment, or cellophane are always negative, but membranes of gelatin, leather, or other protein films are positive or negative according to the conditions of use. Membranes of gelatin or other proteins are insufficiently strong mechanically for practical use. To overcome these weaknesses, composite or mosaic artificial membranes have been prepared and used by Ettisch and others.[104] This has been done by coating collodion, cellophane, sintered or woven glass, porous clay, or alumina with gelatin or other proteins, preferably hardened with chrome alum. Also albumins, gelatin, hemoglobin, glycine, or salmine have been dispersed in collodion before casting membranes.

Recent years have seen the development of membranes of highly selective permeability to anions or cations. Membranes from ion exchange resins are often nearly perfectly permselective for solutions of low concentrations, but become less selective as the concentrations increase in the solution surrounding the membranes. A manual on the theory and use of such membranes in the laboratory has been prepared by the Rohm and Haas Company[104a] to accompany the permselective Amberplex membranes

[104] G. Ettisch et al., Biochem. Z., 266, 422, 431, 441 (1933); 216, 401, 430 (1928). P. Grabar, Cold Spring Harbor Symposia Quant. Biol., 6, 252 (1938).

[104a] Amberplex Ion Permeable Membranes, Rohm and Haas Company, The Resinous Products Division, Washington Square, Philadelphia 5, Pa., 1952.

made by this company. This manual not only treats the theory and practical characteristics of the membranes, but also describes in detail laboratory scale apparatus of several types for use with Amberplex ion permeable membranes. Information on the selection of electrode material
suitable to various applications is included.

3. Apparatus for Electro-ultrafiltration

Figure 22 shows an arrangement for electro-ultrafiltration according to
the description of Bechhold and Rosenberg.[105] Essentially this apparatus
is the ultrafilter of Bechhold and Koenig with electrodes provided for electrolysis. A suction flask, S, is fitted with the funnel plate, c, which holds
the cylindrical ultrafiltering vessel containing the dialyzate. The underside of this vessel is painted with a network of metallic platinum burned
on from a platinic chloride–oil of lavender plating solution. This net is
connected to binding post, c_1. The inner side of the filtering vessel is
covered with a suitable ultrafiltering membrane prepared by the usual
techniques. A small balloon ultrafiltering flask, b, is provided with a

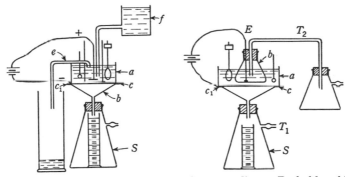

Fig. 22. Apparatus for electro-ultrafiltration, according to Bechold and Rosenberg: a and b, ultrafilter funnels; c, cathodic ultrafilter membrane; e, flow; f,
reservoir for washing solvent.[105]

suitable sieve membrane and a platinum electrode, E, in the form of a small
helix of wire sealed into a glass tube. To carry out an electro-ultrafiltration, suction is applied to both filters by means of pumps connected through
tubulatures T_1 and T_2. Bechhold recommends operating the apparatus so
that there is a slight tendency to transport acid from the anode chamber
into the dialyzate. By regulating the relative flow in any direction, neutral, acid, or alkaline reactions can be maintained in the dialyzate as desired. It is also advantageous to reverse the current at regular or random
intervals for this purpose.

[105] H. Bechhold and A. Rosenberg, *Biochem. Z.*, **157**, 85 (1925).

A number of other arrangements of ultrafiltration apparatus incorporating means for ionic transport by aid of the electric current have been described by Bechhold,[106] who points out that the procedure is quite flexible, can be used for micro to macro quantities, and provides the most rapid method for removing crystalloids from colloidal solutions.

4. Apparatus for Electrodecantation

Figure 23 is a schematic representation of the combined electrodialytic, electrodecantative process as used by Pauli.[107] An apparatus[108] consisting of the normal, three-compartment, horizontal Pauli electrodialyzing device is arranged with the middle chamber divided vertically into three chambers

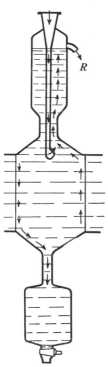

by constriction at two points. The upper portion has an inlet with a tube dipping below the surface to the central portion of the chamber. An overflow, R, is provided for excess water. The lower portion is a vessel fitted with a stopcock for drawing off the sedimented colloids. The flow of fluids caused by the density gradients is indicated by arrows. The lighter solvent layers rise to the upper portion of the chamber and escape through the overflow at R as fresh dialyzate is introduced. The concentrated higher specific gravity material accumulates in the lower third of the middle chamber, where it can be removed as desired.[108]

Stamberger[109] has published a survey of the process of electrodecantation in which the principles, phenomena, as well as applications, are described in some detail. Plans of an electrodecantation unit with a plurality of cells and membranes constructed of Lucite, stainless steel, and Cellophane are given. Among the advantages mentioned for the method, which has been applied to rubber latex,[110,111] gold, silver iodide,[112] and starch sols (see page 110) compared to evaporation or dialysis, are freedom from foaming and elimination of difficulties caused by pH changes as a result of diffusion effects of mixtures of ions of slow and fast diffusion rate.

Fig. 23. Scheme for electrodecantation, according to Pauli.[107]

Nielsen and Kirkwood[113] have also proposed fractionating proteins by superimposing electrophoretic horizontal transport upon convective vertical transport. Transport data for horse hemoglobin, bovine serum albumin, azo-ovalbumin, and fractionation data for mixtures of horse hemoglobin and bovine serum albumin, or hemoglobin and azo-ovalbumin were obtained. Cann, Kirkwood, et *al.*[114] have recently applied the method to the fractionation of diphtheria antitoxin and to bovine serum proteins.

With the rapid growth in electrophoretic techniques both in nonstabilized and stabilized media (zone electrophoresis, see this chapter, Part 4) a variety of commercial apparatus has become available for carrying out preparations or separations by electrodecantation, or electrophoresis-convection (electroconvection)[115] as it is variously termed. Raymond[116] has described an apparatus for electroconvection (Fig. 24) which is manufactured commercially[117] with a cell capacity adjustable from 10 to 200 ml. This apparatus, which can be obtained with graphite or platinum electrodes, is a unitized assembly (Fig. 25), consisting of a dialysis-membrane cell of one-piece construction, a cell frame with a cut-off gate to assist in isolating the fractions, a buffer jar with electrodes, a buffer circulating pump and a power control unit for operation from 110 volt a.c. lines. The dialysis-membrane cell is steam-sterilizable, and the equipment is compact enough to be operated conveniently in a refrigerator or cold room. Another feature of the apparatus is the double channel for the dialysis-membrane cell which permits either increased speed of operation, or electrodecantation of two samples simultaneously, if desired.*

Following the work of Kirkwood,[118] Brown,[119] and others, Raymond has discussed the theory of electroconvection[120] and its application to the design of efficient apparatus. He concludes that for maximum efficiency the

---

* E-C Apparatus Company publishes *Laboratory Manual for the E-C 25 Electroconvection Apparatus*, which treats the subject both theoretically and practically. A bibliography of electrodecantation is included.

[106] H. Bechhold in J. Alexander, ed., *Colloid Chemistry.* Vol. I, Chemical Catalog Co., New York, 1026, pp. 824–825, 834–836.

[107] W. Pauli, *Helv. Chim. Acta*, **25**, 137 (1942). A. Polson, *Biochim. et Biophys. Acta*, **11**, 315 (1953).

[108] Obtainable from E. Schildknecht Ing., Techn. u. wissensch. Messinstrumente und Apparate, Zurich, Neptunstrasse 20, Switzerland.

[109] P. Stamberger, *J. Colloid Sci.*, **1**, 93 (1946).

[110] W. Pauli and P. Stamberger, Austrian Pat. 167/36, 1074/36; Brit. Pat. 492,030.

[111] E. A. Murphy, *Rubber Chem. and Technol.*, **16**, 529 (1943).

[112] E. J. W. Verwey and H. R. Kruyt, *Z. physik. Chem.*, **167A**, 149 (1933).

[113] L. E. Nielsen and J. G. Kirkwood, *J. Am. Chem. Soc.*, **68**, 187 (1946). J. G. Kirkwood, *J. Chem. Phys.*, **9**, 878 (1941).

[114] J. R. Cann, J. G. Kirkwood, *et al., J. Am. Chem. Soc.*, **71**, 1603, 1609(1949).

[115] For a discussion of the terminology of this and allied fields reference should be had to E. R. B. Smith, E. L. Durrum, and S. Raymond, *Chem. Eng. News*, **32**, 2174 (1954).

[116] S. Raymond, *Proc. Soc. Expt. Biol. Med.*, **81**, 278 (1952).

[117] E-C Apparatus Company, 23 Haven Avenue, New York 32, N. Y.

[118] J. G. Kirkwood, J. R. Cann, and R. A. Brown, *Biochim. et Biophys. Acta*, **5**, 301 (1949); **6**, 606 (1950).

[119] R. A. Brown, *et al., J. Am. Chem. Soc.*, **73**, 4420 (1951).

[120] S. Raymond, *Science*, **118**, 388 (1953).

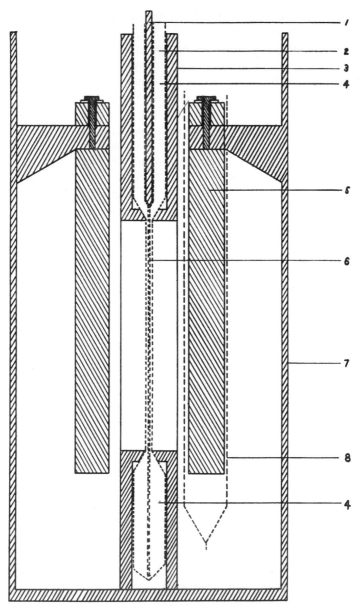

Fig. 24. Electroconvection cell median section:[117] (1) sliding gate; (2) solution;
(3) face plate; (4) reservoir; (5) electrodes; (6) channels; (7) buffer box; and (8) anode
diaphragm.

electrodes should be placed as close to the channel faces as possible to reduce power wastage outside the channel. In addition, the channel should be high and narrow rather than low and broad to obtain short transport times. A practical ratio of height to width is 10:1. A ratio of 20:1 theoretically increases the efficiency by 18%, but introduces unwanted drag effects on the convection currents by the side walls.

Fig. 25. E-C electroconvection apparatus. (Courtesy E-C Apparatus Company.)

Although continuous-flow electroconvection has been practiced industrially for the purification of rubber latex[121] and experimentally for fractionation of protein solution,[122] experience and theory indicate that batch operation is faster and more efficient.[123]

[121] P. Stamberger, Brit. Pats. 505,752 and 505,753 (1936).

[122] S. N. Timasheff, J. B. Shumaker, and J. G. Kirkwood, *Arch. Biochem. Biophys.*, **47**, 455 (1953).

[123] S. Raymond, *Science*, **120**, 542 (1954).

IV. APPLICATIONS OF DIALYSIS AND ELECTRODIALYSIS TO ORGANIC CHEMISTRY

1. Purification and Preparation of Materials

In general it may be said that, when nonelectrolytes such as low-molecular carbohydrates, urea, alcohols, etc. are to be separated from solutions of higher molecular species, the methods of dialysis or ultrafiltration are indicated. Since dialysis is a slow process, sometimes requiring days or months to carry to a satisfactory point of completion, ultrafiltration has been preferred when it could be applied. On the other hand, pure dialysis enjoys an advantage in the extreme simplicity of the apparatus required. Whenever electrolytes must be removed in the course of separations or purifications, as in the removal of ammonium sulfate from protein preparations, the methods of electrodialysis, electrodecantation, electro-ultrafiltration, and electrophoretic transport are especially valuable and offer the great advantage of increased speed, as shown in Table II (page 70). There is, of course, no gain in the speed of removal of nonelectrolytic crystalloids.

Graham[124] demonstated the efficient separation of the polymeric carbohydrate gum arabic from the crystalloidal disaccharide sucrose by means of dialysis through starch-sized letter paper. He obtained the sucrose in a readily crystallizable condition. Since this pioneer work on the subject of dialysis, the methods involving fractionations or separations by semipermeable membranes have been used by experimenters for all manner of substances, inorganic as well as organic. In the organic field, the methods have, as might be expected, played a great part in the study of biocolloids such as the proteins, carbohydrates, enzymes, antibodies, serums, and hormones. Soil chemists have used the methods for studying the organic materials as well as the base-exchange behavior of soils, clays, and minerals. Industrially these methods have considerable importance in the purification of sugar sirups, preparation of medicinals, and, in Europe at least, in the purification and dewatering of clays for the clay-products industries. A particularly valuable review of such applications up to the year 1931 is given by Prausnitz and Reitstötter,[125] and in addition the annotated bibliography at the end of this chapter indicates the scope of the applications and provides supplemental references to the literature particularly since 1931. Since each biocolloid presents special problems of its own, and since in very few cases have investigators studied conditions to determine the optimum method of handling a problem, only a general survey of the field

[124] T. Graham, *Trans. Roy. Soc. London*, **151**, 185 (1861).
[125] P. H. Prausnitz and J. Reitstötter, *Elektrophorese, Elektro-osmose, Elektrodialyse*. Steinkopff, Dresden and Leipzig, 1931, pp. 114 204.

is given here; the reader should have recourse to the literature for complete information on a given substance.

A. PROTEINS AND HORMONES

In 1903 Morse and Pierce[126] applied an electric current across a gelatin solution confined by two parchment membranes for the purpose of removing impurities. Seven years later, apparently independently, Dhéré and Gorgolewski[127] again used electrodialysis to de-ash gelatin and carried out physicochemical studies on the purified preparations. This paper on gelatin de-ashing was followed by others on the same subject as well as papers on the removal of electrolytes from horse serums by electrodialysis. Pauli and co-workers[128–130] carried out systematic studies of the electrodialysis of many proteins and the physicochemical properties of the purified substances. In 1929 Eisler and Spiegel-Adolf[131] described the preparation of typhus and diphtheria serums from horses or dogs using electrodialysis for removing electrolytes according to the method of Pauli and Spiegel-Adolf[129] and the method of Pauli for precipitation of total globulins.

The use of the method of compensating dialysis against saline solutions for protein preparations has been suggested by numerous investigators. A series of papers by Vanzetti and co-workers[132–134] describes a dialyzer, suitable membranes, and the technique of compensating dialysis.

Landsteiner[135] in a study of the size of serologically reactive units in hydrolyzed silk protein carried through fractionations of the hydrolyzates by dialysis and fractional precipitation. Studies of the components of blood complement indicate at least four factors to be present. In a recent study of guinea pig blood complement, three factors were successfully separated and purified by Pillemer, Ecker, Oncley, and Cohn[136] by methods which involved the slow introduction of reactants into the preparations at temperatures of about 1°C. by diffusing them through Cellophane dialyzers. The factors after purification were tested for freedom from contaminants by electrophoretic methods. In studies of the bond between phosphatides and the chromoprotein of visual purple, Broda[137] has employed electrodialysis to advantage.

[126] H. W. Morse and G. W. Pierce, *Z. physik. Chem.*, **45**, 589 (1903).

[127] Ch. Dhéré and M. Gorgolewski, *Compt. rend.*, **150**, 934 (1910).

[128] W. Pauli, *Kolloid-Z.*, **31**, 252 (1922); *Biochem. Z.*, **152**, 355 (1924). W. Pauli and M. Schön, *ibid.*, **153**, 253 (1924).

[129] W. Pauli and M. Spiegel-Adolf, *Biochem. Z.*, **152**, 360 (1924).

[130] W. Pauli and T. Stenzinger, *Biochem. Z.*, **205**, 71 (1929). W. Pauli and E. Weiss, *ibid.*, **203**, 103 (1928). W. Pauli and H. Wit., *ibid.*, **174**, 308 (1926).

[131] M. Eisler and M. Spiegel-Adolf, *Biochem. Z.*, **204**, 28 (1929).

[132] G. Vanzetti, *et al.*, *Biochim. e terap. sper.*, **25**, 159 (1938); *C.A.*, **32**, 7490 (1938).

[133] G. Vanzetti, *et al.*, *Biochim. e terap. sper.*, **24**, 265 (1937); *C.A.*, **32**, 966 (1938).

[134] G. Vanzetti *et. al.*, *Bull. soc. ital, biol. sper.*, **12**, 619 (1937): *C. A.*, **32**, 966, (1938).

[135] K. Landsteiner, *J. Exptl. Med.*, **75**, 269 (1942).

[136] L. Pillemer, E. E. Ecker, J. L. Oncley, and E. J. Cohn, *J. Exptl. Med.*, **74**, 297 (1941).

[137] E. E. Broda, *Biochem. J.*, **35**, 960 (1941).

Methods and schedules for the isolation and purification of hormones have often included dialytic or electrodialytic procedures. Chow and co-workers[138,139] have employed dialysis, centrifugation, fractional precipitation, and filtration to prepare metakentrins from hog and sheep pituitary glands. Kallós and Hoffmann[140] describe membranes and apparatus used by them for preparing β-tuberculin from nutritive broths of cultures of the tuberculosis bacillus. They used ultrafiltration procedures largely in their studies.

Ettisch and co-workers[141] have contributed extensively to the literature on the methods of electrodialysis and the use of electrodialytic techniques for handling animal serums as well as for the study of other types of proteins. The original papers should be consulted by those interested in electrodialytic procedures in general and their applications to protein investigations. Ettisch has used special membranes of collodion containing included proteins or glycine to eliminate or minimize the undesirable membrane phenomena such as the Bethe-Toropoff effect (Sect. II.5). Among other papers appearing in this field are those of Stadie and Ross,[142] Spiegler,[143] and Toth.[144] Toth described a quantitative micro method for electrodialytic fractionation of serum proteins using apparatus based on that of Reiner.[145]

Freeman, Gulland, and Randall,[146] and more recently Cohn, Irving, and du Vigneaud[147] have used electrodialysis in studies of α- and β-hypophamine. Lipovitellin, a protein hormone from egg yolk originally prepared by Hoppe-Seyler in 1867,[148] has been prepared by Chargaff[149] with the aid of dialytic methods. Foster and Schmidt[150] separated the dicarboxylic amino acids from protein hydrolyzates for analytical and preparative purposes by means of electrodialysis. In earlier articles these authors[151] utilized electrodialysis to separate the hexone bases, arginine, lysine, and histidine, from protein hydrolyzates. This method had previously been patented in the United States by Ikeda and Suzuki,[152] who used soluble anodes to avoid pH changes in the electrodialyzed materials.

[138] B. F. Chow, R. O. Greep, and H. B. van Dyke, *J. Endocrinology*, 1, 440 (1940).

[139] T. Shedlovsky, A. Rothen, R. O. Greep, H. B. van Dyke, and B. F. Chow, *Science*, 92, 178 (1940).

[140] P. Kallós and G. Hoffmann, *Biochem. Z.*, 266, 128, 132 (1933).

[141] G. Ettisch *et al.*, *Biochem. Z.*, 266, 422, 436, 441 (1933); 216, 401, 430 (1929); 200, 250 (1928); 195, 175 (1928); 230, 68 (1931); 239, 48 (1931); 203, 147 (1928); 248, 65 (1932); 171, 443, 454 (1926); 230, 129 (1931).

[142] W. C. Stadie and E. C. Ross, *J. Biol. Chem.*, 68, 231 (1926).

[143] R. Spiegler, *Biochem. Z.*, 230, 253 (1931).

[144] A. Toth, *Biochem. Z.*, 189, 270 (1927); 201, 412 (1928).

[145] L. Reiner, *Kolloid-Z.*, 40, 123 (1926).

[146] M. Freeman, J. M. Gulland, and S. S. Randall, *Biochem. J.*, 29, 2211 (1935).

[147] E. J. Cohn, G. W. Irving, and V. du Vigneaud, *J. Biol. Chem.*, 137, 635 (1941).

[148] F. Hoppe-Seyler, *Medizinisch-chemische Untersuchungen.* Berlin, 1867, p. 215.

[149] E. Chargaff, *J. Biol. Chem.*, 142, 491, 505 (1942).

[150] G. L. Foster and C. L. A. Schmidt, *J. Am. Chem. Soc.*, 48, 1709 (1926).

[151] G. L. Foster and C. L. A. Schmidt, *Proc. Soc. Exptl. Biol. Med.*, 19, 348 (1922); *J. Biol. Chem.*, 56, 545 (1923).

[152] K. Ikeda and S. Suzuki, U. S. Pat. 1,015,891 (1909).

Electrolytic desalting in multi-compartment cells equipped with ion-exchange membranes is of special utility in connection with paper chromatography (see Part 4 of this chapter) of amino acids and other substances. Blainey and Yardley[152a] describe appropriate apparatus and methods, and Jepson and Smith[152b] discuss the destruction of thyroxine by such electrolytic desalting.

D. ENZYMES

Lisbonne and Vulquin,[153] following Dhéré's pioneer papers on electrodialysis, applied the method to the removal of electrolytes from malt amylase with a consequent loss of enzymatic activity. With subsequent addition of salts to the deashed material, activity could be restored. Further studies of maltase were made by Kopaczewski,[154] Willstätter and co-workers,[155] and by Fricke.[156]

Fricke and co-workers used electrodialysis followed by electrophoretic partition of a malt diastase. First the maltase was electrodialyzed in a three-chamber cell equipped with a carbon anode and an iron-mesh cathode. Membranes were prepared from 12% glacial acetic acid–collodion solution and these were thoroughly washed out by electrodialysis before use. The membranes were not permeable to the malt diastase. During the electrodialysis the globulins were precipitated, and the diastase activity of the remaining solution rose to 2 to 2.5 times its beginning value. The ash content of the filtered solution fell from 5 to 1%, and the nitrogen content was halved. Following the electrodialysis, the purified solution of diastase was placed in the middle chamber of a five-cell apparatus. The two inner cell membranes, which were permeable to diastase, were of parchment paper or 2% glacial acetic acid–collodion. Starting with a 0.7% diastase solution, the distribution of the material at the end of the run was as follows: 29% in the middle chamber, 32% in the anodic middle chamber, and 16% in the cathodic middle chamber. Only the fraction in the latter chamber showed diastase activity and this was nearly five times as potent as the material before electrophoretic purification. This fraction no longer gave a protein test reaction, only a strong Molisch carbohydrate test. Refinements in apparatus and techniques finally yielded a diastase containing 0.05% ash and sixfold the enzyme potency of the material placed for electrophoretic fractionation in the middle cell. In addition to malt diastase, trypsin and invertin were also purified in a similar manner. The activity of the enzyme solutions purified by the foregoing techniques was less than that of materials purified

[152a] J. D. Blainey and H. J. Yardley, *Nature*, **177**, 83 (1956).

[152b] J. B. Jepson and I. Smith, *Nature*, **177**, 84 (1956).

[153] N. Lisbonne and E. Vulquin, *Compt. rend. soc. Biol.*, **72**, 336 (1912); *J. physiol. et path. gén.*, **15**, 23 (1913).

[154] W. Kopaczewski, *Ann. inst. Pasteur*, **27**, 528 (1913); *Bull. soc. chim. biol.*, **7**, 420 (1925).

[155] R. Willstätter and K. Schneider, *Z. physiol. Chem.*, **133**, 193, 208 (1924). R. Willstätter, K. Schneider, and E. Wenzel, *ibid.*, **151**, 1 (1926).

[156] R. Fricke and P. Kaja, *Ber.*, **57**, 310, 765 (1924). R. Fricke, F. A. Fischer, and H. Borchers, *Kolloid-Z.*, **39**, 152, 371 (1926).

by Willstätter's adsorption method, but the speed of removal of proteins and electrolytes was very much greater. Ornstein[157] has experimented with electrodialytic and electrophoretic purification of rennet enzymes in similar apparatus.

C. STARCHES, SUGARS, AND GUMS

Samec and collaborators[158][160] have made extensive use of diffusion through sieve membranes both with and without applied electric currents in a series of studies of plant colloids. These investigations included fractionations of starches prepared from potato, wheat, maize, rice, arrowroot, *Manihot*, and other sources. Samec and Haerdtl[159] concluded that starches from all sources consisted of an electrodialytically precipitable, highly viscous fraction equivalent to the β-amylose of A. Mayer or amylopectin of Macquenne, and an electrically nonconducting, nonviscous, nonprecipitable fraction equivalent to Macquenne's "amylose." The relative amounts of these components varied with the starch type.

Von Brodowski[161] has published an extensive account of the colloids in molasses. Among other methods discussed by him are those of dialysis, and his paper gives details of special dialyzing equipment which was constructed on the basis of Zsigmondy's[162] and Gutbier's[163] rapid dialyzers. Other carbohydrates which have been purified by electrodialysis include agar-agar by Samec and Ssajevic,[164] by Harvey,[165] and by Hoffmann and Gortner,[166] pectins by Kopaczewski[167] and Emmett,[168] glycogen by Samec and Ssajevic[164] and Kuhn,[169] and mastic sols by Hotta.[170]

Humic acid solutions from organic soils were dissolved with the aid of ammonium ion and were purified electrodialytically by Briesalski and Berger[171] in apparatus using clay-cylinder septa with parchment paper around the anode.

D. RESINS, SYNTHETIC POLYMERS, CELLULOSE, AND CELLULOSE DERIVATIVES

Cragg and Hammerschlag[172] have published a review of the literature on the application of fractional diffusion to such natural and synthetic polymers as rubber, nitrocellulose, polyanethole, polyindene, polyvinyl acetate, polystyrene, and sodium

[157] G. Ornstein, *Z. Hyg. Infektionskrankh.*, **110**, 52 (1929).

[158] M. Samec, *Kolloid-Beihefte*, **10**, 289 (1918).

[159] M. Samec and H. Haerdtl, *Kolloid-Beihefte*, **12**, 281 (1920).

[160] M. Samec and A. Mayer, *Kolloid-Beihefte*, **13**, 165 (1921).

[161] A. Von Brodowski, *Kolloid-Beihefte*, **29**, 261–353 (1929).

[162] R. Zsigmondy, *Z. anorg. Chem.*, **68**, 169 (1919); *Kolloid-Z.*, **8**, 123 (1911).

[163] A. Gutbier, *Z. anorg. Chem.*, **157**, 345 (1926).

[164] M. Samec and V. Ssajevic, *Compt. rend.*, **173**, 1474 (1921).

[165] E. H. Harvey, *Am. J. Pharm.*, **97**, 66 (1925).

[166] W. F. Hoffman and R. Gortner, *J. Biol. Chem.*, **65**, 371 (1925).

[167] W. Kopaczewski, *Bull. soc. chim. biol.*, **7**, 419 (1925).

[168] A. M. Emmett, *Biochem. J.*, **20**, 564 (1926).

[169] R. Kuhn, *Ann.*, **443**, 1 (1925).

[170] K. Hotta, *Biochem. Z.*, **183**, 72 (1927).

[171] E. Briesalski and W. Berger, *Braunkohle*, **23**, 197 (1924); ref. given in *Kolloid-Z.*, **52** 250 (1930).

[172] L. H. Cragg and H. Hammerschlag, *Chem. Revs.*, **39**, 118 (1946).

bivinyl polymer. Many investigators have used the methods of dialysis and fractional diffusion in conjunction with fractional precipitation and ultrafiltration. Krüger[173] separated units of nitrocellulose solutions of varying molecular size by diffusion of the solutions against pure solvent in Oeholm's[174] apparatus. Many investigators consider the methods of ultrafiltration much too slow for practical use.[172] Besides Krüger the following have published data in this field: Beck, Clément, and Riviere,[175] Berl and Hefter,[176] Caille,[177] Duclaux et al.,[178] and Kumichel.[179] Numerous patents have been issued particularly in Germany to Elektro-Osmose A. G.[180]

The dialysis of saturated fatty acids of more than 16 carbon atoms as aqueous colloidal solutions or as soaps and in the presence of bile acids has been studied with Cellophane diffusion membranes.[181] Nowatke[182] has examined the constitution of certain derivatives of caffeine, theobromine, and theophylline with the assistance of dialysis. Harmsen and Kolff[183] have designed special dialyzers with cellophane membranes for cultivation of bacteria, viruses, or fungi. Three arrangements of apparatus are described by them, and special features of the method are the luxuriant cultures, the possibility of maintaining constant nutrient solutions aseptically, accumulating metabolic products, and studying metabolic processes.

General References

GENERAL

Abramson, H. A., *Electrokinetic Phenomena and Their Applications in Biology and Medicine.* Chemical Catalog Co., New York, 1934.

Abramson, H. A., L. S. Moyer, and M. H. Gorin, *Electrophoresis of Proteins and the Chemistry of Cell Surfaces.* Reinhold, New York, 1942.

Abramson, H. A., E. J. Cohn, B. D. Davis, F. L. Horsfall, L. G. Longsworth, D. MacInnes, H. Mueller, and K. G. Stern, "Electrophoresis," *Ann. N. Y. Acad. Sci.*, **39**, 105 (1939).

Bechhold, H., "Ultrafiltration and Electro-ultrafiltration," in J. Alexander, ed., *Colloid Chemistry.* Vol. I, Chemical Catalog Co., 1926, New York, pp. 820–837. Description of principles and design of apparatus.

Bechhold, H., *Die Kolloide in Biologie und Medizin.* 5th ed., Steinkopff, Dresden and Leipzig, 1929, pp. 102–151. Methods for colloid study are discussed including

---

[173] D. Krüger, *Z. angew. Chem.*, **41**, 407 (1928).

[174] L. W. Oeholm, *Z. physik. Chem.*, **50**, 312 (1905).

[175] A. Beck, L. Clément, and C. Riviere, *Chimie & industrie*, **24**, 1068 (1930).

[176] E. Berl and P. Hefter, *Cellulosechemie*, **14**, 65 (1933).

[177] A. Caille, *Chimie & industrie*, **25**, 276 (1931).

[178] J. Duclaux and R. Nodzu, *Rev. gén. colloïdes*, **7**, 241 (1929). J. Duclaux and E. Wollman, *Bull. soc. chim.*, **27**, 414 (1920).

[179] W. Kumichel, *Kolloid-Beihefte*, **26**, 161 (1928).

[180] Ger. Pats. 305,512; 307,701; 307,702; 348,136; 296,053; 305,118; 309;260; 357,057.

[181] F. L. Breusch, *Biochem. Z.*, **293**, 280 (1937).

[182] W. Nowatke, *J. pharm. chim.*, **26**, 481 (1937); *C.A.*, **32**, 7021 (1938).

[183] G. W. Harmsen and W. J. Kolff, *Science*, **105**, 582 (1947).

diffusion, osmotic pressure, dialysis, electrodialysis, ultrafiltration, and electro-ultrafiltration.

Brintzinger, H., "Elektrodialyse," in A. Kuhn, ed., *Kolloidchemisches Taschenbuch*. Akadem. Verlagsgesellschaft, Leipzig, 1948.

Daniels, F. K., "Dialysis," in R. E. Kirk and D. F. Othmer, eds. *Encyclopedia of Chemical Technology*. Vol. V, Interscience, New York-London, 1950.

Ellis, C. B., "Fresh Water from the Ocean," in *Sieve Processes*. Chapter 6, pp. 95–122. Ronald Press, New York, 1954.

Graham, T., *Trans. Roy. Soc. London*, **151**, 183 (1861). Liquid diffusion applied to analysis.

Von Hahn, F. V., "Dispersoidanalyse," in *Handbuch der Kolloidwissenschaft*. Vol. 3, Steinkopff, Dresden and Leipzig, 1928, pp. 125–251.

Pauli, W., and E. Valkó, *Elektrochemie der Kolloide*. Springer, Vienna, 1929.

Prausnitz, P. H., and J. Reitstötter, *Elektrophorese, Elektro-osmose, Elektrodialyse*. Steinkopff, Dresden and Leipzig, 1931. Description is given of methods and materials treated up to 1931 (pp. 113–153); review of patent literature (pp. 193–212); patent index (pp. 281–285); annotated bibliography to 1931 (pp. 261–281).

Schultze, H. E., "Dialyse und Elektro-osmose," in *Ullman's Encyklopädie der technischen Chemie*. Vol. I, Urban and Schwarzenberg, Munich, Berlin, 1951.

Stamberger, P., "Electrodialysis," in R. E. Kirk and D. F. Othmer, eds., *Encyclopedia of Chemical Technology*. Vol. V, Interscience, New York-London, 1950.

THEORY OF DIFFUSION AND MEMBRANES

Adair, G. S., *Trans. Faraday Soc.*, **33**, 1115 (1937). Rate of dialysis and the use of salt solutions in place of pure water as a dialyzing fluid.

Amberplex Ion Permeable Membranes. Rohm and Haas Company, The Resinous Products Division, Washington Square, Philadelphia 5, Pa., 1952. A laboratory manual on ion permeable membranes, their theory and use, two, three and multicompartment cells, laboratory techniques and apparatus design.

Barnes, C., *Physics*, **5**, 4 (1934). Exact solution of the problem of diffusion through a membrane for two stirred solutions.

Bethe, A., and Th. Toropoff, *Z. physik. Chem.*, **88**, 686 (1914); **89**, 597 (1915). Electrokinetic properties of membranes.

Biltz, W., *Gedenkboek van Bemmelen*. Helder, 1910, p. 108; quoted by H. R. Kruyt, in *Colloids;* translation by H. S. van Klooster, Wiley, New York, 1927, p. 149. The effect of molecular size of aniline-dye molecules on diffusion through collodion membranes was studied. The effects of groups such as sulfonic acid residues were noted.

Bolam, F. R., *The Donnan Equilibria*, Bell, London, 1932.

Brintzinger, H., *et al.*, *Z. anorg. allgem. Chem.*, **230**, 381 (1937); comparison of Cuprophane and sintered-glass diaphragms in dialysis. *Z. anorg. allgem. Chem.*, **231**, 337 (1937); effect of foreign electrolyte on dialysis coefficient; *Kolloid-Z.*, **79**, 324 (1937); separation of organic isomers (nitrophenols, nitranilines, etc.) by "diasolysis," *i.e.*, using membranes with special solvent properties.

Brintzinger, H., and H. Osswald, *Kolloid-Z.*, **70**, 198 (1935). Comparison of Cellophane, Cuprophane, and parchment as dialyzing membranes and in electrodialysis of 1% gum arabic.

Brintzinger, H., *et al.*, *Z. anorg. allgem. Chem.*, **224**, 325 (1935); **225**, 213 (1935). Determinations of dialysis coefficients of isomeric and other organic compounds including organic dye ions.

Broyer, T. C., *Botan. Rev.*, **13**, 1, 126 (1947). The movement of materials into plants. (I) Osmosis and the movement of water. (II) The nature of solute movement into plants.

Clarke, H. T., ed., *Ion Transport Across Membranes*. Academic Press, New York, 1954; especially K. Sollner *et al.* "Electrochemical Studies with Model Membranes," pp. 144–189.

Cold Spring Harbor Symposia Quant. Biol., **8**, 9–17, 30–63 (1940). Symposium on cell permeability.

Conway, E. J., "A Redox Pump for the Biological Performance of Osmotic Work, and Its Relation to the Kinetics of Free Ion Diffusion Across Membranes," *Intern. Rev. Cytol.* **2**, 419 (1953).

Davson, H., and J. F. Danielli, *The Permeability of Natural Membranes*. Cambridge Univ. Press, 1943, Chapters I, II, IV–VI, XXI, App. A. The physical chemistry of membranes.

Geddes, L., in Weissberger, ed., *Physical Methods of Organic Chemistry*. Vol. I, Interscience, New York, 1945, pp. 277–310. Methods and applications of the determination of diffusivity.

Höber, R., *Physical Chemistry of Cells and Tissues*. Blakiston, Philadelphia, 1945, pp. 7–23, 59–93, 187–217, 227–355. Diffusion and membrane permeability especially with reference to natural membranes.

Jander, G., and J. Zakowski, *Membranfilter, Cella- und Ultrafeinfilter*. *Akadem.* Verlagsgesellschaft, Leipzig, 1929. I. Working procedures for ultrafiltration. II. Structure of membranes, ultrafine and Cella filters.

Manegold, E., and K. Kalauch, *Kolloid-Z.*, **88**, 257 (1939). Preparation of positively charged dialyzing membranes.

Manegold, E., R. Hoffmann, and K. Solf, *Kolloid-Z.*, **56**, 267 (1931); **57**, 23 (1932). Study of the kinetics and theory of permeability during dialysis, electrolysis, and ultrafiltration of sintered-glass (Jena) plates, porous stoneware filters, etc.

Molecular Physics in Relation to Biology. National Research Council Bulletin No. 69, May, 1929, F. G. Donnan, *Membrane Equilibria and Potentials*, pp. 51–56; L. Michaelis, *Molecular Sieve Membranes*, pp. 119–142; W. J. V. Osterhout, *Permeability and Bioelectrical Phenomena*, pp. 170–221.

Nowatke, W., *Kolloid-Z.*, **75**, 269 (1936). Collodion membranes, their preparation and properties.

Sollner, K., "Ion Exchange Membranes," *Ann. N. Y. Acad. Sci.*, **57**, 177 (1953). A review of the electrochemistry of membranes.

Teorell, H., *Proc. Natl. Acad. Sci. U. S.*, **21**, 152 (1935). Diffusion effect on ionic distribution; theoretical considerations.

Teorell, H., "Transport Processes and Electrical Phenomena in Ionic Membranes," *Progr. Biophys. and Biophys. Chem.*, **3**, 305 (1953). A review of recent advances in the theory of the behavior of membranes.

Urmánczy, A., *Acta Lit. Sci. Univ. Hung. Francisco-Josephinae. Sect. Chem. Mineral. Phys.*, **4**, 239 (1935); *C. A.* **30**, 7011 (1936). The mechanism of dialysis and velocity of dialysis of aqueous solutions of hydrochloric, nitric, sulfuric, and acetic acids, and sodium hydroxide at 25°C., through chrome-tanned calf-intestine membranes.

Voskresenskii, P. I., *J. Chem. Ind. U.S.S.R.*, No. 4, 72 (1934). Theoretical basis for differences in dialyzing power of fresh and aged (dried) viscose films.

Wagner, R., in Weissberger, ed., *Physical Methods of Organic Chemistry*. 2nd Ed., Part I, Interscience, New York, 1949. Osmotic pressure.

Zhukov, I. I., *Uspekhi Khim.*, **12**, 265 (1943); *C. A.* **38**, 5460 (1944). Theory of electrokinetic phenomena associated with electrodialysis.

APPARATUS AND METHODS

Aitken, H. A. A., *J. Biol. Chem.*, **90**, 161 (1931). A simple continuous dialyzer with large ratio of dialyzing membrane surface to dialyzate volume.

Asaba, T., *Arb. med. Fakultät Okayama*, **3**, 561 (1933); *C. A.* **27**, 3248, 5811 (1933). Method of micro-electrodialysis and its use for isolation of serum precipitins.

Bartell, F. E., *Ind. Eng. Chem., Anal. Ed.*, **8**, 247 (1936). A simple and inexpensive electrodialyzer.

Bradfield, R., *J. Am. Soc. Agron.*, **19**, 1015 (1927). An electrodialyzer.

Bradfield, R., *Naturwissenschaften*, **16**, 404 (1928). On the theory of electrodialysis.

Brauns, F. E., *Ind. Eng. Chem., Anal. Ed.*, **13**, 259 (1941). An improved electrodialyzer.

Burlakov, V., *Iskusstvennoe Volokno*, **5**, No. 8, 38 (1934). Tests of various films or membranes of a vegetable nature show parchment to be most suitable for dialysis of caustic soda solutions.

Cann, J. R., J. G. Kirkwood, R. A. Brown, and O. J. Plescia, *J. Am. Chem. Soc.*, **71**, 1603 (1949). Design factors of apparatus for electrodecantation.

Cox, G. J., H. King, and C. P. Berg, *J. Biol. Chem.*, **81**, 755 (1929). Describes the use of hardened (formolized) gelatin membranes in place of parchment paper.

Dahl, O., *Svensk Kem. Tid.*, **51**, 219 (1939). An apparatus for electrodialysis and preparation of organic sols and gels.

Dhéré, Ch., *Kolloid-Z.*, **41**, 243, 315 (1927). Describes apparatus and applications of electrodialysis in field of biochemistry. A bibliography from 1910–1927 is included.

Florence, G., *Bull. soc. chim.*, **51**, 72 (1932). Machine for preparing collodion dialyzing membranes of great uniformity.

Florence, G., and D. Vincent, *Bull. soc. chim. biol.*, **18**, 1167 (1936). A large rotating dialyzer.

Gilding, H. P., and K. A. Webb, *J. Physiol.*, **102**, 2P (1943). A simple rocking dialyzer.

Gutfreund, H., *Biochem. J.*, **37**, 186 (1943). Principles of electrodecantation.

Hamilton, P. B., and R. M. Archibald, *Ind. Eng. Chem., Anal. Ed.*, **16**, 136 (1944). A dialyzer for analytical determination of diffusible components in blood plasma.

Holmes, H. N., *Laboratory Manual of Colloid Chemistry*. 2nd ed., Wiley, New York, 1928, pp. 22–23. Nonaqueous solution dialysis using collodion membranes prepared by washing the alcohol-ether collodion film with toluene instead of water.

Ikeda, K., and S. Suzuki, U. S. Pat. 1,015,891 (1909); Brit. Pat. 9440/09 (1912). Use of soluble anodes of zinc, iron, or aluminum is described to avoid pH changes during electrodialysis or electrophoresis.

Jung, C., *Compt. rend. soc. phys. hist. nat. Genève*, **58**, 100 (in *Arch. sci. phys. nat.*, **23**, Mar.-Apr. (1941); *Chem. Zentr.*, **1942, I**, 3180; *C. A.*, **37**, 3992 (1943)). Preparation of a membrane permeable to urea but not glucose by incorporating copper ferrocyanide in Cellophane foil.

Kahlenberg, L., *Phil. Mag.*, **1** (7), 385 (1926). Dialysis with cholesterol or phytosterol membranes.

King, E. J., *Ind. Eng. Chem., Anal. Ed.*, **4**, 201 (1932). An electrodialyzer using mercury anode.

Kirkwood, J. G., *J. Chem. Phys.*, **9**, 878 (1941). L. E. Nielsen, and J. G. Kirkwood, *J. Am. Chem. Soc.*, **68**, 181 (1946). Chamber apparatus for separating by electroconvection.

Kolff, W. J., and H. T. J. Berk, "Technique and Chemical Results of Dialysis in Vivo. Treatment with the Artificial Kidney," *Arch. neerland. physiol.*, **28**, 166 (1946). Narrow Cellophane tubing wound on a drum which rotates in the dialyzing bath.

Kooij, G. W. van Barneveld, "Principles of Modern Dialyzing," *Brit. Rayon Silk J.*, **26**, 74 (1949). Apparatus suitable for recovery of sodium hydroxide from hemicellulose-containing liquors from viscose rayon "pressings" is described.

Kressman, T. R. E., "Ion Exchange Resin Membranes and Resin Impregnated Filter Paper," *Nature*, **165**, 568 (1950). Description of the preparation of ion-exchange membranes of potential value in electrodialytic separations.

Kristskii, G. A., "Dialyzer for Hastening Dialysis," *Biokhymiya*, **13**, 453 (1948). Cellophane tubes arranged to entrap a bubble of air and moved to force the bubble from one part of the tube to another decreased dialysis time by factor of 5 to 10 times.

Kolloid-Z. and *Beihefte*. General Index, Vols. 1–50. See headings "Dialyse, Druckdialyse, Elektrodialyse, Endosmose, Filtration," etc.

Kratz, L., *Kolloid-Z.*, **80**, 33 (1937). A new type electrodialyzer of high efficiency.

Laporta, M., *Bull. soc. ital. biol. sper.*, **8**, 773 (1933). Dialysis at constant pressure and volume.

Lauffer, M. A., *Science*, **95**, 363 (1942). A check valve for a rocking dialyzer.

Löddesöl, A., *J. Am. Soc. Agron.*, **24**, 74 (1932). A three-compartment electrodialyzer of large volume specially designed for soil suspensions.

Neidle, M., *J. Am. Chem. Soc.*, **38**, 1270 (1916); **39**, 71 (1917). Hot dialysis.

Nelson, I. A., and I. H. Nelson, *Am. J. Clin. Path.*, **3**, 447 (1933). A dialyzer.

Newton, R., and W. M. Martin, *Plant Physiol.*, **2**, 99 (1927). Apparatus for continuous dialysis at low temperatures.

Peniston, Q. P., and J. L. McCarthy, "Lignin I. Purification of Ligninsulfonic Acids by Continuous Dialyzer," *J. Am. Chem. Soc.*, **70**, 1324 (1948).

Raab, H., *Chem. Ztg.*, **55**, 395 (1931). An extraction-type dialyzer for operation at normal or reduced pressure.

Reichel, F. H., and A. O. Russell, U. S. Pat. Appl. July 8, 1943. Assigned to Sylvania Corp., Fredericksburg, Va. A dialyzer for continuous operation.

Reiner, L., *J. Phys. Chem.*, **35**, 423 (1931). A one-piece electrodialyzer with Jena sintered-glass filter plates as membrane supports.

Reiner, M., and R. L. Fenichel, *Science*, **108**, 164 (1948). Dialyzers and use of dialysis for preparing protein solutions for electrophoresis. Apparatus available through American Instrument Co. Inc., Silver Spring, Md.

Renkin, E. M., "Filtration, Diffusion, and Molecular Sieving Through Porous Cellulose Membranes," *J. Gen. Physiol.*, **38**, 225 (1954).

Roche, J., and M. S. Chouaiech, *Bull. soc. chem. biol.*, **22**, 486 (1940). A device for continuous dialysis of solutions under pressure.

Rohm and Haas Company, The Resinous Products Division, Washington Square, Philadelphia 5, Pa., *Amberplex Ion Permeable Membranes*, 1952. A laboratory manual describing apparatus and techniques for use of ion permeable resins in membrane form.

Rose, R. C., *J. Soc. Chem. Ind. London*, **62**, 44 (1943). A rapid method of dialysis in which sodium alginate is added to a turbid solution; the alginate is coagulated with calcium chloride and the gel and liquid phases are separated.

Rutgers, A. J., and R. Swyngedouw, "Fast, Continuous Electrodialyzer for Hydrophilic Colloids, and Fast, Continuous Electrodecanter for Hydrophilic Colloids," *Nature*, **168**, 727 (1951). Apparatus capable of dialyzing 200 ml. of hydrophilic colloid per hour.

Sankaran, G., *Indian J. Med. Research*, **23**, 219 (1935); *Physiol. Abstracts*, **20**, 723; *C. A.*, **30**, 6992 (1936). A simple form of electrodialyzer.

Schlechter, D. C., *Chemist Analyst*, **41**, 11 (1952). A dialyzer is described for obtaining nondialyzable bacterial metabolic products.

Seegers, W. H., *J. Lab. Clin. Med.*, **28**, 897 (1943). A convenient dialyzer using viscose tubing.

Signer, R., Swiss Pat. 244,043 (Aug. 31, 1946); *cf. Chem. Abstracts*, **43**, 8758g (1949). A continuous dialyzer for separation of substances of slightly different dialysis coefficients. A twenty-cell apparatus gave a first fraction from a solution of 40 grams each of sodium chloride and sodium sulfate per liter, which contained less than 1 part per million of sulfate ion.

Smith, C. C., and C. D. Stevens, *Ind. Eng. Chem., Anal. Ed.*, **14**, 348 (1942). A dialyzing evaporator-concentrator.

Taylor, A. R., A. K. Parpart, and R. Ballentine, *Ind. Eng. Chem., Anal. Ed.*, **11**, 659 (1939). A rapid circulating dialyzer.

Stone, G. C. H., *Ind. Eng. Chem., Anal. Ed.*, **7**, 8 (1935). A rapid method for dialyzing large volumes of protein or other solutions which consists of passing dialyzing water through cellophane tubing looped through the protein solution.

Teorell, H., and A. Akeson, *Arkiv. Kemi Mineral. Geol.*, **16**, No. 8 (1942). Micro method of electrophoresis and electrodialysis.

Urbach, K. F., and J. J. Svarz, "Apparatus for Semimicro Electrodialysis," *Science*, **108**, 93 (1948). Description of an all-glass apparatus with 5–20 ml. capacity.

Watson, P. D., *Ind. Eng. Chem.*, **26**, 640 (1934); Electrodialysis of whey proteins; use of a transfer device between cathode and anode chambers to compensate for pH changes.

Watson, P. D., and P. N. Peter, *Rev. Sci. Instruments*, **5**, 362 (1934). A small electrodialyzer with permanent diaphragms of alundum or unglazed porcelain. Siphon transfer from one electrode compartment to another to eliminate pH changes.

Zender, J., U. S. Pat. Appl. July 8, 1943. Assigned to Sylvania Corp., Fredericksburg, Va. A continuous dialyzer.

SPECIAL APPLICATIONS

Albanese, A. A., *J. Biol. Chem.*, **134**, 467 (1940). Estimation of basic amino acids.

Binz, A., H. Bauer, and A. Hallstein, *Ber.*, **53**, 416 (1920). Investigation of silver salvarsan. Dialysis and ultrafiltration.

Coleman, G. H., and A. Miller, *Proc. Iowa Acad. Sci.*, **49**, 257 (1942); *C. A.*, **37**, 5636 (1943). Electrodialysis of glucose and maltose borates.

Collins, F. D., and R. E. R. Grimmett, *New Zealand J. Sci. Technol.*, **27A**, 198 (1945); *C. A.*, **40**, 7270 (1946). Electrodialysis of plant extracts for removal of salts.

Devrient, W., S. Thyssen, and B. Sokoloff, *J. Pharmacol.*, **42**, 299 (1931). Studies on electrodialysis of epinephrine.

Duff, D. C. B., and R. Holmes, *Can. Pub. Health J.*, **27**, 141 (1936). Quantitative estimation of indole by means of dialysis.

Elder, A. L., R. P. Easton, H. E. Pletcher, and F. C. Peterson, *Ind. Eng. Chem., Anal. Ed.*, **6**, 65 (1934). Rapid purification by electrodialysis of acid casein, grape juice, galactose, and arabogalactose.

Elöd, E., and W. Siegmund, *Collegium*, 277 (1934). Textile- and tanning-chemistry investigations by means of electrodialysis.

Fischbach, H., "Electrodialysis in the Field of Antibiotics," *J. Am. Pharm. Assoc., Sci. Ed.*, **37**, 470 (1948). Electrodialysis was used as a method of concentrating solutions of streptomycin sulfate and chloride and bacitracin.

Gaponenkov, T. K., and V. N. Muimrikova, *Colloid J. U. S. S. R.*, **2**, 243 (1936); *C. A.*, **30**, 7902 (1936). Mutual interaction of pectic substances and sugars as determined by dialysis.

Germinal S.-A., "Sugar-Juice Purification by Electrodialysis," Swiss Pat., 252,130 (Sept. 16, 1948). Treatment of sugar juice with resin ion exchangers for cation and anion removal, and electrodialysis and electrodecantation gave very pure sugar solutions which crystallized readily.

Golodetz, A., *Chem. Ztg.*, **37,** 259 (1913). Quantitative dialysis with an apparatus on the Soxhlet principle.

Gordon, A. H., *Am. J. Botany*, **33,** 160 (1946). Study of auxin-protein complexes of wheat grain with the aid of electrodialysis.

Hardy, V. R., *Trans. Illinois State Acad. Sci.*, **26,** No. 3, 30 (1934). Electrodialytic purification of polysaccharide solutions from Jerusalem artichokes.

Harmsen, G. W., and W. J. Kolff, *Science*, **105,** 582 (1947). Cultivation of microorganisms in special dialyzers and the use of such apparatus to recover and separate metabolic products.

Hartley, P., "System of Bacteriology," *Brit. Med. Research Council*, **6,** 259 (1931). Serum purification by electrodialysis and dialysis.

Lightfoot, E. N., and I. J. Friedman, "Ion Exchange Membrane Purification of Organic Electrolytes," *Ind. Eng. Chem.*, **66,** 1579, (1954). The behavior of some typical carboxylic acids and their salts in Amberplex membranes.

Lüers, H., and R. Lechner, *Wochschr. Brau.*, **50,** 49 (1933); *C. A.*, **27,** 5347 (1933). Electrodialysis of amylase solutions.

Martin, A. J. P., *Proc. Symp. Fibrous Proteins* (Society of Dyers and Colourists), May, 1946, p. 1. Use of ionophoresis and partition chromotography for examining partial protein hydrolyzates.

Martin, A. J. P., and R. L. M. Synge, *Advances in Protein Chem.*, **2,** 31 (1945). Ionophoretic methods as used in protein chemistry.

McKeekin, T. L., B. D. Polis, E. S. Dellamonica, and J. H. Custer, *J. Am. Chem. Soc.*, **71,** 3606 (1949). Crystalline dodecylsulfate derivatives of β-lactoglobulin prepared by dialysis.

Müller, A., *J. prakt. Chem.*, **156,** 179 (1940); *C. A.*, **35,** 1934 (1941). Dialysis of components of wormwood and camomile oils.

Moore, J. C., R. J. Reeves, and R. M. Hixon, *Plant Physiol.*, **2,** 313 (1927). Electrodialysis was used to study biochemical differences in abnormal apple tissue.

Narayanamurti, D., and R. V. Norris, *Proc. Indian Science Congr.*, *15th Congr.*, 1928, p. 166. Electrodialysis and electro-osmosis of cholam diastase.

Oldfelt, C. O., *Biochem. Z.*, **251,** 235 (1932). Alkali determination in physiological tissues by means of electrodialysis in a three-celled apparatus.

Régnier, J., A. Quevanviller, and P. Fieyre, *Bull. sci. pharmacol.*, **47,** 15, 20 (1940); *C. A.*, **34,** 1442, 3018, 4153, 7013 (1940). Dialysis of procaine hydrochloride.

Rybak, B., "A Dialyzer with Controlled Pressure," *Compt. rend.*, **235,** 617 (1952). An all-glass thermostatted dialyzer equipped with a modified Warburg manometer for dialysis of proteins and products of enzymic reactions of microorganisms is described.

Schwabe, J. K., and L. Hasner, *Cellulosechemie*, **20,** 61 (1942). Molecular-weight determination of lignosulfonic acids by dialysis and electrodialysis.

Shershnev, P. A., *Arch. sci. biol. U. S. S. R.*, **37,** 376 (1935). Use of electrodialysis to separate carnosine from horse meat.

Sørensen, S. P. L., and M. Hyørup, "Concentration of Proteins by Dialysis under Reduced Pressure," *Compt. rend. trav. lab. Carlsberg*, **12,** 12 (1917–19).

Spandau, H., *et al.*, "Particle Weight Determination of Organic Compounds with the Aid of the Dialysis Method," *Angew. Chem.*, **63**, 41 (1951); **65**, 183 (1953). Dialyzing behavior of a number of organic compounds in water, ethanol, dioxane, and benzene solutions through Cella filters is discussed.

Stange, A., *Pharmacia*, **14**, 282, 298 (1934); **15**, 9 (1935); *C. A.*, **31**, 213 (1937).

Taboury, F. J., and C. Mangin, *Bull. soc. chim. France*, **1948**, 47. Electrodialysis of antipyrine solutions through Cellophane membranes with concentration of the antipyrine in the cathode compartment.

Taylor, T. C., C. E. Braun, and E. L. Scott, *Am. J. Physiol.*, **74**, 539 (1925). Ultrafiltration and electrodialysis of insulin solutions.

Umbreit, W. W., R. H. Burris, and J. F. Stauffer, *Manometric Techniques and Tissue Metabolism*. Burgess, Minneapolis, 1949, p. 213. Points out that proteins of molecular weight lower than 13,000, *e.g.*, cytochrome C, are likely to be lost through the pores of dialyzing membranes.

Vollrath, H. B., *Chem. & Met. Eng.*, **43**, 303 (1936). Application of dialysis for separating spent squeeze liquor from hemicellulose; design of apparatus on a commercial scale.

Wright, M. L., *Discussions Faraday Soc.*, **16**, 60 (1954). Purification of horn keratin membranes by electrodialysis.

Part 4. ZONE ELECTROPHORESIS

I. INTRODUCTION

The technique of separating substances dissolved or suspended in an electrically conducting liquid by virtue of their differing rates of migration in an electric field is called *electrophoresis*. The classic technique of free-solution electrophoresis was discussed in Chapter XXVI of Volume I of this series. The same phenomenon is also employed in the technique called *electrodecantation* which is discussed in Part 3 of this chapter. A modification of these techniques in which the electromigration is carried out in a solution stabilized against convection by a mechanical structure, has been termed *zone electrophoresis, ionography*, or *ionophoresis*.[1,2] Since this technique has some advantages over classic electrophoretic methods, it will be discussed in some detail here.

Although the basic principles of zone electrophoresis are old, the general

[1] H. J. McDonald, E. P. Marbach, and M. C. Urbin, *Clin. Chemist*, **5**, 17 (1953).

[2] A. J. P. Martin and R. L. M. Synge, in *Advances in Protein Chemistry*. Vol. II, Academic Press, New York, 1945.

application is a modern development. Sir Oliver Lodge[3] used agar as a stabilizing substance in electrophoresis experiments as early as 1886. An isolated zone of the substance to be separated was used by Kendall and Clark[4] in 1925. However, the general use of zone electrophoresis began after the publication of the paper of Wieland and Fischer[5] in 1948. Since that time a wide variety of stabilizing substances such as paper, glass beads and wool, asbestos fiber, silk, cotton, sand, agar, starch, and other substances has been employed. The field of application has been extended from inorganic ions to simple organic compounds, proteins, hormones, animal poisons, hemoglobin, and many other complex substances.

Zone electrophoresis has many conveniences that are not shared by the classic free-solution technique. Very small quantities of substances, sometimes as little as twenty or thirty micrograms, may be analyzed. Substances are totally separated from mixtures and, under favorable conditions, may be recovered almost completely. The apparatus is both inexpensive and simple to use. The operating conditions are not as restricted as in the classic technique either with respect to solution composition or operating temperature. The technique may be adapted to continuous operation, thus permitting the separation of relatively large quantities of substances. In some techniques of zone electrophoresis the paper strip containing the separated substances may be retained as a permanent record of the experiment.

Zone electrophoresis also shares many of the advantages of the classic electrophoretic techniques. Separations are made with a minimum chance of changing the nature of the chemical substance. Often organic chemicals and metal ions which are so similar in chemical properties that they can be separated only with the greatest difficulty by chemical techniques may be readily separated by electrophoresis. Several components of a mixture may be detected and quantitatively estimated in a single operation. The direction and rate of migration of a substance often give clues to its chemical nature. Isoelectric points and dissociation and other equilibrium constants may often be calculated from the results of carefully conducted electrophoresis experiments. All these features make the technique of particular interest to biochemists who frequently work with very small quantities of closely related and easily altered compounds.

II. DESCRIPTION AND THEORY OF THE PROCESS

The precautions that must be taken in free-solution electrophoresis to

[3] O. Lodge, *Brit. Assoc. Advancement Sci. Rept.*, **56**, 389 (1886).

[4] J. Kendall and B. L. Clark, *Proc. Natl. Acad. Sci.*, **11**, 393 (1925).

[5] T. Wieland and E. Fischer, *Naturwissenschaften*, **35**, 29 (1948).

prevent convection currents which would quickly remix the separated substances were emphasized in Chapter XXVI of Volume I of this series. The restrictions on the temperature, current, and composition of the solutions are largely removed if the electrophoresis is carried out in a solution containing a stabilizing structure, such as agar, glass beads, paper fiber, etc. to prevent convection. The introduction of the stabilizing substance may, however, cause other difficulties unless precautions are taken.

In the usual procedure, a small zone of the substance to be separated is placed near the middle of a column of buffer solution which saturates the stabilizing structure as shown schematically in Figure 1. An electric potential is then applied at the ends of the column. The substances under study begin to move, and each rapidly reaches a constant velocity of migration through the stabilizing structure. The magnitude of this velocity depends upon the motion of the buffer solution, the magnitude of the

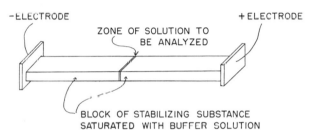

Fig. 1. Simplied zone-electrophoresis apparatus.

applied potential, the charge on the substance, the ionic strength of the solution, the viscous resistance, and the electrical retarding force from its counterion atmosphere which the moving substance encounters. A great variety of substances acquire charges in aqueous solution either by ionizing themselves or by adsorbing the ions of other substances. All these are subject to electrophoresis and, in general, each shows a different mobility, at least under certain conditions. Thus, as the zone electrophoresis proceeds, the original zone breaks up into several zones of different migration velocity. This is quite different from what happens in free-solution electrophoresis, where only the fastest and slowest components become free from the other components of the mixture. Furthermore, in free-solution electrophoresis, even the components which do separate do not do so completely and may only be recovered in fractional yields. Zone electrophoresis, at least in theory, permits total isolation of all the components of a mixture. In practice very good yields of high purity have been recovered.

The quantitative relationships of the techniques are sometimes of value in identifying components or in interrelating various investigations. The mobility, μ, is defined as the proportionality constant relating the distance, d, which the substance moves in time, t, to the gradient produced by the applied potential, V, across the length, l, of the migration path. Thus:

$$d \propto t(V/l) \qquad \text{and} \qquad \mu = (d/t)(l/V) \tag{1}$$

Mobility values calculated directly from zone-electrophoresis experiments are very dependent upon the characteristics of the stabilizing structure used. In order to reduce this dependence and also to permit comparison of zone-electrophoresis mobilities with the many values already measured in free solutions, certain compensating procedures have been devised. Two of these due to Kunkel and Tiselius[6] and to McDonald[7] will be discussed here.

According to the classic relationships the resistance, R, of any conductor is directly proportional to the length, l, and inversely to the cross-sectional area, A. The specific conductivity, k, is defined as the reciprocal of this proportionality constant. From this it may be readily shown that for any conductor:

$$l = kRA \tag{2}$$

If a column of length l and cross sectional-area A were filled with buffer solution of specific conductivity k_0, it would have a resistance R_0. The mobility of a substance in such a column would be the free-solution mobility μ_0. If the same column were filled with a stabilized buffer solution, it would have a different specific conductivity and resistance, k_s and R_s. The mobility measured under these conditions would be that in the stabilized electrolyte, μ_s. Equation (2) may be rewritten for these two cases:

$$l = k_0 R_0 A \tag{3}$$

and:

$$l = k_s R_s A \tag{4}$$

In the case of the stabilized electrolyte one may, however, consider only the buffer solution dispersed in the stabilizing medium. A new cross-sectional area, A', of the buffer solution only may be readily calculated from the volume proportion of buffer and stabilizer in the system. Then, if k' is the specific conductivity of the buffer solution dispersed in the stabilizing structure (which is not the same as k_s, the value for the whole stabilized buffer solution), equation (2) may be written as:

$$l = k' R_s A' \tag{5}$$

[6] H. G. Kunkel and A. Tiselius, *J. Gen. Physiol.*, **35**, 89 (1951).
[7] H. J. McDonald, R. J. Lappe, E. P. Marbach, R. H. Spitzer, and M. C. Urbin, *Clin. Chem.*, **5**, 35 (1953).

Kunkel and Tiselius[6] have substituted k_0 for k' in equation (5) and calculated a new number, l':

$$l' = k_0 R_s A' \tag{6}$$

To this l' they attribute the physical significance of the length of a "tortuous channel" along which the potential acts and through which the migrating charged molecules travel in the stabilized buffer solution. They therefore apply the correction l'/l to both the lengths in equation (1). This results in the rule that to obtain the free-solution mobility, μ_0, from the zone mobility, μ_s, one must multiply the latter quantity by $(l'/l)^2$.

McDonald[7a] recommends that a separate experiment be conducted to measure the "conversion factor" directly. In this experiment, the conductivity of a solution of the migrating substance under study is measured as a function of the amount of stabilizing substance (paper) added to the solution. A special conductivity cell and an alternating current bridge are used in the measurements. The measured conductivities, k_M, are corrected for the amount of solution displaced by the stabilizing substance by multiplying by a factor equal to A/A' above. This derived conductivity $k'_M = k_M A/A'$, is a function of the amount of stabilizing substance also. If the stabilizing substance does not introduce any conducting contaminant, k'_M is less than the free solution conductivity k_{0M}. Assuming that the conductivity of the counter ion to the substance under study is not affected by the presence of the stabilizing structure, it is clear that the ratio of these conductivities k_{0M}/k'_M is equal to the ratio of the mobility of the substance in free solution, μ_0, to the mobility in the stabilized electrolyte, μ_s. Therefore to convert zone mobilities (corrected for buffer drift, see below) to free solution mobilities, they must be multiplied by this conductivity ratio k_{0M}/k'_M.

The limitation on McDonald's technique is that if the migrating substance is not available pure and in sufficient quantities the conductivity experiments may not be possible. It is then necessary to measure the conductivity function with some other substance. Of course, the more the substitute differs from the actual substance under study, the greater the error in the conversion factor. If the buffer solution is used in the conductivity measurements as originally suggested by McDonald,[7] the calculated conversion factor becomes k_0/k', where $k' = k_S \cdot A/A'$ from equations (4) and (5). It may be readily shown from equations (5) and (6) that Kunkel and Tiselius' factor l'/l is numerically equal to k_0/k'. Since k_0/k' is less than k_{0M}/k'_M, the exact conversion factor, it may be that in

[7a] H. J. McDonald, *Ionography*, The Year Book Publishers, Inc., Chicago, 1955.

many cases Kunkel and Tiselius' procedure of using $(l'/l)^2$ is a closer approximation than k_0/k' as originally suggested by McDonald.

Durrum[8] has expressed the view that a more practical procedure is to build up a new and independent set of mobility data in stabilized electrolytes without reference to free solution mobilities. This procedure is the one in general use today.

In any calculation of a mobility, it is the velocity of the migrant with respect to the buffer solution that must be considered rather than the observed velocity with respect to the stabilizing structure. Correction must therefore be made for any streaming of the buffer solution through the stabilizing structure. Eliminating the hydrostatic head between the ends of the migration path, although important, does not prevent buffer flow. Because a boundary potential usually exists between the solid stabilizing structures and the buffer solution, streaming occurs under the influence of the applied migration potential. This streaming, called *electro-osmosis*, has been discussed in Part 3 of this chapter. The direction of the buffer movement depends upon the sign of this boundary potential. The amount of electro-osmosis is much greater in alkaline than in acid solutions. The usual method of measuring the amount of this streaming is to include in the migrating solution some substance which is not charged in the solution. This substance then drifts with the buffer solution. Its position at the end of the experiment is the origin, from which the distance other substances have migrated is measured. A variety of substances have been used as electro-osmosis indicators, such as xylose, starch, sucrose, and dextran; the last has been most popular. Even creatinine and proline have been used under conditions such that they were not ionized. McDonald[7] has shown that all these substances do not migrate at the same velocity under identical electro-osmotic conditions. Since this is presumed to be the result of different molecular volumes, it is recommended that the electro-osmosis indicator be chosen with as nearly as possible the same molecular volume as the substance under electrophoretic study. It has been shown that the ratio of the electro-osmotic drift for a substance under a given set of conditions bears a constant ratio to its electrophoretic migration. Kunkel has suggested that if this ratio is once established, it may subsequently be employed to measure the electro-osmosis in new experiments. An attempt by Michl[9] to minimize electro-osmotic flow by interposing two Cellophane dialysis barriers at each end of the migration path did not prove its value in practice.[7]

McDonald[7a] has suggested a method of calculating an electro-osmotic drift correction which does not involve the use of indicator substances.

[8] E. L. Durrum, *Science*, **113**, 66 (1951).

[9] H. Michl, *Monatsh. Chem.*, **83**, 737 (1952).

He assumes that the mobility conversion factor $(k_{0M}/k'_M$, see page 123 for details) calculated from conductivity measurements may be used to relate the electro-osmotic mobility of different substances. His procedure is to find a calibrating substance for which the free solution mobility is known under the conditions of buffer (type, pH, ionic strength, and temperature) to be used in the zone electrophoresis experiments. Two zone electrophoresis experiments are then conducted with the calibrating substance under different paper wetness conditions. With these two zone mobilities, the corresponding "conversion factors" (k_{0M}/k'_M) and the free solution mobility, two constants are calculated which are independent of ion type and paper wetness but apply to the specified buffer-paper system only. These constants may then be used to calculate the electro-osmotic correction to be applied to the observed zone mobility of any other substance, provided its "conversion function" has also been determined by conductivity.

Tiselius and Flodin[9b] have suggested that the varying drift velocities of uncharged molecules of different types through a stabilizing substance be utilized in a technique of *zone ultrafiltration*. They proposed that a zone of a solution of uncharged molecules of various sizes, such as dextran, be established in a column of stabilizing substance saturated with an electrolyte. By applying a potential to the ends of the column the electrolyte is made to flow through it by electro-osmosis. The zone of mixed substances being carried along by the flowing electrolyte becomes fractionated into various species according to the size and configuration of the molecules. The practicality of such a technique has been indicated by various researches[7,9a] but little use has been made of it.

Many of the substances that may be separated by electrophoresis are more or less strongly adsorbed by the stabilizing media commonly used. If the adsorption is irreversible, the substance becomes spread out in a long band as it migrates. This causes contamination of any component migrating more slowly. If the adsorption is reversible, the solute is desorbed as the zone passes and its concentration decreases.[10] The migrating zone is thus extended into a comet-shaped area which may overlap other zones; the substance, in any case, is difficult to recover. It is always wise to test the combination of a stabilizing medium and the substance to be separated for degree of adsorption previous to conducting an electrophoresis experiment. This may be done by causing the substance to migrate a short distance in the stabilized electrophoretic system and then reversing the potential. In the absence of adsorption the migrating substance returns to its origin in the same time that it took to move away from it. If ad-

[9a] D. L. Mould and R. L. M. Syngr, *Analyst*, **77**, 964 (1952).

[9b] A. Tiselius and P. Flodin in *Advances in Protein Chemistry*. Vol. III, Academic Press, New York, 1953.

[10] R. Weber, *Helv. Chim. Acta*, **36**, 424 (1953).

sorption is found it may sometimes be reduced to an unobjectionable level by changing the concentration of the migrant or the pH of the buffer. In cases where these changes do not solve the problem, it becomes necessary to change to a less objectionable stabilizing substance. Special procedures are sometimes possible, as in the case[11] where a quantity of albumin was added to the migrant in order to ballast the mixture and minimize the adsorption of a very small amount of radioactively labeled albumin present in it. It was also pointed out[10] that the adsorption of the migrant is not an objectionable feature in continuous zone-electrophoresis separations. A convenient means of distinguishing between substances of differing mobility and those spread out by adsorption only is to conduct two successive electromigrations at right angles on a large sheet of paper.[6] The substances differing in mobility lie along a diagonal from the point of origin while their adsorbed tails, if any, lie off the diagonal.

Although in some electrophoresis experiments—as when measuring mobilities—it is necessary to reduce adsorption as far as possible, this is not the case when separation of mixtures is the only object. Several experimenters have made good use of combined electrophoresis and chromatography;[12-17] usually the two operations are applied successively.[18] Electrophoresis is first carried out to separate the mixture into zones of equal mobility which may not, however, be single substances. These zones are then further divided by chromatographic techniques. This experiment is usually performed on filter paper with the two directions of separation at right angles to each other. The separated substances thus become distributed in a two-dimensional array across the paper.

The electrophoretic effect depends upon the fact that many substances take on electric charges when dispersed in water. These may arise either from complete or partial ionization of the substance, or from the adsorption by dispersed solids of ions of other substances in the solution. If all of the substance becomes ionized or if, in the case of a dispersed solid, all the particles of the substance take up equivalent amounts of ion from solution, it moves with a single velocity under the conditions of the experiment. However, if the substance is only partially ionized, the situation is more complex. Only the ions undergo electrophoresis, thus tending to separate

[11] H. Bennhold, E. Kallee, and E. Roth, *Z. Naturforsch.*, **7b**, 324 (1952).

[12] Suzuki, Hagihara, and Takagi, *J. Pharm. Soc. Japan*, **74**, 167 (1954); *Chem. Abstracts*, **48**, 13772 (1954).

[13] J. H. Quastel and S. F. VanStraten, *Proc. Soc. Exptl. Biol. Med.*, **81**, 6 (1952).

[14] B. Kickhöfen and O. Westphal, *Z. Naturforsch.*, **7b**, 659 (1952).

[15] R. Consden and W. M. Stainer, *Nature*, **169**, 783 (1952).

[16] R. Consden and W. M. Stainer, *Nature*, **170**, 1069 (1952).

[17] W. Grassmann, K. Hannig, and M. Plöckl, *Z. physiol. Chem.*, **299**, 258 (1955).

[18] G. Haugaard and T. D. Kroner, *J. Am. Chem. Soc.*, **70**, 2135 (1948).

them from the unionized part.   This separation causes an immediate re-
balance of the ionization equilibrium in both the ionized and unionized
parts.   The result is that all of the substance moves, but with a mobility
somewhat less than that of the ions themselves.   It may be readily shown[19]
that if a substance ionizes with an ionization constant, K, to give a counterion (which may be either hydrogen ion or various other species) of concentration [H], the mean mobility of the substance $\bar{\mu}$ is related to the mobility
of the ion of the substance μ by the equation:

$$\bar{\mu} = \{K/([H] + K)\}\mu \tag{7}$$

Thus, if one measures μ for a substance under conditions in which ionization is substantially complete and then $\bar{\mu}$ at a known [H] at which ionization is not complete, the ionization constant of the substance may be calculated.   Also, by measuring K at different temperatures, the heat of
ionization can be calculated.   Since these determinations may be made with
less than a milligram of substance, the technique is sometimes of considerable value for establishing the nature of functional groups.   The same reasoning may be applied in calculating the mean mobility of a complex formed
between a nonmigrating substance and a component of the buffer solution.
An example of this is the complex formed between certain polyhydroxy
compounds and borate ion.[20]   Since in this case the quantity of borate ion
may be assumed constant, the equation reduces to:

$$\bar{\mu} = \{K/(1 + K)\}\mu \tag{8}$$

The reasoning may also be extended to the case in which two ions of differing mobilities are in equilibrium.

The direction and velocity of migration of a substance are determined
largely by the extent and polarity of its ionization.   A dibasic acid ion
migrates more rapidly than a monobasic, and both migrate in the opposite
direction from an amine.   If the substance contains both cationic and anionic functional groups, the pH of the buffer solution determines both the
direction and the velocity of the migration.   This behavior is most often
noted in amino acids and proteins.   For example, glycine, which at pH 4
migrates toward the cathode, at pH 8 migrates to the anode.   At some
pH value, termed the *isoelectric point*, such substances appear to be unionized.   Thus, a plot of mobility at different pH values provides a very convenient means of measuring the isoelectric point of proteins.[21]   It should
be emphasized that these mobility measurements must be corrected for the
electro-osmotic drift of the buffer solution.   Failure to make this correction

[19] R. Consden, A. H. Gordon, and A. J. P. Martin, *Biochem. J.*, **40**, 33 (1946).
[20] H. Michl, *Monatsh. Chem.*, **83**, 737 (1952).
[21] H. G. Kunkel and R. J. Slater, *Proc. Soc. Exptl. Biol. Med.*, **80**, 42 (1952).

when working with paper fiber as the stabilizing substance leads to high values of the isoelectric point.

It has been shown that the mobility of an ion is inversely proportional to the square root of the ionic strength of the solution.[22] Thus, as the ionic strength is reduced, a given degree of separation is obtained in a shorter time. However, the resistance of the solution is also increased by the reduction in the ionic strength, and a higher potential is, therefore, required to maintain a given current through the apparatus. Since the heat produced is proportional to the square of the potential, this soon becomes a limiting factor. The best practical balance between rate of migration and heat produced is usually found at a buffer concentration between 0.05 and 0.20 molar.

Low mobilities are undesirable, not only because of the inconvenience of long experiments, but also because of loss of resolution as the time is increased. The spreading of a zone by thermal diffusion[23,24] takes place all the time. The broadening is proportional to the square root of the time.[19] It is thus desirable to start an experiment immediately after the migrating zone is produced and to conduct the experiment as rapidly as is consistent with heat dissipation and adequate resolution. When the separation is completed the paper should be dried or the block segmented immediately.

It is usually desirable to adjust the substance to be analyzed to the same ionic strength and pH as the buffer solution. Failure to do this may result in a different potential gradient in the migrating zone than in the buffer. This may result not only in differences in heating in the different zones, but also in variations in the mobility of the substance at the zone boundaries. Both these effects tend to diffuse the zones and reduce the resolution of the technique. Another effect noted particularly when working with blocks of starch or agar is the appearance of swelling at the position of the migrating zone. This may occur when the migrating solution and the buffer are not in osmotic equilibrium. One simple procedure when working with a solid substance is to dissolve it in some of the buffer solution to be used in the column. In other cases, solutions to be analyzed are dialyzed against the buffer solution so that they may come into osmotic equilibrium before being brought together in the zone-electrophoresis apparatus. A similar technique for concentrating the migrant has also been described.[25]

Although it is usual to conduct zone electrophoresis experiments in a medium of constant pH, this is not always the case. Hoch and Barr[25a]

[22] H. J. McDonald, M. C. Urbin, and M. B. Williamson, *J. Colloid Sci.*, **6**, 236 (1951).
[23] M. Lederer, *Anal. Chem. Acta*, **6**, 521 (1952).
[24] Q. P. Peniston, H. D. Agar, and J. L. McCarthy, *Anal. Chem.*, **23**, 994 (1951).
[25] H. J. Mies, *Klin. Wochschr.*, **31**, 159 (1953).
[25a] H. Hoch and G. H. Bar, *Science*, **122**, 243 (1955).

have described a system in which the migrating substances pass through a region in which the pH is graded between two rather widely separated values. The migrants become concentrated in various parts of this region depending upon their dissociation constant or isoelectric point. The technique is rapid but does not work well if the differences in the mobilities of the migrating substances are small.

In zone electrophoresis the temperature need not be restricted to near zero degrees centigrade as in free-solution electrophoresis. Mobilities increase with increasing temperature in a manner directly related to the decrease in viscosity of the buffer solution.[26] This effect is sometimes used to accelerate a separation. It is, however, not uncommon to carry out zone-electrophoresis determinations at low temperatures. This is sometimes done to permit the use of higher currents without excessive heating. At other times low temperatures are used to restrain bacterial action and prevent decompositions in sensitive biological solutions.

Another factor governing the rate of migration of a substance in an electric field is the physical bulk of the migrating particle. This bulk is often largely due to the contributions of many loosely held solvating molecules. The number of such solvating molecules is hard to estimate so that molecular volumes of substances in solution are seldom known. However, in at least one case,[27] the mobility of ribonucleic acid was successfully calculated from the charge and the molecular volume. It is this molecular-volume effect that sometimes permits the separation by zone electrophoresis of substances with equal free-solution mobilities. McDonald[26] has shown, for instance, that the mobility of aspartic acid was practically independent of the grade of paper used in the measurement of the zone mobilities. On the other hand, the zone mobility of polyvinylpyrrolidone varied as much as 50% in the different grades of paper.

Since the principles described govern the conduct and reliability of zone-electrophoresis measurements, they have led to the development of a number of different experimental techniques, each designed to perform a particular task. The principal techniques are described in the next section.

III. TECHNIQUE AND APPARATUS

1. For Analysis

Many techniques of zone electrophoresis have been developed, each of which has some advantage in rate of separation, quantity separated, con-

[26] H. J. McDonald, R. J. Lappe, E. P. Marbach, R. H. Spitzer, and M. C. Urbin, *Clin. Chem.*, **5**, 35 (1953).

[27] R. Markham and J. D. Smith, *Nature*, **168**, 406 (1951).

venience of operation, or information obtained.   In most cases, analytical work has been conducted in thin layers of solution in filter paper.   Thicker layers in columns or blocks have been used for preparative work.   Continuous separations, which are particularly good for preparative work, may be carried out either in filter paper or in thicker beds.   Descriptions of the most common of these techniques are given below with emphasis on the preparative procedures.

The first published report of the use of filter paper as a stabilizing structure seems to have been that of Konig[28] in 1937.   However, it was the publication of the paper by Wieland and Fischer[29] in 1948 that began the flow of reports that has grown rapidly in magnitude ever since.   In 1950 a variety of paper-electrophoresis techniques were described by Durrum, Cremer and Tiselius, McDonald, and others.

The apparatus described by Durrum[30] was very simple.   It consisted of a strip of filter paper hung over a glass rod in an inverted V, with its ends dipping into two vessels containing buffer solution and electrodes.   After the buffer had saturated the paper, the solution to be analyzed was placed in a narrow band across the apex of the paper.   The suspended paper was surrounded by a hood to reduce evaporation (three tumblers were used for electrode vessels and hood in the original apparatus).   When a potential was applied the substances migrated down the strip toward the electrode vessels.   The technique suffers from the disadvantage that the migration velocity is not constant along the strip or proportional to the potential, as is necessary for simple mobility calculations.   Since there is initially less electrolyte near the apex, electrical resistance is greatest at that point and hence there is more heating and evaporation.   This evaporation causes an increase in buffer concentration near the apex of the paper.   Thus, a buffer concentration gradient is soon established along the strip.   Mobilities have been calculated from such data by taking these various factors into account.[31]   The hanging strip, prevents "puddling" of the buffer in the paper, which is sometimes troublesome in horizontal strip techniques.

The factors which make mobility calculations difficult may, however, be employed to improve separations.   It was mentioned that evaporation produces a buffer concentration gradient from the apex of the paper toward the electrode compartments.   As ions move away from the apex they reach regions of lower buffer concentration and therefore higher resistivity and

[28] P. Konig, *Actas trabalhos Terceiro Congr. Sul-Americano Chim., Rio de Janeiro e Sao Paulo*, **2**, 334 (1937).

[29] T. Wieland and E. Fischer, *Naturwissenschaften*, **35**, 29 (1948).

[30] E. L. Durrum, *J. Am. Chem. Soc.*, **72**, 2943 (1950).

[31] M. Macheboeuf, J. M. Dubert, and P. Rebeyrotte, *Bull. soc. chim. biol.*, **35**, 234, 246 (1953).

higher potential gradient. The velocity of the ions increases with distance from the apex, thus enhancing the separation of one ion species from another. However, evaporation also causes a flow of buffer into the strip. The velocity of this flow is greatest near the electrode compartments and decreases to zero at the apex. This velocity opposes the electrophoretic migration. By proper adjustment of conditions it may be arranged that the various substances in the mixture being analyzed move to different positions on the strip and remain there because the flow velocity and their electrophoretic velocity are equal at that point. Volatile buffer substances such as formic acid or triethylamine[32] are especially suited for this type of operation.

Fig. 2. Durrum-type zone-electrophoresis apparatus. (Spinco Division, Beckman Instruments Inc.)

Reproducible separations have been made quickly and conveniently with a wide variety of substances using the apparatus in its original form or as modified by Flynn and DeMayo[33] or by Gordon.[34] One commercial form of the apparatus is shown in Figure 2. Another apparatus of this kind is made in Great Britain by Shandon Scientific Co.

McDonald[22] described a paper-electrophoresis technique in which the filter paper was supported horizontally in air. Later modification of this apparatus led to the use of a rack in which several strips are held under tension by springs. The ends of the strips dip into vessels which are separated from the electrode vessels by porous walls. This procedure reduces the possibility of contaminating the paper with the electrolysis products. The electrode vessels are connected by a small-bore capillary tube which

[32] J. Porath, *Nature*, **175**, 478 (1955).
[33] F. V. Flynn and P. DeMayo, *Lancet*, **261**, 235 (1951).
[34] A. H. Gordon, J. Gross, D. O'Connor, and R. P. Rivers, *Nature*, **169**, 19 (1952).

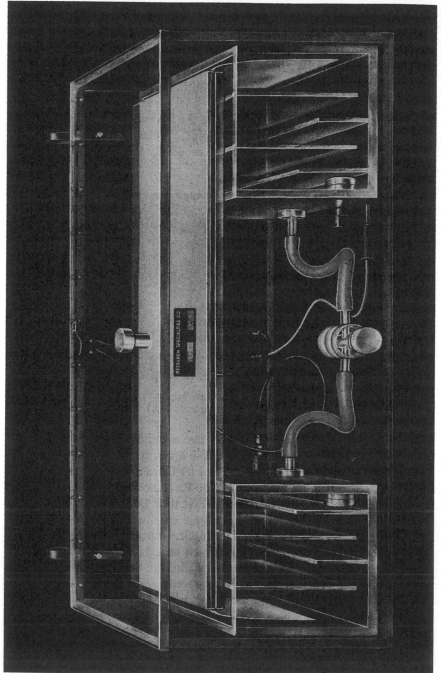

Fig. 3. McDonald-type zone-electrophoresis apparatus.   (Research Specialties Co.)

equalizes any hydrostatic difference that might arise between the compartments. The space around the paper strips, which is made as small as practical, is filled with air or helium[35] saturated with water vapor. Helium aids materially in conducting heat away from the strips. The McDonald apparatus is convenient to use, although not as rapid as certain modifications in which the filter paper strips are placed directly on a thermostated glass plate. This modification permits the use of higher currents and thus shorter runs because of better heat dissipation. The glass–paper boundary, however, introduces some complications. The McDonald apparatus gives migration velocities which are constant throughout an experiment and which vary linearly with applied voltage. The apparatus is therefore particularly useful when mobilities are necessary as in measuring isoelectric

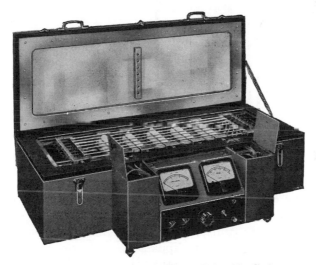

Fig. 4. Ionograph. (Precision Scientific Co.)

points or in identifying substances. Two of the many commercial forms of this apparatus are shown in Figures 3 and 4. Other makers of this type of apparatus are listed below.*

* Makers of apparatus (McDonald-type cells): Matthew Laboratories, 345 Nepperhan Ave., Yonkers 2, New York. Microchemical Specialties Co., 1834 University Ave., Berkeley 3, Cal. Research Specialties Co., 1148 Walnut St., Berkeley 7, Cal. Precision Scientific Co., 3737 W. Cortland St., Chicago 47, Ill. Schaar and Company, 754 W. Lexington St., Chicago 7, Ill. Reco-Research Equipment Co., 1135 Third St., Oakland, Cal. Labline, Inc., Chicago, Ill. E. C. Apparatus Co., 23 Haven Ave., New York 32, New York. Shandon Scientific Co., Ltd., 6 Cromwell Place, London, S.W.7, England. Evans Electroselenium Ltd., Harlow, Essex, England.

[35] H. J. McDonald, M. C. Urbin, and M. B. Williamson, *Science*, **112**, 227 (1950).

The procedure described by Cremer and Tiselius[36] also involves horizontal paper strips, but these investigators pressed the strips between glass plates and submerged the whole system in chlorobenzene to increase heat transfer and eliminate evaporation.   In a modification of this technique, Kunkel and Tiselius[37] omitted the chlorobenzene but sealed the lateral edges of the glass plates with silicone grease.   It was found that considerable care had to be taken in order to insure equal pressure at all points on the glass plates.   Failure to do this produced unevenness in the buffer content and hence in the migration rate through the paper.   It has also

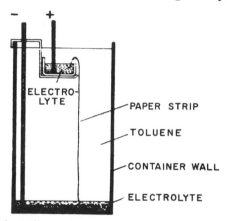

Fig. 5. High gradient paper-electrophoresis apparatus by Michl.[45]

been found that electro-osmosis at the glass–paper interface and smearing of the zone, while removing the glass plates, are serious objections to this technique.   However, Kunkel and Tiselius did make some very good mobility measurements with their apparatus.

Other techniques have been used from time to time.[38–44a]   One by Kickhöfen[45] and Michl[46] is particularly useful for obtaining quite good analyses in unusually short times.   These investigators used a large jar

[36] H. Cremer and A. Tiselius, *Biochem. Z.*, **320**, 273 (1950).

[37] H. G. Kunkel and A. Tiselius, *J. Gen. Physiol.*, **35**, 89 (951).

[38] H. Michl, *Monatsh. Chem.*, **83**, 737 (1952).

[39] R. Consden and W. M. Stainer, *Nature*, **169**, 783 (1952).

[40] R. Consden and W. M. Stainer, *Nature*, **170**, 1069 (1952).

[41] K. A. Kraus and G. W. Smith, *J. Am. Chem. Soc.*, **72**, 4329 (1950).

[42] A. L. Latner, *Biochem. J.*, **51**, xii (1952).

[43] A. J. G. Barnett, H. Lees, and D. K. Smith, *Biochem. J.*, **53**, xxxiii (1953).

[44] H. G. Nöller, *Klin. Wochschr.*, **32**, 988 (1954).

[44a] H. Zentner, *Nature*, **175**, 953 (1955).

[45] B. Kickhöfen and O. Westphal, *Z. Naturforsch.*, **7b**, 655 (1952).

[46] H. Michl, *Monath. Chem.*, **82**, 489 (1951).

with one electrode in buffer solution at its bottom and the other in a small vessel suspended near the top. The paper-electrophoresis strip, saturated with buffer, was suspended between the two buffer solutions. The substance to be analyzed was added to the strip and the jar was filled with an inert organic liquid, such as toluene, as shown in Figure 5. Potential gradients as high as 70 v./cm. could be employed because of excellent cooling of the paper. This permitted them to conduct a separation in 0.5 to 3 hours instead of the usual 12 to 20 hours. The hydrostic head between the two electrode solutions caused siphoning of buffer through the paper strip. By choosing the polarity of the electrodes so that the direction of migration of the ions opposed the hydrostic flow, it was possible to increase the separation of components without increasing the total distance of migration.

It is frequently desirable to carry out several separations at once under identical conditions, as, for instance, when comparing normal and pathological blood serums. To this end, broad sheets of filter paper may be used in the techniques described above. A convenient means of separating the areas in which the various samples are migrating was suggested by Usdin.[47] He described how narrow lines of Teflon Resin Dispersion may be formed in the paper to serve as solvent-proof barriers between adjacent strips.

2. For Preparation

All these techniques are primarily designed for analysis. They separate quantities ranging from tens of micrograms to a few milligrams. Kunkel and Slater[37,48] modified their technique to use several sheets of filter paper in a layer. They were thus able to separate as much as 3 cc. of 1% protein solution in a single operation, but the resolution was rather poor.

Electrophoresis in columns of stabilized solution has been tried by a number of workers.[49,50] Separations are readily obtained in solutions stabilized with solid structures such as glass powder,[51,52] sand, or paper fiber. However, it is very difficult to remove the separated fractions without remixing them. As pointed out by Kunkel[53] the problem is more difficult than in column chromatography. In the latter case, because of ad-

[47] E. Usdin, *Analyst*, **44**, 27 (1955).

[48] H. G. Kunkel and R. J. Slater, *J. Clin. Investigation*, **31**, 677 (1952).

[49] H. H. Strain, *J. Am. Chem. Soc.*, **61**, 1292 (1939).

[50] J. A. V. Butler and J. M. L. Stephens, *Nature*, **160**, 469 (1947).

[51] T. B. Coolidge, *J. Biol. Chem.*, **127**, 551 (1939).

[52] H. Haglund and A. Tiselius, *Acta Chem. Scand.*, **4**, 957 (1950).

[53] H. G. Kunkel, in *Methods of Biochemical Analysis*. Vol. I, Interscience, New York-London, 1954, pp. 141–170.

sorption of the substances, a good deal of solvent must pass through the column to remove each successive layer.   In the case of zone electrophoresis each small addition of solvent causes an equal displacement of all the separated layers.   Thus, any slight irregularity in the flow rates in the column tends to remix the layers.   Gelling substances such as silica gel, starch, agar, and gelatin have been used with much more success.   In this case the column may be sliced apart after the separation, thus preventing remixing.

Potato starch was used successfully as a stabilizing substance by Kunkel and Slater.[54]   A homogeneous block of the starch gel, 38 $\times$ 10 $\times$ 1.5 cm., containing 50% of buffer solution, was cast in a wooden frame and wrapped in waxed paper.   Excess buffer was removed with blotting paper before the solution to be separated was introduced in a narrow slot cut near the middle of the block.   This slot did not extend quite to the edges.   The top was covered with waxed paper and then with a glass plate under about ten pounds pressure.   Opposite ends of the starch block were connected to electrode vessels by thick cloth wicks.   A block 1.5 cm. in thickness, which gave best results, would accept 3 to 5 cc. of undiluted blood serum.   A potential of 450 v. produced a current of 20 to 40 milliamp.   This gave satisfactory separation of the components of blood serum in about 14 hours. At the end of the experiment, the starch block was cut into thin slices and the separated albumin and globulins were eluted from the starch with physiological saline solution.   Although in many cases starch blocks are freer of adsorption than fiber, with certain substances the situation is reversed.   In such cases, blocks of paper fiber which could contain as much as 90% by weight of buffer solution proved useful in the technique described above.   The paper "gels" had to be very carefully torn apart, rather than being cut as were the starch gels.

A similar technique using blocks of silica gel was described by Consden, Gordon, and Martin.[55]   They added paper powder to their silica gel blocks to make them less brittle.   They also employed flowing buffer solution in their electrode compartments to minimize the contamination of the block by electrode reaction products.   Although their separations involved only 0.1 to 0.5 g. of substances, these authors believed that this could be increased about ten times with satisfactory results.   Blocks of agar were used in a similar manner by Gordon and Reichard[56] and others.[57-59]   The use of agar is, however, somewhat limited because of its interference in reactions used for identifying protein fractions.[55]

[54] H. G. Kunkel and X. Slater, *Proc. Soc. Exptl. Biol. Med.*, **80**, 42 (1952).

[55] G. Haugaard and T. D. Kroner, *J. Am. Chem. Soc.*, **70**, 2135 (1948).

[56] A. H. Gordon and P. Reichard, *Biochem. J.*, **48**, 569 (1951).

[57] J. Kendall and B. L. Clark, *Proc. Natl. Acad. Sci.*, **11**, 393 (1925).

[58] Q. P. Peniston, H. D. Agar, and J. L. McCarthy, *Anal. Chem.*, **23**, 994 (1951).

[59] M. Lederer and Cook, *Australian J. Sci.*, **14**, 56 (1951).

The quantities of substances that may be separated by the block techniques described above are determined both by the concentration of the migrating solution and the dimensions of the zone. It was pointed out in the previous section that the migrating solution should be in osmotic equilibrium with the buffer solution. This means that its concentration must be relatively low, since the buffer solution cannot be made very concentrated. The zone to be separated must be kept relatively narrow in the direction of migration or excessive run times will be necessary to achieve the desired separation. The thickness of the block is determined by the ability of the apparatus to dissipate the heat produced by the electric current. It is not normally practical to have the thickness greater than about 2 cm. The width transverse to the direction of migration is limited only by the ability to prepare a uniform slab and to supply a uniform potential gradient across it.

Several authors[49,60-63a] suggested that, by impressing a second velocity transverse to that resulting from electrophoresis, the separated products could be continually removed from the zone of separation, thus permitting the separation of much larger amounts of material. In the simplest of these[64-66] the buffer is permitted to flow by gravity down through a sheet of filter paper, as shown in Figure 6. The substance to be separated is introduced as a band at the middle of the top edge of the paper. A potential is applied between the two vertical edges of the paper. As the substances to be separated flow down with the buffer they are displaced laterally by electrophoresis. The amount of this displacement is dependent upon the mobility of the component substances so that the band breaks up into separate bands of different mobilities. These reach the bottom of the paper at different points and may be collected there. Assuming a uniform field and absence of adsorption and evaporation, the angle, α, of displacement of a substance from the vertical is given by the equation:[67]

$$\tan \alpha - \mu(V/l)(A/F) \tag{9}$$

where μ is the mobility of the substance, V is the potential across the paper, l is the width of the paper between the electrodes, A is the cross-sectional area of the band of migrating substance, and F is the rate of feed of the substance (cm.³/sec.). A modified apparatus of this type was described by

[60] W. Grassmann and K. Hannig, *Z. physiol. Chem.*, **290**, 1 (1952).
[61] T. R. Sato, W. P. Norris, and H. H. Strain, *Anal. Chem.*, **24**, 776 (1952).
[62] I. Brattsten and A. Nilsson, *Arkiv Kemi*, **3**, 337 (1951).
[63] I. Brattsten, *Arkiv Kemi*, **4**, 503 (1952).
[63a] H. A. Saroff, *Nature*, **175**, 896 (1955).
[64] W. Grassmann and K. Hannig, *Naturwissenschaften*, **37**, 397 (1950).
[65] E. L. Durrum, *J. Am. Chem. Soc.*, **73**, 4875 (1951).
[66] J. Pieper and H. Molinski, *Klin. Wochschr.*, **32**, 985 (1954).
[67] H. Svensson and I. Brattsten, *Arkiv Kemi*, **1**, 401 (1950).

Brattsten and Nilsson.[62] With it they obtained good separation of albumin and γ-globulin at a "throughput" of 4 mg. per hour.

Since this rate of separation is still not very high, attempts were made to use thick beds of porous material in the crossed velocity field technique.[67,68]

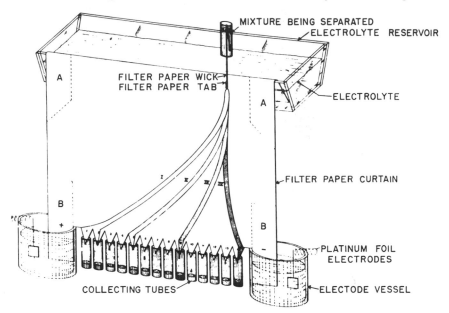

Fig. 6. Continuous crossed velocity paper-electrophoresis apparatus (E. L. Durrum[65]).

Difficulty was encountered in providing entirely vertical buffer flow. Variations in the porosity of the stabilizing substance caused horizontal flow and variations in electrical conductivity. These caused spreading of the migrating bands and thus reduced the resolution.

Probably the most efficient apparatus for the separation of fairly large quantities of substances was described by Brattsten.[63] A box of Lucite $30 \times 30 \times 1$ cm. was filled with powdered glass. The glass was carefully graded to a uniform particle size by repeated fractional settling separations. The particle size of the glass was chosen to give adequate stabilization against convection with minimum resistance to flow. A packing of powder with granules 0.15 mm. in diameter was found to be most widely applicable. The box was filled by allowing the powder to settle through water and then flowing water through the box for a couple of days to achieve a stable packing. A uniform rate of flow in all parts of the box was further assured by supplying the buffer from a large number of separate tubes and removing it in a similar manner at the bottom. A peristaltic pumping system was used to provide the slow, constant addition and removal of buffer solution

[68] W. Grassmann, *Z. angew. Chem.*, **62**, 170 (1950).

at a definite ratio of rates. The electrode compartments were supplied
with electrolyte from separate sources.

A buffer with ionic strength 0.05 was found to permit the best separations.
A protein concentration of 2–5% was most satisfactory. With a current
of 0.5 amp. and a feed rate of 5 ml./hour/cm.², a separation of about 4 cm.

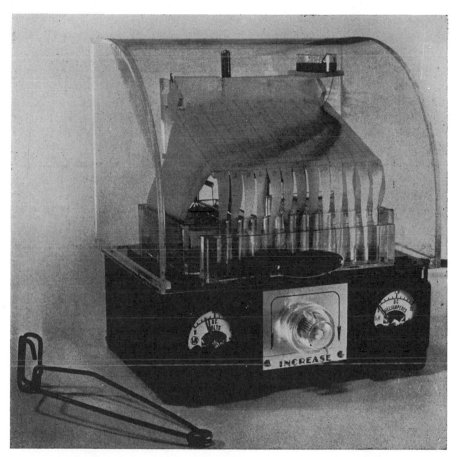

Fig. 7. Continuous paper-electrophoresis apparatus. (Microchemical Specialties Co.)

per mobility unit (cm.²/v.cm.) with good boundaries was achieved at the
bottom of the box. With a band width of 1 cm., as used with blood serum,
a 5% solution and a rate of 10 ml./hour/cm.², the capacity of this apparatus
was 0.5 g./hour of serum protein. With substances of greater mobility
differences, the band width could be increased, thus increasing the capacity.
Although the column thickness could not be greatly increased because of
the heating effect, the length could be increased. This permitted the use
of a smaller displacement angle, α (Eq. 9), and consequently an increased

feed rate and greater capacity. Only very preliminary reports are available in the literature on the performance of Brattsten's apparatus.

Brattsten recently described further refinements of the technique.[69,70] A more stable system is achieved by using an electrical control system which provides constant current to the cell rather than constant voltage. Stability of operation over long periods is improved by governing the applied migration current by an electrical feedback circuit from the rate at which the buffer is pumped to the cell. The ratio of electrical velocity to hydrodynamic velocity is thus maintained constant. "End zones" of concentrated buffer solution have been introduced next to the electrode compartments. These increase the ion transfer and prevent contamination of the migration zone. These refinements have permitted the separation of the components of blood and cerebrospinal serums at a feed rate of 1 ml./hour of whole serum and a resolution of 2.2×10^{-4} mobility unit (cm.^{2} v.$^{-1}$ sec.$^{-1}$)/cm.

Several apparatuses for crossed velocity separations are sold by Microchemical Specialties Co., Berkeley 3, Calif., and Spinco Division, Beckman Instrument Co., Belmont, Calif. One of these is shown in Fig. 7.

3. Two-Dimensional Techniques

In analytical work it is sometimes of value to combine two or more operations. McDonald and Urbin[71] conducted migrations in two electric fields at right angles to each other. They claim a relationship between the distance of migration of the substance and its molecular weight. Sometimes, when analyzing complex mixtures, it is very useful to change the pH of the buffer after conducting the first electrophoresis and conduct a second electrophoresis at right angles to the first.[72] Several substances having the same mobility at the first pH would be separated into individual zones at the second pH. It is very seldom the two substances of equal mobility also respond identically to a pH change. A similar procedure was used by Strain[73] in separating inorganic ions and organic ions. He used a complexing agent in his buffer solution and changed this agent between successive treatments. Successive electrophoresis operations at right angles to each other provide a useful means of distinguishing between differences in mobility and reversable adsorption of the migrating substances.[74]

[69] I. Brattsten, *Arkiv Kemi*, **8**, 205 (1955).
[70] I. Brattsten, *Arkiv Kemi*, **8**, 227 (1955).
[71] H. J. McDonald and M. C. Urbin, *Federation Proc.*, **12**, 243 (1953).
[72] E. L. Durrum, *J. Colloid Sci.*, **6**, 274 (1951).
[73] H. H. Strain, *Anal. Chem.*, **24**, 356 (1952).
[74] H. G. Kunkel and A. Tiselius, *J. Gen. Physiol.*, **35**, 89 (1951).

Analytical work has been carried out with nonaqueous solvents[75] such as nitromethane–glacial acetic acid, absolute methanol–ethanol, and pyridine–glacial acetic acid. The solutes must be highly polar to be effective in such techniques.

4. Methods of Detection and Measurement

Even after the substances are separated in the paper strips or other stabilizing media it is necessary to locate them, estimate their quantity, and possibly identify them. Usually paper strips are first dried rapidly in an oven. Blocks are cut or torn into slices without drying. If the substance is visibly colored, estimation is carried out easily in a colorimeter or densitometer, either directly on the paper strip[76,76a] itself or on the eluted substance.[77] If a paper strip is to be surveyed it may be rendered fairly transparent by soaking in a liquid of proper refractive index such as anisole or a 1:1 mixture of paraffin oil and bromonaphthol.[78] Mechanical devices have been described[79–82] and are available commercially for reading and plotting such curves of density against position on the strip. Suppliers of reading devices are listed below.*

In cases where the substance is not visibly colored, it may sometimes have density[81,83] or fluorescence[84] to ultraviolet light and be measured by this means. It is frequently possible to incorporate a radioactive tracer[85–87] in the substance being analyzed. By radiation counts or autoradiography the substance may be located and its concentration determined.[88] Where none of these assay methods are possible the substance may usually be

[75] M. H. Paul and E. L. Durrum, *J. Am. Chem. Soc.*, **74**, 4721 (1952).

[76] E. M. Crook, H. Harris, and F. L. Warren, *Biochem. J.*, **51**, xxvi (1952).

[76a] J. A. Owen, *Analyst*, **81**, 26 (1956).

[77] H. Cremer and A. Tiselius, *Biochem. Z.*, **320**, 273 (1950).

[78] W. Grassmann and K. Hannig, *Naturwissenschaften*, **37**, 494 (1950).

[79] L. B. Rockland, J. Lieberman, and M. S. Dunn, *Anal. Chem.*, **24**, 778 (1952).

[80] H. Michl, *Monatsh. Chem.*, **83**, 210 (1952).

[81] D. M. Tennent, J. B. Whitla, and K. Florey, *Anal. Chem.*, **23**, 1748 (1951).

[82] A. L. Latner, L. Molyneux, and J. D. Rose, *J. Lab. Clin. Med.*, **43**, 159 (1954).

[83] K. H. Kimbel, *Naturwissenschaften*, **40**, 200 (1953).

[84] L. Robert and F. S. Penaranda, *J. Polymer Sci.*, **12**, 337 (1954).

[85] T. Wieland and E. Fischer, *Naturwissenschaften*, **35**, 29 (1948).

[86] H. Bennhold, E. Kallee, and E. Roth, *Z. Naturforsch.*, **7b**, 324 (1952).

[87] F. Larson, W. P. Deiss, and E. C. Albright, *Science*, **115**, 626 (1952).

[88] W. Maurer and L. Rickenback, *Naturwissenschaften*, **39**, 261 (1952).

* Makers of detecting and measuring instruments: W. M. Welch Scientific Co., 1515 Sedgwick St., Chicago 10, Ill. Nuclear-Chicago, 227 W. Erie St., Chicago 10, Ill. Schaar and Company, 754 W. Lexington St., Chicago 7, Ill. Spinco-Specialized Instrument Corp., Belmont, Cal. Photovolt Corp., 95 Madison Ave., New York 16, New York. Matthew Laboratories, 345 Nepperhan Ave., Yonkers 2, New York.

changed chemically to a colored substance either by reaction with a dye or with a metal ion.[85,89,90]   To do this the strip is bathed in the complexing substance and then washed to get rid of material not held by the migrating substance on the strip.   A second reaction or development may be necessary to produce the color in the strip.

Other workers have used different techniques of analysis.[91,92]   The cut-up paper strips have been analyzed for proteins by micro-Kjeldahl determinations.[93]   Anderson and Lederer[94] determined the amount of copper in various parts of an electrophoresis strip by electrolysis after first dissolving the paper in concentrated nitric and sulfuric acids.   Eluted substances have been assayed biologically[95] and polarographically.[96]

In general, the techniques of analysis and identification are identical with those used in paper chromatography.   These have been described in some detail in texts on this subject, such as Volume V of this series.[97] Other references to identification techniques appear in the next section of this chapter.

IV.   APPLICATIONS

Zone electrophoresis has been used in many ways.   At least two extensive bibliographies are available through the Precision Scientific Company[98] and the American Instrument Company.[99]   The latter work, which covers the whole field of electrophoresis, is particularly valuable because it is kept up to date by frequent supplementary lists.[100]   A number of reviews[101−105] have also been presented which give a more critical

[89] B. Drevon, *Bull. soc. chim. biol.*, **36**, 921 (1954).

[90] L. Jaenicke, *Naturwissenschaften*, **39**, 86 (1952).

[91] F. Hartmann and H. J. Muller, *Naturwissenschaften*, **39**, 282 (1952).

[92] Y. Hashimoto and I. Mori, *J. Pharm. Soc. Japan*, **72**, 1532 (1952); *Chem. Abstracts*, **47**, 1434 (1953).

[93] B. Levin and V. G. Oberholzer, *Nature*, **170**, 123 (1952).

[94] J. R. A. Anderson and L. Lederer, *Anal. Chim. Acta*, **6**, 472 (1952).

[95] G. T. Mills and E. E. B. Smith, *Biochem. J.*, **49**, vi (1951).

[96] W. J. P. Neish, *Rec. trav. chim.*, **72**, 105 (1953); *Chem. Abstracts*, **47**, 8163 (1953).

[97] H. G. Cassidy, "Adsorption and Chromatography," in A. Weissberger, ed., *Technique of Organic Chemistry*, Vol. V.   Interscience, New York-London, 1951.

[98] H. J. McDonald, *Bibliography of Electromigration in Stabilized Electrolytes*.   Precision Scientific Co., Chicago, 1953.

[99] A. Henley and C. L. Schuettler, *Electrophoresis Bibliography*.   American Instrument Co., Silver Spring, Maryland, 1953.

[100] *Aminco Laboratory News*, American Instrument Co., Silver Springs, Md.

[101] H. J. McDonald, R. J. Lappe, E. P. Marbach, R. H. Spitzer, and M. C. Urbin *Clin. Chem.*, **5**, 51 (1953).

[102] M. Lederer, *Research*, **4**, 371 (1951).

[103] H. J. McDonald, *J. Chem. Ed.*, **29**, 428 (1952).

[104] C. Wunderly, *Chimia Switz.*, **7**, 145 (1953).

[105] H. H. Strain, *Anal. Chem.*, **23**, 25 (1951).

summary of the field. Although little work of a truly preparative nature has been reported, it is generally true that if a separation is possible on a micro scale, it may also be performed in preparative work if proper techniques are employed.

The biochemist has been the most active in the field. This is due to the ease with which the technique analyzes minute amounts of complex substances such as hormones or proteins, with a minimum possibility of chemical changes. The technique has been used relatively little by synthetic organic chemists. The following paragraphs outline the breadth of the field, with particular emphasis on topics of interest to the synthetic organic chemist.

A number of papers deal with the application of zone electrophoresis to problems in inorganic chemistry.[106-108] Although Kendall and White[109] were unsuccessful in demonstrating the separation of the isotopes of chlorine[110] by zone electrophoresis, Brewer, Madorsky, and Weshaven[111] did succeed in enriching one of the isotopes of potassium. Michl[112] showed that, although the mobilities of copper and cadmium ions differ by only 2%, they may be separated by zone electrophoresis. Various other metal ions have been separated, such as mesothorium from barium,[113] samarium from gadolinium,[114] yttrium from erbium,[115] and copper from gold, platinum, and palladium.[94] Zone electrophoresis has also been used in studying metal ion complexes with chloride and ammonium ions. Strain[116,117] used two and three successive separations in the presence of different complexing agents to analyze complex mixtures. The technique is simple and rapid, and may be made to yield information on complex ion charges and stability constants.[118] The separation and quantitative determination of the alkali metals K, Na, Mg, Li, Cs, and Rb have been described by Schier.[118a]

The fact that certain polyhydroxy compounds form complex ions with

[106] M. J. McDonald, M. C. Urbin, and M. B. Williamson, *Science*, 112, 227 (1950).

[107] M. Lederer, *Nature*, 167, 864 (1951).

[108] M. Lederer, *Anal. Chim. Acta*, 6, 355 (1952).

[109] J. Kendall and J. W. White, *Proc. Natl. Acad. Sci.*, 10, 458 (1924).

[110] J. Kendall and E. D. Crittenden, *Proc. Natl. Acad. Sci.*, 9, 75 (1923).

[111] A. K. Brewer, S. L. Madorsky, and J. W. Westhaven, *Science*, 104, 156 (1946).

[112] H. Michl, *Monatsh. Chem.*, 82, 489 (1951).

[113] J. Kendall, E. R. Jette, and W. West, *J. Am. Chem. Soc.*, 48, 3114 (1926).

[114] G. V. Hevesy, *Z. anorg. Chem.*, 147, 217 (1925).

[115] J. Kendall and B. L. Clark, *Proc. Natl. Acad. Sci.*, 11, 393 (1925).

[116] H. H. Strain, *Anal. Chem.*, 24, 356 (1952).

[117] T. R. Sato, H. Diamond, W. P. Norris, and H. H. Strain, *J. Am. Chem. Soc.*, 74, 6154 (1952).

[118] K. A. Kraus and G. W. Smith, *J. Am. Soc.*, 72, 4329 (1950).

[118a] O. Schier, *Angew. Chem.*, 68, 63 (1956).

borate ion forms the basis for zone electrophoresis of these compounds which are not in themselves ionized.[119–122] The separations of mixed sugars[120] or other compounds are conducted in columns saturated with borate buffer. The complex acids so formed are stronger than boric acid itself.[90] Michl[119] has shown that only the *cis* (α) forms of sugars form borate complexes. When a sugar is subjected to electrophoresis in borate buffer, it tends to separate into migrating (*cis*) and nonmigrating (*trans*) fractions. Since each form tends to form the other when separated, the migrating and stationary zones are both broadened. Thus, the sharpness of the migrating band depends upon the ratio of the migration velocity to the rate of mutarotation. The polyhydric alcohols mannitol and glycerine migrate as borate complexes but ethylene glycol does not migrate. The orthophenols, phenylcatechol, the methyl ester of gallic acid, protocatechualdehyde, pyrogallol, and tannin all migrate at nearly equivalent velocities. These *o*-isomers are thus very readily separated from their nonmigrating isomers. The rate of migration of these complexes depends upon: (*a*) the number of borate ions complexed per molecule; (*b*) the ionization constant of the complex ion; (*c*) the *p*H of the buffer; and (*d*) the size of the molecule. Jaenicke[90] located the separated sugars by soaking the dried paper-electrophoresis strip in silver nitrate solution and again drying it. The strips were developed in boiling water to reveal the sugars as dark brown spots on a light brown background. Rienits[121] used this technique in the analysis of protein-polysaccharide complexes. Work on carbohydrate derivatives was reported by Gross.[122]

The higher fatty acids—stearic, palmitic, myristic, and lauric—have been separated by a novel technique of countercurrent electrophoresis. In the process described by Barnett, Lee, and Smith,[123] ammonium hydroxide solution was siphoned through a wick in a glass tube. An electric potential was applied between the ends of the siphon in such a manner that the acids introduced near the top of the siphon tended to be carried down by the hydrostatic flow and up by electrophoresis. The ion with the highest mobility, therefore, appeared last at the lower end of the siphon. With a potential of 300 v. and a current of 3 milliamp. the arrival times at the lower end of the siphon were: stearic acid, 9 hours; palmitic acid, 13 hours; myristic acid, 22 hours; and lauric acid, 31 hours. Michl,[112] using a different apparatus, described the separation of malic and succinic acids by zone electrophoresis in paper. The α-keto acids have been separated as

[119] H. Michl, *Monatsh. Chem.*, **83**, 737 (1952).

[120] R. Consden and W. M. Stainer, *Nature*, **169**, 783 (1952).

[121] K. G. Rienits, *Biochem. J.*, **53**, 79 (1953).

[122] D. Gross, *Nature*, **172**, 908 (1953).

[123] A. J. G. Barnett, H. Lees, and D. K. Smith, *Biochem. J.*, **53**, xxxiii (1953).

dinitrophenylhydrazone compounds.[96] These were estimated quantitatively by polarographic determinations. Wieland[124] located and estimated the separated organic acids by forming their copper complexes. The separation of 25 acids and phenols in formic acid buffer was recently reported.[125]

Amines and polyamines have been separated by zone electrophoresis.[126] Successive separations at different pH values have aided in separating complex mixtures. Weber[127] listed the following amines and amino acids in order of decreasing rates of migration in buffer at pH 3.8: methylamine, dimethylamine, ethylamine, putrescine, cadaverine, propylamine, histamine, phenylethylamine, creatine, ephedrine, tyramine, ornithine, gramine, lysine, histidine, arginine, mescaline, glycine, and urea. At pH 7, propylamine and cadaverine migrate together as do lysine, ornithine, mescaline, and arginine; both groups migrate faster than histidine and glycine. Campbell and Muggleton[128] used paper electrophoresis to isolate bisquaternary ammonium compounds occurring in biological fluids.

The amino acids and peptides[126,129−131] have often been investigated because of their biochemical interest. Besides the work of Weber[127] referred to above, there is the classic paper[132] of Wieland and Fischer and the work of Beserte[133] and Durrum.[130] Brattsten and Nilsson[134] separated glycine, alanine, and glycylglycine by their hanging paper continuous electrophoresis technique. Haugaard and Kroner[135] analyzed amino acid mixtures with crossed zone electrophoresis and paper chromatography. Spots of separated amino acids or peptides are frequently made visible by spraying the strips with ninhydrin solution.[130] Wieland and Fischer[132] showed that the retention of copper is a very delicate means of locating and estimating the amounts of separated amino acids. By making a rising chromatogram of a solution of a copper salt in the electrophoresis strip, Wieland[136] devised a simple and direct means of locating and estimating the amount of amino acids in separated spots. The use of radioactive copper[137]

[124] T. Wieland, Angew. Chem., 63, 258 (1951).

[125] H. Berbalk and O. Schier, Monatsh. Chem., 86, 146 (1955).

[126] J. Blasco, O. Lecompte, and J. Polonovski, Bull. soc. chim. biol., 36, 627 (1954).

[127] R. Weber, Helv. Chim. Acta, 34, 2031 (1951).

[128] H. Campbell and D. F. Muggleton, Chemistry & Industry, 1952, 1244.

[129] W. Grassmann, K. Hannig, and M. Plöckl, Z. physiol. Chem., 299, 258 (1955).

[130] E. L. Durrum, J. Am. Chem. Soc., 72, 2943 (1950).

[131] B. Kickhöfen and O. Westphal, Z. Naturforsch., 7b, 655 (1952).

[132] T. Wieland and E. Fischer, Naturwissenschaften, 35, 29 (1948).

[133] G. Biserte, Biochim. et Biophys. Acta, 4, 416 (1950).

[134] I. Brattsten and A. Nilsson, Arkiv Kemi, 3, 337 (1951).

[135] G. Haugaard and T. D. Kroner, J. Am. Chem. Soc., 70, 2135 (1948).

[136] T. Wieland, Angew. Chem., A60, 313 (1948).

[137] T. Wieland, K. Schmeißer, E. Fischer, and H. Maier-Leibnitz, Naturwissenschaften, 36, 280 (1949).

to form the complex with amino acids also provided a very simple means of locating and assaying the amino acid content. The reaction between acetaldehyde and a number of amino acids was studied with paper electrophoresis by Robert and Penaranda.[138]

By far the greatest use of zone electrophoresis has been in the analysis of physiological solutions.[130,139−144] Several papers have shown that good correspondence can be obtained between zone-electrophoresis results and those obtained by the classical Nernst free-solution technique. Serum from normal and pathological subjects has shown some correlations between the pattern of proteins observed and the pathological condition.[145,146] Serum from nursing infants,[147] enzymes,[148−150] cerebrospinal fluid,[151,152] optical humor,[153] urine,[154] gastric juice,[155] saliva,[156] muscle protein hydrolyzate,[157] and bone marrow serum[158] have all been analyzed. Enough of the hormone oxytocin[145,159,160] has been purified by zone electrophoresis in a starch block to permit biological assay of the fractions. The interactions between blood protein and sulfanilamides,[161] iron,[162] radioactive iodine

[138] L. Robert and F. S. Penaranda, *J. Polymer Sci.*, **12**, 337 (1954).

[139] H. Cremer and A. Tiselius, *Biochem. Z.*, **320**, 273 (1950).

[140] H. Svensson and I. Brattsten, *Arkiv Kemi*, **1**, 401 (1950).

[141] W. Grassmann and K. Hannig, *Naturwissenschaften*, **37**, 494 (1950).

[142] A. M. Crestfield and F. W. Allen, *J. Biol. Chem.*, **211**, 363 (1954).

[143] C. Wunderly, *Nature*, **169**, 932 (1952).

[144] R. M. S. Smellie and J. N. Davidson, *Biochem. J.*, **49**, xv (1951).

[145] H. F. Oldershausen, G. Gries, and F. W. Aly, *Deut. Z. Nervenheilk.*, **170**, 254 (1953).

[146] G. Schneider, *Acta Chem. Scand.*, **5**, 1020 (1951).

[147] E. Boussemart and M. Marchand, *Bull. soc. pharm. Bordeaux*, **90**, 206 (1952); *Chem. Abstracts*, **47**, 11297 (1953).

[148] L. R. Wetter and J. J. Corrigal, *Nature*, **174**, 695 (1954).

[149] L. R. Wetter, *Can. J. Biochem. Physiol.*, **32**, 20 (1954).

[150] H. Boser, *Z. physiol. Chem.*, **300**, 1 (1955).

[151] T. Bucher, D. Matzelt, and D. Pette, *Naturwissenschaften* **39**, 114 (1952).

[152] E. Roboz, W. C. Hess, and D. M. Temple, *J. Lab. Clin. Med.*, **43**, 785 (1954).

[153] V. Chingalia and F. Franca, *Am. J. Opthalmol.*, **36**, 1160 (1953); *Chem. Abstracts*, **47**, 11493 (1952).

[154] E. Karverau, *Analyst*, **70**, 681 (1954).

[155] A. L. Latner, C. C. Ungley, E. V., Cox, E. McEvoy-Bowe, and L. Raine, *Brit. Med. J.*, **1**, 467 (1953).

[156] T. Kineraly, *Yale J. Biol. Med.*, **26**, 211 (1953).

[157] A. Meriani and G. Toschi, *Rend. ist. super-sanita*, **16**, 148 (1953); *Chem. Abstracts*, **47**, 10601 (1953).

[158] E. Poli, V. Bevacqua, and R. Curtello, *Plasma* (Milan), **1**, 101 (1953); *Chem. Abstracts*, **47**, 10609 (1953).

[159] H. G. Kunkel, S. P. Taylor, and V. du Vigneaud, *J. Biol. Chem.*, **200**, 559 (1953).

[160] J. N. Cumings, *J. Neurol. Neurosurg. Psychiat.*, **16**, 152 (1953).

[161] H. Kutzim, *Naturwissenschaften*, **39**, 135 (1952).

[162] W. Horst and K. H. Schafer, *Klin. Wochschr.*, **31**, 340 (1953).

131,[163,164] sulfur 35, and phosphorus 32[165] have been studied. Adreno-corticotropic hormone (ACTH),[166] hemoglobin,[167,168] mucopolysaccharides bound to thyroglobin,[169] toxin,[170] steroids,[171] and nucleic acid[172] have all been purified and analyzed by zone electrophoresis. Wieland and Bauer[173] used the technique to separate purine and pyrimidine derivatives. In certain cases,[174] proteins have been identified by incorporating radioactive atoms or by observations with ultraviolet light. In other cases dyes[175] such as bromophenol blue[175] and amidoschwartz 10B[176−177a] were used to stain the zone electrophoretigrams. The mercury[178] compounds of the proteins have also been used for identification. Care must always be taken to establish that the various separated substances on the strip respond equally to the colorant or inaccurate estimates of the amounts of substances may be reached. Special techniques have been discussed for the identification of nucleic acids,[179,180] globulins,[181] and lipides.[182−184]

Zone electrophoresis has been applied in a number of other connections. Dye mixtures, e.g., orange II and methylene blue or amidoschwarz and fuchsin, have been separated;[185,186] the blood sera of various animals,[187,188]

[163] F. Larson, W. P. Deiss, and E. C. Albright, Science, 115, 626 (1952).

[164] W. Maurer and L. Rickenback, Naturwissenschaften, 39, 261 (1952).

[165] W. Maurer, Arch. exptl. Pathol. Pharmakol., 218, 26 (1953); Chem. Abstracts, 47, 12640 (1953).

[166] H. J. McDonald and E. P. Marbach, J. Am. Chem. Soc., 74, 1619 (1952).

[167] A. H. Tuttle, Science, 121, 701 (1955).

[168] D. L. Larson and H. M. Ranney, J. Clin. Investigation, 32, 1070 (1953).

[169] G. J. M. Hoogkwinkel, G. Smits, and D. B. Kroon, Biochim. et Biophys. Acta, 15, 78 (1954).

[170] S. J. Ajl, J. Reedal, E. L. Durrum, and J. Warren, Federation Proc., 13, 485 (1954).

[171] K. D. Voigt and C. v. Beckmann, Acta Endocrinol., 13, 19 (1953).

[172] K. G. Rienits, Biochem. J., 53, 79 (1953).

[173] T. Wieland and L. Bauer, Angew Chem., 63, 511 (1951).

[174] H. Bennhold, E. Kallee, and E. Roth, Z. Naturforsch., 7b, 324 (1952).

[175] B. Drevon, Bull. soc. chim. biol., 36, 921 (1954).

[176] W. Grassmann and K. Hannig, Germ. Pat. 805,339 (May 17, 1951); Chem. Abstracts, 46, 8788 (1952).

[177] R. Wolff and P. Magnin, Bull. soc. chim. biol., 36, 925 (1954).

[177a] E. B. M. DeJong, Rec. trav. chim., 74, 1290 (1955).

[178] G. Thomsen, Naturwissenschaften, 39, 451 (1952).

[179] K. Makino and K. Matsuzaki, J. Biochem. (Japan), 41, 457 (1954); Chem. Abstracts, 48, 13773 (1954).

[180] W. Kanngiesser, Naturwissenschaften, 38, 503 (1951).

[181] F. V. Flynn and P. DeMayo, Lancet, 261, 235 (1951).

[182] E. L. Durrum, M. H. Paul, and E. R. B. Smith, Science, 116, 428 (1952).

[183] R. H. Common, W. P. McKinley, and W. A. Maw, Science, 118, 86 (1953).

[184] A. Fasoli, Acta Med. Scand., 145, 233 (1953).

[185] G. T. Franglen, Nature, 175, 134 (1955).

[186] W. Grassmann and L. Hübner, Das Leder, 5, 49 (1954).

[187] F. M. Antonini and G. Piva, Boll. soc. ital biol. sper., 28, 1887 (1952).

[188] T. L. Gleason and F. Friedberg, Physiol. Zool., 26, 95 (1953).

including dog,[189] horses, rats, monkeys, and rabbits[190] have been studied; the optical humor of the cow has been analyzed by Choisy *et al.*;[191] the soluble protein from the obturator nerve of the ox has been analyzed by Keil.[192] Animal poisons were studied by Neumann and Habermann.[193] The original paper zone electrophoresis work of König[194] was performed with snake venom, as was more recent work by Suzuki, Hagihara, and Takagi.[195] The technique has been used in such diversified studies as the analysis of the components of photographic gelatin,[195a] the hemoglobin of chickens blood,[195b] and the extract from the heads of house flies.[195c] Paper electrophoresis has been used in the study of the ripening of cheese.[196] It has been used[197] to separate indole derivatives from plant extracts. Consden and Gordon[198] used zone electrophoresis in their study of the products of hydrolysis of wool. Blocks of agar gel were used by Peniston, Agar, and McCarthy[199] to separate the products of hydrolysis of lignin. They were able to isolate various phenols, guaiacol, vanillin, and similar substances. Paper electrophoresis has been used to determine the approximate isoelectric pH values of albumins from wheat flour.[200]

General References

R. J. Block, E. L. Durrum, and G. Zweig, *A Manual of Paper Chromatography and Paper Electrophoresis.* Academic Press, New York, 1955.

H. T. McDonald, *Ionography.* The Year Book Publishers, Chicago, 1955.

P. Flodin and A. Tiselius in *Advances in Protein Chemistry,* Vol. III. Academic Press, New York, 1953, p. 1.

M. Lederer, *Introduction to Paper Electrophoresis and Related Methods.* Elsevier Press, 1955, p. 206.

L. F. J. Parker, "Zone Electrophoresis on Filter Paper," *Analyst,* **80,** 638 (1955).

[189] W. Boguth, *Naturwissenschaften,* **40,** 22 (1953).

[190] H. J. McDonald, R. J. Lappe, E. P. Marbach, R. H. Spitzer, and M. C. Urbin, *Clin. Chem.,* **5,** 51 (1953).

[191] A. Choisy, Y. Derrien, and G. Jayle, *Compt. rend.,* **234,** 1918 (1952).

[192] A. W. Keil, *Arch. ges. Physiol., Pflügers* **259,** 146 (1954); *Chem. Abstracts,* **48,** 13742 (1954).

[193] W. Neumann and E. Habermann, *Naturwissenschaften,* **39,** 286 (1952).

[194] D. von Klobusitzky and P. König, *Arch. exptl. Pathol. Pharmakol.,* **192,** 271 (1939).

[195] T. Suzuki, F. Hagihara, and Y. Takagi, *J. Pharm. Soc. Japan,* **74,** 167 (1954); *Chem. Abstracts,* **48,** 13772 (1954).

[195a] H. W. Wood, *J. Photo. Sci.,* **2,** 154 (1954).

[195b] V. L. Johnson and J. S. Dunlap, *Science,* **122,** 1186 (1955).

[195c] W. Chefurka and B. N. Smallman, *Nature,* **175,** 946 (1955).

[196] B. Lindquist, T. Storgards, and M. B. Goransson, *Intern. Dairyman's Cong. Proc., 13th,* **3,** 1224 (1953).

[197] D. V. Denffer, M. Behrens, and A. Fischer, *Naturwissenschaften,* **39,** 258 (1952).

[198] R. Consden and A. H. Gordon, *Biochem. J.,* **46,** 8 (1950).

[199] Q. P. Peniston, H. D. Agar, and J. L. McCarthy, *Anal. Chem.,* **23,** 994 (1951).

[200] J. W. Pence, *Cereal Chem.,* **30,** 328 (1953).

CHAPTER II

LABORATORY EXTRACTION
AND COUNTERCURRENT DISTRIBUTION

LYMAN C. CRAIG, *The Laboratories of the Rockefeller Institute for Medical Research,
New York, New York,* AND DAVID CRAIG, *The B. F. Goodrich Company, Brecksville,
Ohio*
SECTION ON **Increased Quantities** by EDWARD G. SCHEIBEL,

Hoffmann-LaRoche, Inc., Nutley, New Jersey

CONTENTS (*Continued*)

I. INTRODUCTION

Extraction as treated here deals with the transfer of material reversibly or otherwise from one or more phases in which it is dissolved or dispersed to another liquid phase. From the practical standpoint, the purpose of the transfer may be to remove unwanted substances from the phase or phases extracted. Extraction is more frequently employed in order to remove the solute to an environment more suitable for study or isolation. For the latter purpose it has long been one of the most widely used procedures available to the laboratory.

Certainly one of the most basic problems of the research worker in organic chemistry is that of the isolation and purification of individual compounds.   Therefore any study which leads to improvement in the methods for achievement of sharp separations is highly significant.   The importance of extraction procedures and their underlying principles to the experimental organic chemist can scarcely be overstressed and the possibilities of this operation have by no means been exploited to the fullest extent, particularly with regard to fractionation of materials which are closely related and difficult to separate otherwise.   The transfer of material from one phase to another is often a very specific phenomenon capable of precise manipulation as well as of mathematical interpretation.   The distribution of a solute under carefully controlled conditions further offers definite analytical possibilities of characterization and proof of purity.   The phase or phases in which the desired material is dispersed might broadly be called the *extrahend* or, if the material is dissolved in a single liquid phase, this will be called the *solution* or *raffinate phase*.   The *extractant* refers to the arbitrarily chosen liquid phase to which the material is to be transferred. The terms solute and solvent have the customary meanings (see Sec. II.1).

The majority of ordinary laboratory extractions are concerned with liquid phases.   The solid-phase extractions considered here will usually be designed only for isolation or removal purposes.   Though extraction involving a solid adsorbent and a liquid phase may offer a powerful tool for fractionation, this subject is so much a part of adsorption and chromatographic procedures that it will be treated only in a limited way.   Gas–liquid extractions will not be treated.   It is not our intention in this chapter to treat the subject of extraction broadly.   Much has already been written concerning applications in industrial, physical, and analytical chemistry and from the standpoint of chemical engineering (see, however, Section IX). It is rather the intention here to stress a particular analytical viewpoint and to treat only that part of the subject which can be of immediate use to the organic chemist engaged in laboratory, small-scale operations.   Most laboratory workers encounter little difficulty in applying well-established separation procedures such as distillation or crystallization to known compounds with recorded properties but find an unknown with unexpected properties quite a different matter.   Extraction may be particularly useful in such a case.   In this discussion the "empirical approach" will be stressed.

The empirical approach is essentially that of the organic chemist who may believe, as a matter of expediency if for no other reason, in such tenets as the tetracovalency of carbon, the tetrahedral nature of the carbon atom, the ability of carbon atoms to link with each other, and in the tendency of groups to dissociate from carbon atoms to form free radicals.   He believes in these and other tenets as long as they seem to work and as long as they suggest new experiments.   The nature of the organic chemist as an empiricist is further reflected in his interest in the synthesis, purification, characterization, in unique and unexpected behavior, and in naming and cataloging of carbon-containing compounds. The empirical approach contrasts with, but should not conflict with, the classical approach of the physical chemist and the physicist. Greatest progress is achieved when the two points of view are co-ordinated. The empirical approach usually precedes the classical, and the two then continue together. This chapter attempts a relatively new empirical approach to the subject of extraction, embodying the use of higher mathematics (mostly algebra) to a limited degree only. More precise meanings to some terms such as fractionation, identity, and purity have been striven for. With respect to this objective the procedure called *countercurrent distribution* often referred to as C.C.D. has been dealt with in considerable detail (see Section V).

Countercurrent distribution is a strictly stepwise countercurrent process carried out in a series of extraction units in such a manner that the result can be expressed as a plot of the solute fraction in each unit against the unit number.

II. THEORY OF EXTRACTION

1. General

The operative principles of extraction are based on the concepts of heterogeneous equilibria and on the mathematics involved in the dividing and subdividing of unit quantity of material. No attempt will be made here to give a general discussion of the subject of heterogeneous equilibria since it is discussed at length in several textbooks on physical chemistry, particularly by Hill.[1] However, the mathematics involved in extraction will be treated at some length.

Extraction processes are concerned primarily with the fraction or percentage of the total of a given solute which is found in a single phase at equilibrium. The fraction in a single phase is the percentage which will be removed or transferred at a given step when the respective phase is separated. The magnitude of the fraction is determined by a number of factors such as the relative volumes of the phases, the degree of association of the solute with itself in each of the phases, dissociation, association with the solvent, etc. As far as extraction is concerned (*cf.* page 319), solutes may always be regarded as being associated with the solvent in some degree. Thus, any other solute dissolved in the phase plays a role in the solvent action and may or may not associate with the solute of interest.

[1] A. E. Hill, in H. S. Taylor, ed., *A Treatise on Physical Chemistry.* 2nd ed., Van Nostrand, New York, 1930, p. 467.

In spite of the obviously complicated state of affairs determining the fraction of a solute to be found in the extracting solvent at equilibrium, it is perhaps best to develop the theory of extraction first on the basis of a simplified form of the distribution law. Deviation from this will then be treated later. The law, first clearly realized by Nernst,[2] states that a solute dissolved in one phase in equilibrium with another, immiscible phase will distribute itself between the two phases so that the ratio of the concentrations in the two phases is a constant at a fixed temperature. Thus in equation (1) C_1 and C_2 are the concentrations in the lighter and heavier phase, respectively:[1]

$$C_1/C_2 = K \qquad (1)$$

The constant, K, is usually referred to as the *distribution constant* or the *partition coefficient*.

Equation (1), however, holds only for the simplest case in which the molecules in each of the phases are in the same state of aggregation. In case the solute is associated or dissociated, equation (1) must be applied to each individual state of aggregation, if a rigorous treatment is desired. Confusion may arise here since solutes appear to be dissociated in one phase and not at all in another. A similar situation exists with respect to association. For these cases a more complicated form of the law[3] may be written. Hill[1] has summed up the generalizations of Nernst for the simpler cases of association to a dimer and dissociation of a molecule as follows:

phase 1: neither association nor dissociation
phase 2: neither association nor dissociation
$$\left. \right\} \frac{C_1}{C_2} = K \qquad (1a)$$

phase 1: dissociation occurring
phase 2: no molecular change occurring
$$\left. \right\} \frac{C_1(1 - \alpha)}{C_2} = K \qquad (2)$$

phase 1: no molecular change occurring
phase 2: association occurring
$$\left. \right\} \frac{C_1}{\sqrt{C_2(1 - \alpha')}} = K \qquad (3)$$

phase 1: dissociation occurring
phase 2: association occurring
$$\left. \right\} \frac{C_1(1 - \alpha)}{\sqrt{C_2(1 - \alpha')}} = K \qquad (4)$$

"In these formulae C_1 and C_2 represent the concentrations as analytically determined, α and α' the degree of association as determined by independent methods; and the further assumptions are included that the degree of dissociation follows the Mass Law and that the distributed species is the simple molecule. For the more complicated case of association to a molecule $(X)_n$ the denominator would become an nth root."

[2] W. Nernst, *Z. physik. Chem.*, **8**, 110 (1891).
[3] J. A. Campbell, *Ind. Eng. Chem.*, **36**, 1158 (1944).

It is evident that only for the simplest case, which is usually spoken of in extraction as the ideal system, is the partition coefficient independent of the total amount of solute taken. In actual practice, however, it is doubtful if there is any system in which the partition ratio does not deviate more or less at some range of concentration or temperature. In fact, partition coefficients which deviate are so much to be expected that in the literature of chemical engineering[4] the simplified form of the distribution law appears to be regarded as expressing only a limiting case. It is not difficult to understand the reason for this viewpoint since many industrial processes are concerned with concentrated solutions for practical reasons. A different viewpoint may be taken for laboratory extractions in which it is often not at all troublesome to employ extractions involving solutions containing a few per cent or less of solute and in which certain other compensations may be introduced, as will be discussed later (see pages 169, 316).

Since extraction as a separative procedure does not depend on precise information in regard to the cause of changing partition ratios it is not usually necessary to be concerned with equations (2), (3), and (4) and the more complicated derivations. The partition-ratio changes can be investigated and the results can be represented graphically as a partition isotherm, much as Campbell[3] has done. Figure 1 gives a diagram for three examples. The weights may be expressed conveniently as logarithms or the amount of solute expressed in some other way, such as in moles per liter. Where the partition coefficient is constant, a straight line (A) is obtained. Here the same percentage of the total solute is found in the corresponding phase irrespective of the increase or decrease in concentration. Example B is the case in which a relatively larger percentage of the solute is found in the extract phase as the concentration in each phase increases. C is the reverse of B.

The manner of representing adherence to or deviation from constant partition ratios as shown in Figure 1 is usually used only for relatively dilute solutions. The use of triangular co-ordinates becomes useful for representing the equilibria for the more concentrated solutions of three components, in which strong deviation is known to occur (Sect. II.3.C). For four-component systems the corresponding four-component diagrams may be employed.[5]

As far as is known at present, deviation may be ascribed always to the fact that the same molecular species are not present in both phases in the same relative proportions and that, further, in one of the phases an equilib-

[4] J. C. Elgin, in *Chemical Engineers Handbook*. 2nd ed., McGraw-Hill, New York, 1941, p. 1213. Compare J. C. Elgin, R. Wynkoop, and J. A. Lana, *ibid.*, 3rd ed., 1950, p. 713.

[5] T. G. Hunter, *Ind. Eng. Chem.*, **34**, 963 (1942).

rium exists which is the result of an association or dissociation of the solute. The partition coefficient resulting from this equilibrium is a function of the concentration but the relationship is not linear. Where such an equilibrium in one of the phases does exist a modification in that phase such as the addition of a buffer may change the equilibrium so that the partition coefficient can become essentially independent of the concentration, *i.e.*, give a constant partition ratio. Further discussion of the theoretical aspects of the cause of deviations, though interesting, is outside the scope of this chapter.

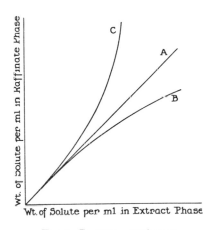

Fig. 1. Partition isotherms.

Since extraction is primarily concerned with the fraction of total solute in a single phase, a simplification results when C_1 and C_2 of equation (1) are expressed in weight per unit volume rather than in moles. C_1 and C_2 thus do not necessarily refer to a single molecular species but are more inclusive in that they refer to over-all amounts present as ions, dissociable dimers, trimers, etc. This broader meaning of the partition coefficient, K, will be used throughout the treatment given in this chapter and, since it may differ from the classical constant, it will be referred to as a *partition ratio*. Such a K will not be restricted to completely immiscible solvents but will also be used for solvents and mixtures of solvents partially miscible with each other.

Fortunately, for most extractions, a certain amount of deviation from constant partition ratios does not detract seriously from the use of the method unless precise mathematical interpretation is desired. Even in this case conditions may often be set up so that the deviations from the ideal behavior have a minimum effect. Unless otherwise stated, the treatment given in this book will refer to ideal behavior, *i.e.*, constant partition ratios.

The underlying causes for the value of the partition ratio are unquestionably related to those forces which determine solubility. However, a partition ratio is not itself a measure of solubility but it may be a ratio which expresses approximately the relative solubilities in the two phases, particularly when the solute is not very soluble in either phase and is not of a type which associates strongly. Obviously, if the limit of solubility has been reached in one phase, then at equilibrium it must also have been reached in the other phase, and at this point the partition ratio approaches or equals a ratio of the solubilities. For ideal solutions the partition ratio would not be significantly different at this point from that at lower concentrations but few solutions are ideal at higher concentrations. Partition ratios are frequently measured for systems in which the solute is very soluble in either or both phases but rarely if ever at the concentration corresponding to the saturation point. The "activity" ratio or K at the lower concentrations usually will be different from the value at the saturation point, that is, the curves of "activity" versus concentration for the two phases would not be linear and would in general not maintain a constant proportionality.

Comparison of solubility and extraction equilibria is valid only at saturation or at some other fortuitous point at which the values might agree. Therefore the value of a partition ratio cannot be predicted accurately from solubility data alone and vice versa. Partition ratios can have a broader application than solubility measurements.

For a given set of conditions, at equilibrium, the two phases have been in intimate contact long enough that the total rate of transfer of solute in one direction across the interface dividing the two phases is identical with the rate in the reverse direction. If the two phases are not in equilibrium, a much more complicated state of affairs exists and the distribution law is usually of little use.

In actual practice, many extractions are made in which complete equilibrium is not reached, but here the quantitative interpretation is made more difficult because of the influence of such factors as diffusion, area of interface films, turbulence, rates of flow, etc. In order to study and properly interpret extractions which do not depend on complete attainment of equilibrium, the experimenter is in need of adequate apparatus to control rates and the several other contributing factors. An extensive study along this line has been reported in the literature for industrial extractions.

The average organic chemist does not have extensive control equipment at his disposal and is generally not concerned with systems on which a large amount of experimentation has already been done. He is more concerned with learning definitely in a short time whether or not there is promise in an extraction process as applied to a new problem rather than with exploitation of all possibilities contributing to efficiency for the investigation of an old problem.   If extraction does not quickly offer promise, some other approach is normally taken.   Equilibrium conditions are thus much more desirable for the laboratory chemist than for the industrialist and are easily within his reach as far as stepwise procedures are concerned.   The result is then quantitative, is quickly checked, and, in most cases, gives information of value.   Only the simplest of equipment suitable for general laboratory use is required.   Even when more intricate continuous extractions are later to be used, a few well planned stepwise experiments frequently will form the basis for the intelligent application of the more extensive procedures.

2. Attainment of Equilibrium

No general rule or procedure can be set up which ensures rapid approach to equilibrium for every system and set of conditions.   Attainment of equilibrium depends upon a variety of factors many of which may be difficult to determine.   Nonetheless a discussion of a number of factors which would seem to have a bearing on the subject will prove helpful.   These can be more sharply defined for stepwise or discontinuous extraction since determination of the partition ratio under two or more sets of conditions will indicate whether or not equilibrium has been reached.   For continuous extraction it is much more difficult experimentally to show the influence of the various factors.

Attainment of equilibrium depends upon the over-all rate of transfer of solute from one phase to the other and equilibrium is established at a phase boundary when the net rate of transfer across it is zero.   However, in order that this can mean that equilibrium conditions have been reached as far as extraction is concerned, the concentration of solute in the region near the boundary must not be different from that in the interior of the same phase.   There must be no concentration gradient except across the phase boundary.

The literature on the rate of transfer of a solute between two phases in contact has been well summarized by Hunter and Nash.[6]   Apparently the experimental observations are best explained by the assumption of resistant stationary films of liquid on both sides of the interface.   This theory assumes that for a fluid in motion past a boundary surface the linear rate of flow is not the same at all distances from the surface, but at a given distance from the boundary is less than that further out in the stream.   On approaching the surface, it rapidly becomes less until there is practically

⁶ T. G. Hunter and A. W. Nash, *J. Soc. Chem. Ind. London*, **51**, 285 (1932).

no flow for a thin layer or film adjacent to the boundary. Thus, in extraction, adjustment of any concentration gradient across this zone could become so low that it would depend entirely on diffusion. These conditions are schematically represented by Figure 2. The films under discussion should not be confused with the monomolecular films of surface-active substances. The former are essentially dynamic in character and their effective thickness is large in comparison to that of adsorbed films. With the approach outlined above it is possible to express the rate of transfer of a solute across an interface not only in terms of the partition ratio but also in

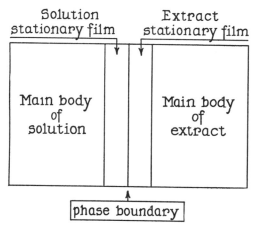

Fig. 2. Schematic diagram of "two-film" theory.

terms of its rate of transfer across the various zones. According to the theory the main body of the solution may be in violent motion and any concentration gradient will be quickly adjusted. Upon passage to the more stationary zone, a definite time is required for the solute to pass across this layer. The time required will depend on the mobility and effective thickness of the layer, diffusion rates, etc. It is assumed that equilibrium is established immediately across the boundary and there is little time involved in the passage of solute to the stationary film of the solvent. Again a definite time is required for passage across the solvent film. The time may be very different from the time of passage across the solution film. Once the solute has reached the main body of the extract no appreciable time is required for establishment of a uniform concentration since the extract again is assumed to be in comparatively violent motion.

This theory on the whole is rather illuminating and undoubtedly represents the true state of affairs for the majority of liquid–liquid extractions. Thus interchange between the two phases is rather slow for most substances unless there is marked turbulence or breaking up of the two phases such as is caused by the shaking of a separatory funnel. Gentle stirring of the two phases in contact does not result in rapid interchange,[7a] an observation often made previously[7b] and experimentally confirmed by the authors in connection with countercurrent-distribution studies. On the other hand, it might be expected that violent shaking would not *necessarily* result in rapid establishment of equilibrium if stable emulsions are formed. Such emulsions may indicate the formation of a stable film at the interface and the film might in part defeat the purpose of continued shaking. The continual formation of droplets of a distribution of sizes, and their coalescing again would appear to offer the optimum state of affairs for rapid interchange. In support of this belief, it has been found that simple repeated inversion of a tube containing the two phases gives essential equilibrium in only a few inversions.[8] Of the many substances and systems thus far studied by the distribution technique, none have failed to be in equilibrium after fifty such inversions. This is accomplished in about 1.5 minutes. Equilibrium would naturally fail to be reached when one phase could not be dispersed in another because of its physical properties.

For the discontinuous process a simple method of studying the rate at which equilibrium is approached is the following: A test tube approximately $\frac{1}{2}$ in. in diameter on the inside, 9 in. in length, and fitted with a ground stopper may serve as the contacting vessel. Standard volumes of the two phases are so chosen that a few milliliters of the volume of the test tube remain unoccupied. A standard sample of the solute to be studied is dissolved in one of the phases. The other phase is carefully stratified either above or below the solution, depending on its specific gravity.

When the tube is suddenly inverted the bubble of air will rise to the upper surface and at this point the tube is quickly righted again to its original position. Inverting and reinverting the tube once will be called a standard inversion. This gives good dispersion of the two phases. If the layers are allowed to separate, the concentration of solute in each may be determined by some suitable analytical method and the ratio of the concentrations in the two phases recorded. Other determinations are made in the same way with different numbers of inversions successively made at such a rate that the bubble of air just reaches the upper end of the tube before the next inversion is started. The logarithms of the concentration ratios for a series of such determinations are then plotted against the number of standard inversions, as given in Figure 3. The lower curve of a pair represents the data when the solute is all contained in the lower phase initially,

[7a] G. C. Green, *Chemical Age, London*, **50**, 519 (1944).

[7b] E. M. P. Widmark, *Biochem. Z.*, **179**, 263 (1926).

[8] G. T. Barry, Y. Sato, and L. C. Craig, *J. Biol. Chem.*, **174**, 209 (1948).

and vice versa for the upper curve.   A certain time, which may be of the order of 10 to 30 seconds, is required for the droplets to coalesce and separate.   The amount of interchange taking place during this period is unknown but is included in the ratios measured.   It does not appear to be large.   Data such as those given in Figure 3 can be reproduced readily and permit operation of a discontinuous extraction process at essential equilibrium without loss of time through excessive shaking.   Obviously equilibrium has been reached when the two curves of a pair have merged.

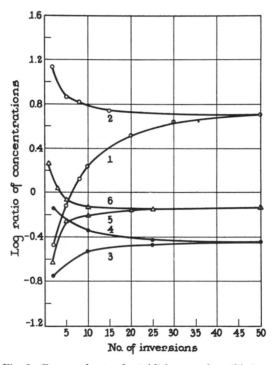

Fig. 3. Curves of rate of establishment of equilibrium.

Figure 3 gives data from several determinations made at 6 °C.   Curves 1 and 2 refer to benzylpenicillin in the system ethyl ether–3 M phosphate buffer at pH 4.6;   curves 3 and 4 represent p-hydroxybenzylpenicillin in ethyl ether–3 M phosphate at pH 4.9;   curves 5 and 6 refer to benzylpenicillin in ethyl ether–2 M phosphate at pH 4.8.

During the course of partition work, in the laboratory of one of the authors, with various solutes and systems it was found that different solutes approach equilibrium at different rates in the same system.   Though the rate for a given set of conditions could be reproduced satisfactorily, it was changed considerably by a different pH of the buffer. It was also changed when the relative volumes of the upper and lower phases were altered. Even more interesting, in the case of the penicillins, as shown by curves 1 and 2 of Figure 3, the rate of approach to equilibrium was different depending on whether the penicillin was all in the upper or lower phase initially. That this effect is not due to the value of the partition ratio (5.2) is shown by the fact that the reverse effect is not shown by curves 3 and 4, where the partition ratio is 0.35. The penicillins are known to be surface active and it is logical to expect them in a mixture to exert a mutual effect on each other in regard to the rate at which equilibrium is established. As far as the authors are aware no quantitative data are to be found in the literature in regard to the effect of small amounts of surface-active substances on the rate of interchange of a solute between two immiscible phases. It would appear that information helpful in extraction might be derived from studies of this nature.

Many different kinds of solutes have now been separated by countercurrent distribution (see Section VII). In nearly all cases something less than 10 tips of the tube is all that is required for essential equilibrium. Molecular size of the solute seems to have little to do with the rate of establishment of equilibrium. Insulin[9] of 6000 molecular size can be fractionated ideally by countercurrent distribution with no more time required for equilibration than with the other smaller solutes.

3. Extraction for Removal Purposes

A. EXTRACTION FORMULAS

Frequently all that is desired in an extraction is the quantitative removal of the solute from a phase unsatisfactory for its further study. This operation may result also in a greater or lesser degree of separation of the desired solute from other undesired solutes. If essentially none of the undesired accompanying materials is extracted by a given solvent, matters are greatly simplified, and the only factor to be considered is the completeness of the extraction in terms of the least labor and least solvent. Provided that equilibrium is reached and the partition isotherm is linear, the labor and solvent required are governed by the value of the partition ratio and the relative volumes of the two phases. Thus the fraction, U, of the total solute found in the upper layer is given by equation (5)[10] where K is the partition ratio, and V_u and V_l are the volumes of the upper and the lower phases respectively, and r is the ratio V_u/V_l:

[9] E. J. Harfenist and L. C. Craig, *J. Am. Chem. Soc.*, **74**, 3083 (1952).
[10] Compare H. E. Hill, in H. S. Taylor, ed., *A Treatise on Physical Chemistry.* 2nd ed., Van Nostrand, New York, 1930, p. 467.

$$U = \frac{KV_u}{KV_u + V_l} = \frac{Kr}{Kr + 1} \tag{5}$$

The fraction, L, remaining in the lower phase is given by equation (6):

$$L = 1 - \frac{KV_u}{KV_u + V_l} = \frac{1}{Kr + 1} \tag{6}$$

Upon re-extracting the lower layer with n successive equal volumes of the upper layer, each nth extract will contain the fraction Y_n of the solute, as given in equation (7):

$$Y_n = \left(\frac{V_l}{V_l + KV_u}\right)^{n-1} \left(\frac{KV_u}{KV_u + V_l}\right) = \left(\frac{1}{Kr + 1}\right)^n Kr \tag{7}$$

and X_n of the solute will remain in the lower layer, as given in equation (8):

$$X_n = \left(\frac{V_l}{V_l + KV_u}\right)^n = \left(\frac{1}{Kr + 1}\right)^n \tag{8}$$

It is obvious from the above formulas that some idea of the value of the partition ratio makes possible a much more intelligent use of the method of extraction. If a partition ratio is not already known, a sufficiently accurate estimate may be obtained by several successive extractions using equal volumes of the extractant. A volume one-third that of the extrahend will be found convenient. The total weights (or other analytical units which are proportional) $W_1, W_2, W_3 \ldots W_n$ of solute in each successive extract will then be determined by some rapid analytical procedure. A value for the partition ratio can then be derived from equation (9) where r is the ratio of the volumes of the two phases:

$$1 - \frac{W_2}{W_1} = \frac{Kr}{Kr + 1} = U \tag{9}$$

If W_2/W_1 is greater than about 0.7, it is advisable to increase the volume of the extractant accordingly for a more accurate evaluation. Values of the partition ratio less than 0.1 obviously make this approach unpractical.

If the value of K obtained from this formula agrees with that obtained from equation (10):

$$1 - \frac{W_3}{W_2} = \frac{Kr}{Kr + 1} \tag{10}$$

then K represents a close approximation of the partition ratio for concentrations not exceeding those in the solutions at hand, but it might also be the *geometric mean* (see page 179) of the partition ratios of more than one solute of similar partition ratio if the solutes were present in equal amount. Otherwise the geometric mean would be weighted according to the amount of each solute. In any case, the approximate total amount of solute in the original solution is now indicated and the factors are known for the intelligent application of simple extraction. This general approach is made much more useful by the multiplicity of rapid analytical procedures which are now available and briefly discussed in a later section.

If the partition ratios derived from Equations (9) and (10) do not agree, either a single solute is present which does not obey the simplified form of the distribution law over the concentration range in question, or two or more solutes are being extracted which have significantly different partition ratios. Several more successive extractions may be advisable in order to learn if the ratios calculated from two successive weights, W_n and W_{n+1}, agree. If they continue to diverge, simple stepwise extraction with the particular solvent is not the most suitable method; a change to some other solvent which yields a more favorable partition ratio is advisable. If this is not possible or desirable, the efficiency of extraction frequently may be improved by addition of some modifying substance to the solution to be extracted. These approaches are taken up later under separate headings. The use of a different method of contacting such as a continuous countercurrent procedure should also be considered.

B. METHODS OF CONTACTING

The method selected for bringing two liquid phases into intimate contact so that the greatest percentage of the solute is extracted varies greatly with the physical properties of the system under consideration. It further depends on the value of the partition ratio, the volume of the solution, and the permissible volume of the solvent to be used for the extraction.

For a given method of contacting, naturally the highest efficiency possible obtains when equilibrium conditions have been reached. The different methods of contacting, however, have a considerable bearing on the experimental procedure which must be employed to approach equilibrium and vice versa. Even assuming that equilibrium is reached, great variation is possible in the degree of extraction simply by contacting the two phases in portions rather than all at one time, and is further influenced by recontacting certain of the extracted portions either with fresh solvent or with portions already contacted with previous portions, etc. This rather involved subject has been treated from the theoretical standpoint by a number of workers, particularly Hunter and Nash,[11] Varteressian and

[11] T. G. Hunter and A. W. Nash, *Ind. Eng. Chem.*, **27**, 836 (1935).

Fenske,[12] and Evans.[13] The underlying cause for the increased extraction can be more readily understood for simplified cases when the percentages in the different portions are considered as terms of the binomial theorem. This aspect of the problem will be taken up in the section on the theory of extraction for fractionation purposes. The methods of contacting to be treated separately now follow.

Discontinuous Extraction. *Single Contact.* In this method a given volume of the solution is contacted with a given volume of the solvent for sufficient time to reach equilibrium and the two layers are then separated. This is the simplest extraction procedure possible and is the most used of any in the laboratory. It is also the preliminary or exploratory operation employed in the study of unknown systems and is designed to yield the quantitative information which will guide in the final choice of the method of extraction. For this purpose it should be rapid and reasonably precise.

Multiple Contact. This method of contacting is done in the same way as in the single stage except that several separatory funnels, tubes, or other vessels are employed. The simplest form amounts to successive single-stage extraction in which the solution always comes in contact with fresh solvent. This has already been discussed since it is part of the preliminary examination of unknown solutions. The Soxhlet extractor for solids is in this category.

Multiple-Contact Pseudocountercurrent. This type of contacting is not a countercurrent process in the strictest sense of the word, according to some authors. It has been discussed by Watanabe and Morikawa[14] and by Hunter and Nash[11] who call it "pseudo countercurrent extraction." As demonstrated by these authors, it can be applied with relatively few individual transfers so that the effect closely approaches the true countercurrent effect.

The procedure can be applied as follows: The solution to be extracted is divided into n convenient portions in any given type of equilibration tube (*e.g.*, separatory funnel) and the tubes are numbered 0, 1, 2, ... r. The first tube, numbered 0, is shaken with an arbitrary volume of the extractant and the upper layer or extract transferred to the next in line, tube 1. A volume of the solvent equal to that used in the first stage is then added to the 0 tube and both 0 and 1 are equilibrated. The upper layer from tube 1 is then transferred to tube 2, the upper layer from tube 0 to tube 1, and a fresh portion of the solvent added to 0. All three are equilibrated and the upper layers are transferred to the next higher tube. Fresh solvent

[12] K. A. Varteressian and M. R. Fenske, *Ind. Eng. Chem.*, **28**, 928, 1353 (1936).

[13] T. W. Evans, *Ind. Eng. Chem.*, **26**, 860 (1934).

[14] S. Watanabe and K. Morikawa, *J. Soc. Chem. Ind. Japan*, **36**, 585 B (1933).

is added to the 0 tube and the process continued in this fashion as long as desired. The process is shown schematically in Figure 4. In this figure and in subsequent ones, a phase is represented by a rectangle, and two phases in equilibrium by rectangles in contact. Transfer numbers are shown vertically and tube numbers or number of other contacting vessel horizontally.

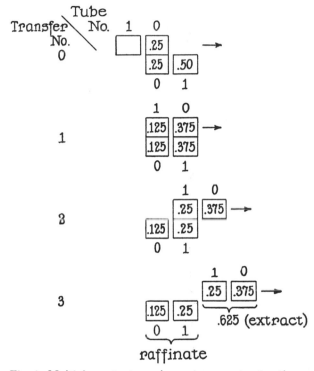

Fig. 4. Multiple-contact pseudocountercurrent extraction.

The relative efficiencies of the three methods of contacting can be shown best by a specific hypothetical problem. Let us assume that there is at hand 100 ml. of a solution containing 1 g. of a single solute and it is desired to transfer as much as possible of the solute to 100 ml. of an immiscible solvent with lower specific gravity. Let the partition ratio of the solute in the two phases be 1. By the single-contact extraction it is obvious from equation (5) that 0.50 g. will be found in the solvent.

In order to apply the multiple-contact method, the solvent could be divided into four portions and each successively contacted with the 100 ml. of solution. From equation (8) it can be calculated that 0.5904 g. will be in the extract when the four portions are combined. Evans[15] has shown that the increase in efficiency in dividing the extracting solvent into more than five portions scarcely is sufficient to warrant further subdividing.

In order to apply the countercurrent principle, the solution could be divided into two equal parts and contacted with two portions of the solvent each containing 50 ml., according to the scheme given above in Figure 4. This is set out in Table I for convenience. The reason for arranging the weights in the manner given will be seen later from the discussion of the binomial theorem under the treatment of fractionation. The weights in the table are the total weights of substance in a tube both in the upper and lower layers where there are two layers in the tube. The numbers at the top of each column refer to the serial number of the tube. It can be seen in this case that the two extracts contain a total of 0.625 g. of the solute as compared to the figure of 0.5904 for the multiple-contact procedure. Four individual operations have been involved in both cases.

TABLE I

MULTIPLE-CONTACT PSEUDOCOUNTERCURRENT EXTRACTION
Solution contacted in two portions

No. of transfers	Tube no.		Extract
	0	1	
0	0.50	0.50	—
1	0.25	0.75	—
2	0.125	0.50	0.375
3	—	0.25	0.25
		Extract =	0.625
		Raffinate =	0.375

If the solution to be extracted is divided into four equal volumes and contacted in the same manner with four portions of the solvent, the results given in Table II will be obtained. A total of 0.7265 g. of material will be in the extract. Though the total volume of the extract is still 100 ml., the process has involved 16 separate operations in all. It is obvious from these two tables that further subdividing the volumes of both solution and solvent, though laborious, will lead to much more complete removal of the solute without increasing the volume of the solvent and will approach complete extraction with an infinite number of subdivisions of each phase.

If a partition ratio other than 1 had been chosen for the foregoing discussion the quantitative comparison of the three methods of contacting

[15] H. M. Evans, *Ind. Eng. Chem.*, **26**, 439 (1934).

would have been different.   Thus at a K of 2 the differences would have been more marked, but at a K of 0.5 the difference would have been less decisive for a few stages.   Many stages are needed when the partition ratio is unfavorable.

TABLE II

MULTIPLE-CONTACT PSEUDOCOUNTERCURRENT EXTRACTION
Solution contacted in four portions

No. of transfers	Tube no.				Extract
	0	1	2	3	
0	0.25	0.25	0.25	0.25	—
1	0.125	0.375	0.25	0.25	—
2	0.0625	0.25	0.4375	0.25	—
3	0.03125	0.1562	0.3432	0.4687	—
4	0.0128	0.0937	0.25	0.4062	0.2344
5	—	0.0467	0.1719	0.3281	0.2031
6	—	—	0.0860	0.25	0.164
7	—	—	—	0.125	0.125

$$Extract \quad = \quad 0.7265$$
$$Raffinate \quad = \quad 0.2735$$

Continuous Extraction.   In continuous extraction either the solvent or solution or both are introduced into the contacting chamber continuously and are removed from some other point of the chamber at the same rate.   Though instantaneous equilibrium may be established at just the point of contact of the two phases, this does not hold for all the liquid in the contacting chamber because of the obvious physical barriers and the degree of stirring required.   Thus, in order to speak of some quantitative measure of the effectiveness of such a system, it has been found expedient to introduce the concept of a "theoretical plate."   This concept will be treated later in the section on fractionation.   (See also Rose and Rose[16] and Section IX of this chapter.)

Single Stage.   This type of extraction is analogous to discontinuous multiple-contact extraction when in the latter the number of successive extractions becomes infinitely large.   It is generally applied by distilling off the solvent from the extract, condensing the distillate, and returning it again to extract the solution in a continuous cycle.   The well known Kutscher-Steudel (see Sect. IV) extractor in which the extracting solvent flows continuously through the apparatus is an example.   The question of the efficiency of the process is ordinarily not raised since the extraction

[16] A. and E. Rose, in *Distillation*, Volume IV of *Technique of Organic Chemistry*, A. Weissberger, ed.   Interscience, New York-London, 1951.

can be allowed to proceed indefinitely without attention. The procedure is so familiar that it scarcely warrants further treatment,[17] except to say that due to inefficiency the process, even though allowed to run for hours, frequently does not lead to high recovery of a solute with an unfavorable partition ratio. Undesired materials often accumulate in the extract part of the system due to the excessively long exposure or carrying-over of slight suspensions (entrainment).

Countercurrent. Theoretically, this is the most efficient form of extraction of all and is particularly useful in the case of an unfavorable partition ratio, as can be seen by extending the reasoning given under treatment of multiple-contact pseudocountercurrent extraction. Even if the partition ratio is favorable, various factors may make the continuous countercurrent process desirable. It is carried out by having a continuous stream of the solution flowing in one direction and contacting a continuous stream of solvent flowing in the other direction (see Fig. 55). There may be discrete contacting units or a long tube which is either filled with only the two liquids or which may be packed with some supporting material to improve the contact. The apparatus for contacting therefore is entirely analogous to a fractionating column, as has been suggested on many occasions.[18,19] As a rule, however, the number of theoretical plates or perfect stages is not high and varies greatly with the nature of the two phases, of the solute, etc. Even so, it may be the type of extraction of choice except for the solutes where the partition coefficient is comparatively favorable.

C.   CASE OF A NONLINEAR PARTITION ISOTHERM

Thus far the treatment has been restricted to the ideal case because here the treatment is simpler and is the most useful from the analytical standpoint. Perhaps this generally is true as far as laboratory extractions are concerned, particularly when an unknown solute is under investigation. Irrespective of this it is not necessary to forego exact calculation for the case of a single solute, when partition ratios shift with concentration. On the contrary most treatments on extraction develop the theory on the basis of changing partition ratios and consider constant ratios to be only a special case of the more general approach. An excellent development along this

[17] For a description of the various types, see A. A. Morton, *Laboratory Technique in Organic Chemistry*, McGraw-Hill, N. Y., 1938, p. 202. H. Kleinmann, in *Handbuch der Pflanzenanalyse*, Vol. I, Springer, Vienna, 1931, p. 126. Thorpe, *Dictionary of Applied Chemistry*, 4th ed., Vol. IV, Longmans, Green, 1940, p. 575.

[18] K. A. Varteressian and M. R. Fenske, *Ind. Eng. Chem.*, **28**, 928, 1353 (1936).

[19] R. N. J. Saal and W. J. A. van Dÿck, *World Petroleum Congr.*, London, *Proc.*, **2**, 352 1933

line which more nearly expresses the viewpoint of the chemical engineer is to be found in a recent review by Frey and Scheibel.[20]

An example of a partition ratio which changes with concentration might be one which would give the hypothetical partition isotherm shown in Figure 5.   Completely immiscible phases are assumed or those not altered appreciably by the solute.   Here the partition ratio is decreasing with the increase of concentration.   An arbitrary solution of the solute in the *heavier* phase, of arbitrary concentration x_0 g. per R g. of pure phase,

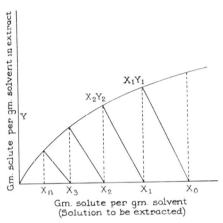

Fig. 5. A nonlinear partition isotherm

might be taken.   This could be contacted and brought to equilibrium with a weight of S g. of the pure lighter solvent.   A line of slope $-R/S$ drawn through x_0 will be found to intercept the curve at the point x_1, y_1.   The concentration of the solute in the heavier phase will thus be x_1 after it has been contacted with S g. of the lighter solvent.   This represents one theoretical transfer.   A second transfer made in the same way starting at x_1 will give x_2, etc.   If it were the objective of the extraction to reduce the concentration of solute in the heavier phase to the concentration x_n, n stages would be required.   Conversely if an extraction were performed in a continuous manner with the solution given above and S g. of the solvent, the equivalent of n theoretical stages would have been accomplished.

For the case in which the partition ratio is constant the isotherm is a straight line or $y = K_x$, and the number of stages required to go from x_0 to any desired concentration is given by equation (11):

$$X_n = [R/(R + KS)]^n x_0 \qquad (11)$$

[20] A. J. Frey and E. G. Scheibel, in *Emil Barrel, Jubilee Volume*, 1946.   Hoffmann-LaRoche and Co., Basle, 1946, p. 446.

If weight is changed to volume this then becomes the extraction formula given in equation (8).

When the extracting solvent is partially miscible with the solution, ternary equilibrium diagrams[18] are useful in explaining the effect and in evaluating the efficiency of a continuous extraction process. If a particular extraction is to be used repeatedly in the laboratory and the utmost efficiency is desired for a particular reason, it may be worthwhile to work out such a diagram.

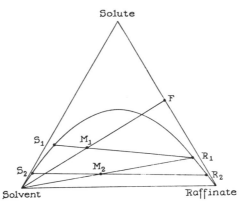

Fig. 6. Ternary equilibrium diagram.

A ternary diagram is shown in Figure 6 above. The solution to be extracted could have the composition F. This could be contacted with an arbitrary volume of the extracting solvent. The mixture will separate into two layers whose composition could be S_1 and R_1, respectively. The curve gives all the possible equilibrium compositions. The relative quantities of the two phases will be the ratio of the segments M_1R_1 and S_1M_1. The raffinate phase, R_1, from this could then be contacted with fresh solvent to give S_2R_2. In this way the number of extractions to give the desired recovery can be derived. For further extension and discussion of this approach see other publications.[18, 20, 21]

4. Extraction for Fractionation

Though the possibilities in the use of extraction for the crude isolation of chemical compounds have been recognized since the beginning of the science of organic chemistry, extraction was little used for the separation of closely related compounds from each other until about 30 years ago.[22]   Jantzen[23]

[21] T. G. Hunter and A. W. Nash., *Ind. Eng. Chem.*, **27**, 836 (1935).

[22] M. Frenc, *Z. angew. Chem.*, **38**, 323 (1925).

[23] E. Jantzen, *Das fractionierte Distillieren und das fractionierte Verteilen*, Dechema Monographie, Vol. V, No. 48.   Verlag Chemie, Berlin, 1932, p. 81.

and Cornish, Archibald, Murphy, and Evans[24] deserve credit for being among the first to recognize the potentialities in the field. For this purpose, extractions can be done in multiple–contact–countercurrent manner, in discrete stages, or in the truly continuous, differential manner in such a way that the theory and the effect are entirely analogous to those of rectification.[25] In fact, the theory of fractionation can be developed and tested experimentally perhaps more completely by the use of extraction, because it is more adaptable to experimental study than is distillation. The partition ratio or the manner of distribution can be adjusted at will over a broad range and with many different solvent pairs. Fractionation as it will be discussed in this treatment is always a countercurrent process even though performed in discrete stages.

A. THEORY FOR STEPWISE PROCEDURES

Theoretical Discussion. In order to reduce the discussion of fractionation by distribution to its simplest form, it will be assumed that, when two solutes are extracted reversibly in a given two phase system, each will behave as if the other solute were not present. Moreover, for purposes of discussion, it may also be assumed that constant partition ratios obtain over the concentration range employed. These conditions may be realized easily in actual practice for most substances by employing sufficiently dilute solutions. Of equal importance where acids and bases are concerned is the use of buffer solutions of high capacity.

In order to simplify the process still further for purposes of discussion, equal volumes of the two phases may be considered and a solute chosen which has a partition ratio of 1 in the solvent pair. Separate contacting units or tubes can be arranged in a series numbered 0, 1, 2, ... r from left to right as in Figure 7. If unit quantity (1.000 g.) of the solute is dissolved in L_0 and U_0 moved over it, the process will be in its initial position at 0 transfer. The two phases in tube 0 are equilibrated and, after they have separated, the upper phases can be shifted so that U_0 will be over L_1 and U_1 will be over L_0. One transfer has now been accomplished. Since the partition coefficient is 1 and the volumes of the two phases are equal, 50% of the solute will have migrated to tube 1 in the upper layer. The total, in both layers combined, of each tube, 0 or 1, will therefore be 0.500 g. In the table of Figure 7 these amounts are given on the appropriate line opposite the figure for the number of transfers.

For the second transfer, both tubes are equilibrated and the upper layers

[24] R. E. Cornish, R. C. Archibald, E. A. Murphy, and H. M. Evans, *Ind. Eng. Chem.*, 26, 397 (1934).
[25] R. N. J. Saal and W. J. D. van Dyck, *World Petroleum Congr., London, Proc.*, 2, 352 (1933).

of both shifted so that U_0 is over L_2, U_1 is over L_1, and U_2 is over L_0.　Two transfers will now have been accomplished and the total fraction of substance in each tube, both layers combined, is given in the table on the line opposite the second transfer.　This process can be continued indefinitely.

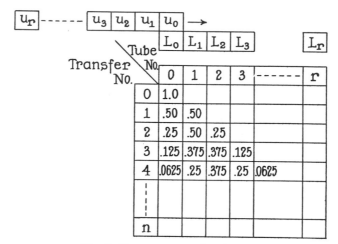

Fig. 7. Countercurrent distribution.

The table (Fig. 7) represents an expansion corresponding to $(X + Y)^n = 1$, where X represents the fraction remaining in the lower phase and Y represents the fraction being transferred; in this case $X = Y$.　The letter n corresponds to the number of transfers made and is the figure given in the first column of the table.　Thus when the tubes are numbered 0, 1, 2, ... r, as given on the top line of Figure 7, each of these numbers corresponds to the rth term of the binomial expansion.

The fraction or percentage of solute in a single tube to be found in each phase is fixed by the partition ratio.　Thus, equation (12) gives the relationship of the fraction Y to be found in the upper phase:

$$Y = K/K + 1 \tag{12}$$

to the partition ratio K at equilibrium.　The fraction X in the lower phase is also fixed by formula (13), since unit quantity was taken initially:

$$X = 1 - \frac{K}{K + 1} = \frac{1}{1 + K} \tag{13}$$

The binomial expansion in terms of the partition ratio, K, as applied to stepwise countercurrent extraction, now becomes:

$$\left(\frac{1}{1 + K} + \frac{K}{K + 1}\right)^n = 1 \tag{14}$$

when equal volumes of the two phases are used.   The expression applies equally well for unequal volumes when K throughout the expansion is multiplied by the ratio of the two volumes.   Thus the percentage of the original material to be found in each tube is fixed for a given K when the number of transfers is fixed.

Fractionation procedures basically depend on the partition, transfer, and recombination of various fractions.   After a few steps these operations become somewhat confusing.   It would appear that a direct and orderly way to carry out the over-all process so that it may be more easily visualized is by way of the binomial expansion.   Therefore the significance and application of the binomial theorem may well be pointed out especially in presenting the subject of fractionation to students.

When carried out as in Figure 7, the amount of substance present in each tube can be calculated directly by the binomial theorem, since the fraction in the rth tube is that of the rth term of the binomial theorem.[26] Equation (15) gives a general formula for calculating the fraction $T_{n,r}$ of substance present in the rth tube for n transfers:

$$T_{n,r} = \frac{n!}{r!\,(n-r)!} \left(\frac{1}{K+1}\right)^n K^r \tag{15}$$

A convenient graphical method for representing such an extraction results when the fraction or percentage present in a tube is plotted as ordinate against the serial number of the tube as abscissa.[27, 28]   This gives a distribution, shown in Figure 8 (curve 1) for a partition ratio of 1 and for eight transfers.   It will be noted that the curve is perfectly symmetrical.   For higher numbers of transfers the curve becomes the normal curve of error (see page 187).   When the partition ratio is 0.333, curve 2 is obtained and, when it is 3.0, curve 3 is obtained.

In order to obtain one of the curves of Figure 8, $(n+1)n/2$ or 36 individual extractions are required.   It is obvious that the high numbers of transfers needed for the separation of complicated mixtures will become too laborious.   Because of this fact, an apparatus has been developed[27] whereby many extractions are accomplished quantitatively in one operation.   This has greatly enhanced the possibilities of extraction for analytical purposes and for characterization of an organic compound.   The name *"countercurrent distribution"* has been given to this particular type of extraction (see page 242).   It is a subject which will be treated in a separate section.

[26] H. L. Rietz, *Mathematical Statistics.* Open Court, La Salle, Ill., 1927, p. 23–24.

[27] L. C. Craig, *J. Biol. Chem.*, **155**, 519 (1944).

[28] S. Stene, *Arkiv Kemi, Mineral. Geol.*, **A18**, No. 18 (1944).   B. Williamson and L. C. Craig. *J. Biol. Chem.*, **168**, 687 (1947).

When two substances are present as solutes each will tend to distribute itself independently as given above, but since the partition ratios will differ at least in some degree, two bands, overlapping or otherwise, will be obtained. To illustrate this point, the case of a mixture of equal amounts of propionic and butyric acids may be taken. Isopropyl ether and 2 M buffer may be employed as the two phases. The pH of the buffer can be so adjusted that the partition ratio of propionic acid is equal to the reciprocal of the partition ratio of butyric acid, *i.e.*, $K_{pr.} = 1/K_{bu.}$. The

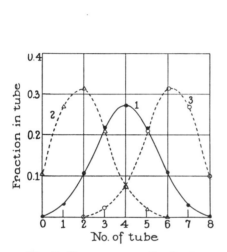

Fig. 8. Countercurrent-distribution
curves.

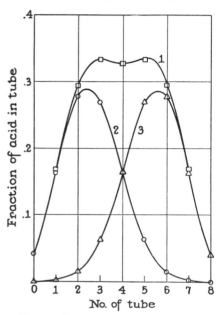

Fig. 9. Countercurrent-distribution
curves.

geometric mean of the ratios is thus equal to 1. The experimental values of $K_{pr.}$ and $K_{bu.}$ at this point have been found experimentally to be 2.06 and 0.485, respectively.

With these values an extraction of eight transfers would give, on the basis of adherence to the binomial theorem (constant partition ratios), the diagram shown in Figure 9, since each solute would migrate nearly independently of the other and at a rate governed by the partition ratio. The total solute in each tube is given by curve 1 and is the sum of curves 2 and 3, which are those of the individual acids. It is obvious that the degree of separation in each tube, as well as the percentage recovery for any given purity, can be calculated.

In the evaluation of rectification processes, it is desirable to consider the process and its efficiency in terms of the relative volatility of the two substances in the mixture. (See Rose and Rose.[29]) Thus, the ratio representing the relative volatility of the two substances under the given conditions gives a measure of the ease with which they may be separated. This ratio is called α. Equation (16) is the equilibrium equation (the Rayleigh equation) and represents for binary mixtures the quantitative relationship in percentage Y of one component in the vapor of its percentage X in the liquid phase:[30]

$$Y = \frac{X\alpha}{1 + (\alpha - 1)X} \tag{16}$$

The same equation may be applied to fractionation by liquid–liquid extraction of binary mixtures and the efficiency of the process likewise evaluated if instead of relative volatility, the separation factor, β, is taken as a measure of the ease with which the two substances can be separated. This can be stated as in equation (17):

$$\frac{Y/X}{(1 - Y)/(1 - X)} = \beta \tag{17}$$

where Y and X are the amounts in terms of weight fraction of one component in the upper and lower phases, respectively, and $(1-Y)$ and $(1-X)$ are the weight fractions of the other component in the upper and lower phases, respectively, all on a solvent-free basis. The equilibrium equation (18) can be derived algebraically from (17) or from (16) with the term β substituted for α:

$$Y = \frac{X\beta}{1 + (\beta - 1)X} \tag{18}$$

The specific problem of the fractionation of propionic and butyric acids will be convenient for illustrating the use of this equation. The experimentally derived partition ratios are 0.485 and 2.06, respectively, and therefore $\beta = 4.25$. The equilibrium curve from equation (18) for such a mixture is given in Figure 10.

The diagonal line, the XY line, is the equilibrium curve when the two partition coefficients become identical. If initially a mixture corresponding to 21.6% of butyric acid is arbitrarily chosen, this could correspond to point A on the diagram. From this point the number of perfect stages or *plates* required to reach point G, 95.5% butyric acid, can be obtained

[29] A. and E. Rose, in *Distillation*, Volume IV of *Technique of Organic Chemistry*, A. Weissberger, ed. Interscience, New York-London, 1951.
[30] K. A. Varteressian and M. R. Fenske, *Ind. Eng. Chem.*, **29**, 270 (1937).

graphically as shown. Three are required. Point G represents the maximum resolution possible in three perfect plates.

The equilibrium curve given in Figure 10 can be derived directly in the stepwise fashion using the highest term of the binomial expansion. The whole expansion forms the basis for the curves similar to those given in Figure 9. Such a derivation permits some interesting deductions. Equal

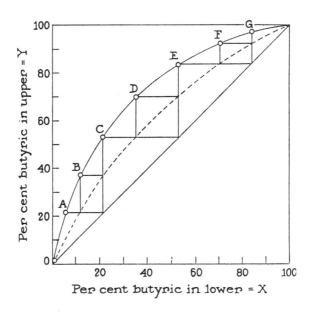

Fig. 10. An equilibrium diagram.

volumes in the two phases will be assumed. Let $K_{bu.}/(K_{bu.} + 1)$ be the fraction of butyric acid transferred for each step. Let $K_{pr.}/(K_{pr.} + 1)$ be the fraction of propionic acid transferred for each step, then $\left(\dfrac{K_{bu.}}{K_{bu.} + 1}\right)^n$ and $\left(\dfrac{K_{pr.}}{K_{pr.} + 1}\right)^n$ are the fractions of the original amount of each acid to be found in the highest term of the binomial expansion, or for n transfers, $(0.673)^n$ and $(0.327)^n$, respectively, for butyric and propionic acids. Then:

$$Y = \frac{\left(\dfrac{K_{bu.}}{K_{bu.} + 1}\right)^n}{\left(\dfrac{K_{pr.}}{K_{pr.} + 1}\right)^n + \left(\dfrac{K_{bu.}}{K_{bu.} + 1}\right)^n} = \frac{21.6\,(0.673)^n}{78.4\,(0.327)^n + 21.6\,(0.673)^n} \quad (19)$$

for the nth stage.   From the partition coefficients 2.06 and 0.485, respectively:

$$X = \frac{\dfrac{21.6\,(0.673)^n}{2.06}}{\dfrac{78.4\,(0.327)^n}{0.485} + \dfrac{21.6\,(0.673)^n}{2.06}} \tag{20}$$

for the nth stage.   Solving this equation for $n = 1, 2, 3, 4, 5$, and 6 will give the values found at points B, C, D, E, F, and G, respectively.   In Figure 10 it is apparent that six such transfers or steps are required to reach G and it would appear at first that, for the case when the partition coefficient of one of the solutes of a binary mixture is the reciprocal of the other, two perfect stepwise transfers would appear to be the equivalent of a theoretical plate in the sense that it is used in rectification.

This, however, scarcely does justice to the stepwise viewpoint since in the same operation the other component is given the same purification and has been moved the same number of steps in the opposite direction.   Calculation of the process for comparative purposes might therefore be started, with stepwise procedures, at point D.   Three steps would then give material at G and also at A.   This would have some analogy to the introduction of the mixture at the center of a perfectly operating continuous column.

The above effect could be more clearly brought out by considering the process of Figure 7 in a somewhat different manner.   If at the end of the first transfer the tubes were equilibrated and then, for the second transfer, the lower layers, instead of the upper layers, were shifted, one tube in the opposite direction, as shown in Figure 11, the band as a whole would not move but be stationary.   On the next transfer, the upper could be shifted to the right and, on the following transfer, the lower could be shifted to the left, etc.   Thus, there would be no movement of the band as a whole at steps 0, 2, 4 etc., but if the process were continued, the band would spread out like heat being introduced at the center of an iron bar.[31]   However, two transfers, one in each direction, would always be required to keep the band from being displaced.

It is further of interest to investigate the effect obtaining when β remains constant and when values of the partition ratios are changed so that one is not the reciprocal of the other.   This effect could be approached for the mixture of propionic and butyric acids by changing the pH of the buffer or perhaps the salt concentration of the solution.   For purposes of discussion, it may be assumed that the partition ratios are 6.18 and 1.455 for

[31] R. E. Cornish, R. C. Archibald, E. A. Murphy, and H. M. Evans, *Ind. Eng. Chem.*, **26**, 397 (1934).

butyric and propionic acids, respectively.   Although β still equals 4.25, the geometric mean is 3.

When these values are substituted in equations (19) and (20), it will be found that twelve transfers will be required approximately to reach point G from point A of Figure 10 instead of the six needed before.   The dotted curve between the XY line and the equilibrium curve is obtained

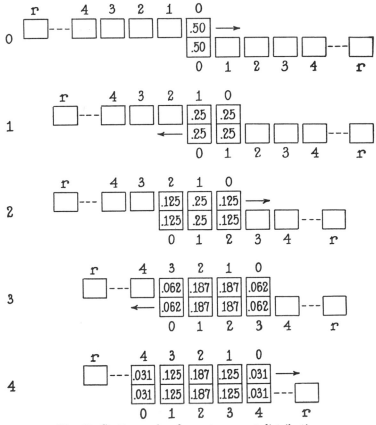

Fig. 11. Stationary-band countercurrent distribution.

by drawing through the corners of the 90° steps and may be considered the "operating" curve. Obviously when the geometric mean of the partition ratios becomes larger (or smaller for ratios both less than 1) this operating curve more nearly approaches the equilibrium curve until at infinity (or 1/infinity) it will coincide with the equilibrium curve.   Here no separation is possible and the effect is equal to that of identical partition ratios.   Obviously in the latter case, the equilibrium curve becomes identical with the XY line. It is thus apparent that, for stepwise extractions involving equal volumes of the two phases, the process is most efficient when the geometric mean of the two partition coefficients is 1. It can also be seen that the ratio of the two partition coefficients is not the sole governing factor which contributes toward the ease of fractionation.

Thus far only equal volumes of the two phases have been considered. Since, however, the percentage of the solute in a single tube which is transferred at a given step is really the controlling factor which fixes the process, substitution of the expression $Kr/(Kr + 1)$, for $K/(K + 1)$, where r is the ratio of the volumes of the two phases, gives the more general calculation of the fraction transferred. This expression may then be used in equation (19) for calculation of the number of steps required. When this is done, it is obvious that for unequal volumes the greatest efficiency is obtained in separating binary mixtures when the geometric mean of the product of the partition ratios and the ratio of the two volumes is equal to 1, as given in equation (21): [32,33]

$$\sqrt{K_{\text{bu.}} r \times K_{\text{pr.}} r} = 1 \qquad (21)$$

If the volumes of the two phases for the calculated separation above in which the partition coefficients were 6.18 and 1.455 had been adjusted so that the volumes of the lower phases were three times those of the upper, the highest efficiency would have been obtained. Adjustment of the volume in stepwise extractions can therefore be used for obtaining the best separation for a given number of transfers. Conversely selection of volumes not in conformance with equation (21) would have the same effect in shifting the operating curve of Figure 10 as improper choice of partition ratios.

The understanding of a stepwise extraction for fractionation can be obtained most satisfactorily as given for Figure 7 and the result of the process can be represented as in Figure 8. Such an operation may require experimentally as little as 2 hours for 12 stages including the estimation of the amount in each tube. It is a scheme which certainly can be recommended as a routine laboratory procedure for the examination of reaction products, crude materials, etc., although variations of the scheme[32] are just as satisfactory.

If a theoretical curve should be obtained, as in Figure 8, one may not need to go further. On the other hand, if this is not the case, the general shape of the curve will indicate whether separation is possible and will

[32] M. T. Bush, A. Goth, and H. L. Dickison, *J. Pharmacol. Exptl. Therap.*, 84, 262 (1945). M. T. Bush and P. M. Densen, *Anal. Chem.*, 20, 121 (1948).
[33] W. J. D. van Dyck and A. Schaafsma, U. S. Patent 2,245,945 (1941).

suggest the best procedure. Also the general shape will disclose approximately the degree of separation obtained. Should the curve turn out to indicate a binary mixture, as in Figure 9, separation will be easy. However, the restriction imposed by the required labor, after 14 to 16 tubes are in the series, again enters as pointed out on page 248.

Procedures. An approach alternative to the use of a special apparatus (see Sect. V) for making multiple extractions lies in the variations in systematization which may be introduced. The possibilities along this line may be classified as follows: (*A*) fundamental, (*B*) single withdrawal, (*C*) double withdrawal, (*D*) alternate withdrawal, (*E*) completion of the square, and (*F*) recycling.

Fundamental. This is the procedure which has been treated thus far in the theoretical discussion. Here nothing is withdrawn from the system until the whole operation is completed. The binomial theorem exactly

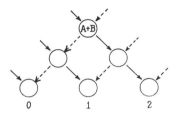

Fig. 12. Fundamental pattern.

expresses the effect. If one could actually employ very high numbers of tubes with a reasonable expenditure of time and effort, it would not be necessary to use the withdrawal modifications which follow.

One way of visualizing the process for a series of three funnels is by the scheme of Figure 12. Here each circle represents an equilibrium contact. The movement of the lighter phase is shown by the solid arrows, that of the heavy phase by the dotted arrows. The volumes of each equilibration must be the same as that for the initial equilibration.

Single Withdrawal. In this procedure only a fixed number of tubes is used. The process may be illustrated by continuing from Figure 9, a situation which has been achieved by use of the fundamental procedure. The extraction may be continued by setting aside tube 8, which contains essentially butyric acid with little propionic acid in it. Tube 8 in this case need not contain a lower phase and may be replaced in the series by an empty tube in order to go one step further. After proceeding one more step, tube 8 is again withdrawn. This process may be continued indefinitely. The withdrawn tubes are numbered consecutively and form a different series from the fundamental. The new series can be given graphically also by a curve.[34] (See page 259.) Soon, however, propionic acid would emerge in the withdrawn tubes in significant quantities. The withdrawn curve is analogous to the effluent curves obtained by chromatographic procedures.[35]

If the process is interrupted before all the solute has been withdrawn, two curves can express the results of the process. One will give the amount in each tube remaining in the system and can be calculated by the binomial expansion or equation (15). (See also pages 173 and 246.) The other will give the amount in each of the withdrawn tubes. This curve represents a Pascal distribution[34] and is not too difficult to calculate. For some purposes, single withdrawal is not as efficient as double or alternate withdrawal. Single withdrawal may be considered as shown in Figure 13.

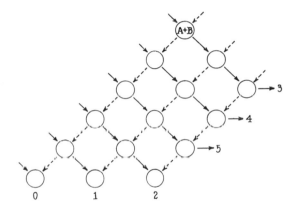

Fig. 13. Single-withdrawal pattern.

Double Withdrawal. In this again the fundamental procedure is first used and only a fixed number of tubes are employed. For example, if nine tubes are used and the state of affairs shown in Figure 9 is reached, both tubes 0 and 8 may be withdrawn and set aside. Now two further stages may be accomplished and again the two tubes on the extremities set aside, having been numbered appropriately. Two further stages give two more withdrawn tubes, etc. Three series of tubes will be obtained in this way. The ones withdrawn from the left will contain only the lower layer and will form one series. Those remaining in the system will contain both layers and will form a second series. Those withdrawn from the right will contain only the upper layer and will form a third series. The amount of substance in each of the tubes of the three series may be repre-

[34] S. Stene, *Arkiv Kemi, Mineral. Geol.*, **A18**, No. 18 (1944).
[35] S. Moore and W. H. Stein, *Ann. N. Y. Acad. Sci.*, **49**, 265 (1948).

sented graphically, but here the calculation of curves is much more complicated and a completely satisfactory method has not as yet been developed.

For purposes of visualizing the process a total of four additional transfers might be applied by the method of double withdrawal to the state of affairs given by Figure 9. This would give three tubes withdrawn from each side.

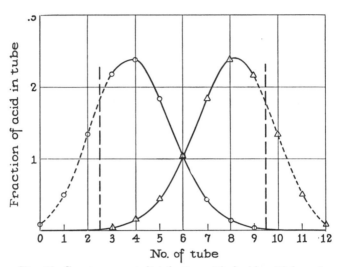

Fig. 14. Countercurrent distribution with double withdrawal.

In Figure 14 these are represented by dotted lines. The amounts shown in tubes 3 and 9 in particular are in error, being considerably less than shown since they have already been pulled out to a certain extent into the withdrawn tubes.

The procedure amounts to the scheme proposed by Jantzen,[36] given diagrammatically in Figure 15. (See page 183.)

Although Figure 14 is not entirely correct, it serves to show that propionic and butyric acids could be almost completely separated by the scheme in a high degree of purity in a short time. The fractions withdrawn at each extremity of the process have had the equivalent of four theoretical plates applied with respect to the original mixture but eight with respect to each other. (See page 177.) This has been done in about the time required to get a fractionating column set up and operating.

Alternate Withdrawal. This procedure is only a slight variation from the previous method and is particularly useful in connection with the distribu-

[36] E. Jantzen, *Das fractionierte Distillieren und das fractionierte Verteilen,* Dechema Monographie, Vol. V, No. 48. Verlag Chemie, Berlin, 1932, p. 81.

tion machine (see Sect. V).   In this method, if applied with nine tubes, the state of affairs in Figure 9 would be reached, then 0 set aside.   One stage further would be accomplished by adding a new tube at 9.   This ninth tube would be withdrawn and replaced by a new tube in the same position.   On the next transfer, tube 1 would be withdrawn and a new tube introduced at 10.   Tube 10 is set aside on the next step.   This process can be continued indefinitely and can be represented by three curves as in the double-withdrawal scheme.

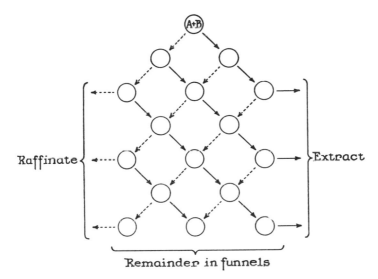

Fig. 15. Extraction pattern of Jantzen.

The method is particularly advantageous for separating substances closely related which require many transfers.   In such a case, the distribution apparatus[27] can be operated so that it takes advantage of this scheme.   Obviously with a limited number of tubes a withdrawal scheme must be used, and if the optimum range of partition coefficient is chosen (see page 179) the mixed solute will migrate from the apparatus with the single-withdrawal technique before a sufficient number of transfers has been applied to effect separation.   However, the alternate-withdrawal method permits removal of only those tubes which have essentially no solute in them or only a small amount of one solute free of the others.   Thus the mixture can be kept in the apparatus as long as possible so that more work can be done on it.   A detailed example of the process will be given on page 263.

Alternate withdrawal may be represented as in Figure 16, where a withdrawal is made from each end of the series on every other transfer. Here on one transfer the series may be considered an "enriching" section of a fractionation column with center feed but on the next transfer it becomes

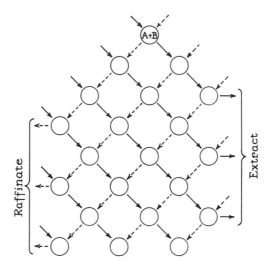

Fig. 16. Alternate-withdrawal pattern.

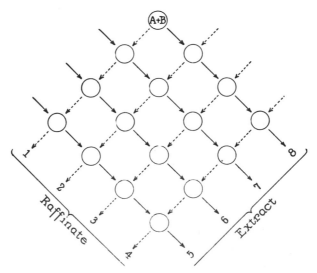

Fig. 17. "Diamond" pattern of Bush and Densen.

a "stripping" section (see Sect. IV). It is a slightly more efficient procedure than double withdrawal.

Completion of Squares. A novel and interesting extraction scheme is that of Bush and Densen,[37] shown schematically in Figure 17. Following the previous treatment the process is more or less self-explanatory. It can be carried out with individual transfers or with the distribution apparatus. Bush and Densen have also devised formulas based on the binomial theorem for calculating the fraction to be expected in each of the fractions numbered 1–8 in Figure 17 or for any size "diamond" pattern and can thus plot a distribution much as in Figure 9. In the schemes shown in Figures 15, 16 and 17 it is important to adjust either the volumes or the system or buffer so that $\sqrt{K_a r \times K_b r} = 1$, where K_a and K_b are the partition ratios of the two components, respectively, and r is the ratio of the volumes of the phases.

Recycling. When the extraction train contains a large number of cells and a single solute or mixture of solutes with similar partition ratios is being distributed the fundamental procedure can be completed and from this point the upper phases emerging can be introduced again into tube 0. This can be continued until the front of the solute band begins to overtake the trailing edge. It amounts to the double-withdrawal or alternate-withdrawal procedure for the case where no solute is taken from the apparatus. It accomplishes most of the objectives of reflux. This procedure will be treated in detail in the section dealing with automatic distribution equipment.

B. THEORY FOR LARGER NUMBERS OF TRANSFERS

As a result of the development of apparatus for making many individual extractions in a single operation and in an almost quantitative manner, the greatly increased possibilities inherent in the use of extraction and partition ratios for the separation and characterization of a wide variety of organic compounds became apparent. Larger numbers of transfers can be systematized in such a manner as to permit use of the mathematics developed for statistics to be employed in precisely interpreting the effect obtained. The apparatus and its practical application will be treated in detail in Section V.

Although the underlying theory is included in the treatment previously given for discontinuous extraction it appeared advisable to devote space to the further treatment of stepwise extraction where high numbers of transfers are concerned, before treating the theory of continuous extraction.

Theoretically there is no limit to the number of transfers which may be applied to a discontinuous extraction process. It is therefore instructive to follow the effect for a given single solute as more and more transfers are

[37] M. T. Bush and P. M. Densen, *Anal. Chem.*, **20**, 121 (1948).

applied. This is shown graphically in the distribution patterns in Figure 18 when the partition coefficient is 1 and equal volumes of the two phases are used. The progressive shift of the solute in the various tubes as the process continues is clearly shown. A, B, C, and D are the curves obtained for 24, 50, 100, and 200 transfers, respectively.

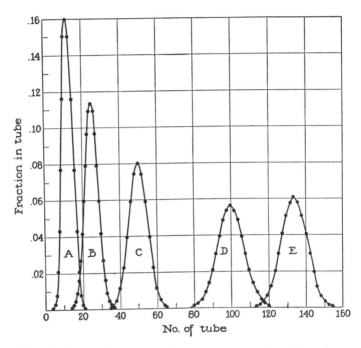

Fig. 18. Distribution patterns for increasing number of transfers.

In reality, however, these curves do not give the full picture and neglect entirely concentrations below a certain level. This is done for practical reasons. Basically, all fractionation procedures only change the relative concentrations of the different solutes present in a given mixture. They do not remove *completely* one solute from the others but in many cases may be employed in such a manner that, as far as any practical purpose is concerned, a solute may be considered removed. (See also page 172.) Thus tube 200 for the distribution of 200 transfers actually contains a fraction, $(0.5)^{200}$ or $1/(1.6 \times 10^{60})$, of the original material. This is such a small fraction that it may be neglected entirely. The level below which it is permissible to neglect the presence of a solute will naturally vary with the purpose of the fractionation and is a somewhat arbitrary figure. For practical purposes in treating the theory in this chapter, a fraction less than 0.1% of the total weight of a component will be neglected.   Thus the ordinates of Figure 18 are of such size that they do not show amounts less than 0.1% of a particular band.

Since the numbers given on the abscissa correspond to the consecutive cells of the distribution apparatus, it is apparent from Figure 18 that the process may be thought of much as a moving-boundary method in which there could be some analogy to the migration of a band in the electrophoresis apparatus or the ultracentrifuge.   The rate at which the band migrates will be proportional to the fraction of the material in each tube in the upper layer and which is moved forward with each step.   In terms of the partition ratio, this will be $Kr/(Kr + 1)$, where r is the ratio of the volumes of the upper and lower phases.   From this the position of the maximum for any given number of tubes after the band has cleared the 0 tube will be given by equation (22):

$$N = nKr/(Kr + 1) \qquad (22)$$

where n is the total numbers of transfers and N is the position of the maximum on the abscissa.

Since the process is discontinuous, formula (22) gives a real value only when N happens to be a whole number.   However, for practical purposes and for plotting a curve the position of the maximum may be located at any point intermediate between two tubes where it may chance to fall. An example of this would be the case of 200 transfers performed with equal volumes of the two phases and a solute with a partition ratio of 2 in the system.   From equation (22), N would equal 133.33.   The distribution under these conditions is shown in Figure 18 (curve E).

For the case of large numbers of transfers it becomes laborious to calculate distributions by equation (15), the binomial expansion.   However, a distribution may be calculated with sufficient accuracy for the purpose when partition ratios are in the range of 0.2 to 5 and with more than twenty transfers by assuming a continuous function in order to plot a curve.   This permits use of equation (23), which is essentially the formula used for calcuating the normal curve of error:[38]

$$y = \frac{1}{\sqrt{2\pi n \, K/(K + 1)^2}} \, e^{-x^2/[2nK/(K+1)^2]} \qquad (23)$$

In this equation y is the fraction of substance in a given tube, K is the partition ratio, n is the number of transfers, and x is the distance from the maximum of the tube in question.   The curve is thus plotted in the same

[38] H. L. Rietz, *Mathematical Statistics.*   Open Court, La Salle, Ill., 1927, p. 23–24.

way that the curve for diffusion[39] is ordinarily plotted as given in Figure 19. If a curve calculated in this way is plotted so that its 0 point or maximum coincides with the maximum of an actual distribution, the positions of the other points follow. When the maximum chances to fall at a position intermediate between two tubes, each of the calculated values will also fall at their respective intermediate positions. Upon drawing a smooth curve through the points, the real values can then be obtained from the positions where the curve crosses the tube lines. Curve E of Figure 18 was calculated and plotted in this way.

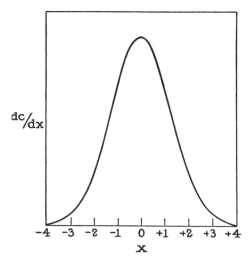

Fig. 19. Diffusion curve.

That the picture as presented is essentially the correct one for a single substance and that all the factors needed to obtain the result experimentally e.g., essential equilibrium, precision in transferring, etc., can be achieved easily have been demonstrated for a wide variety of substances.[40]

The different methods of carrying out discontinuous extraction given on page 180, including the "completion of squares,"[37] can all be accomplished in the distribution machine. The withdrawal variations permit application of higher numbers of transfers without increasing the number of tubes in actual operation. However, these variations take on a slightly different aspect when considered in terms of curves such as those given in Figure 18.

In practice, the fundamental method was restricted with the steel machine to not more than 53 transfers, since the machine with the largest number of tubes thus far constructed had only 54 tubes.   If at 53 transfers withdrawal were begun by single-withdrawal technique, at tube 53 more transfers could be applied until significant quantities of the band had begun to emerge.   For a partition ratio of 1 and equal volumes of the two phases this could be about 80 transfers.   The distribution curve could then be plotted for the tubes of the machine exactly as if no withdrawal had been made.   Of course, further transfers could be applied and the withdrawn curve calculated by the Pascal distribution.[41]

If the double- or alternate-withdrawal technique were applied at the end of the fundamental operation, material would be withdrawn at both tubes 0 and 53 and the band of interest would be carried along in the machine before significant amounts would emerge for a much longer time, as it moved on the pattern from left to right.   However, it would slowly spread out in the machine until appreciable amounts of the desired solute would be contained in every tube.   This would be somewhat analogous to the diffusion of heat from the center of an iron bar.[42]   For a partition ratio of 1 and for equal volumes of the two phases it can be calculated that material would begin to emerge in significant quantities from both extremities of the band in about 325 transfers in an apparatus with 54 tubes. This is the case for the most rapidly spreading band, i.e., that where $K = 1$.   Where K is either greater or less than 1, the band spreads less rapidly.   Up to the point of emergence, formula (23) could be used for calculating the distribution for the tubes of the machine.   The advantages of the alternate-withdrawal technique are obvious when curves D and E of Figure 18 are considered.   Although a slightly better separation could be reached for a binary mixture of substances giving D and E for the given number of transfers by adjustment of the volumes as given on page 179, more actual tubes would be required for this case in order to permit a calculated curve to be fitted.

In considering the effect of passing to higher and higher numbers of transfers a certain perspective is desirable since the solutions become progressively more dilute because the solute becomes scattered in more and more tubes as the distribution proceeds.   In Figure 18 it is seen that for 24 transfers the maximum tube contains 16.4% of the original, while in 200 transfers it contains only 5.6%.   For higher numbers of transfers it is accordingly desirable to begin with a greater amount of solute.

[39] H. B. Bull, *Physical Biochemistry*.   Wiley, New York, 1943, p. 272.

[40] L. C. Craig, C. Golumbic, H. Mighton, and E. O. Titus, *J. Biol. Chem.*, 161, 321 (1945).   Y. Sato, G. T. Barry, and L. C. Craig, *ibid.*, 170, 501 (1947).   G. T. Barry, Y. Sato, and L. C. Craig, *ibid.*, 174, 221 (1948).

[41] S. Stene, *Arkiv Kemi, Mineral. Geol.*, A18, No. 18 (1944).

[42] R. E. Cornish, R. C. Archibald, E. H. Murphy, and H. M. Evans, *Ind. Eng. Chem.*, 26, 397 (1934).

Of considerable interest in getting a useful perspective is an alternative method of plotting the result of a distribution, as is done in Figure 20 ($K = 1$; equal volumes in each phase). In this figure the ordinates are expressed in weight rather than in percentages (or a fractional part).

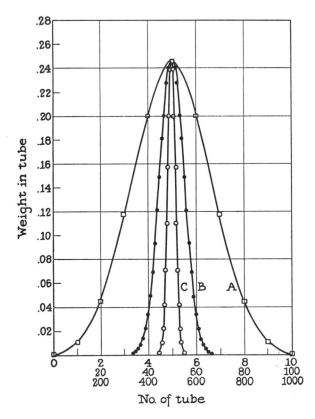

Fig. 20. Comparative distributions with increasing numbers of transfers.

When a comparison of two distributions is made, such as one of 10 transfers with one of 100 transfers, 3.08 times as much solute should be used for the latter. This then gives a maximum tube, at the completion of the distribution, which contains the same total solute for both cases. For 1000 transfers 9.78 times the solute should be used. Thus the arbitrary level at which solute is neglected is comparable in each case. This level usually represents also the limit of error in determining the amount of solute in a given tube. The comparative amounts which should be used for beginning the distribution can be calculated from the y_0 values of equation (23), *i.e.*, 0.246, 0.0796, and 0.0239, respectively, for 10, 100, and 1000 transfers.

The units used for the abscissa of Figure 20 also require explanation. Since the binomial theorem expresses the process of dividing and sub-dividing unit quantity of material and when applied to extraction is independent of the particular volume of solvent chosen, the solvent from a theoretical standpoint may be regarded as indefinitely expandable or contractable. A 10-, 100-, or 1000-transfer distribution may be run with the same total amount of solvent. Such a viewpoint could properly be expressed by plotting comparative distributions on an abscissa of fixed length. This is done in Figure 20 by using 10, 100, and 1000 subdivisions, respectively, on the abscissa.

It can be seen from curve A that insufficient space is present for the clear resolution of any other band even though it might have a partition ratio considerably different from 1. However, space could be provided for one other band by selecting an effective partition ratio greater or less than 1 for the main substance, *e.g.*, 3 or ⅓. Curve B, 100 transfers, provides considerable space for the resolution of other components, at least two on each side, if they should possess the proper partition ratio. Curve C, 1000 transfers, would permit at least four other components on either side and still allow excellent resolution. Thus it can be calculated by equation (22) that the maximum for a solute of partition ratio 1.5 would occur at tube 600 and separation from curve C would be of the order of 99% complete.

In the resolution of two or more substances by a countercurrent distribution, it may be considered that the separation depends upon the relative rate of migration of the independently migrating band of the one substance as compared to that of the other. The rates are governed by equation (22). However, the progressive broadening and lowering of the band as it migrates operate in such a manner that the effect of the different rates of migration is in part defeated. Table III shows the broadening of the band with increasing numbers of transfers for $K = 1$.

As far as the separation of two components is concerned, the most favorable balance of these two effects theoretically possible is obtained when equation (24) is met:

$$\sqrt{K_a r + K_b r} = 1 \tag{24}$$

In fractionation by stepwise extraction, progressive dilution cannot be escaped. That is to say, the spreading of the band cannot be avoided since it is fundamentally part of the process. This subject will be treated further in the section on continuous extraction. The reflux principle also is interesting in this connection. (See page 208.) Figure 20 gives a ready

TABLE III

BAND SPREAD

No. of transfers	Curve spread	Total tubes occupied by band, %
25	15	60
50	21	42
100	30	30
200	42	21
400	60	15
1000	95	9.5

picture of the spreading of the band relative to the total transfers used. Recovery of solute from a very dilute solution is not usually troublesome as a laboratory procedure.

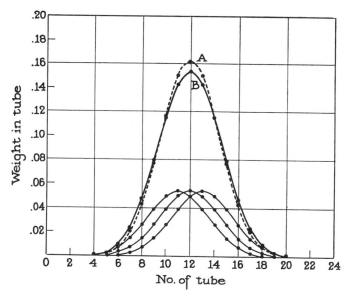

Fig. 21. Distribution begun in three tubes.

From the practical standpoint with higher numbers of transfers, if the amount of solute at the beginning is increased, difficulty is encountered, since, in general, partition ratios do not remain sufficiently constant to permit use of the higher concentrations. A possible way of avoiding higher concentrations lies in the scattering of the solute equally among several tubes at the start of the process. The effect would then be to achieve a distribution which is the sum of as many overlapping separate distributions as the number of tubes in which the solute was placed at the start.   This can be visualized better perhaps by an actual example, *e.g.*, the case of unit quantity of material, with a partition ratio of 1, equal volumes of the two phases, and 24 transfers.   Let one-third be placed in the 0 tube, one-third in the tube numbered 1, and one-third in an extra tube which is adjacent to the 0 tube on the other side.   At the end of the distribution, three overlapping curves will be obtained as shown in Figure 21.   The sum of these three curves will be the distribution actually

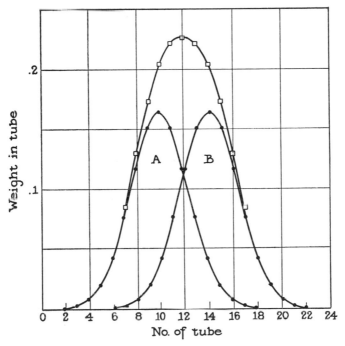

Fig. 22. 24-transfer distribution of a binary mixture. K_A 0.707; K_B 1.414.

obtained and will equal curve B.   Had all of the solute been placed in the 0 tube at the start, the distribution shown by A would have been obtained. For practical purposes A is not significantly different from B, yet it permits the distribution to be made with one-third the initial concentration of solute

The same reasoning can be extended to higher numbers of transfers. Here a slightly greater deviation is obtained for the same percentage of tubes containing solute at the start, but, if solute is placed in not more than 5% of the total tubes used, the effect is small.   Thus for 100 transfers, the solute could be placed in five adjoining tubes.   For 1000 transfers, it could be placed in up to a total of 50 tubes.

The theory involved in the separation of a binary mixture can be visualized best in terms of a specific problem. For this purpose the separation of a mixture of equal parts of two substances whose partition ratios are 0.707 and 1.414 is suitable. Equal volumes of the two phases may be chosen so that the relationship of equation (24) will hold. The separation expected from 24 transfers is shown in Figure 22. The upper curve is the sum of the two individual curves and it is a simple matter to calculate the degree of separation obtained. Just as has been the custom in the evaluation of fractional-distillation columns, it is advantageous here also to specify

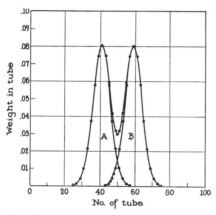

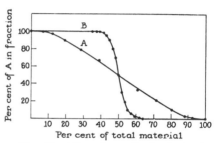

Fig. 23. 100-transfer distribution of a binary mixture. K_A 0.707; K_B 1.414.

Fig. 24. Alternate method of plotting countercurrent-distribution data. Per cent purity vs. per cent in tube.

a standard separation. Rose and Rose[43] have given as a standard separation a recovery of 80% of each component at a purity of 95% or better. The separation given in Figure 22 would not permit this, but a distribution involving 50–55 such transfers would be sufficient.

If 100 transfers were applied to the above problem, the separation given in Figure 23 would be obtained. Here some 96% of each component could be recovered at a purity of better than the prescribed 95%. If higher purity is desired, more transfers are required. In Figure 22 only 15.5% of each component could be recovered for a purity of 98% as contrasted to 93% recovery in Figure 23.

In fractional distillation work it is customary to express the effect in a curve plotting fraction distilled versus temperature. Multiple-extraction results can be treated in an analogous way. Here, instead of overhead temperature, the ordinate might be per cent composition of the fraction.

[43] A. and E. Rose, in *Distillation*, Volume IV of *Technique of Organic Chemistry*, A. Weissberger, ed. Interscience, New York-London, 1951.

The results of Figures 22 and 23 expressed in this way might be arranged to give curves A and B, respectively, of Figure 24. The ordinate could be the resulting partition ratio just as well but in this case, in order to keep the pattern symmetrical, the reciprocal of the ratio for values less than 1 could be used. The abscissa represents the progressive fractions of the pattern of Figures 22 and 23 from left to right. These fractions, however, have been weighted on the scale of Figure 24 according to the per cent of the total they represent. Such a diagram in no way minimizes the difference between this type of process and that with a distillation column, in which there is actual reflux.

In the case of a fractionation column, one cannot reach beyond a certain efficiency, that is, number of theoretical plates. That limit is the case of total reflux under control conditions optimum in other respects, such as vapor velocity, etc. In the case of countercurrent distribution, the limiting factor is the number of tubes in the system. Thus the problem set forth in Figure 22, at 24 transfers it can be considered that mixed solute not sufficiently fractionated for the required 98% purity of either component occurs in tubes 6 to 18 inclusive or in twelve tubes. Tube 6 contains 98.5% A, and tube 18 contains 98.5% B. By the time 100 transfers have been applied, as in Figure 23, insufficiently fractionated solute occurs in tubes 44 to 56 inclusive or still in only 12 tubes. It is thus apparent that a distribution machine with 13 tubes would permit separation of the mixture by the method of alternate withdrawal (or double withdrawal) where only A at a purity of 98% is withdrawn from the left and B with a similar purity is withdrawn from the right. One side may be considered the extract and the other the raffinate.

With 11 tubes, only A containing about 3% of B could be withdrawn from the left and the inverse of this from the right. A certain minimum of tubes is thus required for any given separation if it is to be made in a single run by the scheme given.

Although a higher separating power in terms of purity and yield can be reached for a binary mixture by the procedure of alternate withdrawal just outlined, the result cannot always be interpreted conveniently by a calculated countercurrent-distribution pattern. The mathematics have been worked out for restricted cases,[44,44a] but have proved too involved for others. However, a distribution pattern of weight versus fraction number can be plotted from experimental data for both the extract and raffinate withdrawals.

The distribution apparatus operated as given above is analogous to a continuous fractional-distillation column when the feed is inserted at the

[44] P. Karlson and E. Hecker, *Z. Naturforsch.*, **5b**, 237 (1950).
[44a] E. L. Compere and A. L. Ryland, *Ind. Eng. Chem.*, **46**, 24 (1954).

central part of the column so that the enriching section contains the same number of theoretical plates as the exhausting section.   This will be more apparent in the light of the discussion of page 176.   In fact the distribution apparatus can be operated semicontinuously rather than batchwise (though still by discrete steps) by injecting a standard portion of the mixed solute on each transfer at a tube midway from the extremities of the two bands.

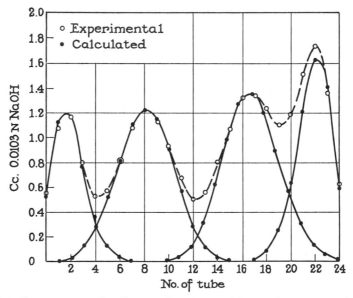

Fig. 25. Countercurrent distribution of a mixture of four acids.   Maxima, left to right, are acetic, propionic, butyric, and valeric acids, respectively.

After beginning the withdrawal (see page 263) this would be at tube halfway round the circle from the tube of withdrawal.   When operated in this manner a 13-tube apparatus would offer twelve theoretical plates in the exhausting section and 12 in the enriching section.   This is true by virtue of the fact that essential equilibrium is reached at each stage and the mechanical aspect of the transfer can be 99% perfect.

For analytical work, it is better to have many times the minimal number of tubes required for a separation since usually the mixtures fractionated have more than two components, and it is desirable to have a sufficient number of tubes so that the several bands will show up plainly.   An example of this is an actual distribution made with an artificial mixture of acetic, propionic, butyric, and valeric acids, shown in Figure 25.   An apparatus with 25 tubes in it was used for the separation.[45]   If only half the number

[45] Y. Sato, G. T. Barry, and L. C. Craig, *J. Biol. Chem.*, **170**, 501 (1947).

of tubes had been available and the partition ratios known, it would have been necessary to first separate the two right-hand bands, valeric and butyric acids, in one fraction while the two left-hand bands, acetic and propionic acids, would be in the other. Each of these fractions would then be subjected to further fractionation. The sum total of this work would be several times that needed for Figure 25, which at once gives an excellent perspective both qualitative and quantitative in nature.

C. THEORY OF FRACTIONATION BY CONTINUOUS EXTRACTION

When restricted to ideal conditions the theory of extraction for continuous processes should bear the same relationship to discontinuous extraction which the mathematics of calculus bears to the mathematics of algebra. For this reason discontinuous processes have been treated at length before attempting to treat the continuous theory. In the discontinuous case, each assumption which contributes to ideality can be studied separately and proved to hold experimentally or, if not, the conditions can be modified frequently so that the assumption does hold. Unfortunately, this state of affairs is never possible in the continuous case and consequently the theory is on a much less certain basis. In fact, one of the basic assumptions, namely, that the partition ratio is instantaneously satisfied, has never been realized for any continuous process as far as the authors are aware. Nevertheless, development of the theory on such a hypothetical basis may be helpful in understanding certain of the principles.

Most fractionations by continuous extractions are of necessity true countercurrent processes. The simplest type may be set up so that in a contacting apparatus of some sort, called the *column*, a continuous stream of one phase, arbitrarily called the *extract* phase, comes into intimate contact with a continuous stream of the other phase, the *raffinate* phase. The second phase usually flows in the opposite direction to the first.

Solute Introduced in One Portion. In the simplest case to be treated, the solute to be fractionated is introduced near the middle of the column all in one portion. The stage is thus set for a process exactly analogous to that of "double" or "alternate" withdrawal described previously in the discontinuous treatment, except that a continuous flow replaces the movement of the phases by discrete steps. Under these conditions a single solute operating perfectly should form a migrating *band* just as in countercurrent distribution. The band should move toward either end of the column or not move at all, depending on the partition ratio, the relative rates of flow of the two phases and their volumes, the rate of interchange of the solute and other factors perhaps many of them as yet unknown. In the case in which the band does not move, it will steadily spread until it covers the whole column and finally will emerge partly at each end.

The rates of flow chosen for each phase may be entirely arbitrary. In fact, the rate of flow for one of the phases could be zero with respect to the stationary apparatus or theoretically could even be a negative quantity and thus move in the same direction as the other phase. In the latter case, the second phase must move at a slower rate than the first. Thus in the broader sense, all that is required to satisfy the conditions is a rate of flow of the two phases sufficiently different so that a band will be formed. The perspective of this reasoning is obtained perhaps better when a column of infinite length (or better still, of 100% efficiency) is visualized. The stationary structure of the column could then be dropped entirely from consideration. In such a case, the point of reference for calculating rates could arbitrarily be that of the average position of any migrating band. However, it is easier to develop formulas on the basis of a rate relative to the fixed position of the column, as is given in the following treatment.

In the section on countercurrent distribution equation (22) was developed for the discontinuous process in order to express the movement of a band in terms of the number of steps, the relative volumes of the two phases, and the partition ratio. One of the phases was arbitrarily held stationary so that the movement of the other phase was the only movement consideration necessary. Accordingly, the movement of the mobile phase was expressed by the total number of steps, n. Similarly for the continuous case, one of the phases could be held stationary. Substitution of tR_1 for n of equation (22) then gives equation (25), where t represents a unit of time and R_1 the rate of flow of the mobile phase. N_c represents the position of the band at a given time and, again, r represents the relative volumes of the two phases.

$$N_c = tR_1Kr/(Kr + 1) \qquad (25)$$

It is assumed that the relative volumes of the phases are constant throughout the column in any given section. It is further assumed that the rates of flow are uniform and that the partition ratios are reached at every point.

For the case in which the second phase also moves, equation (25) can be modified to take this into account. Let R_2 be the rate of flow of the second phase. If $R_1 + R_2$ is substituted for R_1 in equation (25), the equation expresses the rate of movement of the band with respect to the phase which was previously held constant and thus was the same reference point in that case as the stationary column. Subtraction of the quantity tR_2 then refers the rate of movement back to the stationary column and equation (26) thus gives the more general expression for relating the various factors to the rate of migration of the band. N becomes a negative value when R_2 is greater than R_1:

$$N = [t(R_1 + R_2) Kr/(Kr + 1)] - tR_2 \qquad (26)$$

From equation (26) it can be derived that for the case of a partition coefficient of 1, for equal but opposite rates of flow of the two phases and for equal volumes of the two phases, N becomes zero and the band will not move but becomes stationary as has been stated on more than one occasion.[46] Likewise a partition ratio other than 1, such as 2, can be compensated for by either increasing the rate of flow of one of the phases or by doubling the volume of one of the phases so that the band remains stationary.

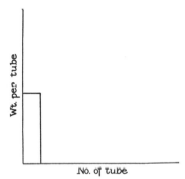

Fig. 26. Pattern for beginning of a perfect distribution in a continuous column.

The picture presented thus far is an attempt to carry over the reasoning of the discontinuous process to that of the continuous simply by infinitely multiplying the number of discontinuous steps. Although this can be done on the basis of the simplifying assumptions given above, closer inquiry into the assumptions reveals serious shortcomings—in particular, the assumption that the partition ratio is met at every point.

It would appear[47] from the results of chromatography that, for the ideal case, a continuous column, even a short one, would have nearly an infinite number of theoretical stages. This follows from the reasoning of calculus. Chromatography from a theoretical standpoint may be considered extraction in which one of the phases concerned is a solid and it may be treated also on a discontinuous basis.[48] The implication of nearly an infinite number of theoretical stages is clarified by the reasoning presented in Figure 26 and on page 189. Here it can be seen that, as the

[46] R. E. Cornish, R. C. Archibald, E. A. Murphy, and H. M. Evans, *Ind. Eng. Chem.*, 26, 397 (1934).

[47] S. Stene, *Arkiv Kemi, Mineral. Geol.*, **A18**, No. 18 (1944).

[48] L. C. Craig, C. Golumbic, H. Mighton, and E. O. Titus, *Science*, **103**, 587 (1946).

number of discrete stages is increased, the relative percentage of the volume occupied by the band in the apparatus becomes progressively less. At an infinite number of stages, further plotting of the results as in Figure 20 would give essentially a line with each tube having vanishingly small capacity. It would therefore be necessary to begin the process by placing the sample (a pure substance) in a series of tubes to form a band. The band would have essentially the shape given in Figure 26 and upon migrating would appear to hold its shape. Any changes in shape of the front or rear of the band for a linear partition isotherm would be of such a small order that they could not be shown on the graph. Since bands with both such sharp front and rear edges have never been observed experimentally, either in liquid–liquid extraction or in liquid–solid extraction including chromatography, the conclusion is logical that true equilibrium is actually never reached at any point in a continuous column.

This is certainly the most likely conclusion as far as liquid–liquid extraction is concerned, particularly when studies of the rate of transfer of a solute across a liquid–liquid interface are considered. The subject has been considered in detail in Section 2. In many cases equilibrium will be established with equal speed for a given predominance of solute in either phase, and, for these cases, the effect of the disequilibrium will be to produce a symmetrical curve approximating the shape of some particular curve of error. On the other hand, in many cases equilibrium will not be established at the same speed with a given predominance of solute in either phase and here the band will be a skewed curve with one edge more trailing than the other.[49] In such a case, the skewed curve is not the result of deviation from a linear partition isotherm. Equation (26) will still hold for the former case but will be in error for the latter.

On the basis of such reasoning it might be possible theoretically to resolve partially a binary mixture of solutes with identical partition ratios provided the rate of approach to equilibrium was not the same from either phase and at the same time relatively different for the two solutes. This interesting possibility inherent in operating at disequilibrium can be revealed by a hypothetical case of the discontinuous process given in Figure 27. When operated at complete equilibrium two individual substances of identical partition ratios would give curves which would be superimposable, for example, curve 1. However, when operated at a critical stage of disequilibrium, curves 2 and 3 could theoretically be obtained for the respective solutes. The degree of resolution is apparent from the curves. Thus the actual effect disequilibrium might have on a separation by continuous extraction is not entirely certain, though in most cases it

[49] G. T. Barry, Y. Sato, and L. C. Craig, *J. Biol. Chem.*, **174**, 209 (1948).

probably is not favorable.   However, this hypothetical example is sufficient
to show one uncertainty in the use of individually determined partition
ratios in the evaluation of the efficiency of a continuous column.

An interesting experimental finding supports this viewpoint.   With
certain substances of relatively high molecular weight experimental curves
definitely more narrow than the calculated band such as curve 4 in Figure
27 have been obtained.   This is unquestionably caused by some type of
departure from ideality, either disequilibrium or a combination of disequilibrium with a certain type of partition isotherm.

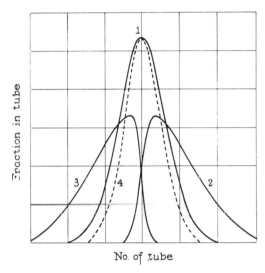

Fig. 27.   Hypothetical countercurrent-distribution
patterns caused by disequilibrium.

Actually the ideal process described in the first part of this section and
to which equation (26) could be applied has not even remotely been
approached for two streams of immiscible liquid phases flowing past each
other in the most simple way.   Interchange of solute is apparently not
rapid enough even when one of the phases is dispersed in tiny droplets
moving countercurrent to the phase in which it is suspended.

The patented extractor of Podbielniak[50] is an attempt to approach the
ideal continuous process.   This apparatus is of such size as to be outside
the scope of this section and is of more interest to the chemical engineer.
The smallest Podbielniak extractor is the Pup model.   A good description
of its characteristics is given by Barson and Beyer.[50]   Although the larger

[50] N. Barson and G. H. Beyer, *Chem. Eng. Progress*, **49**, 244 (1953).

commercial models are constructed somewhat differently the principle on which they operate is the same as for the Pup.

In these extractors contacting of the two phases takes place in the centrifugal field of a rotor in order to promote rapid separation of the phases.   Inside the rotor are eighteen concentric annuli machined out of the two mating discs forming the rotor.   The annuli are connected at 180° intervals by slots approximately 0.040 in. x 0.120 in. in size.   The slots in adjacent rings are rotated 90°.   The perforations make up only about 2% of the cylindrical area and permit two-way flow of liquid.

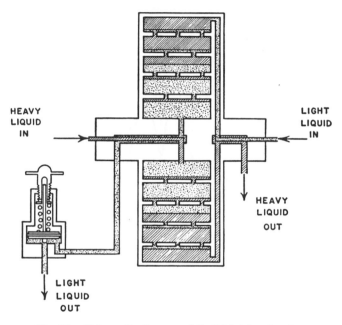

Fig. 28.   Schematic diagram of Podbielniak extractor.

The heavier phase is introduced at the central annular ring and leaves through the outer as shown in the schematic drawing of Figure 28.   The lighter phase is introduced at the outer concentric space and leaves through the central one.   The flow of the two phases is separately controlled by valves and pressure equipment.   New interfac es are constantly formed by the passage of the liquids through the slots.

The extractor operates under a rotational speed of 2000 to 5000 r.p.m. It has a holdup volume of about 600 cc. of which only 65 cc. is in the contacting elements.   The combined flow rate of both liquids through the extractor can be as high as 7 gal./hr.

The number of theoretical stages obtainable varies greatly with the system, the solute, rates of flow, centrifugal speed, etc.   Its greatest advantage is in the high capacity and very short time of contact.   This latter advantage is extremely important for manipulation of sensitive natural products.   Extraction with reflux or with center feed is not possible.   These extractors can be used for extraction from crude mixtures which still contain fine solids dispersed and which easily form emulsions.

The spray columns [51] and spinner columns [52] are also attempts to improve interchange.   Here the possible momentary movement of a portion of a phase in the wrong direction must enter.   Packed columns represent an attempt to overcome this latter possibility as well as to improve contact. However, continuous, fractional, solid–liquid extraction or chromatography does more nearly approach[53] the ideal process in certain cases [54] and will therefore be treated later in a special section in connection with partition chromatography (see also page 237).

Here the tendency to use extraction apparatus more complicated than necessary may be mentioned.   Thus Short[55] described a small rotating pole column for continuous liquid–liquid extraction for removal purposes. The column had novel features, including a liquid spiraling effect, and considerable data were presented to disclose its operability.   Thus the column could remove 87% of the acetic acid from 90 ml. per hour of a dilute aqueous solution in a single extraction with methyl isobutyl ketone.   The solvent-extrahend volume ratio was chosen so that $K = 0.5$ (approximately).   The throughput amounted to 90 ml. per hour.   Four separatory funnel extractions requiring about thirty minutes with the same phase ratio would result in the removal of all but $(0.5)^4$ or 93% of the solute.   There would appear to be no trouble in extracting ten l. per hour equal to a rate 100 times that of the continuous extractor.   Since for most laboratory quantities and conditions such as this a separatory funnel extraction is rapid and simple, the use of the more complicated continuous apparatus would not be warranted unless some special factor were involved.   We shall see later that the discrete stage extractions even for fractionation purposes may have advantages in many cases over the continuous methods. This is due in part to difficulty in the attainment of equilibrium but also depends on deviations from ideality, mechanical difficulties, etc.

Continuous Stage.   Several attempts to modify a liquid–liquid con-

[51] T. K. Sherwood, J. E. Evans, and J. V. A. Longcor, *Ind. Eng. Chem.*, **31**, 1144 (1939).

[52] W. O. Ney, Jr., and H. L. Lochte, *Ind. Eng. Chem.*, **33**, 825 (1941).

[53] A. J. P. Martin and R. L. M. Synge, *Biochem. J.*, **35**, 1358 (1941).

[54] S. Moore and W. H. Stein, *Ann. N. Y. Acad. Sci.*, **49**, 665 (1948)

[55] J. F Short *J Chem. Soc.*, **1953**, 1278.

tinuous-extraction process experimentally so as to ensure equilibrium and thus approach the ideal process mentioned above are well worth attention.   These are the extractors of Cornish, Archibald, Murphy, and Evans,[56] who attempted the separation of vitamins by the procedure, the extractor of van Dyck and Ruys,[57] and the extractor of Martin and Synge,[58]

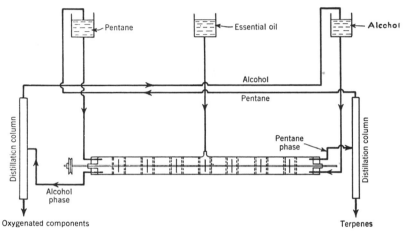

Fig. 28a. Continuous countercurrent stage extractor.

who applied their apparatus to the fractionation of amino acids.   An extractor of this type on a somewhat larger scale has been studied by Knox, Weeks, Hibshman, and McAteer[59] and by Scheibel[60] (see Section IX).   The Scheibel column has had extensive testing and is available commercially. The various workers in this field have developed their theory along similar lines.   Figure 28a is a schematic diagram of the van Dyck and Ruys extractor.   In the extractors mentioned the column itself is not continuous but is divided into compartments with alternate stirring and settling chambers. The process thus might be called "countercurrent stage extraction."   The two phases pass from compartment to compartment in opposite directions in a continuous stream but a large portion of each phase is not in steady flow.   According to the binomial theorem, the columns therefore are based on a fundamentally different process from the continuous theoretical

[56] R. E. Cornish, R. C. Archibald, E. A. Murphy, and H. M. Evans, *Ind. Eng. Chem.*, **26**, 397 (1934).

[57] W. J. D. van Dyck and J. D. Ruys, *Perfumery Essent. Oil Record*, **28**, 91 (1937).

[58] A. J. P. Martin and R. L. M. Synge, *Biochem. J.*, **35**, 91 (1941).

[59] W. T. Knox, Jr., R. L. Weeks, H. J. Hibshman, and J. H. McAteer, *Ind. Eng. Chem.*, **39**, 1573 (1947).

[60] E. G. Scheibel, *Chem. Eng. Progress*, **44**, 681 (1948).

columns treated above but appear to possess certain characteristics of a modified countercurrent-distribution series.

The distribution apparatus could be modified so that it would give a result which would be analogous to this series by using two sliding sections as shown in Figure 29 instead of the original one of Figure 7.   In this scheme each cell has three sections A, B, and C.   The meniscus between the two phases occurs near the center of B.   A single solute introduced at 0 and equilibrated will give stage 0.   Then the A sections are moved one step to the left while the C sections are moved one step to the right.   Section B remains stationary.   The shaded areas represent a phase which contains solute, while the clear areas represent only pure phase.   After equilibration the A sections are again moved one step to the left while the

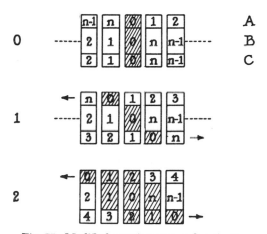

Fig. 29. Modified countercurrent distribution.

C sections are moved one step to the right.   This gives stage 2.   Upon continuing the process further, a bell-shaped band will be formed but the rate of migration and the rate of spreading of the band in terms of the partition ratio and the number of stages will be quite different from that given by equation (23) which is the result of the direct binomial expansion.

Further treatment of the theory of this process will not be given here. However, it would appear to be a less efficient process in terms of labor for separating two substances than countercurrent distribution as shown in Figure 7.

The extractor of Cornish et al.[56] contained 210 mixing and settling chambers while the Martin and Synge extractor contained 40.   The former workers calculated their plate efficiency on the basis of the spreading of the band with a single solute and came to the conclusion that they were achieving about the equivalent of 115 theoretical plates. The basis for the calculation, however, is open to some doubt. Martin and Synge gave data for the separation of a two-component system, acetylleucine and acetylproline ($\beta = 1.9$), from which the efficiency of their column can be derived. Calculations based on the alternate-withdrawal countercurrent-distribution method (page 195) would indicate that about 13 tubes by the discontinuous method should give a separation of the same order. Since it is probable that equilibrium was nearly established in the mixing compartment, it follows that other factors including the basic nature of the process were the limiting factors. Entrainment probably played a certain role. In any case further work with either extractor was not reported. The mechanical difficulties in either design were large and the process was obviously not a very flexible one. Industrial extraction processes operating on the principle are not uncommon but usually involve only a small number of alternate stirring and settling chambers.

The difference between stage processes in which the phases pass continuously through discrete contacting units and the completely discontinuous type in which at the completion of equilibration an entire phase is transferred to the next unit in the series has been well recognized. More than twenty years ago Ravenscroft[61] came to the conclusion that in order to produce comparable separations by the two methods it was necessary to have more units for the former process. He derived the relationship given by formula (27) for the two processes:

$$N_d = (N_c + 1)/2 \qquad (27)$$

where N_d is the number of discontinuous units (batch process) and N the number of contacting units for the phases flowing continuously through from one cell to the next. The reason for this can be derived from Scheibel's[62] excellent treatment of the relationship between the discontinuous and continuous processes. In the alternate-withdrawal scheme the series of contacting cells can be considered to form first an enriching section but on the next step to form an exhausting section.

Solute Introduced Continuously in Middle of Column. The principle involved in this case is identical with that described in the previous section except that there is no single migrating band. The single band is replaced by an infinite series of migrating bands each behaving as if it were introduced independently. For the case of two solutes, flow rates and relative volumes or systems can be chosen so that essentially only one solute can emerge at one end of the column while the other can emerge

[61] E. A. Ravenscroft, *Ind. Eng. Chem.*, **28**, 851 (1936).
[62] E. G. Scheibel, *Ind. Eng. Chem.*, **43**, 242 (1951).

only at the opposite end. For the best separation when the solutes are introduced near the middle of the column conditions should be chosen so that N (equation 26) for each solute for a given time will be equal but of opposite sign. However, since the partition ratio is actually not satisfied it is necessary to find experimental conditions for inducing the solutes to flow in opposite directions. Mixtures more complicated than binary mixtures may be progressively separated into groups by dividing into two and subdividing until the single members are obtained.

Solute Introduced at One End of Column. An alternative method of operating the column is that of introducing the solute at one end rather than in the middle. This is an obvious modification of the above and will often lead more quickly to a single pure substance. In a binary mixture, however, this is usually done at the expense of the purity of the other component.

This latter method of operating the column is more analogous to the laboratory fractional-distillation column and is made more so as well as more efficient by continuously returning to the system a portion of the desired solute emerging at one end. This is done by placing solute, at the end from which it has just emerged in the solvent phase entering the column. Some procedure such as evaporation or extraction must be employed for removing the solute from the emerging phase so that it may be transferred to the pure entering phase. Returning the extract to the system in the manner described constitutes *reflux* and permits the entire process to be considered on nearly the identical basis[63] with that in fractional distillation. Since the theory of such a process has been well treated in another book of this series by Rose and Rose[64] it would appear unnecessary to treat it again here.

Fractionation by Continuous Extraction with One Solvent Only. When operating in a manner so that reflux is employed, it may not be necessary to use two immiscible solvents for the case when the solutes are liquids themselves. A single solvent may be chosen in which the solute is only partially miscible. This will then furnish two phases which may be treated experimentally as given above so that the necessary concentration gradients are set up and thereby separations achieved. For such cases it is difficult to know or to visualize all the factors involved in the separation. Partition ratios are progressively changing even if they should happen to be largely responsible for the process.

Much insight into the process can be derived from the case in which only a binary mixture is being fractionated, through the use of triangular

[63] R. N. J. Saal and W. J. D. van Dyck, *Proc. World Petroleum Congr.*, 2, 352 (1933).

[64] A. and E. Rose, in *Distillation*, Volume IV of *Technique of Organic Chemistry*, A. Weissberger, ed. Interscience, New York-London, 1951.

co-ordinates,[65] which show the composition of the two phases for each theoretical step. In this the solvent is the third component. (See Sect. 3.) Obviously a considerable amount of information must be obtained before full advantage can be taken of such an extraction process. Because of this and because its theoretical treatment is restricted mainly to binary mixtures, the theory of this type of extraction is of less interest in laboratory extraction but is of great interest from the industrial standpoint. For this reason its theoretical treatment will be left to the more technical treatises on industrial extraction. Lack of understanding of the events occurring during the process, however, should not discourage the empirical use of a laboratory column designed to operate in such a manner.

Principle of Reflux. In a fractional distillation, part of the ascending vapors are constantly condensing and the condensate is steadily flowing back to the lower sections. It was found many years ago that this contributed to the efficiency of the separation and that still greater improvement could be obtained by a steady return of the greater proportion of the distillate reaching the column head when the column itself was more or less thermally isolated. Reflux may thus be defined very simply as far as rectification is concerned. However, an explanation of the cause of the greatly improved separation is much less simple.[64] Many factors are involved. Since stepwise extraction often lends itself to an easy analysis of the factors involved in separation processes, manipulation of a stepwise extraction system so that some of the effects of reflux are achieved could prove of interest.

For rectification under total reflux the distillate which would emerge at one end of the column is all being returned. This might correspond in part to the return of the solute at each withdrawal step, during a counter-current-distribution, single-withdrawal procedure, to the previous tube in the series. This would, however, simulate only part of the effect of reflux as achieved in rectification. In a rectifying column, as more of the liquid builds up at the top of the column its rate of flow back down the column becomes greater. The state of affairs becomes something like a treadmill whose rate is automatically adjusted and at total reflux the downward rate of flow of the liquid becomes exactly equal to the over-all supply from the rising vapors. The whole system is then in equilibrium. Interchange between the vapor and the liquid takes place at the surface only. Therefore as the rate of flow increases the effect is similar to that of providing much more surface for interchange. If interchange were instantaneous the separation would be improved accordingly.

An analogous state of affairs can be produced by the countercurrent-

[65] T. G. Hunter and A. W. Nash, *J. Soc. Chem. Ind. London*, **53**, 95 (1934). K. A. Varteressian and M. R. Fenske, *Ind. Eng. Chem.*, **28**, 928, 1353 (1936).

distribution process. For discussion of this point the scheme given in Figure 11 will be helpful.   Here a partition ratio of 1 and equal volumes of the two phases were assumed.   After the required number of transfers, solute will begin to emerge on the right-hand side of the diagram if no more tubes in the series are provided at that point.   If at this time, however, the rate of movement of the lower phases in the direction of the left hand is increased with respect to the rate of movement of the upper

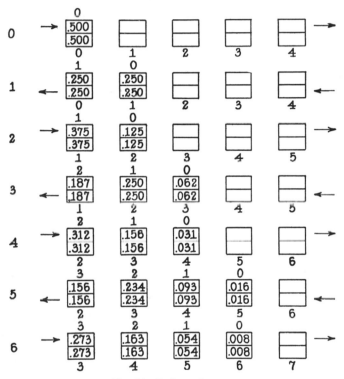

Fig. 30. Reflux scheme.

phases in the opposite direction, a rate can be found which will just prevent the emergence of solute on the right.   Or if the solute were permitted to emerge slowly many more transfers would have been applied before it could emerge and thus a greatly improved separation would be achieved. This, however, has not taken into account the events occurring at the left-hand side of the scheme.   Obviously the solute would be migrating at the same time more rapidly toward the left, if the number of tubes available for it were not restricted in some manner.   A very dilute solution would be reaching the right-hand side.

The latter difficulty can be overcome by preventing the movement of solute toward the left as given in the scheme of Figure 30. Thus at stage 2 the solute of the withdrawn tube 2/0 could be transferred back to tube 1/1 (by evaporation to dryness or by extraction). At stage 4 the solute of the withdrawn tube 3/1 could be returned to tube 2/2, at stage 6 the solute of the withdrawn tube 4/2 could be returned to 3/3, etc. Thus no solute could escape toward the left. The reflux principle in this scheme could also be visualized as something operating like a treadmill and which would permit a greater number of transfers to be applied with a fixed number of contacting cells. It could require the recovery of solute at every other stage, perhaps at every third stage or perhaps at two consecutive stages with an intermediate stage at which no recovery would be required. This could adjust the rate of movement of solute as desired.

From this reasoning it would appear that for the case of fractionation by continuous extraction in which only a single solvent is required, as treated in the previous section, the operation can be performed in a manner entirely analogous to rectification. Perhaps a certain basic difference does occur when two immiscible solvents are used but this difference can be compensated for in part by adjusting the relative rates of flow of the two phases.

It should be emphasized that regardless of the theory the proper experimental conditions for optimum separation of a given mixture by the continuous process can only be found more or less empirically. However, the use of the reflux principle is especially important and has resulted in greatly improved separations in line with the theory. One must assume, therefore, that the theory is helpful even though it may not be entirely correct in its present form.

As far as the discontinuous process is concerned use of the reflux principle involves more labor. Nonetheless the scheme given in Figure 30 can have its practical applications for many cases in which the recovery of the solute is easy.

D. PARTITION CHROMATOGRAPHY

In a series of outstanding studies on small-scale fractionation Martin and Synge[66] undertook the problem of the separation of amino acids or their derivatives by the use of countercurrent liquid–liquid extraction. Their earlier studies first led them to the development of the extraction scheme discussed on page 204, which they later abandoned in favor of an apparently related separation scheme of the utmost simplicity as far as the experimental procedure is concerned. An aqueous phase was im-

[66] A. J. P. Martin and R. L. M. Synge, *Biochem. J.*, **35**, 91, 1358 (1941).

mobilized by adsorption on a solid such as silica gel which was thought to be otherwise inert.   The material to be fractionated was dissolved in a small volume of an organic solvent immiscible in water and allowed to filter through a column of such material.

Pure organic phase was then allowed to flow in from the top of the column in exactly the same manner customarily used for the development of a chromatogram.   Different solutes often passed through the column at different rates and formed more or less distinct bands which could be collected either separately when they emerged as effluent at the bottom of the column or the column could be cut at points between the bands at any given stage of development.   The process was called "partition chromatography" presumably because it was thought to depend almost entirely on liquid–liquid extraction.   However, it should be pointed out that all chromatography is a partition process involving interchange between phases whether or not two liquids immiscible in each other are added to the column.

In the beginning Martin and Synge were able to correlate the relative rates of migration through the column of known amino acid derivatives with their partition ratios in water and the organic phase used for the development of the column.   Such good correlation was obtained that they came to the conclusion that the process was really an extraction process rather than an adsorption process.   Irrespective of the correctness of this assumption, a point to be treated in more detail further on, a theory of operation was proposed which is well worth considerable study and which in fact can be applied just as well to the theory of chromatography where only one liquid phase is probably present.

In their theory the immobilized phase was visualized in terms of a stationary liquid phase in what might be a series of many separatory funnels with a continuous stream of the other phase slowly passing through the series from one end to the other.   The stationary units or separatory funnels were assumed to be so small that equilibrium was immediately established.   This permitted development of the theory on the basis of the binomial expansion in a manner analogous to that later done by Stene[67] for systematic extraction as well as that for the countercurrent-distribution apparatus treated in a previous section.   However, the process was continuous in reality and since there were no discrete steps it was necessary to use the concept of the "height equivalent to a theoretical plate" in the development of the theory.   In the resulting calculations many factors were taken into account such as the partition ratio, the volume of the mobile phase employed, and several cross-sectional areas such as that of the column, the mobile phase, the nonmobile phase, and

[67] S. Stene, *Arkiv Kemi, Mineral. Geol.*, **A18**, No. 18 (1944).

the inert solid. For the full development of the theory, the reader is referred to the original literature.

An expression was developed for the rate of migration of a given solute through the column in terms of the different factors involved. Later with the introduction of other adsorbent materials such as starch and filter paper an expression R_f was substituted. R_f is equal to the rate of movement of the solute divided by the rate of movement of the solvent phase. R_f is thus analogous to the expression $Kr/(Kr + 1)$ used in equation (22) under the treatment of countercurrent distribution.

On the basis of their theory and the rate of spreading of the band as it migrated down the column, Martin and Synge calculated the height corresponding to a theoretical plate in their column and found the surprisingly low value of 0.002 centimeter. This would mean that a 10-cm. column would be the equivalent of approximately 5000 theoretical plates. Since no other liquid–liquid extraction process has even remotely approached such an efficiency, the desirability of further inquiry both into the process itself and into the theory is indicated.

The first assumption which might be questioned is the basic nature of the process, namely, whether it is primarily liquid–liquid extraction or whether adsorption plays a significant role. If the latter is the case, the calculations which involve the use of a partition ratio determined from the two liquid phases in equilibrium and not in the presence of the adsorbent or of each other would scarcely seem to be permissible. One of the most interesting observations in connection with the attempts to fractionate mixtures by extraction is that the spread of partition ratios, i.e., the β values of equation (17), can frequently be improved by modifying in some manner the solvent properties of either or both of the phases. This subject will be treated more in detail at a later time (see page 301). Also it has been found that where improvement in β values for two members of a closely related series of homologs such as the fatty acids has been obtained by modification of a phase, almost the same quantitative improvement will also be found between the other members of the series. Although it is not known to what degree the adsorption of an aqueous phase on silica gel will change the solvent properties of that phase or whether this in fact does improve β values, such an effect is entirely possible. In any case, the correlation of partition ratios with band rates in a homologous series is not valid evidence for ruling out the effect of adsorption in improving separation by giving improved β values. If the latter is true, and the effect of the different solutes on each other is considered, the assumption of such high numbers of theoretical plates may not be necessary.

Such a view on the one hand could appear more in line with the comparative picture presented by the relative separations obtainable by the countercurrent-distribution apparatus and partition chromatography. The former is unquestionably a true extraction process operating at essential equilibrium and with present-day automatic equipment it is not difficult to apply several thousand actual transfers.   In the separation of fatty acids,[68] the penicillins, amino acids,[69] etc., countercurrent distribution has often given comparable separations with several hundred transfers or less, while in other cases even several thousand transfers have given a result far inferior to partition chromatography.

On the other hand, in support of the viewpoint of high numbers of theoretical plates in a column of this type, the careful work of Moore and Stein on the separation of amino acids on starch columns should in particular be mentioned.   The changes in their experimental procedure[70] which led to improved separations were also of the type which would indicate the equivalent of high numbers of perfect transfers.

A considerable number of cases are now on record in which the solute does not migrate at all according to its partition ratio in the two liquid phases used in partition chromatography.   Patterson and Ramsey[71] were able to show this in the fatty acids by a study of the effect of variation of the total amount of the nonmobile phase on the volume of mobile phase (the threshold volume) required to carry an acid such as butyric acid

TABLE IV

DATA OF PATTERSON AND RAMSEY

Volume of H_2O absorbed on silica gel, ml.	Threshold volume of mobile phase, ml.
5.0	53
7.5	42
10	31
11.5	30

through the column.   15 g. of silica gel was used for each experiment.   The mobile phase was hexane.   As Table IV shows, the effect obtained is the reverse of that expected from an extraction process (see equations 22 and 26) but is in line with the effect to be expected on the basis of adsorption.

When the use of starch as an adsorbent in partition chromatography was

[68] S. R. Elsden, *Biochem. J.*, **40**, 252 (1946).   L. L. Ramsey and W. I. Patterson, *J., Assoc. Official Agr. Chem.*, **28**, 644 (1945).   E. H. Ahrens, Jr., and L. C. Craig, *J. Biol. Chem.*, **195**, 299 (1952).

[69] L. C. Craig, W. Hausmann, E. H. Ahrens, Jr., and E. J. Harfenist, *Anal. Chem.*, **23**, 1236 (1951).

[70] S. Moore and W. H. Stein, private communication.

[71] W. I. Patterson and L. L. Ramsey, private communication.

introduced, it was found that amino acids could be separated directly with butanol–water forming the supposed liquid phases. Again the water was first adsorbed on the adsorbent. It was soon found, however, that the aromatic amino acids did not migrate on the column in proportion to their partition in butanol–water.[72]   A similar result was also encountered in the laboratory of one of the authors in connection with paper chromatography. The most likely explanation of this experience would appear to be that the separation is largely caused by adsorptive forces. In the aliphatic amino acids the relative adsorptive forces could be very similar to the relative partition ratios but an aromatic ring introduced into the side chain would be expected to have more of a contribution of its own to make to the adsorptive forces and thus its rate of migration down the column could be retarded.

A precise understanding of a column of this type is difficult to obtain. However, it is known that the aqueous phase is bound with considerable energy and that the amount of the aqueous phase with respect to the adsorbent is a rather critical point. The amount of the adsorbent is greater in such columns than the aqueous phase and it would seem that such an adsorbed phase would be more like a solid phase than a liquid phase in certain respects. If there is any basis for the theory of solute interchange given in Section 2, the aqueous phase could have very little if any fluidity and conditions which would certainly hinder interchange would exist. On the other hand, if the layer of aqueous phase were only a few molecules deep, it could scarcely act as the aqueous phase in the sense pictured in liquid–liquid extraction.

It would appear that an entirely satisfactory answer in all cases to the problem of the basis for the often extremely good separations obtained with the type of chromatography introduced by Martin and Synge cannot be given at the present moment. The process is clearly a chromatographic process since it is carried out in the same manner as chromatography and cannot be achieved without the presence of a solid adsorbing phase. Whether or not liquid–liquid extraction plays a role has not been clearly demonstrated thus far and in fact is brought more into doubt by the excellent results Moore and Stein[72] obtained in separating amino acids on starch columns by substituting propyl alcohol for butyl alcohol in the process. In the latter case, relative band rates were similar to those with the water–butanol system on starch, but the presence of a second liquid phase under such conditions is certainly open to doubt.

If the limiting factor in fractionating mixtures by true liquid–liquid countercurrent extraction really is the resistance to interchange of the solutes between the phases, as clearly appears to be the case, substitution

[72] S. Moore and W. H. Stein, *Ann. N. Y. Acad. Sci.*, **49,** 265 (1948).

of one of the liquid phases by a solid phase should result in greater efficiency as far as the equivalent of numbers of stepwise perfect transfers is concerned. In line with this view is the well-known effectiveness of the chromatograph and especially the recent results obtained in amino acid separations by Moore and Stein. The many spectacular separations obtained by paper chromatography[73] must also be considered. At the present time the difficulty in properly evaluating such processes in terms of "theoretical plates" is the inability to measure experimentally the effect of a single stepwise transfer under conditions which might be those really operating in the column, when the solutes exert an effect on each other. Mayer and Tompkins[74] have in part overcome this difficulty by determining a partition ratio with an arbitrary volume of solvent and weight of the ion-exchange resin used as the adsorbent. This was done in the same manner as was previously done by Craig et al.[75] for adsorption with alumina. Mayer and Tompkins were concerned with a theoretical study of the performance of columns of ion-exchange resins with radioactive inorganic salts. They obtained better results than most chromatographic separations when very slow rates of flow were used and with very dilute solutions, which could be accurately measured by virtue of the radioactivity. Even such a determined ratio on theoretical grounds would not appear to clarify entirely the picture of the fractionation process because of the many unmeasurable contributing factors among which is the resistance to flow of a liquid near a surface.

Although in the opinion of the authors "partition chromatography" represents a milestone in the development of the analytical aspects of organic chemistry, it will not be treated further. However, all chromatography can well be considered one type of distribution, i.e., solid–liquid extraction performed as a countercurrent process for the fractionation of mixtures.[76] Liquid–liquid extraction can play a role in the same process. Martin has presented the arguments in favor of this in considerable detail[77] (see also Moore and Stein[78]).

III. EXTRACTION OF SOLIDS

Extraction from solids is an operation which frequently requires a considerable amount of time, except when the desired solute is adsorbed only on the surface of the solid. Thus the continuous process is nearly always

[73] R. Consden, A. H. Gordon, and A. J. P. Martin, *Biochem. J.*, **38**, 224 (1944).

[74] S. W. Mayer and E. R. Tompkins, *J. Am. Chem. Soc.*, **69**, 2866 (1947).

[75] L. C. Craig, C. Golumbic, H. Mighton, and E. O. Titus, *Science*, **103**, 587 (1946).

[76] H. G. Cassidy, *J. Chem. Ed.*, **23**, 427 (1946).

[77] A. J. P. Martin, *Ann. Rev. Biochem.*, **19**, 517 (1950).

[78] S. Moore and W. H. Stein. *Ann. Rev. Biochem.*, **21**, 521 (1952).

the method of choice.   The principles given in the discussion of extraction of liquids likewise apply to solids.   However, the establishment of equilibrium conditions when one of the phases is a solid, except for absorbed solutes, usually proceeds very slowly and therefore, for practical reasons, the experiments are not carried out under equilibrium conditions.   Even though equilibrium conditions are not reached, it is possible to influence greatly the rate of extraction as well as the degree, by the choice of the solvent, the manner in which extraction is carried out, etc.   Since the diffusion of a solute throughout the body of a solid is a very slow process, it goes without saying that the material should be ground finely for the most intimate contact.

The manner of contacting in the sense discussed under liquid–liquid extraction is often relatively not so important with solids.   However, solids are ideal for application of the countercurrent principle since all that is necessary in satisfying the conditions is the percolation of the solvent slowly through a uniform bed of the solid.   For the case in which only adsorption plays a role, this is then analogous to continuous countercurrent extraction of liquids except that the adsorption isotherm takes the place of the partition isotherm.

The choice of the proper solvent and the addition of other substances to improve extraction is often of much more significance in dealing with solids than the method of contacting.   It is well known that, in the extraction of plant material, the addition of a small amount of water or of acid or alkali will greatly increase the extractability of the desired solute. Often this causes the material to swell, and precautions must be taken in the type and size of the vessel used.   Frequently it is found desirable first to extract some interfering substance, such as wax or gum, by a solvent in which the desired solute is insoluble.

Adsorption will often interfere with simple extraction from solids. Where adsorption does play a large role, it is particularly desirable to operate the extraction in a countercurrent manner, like the chromatograph, since most adsorption isotherms are such as to improve extraction or elution under these conditions.   The displacement of adsorbed substances has received considerable attention in connection with chromatographic procedures and the information may well be applied in order to improve extraction.   Good developers or displacing solvents are known to be methanol, water, and, more recently, phenol.[79]   Methanol and water have long since been known to improve certain extractions from solids and perhaps phenol might also prove useful in this respect.

The simplest form of apparatus for the extraction of a solid could be any vessel such as a beaker in which the solid is treated with the solvent

[79] A. Tiselius, *Advances in Protein Chem.*, **3**, 78 (1947).

and the extract then decanted.   Probably the most familiar apparatus for
the extraction of solids is that for "making" coffee.   The process involved
can also be classified as "leaching" since water is used as the solvent.   It is
well known that with a given coffee the flavor obtained will be influenced
greatly by the manner in which the leaching is accomplished.   If the
extraction process is too efficient, the coffee may be too strong and probably
have a less pleasing taste because more of the bitter principles have been
extracted.   If the extraction is not efficient enough, the coffee is weak and

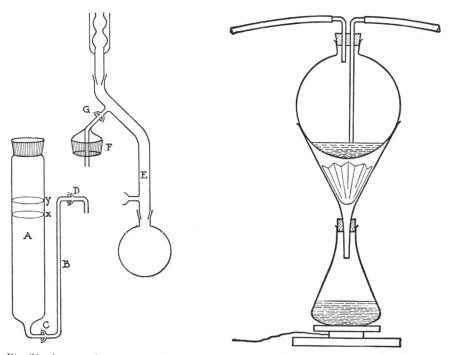

Fig. 31. A versatile extraction device.   Fig. 32. Extractor of Clarke and Kirner.

tasteless.   The size of the grind has an effect and is varied to suit the different methods of making the coffee.   If the water is boiled with the grind
in the old-fashioned way, the time of the boiling process is important.
When boiling has actually taken place the solution may be called a "decoc-
tion" but if the mixture has been merely heated the process may be called
"digestion."   In one form of coffee maker the hot water merely drips
through a fine grind of the coffee and does not come into contact with the
solid again.   In another type called the percolator the hot extract is intermittently pumped over the grind by the steam generated.   During the

treatment a certain amount of chemical transformation is probably taking place. Atmospheric pressure can have an effect since this alters slightly the temperature of contact. It is thus apparent that the simple every-day operation of making coffee involves most of the variables which are so important in the more refined extractions of the laboratory. However, most extractions by the chemist are conducted for the purpose of removing the desired solute as quickly and efficiently as possible and with the intention of avoiding transformation.

Speed often is important with less stable solutes. An illustration of this might be the purification of a polymer of acetaldehyde known as paraldol. The highest melting point recorded for this substance is 95°C. By extraction with ether in a beaker followed by prompt evaporation *in vacuo* the melting point may be raised to 112°. Since the crystals of this substance appear to be unstable in contact with ether the time of contact should be as short as possible.

The work of Polonsky and Kinney[80] is an illustration of speed and simplicity. In this work a search was made for a suitable solvent for the extraction of humic acids from coal treated with nitric acid. 250 solvents were tested by treatment of the extrahend with the solvent on watch glasses. The interesting solvents were then investigated by a more quantitative procedure in which the extract was separated by centrifugation.

Most laboratory houses list percolators. These are merely conical glass vessels with the larger end open and with a short tube attached to the smaller end in order to drain off the extract. An attached stopcock could be helpful. A filter of some sort, usually a plug of cotton, is placed at the lower end and a slurry of the material with the solvent is then filled in. Sometimes the material to be extracted is placed in a filter bag. The percolator has long been used for the extraction of plant tissues and is known to be efficient.

A useful modification of it is that shown schematically in Figure 31, parts A, B, C, and D. A plug of cotton may be thrust into the lower opening of A to act as a filter but would not always be necessary. The slurry is placed in A. An amount should be used so that the top layer of the extrahend, x, would not be higher than the exit of tube B. If less than this were at hand the opening of B could be lowered by virtue of the spherical joint at C. This apparatus permits an extraction to be made in the manner of a chromatographic separation and thus takes full advantage of the countercurrent principle. In fact the apparatus is very convenient for making chromatographic separations. A constant flow of fresh solvent to the upper part of A, y, could be maintained by a siphon arrangement which leads from a larger reservoir of the solvent. Other functions of this apparatus will be described later.

[80] T. S. Polonsky and C. R. Kinney, *Ind. Eng. Chem.*, **39**, 925 (1947).

Clarke and Kirner[81] assembled an extractor as shown in Figure 32 from simple pieces of glassware used for other purposes.   The solid to be extracted, up to 500 g., was placed in a fluted filter in the funnel.   The round-bottom flask served as the condenser and permitted the condensed solvent to drip over the extrahend.

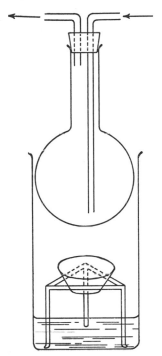 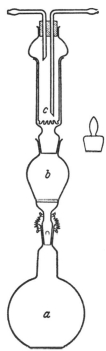

Fig. 33. Extractor of Tanner.   Fig. 34. Extractor of Kuhlmann and Gerschson.

A modification of the same principle, proposed by Tanner,[82] is shown in Figure 33.   The extractor is a tall beaker and again a round-bottom flask serves as the condenser.   The solid is placed in a folded filter paper resting on a 35 by 70 mm. crystallizing dish supported by a glass tripod. The condenser could also be a round-bottom flask or watch glass containing "dry ice."

A quick extraction made in this manner at the boiling temperature of the solvent, followed by crystallization, can be an especially neat method

[81] H. T. Clarke and W. R. Kirner, in Gilman, ed., *Organic Syntheses.*   Coll. Vol. I, Wiley, New York, 1932, p. 375.

[82] H. G. Tanner, *Ind. Eng. Chem., Anal. Ed.,* **4,** 397 (1932).

of purifying a crystalline substance with a minimum volume of the solvent. It is particularly useful when the undesired component is not extracted as rapidly as the desired one.   (See also page 201.)

A slightly different method of accomplishing the same objective is possible with the apparatus of Kuhlmann and Gerschson[83] shown in Figure 34.   When the solvent in the lower flask is boiled, vapor will pass through the fritted filter and condense either in the flask or in a condenser which may be fitted to the top.   This gives good contact.   When the extraction

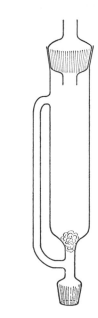

Fig. 35. Soxhlet extractor.

Fig. 36. Continuous-infusion extractor.

flask becomes full, simple cooling of the boiling flask causes the extract to enter the boiler.   The apparatus has been tested extensively for the extraction of flour.   40 to 50 minutes of alternate boiling and filtering is stated to be the equivalent of 12 to 24 hours of Soxhlet extraction.   The possibilities of this apparatus in fractional crystallization are obvious.

When complete removal of the solute from the solid extrahend is possible only by prolonged treatment with the solvent, some form of continuous extractor is indicated.   For this purpose the extractor first published by Soxhlet and Szombathy[84] and now known simply as the "Soxhlet," is

[83] A. G. Kuhlmann and A. I. Gerschson, *Z. anal. Chem.*, **106**, 145 (1936).
[84] F. Soxhlet and Szombathy, *Dinglers Polytech. J.*, **232**, 461 (1879).

perhaps the best known of all, although it is not necessarily the most efficient. It is shown in Figure 35, but it is so familiar that a description is scarcely warranted. With this apparatus, as with nearly all continuous types, fresh solvent is furnished by continuous distillation of the extract. Electrically controlled heating devices such as the Glas-Col heating unit or a battery of electrical heaters make steady distillation comparatively simple.

Of the extractors, two basic types should be mentioned. They are the discontinuous-infusion type and the continuous-infusion type. The Soxhlet is an example of the first class. One of the simplest of the second type could be the extractor of Figure 36. It possesses certain disadvantages. Unless the tube which holds the extrahend is quite narrow the solvent will tend to channel as it flows through the solid and thus will lead to inefficiency. This is a difficulty which may be overcome in part by using a filter or wad of cotton of sufficient resistance and a rate of distillation of such speed that the extrahend is always covered with pure solvent. A better method of insuring a layer of fresh solvent over the extrahend is offered by the extractor of Figure 31, in which the extrahend can never run dry. When the short drip tube is removed at the ball joint D, the apparatus for continuous supply of the solvent by distillation can be attached by E and F. A condenser is connected at the top and any size flask can be used for collection of the extract. The flow of solvent through the extrahend will not become too rapid since solvent will merely overflow back into E when G fills with liquid.

Both the discontinuous- and continuous-infusion types of extractor generally require a filter of some sort. In the Soxhlet extractor this is usually an extraction thimble made for the purpose but it can be filter paper, cloth, fine-wire screen, etc. In the continuous-infusion type it can be a filter paper, a fritted-glass filter, a plug of cotton or glass wool, etc.

Neustadt[85] has called attention to the plugging of extraction thimbles during the extraction of soybean flour. He suggested raising the extraction thimble so that it would not rest on the bottom of the extraction chamber. Later it was suggested[86] that the sample be placed in the annular space between nested extraction thimbles. (Compare also the work of Kardos and Schiller.[87]) The inner thimble could be filled with glass beads to decrease the time between the siphonings. This procedure can also be used when only an extractor of size larger than is required for the purpose is at hand.

The literature contains variations of the two types of continuous ex-

[85] M. H. Neustadt, *Ind. Eng. Chem., Anal. Ed.*, **14**, 431 (1942).
[86] I. C. P. Smith and M. H. Neustadt, *Ind. Eng. Chem., Anal. Ed.*, **19**, 618 (1947).
[87] M. Kardos and W. Schiller, *Chem. Ztg.*, **37**, 920 (1913).

tractors in confusing number.   Presumably these each have their advantages for a specific extrahend but quantitative data are not available in regard to their efficiency.   It would appear that many chemists prefer to design and build their own modification for a particular purpose.   In view of this and in order to offer suggestions, several pages are devoted to a brief description of some of the extractors together with the specific advantages claimed.   Catalogs of supply houses usually contain excellent diagrams and are worth consulting.   As regards reviews, the most complete treatment of the subject is to be found in Thorpe's *Dictionary of Applied Chemistry*[88]; see also Morton [89] and Kleinmann.[90]   It is especially notable that reviews

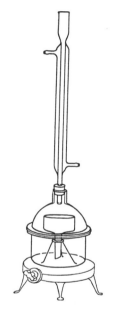

Fig. 37. Extraction arrangement of Ruderman.

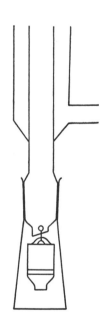

Fig. 38. Microextractor.

of extraction apparatus usually overlook devices designed for use with other laboratory operations such as distillation, recrystallization, adsorption, or chemical reaction.

[88] J. F. Thorpe and M. A. Whiteley, *Dictionary of Applied Chemistry*.   4th ed., Vol. IV, Longmans, Green, New York, 1940, p. 575.

[89] A. A. Morton, *Laboratory Technique in Organic Chemistry*.   McGraw-Hill, New York, 1938, p. 202.

[90] H. Kleinmann, in Klein, *Handbuch der Pflanzenanalyse*.   Vol. I, Springer, Vienna, 1931, p. 126.

Ruderman[91] described an extractor designed to permit the following sequence of operations to be conducted in the same apparatus: collection of the crude material on a Büchner funnel, continuous extraction, and finally evaporation of the extraction to dryness under the pressure desired. In Figure 37 the Büchner funnel (106 mm.) serves as the extraction thimble. It is supported by a glass tripod resting on the flat bottom of a

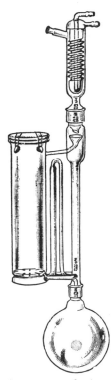

Fig. 39. An analytical extractor.   Fig. 40. An extractor for intermediate amounts.

commercially available (Corning Glass Works Catalog No. 3480) distillation apparatus. The Pyrex distilling apparatus is constructed on the order of a desiccator. The dome is fitted with a ground joint. For extraction a reflux condenser can be inserted, but for removal of the solvent this can be replaced by a distilling tube.

The size of the extractors considered in the remainder of this section vary from the micro size of Blount,[92] in which 1 ml. of solvent may be

[91] I. W. Ruderman, *Ind. Eng. Chem., Anal. Ed.*, **16**, 332 (1944).
[92] B. K. Blount. *Mikrochemie*, **19**, 162 (1936).

used (Fig. 38), to that in which the extracting section has a capacity of many liters. A number of these extractors can be obtained commercially.

Batt and Alber[93] in a general study of the extraction of solids came to the conclusion that the semimicro Soxhlet had several advantages over the macro apparatus and that among other things it required a shorter extraction time. They also concluded that the continuous-infusion types of extractors were superior to the siphoning type. They included in their study a number of different extractors.[94]

A common type of extractor used mainly for analytical purposes is that shown in Figure 39. It is used especially in the rubber industry for determining acetone extracts. In connection with the extraction of rubber, Stevens and Rowe[95] reported an interesting observation. The extraction of crude rubber in the light produced a larger extract than that obtained in the dark.

Most Soxhlet extractors are operated so that the contact of the solvent with the extrahend is near the boiling point of the solvent. If the extract is at the boiling point, vapor locking may result in the siphon tube and prevent siphoning action.[96] This is an objection to the location of the siphon tube on the inside of the extraction chamber. In some cases, for reasons of stability and also for efficiency of extraction, modifications have been introduced for cooling the condensed solvent before it enters the extraction chamber.[97] The usual apparatus for the extraction of rubber was modified by Lindsly[98] so that vulcanization during the extraction could be avoided. The commercially available apparatus of Figure 40 for the extraction of intermediate amounts permits a cooler extrahend during extraction. It also offers ready access to the extrahend during the extraction if test samples are desired. Soxhlet apparatus of large capacity have been described by Drake and Spies[99] and by Jonnard.[100]

Of the continuous-infusion types, one of the simplest and frequently referred to extractors is the Butt extractor.[101] It consists of a straight adaptor with the narrow end fitting into the boiling flask and the upper end

[93] W. G. Batt and H. K. Alber, *Ind. Eng. Chem., Anal. Ed.*, **13**, 127 (1941).

[94] L. Titus and V. W. Meloche, *Ind. Eng. Chem., Anal. Ed.*, **5**, 286 (1933). G. Gorback, *Mikrochemie*, **12**, 161 (1933). H. Hetterich, *ibid.*, **10**, 379 (1932). A. Wasitzky, *ibid.*, **11**, 1 (1932). E. B. Colgrave, *Analyst*, **60**, 90 (1935).

[95] H. B. Stevens and J. W. Rowe, *Rubber Chem. and Technol.*, **12**, 604 (1939).

[96] R. Wollny, *Z. anal. Chem.*, **24**, 48 (1885).

[97] M. Moskowitz, *Science*, **105**, 624 (1947). F. W. Neumann, *Chem. Fabrik*, **8**, 326 (1935).

[98] C. H. Lindsly, *Ind. Eng. Chem., Anal. Ed.*, **8**, 179 (1936).

[99] N. L. Drake and J. R. Spies, *Ind. Eng. Chem., Anal. Ed.*, **5**, 284 (1933).

[100] R. Jonnard, *Ind. Eng. Chem., Anal. Ed.*, **16**, 61 (1944).

[101] C. A. Butt, *Ind. Eng. Chem.*, **7**, 130 (1915).

connected to a reflux condenser.   The sample to be extracted is placed in
the adaptor.   Barthel[102] modified the Butt extractor as shown in Figure
41 so that the extraction could be run at reduced pressure and also in an
inert atmosphere if necessary.   The modification embodies, as part of the
extractor, a thimble, D, containing an overflow tube with a wad of cotton
in it.   This allows passage of only the solution.   The boiling flask, C,
has a side arm for a capillary through which a small amount of an inert
gas can be introduced.   The gas insures regular boiling and excludes

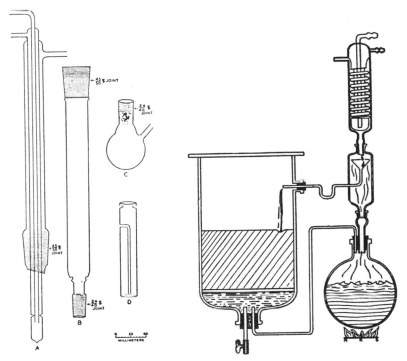

Fig. 41. Extractor for reduced pressure.   Fig. 42. Large continuous-infusion
extractor.

oxygen.   The condenser, A, extends below the 45/50 standard-taper joint
of the extracting section, B, in order to avoid contamination with grease
from the joint.   This extractor was used in concentration of the heat-labile
pyrethrins.

Kaye, Liebner, and Sobel[103] discuss the factors such as reduced pressure,

[102] W. F. Barthel, *Ind. Eng. Chem., Anal. Ed.*, **17**, 53 (1945).
[103] I. A. Kaye, I. W. Leibner, and A. E. Sobel, *J. Biol. Chem.*, **138**, 643 (1941).

inert atmospheres, moisture content, peroxide formation, etc. (See also Crampton and Purdy.[104])

The extraction of wet tissues often will proceed faster than dry-tissue extraction. Holmes[105] published evidence indicating that the simultaneous extraction and drying of lipides with chloroform from wet tissues is more complete than when previously dried samples are extracted or when the sample is allowed to remain wet during the extraction. He described a microextractor and two large extractors equipped with water traps for collection of the water. These extractors will not be described here. They apparently require expert glass blowing. The paper by Holmes is worthy of study.

A continuous extractor for the hot-solvent separation of tarry material has been described by Gibb.[106] Since this extractor has a specialized use it will only be mentioned here. The apparatus would be suitable for extracting either large or small quantities of material difficult to handle by other procedures.

A convenient large extractor has been described by Applezweig[107] and is shown in Figure 42. The continuous-infusion type of extraction was found to be more efficient than the discontinuous type. The construction of the apparatus is obvious from the figure. Although rubber stoppers were used these could be replaced by ground-glass stoppers. Simple large extractors of the continuous-infusion type which can be assembled from common laboratory equipment have been described in other places.[108]

IV. APPARATUS AND PROCEDURES FOR LIQUID–LIQUID EXTRACTION. REMOVAL

The apparatus and procedures described in this section will apply chiefly to the objective of removing a solute from a given extrahend. When a discussion of fractionation is desired, Section V, dealing with apparatus and procedures for countercurrent distribution, should be consulted for the discontinuous approach. Almost any one of the column extractors described in Sect. IV.2.B is potentially useful for fractionation as well as for removal. Their use for this purpose, however, will not be described because of the special conditions required for each mixture of solutes in connection with a given extractor. It is felt that the reader can more profitably consult the original literature for this information.

[104] E. W. Crampton and T. L. Purdy, *Can. J. Research*, 116 **19 B,** (1941).

[105] F. E. Holmes, *Ind. Eng. Chem., Anal. Ed.,* **13,** 918 (1941).

[106] T. R. P. Gibb, *Ind. Eng. Chem., Anal. Ed.,* **10,** 547 (1938).

[107] N. Applezweig, *Ind. Eng. Chem., Anal. Ed.,* **16,** 472 (1944).

[108] Beal, in Gilman, ed., *Organic Syntheses.* Coll. Vol. I, Wiley, New York, 1941, p. 539; *Synthetic Org. Chemicals,* **13,** No. 4 (1941).

1. Discontinuous

Extraction for many organic chemists brings to mind the recovery of a solute from an aqueous phase by shaking with ether in a separatory funnel. For simplicity and effectiveness this often leaves little to be desired. In fact the use of separatory funnels is so common that description of them in current scientific literature is rare. However, descriptions are abundant in catalogs of supply houses. The globe-shaped type, the Squibb pear-shaped type, and the French type with a long conical section below a globular section are listed in sizes ranging up to 12 liters. In practice the conical shape just above the stopcock enables a separation that is sharper than would be the case if the vessel were spherical. Many useful types are graduated cylindrical shapes with a conical section just above the stop-cock.

The reasons that the globe shape is the most common may be the cost, the relatively great mechanical strength, the compactness, the rate of layering out, etc. The cylindrical and elongated Squibb types, often the most popular among organic chemists, are frequently used when violent shaking of the two phases is to be avoided because of emulsifying tendencies. The highest rate of layering-out is generally realized when the interface is as broad as possible, i.e., the elongated funnel is on its side; but sometimes the reverse is true. When a large volume of the organic phase is desired in order to avoid stable emulsions the Squibb or French type appropriately provides a small-diameter section just above the stopcock for drawing off the desired layer. Funnels are also available with small-diameter upper sections for withdrawal of the upper layer when it is present in smaller volume. When the removal of the upper layer completely free from the lower layer is desired, the top of the funnel may be fitted with a ground joint which carries a stopcock above it. After removal of the lower phase the funnel may then be inverted and the upper phase removed through a stopcock not wet with the lower phase.

Heating mantles of the Glas-Col type, covered with glass cloth, are convenient for separatory funnels in which hot extractions are to be made. In exploratory operations and for many other purposes even simpler apparatus than separatory funnels can be recommended. For example, the two phases can be contacted in centrifuge tubes. These preferably should be narrowed at the bottom. Sharp layering-out can be quickly realized by centrifuging, after which the phases may be separated by one of several procedures. The desired layer may be withdrawn by a transferring pipet with a rubber bulb attached, by a dip tube of stainless steel or glass actuated by suction or by air pressure, or by a suitable hypodermic syringe with a long steel or flexible glass tube attached to the glass joint. Fine needles allow even the lower layer to be withdrawn without serious contamination from the upper.

Where the lower layer is desired free of the upper for analytical purposes a rather large needle attached to a syringe can be thrust through the upper layer, a bubble of air expelled from the syringe, and the needle disconnected from the syringe. A smaller needle attached to the syringe is then thrust through the larger needle in order to obtain the uncontaminated sample. Where needles of the desired length are not obtainable they can be fabricated from tubing of the correct size obtained from the syringe supply houses. These can be soldered into the ground joint of the standard needle.

A syringe itself can be used as a separatory funnel. A stopcock with ground joints for attachment to a standard syringe is also obtainable from syringe supply houses. This even permits small-scale extractions to be carried out under pressure. In a technique[109] developed in the synthetic-rubber program during the second world war, reactions were carried out in bottles closed with crown-cap metal seals. The gasket material was of oil-resistant synthetic rubber. A small hole in the rubber which was self-sealing permitted the needle of such a syringe to be thrust through into the bottle for the addition or removal of solutions. Extractions at elevated pressures could be made conveniently in this way.

Occasionally one of the layers can be fixed in position by cooling, if it is sufficiently viscous or crystallizes at such a temperature, and the other layer decanted. When large volumes of the two layers are required the extraction can be done most conveniently in an appropriate bottle with the use of a siphon for separation of the layers.[110]

Although the countercurrent distribution apparatus described in Section V could be used for removal purposes, it was primarily designed for fractionation.

2. Continuous

Many different types of apparatus for continuously contacting two liquids for extraction purposes have been reported in the literature. Because of the great diversity of types and special features even a classification is difficult. No attempt will be made here to cover all the types. A good review of the subject is given in Thorpe's *Dictionary of Applied Chemistry*.[111]

[109] S. A. Harrison and E. R. Meinke, *Ind. Eng. Chem., Anal. Ed.*, **20**, 47 (1948).

[110] C. F. H. Allen and J. R. Thirtle, *Org. Synthesis*, **26**, 17 (1946).

[111] J. F. Thorpe and M. A. Whiteley, *Dictionary of Applied Chemistry*. 4th ed., Vol. IV, Longmans, Green, New York, 1940, p. 575.

A.   SINGLE STAGE

In this type of extractor the solvent is continuously furnished to the extrahend by some process such as distillation and passes either steadily or intermittently through it.   If the solvent is lighter than the extrahend it is admitted at the bottom of the contacting vessel but if it is heavier it must rain down from the upper part.   An example of the former for small volumes is the commercially available extractor of the Kutscher-Steudel type[112] shown in Figure 43.   An example of the latter is the apparatus of Wehrli[113] shown in Figure 44.   Both are for relatively small amounts but can be enlarged to any size.   In Figure 43 the condensed solvent drips into the central tube and passes out through the bottom.   It extracts as it rises through the extrahend.   The extrahend must not be of large enough volume to flow out through the side tube.   The extract only flows into the side tube.   The process in Figure 44 is obvious.   Wehrli's extractor could be modified easily for either light or heavy solvents by inserting a stopcock in the side arm.   The Hemmings[114] "all-purpose" extractor combines the important features of these extractors into a single apparatus and at the same time makes possible an easy conversion to a percolator. The Soxhlet extractors common in most laboratories (or the design of Figure 31) can be modified easily to accomplish either of these processes in a very simple manner as has been shown by Gould[115] (Fig. 45).   For the case of a solvent lighter than the extrahend the latter can be placed in a short, wide test tube which will just fit into the extraction chamber of the Soxhlet.   A thistle tube conducts the condensed solvent to the bottom of the extrahend as shown.   The tube to be inserted can be modified as given in extractor 2 of Figure 45 to accommodate the heavy solvent.

The extractors described above are all relatively inefficient because the extractant does not extract sufficient solute to satisfy the partition ratio on a single passage through the extrahend.   Even though this is so, the extractors will be good enough for many purposes and are widely used.   Their efficiency may be increased greatly by the use of a diffuser plate made of sintered glass for introducing the solvent.   These are available from a number of supply houses.   This diffuser plate simply furnishes many tiny droplets of the solvent instead of large drops.   The efficiency of the diffuser plate can be further improved by recycling the extract through the diffuser plate before it passes into the distillation chamber.   The extractor of Long[116] (Fig. 46) does this by making use of the air-lift principle.   The

[112] F. Kutscher and H. Steudel, *Z. physiol. Chem.*, **39**, 474 (1903).

[113] S. Wehrli, *Helv. Chim. Acta*, **20**, 927 (1937).

[114] A. W. Hemmings, *Analyst*, **76**, 117 (1951).

[115] B. S. Gould, *Science*, **98**, 546 (1943).

[116] W. D. Long, *Ind. Eng. Chem., Anal. Ed.*, **16**, 180 (1944).

air or inert gas entering at tube 1 forces liquid through tube 2 into the reservoir 3.

Other devices for improving the efficiency, *i.e.*, causing the solvent leaving the extracting chamber to be more nearly in equilibrium with the

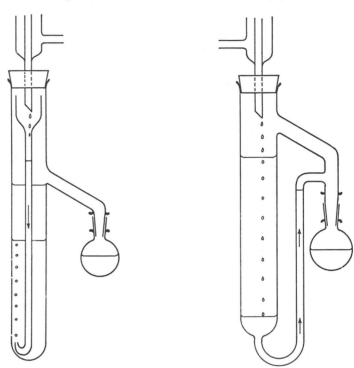

Fig. 43. Kutscher-Steudel extractor.   Fig. 44. Wehrli extractor.

solution, include a mechanical stirring device in the contacting chamber, stirring by injection of the vapor from the distillation of the extract, injection of the solvent from a fine jet under pressure or from several such jets, providing a long spiral for the solvent to be in contact with the solution, etc.

Neuberger[117] described the apparatus shown in Figure 47, which has a mechanical stirring device. (See also Wilson.[118]) Synge[119] found this apparatus to give a plate efficiency of 70–80% for the removal of acetylated amino acids with chloroform from aqueous solution. Unfortunately such

[117] A. Neuberger, *Biochem. J.*, **32**, 1435 (1938).

[118] W. C. Wilson, in H. Gilman, ed., *Organic Syntheses.* Coll. Vol. I, Wiley, N. Y., 1941, p. 277.

[119] R. L. M. Synge, *Biochem. J.*, **33**, 1913 (1939).

a result does not mean that high efficiency will necessarily be obtained with other extractions in which different phase pairs are employed. High efficiency obviously depends on the rate at which equilibrium is established and, as has been discussed in the section on establishment of equilibrium, this rate is very variable. It depends on the value of the partition ratio, the relative volume of the two phases, the viscosity of the solutions, and other factors. The data of Kolfenbach, Kooi, Fulmer, and Underkofler[120] show the stirring device to be definitely superior to the diffuser plate

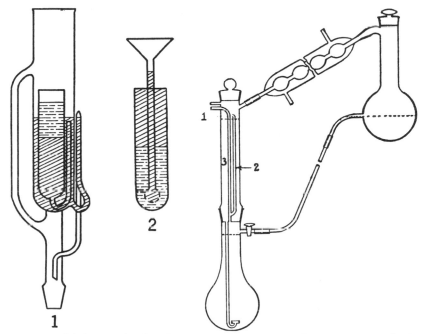

Fig. 45. Modification for Soxhlet.   Fig. 46. Diffuser-plate extractor with air lift for recycling.

for the particular extraction studied by them. It is reasonable to expect this generally to be the case.

Mameli[121] designed an extractor (Fig. 48) on the injection principle. Vapor from the distillation of the extract is forced through tube t directly into the solution where the majority of the vapor condenses. The condensate, which is now the extract, flows intermittently or steadily back into the distillation flask through the tube s. This extractor should prove to

[120] J. J. Kolfenbach, E. R. Kooi, E. I. Fulmer, and L. A. Underkofler, *Ind. Eng. Chem.*, *Anal. Ed.*, **16**, 473 (1944).

[121] F. Mameli, *Gazz. chim. ital.*, **36I**, 123 (1906).

be a very efficient extractor of its type and might be improved by cooling the solution during the extraction by some more efficient means. A somewhat more complicated design of this type is the extractor of Wollny.[122]

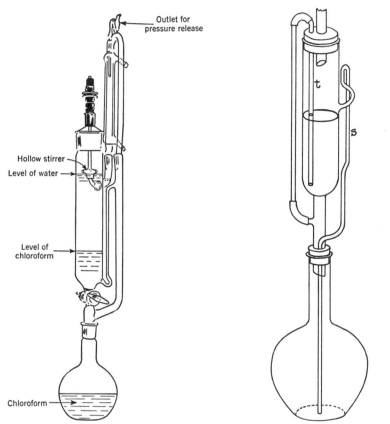

Fig. 47. Extractor with mechanical stirring device.

Fig. 48. Vapor-jet extractor.

The Friedrichs extractor[123] (Fig. 49) is an attempt to satisfy more nearly the partition ratio by providing a long spiral, as shown in the figure, for the solvent to pass through as it rises. The extractors of Wayman and Wright[124] make use of the same principle but are more simple in construction. They should be efficient and convenient for extraction of small volumes. Figure 50 is an extractor for liquids heavier than the extractant;

[122] R. Wollny, *Z. anal. Chem.*, **24**, 147, 202 (1885).
[123] F. Friedrichs, *J. Am. Chem. Soc.*, **34**, 285 (1912).
[124] M. Wayman and G. F. Wright, *Ind. Eng. Chem., Anal. Ed.*, **17**, 55 (1945).

Figure 51 is for liquids lighter than the extractant. The extraction chamber is part C of the apparatus. For full directions of operation the reader is referred to the original paper. The authors state that in one case 90 minutes of operation was found to be the equivalent of 20 successive hand extractions.

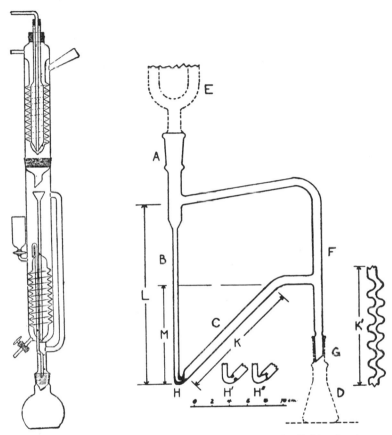

Fig. 49. Friedrichs extractor.   Fig. 50. Microextractor for light solvents.

Often extraction is much more rapidly and efficiently done at the boiling temperature of the solvent but sometimes it is desirable to cool the solution during the process in order to increase extraction. Certain solutes are not sufficiently stable for the higher temperatures. A simple modification of the extractor of Neuberger[117] or of Figure 31 would permit the extraction chamber to be cooled. Another means of lowering the temperature is by reduction of the pressure.

Woolley[125] has described an apparatus for the extraction of amino acids with butanol under reduced pressure. Adaption of nearly any extractor to reduced-pressure operation is not difficult.   In the amino acid extraction of Dakin boiling butanol resulted in a substantial amount of amino acid anhydride formation. Woolley's apparatus (Fig. 52) permits reduction of the pressure to the point where an extraction temperature of approxi-

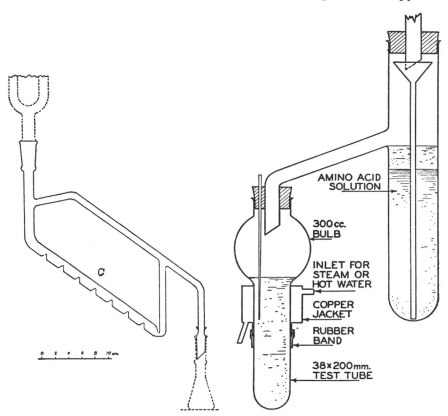

Fig. 51. Microextractor for heavy   Fig. 52. Extractor for heat-sensitive
          solvents.   solids.

mately 50° is obtained.   It provides for steady boiling by the use of a capillary which extends only to the bottom of the heated zone.   A novel feature of heating only the upper part of the boiling tube is provided for. Since the lower section of the tube is cold the amino acid crystallizes there during the extraction.

Control of the temperature of extraction is perhaps easier when some

125 D. W. Woolley, *Ind. Eng. Chem., Anal. Ed.*, **39**, 433 (1937).

means other than distillation is used for circulating the solvent and recovery of the solute.   The extractor of Chapman and Hammett[126] could be used for this purpose although it was used for the extraction of benzoic acid. The solvent was circulated by the air-lift principle and in one stage of the cycle the benzoic acid was recovered by passage of the extract through a solution of alkali.

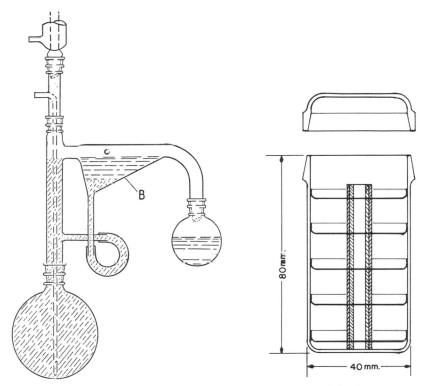

Fig. 53. Continuous extractor for emulsi-   Fig. 54. Sol-gel extractor.
fying extrahends.

A vacuum-operated continuous extractor consisting of four separable parts connected by standard-taper ground joints was described by Shelesnyak, Biskind, and Schwarzschild.[127]   In this device rhythmic flow of solvent through the extraction chamber was effected as a result of pressure changes instead of by means of a boiling–condensing mechanism.

When emulsions tend to form, difficulty is experienced with continuous

[126] R. P. Chapman and L. P. Hammett, *Ind. Eng. Chem., Anal. Ed.,* **5,** 346 (1933).
[127] M. C. Shelesnyak, M. S. Biskind, and M. Schwarzschild, *Am. J. Clin. Path., Tech. Sect.,* **6,** 96 (1942).

extractors because the phases do not separate rapidly enough. (See Sect. VII.) A design for overcoming this difficulty is shown in the apparatus of Pearl[128] (Fig. 53). (See also Kieselbach[129] and Holmes.[130]) The two phases are stirred by a stream of air or inert gas entering through the side tube. A broad chamber, B, is furnished in which the layers may separate.

Other means of avoiding emulsions will be discussed under the counter-current types and in the section on prevention of emulsions. For washing out some unwanted solute LeRosen[131] has suggested a very convenient apparatus.

The most appropriate type of extraction for a solid or liquid extrahend may be difficult to recognize in the absence of actual tests. Thus Yanko[132] described a simple sol-gel apparatus (Fig. 54) for use with 0.3 g. samples of GR-S rubber. It consists of five 50-mesh stainless-steel screens mounted on a hollow center pole, the ensemble being inserted in a 40 x 80 mm. 45/12 ⚬ weighing bottle containing 75 ml. of benzene. When Sweitzer, Goodrich, and Burgess[133] wished to extract unbound from bound GR-S in carbon black mixes they used a Soxhlet with warm benzene only to find that the results were nearly the same as those with the sol-gel procedure with cold benzene. In this type of work it is sometimes found that the strength of the extrahend—in this case the gel—is not sufficient to withstand the mild mechanical action of the Soxhlet extraction. A useful guide in extraction work thus seems to be to try the simplest procedure first.

A concept of interest here is that of Bewick, Currah, and Beamish.[134] They proposed the "half extraction volume defined in effect as the volume, V, of solvent required to decrease the amount of solute to one-half its initial value." Thus, if W is the original volume of solution and k the ratio of the concentration of solute in extracting solvent to the concentration in the solution, then:

$$V = 0.693W/k$$

Thus, a small V and large k are characteristic of favorable extraction. The value k is called the distribution factor and is similar to the rate constant in a first-order reaction,[135] but, it should be emphasized, is not the partition constant at equilibrium. Just as a first-order reaction can be characterized

[128] I. A. Pearl, *Ind. Eng. Chem., Anal. Ed.*, **16**, 62 (1944).

[129] R. Kieselbach, *Ind. Eng. Chem., Anal. Ed.*, **15**, 223 (1943).

[130] F. E. Holmes, *Anal. Chem.*, **23**, 936 (1951).

[131] A. L. LeRosen, *Ind. Eng. Chem., Anal. Ed.*, **14**, 165 (1942).

[132] J. A. Yanko, *J. Polymer Sci.*, **3**, 578 (1948).

[133] C. W. Sweitzer, W. C. Goodrich, and K. A. Burgess, *Rubber Age (N. Y.)*, **65**, 651 (1949).

[134] H. A. Bewick, J. E. Currah, and F. E. Beamish, *Anal. Chem.*, **20**, 740 (1948).

[135] F. Daniels, *Chemical Kinetics.* Cornell Univ. Press, Ithaca, 1938, p. 22.

by the half-life so nonequilibrium extraction can be characterized by the half-extraction volume.   Among organic chemists this quantity apparently has not received widespread use.

B. COUNTERCURRENT

Theoretically this usually is the most efficient form of extraction for the case of an unfavorable partition ratio.   The reason for this has been given under the theoretical treatment in Section II.   Even if the partition ratio is favorable, various factors may make the countercurrent process desirable.   Large volumes of solution can frequently be extracted with a small apparatus and with comparatively little solvent.

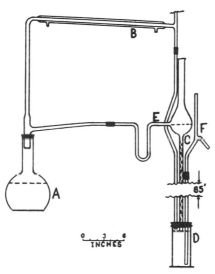

Fig. 55. Countercurrent extractor.

The simplest type of countercurrent-extraction device is that in which the contacting chamber or column is simply a long tube in which the two phases are caused to flow counter to each other.   In this case the rate of interchange of the solute between the two phases, however, is so slow that modifications must be employed in order to reach an efficiency which will make the process at all worth while.

One of the earliest laboratory extractors employing the countercurrent principle is the extractor of Veler, Thayer, and Doisy,[136] developed for the extraction of large quantities of urine.   It is shown schematically in Figure 55.   The column contains baffles to improve interchange.

[136] C. D. Veler, S. Thayer, and E. A. Doisy, *J. Biol. Chem.*, **87**, 357 (1930).

The column C is connected to two separators. Urine is allowed to flow in at the top of the upper separator. It passes out through the overflow tube, F, which can be adjusted to the required height by virtue of the two telescoped glass tubes which form F. These two tubes are connected by rubber tubing below the overflow. The arrangement for circulation of the organic solvent by distillation from flask A is obvious.

Perhaps a simpler and more efficient modification of the column involves the introduction of one of the phases into the column in the form of a spray. A number of extraction devices of this general type, which can take advan-tage at least in part of the countercurrent principle, are either available on the market or have been described in the literature. Three of these[137-139] are very similar. Two have been used to advantage for the extraction of fermentation liquors, always a troublesome problem. In these the ex-traction column is something over a meter in length. It is filled, as shown in Figure 56,[137] almost entirely with the extracting solvent while the phase to be extracted is introduced as a spray and allowed to pass gently through the solvent by gravity.

It should be noted that in Figure 56 a small volume of the solution is constantly being extracted with a large volume of the solvent—the reverse of the relative volumes in the majority of the continuous single-stage ex-tractors. This will usually tend to reduce troublesome emulsification and probably promotes more rapid interchange.

Mair and Streiff produced a spray in their apparatus[139] by introducing the solution through a mechanically rotated drum with holes in it. In Fig-ure 56 the solution is injected into the solvent from a single jet so that a spray is formed which passes through the solvent due to the difference in specific gravity. Bush and Goth[138] found a jet with many openings of carefully controlled size to be superior to a single opening from the stand-point of avoiding emulsions and of efficiency. The jet size and the speed of injection of the solution unquestionably are important and can be changed as the particular extraction requires.

In the Bush and Goth extractor only one passage of the solution was necessary to accomplish 80–85% extraction of penicillin from acidified broth when the total volume of solvent was half that of the broth. The partition coefficient was approximately 15. Instead of evaporation by distillation, re-extraction at low temperature with bicarbonate solution was employed to remove unstable penicillin from the extract. The time of exposure to the acidified media was reduced greatly by the procedure.

[137] J. J. Kolfenbach, E. R. Kooi, E. I. Fulmer, and L. A. Underkofler, *Ind. Eng. Chem., Anal. Ed.*, **16**, 473 (1944).

[138] M. T. Bush and A. Goth, *Ind. Eng. Chem., Anal. Ed.*, **16**, 528 (1944).

[139] B. J. Mair and A. J. Streiff, *J. Research Natl. Bur. Standards*, **24**, 395 (1940).

In the extractor of Kolfenbach *et al.* shown in Figure 56, the solvent was circulated by continuous distillation.   A pumping device driven by a motor was used to circulate the extrahend.   A stream of air bubbles introduced at the bottom of the contacting chamber was found beneficial in breaking emulsions.

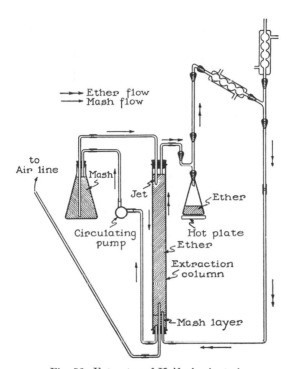

Fig. 56. Extractor of Kolfenbach *et al.*

For many purposes the rubber connections of Figures 55 and 56 could be replaced by suitable ground-glass joints and a different type of circulating pump, such as those used for the circulation of the distilland in molecular distillation, could be used.

The data presented by Kolfenbach *et al.* (Fig. 57) show the definite advantage of this type of extraction.   Curve 1 gives the per cent of solute extracted with time by the extractor with a diffuser plate.   Curve 2 shows the extraction obtained with the Hossfeld extractor,[140] which has a stirring device in the contacting chamber.   Curve 3 gives the result obtained with the extractor of Figure 56.

The data appear more interesting in the light of a series of partition

[140] R. Hossfeld, *Ind. Eng. Chem., Anal. Ed.*, **14,** 118 (1942).

coefficients determined approximately and given in Table V. Concentrations are expressed in grams per 100 milliliters. As is seen in the table,

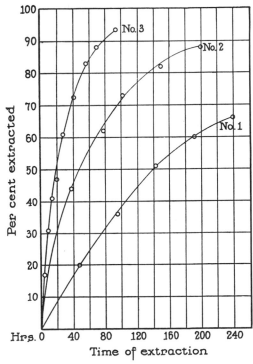

Fig. 57. Comparison of efficiency of several types of extractors.

TABLE V[a]

PARTITION RATIOS OF 2,3-BUTYLENE GLYCOL

C_w (water)	C_e (ether)	C_e/C_w
17.72	0.976	0.055
8.86	0.392	0.044
4.46	0.164	0.037
0.89	0.024	0.027

[a] Data kindly supplied by L. A. Underkofler (private communication).

the partition coefficient is unfavorable at any concentration. Furthermore, the partition isotherm is not linear and the partition ratio shifts with concentration, so that as extraction proceeds the ratio becomes increasingly unfavorable.

One of the most ingenious modifications of the straight tube for contact-

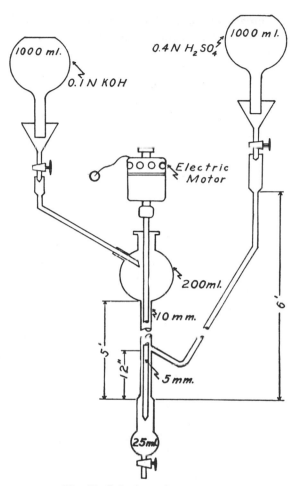

Fig. 58. Spinning-tube extractor.

ing two phases in a countercurrent manner is the contactor of Podbiel-niak[141] (see page 202).

Another ingenious attempt to improve the efficiency of interchange in an unpacked column is by the use of a spinnning tube first introduced by Jantzen[142] and later improved by Schutze, Quebedeaux, and Lochte.[143]

---

[141] Podbielniak, Incorporated, Chicago, Circulars No. 13–15. U. S. Pats. 2,003,308 and 2,004,011 (June 4, 1935). See also N. Barson and G. H. Beyer, *Chem. Eng. Progr.* **49**, 243 (1953).

[142] E. Jantzen, *Das fractionierte Distillieren und das fractionierte Verteilen*, Dechema, Monographie, Vol. V, No. 48. Verlag Chemie, Berlin, 1932, p. 81.

[143] H. G. Schutze, W. A. Quebedeaux, and H. L. Lochte, *Ind. Eng. Chem., Anal. Ed.*, **10**, 675 (1938).

Figure 58 is a schematic drawing of their extractor and is more or less self-explanatory. The spinning central tube keeps both phases dispersed and when the two phases have the proper relative specific gravity, viscosity, etc. improved efficiency is achieved. The dimensions of the column which are optimum depend on the viscosity, density, etc. of the phases employed. Apparently throughput is slow, and is of the order of 250 to 500 ml. of each phase per hour. This is a rate which could be achieved easily by the countercurrent-distribution apparatus in a discontinuous process.

Other attempts to improve the efficiency of interchange in a column involve the use of packing. Most of the packings used in rectifying columns have been studied in this connection. These include wire or glass helices, Berl saddles, and carbon rings, among others. For the same size column throughput is similar to that of the spinner-type column.

A number of studies have been made[144] in comparing the effectiveness of the different type columns. The relative efficiencies were found to vary considerably with the different phases employed but gave heights corresponding to a theoretical plate of from 0.5 to 4 feet. Ney and Lochte found the packed columns to be only about three-fourths as efficient as the spinning-tube columns for several different systems.

V. APPARATUS AND PROCEDURES FOR COUNTERCURRENT DISTRIBUTION

1. Individual Transfers

For this purpose the contacting vessels may be any one of a variety of types depending on the volumes of the phases to be used at each step. A series of separatory funnels may be the easiest collection to assemble. Centrifuge tubes, burets, or graduated cylinders are also suitable, but for large volumes, bottles of appropriate size are the most satisfactory.

If many such extractions are to be made, a unit arranged as shown in Figure 59 is useful. Here the separate contacting units numbered 0 to 12 are attached to a rod, A, by means of some suitable clamp such as B. The rod extends through a bearing, C, at each end and has a crank, D, attached to it. The contacting tube or unit can be a standard test tube with a small ground-glass stopper at the top. It is often convenient to have the tubes graduated so that the volumes can be checked, but this is not a necessary requisite. During a distribution the tubes are filled with arbitrary volumes of the phases except that a few cubic centimeters of air space must be allowed for good mixing. Equilibration of the

[144] T. K. Sherwood, J. E. Evans, and J. V. Longcor, *Ind. Eng. Chem.*, **31**, 1144 (1939). W. O. Ney, Jr., and H. L. Lochte, *ibid.*, **33**, 825 (1941).

phases is accomplished by turning the crank D through a semicircle and back again so that the air bubble flows from one end of the tube to the other at the maximum rate.   This has been found by experiment to give excellent interchange of the solute between the two phases.

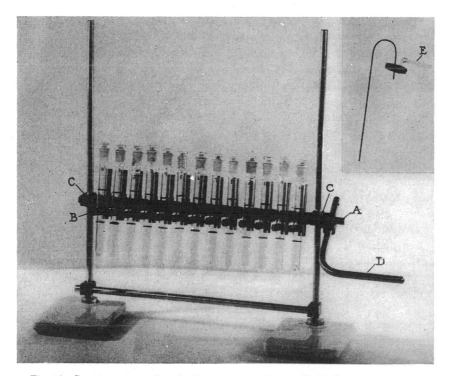

Fig. 59. Countercurrent–distribution apparatus for small numbers of transfers.

The stopper is more convenient when it is of small diameter.   In this case the use of a spring or clamp is not necessary in order to hold it in position when the tube is inverted.   Simply forcing the stopper in position with a slight turn will cause it to stick with sufficient force for the purpose except when pressure is developed during the equilibration by the solvents. The loss of time involved in taking the spring off and putting it on again at each individual transfer is thus avoided.

Individual transfers can be made most conveniently by means of the siphon shown in Figure 59 (upper right).   The siphon may be constructed of glass tubing but is preferably made of stainless steel.   Such tubing in a variety of sizes may be obtained from manufacturers of hypodermic syringes.   Steel tubing does not break and does not scratch the glass contacting cells. The tubing extends through a small flexible rubber collar. A glass tube, E, also extends through the rubber collar and has a small opening at the curve of the tube. The end of the tube is attached to a piece of small-bore, flexible rubber tubing which in turn is connected to a vacuum line.

In using this device the long arm of the siphon is thrust into the phase to be transferred and the rubber collar is placed over the mouth of the tube receiving the phase. When the operator places his finger over the opening at the curve of E, sufficient vacuum is created so that the phase can be transferred rapidly and with immediate control by the finger. Added control may be obtained through a second opening in the vacuum line to which a rubber tube is attached. This rubber tube can have its opening on the floor near the operator's foot. When needed, additional vacuum can then be applied by stepping on the tubing. Passage of unnecessary air through the siphon could cause appreciable evaporation of volatile solvents and is often to be avoided. With a suitable siphon it is somewhat easier to transfer the lower phase in a quantitative manner. If this is to be done, it is helpful to have the contacting tubes blown to a blunt tip at the bottom so that a sharper separation of the phases may be made.

In order to illustrate the procedure, an actual example of an eight-stage distribution will be given in which the solute was 6-methoxy-8-aminoquinoline. The upper phase was isopropyl ether and the lower phase was a mixture of 76 parts of a concentrated solution of citric acid and 24 parts of a citrate buffer solution. The citric acid solution contained 420 g. citric acid monohydrate per liter. The buffer contained 420 g. sodium citrate dihydrate, 105 g. citric acid monohydrate, and 622 ml. 2.42 M potassium hydroxide per liter. No particular importance should be attached to the composition of the buffer solutions. This particular composition had been used for another purpose in the authors' laboratories and, by chance, gave a system suitable for the distribution of the particular solute.

Equal volumes (150 ml.) of each of the phases were shaken together in a separatory funnel and separated. 15 ml. of the upper phase was placed in each of nine equilibration tubes numbered 0 to 8 in the apparatus of Figure 59. 80 mg. 6-methoxy-8-aminoquinoline was then added to tube 0 and the tube was shaken to effect solution. 15 ml. of the lower phase was then added and equilibration accomplished by inverting the tubes 50 times. The rate of tipping was such that the bubble of air just reached the top before it started back again. After the two layers were separated the lower layer was transferred quantitatively to the tube numbered 1, and 15 ml. of fresh lower phase was added to the 0 tube. Equilibration was then accomplished and a period allowed for the phases to settle. The lower phase of 1 was transferred to 2, the lower phase of 0 then transferred to 1, and a fresh 15-ml. portion of lower phase added to 0.   The process was continued until all the tubes contained equal volumes of each of the phases.   Usually at this point tube 8 will be found to contain a somewhat smaller volume of the lower phase.   This could be avoided by passing a volume of the pure lower phase through the series before the distribution was begun or the volume of the first advancing portion of the lower phase could be corrected at each step by addition of a few drops of the correct phase.

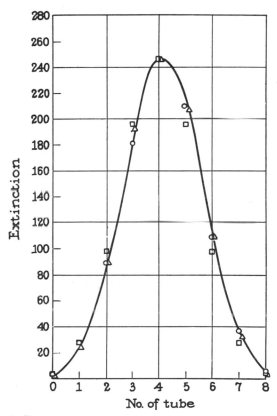

Fig. 60. Eight-stage distribution curve. O, Experimental; Δ, calculated for K of 1.05; □, calculated for K of 1.0.

At the completion of the distribution 1 ml. 6 N sodium hydroxide was added to each of the tubes and the whole equilibrated by inverting the tubes fifty times.   This operation transferred all of the organic base present in the lower phases to the corresponding upper phases.   The amount per milliliter present in each of the upper phases was then determined by measuring the extinction at 360 mμ in the Beckman quartz spectrophotometer. The extinction obtained was plotted as ordinate against the corresponding tube as shown in Figure 60. The shape of the curve will be found to be rather insensitive to small variations in the volume of any one phase. Loss of a milliliter of solvent in one tube would not cause a serious deviation in the curve. Similarly a corresponding error could be made in transferring one of the phases without much effect on the curve. The explanation of this fortunate fact is more obvious when it is realized that the process amounts to an automatic averaging or summation of many separate transfers according to the mathematics of probability. When sufficient cases are involved such is indeed the basis for the reliability of statistics.

If the system has been a perfectly operating one and the preparation used initially was pure, the fraction of solute present in each tube can be calculated by the binomial expansion. (See Sect. II.) Conversely, if the solute is known to have constant partition ratios in the system, the values expected can be calculated and then the divergence obtained, if any, will give quantitative information concerning the amount of impurity present in the sample.

The fraction of the solute expected in each tube can be calculated by equation (15), Section II 4A, which is repeated here for convenience (see also Williamson and Craig[145]):

$$T_{n,r} = \frac{n!}{r!\,(n\text{-}r)!}\left(\frac{1}{K+1}\right)^n K \qquad (28)$$

$T_{n,r}$ is the rth term for a distribution of n transfers.

For an eight-transfer distribution, $n = 8$ and $r = 0, 1, \ldots .8$. K is the effective partition ratio when equal volumes of the two phases are used. If unequal volumes are used, K should be multiplied by the ratio of the volumes of the two phases. Equation (28) is set up for the case in which the upper phase is the one transferred. If the lower phase is transferred, as in the above example, $1/K$ should be substituted in the equation for K.

Thus for an eight-transfer distribution, nine values must be calculated. Rather than calculate each value independently from equation (28), a more rapid method is possible which in principle calculates only one term directly; the others are then calculated from it. One can derive from the binomial expansion that adjacent terms are very simply related to one another. Thus, for eight transfers: the 0th term, $T_{8,0}$, is $[1/(K + 1)]^8$; $T_{8,1}$ is $8\,KT_{8,0}$; $T_{8,2}$ is $\frac{7}{2}\,(KT_{8,1})$; etc. In general terms the rth term is

[145] B. Williamson and L. C. Craig, *J. Biol. Chem.*, **168**, 687 (1947).

related to the $(r-1)$th and the $(r+1)$th term by equations (29 and 30),
respectively:

$$T_r = FKT_{r-1} \qquad\qquad (29)$$

$$T_r = F'\,(1/K)T_{r+1} \qquad\qquad (30)$$

where $F = (n+1-r)/r$ and $F' = (r+1)/(n-r)$.

A simple table of these factors is convenient and is given in Table VI
for eight and ten transfers. However, the relationship of the various
F and F' terms is very simple and can be set up easily for any number
of transfers.   In actual practice the difficulty with such an approach is the
fact that if a mistake should be made in one of the earlier calculations all
the other values will be in error.   It is therefore advisable to add up all
the terms after they have been calculated in order to see if their sum is
equal to 1.   If a result other than 1 is obtained, a mistake has been made
in calculating at least one of the terms.

Before a suitable curve can be calculated the partition ratio of the pure
solute in the exact system must be known with sufficient accuracy.   There
are at least two reasons for not using a K individually determined on a
single partition for this purpose.   The system and conditions under which
the individual value was determined may be slightly different and thus in

TABLE VI

FACTORS FOR EIGHT- AND TEN-TRANSFER DISTRIBUTIONS

	Eight-transfer distribution		Ten-transfer distribution	
	F	F'	F	F'
0	—	1/8	—	1/10
1	8/1	2/7	10/1	2/9
2	7/2	3/6	9/2	3/8
3	6/3	4/5	8/3	4/7
4	5/4	5/4	7/4	5/6
5	4/5	6/3	/5	6 5
6	3/6	7/2	5/6	7/4
7	2/7	8/1	4/7	8/3
	1/8	--	3 8	9/2
9	—	—	2/	10/1
10	—	—	1/10	—

the case of a sensitive system may differ from the one operating during the
distribution.   Secondly, a pure sample must be used for the determination
of the ratio.   Since the value of the partition ratio actually operating
during the distribution can be derived easily from the curve itself by equation (22) of Section II.4.B and also by other procedures,[145] the objections raised above can be circumvented very easily.   The equation:

$$N = nKr/(Kr + 1) \tag{31}$$

gives the center of gravity of the solute on the diagram in terms of a tube number but in reality will do so only when N is a whole number. However, if a smooth curve is drawn through the experimental points as has been done in Figure 60, then for the purpose of estimating K, the curve can be assumed to be a continuous function and hypothetical fractional tube numbers can be derived. Thus from the experimental curve the center of gravity can be estimated to be 4.1. Substituting this value in equation (31) the partition ratio 1.05 can be derived. For the reason now apparent we have chosen to draw smooth curves through all the experimentally derived points rather than straight lines joining the experimental points as has been done by others.[146]

The calculated values represent the fractions or amounts in the tubes when unit quantity of substance was used at the start, but the experimental curve in Figure 60 was determined with 80 mg. material. In order to correct for this the maximum tube of the experimental curve may be assumed to be correct and the theoretical curve arbitrarily adjusted to this point. It has a value of 0.246, while the same tube from the calculation of Table VI has the value 0.271. Therefore all the calculated values are multiplied by the factor 0.246/0.271 and the values so obtained plotted on the same graph as the experimental curve. If the calculated values agree within the experimental error, this graph represents a theoretical distribution. If several of them diverge a better fit may be obtained by using a slightly different K value in the calculation. The curve must be adjusted in this manner so that the greatest number of points fit the experimental curve within the experimental error. Usually in a distribution it is the *relative fraction* of solute in each tube which is important rather than the *absolute position* of the curve.

The partition ratio determined by a single distribution prior to the multiple distribution was 1.0. Had this constant been employed for the calculation of the theoretical values, they would not have fallen on the experimental curve as shown in Figure 60. When a distribution is made and an appreciable fraction of solute is in tube 0 or the nth tube, the partition ratio cannot be derived as accurately from the experimental curve and more attempts through trial and error are required in fitting the curve.

2. Multiple Transfers

Obviously the number of transfers practicable in systematic extraction is limited when individual contacting units are used because of the time

---

[146] S. Stene, *Arkiv Kemi Mineral. Geol.*, **A18**, No. 18 (1944).

and labor involved.   For this reason an apparatus has been devised which permits many extractions to be made simultaneously and under almost identical conditions.   Instead of transferring a phase in each unit individually the operation is achieved in numerous units simultaneously by a very simple movement.   One type of apparatus is shown schematically in Figure 61.   It is now obsolete but is useful for describing the process.

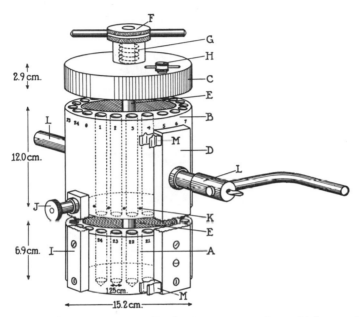

Fig. 61. 25-tube countercurrent-distribution apparatus for multiple transfers.

It is constructed from a stainless-steel cylinder 15.2 centimeters in diameter which has been machined from a solid rod.   Holes 1.25 cm. in diameter are drilled in the outer shell and these holes form the tubes or cells of the apparatus.   They are symmetrically placed 0.6 cm. from the outer edge of the shell, 0.6 cm. from the inner edge of the shell, and 0.3 cm. apart.   They extend through the upper section, B, but not quite through the lower section, A.   The lower section of each tube has a volume of 8 milliliters.   The volume of the upper is nearly 16 milliliters.   The top section, C, forms the cover.   The three parts are held together by a central rod, E, which is attached to the solid part of the bottom section A. It is threaded for a wing nut at the top.   A spring, G, lies under the wing nut.   In the central part of section B sufficient stock is left so a hole drilled in it forms a bearing through which E passes.   B can be rotated on this bearing.   The upper surface of A and the lower surface of B are ground flat with great precision similar to the parts of a desiccator so that when B drops down over A the solvents contained in the tubes will not escape between the surfaces.   No lubricant is used.   Similarly the upper surface of B and the lower surface of the cover C are flat so that all the tubes will be closed at once.   With this arrangement a single opening and plug H in the cover will permit access to any tube by revolving C around E.

The apparatus is supported by two arms, D, one on either side.   Two short rods, L, attached to the arms, form bearings which rest on two supports not shown in Figure 61.   A crank for equilibration is attached to one

Fig. 62. Countercurrent-distribution apparatus containing 54 tubes.

of the rods.   A pair of clips, M is attached to the arm D, as shown for the attachment of a glass dummy tube.   J is a machine plug with a spring attached.   When the upper section, B, is rotated over A the plug will snap into one of the small shallow holes K and thus stop B in the correct position so that all the tubes of section B are exactly superimposed on the tubes of A.

A slightly different model was made from individual tubes which contained a total of 54 tubes[147] as shown in Figure 62.   In this model the plates closing the top and bottom were glass and permitted the exact time of separation of the phases to be observed.   Experience with these steel distributors soon showed their limitations for the application of higher numbers of transfers and an all-glass type of apparatus operating on a different principle was developed.   The steel type of equipment can now be considered as obsolete.

The first type of glass apparatus to be really successful was that shown

[147] L. C. Craig and O. Post, *Anal. Chem.*, **21**, 500 (1949).

in Figure 63.   It is a train of interlocking individual units which can be made of any length or size desired.[147]   The upper left figure shows a single unit.   A, the equilibrating chamber, is a glass tube approximately 12 inches long and with an 0.5 inch inside diameter.   The two phases are inserted together with the solute through opening E.   Equilibration is accomplished

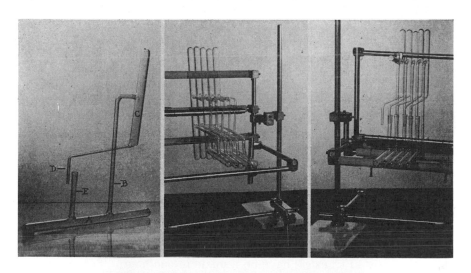

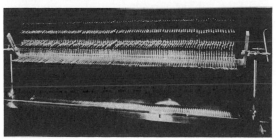

Fig. 63. Glass countercurrent-distribution machine.

by tilting back and forth at an angle of about 35°.   The unit tubes interlock with exit tube D inserted into the opening of the adjoining tube as shown at the upper right of Figure 63.   The units may be held in place by Flexa-frame rods and clamps.   Those rods which touch the glass tubes are covered with rubber tubing.   The frame holding the tubes is supported by bearings (Flexaframe clamps will do) at each end of the train of tubes.   An upright rod from each end of the frame to the corresponding bearing permits adjustment of the center of gravity of the whole unit so that it will return of its own accord to a position midway between that shown in the upper center and upper right of Figure 63.   This is the settling position used after the equilibration has been accomplished.

After the layers have separated the tubes are tilted to an angle slightly more than 90° (Fig. 63, upper center) where the upper phase will decant through tube B into C.   On righting the tubes to the position shown in the upper right the contents of C will flow through D into the next adjoining tube of the series.   In the decanting position, the heavier layer remains in A because its volume is such that none will flow out through B.   The small amount of the lighter phase which does not flow out represents a constant error and accordingly does not interfere with the process.   Thus the volume (10 ml.) of the part of tube A extending from the end to the decanting tube is the only critical dimension of the entire apparatus.   Actually this need not be very exact because of the large number of extractions to be made.   Variation from tube to tube of as much as several per cent has not appreciably distorted the distribution curves experimentally obtained.   When an apparatus with considerable variations in the volumes of the tubes is used, the distribution curve should always be determined and plotted as weight per milliliter or some proportional unit rather than as total amount per tube.

The lower picture of Figure 63 shows a train containing 108 units.   With this apparatus 40 transfers have been made in one hour.   The opening of each tube is closed by a rubber cap cut from the rubber bulb of a medicine dropper.   A hole of the correct size is cut through the rubber cap for the emptying tube D to pass through.   During operation the movement of the solutions creates a pumping action and if the openings were not closed, considerable evaporation would take place.   A snugly fitting rubber cap prevents this but does not come in actual contact with the solutions.   It is easily pulled up on D for cleaning and filling the apparatus.   If desired, samples may be withdrawn at any time from appropriate tubes by use of a hypodermic syringe with a needle sufficiently narrow to pass by tube D but inside the opening of E of the tube selected.

Following the initial success of this distributor a number of distributors of similar design have been reported.[148-150]

The apparatus of Figure 63 practically amounts to a spiral with offset chambers which trap the heavier phase and prevent it from migrating along the spiral.   One of the earliest types of discontinuous extractors built was a spiral designed by Jantzen.[142]   Improved models of this type have been

[148] N. Grubhofer, *Chem. Ing. Tech.*, **22**, 209 (1950).

[149] F. Weygand, *Chem. Ing. Tech.*, **22**, 213 (1950).

[150] L. C. Craig, W. Hausmann, P. Ahrens, and E. J. Harfenist, *Anal. Chem.*, **23**, 1236 (1951).

reported by Tschesche and Konig[151] and by Lathe and Ruthven.[152] Although there are certain advantages to this type of apparatus, such as simplicity and flexibility in that either the heavier or lighter phase can be transferred at will, there are also certain disadvantages. For complete descriptions of these extractors, the reader is referred to the original literature.

The apparatus of Figure 63 which can be made even by an unskilled glassblower was designed with the ultimate purpose of attaching an electrically operated robot to it so as to minimize the labor which would limit the practical number of tubes that might be put into a single train. However, before the automatic features were accomplished a change in design of the tube seemed worthwhile.[150]

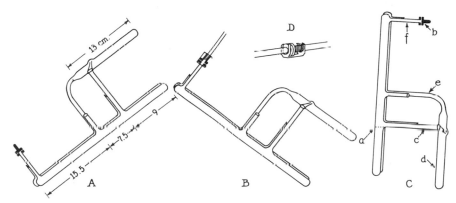

Fig. 64. Cells of distribution train.

This latest design is somewhat more expensive than that of Figure 63 but is well worth the difference in cost. A line drawing is shown in Figure 64. Like the tube of Figure 63 it operates by rocking from position A to B and back for equilibration. The layers separate, following equilibration, in position B. On tipping to position C the upper layer passes through the decantation tube c into the decantation cell d and on tipping to position A again it flows through the transfer tube e into the next tube of the series. Tube c extends through a ring seal nearly to the opposite wall of d so that any back flow through c on tipping to position A is prevented.

Each tube has an opening tube attached to the front end which is 7 cm. in length. This tube is closed by a ground butt joint which is held in place with a spring clamp, D, which is designed for quick attachment or removal. Each unit is sealed to the next through tube e except every tenth unit. On

[151] R. Tschesche and H. B. König, *Chem. Ing. Tech.*, **22**, 214 (1950).
[152] G. H. Lathe and C. R. J. Ruthven, *Biochem. J.*, **49**, 540 (1951).

this unit the transfer tube projects a little beyond the others and is joined to the next unit with a butt joint and a small clamp. This permits the train to be easily assembled or taken apart in banks of 10 units.

The glass units are mounted on a rigid cross bar of aluminum which is notched to receive each tube. A thin strap of stainless steel passes around the glass tube slightly behind the decantation tube c. Both ends of the strap are attached to a threaded rod which passes through the aluminum bar and is held on the other side of the bar with a knurled nut. Such a clamp on every second tube is sufficient. Each end of the aluminum bar is attached to a short cross rod of adjustable length. The cross rods are attached to bearings. An apparatus of this type containing 30 tubes is shown in Figure 65.

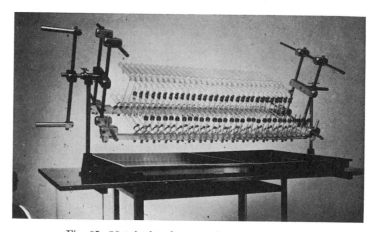

Fig. 65. 30-tube hand-operated distribution train.

With any of the various distributors which operate on the decantation principle a single transfer is completed when the layers are recombined after decantation. This accomplishes the same thing that advancing the upper section of the steel apparatus one tube accomplishes. Each of the distributors mentioned above is capable of giving experimental distribution patterns which agree well with calculated curves. However, in order to assess properly the ultimate worth of each of the types it must be considered in terms of its suitability for performing each of the various procedures given on page 180 for extending the usefulness of extraction. In the authors' opinion the automatic apparatus described later in Section V.5 comes nearer the over-all ideal than any other developed thus far. It will be treated in a separate section because the procedures best suited to its use are different than those for the hand-operated types.

A. FUNDAMENTAL PROCEDURE

The method can best be illustrated by an actual 24-transfer distribution made in the steel machine of Figure 61 at 5°C. with a colorless sample (m.p. 180°) of 2-mercaptobenzothiazole.

Two phases were prepared by shaking 250 ml. of diethyl ether and 250 ml. 2 M phosphate buffer, pH 10.6, in a separatory funnel. The cover, C, was removed from the apparatus and the central section, B, then rotated slightly so that its tubes were directly over the metal partition separating the lower tubes, e.g., midway from being superimposed. Each of the upper tubes at this position will partly open into two of the lower tubes and thus all the tubes in the apparatus are connected. 200 ml. (25 × 8) of the lower phase was then poured into one of the tubes. After waiting a short time for the solution to flow around and fill all the lower segments, an equal level in each was insured by rotating the upper section, B, one complete circuit around the lower so that upper 0 was again over lower 0. The machine plug, J, was then allowed to snap into position.

8 ml. of the upper phase was placed in each of the tubes. This operation can be done most conveniently by means of a hypodermic syringe. It should be noted that the meniscus separating the two layers occurs at the point where the upper and lower sections join. Thus essentially all the upper phase is contained in B so that when it is rotated over A all the upper layers are transferred simultaneously. After the cover was placed on the apparatus, 100 mg. solute was introduced into tube 0/0. This operation can be done most conveniently by withdrawing the contents of tube 0/0 into a glass tube containing the sample. The glass tube should be of the same dimensions as a tube of the apparatus. After solution it is advisable to equilibrate the contents of the tube by inverting it several times and recording the time required for the two layers to separate. Any tendency to form a stable emulsion and whether or not the solute has influenced the relative volumes of the two phases should also be noted. If neither has occurred the phases are returned to the apparatus.

The phases in the apparatus were equilibrated by inverting the barrel, then righting it again 50 times with the crank. The glass tube mentioned above was filled with 8 ml. of each of the pure phases and attached to the apparatus by means of the clips, M. It served as a guide to control the rate of shaking. Good dispersion of the phases was maintained by pausing before each inversion just long enough for the bubble of air to reach the top of the tube. A period of 3 minutes was then allowed for the layers to separate. The plug, J, was pulled out and the wing nut, F, was unscrewed one half turn. While the apparatus was in the upright position, the upper section, B, was rotated slightly in the clockwise direction and the plug then allowed to snap back against the barrel. Upon rotating the barrel further the plug found its way into the next adjacent hole. The contents of the upper sections of each tube had thus been transferred so that they were now over the lower sections of the next tubes in the series. The wing nut was tightened again and the next step was accomplished in exactly the same manner as was the first. Upper 0 was then over lower 2. This process was repeated until upper 0 had migrated until it was over lower 24.

The contents of each of the tubes were then withdrawn into appropriate glass tubes with ground stoppers. These tubes were numbered 0 to 24, the numbers arbitrarily being made to correspond to those of the lower section A. This operation can be done best by means of the siphon described in

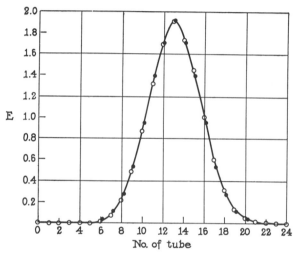

Fig. 66. Distribution curve of 2-mercaptobenzothiazole. O, Experimental; ●, calculated.

Figure 59 but may also be accomplished by means of a hypodermic syringe with a long needle. For practical reasons the tubes were not rinsed.

The problem now was to find as quickly as possible the total amount of solute present in each of the 25 tubes, both phases combined. The manner of accomplishing this will vary greatly with the nature of the system and with the nature of the solute. In some cases for purity studies[153] it is advisable also to determine the concentrations in each of the phases so that partition ratios may be plotted as well as amounts. If each of the phases contains only volatile solvents, the first objective may be accomplished

[153] L. C. Craig, G. H. Hogeboom, F. H. Carpenter, and V. du Vigneaud, *J. Biol. Chem.*, **168**, 665 (1947).

by addition of a standard volume of some third solvent to each tube which will cause the two phases to be mutually soluble.   In some cases addition of a few milliliters of a particular solvent or perhaps another solute will cause the solute of interest to migrate quantitatively to one of the two layers where it can be determined.   When the solute is acidic or basic this is frequently the method of choice.   In the experiment above 1 ml. 8 M phosphoric acid was added to each tube and all were then equilibrated. The amount of solute in the ether phase in each tube was determined spectroscopically with the Beckman quartz spectrophotometer.

For purposes of plotting a curve any unit which is directly proportional to the amount of solute may be used as the units of the ordinate.   In the present case the determined extinction was suitable and gave the curve shown in Figure 66.   The calculation and the "matching" of a theoretical curve became the next step in the interpretation of the result.

The steps involved in the calculation of a curve are the same as in Section II, page 187, with certain exceptions.   From Figure 66 the maximum can be estimated to occur at 13.2.   Thus from equation (31) the operating partition ratio is 1.22.   With this value the distribution of interest can be calculated by the binomial approach as given on page 247 if desired, but it can be more quickly calculated by the approximation of equation (23) in Section II.   This equation is repeated here for convenience:

$$y = \frac{1}{\sqrt{2\pi n \ K/(K + 1)^2}} \ e^{-x^2/[2nK/(K+1)^2]} \tag{32}$$

Although this equation may appear somewhat formidable at first, its application can be simplified as follows: The expression $2nK/(K + 1)^2$ is used in calculating each term.   It is therefore calculated first and for the problem above is equal to 11.9. y_0 is thus 0.164.   The other terms, y_1, y_2, etc., can be calculated from y_0.   When logarithms are used, the logarithm 0.434/11.9 or 0.0365 appears in each calculation.   Thus y_1 = 0.164 divided by the antilog of 1×0.0365 or $0.164/1.086 = 0.151$; y_2 = 0.164 divided by the antilog of $2^2 \times 0.0365$ or $0.164/1.4 = 0.117$; etc.   The use of a slide rule permits an entire curve to be derived in 10–15 minutes.   Furthermore, for higher numbers of transfers calculation of every second, third, or fourth term may be sufficient for plotting a curve.

The calculated maximum is 0.164.   That of the experimental is 1.92 in terms of extinction units.   Each of the calculated values must therefore be multiplied by the factor 1.92/0.164 before plotting on Figure 66.   This calculation is avoided by simply using 1.92 rather than 0.164 for y_0 in the calculation above.   When this is done agreement between calculated and experimental is shown to be nearly perfect.   If calculated values are higher than experimental on one side of the curve but lower on the other, it is probable that the value of K used for the calculation has been slightly in error and it is then permissible to move each of the values horizontally the same distance in order to get a better fit. For distributions of higher transfers, the shape of the curve is less sensitive to the absolute value of the partition ratio. Thus a curve for 24 transfers calculated on the basis of a K of 1 is not much different in shape from a curve calculated for a K of 0.95 or 1.05. The difference in position, however, is easily seen.

If, at the beginning of the distribution, when the solute is being initially studied in the glass tube, the volumes of the phases are markedly shifted, a number of individual transfers may be made whereby changes in volumes may be adjusted. Where too stable an emulsion has been formed, the tubes may be centrifuged to cause separation. After several transfers the concentration in any one tube will then be only one-third or less of its initial concentration. At the lower concentration it may behave satisfactorily. The upper section, B, can then be shifted a corresponding number of tubes and the contents of each glass tube transferred to the correct tube of the apparatus (after removing the solvent phases).

If a shift of volume should occur, the question of the effect of such a shift on the final curve is logically raised. It has been found experimentally that small shifts in the beginning have an almost imperceptible effect on the final curve. Similarly a small effect is observed if the volume of one of the phases in a single tube becomes lowered through loss or some other mistake. Even a shift of 10% in the volume of one of the phases is not serious when the number of transfers applied is 25 or more. The explanation for this lies in the fact that a curve itself represents the most rational method for averaging a great many determinations. It is a statistical approximation and thus is fortunately a very stable measure. On the other hand, if an error should be additive in each tube, the error will be registered plainly in the final curve.

For the reason given above, it is not highly important that the meniscus occur exactly at the place where the two sections of the apparatus join. If the upper phase should be omitted from one of the tubes it will be found that this upper section will have practically no upper phase in it at the end. This of course would not hold for systems which build up pressure during the run. Actual experimental work has shown that the error in mechanical carry-over from tube to tube of the stationary phase can be less than 1.0% for a system separating reasonably well.

B. SINGLE-WITHDRAWAL PROCEDURE

The principle in this procedure has been discussed in Section II.4.A. In general, the procedure will be found most useful when a mixture of solutes of unknown and widely differing partition ratios is encountered.   It is also to be recommended when, for isolation purposes or analysis, it is desirable to have the solute only in one of the phases at the end of the run.

In accomplishing single withdrawal, the fundamental procedure given above is first followed until upper 0 reaches lower 24.   If the effective K is approximately 0.1 or less than 1, the contents of tube 0/24 is siphoned out and set aside.   Both layers are withdrawn because it is difficult to

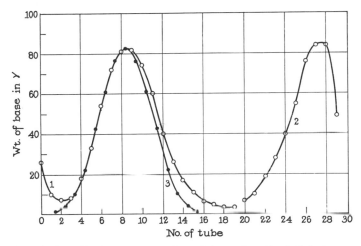

Fig. 67.   Distribution pattern of a mixture of antimalarial drugs. Single-withdrawal.

withdraw only the upper phase and not the lower.   The empty tube is filled with the fresh phases and one more stage is applied.   Tube 1/24 is then withdrawn.   The next tube will be 2/24, etc., to n/24.   After a withdrawal has been made the empty tube is always filled with fresh phases. If, for example, the effective K were 10, or larger than 1, at the end of the fundamental procedure tube 24/0 would have been withdrawn first, then tube 24/1, then tube 24/2, ...24/n.

At the end of the distribution the solute in each of the tubes is determined as given in the above section.   The tubes remaining in the apparatus are plotted as a continuous curve as in the fundamental procedure but those withdrawn form a different series and may be represented by an adjoining curve as shown in curve 2 of Figure 67.   The tube withdrawn first will be on the far extremity; that withdrawn last will be placed next the curve representing the concentrations of those remaining in the apparatus until the end.

Figure 67 is the result of an actual experiment made in connection with the study of an antimalarial drug.   In this study the drug, 4-(4-diethyl-amino-1-methylbutylamino)-7-chloro-3-methylquinoline, was given to a human patient and the basic fraction was recovered by extraction from the urine. After evaporation of the extract an oily residue remained in small amount. Identification of the oil and an estimation of its purity was desired. Approximately 1.5 mg. residue was distributed in a 20-tube apparatus in the system ethylene dichloride – 0.2 M phosphate buffer, pH 6.7. Ten tubes were withdrawn; thus a total of 29 transfers was applied. The withdrawal was made so that the solute of higher K would emerge first. Analysis of each tube was made spectroscopically in the organic layer after addition of excess alkali and equilibration of the tube. A partition ratio of 0.42 was estimated from the main band by equation (31). This was in good agreement with the value determined for the original drug. A considerable fraction of the drug was thus not transformed in passing through the body. When a theoretical curve was calculated for a K of 0.42 and fitted, curve 3 was obtained. The divergence noted could have been due to a small amount of a transformation product whose partition ratio might be approximately 0.8.

Curve 2 clearly represented a transformation product, since basic material with the properties of these substances could not be isolated from control urine. It is also possible to calculate a theoretical curve for these tubes since they form a Pascal distribution. In this series each succeeding tube (from 30 to 20) has had one more transfer applied than its predecessor. This type of calculation has been treated by Stene.[154] See also p. 262.

It is clear from a diagram such as Figure 67 that countercurrent distribution should offer great possibilities in following the fate of many drugs or other substances taken into the body. A beginning along this line has been made with synthetic antimalarial drugs.[155] The isolation of metabolites from tissue and from biological fluids has always been a difficult problem.

With systems which do not build up pressure, an alternative procedure is possible which gives only one phase in the series withdrawn. In this the fundamental procedure is followed only until upper 0 has reached the second tube from the right of lower 0, lower 23. The contents of tube 24/24 are then withdrawn and discarded since no solute can be present in these solvents as yet. The tube is left empty for the next transfer. When the upper section is advanced only the upper phase from tube 0/23 will fall into the empty tube. However, at this point tube 24/0 will contain no upper phase. The appropriate volume is accordingly added from a syringe through the opening in the cover and the equilibration is then performed.

[154] S. Stene, *Arkiv Kemi, Mineral. Geol.*, **A18**, No. 18 (1944).

[155] O. E. Titus, L. C. Craig, C. Golumbic, H. Mighton, I. Wempen, and R. C. Elderfield, *J. Org. Chem.*, **13**, 39 (1948).

While the phases are separating, the upper phase present in tube 0/24 is withdrawn.   It constitutes the first member of the withdrawn series.

Another transfer again gives only upper phase advancing into the empty tube.   It will be number 2 of the withdrawn series.   The process may be continued until all the solute has been removed in the upper phase.   Often this process will simplify analytical difficulties since only one phase need be dealt with.   The use, for a distribution, of a lower phase which would otherwise interfere with the final analysis is thus permitted.

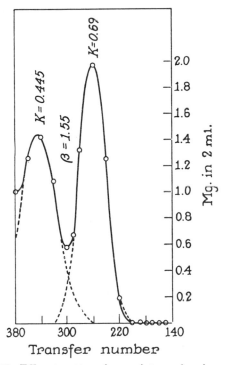

Fig. 68. Effluent pattern for a mixture of amino acids.

The single-withdrawal procedure is analogous to operating a chromatogram by the elution technique.   With the latter there is a certain optimum range in the degree the adsorbent retards the solute as it passes through. It must not pass through too rapidly nor yet too slowly.   Similarly, with a distribution train operated by single withdrawal there would appear to be an optimum rate of travel, *e.g.*, that given by an effective partition ratio in the range of 0.1 to 0.2.

Since now with the glass apparatus the single-withdrawal technique becomes much more important, a rapid method of calculating a theoretical withdrawal curve is highly desirable. Fortunately, a minor change in the approximation for the normal curve of error has made this possible. In order to show the method of calculating such a curve, an actual example will be given:

A synthetic mixture of amino acids was distributed in a 108-tube train using a system containing aqueous ammonium sulfate, propanol, and acetic acid. The first two bands to emerge from the end of the train were tryptophan and phenylalanine. For illustration of the point, we shall deal only with these two and omit the remainder of the experiment. In plotting withdrawal curves we have found it convenient to assign the corresponding transfer numbers (as in Fig. 68) to the successive upper phases withdrawn with the first to emerge on the right. This procedure seems better than the method given on page 259, when many transfers are involved.

Each successive phase that emerges has had one more transfer applied than the previous one. It is immediately apparent that exact calculation by the binomial expansion is out of the question because of the labor involved. Let us therefore for the moment neglect the exact mechanism by which the curve is achieved and consider it as a curve to be matched by some suitable formula that must include the partition ratio, the average number of transfers involved in the band, and the units used for the abscissa and the ordinate. Let n be the average number of transfers in the band, $i.e.$, the transfer number at the maximum. Let u be the number of units in the train. Then it is possible to derive easily from equation (22) in Section II.4.B. that $K = u/(n - u)$. Equation (33) can now be

$$y = \frac{1}{\sqrt{2\pi n/K}} \, e^{-x^2/(2n/K)} \tag{33}$$

derived easily from the approximation of equation (32). The abscissa and ordinates are x and y respectively.

Thus K for the tryptophan band of Figure 68 is 0.69 and n is 240. The experimentally found value for y_0 (from the experimental curve) is 1.97; y_1, y_2, y_3, etc. are calculated from y_0, as on page 257, by multiplying 1.97 by $e^{-x^2/(2_i/K)}$. Thus, calculating and matching a theoretical curve in a withdrawal series is even simpler than for the fundamental series. Naturally such an approximation will hold only for rather high numbers of transfers. It has been checked experimentally with an extraction train containing of the order of 100 tubes but if the K is 1 or less, fair agreement should be obtained even with 25 tubes. A withdrawal curve is always slightly skewed, but the agreement obtained by the above approximation is good enough for practical purposes, as can be seen from Figure 68.

C. ALTERNATE-WITHDRAWAL PROCEDURE

The principle of this procedure is given in Section II.4.A. It is often the procedure of choice for complicated mixtures and for substances whose partition ratios are closely related. It approaches the true counter-current process more nearly than any of the others and is correspondingly the most efficient for some purposes.

The fundamental procedure is first accomplished. Then with the steel machine of Figure 61 (p. 249) tube 24/0 is first withdrawn and set aside on the left. At the next stage, tube 0/0 is withdrawn and set aside on the right. It forms the first tube of that series. At the next stage tube 0/1 is withdrawn and forms the second tube in the left series. It has had two more transfers applied than has the 0 tube of that series. At the next stage 1/1 is withdrawn and forms the second tube in the right series.

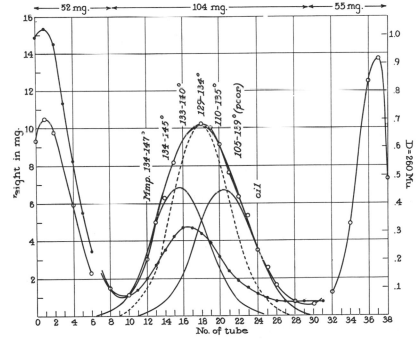

Fig. 69. Alternate-withdrawal pattern of an artificial mixture of penicillins: O, weight, in milligrams, of triethylamine salt; ● extinction at 260 mμ; —theoretical curves (assuming K of 0.7 + 1.05); - - - theory for one substance (K of 0.9).

The next withdrawn tube is 1/2 for the left series and the next after that is 2/2 for the right series, etc.

In plotting the results of such a distribution three curves are required.

The series on the left gives one curve. Those remaining in the apparatus until the end form the central curve. Those on the right represent the other withdrawn series. An actual example of such a distribution, given in Figure 69, was made on an artificial mixture of four penicillins,[156] p-hydroxybenzylpenicillin, benzylpenicillin, Δ^2-pentenylpenicillin, and n-heptylpenicillin. The left-hand curves represent p-hydroxybenzyl-penicillin; the central curves represent partially separated benzylpenicillin on the left and partially separated Δ^2-pentenylpenicillin on the right; the right-hand curve represents n-heptylpenicillin. A total of 38 transfers had been applied. A theoretical curve could be calculated for the bands located in the tubes remaining in the machine until the end but only if insignificant amounts of the solute of that band had been withdrawn. In this case, the two overlapping bands could be accurately estimated. The problem of calculating a curve in a simple manner for either of the withdrawn bands has not as yet been solved. The difficulties of this calculation have been treated by Karlson and von Hecker[157] who have provided formulas for calculating the withdrawn curves under certain restrictions. Those interested in this problem and a good general treatment of the mathematics of countercurrent distribution can well refer to their paper.

It is almost always advisable even in the preliminary phases of an investigation to go a little further than the fundamental procedure by applying several extra transfers by the withdrawal method. Thus with the 25-tube machine three tubes might be withdrawn on each side. With the 54-tube machine six tubes might be withdrawn on each side. In this case the solute in the withdrawn tubes will have a partition ratio either of 0.1 or less, or of 10 or greater. The efficiency of the separation of any material in these tubes is therefore not too great. In order to get a quantitative picture of the mixture little error is introduced if these tubes are plotted as part of the same curve formed by the tubes remaining in the apparatus until the end. For an example, see Craig et al.[156]

Since it is desirable to keep all of the band comprising the solute of interest in the apparatus until the end so that a calculated curve can be applied to it, some rapid method of knowing exactly the limits of the band at any time during the distribution is desirable. A very convenient method of estimating them is available from the mathematics of probability. Thus $\sqrt{pqn}$ or $\sqrt{\left(\dfrac{K}{K+1}\right)\left(\dfrac{1}{K+1}\right)}\,n$ is the mean probable error and six times this amount would include approximately 99% of the total cases.

[156] L. C. Craig, G. H. Hogeboom, F. H. Carpenter, and V. du Vigneaud, J. Biol. Chem., 168, 665 (1947).

[157] P. Karlson and E. von Hecker, Z. Naturforsch., 5b, 237 (1950).

Accordingly $6\sqrt{nK}/(K + 1)^2$ would give a width of the band in terms of tube number which would include approximately 99% of the solute. The position of the maximum can be located quickly by the equation $N = nK/(K + 1)$. $3\sqrt{nK}/(K + 1)^2$ tubes from this point on each side gives the edge of the band.

In using alternate withdrawal it is not necessary to withdraw equal numbers of tubes from each side. If the solute of interest has a partition ratio greater than 1, for instance 3, for each tube withdrawn from the upper layer (the right-hand side of the pattern) five should be withdrawn from the lower (the left-hand side of the pattern). Using the calculation discussed above, withdrawal can be controlled so that for a considerable time none of the solute of interest emerges.

D. COMPLETION OF SQUARES

This procedure is very easily accomplished by the glass distribution trains. The fundamental procedure stage is first reached and then the train is operated further without adding fresh upper phase at the 0 tube. The upper phases are collected and numbered as in single withdrawal. After the last upper phase has emerged from the apparatus and analysis has been made, the diamond pattern can be drawn. As in the single-withdrawal procedure two adjoining curves are to be considered. Since the lower phases remaining in the apparatus also represent a withdrawn series, in plotting, the tube numbers are replaced by transfer numbers, adding to each tube number the transfer number at which it became free of upper phase.

Bush and Densen[158] give the mathematics for calculating theoretical curves. For larger numbers of transfers approximations are well suited for calculating theoretical curves. That of the effluent upper phases is identical with the withdrawn series of single withdrawal, while that of the heavier phases is the mirror image. Therefore, $1/K$ should be substituted for K in equation 33. K in this case can be calculated from equation (34) where S is the number of lower phases remaining without upper phase at the time the last upper phase

$$K = S/(n - S) \qquad (34)$$

leaves the lower phase of highest solute concentration.

It may not be desirable to produce a symmetrical diamond pattern. An unsymmetrical pattern can be produced by interrupting the addition of fresh upper phase before all the tubes of the series are full and then proceeding to the point where all the upper phases have emerged as effluent.

[158] M. T. Bush and P. M. Densen, *Anal. Chem.*, **20**, 121 (1948).

A higher number of transfers will be accomplished by continuing addition of upper phases for an arbitrary time after the fundamental procedure point is reached as in single withdrawal before permitting the upper phases to leave the lower.

Recycling. This procedure is of real value only when relatively high numbers of tubes are in the distribution train. It is accomplished very easily. If, at the point of completion of the fundamental procedure, analysis shows an overlapping band formed by solutes with partition ratios nearly equal, the higher numbers of transfers required to cause their separation may be reached by reintroducing each effluent upper phase again into the train at tube 0. Before this the solute in any separated band could have been removed from the train and the solvents replaced. The longer distribution trains discussed later (see page 277) in connection with automatic equipment are arranged so that return of an effluent phase to the 0 tube can be automatic. It is the most effective procedure for separating mixtures with very similar partition ratios, but must be carefully controlled by analysis from time to time during the course of the prolonged run to make certain that remixing of separated solutes does not occur.

3. Separation of Mixtures with Many Components

The separation and analysis of mixtures with many components has always been a difficult and tedious problem except in certain fortunate cases. Only recently has the technical development of fractional distillation[159] and of the chromatogram[160] made possible solutions to such a problem. The problem of the separation of the amino acids resulting from the hydrolysis of a protein may be given as an example. Countercurrent distribution offers certain possibilities along the same line.

As an example the separation and estimation of the components of a mixture of pentanoic, hexanoic, heptanoic, and octanoic acids may be taken. Figure 70 is an actual example[161] of such a separation, made in a 25-tube apparatus (see also page 196). It can be seen from this pattern that if yet another component had been present there would not have been a sufficient number of tubes for clear resolution. However, if the apparatus had contained 50 tubes, two or three more bands could have been revealed with equal precision. A 100-tube apparatus could have theoretically accommodated nine or ten such bands if their partition ratios were properly

[159] A. and E. Rose, in *Distillation*, Volume IV of *Technique of Organic Chemistry*, A. Weissberger, ed. Interscience, New York-London, 1951.

[160] A. J. P. Martin and R. L. M. Synge, *Biochem. J.*, **35**, 1358 (1941). R. L. M. Synge, *ibid.*, **38**, 285 (1944). R. Consden, A. H. Gordon, and A. J. P. Martin *ibid.*, **38**, 224 (1944).

[161] Y. Sato, G. T. Barry, and L. C. Craig, unpublished results.

spaced. An apparatus with many tubes is thus highly desirable for the separation of mixtures containing many components.

However, most mixtures encountered will not have components with partition ratios ideally spaced. For this case, regardless of the number of tubes available, it will be necessary to separate out certain overlapping bands together and then in a subsequent run take up their separation under more ideal conditions.

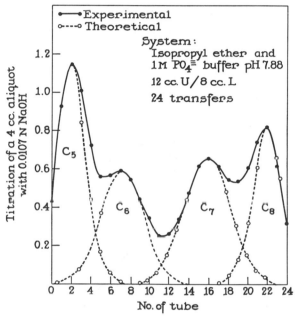

Fig. 70. Distribution pattern of an artificial mixture of normal fatty acids.

A single distribution can only rarely be carried out so that it will answer all the questions which may come up concerning a mixture. Thus, the requirements for a preliminary separation are quite different from those for the establishment of the purity of a preparation or in turn from those designed to give the greatest yield of one component from a given mixture.

4. Application of Countercurrent-Distribution Data to the Problem of Identification of a Substance and Proof of Purity of a Given Preparation

Experimentally the classical identification of a single unknown organic compound involves the determination of the simplest empirical formula through the ultimate analysis for as many elements as the compound contains. The determination of molecular weight is required to supply the actual empirical formula. Finally, from the observance of a number of chemical and physical properties, a structural formula including configuration may be inferred.

There are, as is generally recognized, many abbreviations of the classical procedure. Thus, neither qualitative nor ultimate analysis may be required if suitable authentic specimens are available for direct comparison to the unknown specimen. Such comparisons are usually done with respect to several physical and chemical properties. If the unknown is crystalline with one or more reproducible melting points, the well known mixed melting point may be used. If the melting point or points of any mixture of the known and unknown specimens is higher or lower than those of the individual components the conclusion is drawn that the specimens constitute different compounds. If the melting points of several mixtures of the specimens differing widely in composition are the same as those of the separate components, it is quite probable that they are the same compound. However, it is by no means proved that such is the case. Due to solid solution formation or possibly to lack of the solubility of one solid in the melt of the other, occasionally the mixed melting point method fails. (See also Section VIII.) Obviously it fails where the unknown is too unstable to have a reproducible melting point. In such cases a mixed solubility determination often is reliable.

The practice of crystallizing to constant melting point as a procedure is common and reliable. It warrants little comment here. A criterion of purity not commonly recognized but sometimes useful is that a compound may display polymorphism when sufficiently pure. Thus, in the case of oleic acid, a sample which has been carefully crystallized and fractionally distilled has a melting point at 16.25° as well as at 13.26°. The lower melting form readily changes to the higher melting form in the case of sufficiently pure samples, thus making possible a more rigorous identification and criterion of purity.

Absolute proof of the identity of two specimens as well as the *absolute* proof of the purity of a single specimen is unattainable. The concepts of purity and identity are useful but can only be established by operational techniques. Naturally certain techniques are more rigorous than others. A rigorous approach appears to have been achieved for a number of *stable* hydrocarbons by Rossini and collaborators,[162] by use of a freezing-point technique for estimating the degree to which purity has been attained. They expressed the amount of impurity in a given sample on a mole per cent basis.

[162] F. D. Rossini, *Anal. Chem.*, **20**, 110 (1948).

The concepts of purity and its attainment for biological chemicals are, of course, no different basically from those which apply to other organic compounds.   The former are prone to form solid solutions, to have more than one melting point near the same temperature (this is sometimes an advantage), to be unstable, and to be of high molecular weight.   These properties are not favorable with respect to the use of the freezing-point method and of many other techniques.   Yet biological chemists have done well in the development of methods applicable to their field.   Indeed, the solubility determination, which Northrop applied to proteins, is a good illustration.

The problems of identification and measurement of purity are always related.   They may be solved frequently by the interpretation of the same set of unrelated properties such as neutral equivalents and freezing point. There are many other properties useful in identification work, such as boiling point, refractive index, light absorption, X-ray diffraction, density, viscosity, surface tension, solubility, bioassay, behavior toward acids and bases and other reagents, and thermal stability.   These properties, however useful, of themselves rarely are sufficient to establish purity.   If it can be shown, however, that the unknown has an acceptable degree of purity, as for example, by the freezing-point technique, most of the properties mentioned can be used in the final identification.   Countercurrent distribution is a technique which shows promise of even greater usefulness than freezing-point techniques for the measuring of the purity of organic compounds.   Extraction may be applied to *stable* as well as to *unstable* substances.

One of the advantages of extraction as a laboratory tool is that it permits the study of reactive compounds without isolating them in the "pure" state.   For example, a solvent such as water may be required for the stabilization of a certain pair of solutes A and B.   The separation of A and B may be entirely feasible by extraction.   Furthermore, the course of the separation may be conveniently expressed.   Thus, the countercurrent-distribution technique constitutes a rigorous approach to the degree to which such a separation is realized.   The purity of A would be 98% if this solute had been separated to the extent that it contained 98% of A and 2% of B on a solvent-free basis.

A main approach to the problem of purity may be classified as the fractionation approach.   To be sure, certain approaches may be considered hybrids involving two classes.   The sample is subjected to fractionation attempts until its physical properties can be changed no longer.   This is the method most used by organic chemists and is a time-consuming procedure. The main fractionation schemes available for separations are the following: crystallization, distillation, adsorption, extraction, electrical transport, diffusion, and centrifugation.   In more recent times hybrids of these methods such as extractive distillation[163] and partition chromatography[164] have been developed. All these schemes may be useful for estimating purity provided they have sufficient resolving power. Thus fractional crystallization may be adequate in some cases but may fail entirely in others because the solid phase collected does not differ appreciably in composition from the liquid (excluding the solvent). This is more or less true

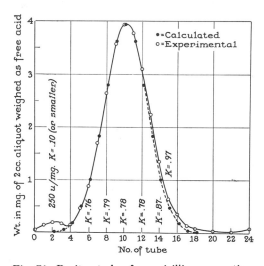

Fig. 71. Purity study of a penicillin preparation.

of all the methods of fractionation listed above but is basically less true of extraction than of any of the others, because extraction is a much more flexible method generally and can be applied under a very wide variety of conditions. Thus if a preparation behaves as a single solute in one system and with many transfers applied, it may be tried profitably in an entirely different environment where the physical forces affecting the solute may be quite different. The remainder of this section will be concerned with the application of extraction data to the measurement of purity.

The application of the countercurrent-distribution method to the problem of purity has been discussed in several publications.[165,166] When a

[163] M. R. Fenske, C. S. Carlson, and D. Quiggle, *Ind. Eng. Chem.*, **39**, 1322 (1947).

[164] A. J. P. Martin and R. L. M. Synge, *Biochem. J.*, **35**, 1358 (1941).

[165] L. C. Craig, H. Mighton, E. O. Titus, and C. Golumbic, *Anal. Chem.*, **20**, 134 (1948). E. O. Titus, L. C. Craig, C. Golumbic, H. Mighton, I. Wempen, and R. C. Elderfield, *J. Org. Chem.*, **13**, 39 (1948). G. T. Barry, Y. Sato, and L. C. Craig, *J. Biol. Chem.*, **174**, 221 (1948).

[166] L. C. Craig, G. H. Hogeboom, F. H. Carpenter, and V. du Vigneaud, *J. Biol. Chem.*, **168**, 665 (1947).

distribution diagram has been experimentally achieved which agrees with the calculated within the experimental error, the solute is assumed to be pure within certain limits.   If it does not agree three possibilities must be considered.   In discussing these three possibilities an actual experimental diagram will be considered.   The diagram of Figure 71 was made with a sample of benzylpenicillin[166] recrystallized several times.   A divergence from the theoretical curve was noted in at least two places.   The shape of the first divergence on the left leaves little doubt but that it represents impurity.   Determination of the partition ratio of the solute in tubes 1, 2, and 3 or even isolation would confirm this assumption. The interpretation of the small amount of divergence on the right side of the main band, however, requires more study.   It could possibly have been due to the fact that equilibrium had not been reached or that the partition ratio was not constant over the concentration range employed.   Both of these possibilities may be eliminated by determining the partition ratios of the solutes in the tubes concerned.   If they should prove to be the same as that of the solute on the other side of the main band, neither of these possibilities could be the cause.   Such possibilities are treated more thoroughly in Sections II and VIII.   On the other hand, the ratios actually determined showed the material in the tubes concerned to be different from the main body of the band.   It therefore represented impurity in small percentage but the actual amount cannot be estimated with high precision from Figure 71.   Precise estimation would require several times the number of transfers.   Where any doubt exists, therefore, as to the cause of a divergence, it is always advisable to determine for comparison the partition ratios of the solutes on each side of the main band at similar concentration ranges.   After several times the number of transfers have been applied the evaluation is repeated for more convincing data.

If a perfectly operating system is available and a countercurrent-distribution pattern is experimentally run which agrees with the calculated curve[167] within the experimental error, the impurities that may be present are limited to two types, those which escape the analytical method employed and those which have partition ratios sufficiently near the value for the solute of interest that if present they are not detected.   The first type may be detected by using an analytical method which is more inclusive.   It is for this reason that determination of weight[166] is the method to be recommended wherever possible.   The second possibility requires a more thorough discussion.

If impurity is present with an identical or nearly identical partition ratio in one system and, thereby, escapes detection it will usually be revealed by a change of system or temperature.   There is, however, no absolute

[167] B. Williamson and L. C. Craig, *J. Biol. Chem.*, **168**, 687 (1947).

guarantee that it will be revealed by such a change. The method does not guarantee purity in the absolute sense nor can any other known method achieve such an ideal.

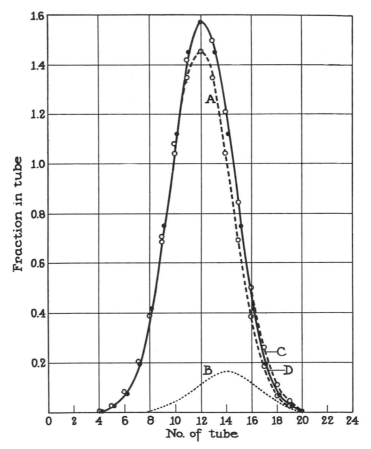

Fig. 72. Hypothetical distribution patterns of a mixture. $n = 24$; $\beta = 1.4$.

The extraction technique can be used so that the probability of the presence of a spurious solute becomes so slight that, for all practical purposes, the objective is accomplished.

Two general approaches may be taken in improving the reliability of extraction in proving purity. The first is mechanical and involves the application of higher numbers of transfers to a given system. This simply reduces in a mathematical way the permissible limits of partition ratio that an impurity might have and still escape detection. The second involves the discovery of a more selective or specific system for the extraction, and up to the present time has been a matter of experience.

The effect of higher numbers of transfers can be appreciated best by a consideration of 100 mg. of a hypothetical mixture.   Figure 72 shows the effect to be expected with 24 transfers and equal volumes of the phases from a mixture of 90% A, $K = 1$, and 10% B, $K = 1.4$.   The sum of curves A and B gives curve C.   If this mixture had been encountered as an unknown, curve C would have been determined as a weight curve.   An

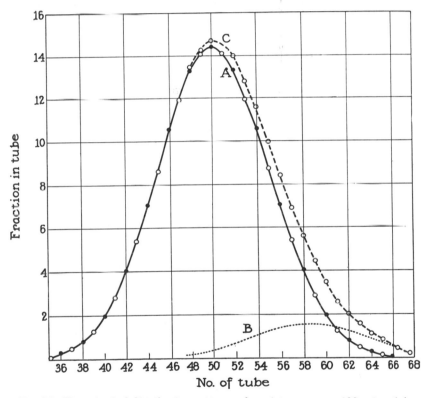

Fig. 73. Hypothetical distribution patterns of a mixture. $n = 100$; $\beta = 1.4$.

aliquot should have been so selected for the determination of weight that the weight of residue in the maximum tube would be at least 100 times that of the error in weighing.   Then a theoretical curve[167] would have been matched, in this case curve D.

Although the divergence of C from D appears slight at first glance, it is appreciable.   At tube 17 the determined weight is 2.6 mg. while the theoretical is 1.9 mg., a difference of 0.7 mg.   The error in weighing could be ±0.1 mg. Thus the divergence would be six times the experimental error. Such a divergence would also be supported by the divergence at tubes 16 and 18.

If this same mixture were subjected to 100 transfers, a much clearer picture would be obtained, as is shown in Figure 73. Here the two bands are far enough separated so that nearly half the curve of A on the left side

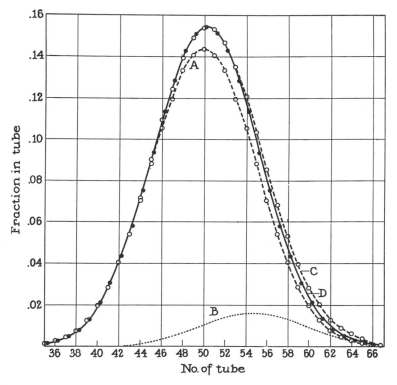

Fig. 74. Hypothetical distribution patterns of a mixture. $n = 100$; $\beta = 1.2$.

is essentially pure and it is therefore available for the matching of a theoretical curve. The theoretical curve now coincides with A and the difference between this curve and the one which would be experimentally determined, curve C, would give curve B. It is plain that for these partition ratios, 1% of B in A could be detected.

It is now instructive to consider a mixture of substances whose partition ratios are closer together. Such a mixture could be one containing 90% of A with the partition ratio of 1 and 10% of B with the partition ratio of 1.2. 24 transfers obviously would not be sufficient to show the presence of the mixture if weights only were used for the determination of the curve. However, 100 transfers would give the picture shown in Figure 74.

The question of the selectivity of the system cannot be answered so methodically. Nonetheless, an actual study here also will serve to give the viewpoint. The problem of the separation of benzylpenicillin and Δ^2-pentenylpenicillin will be a good example. Table VII gives the partition ratios of the two penicillins determined in a number of different systems.[168] The choice of a system will be treated more fully in Sect. VIII.

If, for instance, the purity of a benzylpenicillin preparation were being studied, several per cent of Δ^2-pentenylpenicillin would escape detection with system 1, using 24 transfers. This would not be the case with 7, 8, or 9 in Table VII.

The interesting conclusion to be drawn from this table is that the β values are in each case shifted by the change in the system. This shift is not of large magnitude, in accord with the experience of others[169] for

TABLE VII

PARTITION RATIOS OF BENZYLPENICILLIN AND Δ^2-PENTENYLPENICILLIN

System no.	Organic solvent	Phosphate buffer	K of benzyl-penicillin (G)	K of Δ^2-pentenyl penicillin (F)	Ratio β
1	Ethyl acetate	1 M, pH 5.12	1.24	1.05	1.20
2	Ethyl ether	3 M, pH 4.60	5.20	8.9	1.71
3	Ethyl ether	3 M, pH 4.93	2.54	4.00	1.57
4	Chloroform	2 M, pH 4.85	1.32	0.93	1.42
5	Furan	3 M, pH 4.93	0.34	0.50	1.47
6	Ethyl ether	2 M, pH 4.85	0.75	1.18	1.57
7	50–50 Ethyl and isopropyl ethers	3 M, pH 4.93	0.96	1.72	1.80
8	Isopropyl ether	3 M, pH 4.93	0.34	0.68	1.97
9	Isopropyl ether	3 M, pH 4.93	0.26[a]	0.61	2.3

[a] Determined at 25 °C.

closely related substances. Irrespective of this, the practical problem of determination of purity of a preparation by countercurrent distribution resolves itself into the application of a sufficient number of transfers together with adequate analytical precision so that the limiting β value which would permit a mixture to escape detection is small as compared to the β value for any likely impurity. The advantage to be gained by studying several systems is shown by Table VII.

[168] G. T. Barry, Y. Sato, and L. C. Craig, *J. Biol. Chem.*, **174**, 221 (1948).

[169] A. J. P. Martin and R. L. M. Synge, *Biochem. J.*, **35**, 91 (1941). R. E. Cornish, R. C. Archibald, E. A. Murphy, and H. M. Evans, *Ind. Eng. Chem.*, **26**, 397 (1934).

In the case of Figures 72 and 74 the sensitivity of the method is decreased because of the inability to place correctly the theoretical curve when weight only is used to determine the actual experimental curve. However, if a method of analysis specific for A only in contrast to B, or vice versa, such as biological assay, infrared absorption, etc., is at hand, the procedure then becomes much more sensitive and here again would permit limiting β values of 1.2 and 1.1 for 24 and 100 transfers, respectively, and yet permit detection of a few per cent of the one constituent.

Where the question of purity is very important confirmation of the conclusions derived from direct distribution of the sample can be obtained by distribution of a reaction product or products obtained by the action of some

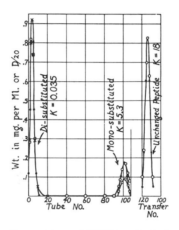

Fig. 75. Distribution pattern of DNP products from gramicidin-S.

mild reagent which will cover or liberate a hydrophylic group. A good example of such an approach is found in a study of the polypeptide gramicidin-S.[170] This peptide was thought to be a pentapeptide although diffusion data had shown that the molecular weight could be higher. Countercurrent distribution soon showed that material isolated by fractional crystallization was not entirely pure but that a single band could be obtained by distribution which had the appearance of homogeneity. This material was then treated with the Sanger reagent, fluoro-2,4-dinitrobenzene, to make a dinitrophenyl derivative. An amount of reagent insufficient to cover all the amino present was used with the intention of revealing whether or not the peptide molecule contained more than a single amino group.

If the preparation was pure and only one amino group was present two bands, one for the derivative and the other for the original peptide, would

[170] A. R. Battersby and I . C. Craig, J. Am. Chem. Soc., 73, 1887 (1951).

be expected.   However, the result shown in Figure 75 was obtained.   This result showed that two amino groups are present and permitted a molecular weight to be calculated from weight-optical density ratios (or Van Slyke amino nitrogen).   Only clean-cut bands agreeing with theoretical distributions and ascribable to the derivatives of a single peptide were obtained. Such a result gives considerable added proof for the thesis of purity.

5. Automatic Countercurrent-Distribution Equipment

It should be obvious to anyone who has read even part of the foregoing treatment that an apparatus with very high numbers of tubes would be desirable from almost any standpoint were it not for the labor involved in making the transfers.   There is also the analytical problem presented by

Fig. 76. 420-tube automatic countercurrent-distribution apparatus.

the high numbers of tubes at the end of the run.   The first of these difficulties has been met in part by the development of automatic equipment. The second can be minimized by the proper systematization of analytical techniques.   Great improvement along both lines can still be achieved. At the present time, however, the development in both directions has reached the stage where a single train with 420 tubes has not proved unwieldy.   It has permitted separations involving thousands of transfers to be carried out routinely.

Description of this type of apparatus[171] was reserved for a separate section in the thought that it is more suited for the specialist.   It admittedly

[171] L. C. Craig, W. Hausmann, E. H. Ahrens, Jr., and E. J. Harfenist, *Anal. Chem.*, **23**, 1236 (1951).

requires a considerable outlay of time and money, perhaps of the same order as an ultracentrifuge or an electrophoresis set-up. The entire apparatus consists of an extraction train, a glass hood in which the train operates, a mechanical robot for driving the train, an automatic filling device, and an automatic fraction collector. A photograph of such an assembly with 420 tubes is shown in Figure 76. This apparatus can now be purchased in part or in its entirety from H. O. Post, 6822 60th Road, Maspeth, N. Y.

The hood of showcase construction is mounted on a long table covered with stainless-steel sheeting. A table height of 28 inches has been found convenient. The robot is mounted outside the hood beneath the table and drives the train by a rack which extends from the arm of the robot through a small hole in the table to the gear wheel attached to one of the bearings. Thus, no electric circuits or switches are inside the hood to ignite chance vapors of combustible solvents. The frame of the hood is made of wood covered with stainless steel. The sides and top are made of plate glass; any glass section can be removed at will. The side sections are mounted on tracks to permit them to slide to one side. The exhaust through the top of the hood has a damper for regulation of the draft. The room in which the assembly is placed is air conditioned with temperature variations of $\pm 1°$. However, when the hood is closed temperature variations in the train are less than $\pm 0.2°$.

The extraction cells are identical to those shown in Figure 64. They are mounted in the same way except that they are arranged in two rows, one above and slightly to the rear of the other. This arrangement makes the apparatus shorter but has in fact a more important purpose. In the upper row the transfer tube carries the upper phase in a direction away from its point of entry. At the end of this row the transfer tube carries the upper phase to the lower row. In the lower row the transfer tubes lead to the next cells toward the point of entry and on the last cell of the lower row the decantation tube is extended so that the decantation cell of this tube is mounted beside the decantation cell of tube 0. Thus, the end of the train has returned to its beginning. This permits the train to be operated in the single-withdrawal procedure by attaching the effluent tube to the decantation cell of the terminal tube or in the recycling procedure by replacing the effluent tube with a short glass tube leading to cell 0 again.

A. FILLING DEVICES

Several different types of filling devices have been made and tested. Devices employing hypodermic syringes and valves have been avoided because of the danger of their sticking when the apparatus operates unattended. The final model which appears to be satisfactory under any conditions is probably a little too intricate for an unskilled glass blower to make.   However, it can be purchased commercially from H. O. Post, Scientific Apparatus Co., 6822   60th Rd., Maspeth, N. Y.   One type of filling apparatus has been described in the literature[171] and will not be described again here.   It works on the dipping principle.   Its disadvantage is in the difficulty of assembly for each run, and in additional room required in the hood.

A simple device has been used for some time in the laboratory of one of the authors.   It is simple and easy to build but is very sensitive to changes in external conditions.

The solvent reservoir, a (Fig. 77), is a 5-liter flask with a flat bottom and a standard taper joint.   It rests on a small platform, b, attached to the frame of the apparatus and inside the hood in front of and to one side of the bearing.   Two glass

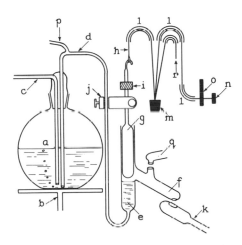

Fig. 77. Filling device operating by a plunger.

tubes extend through the stopper: c is for the entrance of air, d is the siphon. Near the top bend in the siphon is a side tube, P, closed with a rubber tube and clamp for starting the siphon.   The siphon is made from 7-mm. tubing.   It empties into a chamber, e, of shape shown in the figure.   The solvent will rise in e to a point approximately 1 cm. below the side arm f.   It will not rise further because the level is controlled by the level of the air inlet tube, c, in the reservoir.

A glass plunger, g, hangs from a nylon cord.   At the decantation position the cord permits the plunger to drop a controlled distance into e.   This displaces a measured volume of solvent from e which flows out through f into a funnel, K.   K is attached to the first decantation cell of the distribution train in such manner that it moves under f at the decantation position of the train and permits the solvents to flow into the first decantation cell.   The volume of solvent displaced by g is controlled by the rubber stop, i, which is a small one-hole rubber stopper which fits tightly around the stem of g and strikes the ring of a clamp, j. This clamp is attached to the siphon. Its position on d can easily be adjusted.

The nylon cord which pulls the plunger up passes through bent glass tubes, l. Its other end is attached to a weight, m. Another nylon cord attached to m passes through two glass tubes as shown and is attached to a post, n, of the frame at its other end. A rod, O, is mounted to the support of the train in such a way that it strikes the nylon cord between n and L in the decantation position of the train. This pulls up the weight m and lets the plunger g drop.

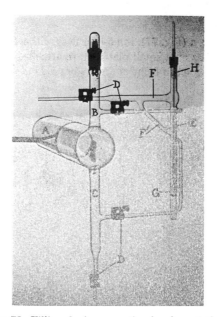

Fig. 78. Filling device operating by decantation.

Experience has shown that during most runs it is advantageous to add a small amount of the heavier phase as well to make up for losses due to entrainment and for distortion of phases due to the solute. A second filling device about one-tenth the size of the one shown here is ideal for this purpose. It is mounted so that its side arm, q, empties into an opening in the upper side of the bigger side arm, f, of the main filling device. The plunger of this smaller filling device is actuated by a third nylon cord attached to m.

A reproducibility of 0.1 to 0.2 ml. in upper phases injected is desired. That very steady conditions surrounding the reservoir a are required will be appreciated when it is pointed out that the volume of a is 5 liters. A change in pressure of one part in 10,000 will cause the level in e to rise or fall sufficiently to cause a variation in the volume displaced of 0.1 ml. Any draft or change in temperature around a will have a similar effect. It was found that a door to the room which was shut by a spring caused errors until the transom above the door was left open. Highly volatile solvents such as ethyl ether gave more trouble than less volatile ones.

The most reliable and satisfactory filling device is shown in Figure 78. In Figure 79 a photograph of the whole assembly is shown.

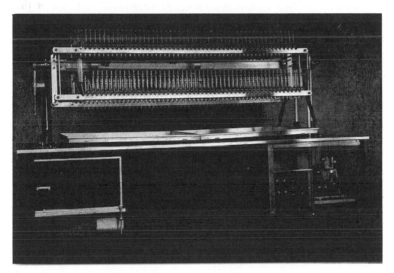

Fig. 79. 100-tube completely automatic distribution apparatus.

A is the solvent reservoir. It is made from large glass tubing of appropriate size depending on the size of the machine and the volume required for an overnight run. It can be of such length that its volume can be easily 6 to 8 liters. The clamp holding A in the photograph is not the one holding it to the apparatus. However, two similar strap clamps hold it to a large piece of aluminum mounted so that it is between the two rows of equilibration tubes and between the two bearings which support the train (Fig. 79) and permit it to turn. Tube A is on the axis with the front bearing at the center and slightly in front of A. The tubes B and C, made from 20-mm. tubing, pass in front of the 0 tube of the train. A is filled through the top of B. The solutions can be drained out through the butt joint at the bottom of C. A is mounted with a slight tilt toward C for draining the solvents. The various parts are joined by butt joints and clamps D.

A tube E measures the volume of solution which passes into the apparatus in the transfer position. It is joined to B and C by two 7-mm. pieces of glass tubing. The solution flows through the lower tube attached to C and E when the train is tipped to the transfer position. At this point it even reaches nearly up to tube F which leads off into a decantation tube just above tube 0 of the train. But on tipping back to the settling position any excess drains back into C and leaves only the volume trapped below the inlet tube on E.   The volume of solution trapped is adjustable by the plunger G which has a glass rod attached which extends through a stainless-steel cap closing, E.   Friction on the cap holds G at the desired position. The rod also passes through a small inverted cup, H, sealed onto the rod.   This is to catch any solvent which might flow down the rod when it is tipped to the transfer

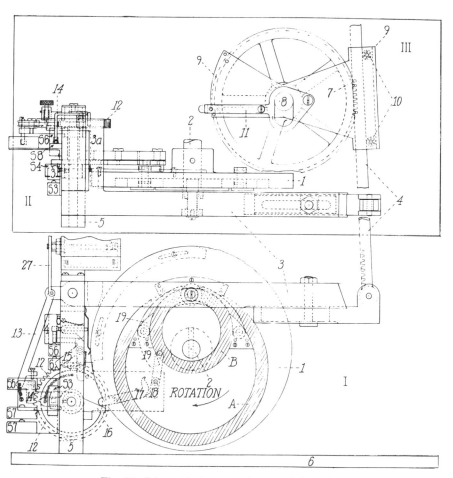

Fig. 80. Schematic drawing of parts of the robot.

position and comes in contact with the steel cap.   The solvent trapped in E passes through F′ into the train when the assembly reaches the transfer position   Figure 79 shows this filling device on a 100-tube automatic machine.   It is mounted between the two rows of tubes.

B. THE ROBOT

The movements which operate the extractor are relatively simple tipping movements designed to place the cells in the positions shown in Figure 64. Nonetheless, the design now in use is somewhat complicated in order to give versatility and permit each movement and interval to be adjusted independently of the others.   Detailed drawings of the various parts of the robot are given in Figures 80 and 81; each figure gives several views. In Figure 80 two side views, I and III, and two top views, II and IV, are given.   An end view, I, is given in Figure 81.   A drawing of the "combiner" is given in II, Figure 81, and III and IV are side and end views, respectively, of the timer.

A solid iron wheel (1), 22 cm. in diameter and 1.7 cm. thick, is mounted on the drive shaft (2) of the reduction gear of the electric motor.   Two circular tracks, A and B, which merge at one place, are cut into the wheel.   Each track is 12 mm. wide and 9 mm. deep.   The circle of the larger track, A, is 17.2 cm. in diameter; B is 8.6 cm. in diameter

An aluminum bar (3) approximately 30 cm. in length and 2.5 cm. in width and breadth, acts as a lever arm to drive the rack (4).   The effective length of the arm and hence of the stroke is adjustable by virtue of the bolt and sliding section near the rack bearing.   On its other end, the bar carries a side L extension (3a in view II of Fig. 80) so that the bar can be attached by two bearings to a rigid broad piece of aluminum metal (5) 18 cm. in height, 10 cm. thick, and 2.5 cm. wide.   Part 5 is in turn attached by screws to the base plate (6) of the robot.   The base (6) is an aluminum plate 1.3 cm. thick, 46 cm. long, and 23 cm. wide.

At nearly the central part of the arm (3) is attached a pin held in the arm by two roller bearings.   The large end of the pin or shaft extends into the track in 1 and rolls on the sides of the track as wheel 1 revolves.   This drives the arm up and down. The two bearings by which 3 and 3a are attached to 5 prevent the arm from moving away from the wheel.   The roller remains in the smaller track, B, for the equilibration period.   It is shifted to the larger track, A, in order to reach the higher position required for the decantation, C of Figure 64.   This position is reached when wheel 1 is stopped 180° from the position shown.   The settling position, B of Figure 64, is that shown in view I of Figure 80.   The transfer position, A of Figure 64, is reached when the roller is in the smaller track, B, and the wheel is stopped 180° from the position shown in I.

The movement of the arm is transmitted through the rack (4) to the spur gear (7) shown in view III of Figure 80.   This gear is mounted directly on the rod (8) which serves as the bearing on which the aluminum bars carrying the extraction cells are mounted.

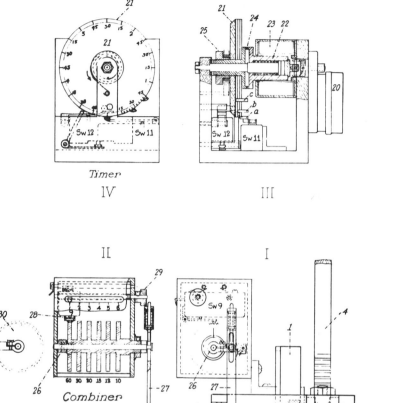

Fig. 81. Schematic drawing of parts of the robot: end view.

The rack (4) can be disengaged from the spur gear (7) in order to permit hand operation of the cells.   It is held against the spur gear by a broad brass piece (9) which extends to the opposite edge of the spur gear and on both sides of it, as shown in view IV.   The shaft (8) passes through a short slot set at an angle in 9.   Part 9 carries two roller bearings (10) which press against the back of the rack and normally keep the teeth engaged.   Part 11 together with 9 forms the bearing around 8. The former is attached to 9 at its right-hand end by means of a short bolt, so that it is movable.   The left-hand end of 11 is held in position at the lower edge of part 9 by a flat spring on 11 and a pin which snaps into the hole shown in 9.   Near the upper left-hand corner of 9 another hole is provided, so that the arm (11) can be moved to it.   This movement forces 9 along its slot and to the right a sufficient distance to disengage the rack from the spur gear.

The number of strokes per equilibration is adjustable from 5 to 50 by means of the small spur gear (12) which is mounted on the aluminum piece (5).   It is 8 cm. in diameter.   The L extension of the lever arm (3a) extends beyond the bearing on 5, so that a push rod (13) can be attached.   The push rod moves a metal part (14) which is held against 12 by a spring and is adjustable by a screw in 13.   Each time a downward stroke of 13 is made during the equilibration 12 is advanced one tooth; 12 is spring loaded but is held in position during the upward stroke of 13 by the rachet part (15) which is pressed into position by a spring.

The spur gear returns to its original position when the decantation is made.   At this point the push rod (13) travels far enough so that 14 disengages itself.   At the same time 15 is pushed out by the pin on 12 and is held out by a spring ratchet attachment, which is released again when the spur gear returns to its starting point.

The spur gear (12) carries an adjustable outer arm mounted on its shaft, which carries a pin and determines the distance the gear travels on being released and must return again stepwise in order to reach the 0 position.   Near the outer edge of the spur gear, a series of holes numbered 1 to 50 are drilled as shown in Figure 80, one for each tooth of the gear.   The pin on the arm snaps into any desired hole and is thus adjustable.   Another pin in place of the 0 hole on the spur gear presses against 15 when it reaches the upper position; 15 in turn presses switch 3 and stops the motor for the settling interval.

Part 16 is rigidly attached to the shaft of the spur gear, so that it reaches the position shown in I at the settling position.   When the motor starts again, 16 pushes up on 17, which pushes down on the lower tip of 18; 17 and 18 are held by a brass plate attached to the stationary piece (5).   18 carries a pin on its upper end which pushes 19, attached to wheel 1, outward and holds it out as the wheel moves forward.   Thus, the other curved wedge-shaped end of 19 is moved from the outer edge of the track to the inner edge and held there for a time sufficient for the roller on the arm (3) to enter the outer track, A.   19 is therefore the track switch, which is normally held by a spring in the position shown.   The corresponding part on the right is merely held in position by a spring.   The roller pin forces it open on passing through.

The timing mechanism is shown in views III and IV of Figure 81.   It provides for three independently adjustable intervals corresponding to the settling period, a shorter time for draining at the decantation stage, and a third short time for drainage at the transfer stage.   This mechanism is mounted on the gear box of the electric motor.

The time clock (20) is a Haydn timing meter of 0.2 r.p.m.   It is mounted on an aluminum base and two upright pieces.   It drives a wheel (21) by means of a shaft (22).   The wheel (21) carries three circular plates attached to it.   Each plate carries a metal flap, a, b, and c, attached as shown in Figure 81, III.   Each flap depresses switch 11 as it passes over.   Thus, flap a starts the motor at the end of the settling period, b after the decantation, and c after the transfer interval.   The time clock is set in motion when switch 3 is closed by the metal piece (16) at the end of the equilibration stage.

After c has passed switch 11, the equilibration stage has begun.   At the second and third strokes of arm 3, wheel 21 is released from the timer shaft at a sawtooth clutch (24).   A solenoid (23) operating around the shaft (22) and energized by switch 8 disengages the clutch.   Wheel 21 is spring loaded and therefore returns to its starting point.   The power to the solenoid is then turned off and the teeth at 24 are engaged again by a spring on the shaft.   The relative positions of the metal flaps are adjustable by loosening the nut (25) which holds the three circular metal plates on the wheel.   The wheel is calibrated in minutes and seconds.   If the parts should be moved so as to upset the sequence, the next cycle will automatically correct the change.

The robot includes a device for combining fractions, which can be set so that the collector turn table is advanced every transfer or only every 2nd, 3rd...6th transfer as desired.   This automatically combines adjacent effluent phases and reduces the number of test tubes required for a given fractionation.   The device is called a "combiner" and is shown schematically in view II of Figure 81.

Six V-grooved wheels numbered 1 to 6 are attached rigidly to a hollow shaft (26). The wheels are rotated the distance of 1 groove each time the arm (3) moves to the decantation position by a small push rod (27) and arm attached to one end of a rod extending through 26.   On the other end of the rod is attached a ratchet mechanism (30) which pushes the sheels.   The push rod does not move far enough to engage the ratchet arm on the other movements of the lever arm (3).   The first wheel has 60 grooves.   Each time a groove moves into position switch 9 is allowed to close at 28 and the fraction collector motor is activated.

In the grooved wheel numbered 2 every other groove is omitted.   Thus, switch 9 closes only every other transfer.   Similarly, 3, 4, 5, and 6 have only $1/3$, $1/4$, $1/5$, and $1/6$ the grooves, respectively.   28 can be moved to any desired wheel by means of a screw thread turned by the knob at 29.   The combiner is enclosed in a small metal box.

The wiring scheme is given in Figure 82.   The driving motor available at the time happened to be a direct current motor; hence, both direct current and alternating current power are used.   Both sources of power can be turned off simultaneously at a main switch, SW1, which is a double-pole, double-throw switch.

The driving motor, M1, is a shunt-wound, 1/30 h.p., Janette direct current motor geared down to a range of 20 to 30 r.p.m.   The speed within these limits is variable by virtue of R, an adjustable resistance in series with the field.   In order to assure a slower, smoother movement when the cells are tipped to the higher position required for decantation, an alternating current relay, RY3, has been inserted which shorts R and slows the motor to the minimum speed until the transfer is completed.

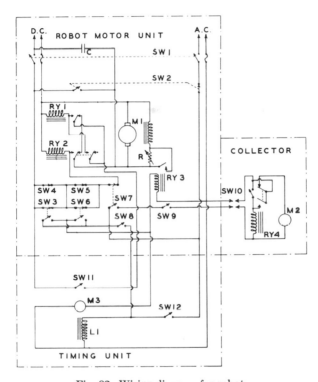

Fig. 82. Wiring diagram for robot.

Switches 3, 4, 5, and 6 are motor-controlling switches (GE switchettes) whose normal position is closed as shown in Figure 82.   Switch 3 is opened by the advancement of the spur gear (12) of Figure 80, after the required number of strokes of the lever arm (3).   However, the apparatus must be stopped at the proper angle for the phases to settle.   This is accomplished by switch 4 which is opened by an adjustable plate attached to the side near the periphery of the wheel (1).   It is opened every time the lever arm reaches the highest point of the equilibration stroke.   The latter is the correct position for settling.   Both switches 3 and 4 must be open before the motor stops.

Switch 5 is opened by the push rod (13) every time the highest position of the arm (3) is reached.   Switch 6 is opened when the ratchet arrangement (15) permits the spur gear (12) to return to its original position.   Switches 5 and 6 must both be open to stop the motor in the decantation position.   Switch 7 is opened by a short extension on the arm (3) and stops the motor in the transfer position.   At this time switch 6 has not yet closed.   Both 6 and 7 must be open before the motor stops.

Riding pick-a-back on switches 3, 6, and 7 are three other switchettes whose normal position is open.   These act oppositely to their companions and activate the timing mechanism.

Switch 8 is the reset switch which energizes the solenoid, L_1, and disengages the timing motor clutch in order to permit the wheel (21) to return to the 0 position. At the same time the timing motor is stopped by the opening of switch 6.   In case switch 8 fails to act, an emergency manual reset switch (12) is activated by a pin on the third circular plate attached to the sheel (21).   The timing motor is started again by switch 3 at the end of the equilibration.

RY1 and RY2 are 110-volt direct current relays used to assure that switch 11 has control of the motor only until switches 3, 4, 5, 6, and 7 are all closed again.

C is a 4-microfarad 600-volt paper condenser placed across all the switches in the direct current circuit so that arcing across the switch contacts is minimized.

A number of robots based on different principles have been described in the literature.[172]

C. THE FRACTION COLLECTOR

The fraction collector is essentially that designed by Moore and Stein for chromatography.   A turntable, 61 cm. in diameter and shown in Figure 83, carries the test tubes.   It may be made from three sheets of Bakelite

Fig. 83. Fraction collector turntable.

or preferably from stainless steel.   The sheets are held 5 cm. apart by 5 short brass sticks.   200 holes in four rows symmetrically placed and drilled

[172] F. A. Metzsch, *Chem.-Ing.-Tech.*, **25**, 66 (1953); *Angew. Chem.*, **65**, 586 (1953). F. C. Hickey, *Anal. Chem.*, **24**, 1993 (1952).   E. S. Perry and W. H. Weber, *ibid.*, **26**, 498 (1954).

through the top two sheets near the outer edge hold the test tubes. The holes are slightly larger than 20 mm. in diameter to provide for a 20 × 150 mm. standard test tube.

The turntable rests on a central bearing and shaft which holds it in a horizontal position. It may be lifted off the bearing at will and thus can serve as a rack to carry the test tubes to some other place for analysis. A shallow circular pan of stainless steel is built into the turntable and rests on the lower sheet. This catches any effluent that fails to go into a test tube due to failure of the apparatus or breakage of test tubes.

An effluent fraction enters the fraction collector through a shallow funnel placed slightly above and to one side of the turntable. The exit tube of the funnel is bent at a sharp angle so that it may be swung as an arm out over the rows of test tubes. Provision is made for the arm to be held in five different positions, one for each row of test tubes and one over a narrow funnel held by the outer part of the fraction collector. This funnel discards into a large bottle beneath the fraction collector.

The turntable is advanced by a small motor which is actuated by a switch on the robot. This switch is closed at the decantation position of the distribution train. A set of reduction gears attached to the motor is arranged so that the slowest moving one makes one complete circuit before it trips a second switch and stops the motor. This second switch is held out by a solenoid as long as the fraction collector switch on the robot is closed. A driver and arm is also attached to the slowest moving gear which advances the turntable one test tube for every circuit of the gear and then resets itself by a ratchet arrangement.

The "combiner" described earlier prevents the motor from being actuated at certain transfers, every other transfer, every second or third, etc. Thus, set numbers of effluents can be collected in each test tube. Since each test tube holds over 30 ml., three 10-ml. effluents or six 5-ml. effluents can be collected in each tube.

At the beginning of collection the arm of the entrance funnel is placed with its opening over the first tube of the inner row. After the turntable has made nearly one complete circuit a small metal projection on the turntable trips a ratchet arrangement which swings the arm over the next row so it empties into the first tube of the second row. On the second circuit of the turntable the arm is swung to the third row, on the third to the fourth row, and finally away from the turntable to the discard funnel.

The fraction collector is placed in a housing which is attached by hinges to one leg of the table supporting the hood. When the distribution train is in operation its position is beneath the table under the filling device so that effluent fractions flow by gravity directly into the entrance funnel. The hinges permit the whole fraction collector to be swung out from under the table where individual samples or the whole turntable can be conveniently removed.

D. CARE AND WASHING OF APPARATUS

Two large stainless-steel pans lie beneath the train. An outlet from these pans leads to the drain in the floor. If a break should occur in a glass tube during the night when the machine is operating unattended, inflammable solvent would then not accumulate but would run down the drain.

The main use of the pans is in washing out the cells at the completion of a run. For this purpose all the stoppers are removed from the cells and unwanted solvent is dumped into the pans by disconnecting the train from the robot and tipping it forward. Each cell is then flooded with water from a rubber hose attached to the tap. After the tubes have been inverted so that the rinse water reaches all parts, it is emptied into the pans. A wash of distilled water is similarly given. Finally, about 10 ml. of acetone is placed in each cell from a wash bottle for the final rinse. The acetone evaporates overnight through the open stoppers or it may be quickly removed by restoppering and drawing air through the train. A 220 tube apparatus can easily be washed by one person in less than one hour.

E. METHODS OF OPERATION

The apparatus can be operated in a variety of ways, depending on the purpose of the distribution, the quantity of the solute, the complexity of the mixture, and the number of transfers required. The different procedures previously described for hand-operated equipment can be carried out automatically except double or alternate withdrawal. These can be carried out by adding and removing the proper fractions by hand.

For the fundamental procedure all the lower phase—2200 ml. for a 220 tube apparatus—is first filled into the apparatus plus a slight excess. This excess drains off as the run is made and insures the proper level in each tube. A convenient way of filling in the lower phase is to tip the train to the decantation position. 250-ml. portions are added at points approximately 20 cells apart, beginning a few tubes in advance of those which will receive the sample. A short funnel with a flat joint which can be attached to the opening of each tube is useful for this purpose. All openings are then closed and the apparatus is moved from the decantation to the transfer position a number of times. The lower phase is distributed automatically by this maneuver to every cell, and as the distribution proceeds the small excess finally flows into the fraction collector in front of the advancing upper phases.

The phases containing the solute are inserted by means of a syringe into cell 0 or into as many consecutive cells as may be required. This point has been discussed elsewhere. Upper phase free of solute is placed in approximately 10 cells in front of the solute band in order to insure conditioning of the lower phases in advance and thus minimize volume distortion.

The automatic filling device is then attached and the apparatus is operated with the desired number of strokes, settling interval, etc., until 220 − b transfers have been applied. Here b is the number of cells initially required for the solute. In the event that a shorter distribution gives sufficient resolution, it is not necessary to use the full 220 transfers. The analysis of the distribution is made before any of the upper phase which has carried solute has had an opportunity to leave the train. The data are treated as before for the fundamental series.

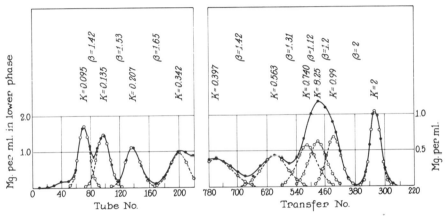

Fig. 84. Distribution patterns for a mixture of ten amino acids.

Single Withdrawal. The maximum transfers of the previously discussed procedure are reached and the extraction is continued by allowing effluent upper phases to collect in the fraction collector. In this manner of operation the method is most nearly analogous to chromatography. For expression of the analytical results after an arbitrary time of operation it is best to give each effluent fraction the transfer number which caused it to emerge from the train. A definite advantage of single withdrawal lies in the fact that the analysis of the effluent fractions involves only one phase. The results are best represented by a plot of the weight per effluent fraction (or some figure proportional to it) as ordinate against the transfer number as abscissa, as shown in Figure 84.

The analysis may show that all the solute has not emerged from the train and that satisfactory separation has been accomplished. Here expression of the results involves two patterns. The fundamental pattern representing the cells is plotted as given in Figure 84, left.   It is the convention of this laboratory to place the effluent pattern to the right of the fundamental pattern, with the highest transfer number nearest the highest cell number of the fundamental pattern, as in Figure 84, right.   This arrangement gives the truest expression of the over-all result, since there is little difference between the composition of the last effluent and the upper phase of cell 219.

The method of operation and the treatment of results are well shown by an actual experiment on an artificial mixture of 10 amino acids.   The mixture chosen contained 300 mg. of each amino acid.   At the start the sample was dissolved in a mixture of 80 ml. of each phase, sufficient to fill the first 8 cells.   The system was made by equilibrating an equal volume of 5% hydrochloric acid with n-butyl alcohol.   15 strokes at each stage were applied, and 30 seconds were required for the phases to separate. The apparatus was permitted to operate until 780 transfers had been applied, approximately 20 hours.   The analysis was made by weight as the hydrochloride residue.

For convenience, only the lower phase of the fundamental series was analyzed, as only amino acids of low partition ratio remained in this series. The total weight per tube can be calculated, if desired, as the partition ratio is known.   The identities of the bands from right to left are: tryptophan, phenylalanine, leucine, isoleucine, tyrosine, methionine, valine, α-aminobutyric acid, alanine, and glycine.   This was confirmed by spotting appropriate samples on a broad paper chromatogram.   All the bands were reasonably well separated except the phenylalanine, leucine, and isoleucine triplet, which could be resolved by recycling or by changing to a more favorable system.   In the former case effluents 380 to 560 could be introduced into a freshly charged apparatus at cell 0 in the order in which they emerged and then recycled several times.   An actual example of the latter method of resolving the triplet will be given under the recycling procedure.

Recycling Procedure.   If on analysis at the fundamental stage only overlapping bands of similar partition ratios are revealed, it is wasteful of solvent to use the single withdrawal procedure, as the upper phases in most of the cells would be free of solute.   On the other hand, if the phases contain no solute, they can be used over again without further treatment. The decantation compartment exit of cell 219 is therefore connected to cell 0 and the upper phase, which would have been an effluent phase, is thus caused to enter the system again to begin a second passage around the series.   In fact, when the band has been narrowed to only two or three closely related components, several thousand transfers can be applied by continued recycling.

The fractionation of the triplet phenylalanine, leucine, and isoleucine, insufficiently separated in Figure 84, can be taken as an example. The free amino acids were distributed in the system *n*-butyl alcohol–water, using five cells for the initial charge. Recycling was begun at 240 transfers. The machine was permitted to run until 1137 transfers had been accomplished. No solvent was added during this time.

Analysis of the lower phases gave the pattern shown in Figure 85 (up-

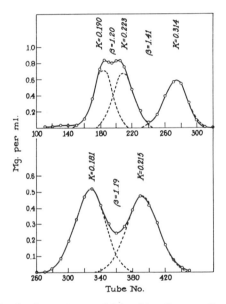

Fig. 85. Distribution patterns obtained by the recycling procedure.

per). It was plain that all solute had cleared the cells below 150, but that many of these had been refilled by the advancing phenylalanine band. Therefore, cell 0 becomes 221, 1 becomes 222, etc.

When the extraction was interrupted, the phenylalanine band was well resolved, but the leucine-isoleucine band was still an overlapping doublet. The former band was accordingly removed and replaced by fresh solvent. The machine was then permitted to operate until 2772 transfers had been reached. Analysis now gave the pattern shown in Figure 85 (lower), which is regarded as a sufficiently good separation, even though further separation only involves permitting the machine to continue operation.

In the event of a binary mixture with β values of 1.1 or less, the width of the overlapping bands would extend over more than 220 cells before complete separation was achieved. But the advancing edge of the band would contain A of satisfactory purity. Perhaps 20 cells of each might be withdrawn. After filling with fresh solvent, a calculated number of transfers could be made before repeating the double withdrawal. This method of accomplishing alternate or double withdrawal does not require the constant attention of the procedure proposed earlier (see page 263) for the fewer cells in the series and is the one recommended for automatic equipment.

High fractionating power in general requires relatively more solvent. Obviously, assuming a standard sized cell, the volume of solvent required is directly proportional to the number of cells involved. Thus, the 220 cells of this apparatus require 2.2 liters of each phase to complete the "fundamental" series. "Single withdrawal" might require tenfold this amount where a higher degree of separation is desired. Unless solvent is extremely cheap and pure, it would appear best to develop some procedure for using the same solvent again and again. The "reflux" principle of fractional distillation is brought to mind.

In a general way, the effect of the reflux of distillation might be viewed in the following manner. Interchange between vapor and liquid takes place only at the surface of the liquid. There is a fixed length of the column to be traveled by the vapor, but because the liquid is constantly flowing back down the column at a rapid rate, the vapors contact a much longer liquid surface than is presented by only the length of the column. The length actually contacted is a function of the speed of back flow, although at higher speeds a point is reached where efficiency falls due to other factors. The proper state of affairs is conveniently created by the concentrating action of the reflux condenser.

It is theoretically possible to simulate an analogous state of affairs with regard to the movement of the individual solutes in an extraction column and likewise provide more opportunity for repeated interchange. Such a procedure involves removal of the solute from the appropriate fractions and its movement systematically backward in the column. Obviously, this would be very laborious. However, a different approach accomplishing nearly the same purpose is practical.

Fractionation according to the binomial expansion methodically divides and repeatedly subdivides a unit quantity into fractions each becoming smaller as the process continues. The fractions, beyond a certain point on each side of the "band," become so small that they may be neglected entirely (see page 186). The solvent in these can therefore be regarded as free of solute and reintroduced into the system. The "recycling process" does this work automatically. The effect achieved is that of greatly increasing the number of transfers or contacts. When applied to complex mixtures, a preliminary distribution can be made for the purpose of sorting the mixture into groups each containing solutes with similar partition ratios. A distribution is then made on each group by the "recycling" processes as outlined in the example with leucine, isoleucine, and phenylalanine. At the end of the distribution, the solute can be recovered in a few simple operations from the dilute solutions comprising the appropriately combined fractions. The net effect here is not greatly different from reflux. Thus, with the 220 tube apparatus, recycling ten times would give nearly the same effect as the "fundamental" procedure in a train containing 2200 cells.

Recycling approaches the experimental ideal more nearly with large numbers of cells in the train. In the original steel machines of 25 tubes, recycling to 50 transfers would be the upper limit, since a single solute with a partition ratio of 1 would then yield a significant amount of solute in every tube. There would be little room for throwing off impurity. A significant amount of solute for purposes of discussion may be defined arbitrarily as an amount greater than 1.0% of the solute present in the cell containing maximum material. However, with 220 tubes in the series, 5260 transfers can be applied to the same solute by recycling before significant amounts of solute would be in every tube. The upper phase here has passed through the train 24 times. The concept of band spread with increasing numbers of transfers has been treated elsewhere (Sect. II.4.B).

The band spread, in terms of transfers applied, is a function of the value of K. Thus, with a K of 0.2 the band spread would not be as wide as 220 tubes until 8000 transfers had been reached and 14,800 transfers would be required for a K of 0.1. As pointed out on page 179 the best separation of a binary mixture in terms of transfers is obtained when the geometric mean of the K values is 1. However, with automatic equipment a different emphasis is reached, since there is no labor involved in making transfers. K values with a geometric mean of 0.2 give a better resolution, even though a somewhat longer time is required. Even better resolution is obtained with lower K values, but here the migration rate becomes slow. By way of analogy, it is interesting that the high resolutions recently obtained in chromatography and ion exchange require slow migration of the solute through the column and relatively large volumes of effluent. There is thus offered the opportunity for many more interchanges between the phases.

With automatic equipment in general there need be less emphasis on the selectivity of the system and the range of K values. Likewise, adjustment of relative phase volumes is less important. With the hand-operated equipment, a practical K range appeared to be 0.2 to 5, whereas with the equipment reported here the satisfactory K range is extended to a range of 0.01 to 100. This naturally means that mixtures containing a dozen or more components can be separated in a single run.

More analytical work at the end of a distribution is required for the higher number of transfers in which more components are revealed. However, the number of analyses is not in direct proportion to the number of transfers or cells. Only a sufficient number of analyses per band is required to show definitely its position, height, and width. Approximately 10 analyses or points on the pattern are adequate per component, whether 100 or 1000 transfers have been applied. This obtains because the concentration changes are more gradual with the broader bands produced by higher numbers of transfers. In cases of overlapping bands, a few more points may be required. If complicated mixtures are to be separated then an apparatus with as many tubes as are practicable experimentally is certainly the best all-around approach. Up to the present time (to the authors' knowledge) a train with 420 units is the longest one that has been built.* It has not proved unwieldy with our present development and systematization of supporting techniques. Construction of one with twice this number has been begun. In the interest of versatility it would appear desirable to have such a train built in sections so that it could be used as a single train only when very high numbers of transfers are required but could be used separately for less difficult separations. The apparatus shown in Figure 76 was designed with this in mind. It is actually a combination of two separate apparatuses, one containing 220 tubes and the other 200. Both are in the same hood but have separate robots, filling devices, and fraction collectors and can be used separately or joined to provide a single train with 420 units. Either robot, filling device, or fraction collector can be used to operate the 420 tube train.

It would seem possible to lengthen a train almost indefinitely. However, very large volumes of solvent become a problem. Compensation for this can be made by reducing the volume in each unit since a larger number of tubes not only improves the separating power but also gives greater capacity. As pointed out earlier, solute may be scattered in several tubes initially without materially reducing the separating power provided that sufficient transfers are applied. We have found that a useful rule for guidance in deciding how many tubes to scatter the solute in initially is to employ a number up to 20% of the width of the final band of the component of interest. Thus, with a K of 1 and 100 transfers applied, the band is approximately 30 tubes wide. Little efficiency would be lost if the samples were scattered initially in equal amounts in the first six tubes and the distribution was then run as if the entire sample had been placed only in a single tube.

The scattering of sample is also important for another reason. When a total of 25 transfers is applied, considerable variation in the value of the partition ratio at different concentrations can be tolerated. A 10 or 20%

* Since this manuscript was prepared, a train containing a total of 1000 tubes arranged in four rows has been built. Preliminary tests indicate it to be entirely practical.

variation over the concentration range covered can scarcely be detected in the final curve. But if several hundred transfers are applied, considerable separation can be obtained in a binary mixture in which the components themselves differ in their partition ratios by 10 or 20%. Thus, for the higher numbers of transfers, a much more exact adherence to the ideal is also required. This requirement can be compensated for in part by scattering the sample in a larger number of tubes at the beginning in order to cover a narrower range of concentration shift.

For example, if a distribution were made by single withdrawal using 100 tubes, an initial concentration (all in one tube) of 85 mg./ml. in the upper phase, and a K of 0.41, then the maximum concentration which would emerge at the end of the train would be of the order of 4 mg./ml. The minimum concentration of interest in the withdrawn band would be 0.04 mg./ml. However, if the same total weight of sample was placed initially in 10 tubes, a concentration of only 8.5 mg./ml. would be the initial and highest concentration during the run. Yet the band emerging would have practically the same concentration as in the first case. A narrower range of concentration change is accordingly involved.

VI. DETERMINATION OF PARTITION RATIOS

In quantitative discontinuous extraction it is of primary importance to know the true value of the partition ratio. Superficially the ratio would appear a very easy constant to determine since this only involves equilibration of an arbitrary weight of the solute with the two phases and subsequent determination of the weight of solute per unit volume in each of the phases. However, if such a constant is to be used for identification purposes, its reliability or specificity will become much greater as the precision of its determination increases. Thus a partition ratio accurate to 10% is frequently all that is required for reasonably intelligent application of extraction as far as separations are concerned, but for identification it would be desirable to have it accurate to within 1% or even less. The higher accuracy is not as easy to reach as may appear on first thought and for this reason a discussion of the determination of partition ratios is given in this chapter as a separate section.

When partition ratios are to be determined with the greatest accuracy possible, all the conditions which might cause the absolute value of the constant to vary must be standardized with sufficient precision. The chief points to be considered in this connection are the composition of the phases, the temperature of equilibration, and the final concentrations of the solute being partitioned.

If the two phases are mutually insoluble in each other, or nearly so, and

are pure compounds, the first point is easily satisfied.   The same applies
if the solvents used to make up the two phases are pure individual compounds but yet mutually soluble to a certain extent.   Somewhat more care
must be used in making up the system when one or both phases are mixed
solvents but mutually insoluble in each other.   On the other hand, if the
two phases are mutually soluble to an appreciable extent and more than
two pure solvents are used to make up the system, the greatest care must
be taken in the relative volumes of solvent used in their preparation.   In
fact, for the latter case, it is frequently difficult to duplicate the absolute
value of the constant.   When salt or a buffer is present in one of the phases,
the systems are likely to be very sensitive to a change in salt concentration.

The effect of a change in temperature must be learned before any
reliance can be placed on the absolute value of the partition ratio.   This
point can be settled quickly by determining the value at more than one
temperature and by plotting a curve with the ratio as a function of the
temperature.   The temperature control required for the determination will
be evident from the curve.   In general, values of partition ratios are relatively insensitive to changes in temperature where relatively dilute solutions are employed and where the two phases are mutually immiscible.
Attempts to obtain more favorable partition ratios for separations by
changing the temperature considerably have been made[173] with more or
less success.   However, if the two phases are soluble in each other to a
considerable extent and particularly where more than two solvents are
used to make up the system, the ratio is likely to be very sensitive to changes
in temperature.   For these cases the temperature must be controlled with
the required accuracy.

The effect of a change in concentration on the partition ratio, like the
effect of changing temperature, is a factor which should never be taken for
granted but must always be studied when a new system is to be used.
For the sake of convenience, it will usually be desirable to choose a concentration range which shows little shift.   However, this again is not a
requisite for the use of partition ratios.   The change of ratio as a function
of the change of concentration can be shown graphically as in Figure 1,
or alternatively as in Figure 89.   When the purity of the preparation used
to determine the curve has been established, such a curve presents a picture
which is very characteristic of the solute.   If a concentration of the solute
greater than several per cent is used and the two phases are two pure solvents which have appreciable mutual solubility, the concentration may be
sufficient to shift the composition of the phases to an appreciable extent.

[173] A. J. P. Martin and R. L. M. Synge, *Biochem. J.*, **35**, 91 (1941).   R. E. Cornish,
R. C. Archibald, E. A. Murphy, and J. E. Evans, *Ind. Eng. Chem.*, **26**, 397 (1934).

Here the equilibria involved can be represented better by triangular coordinates as in Figure 6.

The problem of determining a partition ratio is simplified when the determination of partition ratio is made on a pure preparation of a single compound.   In this case the choice of an analytical method for determining the phase composition is immaterial as long as it has the required precision.   On the other hand such pure preparations are no usually at hand and the choice of an analytical method which does not include the impurity present will naturally give the correct ratio with respect to the pure compound but will not give the correct ratio with respect to the particular preparation.   For this reason an analytical method which is the most inclusive yet has the required precision and can be applied readily is the method of choice.   On the other hand for substances which have already been studied to a considerable extent some specific method such as spectroscopic analysis may be employed and a result obtained on an impure solute by considering that part of the solute inert which is not registered by the method of analysis.   A discussion of the choice of analytical methods will be given in Section VIII.

Partition ratios may be calculated reliably from a countercurrent-distribution pattern.[174]   At the same time the purity of the sample used becomes evident and impurity does not interfere unless it has a ratio nearly identical with the solute of interest.   Even so the impurity would not cause the partition ratio calculated to be in serious error.   In case the partition ratio did shift with concentration, the curve obtained would be a skewed curve, as discussed in Section VIII.   Thus countercurrent distribution is a convenient method for determining partition ratios, since a single determination gives the true ratio even though the sample used might be impure.   At the same time the pattern will show whether or not the partition ratios are constant with different concentrations of solute.

In order to obtain the greatest accuracy in the value of the individually determined partition ratio, with a given analytical precision, it naturally follows that the value of the partition ratio and the amount of material must be selected so that not less than the required analytical precision is always obtained.   Thus for the determination of a partition ratio with a minimum amount of solute the phases usually should be selected so that the partition ratio is roughly 1.   In this case, if for instance the analytical method for determining the concentration in each of the phases is accurate to ± 0.005 unit, the ratio itself would be accurate to 0.01.   On the other hand, if the determination of a ratio in the range of 0.1 or 10 is necessary, correspondingly more solute will be required, in order to obtain the required

[174] L. C. Craig, *J. Biol. Chem.*, **155**, 519 (1944).

analytical precision. As a possible alternative in weight analysis a correspondingly larger volume of the phase in which it exists in less amount can be used. A specific problem may better express the meaning of these requisites.

If the partition ratio is to be determined by weight and a balance is available, sensitive to 0.01 mg., a partition ratio accurate to ±0.01 could be determined on slightly more than a total of 4 mg. using equal volumes, when the partition ratio is 1. In this case practically all of each phase would be evaporated to dryness for the weight determination. But, if the ratio happened to be 10, the lower phase would contain only 0.363 mg. and the constant would be 10 ± 0.27. 22 mg. solute would be required in order to give the necessary 2 mg. in the more dilute phase. Alternatively ten times the volume of the more dilute phase could be used with 4 mg. as the starting weight. In the latter case again it would be necessary to evaporate all the phases in order to obtain the required weight. For determining partition coefficients by weight the thin-walled glass shells described by Craig et al.[175] are particularly suitable.

For the determination of partition ratios by individual extractions the extraction should be carried out in such a manner that it is rapid and reasonably precise. Small volumes of the phases are preferable and a technique which could make use of the centrifuge for clear-cut separation of the layers, if necessary, is advisable. The small conical tubes of the hand centrifuge will be found convenient when fitted with ground-glass stoppers, though somewhat larger tubes used in conjunction with a mechanical centrifuge often will be desirable. The upper layer may then be withdrawn by means of a transferring pipet with a rubber bulb attached or by a hypodermic syringe with either a steel needle or a flexible glass capillary attached at the ground-glass joint. A fine needle even permits the lower layer to be withdrawn without serious contamination from the upper.

For more precise sampling of the lower layer without contamination from the upper, a thin-walled pipet or rather coarse, long hypodermic needle may be carefully thrust through the upper layer and any of the upper phase kept out of the inside by the air pressure from the top. Either the bulb or syringe may then be removed but the pipet or needle left in place. The desired sample may now be withdrawn at will with a thinner pipet or needle which will pass through the first. Separation of the two phases in this way is usually sufficiently sharp so that spectroscopic measurements may be performed directly, or the majority of other analytical procedures applied without further treatment of the phase.

[175] L. C. Craig, W. Hausmann, E. H. Ahrens, Jr., and E. J. Harfenist, *Anal. Chem.*, **23**, 1326 (1951).

VII. CHOICE OF SOLVENTS AND COMPOUNDING OF SYSTEMS

The choice of a solvent for a particular purpose in extraction is certainly one of the major problems. Not only is one confronted with almost limitless possibilities as far as different solvents are concerned but also the choice is always made, consciously or unconsciously, with many different factors in mind. Some of the factors to be considered in making a choice are given in the following list under the headings of Purpose, Systems, Apparatus, and Analysis.

1. Purpose:
   Removal   Amount of pure substance desired
   Fractionation   Purity required
2. Systems:
   Stability   Distorting effect of solutes
   Partition ratio   Recovery of solute
   Partition isotherms   Speed of interchange of solute
   Selectivity of system   Complexity of mixture
   Rate of break of dispersions   Molecular size and complexity of solutes
3. Apparatus:
   Single stage   Cost of apparatus and availability
     Discontinuous   Selectivity
     Continuous   Reproducibility
   Multiple stage   Labor involved
     Discontinuous   Time involved
   Countercurrent
     Discontinuous
     Continuous
4. Analysis
   Direct weight   Titration
   Spectroscopic   Time for analysis

It happens only too frequently that a particular solvent has been chosen hastily without considering some one of the important factors and material or time thereby lost. Quick review of a list such as that above may be helpful. To be sure, the information for evaluating many of the points can be obtained only through new experiments but usually the majority of them can be rapidly checked by previous experience.

Often it will be impossible to find a solvent for which every point mentioned above will be most favorable, and a decision must be made as to the relative importance of each. Thus a solvent may have the highest selectivity in bringing about a separation of the desired solute from accompanying substances but may have undesirable properties such as a high viscosity or may make difficult the recovery of the solute. No general rule can be offered for such a choice because of the multiplicity of conditions and combinations possible. Considerable thought and ingenuity may be required in balancing the relative merits of one solvent against the advantages of the other. The choice of a solvent for an extraction has always been part of the art of organic chemistry. An experienced organic chemist is often so familiar with the properties of his solvents that he appears to have a certain intuition in making the correct choice. Several books are available with pertinent data for many solvents.[176,177]

A list of common solvents to be considered is given below:

pentane	benzene	o-dichlorobenzene
isopentane	toluene	carbon disulfide
hexane	ethylene dichloride	the higher ethers
heptane	tetrachloroethylene	diisopropyl ether
2,2,4-trimethylpentane	methylene chloride	diethyl ether
cyclohexane	carbon tetrachloride	furan
cyclopentane	chloroform	furfural
thiophene	pentanol	pyridine homologs
methyl ethyl ketone	tertiary pentanol	pyridine
methylcyclohexanone	butanol	morpholine
acetone	secondary butanol	aniline
dioxane	propanol	phenol
amyl acetate	ethanol	acetic acid
isopropyl acetate	methanol	formamide
ethyl acetate	acetonitrile	water
methyl acetate	nitromethane	hydrochloric acid
nitrobenzene	nitroethane	sulfuric acid
cyclohexanol	methoxyethylene glycol	salt solutions

The choice of solvents does not end when the list of common solvents has been checked. Often the key to the solution of a problem lies in the use of solvents mixed in the correct proportion. Thus the possibilities to be considered are very greatly increased.

In this list the solvents with the lowest dielectric constant are given first. These, with few exceptions, are the least miscible with those at the end. Solvents near each other in the list are completely miscible with each other. It is of interest in connection with adsorption procedures that this list corresponds roughly to the "eluotropic" series in chromatography first

[176] A. Weissberger, E. S. Proskauer, J. A. Riddich, and E. E. Toops, *Organic Solvents*, 2nd ed. (*Technique of Organic Chemistry*, Vol. VII.) Interscience, New York-London, 1955.

[177] L. Scheflan and M. B. Jacobs, *The Handbook of Solvents*. Van Nostrand, New York, 1953.

discussed by Trappe[178] (see also page 212). Therefore, it is likely that
two substances which form bands close together in a chromatogram will
often have similar partition ratios and thus be more difficult to separate
also by extraction procedures. However, many exceptions to this generalization might be expected because the relative position of two solutes on a
chromatograph is often reversed by changing either the developer (solvent)
or the adsorbent.[179]

An analogous phenomenon can occur in liquid–liquid extraction as
shown by the series of partition ratios of benzylpenicillin and Δ^2-pentenyl-
penicillin given in Table VII. These data show that a considerable selectivity can be obtained by a careful study of solvent pairs. The more favorable ratio of the partition coefficients obtained when diisopropyl ether was
used led to a much easier separation by countercurrent distribution.[180]

A similar table could be constructed from the data of Cornish, Archibald, Murphy, and Evans[181] in their attempt to separate sterols by extraction. Prior to this work, Archibald[182] had investigated the relative partition ratios of a considerable number of fatty acids in different combinations of immiscible solvents. Certain combinations were found to be much
more efficient than others. One of the best was diisopropyl ether–water.
This system has been further improved by the use of concentrated phosphate buffer for the aqueous phase.[183]

Although the partition ratios of two solutes may be very close together
in one solvent pair and the solutes may be similar structurally, it will
usually be found not too difficult to shift the relative ratios by selecting
a different solvent pair so that a ratio of the ratios, β, of at least 2 can be
obtained. Even with this ratio, however, a considerable number of perfect
stages will be necessary for a separation approaching purity and in high
yield. For this purpose either some mechanical method of making multiple
transfers or a continuous fractionating column will be required. If in the
separation of a binary mixture the first system investigated shows a ratio
of partition coefficients, perhaps on the borderline of a value which could be
employed profitably for separation, it is worth while to investigate one or
more other systems. A ratio of the partition coefficients, or β, of 3 might
be considered such a borderline case, if a countercurrent-distribution apparatus were not available. When an automatic countercurrent-distribu-

[178] W. Trappe, *Biochem. Z.*, **305**, 150 (1940).

[179] H. H. Strain, *Chromatographic Adsorption Analysis*, Interscience, New York-
London, 1942; *Ind. Eng. Chem., Anal. Ed.*, **18**, 605 (1946).

[180] G. T. Barry, Y. Sato, and L. C. Craig, *J. Biol. Chem.*, **174**, 221 (1948).

[181] R. E. Cornish, R. C. Archibald, E. A. Murphy, and J. E. Evans, *Ind. Eng. Chem.*,
26, 397 (1934).

[182] R. C. Archibald, *J. Am. Chem. Soc.*, **54**, 3180 (1932).

[183] Y. Sato, G. T. Barry, and L. C. Craig, *J. Biol. Chem.*, **170**, 501 (1947).

tion apparatus is available separation of mixtures with β values of 1.2 is not difficult.

In general, if the solutes are known to be considerably different structurally but by chance give partition ratios close together with the first phase pair studied, selection of another phase pair will almost always provide a more favorable separation factor. Those solvents which are furthest removed from each other in the list of solvents above ordinarily give the greatest differences in partition ratios for two given solutes.

When the optimum partition ratio cannot be obtained by combinations of solvents or when the desired solvent does not give a favorable partition ratio, the use of modifying solutes may be important. The addition of neutral salt, acid, or alkali to an aqueous solution in order to favor extraction is a common practice in organic chemistry. Salts of acids or bases with more favorable ratios may be formed. Even the partition ratios of neutral, though highly water-soluble, substances are often greatly influenced by the formation of addition compounds. However, contrary to the desired effect the addition of salt sometimes influences the ratio in such a way as to favor the aqueous phase. In this case it is probable that some sort of association with the salt occurs. The effect is sometimes called "salting in" or a "hydrotropic phenomenon" [184] (see also page 156). The salts which produce this effect are usually neutral salts of aromatic carboxylic acids, such as sodium benzoate, or sulfonic acids such as sodium xylene sulfonate.[185] Many substances with slight solubility in water may be dissolved readily in solutions containing from 5–50% of these salts.

When the solute is highly soluble in water but not sufficiently soluble in water-immiscible solvents for the use of extraction, salts such as ammonium chloride, sodium chloride, sodium sulfate, etc. can be added to the aqueous solution. After this is done methanol, ethanol, or one of the solvents nearer water in the series given in the preceding section can be used for the immiscible extractant.

When the extraction of organic acids or bases is under investigation, it is customary to expect that salt formation by the addition of the required acid or base will favor transfer to the aqueous phase. Though this appears to be nearly always true when hydrocarbons or ethers are used for the organic phase, it is by no means the case when chlorinated hydrocarbons or alcohols (and sometimes even ethers) are used. The hydrochlorides of certain aromatic amines are often completely extracted with chloroform from aqueous solution. Many alkaloids also fall in this category and the specific property has been used to advantage by Manske[186] in his systematic

[184] C. Neuberg, *Biochem. Z.*, **76**, 107 (1916).

[185] R. H. McKee, *Ind. Eng. Chem.*, **38**, 382 (1946).

[186] R. H. F. Manske, *Can. J. Research*, **B14**, 347 (1936); *Can. Chem. Process Industries*, **23**, 199 (1939).

work on the isolation of alkaloids. Further possibilities along this line have been brought out by Brodie et al.[187] in the use of sulfonic acids for the removal of bases from aqueous solution. They found the helianthin salts of some synthetic antimalarials to favor chloroform so greatly that this property could be used in the colorimetric estimation of small amounts of the drugs in biological fluids. Methyl orange itself remained entirely in the aqueous phase and thus the color appearing in the chloroform served as a basis for determining the amount of base present. Conversely it would appear that all the methyl orange could be transported to the organic phase by the use of an excess of an organic base.

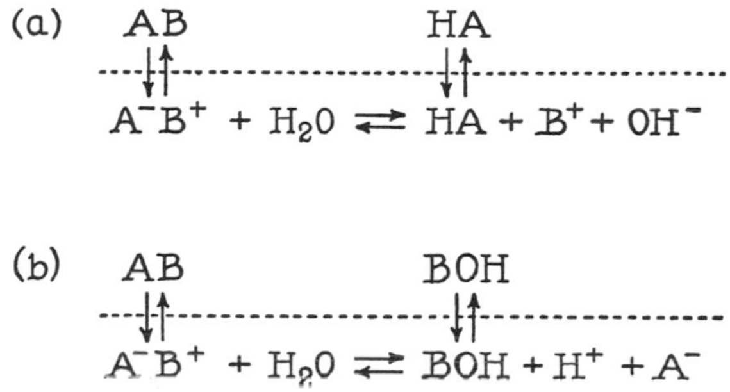

(a)   AB   HA

A⁻B⁺ + H₂0 ⇌ HA + B⁺ + OH⁻

(b)   AB   BOH

A⁻B⁺ + H₂0 ⇌ BOH + H⁺ + A⁻

Fig. 86. Buffer equilibrium.

Titus and Fried[188] have obtained a favorable partition ratio in butanol–water for the countercurrent-distribution analysis of streptomycin by the use of p-toluenesulfonic acid. The free base is slightly soluble in most organic solvents. This lead was further exploited by O'Keeffe, Dolliver, and Stiller[189] who found that a number of different anionic detergents such as lauric acid were effective in this way when the aqueous solution was buffered. They called this phenomenon the "carrier" effect. Similar reasoning was used in choosing a system for the distribution of heparin.[190]

Another example is in the behavior of certain penicillins. The triethylammonium salts of these acids can be extracted almost quantitatively with chloroform from aqueous solutions containing inorganic salts.

A number of amphoteric, highly water-soluble substances have been found to be more readily extracted from urine with butanol after the addition of ammonia or certain amines. Removal of amphoteric substances from aqueous solutions, particularly biological fluids, is frequently

[187] B. B. Brodie, S. Udenfriend, and W. Dill, J. Biol. Chem., 168, 335 (1947).

[188] E. O. Titus and J. F. Fried, J. Biol. Chem., 168, 393 (1947).

[189] A. E. O'Keeffe, M. A. Dolliver, and E. T. Stiller, J. Am. Chem. Soc., 71, 2452 (1949).

[190] A. E. O'Keeffe, F. M. Russo-Alesi, M. A. Dolliver, and E. T. Stiller, J. Am. Chem. Soc., 71, 1517 (1949).

difficult and the possibilities inherent in the use of extraction of the salts produced by the addition of either acids or substituted amine bases should not be overlooked. Recovery of the amphoteric substance is frequently made easy by the choice of volatile acids or amines.

In the extraction of acidic or basic substances, the addition of buffer salts to the aqueous phase aids in the attainment of reproducible, constant partition ratios. This practice has in many cases provided a suitable phase for otherwise unstable solutes and has increased selectivity.[192] Thus extraction procedures involving buffers have been one of the most important factors which have contributed to the isolation,[191] fractionation, and characterization of the individual penicillins. The same approach has been used repeatedly in purifying and proving the purity of preparations of synthetic antimalarials,[192] where other more conventional methods failed to yield a reliable result.

The reason for the improved selectivity often realized in extractions involving buffers can be shown schematically by Figure 86 for acids and bases. The dotted line represents the interface. From a practical standpoint one is concerned in extraction only with the percentage of the total solute present in either layer. It does not matter in the end whether the solute is present in a single form or as several molecular species such as ions, unionized molecules, reversible dimers or polymers, or molecules associated with some other constituent of the solution, so long as there is equilibrium and an over-all partition ratio which does not change appreciably over the concentration range in question. It is obvious from Figure 86 that other factors come into play aside from the partition coefficient of the unionized solute, such as the dissociation constant of the acid or base. In the presence of a fixed hydrogen ion concentration, the per cent of either acid or base in the ionized form is fixed. This contributes to the constancy of the partition ratio and to the selectivity as well. Buffer salts increase the dielectric constant of the water phase and move it even lower in the series given on page 302. This contrasts further the properties of the two phases of a system to be used for fractionation and offers greater selectivity. Aside from maintaining a constant pH, the more concentrated buffers seem to associate more or less with certain solutes and thus play a solvent role. Buffers further permit adjustment of the value of the effective partition ratio to the optimum range in a very convenient manner. For the best results the buffer should be essentially insoluble in the organic phase. Phosphate buffers are admirable from this standpoint.

[191] F. C. Whitmore et al., Ind. Eng. Chem., 38, 942 (1946).

[192] R. C. Elderfield et al., J. Am. Chem. Soc., 68, 1516 (1946). L. C. Craig, H. Mighton, E. O. Titus, and C. Golumbic, Anal. Chem., 20, 134 (1948).

It is apparent from the foregoing discussion that great ingenuity can be used in the compounding of a good system.   In spite of this and the greater skill which comes with practice the selection of the proper system for a given separation is one of the greatest difficulties in the use of countercur-

TABLE VIII
ACIDS

Solutes separated	System	Reference
Fatty acids..............	Isopropyl ether, PO$_4$ buffer	*J. Biol. Chem.*, **170**, 501 (1947).
	Heptane, PO$_4$	*Ibid.*, **188**, 299 (1951).
Benzoic acid............	92% methanol, CCl$_4$	*Biochem. J.*, **49**, 540 (1951).
Benzoic and naphthoic acids................	Hexane, benzene, 80% methanol	*J. Biol. Chem.*, **189**, 637 (1951).
β-Nitropropionic acid.....	Ether, 2 *M* NaH$_2$PO$_4$	*Ibid.*, **188**, 690 (1951).
Isobutyric acid, propionic acid.................	Isopropyl ether, 2.2 *M* PO$_4$ buffer	*Ibid.*, **176**, 123 (1948).
Higher fatty acids........	Heptane, methanol, form-amide, acetic acid	*Ibid.*, **195**, 299 (1952).
	Isooctane, methanol, form-amide	"
	Heptane, acetonitrile, form-amide, acetic acid	"
	Heptane, acetonitrile, acetic acid, methanol	"
	Heptane, acetonitrile, acetic acid	"
	Heptane, acetonitrile, acetic acid, methyl Cellosolve	"
α-Lipoic acid............	CHCl$_3$, 0.5 *M* phosphate	*J. Am. Chem. Soc.*, **7**, (1951).
α-Lipoic acid............	Organic solvents, buffer	*Ibid.*, **73**, 5920 (1951).
Lipoic acid..............	Benzene, 50% acetic acid	*Ibid.*, **75**, 1271 (1953).
α-Lipoic acid............	Benzene, 50% acetic acid	*Ibid.*, **75**, 1267 (1953).
Formic acid.............	Methyl isobutyl ketone, water	*Ind. Eng. Chem.*, **45**, 2119 (1953).
Taurocholic acid.........	2-Butanol, 3% aq. acetic acid	*J. Biol. Chem.*, **195**, 763 (1952).
Glycolic acid............	*n*-Butanol, heptane, acetic acid	"
Free bile acids...........	Heptane, acetic acid, water	"
	Isopropyl ether, heptane, HAc	"
Conjugated bile acids.....	Heptane, isopropyl ether, acetic acid, 2-butanol, 3% acetic acid, heptane, 97% acetic acid	"
Acids from *Aspergillus ustis*	Cyclohexane, pyrophos-phate buffer	*J. Biol. Chem.*, **162**, 363 (1946).
Dichlorophenoxyacetic acid.................	Tributyl phosphate, phos-phate buffer	*Anal. Chem.*, **22**, 460 (1950).
Chlorogenic acid.........	Ethyl acetate, phosphate buffer	*J. Am. Chem. Soc.*, **69**, 1470 (1947).
Isochlorogenic acid.......	Butyl acetate, phosphate buffer	*J. Am. Chem. Soc.*, **72**, 4187 (1950).

rent distribution. However, with distribution machines easily available applications have greatly increased and the literature now contains accounts of many different systems.[193] Metzsch[194] has given an excellent review of the subject.

TABLE IX
AMINO ACIDS AND DERIVATIVES

Solutes separated	System	Reference
Amino acids.............	n-Butanol, 5% HCl	*Anal. Chem.*, **22**, 1346 (1950).
	n-Butanol, 2-butanol, 5% HCl	*J. Biol. Chem.*, **198**, 405 (1952).
	n-Butanol, 17% acetic acid	*Biochem. J.*, **50**, 114 (1952).
	2% HCl, phenol	*J. Biol. Chem.*, **199**, 865 (1952).
	2-Butanol, propanol, 10% ammonium acetate	*J. Am. Chem. Soc.*, **74**, 4019 (1952).
Arginine and arginine methyl ester..........	5% lauric acid in n-butanol, 15% sodium acetate	*Z. physiol. Chem.*, **292**, 109 (1953).
Acylamino acids........	Ethyl acetate, PO₄ buffer	*J. Chem. Soc.*, **1952**, 2069.
DNP-amino acids.......	n-Butanol or ethyl acetate, dil. ammonia or PO₄ buffer	*J. Biol. Chem.*, **199**, 563 (1949).
Benzoyl threonine........	Ethyl ether, water	*Biochem. J.*, **45**, 429 (1949).
Pipsylamino acids........	CHCl₃, 0.2 N HCl	*J. Biol. Chem.*, **190**, 721 (1951).
Carbobenzoxyglutamic esters.................	Ethyl ether, PO₄ buffer	*Coll. Czechoslov. Chem. Communs.*, **16**, 615 (1951).

TABLE X
BASES

Solutes separated	System	Reference
Various organic bases.....	Liquid paraffin, phosphate buffer	*J. Chem. Soc.*, **1953**, 1619.
Aromatic amines.........	Cyclohexane, water, Ag⁺	*J. Am. Chem. Soc.*, **74**, 5777 (1952).
Quinoline..............	Ethyl ether, 0.75 N acetic acid	*J. Biol. Chem.*, **187**, 787 (1950).
Pyridine bases..........	Cyclohexane, citrate buffer	*J. Am. Chem. Soc.*, **72**, 4145 (1950).
Diethylamine............	Toluene, water	*Ind. Eng. Chem.*, **42**, 1078 (1950).
Degradation products from antimalarial bases......	n-Butanol, buffer	*J. Org. Chem.*, **13**, 39 (1948).
Substituted anilines......	Cyclohexane, citrate buffer	*J. Am. Chem. Soc.*, **73**, 3966 (1951).
Methadone.............	Ethylene dichloride, 0.67 M acetate buffer	*J. Pharmacol. Exptl. Therap.*, **101**, 249 (1950).
Purines, pyrimidines......	n-Butanol, phosphate	*J. Biol. Chem.*, **173**, 585 (1948).
Quinoline antimalarials...	Org. solvents, buffers	*Anal. Chem.*, **20**, 134 (1948).

[193] L. C. Craig, *Anal. Chem.*, **26**, 110 (1954).
[194] F. A. von Metzsch, *Angew. Chem.*, **65**, 586 (1953).

In Tables VIII to XIV a number of systems used for actual separation of different classes of compounds are given. No attempt has been made in these tables to give a complete survey. They are included in this chapter in the hope that a short survey will offer valuable suggestions. Many of

TABLE XI
ALKALOIDS

Solutes separated	System	Reference
Alkaloids of veratrine.....	$CHCl_3$, CCl_4, 2 M acetate buffer	*J. Am. Chem. Soc.*, **74**, 5107 (1952).
Desacetylneoprotovera-trine.................	Benzene, 2 M acetate buffer	*Ibid.*, **75**, 3595 (1953).
Alkaloids of veratrine.....	Cyclohexane, benzene, 2 M acetate buffer	*Ibid.*, **74**, 1871 (1952).
Zygadenus alkaloids......	$CHCl_3$, 2 M acetate buffer	*Ibid.*, **74**, 3202 (1952).
Zygadenus alkaloids......	Benzene, phosphate buffer	*Ibid.*, **74**, 2383 (1952); **75**, 1025 (1953).
Neorgermitrine..........	Benzene, 2 M acetate buffer	*Ibid.*, **74**, 3041 (1952).
Alkaloids of veratrine.....	Benzene, phosphate buffer	*Anal. Chem.*, **24**, 1918 (1952).
	Benzene, 2 M acetate buffer	*Nature*, **170**, 932 (1952).
	$CHCl_3$, acetic acid, water	*J. Am. Chem. Soc.*, **75**, 1942 (1953).
	0.5 N HCl, $CHCl_3$	*Helv. Chim. Acta*, **36**, 1571 (1953).
Germbudine, isogermidine.	Benzene, 2 M acetate buffer	*J. Am. Chem. Soc.*, **74**, 3198 (1952).
Wilforgine..............	Benzene, hexane, 2% HCl	*Ibid.*, **74**, 1585 (1952).
	Benzene, 1.8% HCl	*Ibid.*, **74**, 1585 (1952).
	Benzene, hexane, 2% HCl	*Ibid.*, **75**, 2136 (1953).
Ryanodine.............	Ethyl ether, water	*Can. J. Chem.*, **29**, 905 (1951).
Corynanthein...........	Ethyl ether, citrate buffer	*Helv. Chim. Acta*, **36**, 337 (1953).
Tar bases..............	Cyclohexane, phosphate-citrate buffer; $CHCl_3$, phosphate-citrate buffer	*Anal. Chem.*, **24**, 1849 (1952).
Pyridine alkaloids........	*tert*-Amyl alcohol, various buffers	*J. Am. Chem. Soc.*, **74**, 4096 (1952).
Gerraya alkaloids........	$CHCl_3$, phosphate-citrate buffer	*Can. J. Chem.*, **30**, 608 (1952).
Cinchona alkaloids.......	Isoamyl alcohol, 1 M phosphate buffer	*J. Biol. Chem.*, **188**, 567 (1951).

the systems given in Tables VIII to XIV involve systems with three or more components. Obviously considerable time has been spent in finding the optimum proportions of each solvent to use. This need not be entirely trial and error; graphic systematization can help. An outstanding example of this approach is to be found in the work of Engel and co-workers[195] in setting up quaternary systems for separating neutral steroids. Nomograms were employed in a very ingenious way.

[195] L. L. Engel *et al.*, *Anal. Chem.*, **26**, 639 (1954).

TABLE XII
LIPIDES AND STEROLS

Solutes separated	System	Reference
Lipides from placenta....	Mixtures of CCl_4, $CHCl_3$, CH_2Cl_2, CH_3OH, and H_2O	Biochem. J. (London), **55**, 17 (1953).
Lipides from brain.......	CH_3OH, CCl_4, H_2O	Ibid., **54**, 449 (1953).
Phospholipides from ox brain................	Petroleum ether, ethanol, H_2O	Ibid., **51**, 464 (1952).
Linseed phosphatides.....	Hexane, methanol, water	J. Am. Oil Chemists' Soc., **28**, 328 (1951).
Uridine-5-pyrophosphate derivatives...........	Phenol, sulfate buffer	J. Biol. Chem., **194**, 877 (1952).
Methyl esters of higher fatty acids............	Pentane, hexane, nitromethane, nitroethane	Anal. Chem., **24**, 1530 (1952).
Peroxides of methyl linoleate.................	Pentane, hexane, ethanol, water	J. Am. Oil Chemists' Soc., **29**, 244 (1952).
Urinary estrogens........	CH_3OH, CCl_4, H_2O, ethanol, cyclohexane, ethyl acetate, water	J. Clin. Endocrinol. Metabolism, **13**, 674 (1953).
Steroid mixtures.........	Cyclohexane, ethyl acetate, ethanol, water	Federation Proc., **12**, 200 (1953).
Adrenal cortex hormones..	Petroleum ether, water	Arch. exptl. Path. Pharmakol., **214**, 165 (1952).
Cholesterol..............	Heptane, 90% ethanol	J. Biol. Chem., **195**, 357 (1952).
Cephalins, DNP-ethanolamine, DNP-serine.....	Benzene, 5 N HCl, methyl butyl ketone, citrate buffer	Ibid., **204**, 903 (1953).
Phospholipides...........	Petroleum ether, acetone, ethanol, water	Biochim. et Biophys. Acta, **10**, 493 (1953).
Phospholipides...........	Hexane, 95% methanol	J. Am. Oil Chemists' Soc., **25**, 368 (1948).
Estrogens...............	Dil. NaOH, toluene CCl_4, methanol, dil. NaOH Various other systems	J. Biol. Chem., **185**, 255 (1950).
Steroids.................	75% methanol, CCl_4 + $CHCl_3$	Chem. Ing. Techn., **25**, 505 (1953).
Cholesterol..............	n-Heptane, 80% ethanol	J. Biol. Chem., **195**, 357 (1952).

TABLE XIII
PEPTIDES

Solutes separated	System	Reference
Actinomycins............	Methyl butyl ether, sodium naphthalenesulfonate soln.	Naturwissenschaften, 224 40, (1953).
Actinomycins............	Ethyl ether, 5.6% HCl	Ibid., **39**, 429 (1952).
Actinomycins............	Methyl butyl ether, 30% urea	Z. physiol. Chem., **292**, 77 (1953).
Rhodomycins............	Butanol, 0.1 N phosphate	Ber., **84**, 700 (1951).
Rhodomycins............	Butanol–ether, HCl soln. (pH 3)	Ibid., **86**, 261 (1953).

Table Continued

Table XIII *Continued*

Solutes separated	System	Reference
Oxytocin...............	2-Butanol, 0.5 *N* aq. acetic acid; 2-butanol, 0.01 *M* ammonia	*J. Biol. Chem.*, **199**, 929 (1952). *Ibid.*
Desulfurized oxytocin....	2-Butanol, water	*Ibid.*, **193**, 359 (1951).
Bromine oxidation products of oxytocin........	2-Butanol, 0.5% acetic acid	*Ibid.*, **204**, 861 (1953).
Hog vasopressin.........	1-Butanol, 0.09 *p*-toluenesulfonic acid	*J. Am. Chem. Soc.*, **74**, 3713 (1952).
Oxidized oxytocin........	1-Butanol, 6% acetic acid	*J. Biol. Chem.*, **191**, 309 (1951).
Partial hydrolysis products of vasopressin.........	2-Butanol, 0.1 *N* acetic acid	*J. Am. Chem. Soc.*, **75**, 4879 (1953).
Synthetic oxytocin.......	2-Butanol, 0.1 *N* acetic acid; 2-butanol, 0.01 *N* ammonia	*Ibid.*, **75**, 4880 (1953).
ACTH.................	2-Butanol, 0.2% aq. trichloroacetic acid	*Ibid.*, **75**, 503 (1953).
	2,4,6-Collidine, water	*Ibid.*, **74**, 4956 (1952).
	2-Butanol, 0.5% aqueous trichloracetic acid	*Ibid.*, **74**, 2120 (1952).
	2-Butanol, 0.1% aqueous trichloroacetic acid	*Ibid.*, **75**, 1955 (1953).
Benzoyl peptides	Ethanol, water, $CHCl_3$, cyclohexane	*Ibid.*, **75**, 704 (1953).
Hydrolyzate of gramicidin.	1-Butanol, dil. acetic acid	*Biochem. J. (London)*, **50**, 109 (1951).
Peptide from *Bacillus subtilis*................	1-Butanol, 0.1 *M* phosphate buffer	*Nature*, **170**, 618 (1952).
Nisins................	Methanol, butanol, acetic acid, water, NaCl, NaAc	*Ibid.*, **169**, 707 (1952).
Nisins A, B, C, D........	Methanol, 1-butanol, acetate buffer	*Biochem. J. (London)*, **52**, 529 (1952).
Licheniformins..........	Phenol, dil. HCl	*Ibid.*, **51**, 558 (1952).
Micrococcin............	Ethanol, acetic acid, $CHCl_3$, CCl_4, water	*Ibid.*, **50**, 247 (1951).
Clupein, salmine........	1-Butanol, lauric acid, NaAc buffer	*Z. physiol. Chem.*, **292**, 101 (1953).
Pipsyl derivs. from peptides................	Various org. solvents with water	*J. Biol. Chem.*, **199**, 563 (1952).
	"	*Ibid.*, **201**, 371 (1953).
Bacitracins............	Pentanol, butanol, phosphate buffer	*Biochem. J. (London)*, **53**, 597 (1953). *Brit. J. Pharmacol.*, **6**, 417 (1951).
	2-Butanol, 3% acetic acid	*J. Biol. Chem.*, **199**, 259 (1952).
Amino acids from bacitracin..................	2% HCl, phenol	*Ibid.*, **199**, 865 (1952).
DNP derivs. of bacitracin.	2-Butanol, 3% acetic acid, $CHCl_3$, water	*Ibid.*, **200**, 765 (1953).
Polypeptin.............	2-Butanol, isopropyl ether, dilute HCl	*Ibid.*, **198**, 405 (1952).
Tyrocidines............	Methanol, $CHCl_3$, 0.1 *N* HCl	*J. Am. Chem. Soc.*, **74**, 4019 (1952).
Tyrocidine A derivatives..	Methanol, benzene, $CHCl_3$, 0.1 *N* HCl	*Ibid.*, **74**, 4023 (1952).

Table Continued

TABLE XIII (*continued*)

Solutes separated	System	References
Penicillins.............	Ethyl ether, PO₄ buffer	*J. Biol. Chem.*, **168**, 665 (1947).
	Isopropyl ether, PO₄ buffer	*Ibid.*, **174**, 209 (1948).
	CHCl₃, PO₄ buffer	
	Ethyl acetate, PO₄ buffer	
Subtilin...............	2-Butanol, water	*J. Am. Chem. Soc.*, **73**, 330 (1951).
Gramicidins...........	CHCl₃, benzene, methanol, water	*J. Biol. Chem.*, **182**, 839 (1948).
Gramicidin-S...........	Methanol, CHCl₃, 0.1 *N* HCl	*Cold Spring Harbor Symp. Quant. Biol.*, *XIV*, 23 (1950).
Amicetin..............	Methylene chloride, water	*J. Am. Chem. Soc.*, **75**, 499 (1953).

TABLE XIV
MISCELLANEOUS SOLUTES

Solutes separated	System	Reference
Phenol................	Phthalate buffer, CCl₄	*Anal. Chem.*, **20**, 951 (1948).
Various phenols.........	Cyclohexane or benzene, phosphate	*J. Am. Chem. Soc.*, **71**, 2624 (1949); **72**, 1939 (1950).
Lignin................	Dilute alkali, ethanol, CHCl₃	*J. Am. Chem. Soc.*, **72**, 3838 (1950).
Homologs of cyclopentenophenanthrene.........	Pentane, nitromethane	*Z. Naturforsch.*, **96**, 288 (1954).
Azulenes..............	Petroleum ether or CCl₄, H₂SO₄ or H₃PO₄	*Helv. Chim. Acta*, **32**, 547 (1949).
Isomers of nitrochlorobenzene................	Petroleum ether, 85% methanol	*Ind. Eng. Prog.*, **44**, 772 (1948).
Gliotoxin.............	Water, CHCl₃	*J. Am. Chem. Soc.*, **75**, 2103 (1953).
Mycomycin............	CHCl₃, phosphate buffer	*J. Am. Chem. Soc.*, **74**, 2245 (1952).
Flavines..............	*n*-Butanol, 0.02 *N* HCl	*Z. physiol. Chem.*, **287**, 216 (1951).
Porphyrins............	Ethyl ether, HCl	*J. Biol. Chem.*, **202**, 781 (1953).
Bitter principles from hops	Isooctane, phosphate buffer	*J. Am. Chem. Soc.*, **74**, 6118 (1952).
Streptomycin..........	Pentasol, aq. buffered stearate	*J. Am. Chem. Soc.*, **74**, 5461 (1952).
Biocytin..............	CHCl₃, cresol, dil. HCl....	*J. Am. Chem. Soc.*, **74**, 1996 (1952).
Vitamins B₁₂, B₁₂b, etc.....	Phenol, CCl₄, water	*J. Am. Chem. Soc.*, **73**, 3569 (1951).
Cardiac glycosides.......	Ethanol, water, CHCl₃	*Ber.*, **85**, 1042 (1952).
Heparin..............	Isoamyl alcohol, laurylamine, buffer	*J. Am. Chem. Soc.*, **71**, 1517 (1949).
Noradrenaline..........	0.02 *N* HCl, phenol	*Acta Physiol. Scand.*, **20**, 101 (1950).
Cozymase..............	0.05 *N* HCl, phenol, ether	*J. Biol. Chem.*, **176**, 935 (1948).
Growth hormone........	2-Butanol, aq. toluenesulfonic acid	*Biochem. J.*, **57**, 16 (1954).
Insulin...............	2-Butanol, 1% dichloroacetic acid	*J. Am. Chem. Soc.*, **74**, 3083 (1952).

VIII. MISCELLANEOUS SUBJECTS OF INTEREST IN CONNECTION WITH EXTRACTION

1. Choice of Temperature

In general extraction is relatively insensitive to changes in temperature when relatively dilute solutions are employed and the two phases are not partially miscible. Attempts to obtain more favorable partition ratios by changing the temperature considerably, however, have been made with more or less success. (See Sect. VI.) More favorable separation factors can frequently be achieved by use of a certain temperature of operation. Usually extractions are made at room temperature because of the convenience when the discontinuous process is the one of choice, but the continuous processes may be carried out easily under a wide range of temperature conditions. No general rule can be given in connection with the choice of temperature. Stability of the solute is an important consideration.

2. Problem of Emulsions

The advantage of stepwise extraction lies largely in the fact that equilibrium can be attained quickly and a single transfer made without delay. It is always annoying to find that the solution to be extracted forms a stable emulsion which in some cases cannot be broken satisfactorily even with centrifuging at rather high speeds. Centrifuging involves delay. There would appear to be no general procedure for avoiding emulsions, but a few suggestions may prove of value.

Emulsions usually occur during the extraction of an aqueous solution containing surface-active agents such as proteins, long-chain fatty acids, biological fluids such as blood and urine, and some plant material containing saponins. Changing the pH of the solution usually influences greatly the tendency to emulsify. As a rule alkaline solutions emulsify more readily than acid solutions. Addition of neutral salt often reduces this tendency, perhaps by increasing the surface tension or the density. Some organic solvents show in themselves a greater tendency to emulsify than others. If a hydrocarbon or higher ether is the solvent, addition of a small amount of ethanol or of a higher alcohol such as octanol may be beneficial. In many cases simply increasing the relative volume of the organic solvent will greatly assist the layers to separate. The possibility of addition of a different surface-active agent might also be considered.

It will often be found that emulsification is produced by a small amount of a solid phase which resides at the interface. Filtration of both phases will then prevent the trouble. A common procedure in biological work in which it is necessary to extract solutions containing protein is the preliminary precipitation of the protein by denaturation.   Other means of preliminary removal of the interfering substance might be suggested.   If the desired solute is known not to be adsorbed on an adsorbent such as alumina filtration through a thin bed of the adsorbent may be sufficient to remove the surface-active emulsifying agent.   If the solutes desired are freely dialyzable preliminary passage through a membrane may give a mixture which can be distributed without trouble.   Such a dialysis is simple to perform (see chapter on Dialysis).

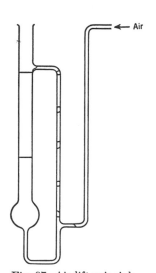

Fig. 87. Air lift principle.

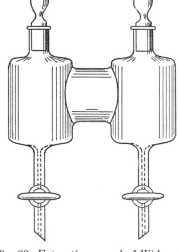

Fig. 88. Extraction vessel of Widmark.

The continuous types of extraction are very useful for the removal of solutes from aqueous solutions which tend to emulsify.   In most cases, the droplets of solvent which continuously pass through the solution are relatively large or their size can be controlled[196]; thus the difficulty due to emulsification is avoided.   Even though the amount of solute which is extracted at a single passage may be small and the extraction correspondingly inefficient, a continuous extraction can be allowed to run for days and an otherwise troublesome operation accomplished.

A particularly good example is to be found in the work of Veler, Thayer, and Doisy[197] in which sex hormones were extracted from urine.   Here the countercurrent principle was helpful.   Recirculating the extract continuously by the air-lift principle as shown in Figure 87 until the partition

[196] M. T. Bush and A. Goth, *Ind. Eng. Chem., Anal. Ed.,* **16,** 528 (1944).
[197] C. D. Veler, S. Thayer, and E. A. Doisy, *J. Biol. Chem.,* **87,** 357 (1930).

ratio is satisfied has been proved useful.[198,199] Allen and Goetsch[200] found that dripping methanol slowly into the upper separator of the countercurrent extractor of Veler, Thayer, and Doisy effectively broke emulsions and permitted extraction of urine with petroleum ether.

The extractor of Bush and Goth[196] would appear to offer particular advantages since it uses to a considerable extent the countercurrent principle and yet gives drop sizes just large enough to avoid emulsification. A further technique in avoiding emulsification is the arrangement whereby a small amount of the aqueous solution comes in contact with a relatively large amount of the organic solvent. Bush and Goth were able to extract rapidly the penicillins from culture broth and yet avoid emulsification. The extractor of Kolfenbach, Kooi, Fulmer, and Underkofler[199] makes use of essentially the same conditions. This extractor was developed for the extraction of fermentation liquor. A stream of air bubbles introduced at the bottom of the contacting tower was helpful in breaking the emulsions formed. In some cases, however, bubbles will form emulsions in an otherwise satisfactory system. Kieselbach[201] has designed a continuous extractor with a flat settling compartment in which the emulsions separate.

The literature contains many references to extractions done in such a way as to avoid emulsification. One of these[202] refers to the use of a large flat surface so that the surface area between the phases may be increased. The two phases are stirred gently by slow rocking without the production of sufficient turbulence to produce emulsification. Another[203] slowly rotates mechanically a bottle lying on its side which is half filled with the two phases. The rate of extraction is improved because the film of the aqueous phase is constantly carried up on the wall of the bottle.

An interesting device in many respects for exhausting acids and bases from small volumes of biological fluids has been suggested by Widmark.[204] It is shown schematically in Figure 88. Two flat-bottomed vessels are connected by a wide joining tube. In one vessel is placed the solution to be extracted and in the other is placed acid or base as required for removal of the solute from the extract. Both these solutions do not reach the broad tube joining the two vessels. Solvent is then stratified above the two in such amount that, when the tube is tilted, the upper layer runs gently from

[198] Moore, *Chemist-Analyst*, **19**, 23 (1930). P. F. Holt and H. K. Callow, *J. Soc. Chem. Ind. London*, **61**, 84 (1942); **62**, 32 (1943).

[199] T. T. Kolfenbach, E. R. Kooi, E. I. Fulmer, and L. A. Underkofler, *Ind. Eng. Chem., Anal. Ed.*, **16**, 473 (1944).

[200] W. M. Allen and C. Goetsch, *J. Biol. Chem.*, **116**, 653 (1936).

[201] R. Kieselbach, *Ind. Eng. Chem., Anal. Ed.*, **15**, 223 (1943).

[202] C. E. Parker, *J. Am. Chem. Soc.*, **35**, 295 (1913).

[203] A. Bruno, *Bull. soc. chim. France*, **35**, 422 (1924).

[204] E. M. P. Widmark, *Biochem. Z.*, **179**, 263 (1926).

one vessel into the other without allowing either of the other two phases to mix. The apparatus is rocked mechanically at such a rate that there is not sufficient turbulence for emulsification. Samples can be withdrawn periodically and the rate of exhaustion plotted against time. The quantitative data which can be derived from this simple apparatus would appear to offer interesting possibilities.

When emulsification develops during the attempt to carry out a countercurrent distribution it is an annoying complication. In addition to the suggestions made at the beginning of this section a number of other possibilities can be considered. One approach involves proceeding with the distribution in test tubes that can be centrifuged at each step, up to about 10–12 transfers. By this time it may be noted that the layers fail to separate in only two or three tubes and analyses at this point may show that the solute of interest is not in these tubes. If so the troublesome solutes may be removed and the distribution continued by placing the satisfactory solutions in the appropriate tubes of a countercurrent distribution machine.

It has often been noted that increasing the volume of the organic phase tends to prevent emulsification. Thus, where volume ratios of 5:10 caused trouble, 10:10 or 15:10 have been satisfactory.

A slower rate of shaking with less violent dispersion tends to minimize emulsification. In fact, the rate of rocking the tubes can be reduced with the automatic equipment to the point where there is no dispersion but only gentle stirring of the two phases. In this case a much longer time of equilibration would be required except for those systems and solutes where equilibrium is reached very easily. The loss in time caused by the longer equilibration is in part compensated for by the fact that there need be no settling period. Some success along this line has been reported in private communication to one of the authors.

As a rule it will be found that true equilibrium is not reached if a stable emulsion forms even though the layers can be separated by centrifugation. The emulsion prevents free interchange of the solutes. However, it will be found that proceeding with a distribution in spite of some emulsification often gives quite good separation. Here the experimental curve will not agree with the calculated.

3. Countercurrent Distribution and Changing Partition Ratios

Most treatments of fractionation develop the theory on the basis of more or less ideal behavior for the components. The usefulness of the theory then suffers in actual application for the reason that the majority of substances encountered show varying amounts of deviation. Often experiments must be performed empirically only to find that the separation ex-

pected has not been achieved.   This need not be the case in stepwise
laboratory extraction where the amount of solute is not large enough to
alter seriously the solvent properties of either phase.   In order to come
within this category the amount of solute tolerated will vary with the system as well as the solute itself but often may be as much as 5 to 10% of one

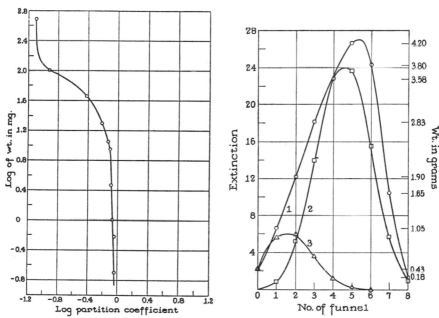

Fig. 89. Partition isotherm of plasmochin.   Fig. 90. Fractionation of plasmochin
mixture.

of the phases.   Preliminary experiments can readily indicate conditions
and concentrations for reducing the difficulty to a minimum and even may
permit taking advantage of a certain type of deviation for improved separations.

When choosing a system for extraction it is desirable to learn quickly
the extent of deviation from the ideal as well as the direction of the deviation.   This information may be obtained in a preliminary way by the systematic approach suggested on page 162, which involves successive extractions.   In selecting a system for fractionation, however, a better procedure is the direct determination of partition ratios at several dilutions
which cover the concentration range in prospect.   The result may then be
plotted as shown in Figure 89, which is an actual determination[205] with the

[205] L. C. Craig, C. Golumbic, H. Mighton, and E. O. Titus, *J. Biol. Chem.*, **161, 321**
(1945).

antimalarial drug plasmochin, using 10 ml. of each phase. The data could also be plotted so that the concentration in one phase is shown as a function of the other but their significance for the problem of fractionation is often more evident if partition ratios are plotted.

It can be predicted from Figure 89 that little difficulty will be encountered if the total weight per milliliter of each phase is less than 1 milligram. In fact, for many fractionation purposes, several times this amount could be used initially without encountering serious deviation in the final result, since, after a few transfers at a partition coefficient approximating 1, the concentration is reduced so that it comes into the linear range.

An example will illustrate the application of these data. Commercial plasmochin available at the time showed approximately 10–15% of an isomer[206] by countercurrent-distribution analysis. The isomer was found to have a partition coefficient approximately three- or fourfold that of plasmochin in the dilute range in the system diisopropyl ether – 2 M phosphate at pH 5.22. Though a small amount of the isomer could readily be separated by the distribution machine, much larger amounts of the pure drug were needed for clinical study. Attempts to remove the isomer by distillation and fractional crystallization of the available salts from a variety of solvents were to no avail. However, an eight-stage distribution[205] carried out in separatory funnels with 1800 ml. of each phase and 19.5 g. of the base gave the result indicated in Figure 90, curve 1. The material in funnels 6 and 7, when redistributed in the distribution apparatus, gave a curve in agreement with that calculated for pure plasmochin.

Initially, the concentration of the plasmochin was 10.8 mg. per milliliter of each phase. This is a concentration tenfold that within the linear range of the partition isotherm, and it is to be expected that the distribution curve would be skewed toward the right as was actually observed in Figure 90. From the isotherm given, it can be seen that the higher concentrations increase the percentage in the lower layer and accelerate the migration when the lower layer is the one transferred as in this experiment. A normal curve (curve 2) for a K of 0.78 is given for comparison. The approximate curve of the isomer is also shown by curve 3. It can be seen that the skewness and thus the deviation from a constant distribution ratio has placed more material in tubes 6–8 than afforded by a linear partition isotherm. Hence, the deviation has permitted a better separation than would have been obtained had more dilute solutions been used.

A similar effect has previously been shown in chromatography.[207] The curvature of the adsorption isotherm often produces a steep advancing

[206] R. C. Elderfield *et al.*, *J. Am. Chem. Soc.*, **68**, 1516 (1946). L. C. Craig, H. Mighton, E. O. Titus, and C. Golumbic, *Anal. Chem.*, **20**, 134 (1948).

[207] D. DeVault, *J. Am. Chem. Soc.*, **65**, 532 (1943).

front and a trailing rear of the band. If a mixture is being separated, an extremely good separation is obtained in the first effluent but, when the second component emerges, it is overlapped by the trailing part of the first.

The deviation noted in Figure 90 is probably caused by association in one of the phases. It is reasonable to expect that, if the diisopropyl ether phase is the one involved, increasing the volume of the organic phase would permit a greater amount of the solute to be used. The buffer could be maintained at its original volume by adjustment of pH so that it still would contain the same fraction of the solute at equilibrium.

For most cases encountered in laboratory extraction, it is likely that deviations may be reduced or eliminated by using more dilute solutions. However, it is better to choose a solvent which does not show deviation at the higher concentration, provided the desired selectivity can be obtained.

In general, solutes containing polar groups, particularly acids and bases, tend to show deviations when one of the solvents is a hydrocarbon or chlorinated hydrocarbon. Less deviation usually occurs when the non-aqueous solvent is an ether, ketone, or a hydroxylated solvent. Addition of a small fraction of an alcohol often reduces deviations.

Deviations from a linear partition isotherm are commonly ascribed to the reversible association of the solute, in one of the phases.[208] In some cases, association may be so great that, even with dilute solutions, the solvent cannot be used for quantitative work unless modified by the addition of another solvent such as alcohol. It has been suggested[209] that solvents of more polar character prevent deviation from the ideal by themselves associating with the solute. The monocarboxylic acids are known to deviate strongly when the organic solvent is benzene or chloroform, but they show much less deviation in an ether.

The higher fatty acids associate strongly. In most systems they do not give linear partition isotherms and skewed countercurrent-distribution patterns result. However, if glacial acetic acid is used as one of the components of the system the tendency of the higher fatty acid molecules to associate with each other is replaced by the association with the acetic acid molecules which are present in overwhelming concentration. Such systems give linear partition ratios and good β values as well. The higher fatty acids can be separated rather easily. Even such strongly associating solutes as the conjugated bile acids can be made to behave as ideal solutes or at least closely enough to permit ready separation.

There is a certain analogy between the phenomenon of skewed distribu-

[208] F. Daniels, *Outlines of Physical Chemistry*. 6th ed., Wiley, New York, 1951, p. 292.

[209] A. E. Smith and J. W. Norton, *J. Am. Chem. Soc.*, 54, 3814 (1932). S. Glasstone, *Textbook of Physical Chemistry*, 2nd ed., Van Nostrand, New York, 1946, p. 737.

tions in countercurrent distribution and the phenomenon of azeotropy in fractional distillation. In the latter a constant-boiling mixture results when there is a deviation from the expected partial pressure caused by association (hydrogen bonding) in the liquid state. The distillate has a composition in proportion to the modified escaping tendencies. In countercurrent distribution two solutes which deviate from a constant partition ratio could give two overlapping skewed bands as in Figure 91. Most of the band to the right, compound A, is free of the one to the left. But as its concentration becomes less a point is reached where the partition ratios become identical and no separation results. If, on the other hand, B had

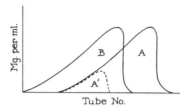

Fig. 91. Overlapping skewed distribution patterns.

been present originally in a concentration less than the critical concentrations then A' could have been obtained. Here the right-hand part of B would have been free of A but soon the critical concentrations would have been reached again where no separation would result. Figure 91 is a fundamental pattern. The analogy to constant-boiling mixtures in distillation would be more apparent if the hypothetical separation in Figure 91 were carried on into alternate or double withdrawal.

Obviously countercurrent distribution can still be very useful in spite of deviations just as azeotropy does not always defeat rectification. However, it does make the approach more complicated. It is to be expected that the larger complicated molecules encountered in biochemistry will be those most likely to deviate. On this score it is encouraging to note from the tables given in Section VII that many successful separations have been reported with substances such as peptides, bile acids, etc., which are known to associate strongly and act as detergents.

4. Analytical Control

In order to apply extraction intelligently in any process except the most simple and where partition ratios are known, one must be able to determine quickly the percentage transfer for any given step. All analytical methods are thus of interest in extraction and particularly those which are

simple, rapid, and general. For most cases, an accuracy to within a few
per cent is sufficient. An approximate method which is simple and rapid
is usually more useful than a more precise method which requires considerable time and effort. Many rapid methods of estimation are now available

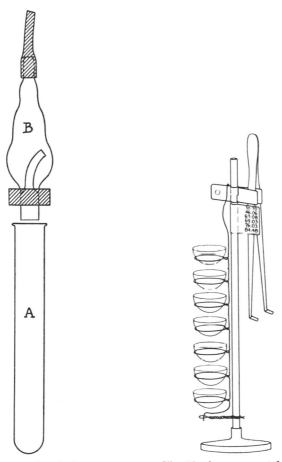

Fig. 92. Evaporation device.   Fig. 93. Arrangement for glass shells.

to the organic chemist. Some of the more readily available ones are direct
weighing, titration, spectroscopic estimation, colorimetry, biological assay,
polarimetry, refractometry and interferometry, polarography, use of
tracer elements, molecular-weight measurement, and paper chromatography.

Weight determination is the most general, most reliable, and often the
most rapid analytical procedure of all. It may involve a quantitative

precipitation and determination of the weight of the residue but more often it consists in simple evaporation of a small aliquot of the extract to dryness. Naturally, it is not applicable to highly volatile substances or to the cases in which appreciable amounts of other products are extracted together with the substance desired.   In a simple weight procedure which requires little time, a small aliquot of the phase is placed in a tared test tube such as A in Figure 92.   A glass trap, B, which is connected to a water aspirator or oil pump, is then brought to the top of A as shown.   B has a rubber collar which forms a tight seal when the vacuum is applied.   This permits rapid evaporation to dryness by shaking under warm water or on the steam bath. A small test tube will quickly come to within a milligram of its original weight when brought to room temperature by immersing in water adjusted to the temperature of the room and then removing the excess water by wiping with a clean cloth.

Where many weight analyses are to be made the following method has been found most satisfactory.[210]

Thin glass shells serve as both evaporation and weighing vessels.   They are made by blowing a round bulb, approximately 3.3 cm. in diameter, from soft glass ampoules.   The lower half of the bulb is detached by scratching a line on the fragile wall with a diamond point and then cracking off the hemisphere with the hot wire of a glass cutter.   The cracked edges are strengthened by fire polishing.   A sufficient number are made so that shells weighing within ±50 mg. of each other can be selected.   The weight of a finished shell should approximate 0.5 g.

The shells are arranged in order of increasing weight on a wire frame, as shown in Figure 93.   The frame can be made by twisting a series of copper wire loops around a glass tube 3 cm. in outside diameter.   The wire frame is hung on a small ring stand, which also supports a pair of small forceps for manipulating the shells. The jaws of the forceps can be covered with small pieces of rubber tubing to avoid damaging the shells.

The evaporator is a small steam bath placed on an electric hot plate.   The cover of the bath is fashioned from a flat sheet of stainless steel with five holes drilled in it.   One of the holes permits a reflux condenser to be attached, and the other four are of such size (3.0 cm.) that the glass shells are exposed to the hot vapors when the shells rest in the holes.   A glass tube, 10 mm. in inside diameter, with its opening approximately 2 cm. above the shell, serves as an air jet.   Air to the jet is filtered through a cotton plug.   The top shell of the series is a control tare.   If the solvent system itself contains a measurable residue, it may be advisable to evaporate an appropriate aliquot of the solvent as a blank in the tare shell each time a series of determinations is made.   In this manner the weight of each fraction subsequently determined is automatically corrected.   Otherwise, the tare receives the same final drying treatment as the other members of the series.

An aliquot of the solution to be analyzed, 0.1 to 3.0 ml., is added to the second

[210] L. C. Craig, W. Hausmann, E. H. Ahrens, Jr., and E. J. Harfenist, *Anal. Chem.*, **23**, 1326 (1951).

shell after the latter has been placed on the steam bath. A hypodermic syringe is ideal for this purpose, and can be fitted with a fine glass tip drawn out from an adapter (available from Becton Dickinson & Co., Rutherford, N. J.). A current of air from the jet is blown at the solution at such a rate that the surface of the solution is barely disturbed. If an aqueous solution is to be analyzed, it requires 2 to 3 minutes for a 1-ml. aliquot to be brought to dryness at 100°C. Higher or lower temperatures can be reached as desired by placing liquids of suitable boiling temperature in the bath.[211] During the time required for the evaporation of the first aliquot, others can be started on the remaining three holes of the bath.

As soon as the solution comes to dryness, the liquid clinging to the bottom of the shell is touched off with cotton gauze, and the shell is placed in its proper position on the wire frame. When all the shells have been so treated, the wire frame with its shells is placed in a large glass test tube fitted with a rubber collar near its upper end. The tube and its contents are supported in a steam bath by means of this collar, and the open end is closed by a one-hole rubber stopper with a glass tube and rubber hose connection to a high-vacuum oil pump. All the samples and the tare are dried together at 100°, 0.2 mm., for the required time, usually about 5 minutes. The shells are then weighed on a semi-microbalance to ±0.01 mg. In weighing, the tare always nearly counterbalances the shell containing the residue.

The Seederer-Kohlbusch balance used in this laboratory utilizes riders for weights up to 100 mg., and hundredths of a milligram are measured by the degree of deflection. As the shells differ from the tare by no more than 100 mg., the entire series of shells can be weighed by use of the riders alone. The balance is magnetically damped, and each weighing requires no longer than 1.5 minutes. Thin shells have been found preferable to heavier ones. Because they provide less resistance to the interchange of heat, evaporation of solutions is more rapid, and in the steam bath the final drying temperature is reached more quickly. Even more important is the rapid adjustment to atmospheric temperature. This permits reliable weighing immediately after removal from the steam bath. Finally, there is the added precision of weighing very small residues in containers of the smallest possible weight.

The method of evaporation presents several advantages. The stream of air not only carries away solvent vapors but also prevents particles of dust from falling into the shells. The shells are sufficiently large so that the level of the liquid is well below the rim of the hole in the steam plate, even with a 3-ml. aliquot. Thus, any solution tending to creep up the wall evaporates before it travels beyond the heated surface. It is advisable to evaporate sufficient solution so that a residue of 0.5 mg. is obtained. With samples of this size there is no loss by spattering, even with crystalline residues. Usually a thin layer of the residue covers the bottom of each shell, and conditions for final drying are optimal.

The fragile shells can be washed out easily without removing them from the wire frame by flooding them two to three times with an appropriate solvent. Solvent remaining in the shells is aspirated conveniently by a rubber tube with a syringe needle attached for a nozzle. The empty shells return to their original weight after washing. It is therefore necessary to recalibrate their weights only at infrequent

[211] E. H. Ahrens, Jr., and L. C. Craig, *J. Biol. Chem.*, **195**, 299 (1952).

intervals, or when there is reason to suspect an insoluble residue. Thus, the clean, wet shells can be placed directly on the evaporator for the next series of determinations. As the bottom of each shell is of clear glass, a residue of 0.10 mg. can be seen with the naked eye.

The above procedure has been in use in this laboratory for the past two years, and has been applied successfully to the measurement of partition ratios and to the analysis of countercurrent distributions of amino acids, polypeptides, bile acids, and lipides. The volatility of some fatty acids requires that water be replaced by ethyl alcohol in the evaporator, and some proteins and lipides can be freed of water only by final drying in the steam bath for 15 to 20 minutes.

Another type of shell has also been used with considerable success. It is made from platinum (currently obtainable from the American Platinum Works) and is smaller than the glass shell but permits the evaporation of 1 ml. of solvent. The weight is slightly more than 1 gram. The advantage of platinum is that it can be cleaned rapidly by holding it over an open flame unless the solute or solvents contain salt. After burning the shells return to their original weight; no tare is required. With a microbalance it has been possible to achieve comparable accuracy to the glass shells with one-third the sample and with equal speed. However, somewhat more care in handling is required.

In order to minimize the weight of the shells they are very thin walled, and bend too easily to be handled routinely with forceps. Instead they can be conveniently picked up with a small fork made by twisting a piece of platinum wire. The twisted end of the wire extends into a glass tube which serves as the handle of the fork. The two prongs of the fork are set a distance apart slightly less than the diameter of the rim of the platinum shell. The fork is ideal for holding the platinum shell in the flame of a bunsen burner for cleaning and for other manipulation.

If an acid or base is being extracted direct titration is a rapid and satisfactory method of analysis. Often the acid or base may be directly estimated in this way in the presence of the extracting solvent, if necessary by the addition of a third solvent such as methanol to avoid two liquid phases. In some cases, after addition of a few milliliters of water the titration may even be done in the presence of an immiscible organic phase by constant equilibration of the two phases. In such a case, however, the partition ratio must not favor the organic phase too greatly since the end point would then not be sufficiently sharp and would be in appreciable error. Graduated pipets are especially convenient for this type of estimation. The amount delivered is controlled by a small rubber bulb at the top held between two narrow plates which are controlled by a micrometer screw, as shown in Figure 94. This arrangement permits almost any volume from

0.002 to 5 ml. to be delivered by choosing a pipet and rubber bulb of the desired volume.   Other volumetric methods, such as iodimetry, can be used similarly.

If the substance to be extracted absorbs light in the ultraviolet or the visible, an especially convenient method of control is offered by the Deck-

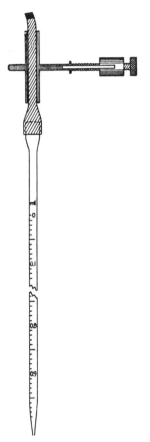

Fig. 94. Titration device.

man quartz spectrophotometer.   A series of cells varying in length from 0.5 mm. to 10 cm. will often save time by avoiding the dilution to an extinction within the range of operation.   If dilutions are required, hypodermic syringes are convenient and will often give the desired precision.

Colorimetry is not necessarily limited to colored substances since many colorless substances may be subjected to color tests which are quantitative in character and which may be applied conveniently.   A good example of this is the ninhydrin color test, which has been used for the quantitative estimation of amino acids.[212]

Biological assay has become more prominent in recent years and is especially valuable in the preliminary attempts to isolate active principles from their natural environment. Often these assays are surprisingly accurate and require only a few hours' time for a whole series of determinations. A good example of this is to be found in penicillin studies.[213]

5. Recovery of Solute

It is obvious that fractionation by extraction procedures requires repeated recovery of solute from dilute solutions. Following an extensive fractionation by countercurrent distribution it is not unusual to have 10 or 12 cuts which require the separate removal of solvent from each one. The method chosen for accomplishing this varies with the solvent and solute but usually involves an evaporation or concentration operation of some sort. The well-known way of doing this is by distillation in a distilling flask under reduced pressure. A decided improvement over this procedure is to be found in the rotary evaporator of Craig, Gregory, and Hausmann.[214] It is shown schematically in Figure 95.

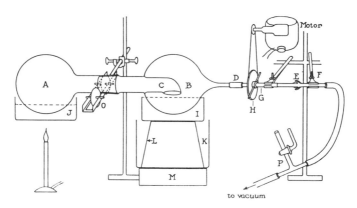

Fig. 95. Rotatory evaporator.

The solution to be concentrated is placed in a roundbottomed flask, A. B is a bulb which is at least as large or larger than A and has an inlet tube, C, whose width and opening are not smaller than the standard taper connecting A and C. The

[212] S. Moore and W. H. Stein, *Ann. N. Y. Acad. Sci.*, **49**, 265 (1948); *J. Biol. Chem.*, **176**, 367 (1948).

[213] J. G. Vincent and H. W. Vincent, *Proc. Soc. Exptl. Biol. Med.*, **55**, 162 (1944).

[214] L. C. Craig, J. D. Gregory, and W. Hausmann, *Anal. Chem.*, **22**, 1462 (1950).

other opening in B is a 7-mm. glass tube which is located opposite and in line with C. The smaller opening is connected by a short piece of rubber tubing, D, to a 7-mm. glass tube approximately 15 cm. in length which has a standard ball joint (2/5), E, at its further end. The other part, F, of the joint is held stationary by a clamp attached to a ring stand and connects to the vacuum pump through a rubber tube.

The glass tube which connects D and E passes through a cork borer, G, which is supported by a clamp attached to the ring stand to serve as a bearing. The tube also passes through a rubber stopper which is forced into a hole in the center of the wooden pulley, H, and this is made to grip the tube tightly. The pulley is turned by a leather belt and a smaller pulley attached to an electric motor which has a reduction gear (20:1 ratio) and an appropriate slide-wire resistor. Flask A and bulb B are supported by two small wheels with solid rubber tires.

For operation, joint E is well greased with a heavy stopcock lubricant and evacuation is begun. The motor is then started and the speed is so adjusted that the steady rotation of A and B does not greatly disturb the surface of the liquids in either vessel. B serves as the condenser. It may be cooled by the ice and water contained in the flat pan, I. Ice is added to the pan and the maximum surface of B is cooled because it is rotating constantly. Heat at any desired temperature is supplied to A by water in pan J. Because A rotates steadily, a film of the liquid is constantly being pulled up on the upper inside wall and a relatively large heated surface is thereby furnished for vaporization. Thus, distillation takes place rapidly without ebullition as in molecular distillation[215] and there is little or no tendency for bumping when pressure and temperature are properly adjusted. Even salt solutions have often been quietly brought to dryness. The familiar capillary leak or boiling stone is completely unnecessary. For solutes of poor stability, the level of the warm water in J can be reduced as the solution in A decreases; thus, overheating of the dry residue is avoided. Moreover, if evaporation at a low temperature is desired, dry ice and acetone can be placed in I and a high vacuum can be supplied with an oil pump. The apparatus then becomes a convenient freeze-dry assembly.

Where volumes of 0.5 to 2 liters are to be evaporated a different type of condenser is found to give more rapid evaporation. It is shown in the simple drawing in Figure 96. The condenser is made from a thin-walled glass tube 8 cm. in diameter and 24 cm. in length. A discarded 1-liter blood serum Pyrex bottle is excellent for making it. A short 8-mm. tube is sealed to one end and the 24/40 standard taper joint is sealed to the other end. In this case the vessel holding the ice–water (or acetone–dry ice) must be elongated as B in Figure 96. The level of the cooling solution must be of such height C that A dips into it about 1 cm. as it is turned by the motor. This condenser is particularly good when the distillate freezes on the condenser as when dry ice–acetone is used as a coolant.

[215] K. C. D. Hickman, *Ind. Eng. Chem.*, **29**, 968 (1937).

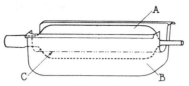

Fig. 96. Elongated condenser for rotatory evaporator.

Experiments with an elongated evaporation vessel instead of a round-bottomed flask (A of Fig. 95) indicated that this would further increase the rate of evaporation due to the increased surface. However, the convenience and ready availability of a round-bottomed standard flask speaks in its favor. Nearly the same effect can be obtained by using a larger round-bottomed flask.

Several evaporators of the type shown in Figure 96 can be set up and operated simultaneously by one operator. However, if the extraction process is to be carried out on a scale which would yield several liters in each cut, then a different type of evaporator such as the commercially available type operating with steam should be considered.

6. Extraction and Distribution of High Polymers

A considerable literature now exists on the distribution of high polymers between liquid phases. Such distribution has been mostly analytical in purpose, i.e., to get at the molecular-weight distribution and composition, but has sometimes been preparative. A survey by Cragg and Hammerschlag[216] through 1944 listed 312 references. They classified the methods

TABLE XV
DISTRIBUTION OF HIGH POLYMERS

Method	Principle
I. Solubility methods	Solubility decreases with molecular weight
1. Fractional precipitation	
a. By addition of precipitating solvent	
b. By cooling	
2. Fractional solution	
a. Solvent of varying composition	
b. By varying temperature with a single solvent	
3. Distribution between immiscible solvents.	Coefficient depends on molecular weight
II. Rate of solution methods	Small molecules diffuse faster
III. Ultracentrifugation	Sedimentation velocity increases with molecular weight
IV. Chromatographic adsorption	Small molecules adsorb preferentially
V. Ultrafiltration	Sieving action
VI. Molecular distillation	Large molecules are less volatile

[216] L. H. Cragg and H. Hammerschlag, Chem. Revs., 39, 79 (1946).

into six types as indicated in Table XV along with the various principles involved.

Methods I and II may be considered as extraction techniques within the purview of this chapter. Other separative methods such as centrifuging, dialysis, electrodialysis, electrophoresis, electro-osmosis, electro-ultrafiltration, and the various forms of chromatography are discussed in other places in this series of books. They and methods III, IV, V, and VI alone are often used for removal of electrolytes and small molecules from macromolecules and less frequently for fractionation purposes. Creaming under the influence of gravity or by centrifuging is often used as a separation technique with high polymers.

Interaction between high polymers and finely divided solids[217] can be adapted as an extraction process to the fractionation of polymers. For example, when carbon black is mixed with rubber it produces a sort of gel from which a portion of the initial rubber can be extracted. The rubber may be dissolved in a suitable solvent and the pigment added last. Certain blacks are said to take up high molecular weight polymer preferentially but at least one, Graphon, tends to absorb preferentially the low molecular weight fraction of GR-S. Such a separation has some of the aspects of extraction and incorporates some of the principles supposed to obtain in partition chromatography.

The nature of the swelling and eventual solution of high polymers in solvents has been presented by Hildebrand and Scott.[218] According to their treatment of linear high polymers the solubility of any actual specimen varies with the amount of undissolved polymer. This follows because high polymers are not homogeneous with respect to molecular weight and the lower molecular weight portions are the more soluble. Also, the "insoluble" portion is actually a gel, i.e., it is polymer swollen by the solvent and may actually flow like a liquid. A "good" solvent for a high polymer is one in which it is or tends to be infinitely soluble just as for low molecular weight solutes. In the case of a good solvent a high viscosity is to be expected because solvent-solute interaction (compare the effect of acetic acid on the association of acid solutes, page 319) makes it possible for the long polymer molecules to extend themselves. With a poor solvent, however —and these are more numerous than good ones—two phases can be expected in a sufficiently low temperature range. One of these is a gel, apparently not soluble although it is mostly solvent, and the other a liquid having nearly the viscosity of the pure solvent. When the temperature is raised the viscous layer may suddenly disappear to give the nonviscous

[217] M. A. Golub, *J. Polymer Sci.*, 11, 583 (1953).

[218] J. Hildebrand and R. L. Scott, *Solubility of Nonelectrolytes.* 3rd ed., Reinhold, New York, 1950.

solution. The reverse of this dissolving of the gel is called *coacervation* and the gel may be referred to as the *coacervate*. *Syneresis* is a related process. When a coacervate is cooled it is usually found to "sweat," *i.e.*, droplets of nearly pure solvent appear to be squeezed out on the surface. Syneresis is the older term, having been used in rubber and protein technology for many decades. Coacervation originated with Kruyt for proteins and was demonstrated for rubbers by Alfrey, Bartovics, and Mark[219] (see also Bosu and Bhattacharya[220]).

The theoretical approach to fractionation, molecular-weight distribution, and structure of high polymers is reviewed ably by Flory in his recent book.[221] Flory comments that the conventional precipitation fractionation of high polymer in the presence of a good plus a poor solvent actually amounts to the distribution of the polymer between liquid phases. On page 318 he makes the statement: "Sharp separations are never achieved and reliable results require time-consuming fractionation and refractionation into a large number of cuts.... The most significant progress toward the elucidation of molecular weight distribution has been achieved through application of theory." This state of affairs, if true, presents a challenge to the experimentalist. It would appear that the knowledge gained through the countercurrent distribution approach, which is largely empirical, could substantially supplement or change this state of affairs. We could hardly treat such a possibility in the present section even in a very limited way. We can point out, however, that in at least one case, that of polyethylene, the possibility of extraction has been put to a practical test. Desreux and Spiegels[222] described a temperature-controlled column extractor somewhat like an adsorption column which could well have general utility in the fractionation of high polymers. The polymer was supported on a solid. (See also Desreux[223] for apparatus for continuous mixing of good with poor solvents, fraction collectors, etc.)

The possible value of countercurrent distribution in polymer fractionation is suggested by a recent note.[224] The point was made that "polymer distributions show that, for a constant weight of polymer, middle fractions have smaller spread of chain lengths than fractions at either extreme." The usual precipitation procedure removes high molecular weight material first, but simple extraction technique—such as that of Desreux—removes the lowest molecular weight preferentially, whereas a true countercurrent distribution would separate various bands simultaneously.

[219] T. Alfrey, A. Bartovics, and H. Mark, *J. Am. Chem. Soc.*, **64**, 1557 (1942).
[220] S. Bosu and G. Bhattacharya, *Science*, **115**, 544 (1952).
[221] P. J. Flory, *Principles of Polymer Chemistry.* Cornell Univ. Press, Ithaca, 1953.
[222] V. Desreux and M. C. Spiegels, *Bull. soc. chim. Belg.*, **59**, 476 (1950).
[223] V. Desreux, *Proc. Intern. Colloquium Macromolecules, Amsterdam*, **1949**, 346.
[224] W. F. Watson, *J. Polymer Sci.*, **13**, 595 (1954).

7. Comparison of Extraction to Other Procedures

A treatment of extraction would scarcely be complete without devoting a small part of it to a discussion of the relative merits and shortcomings of this method compared to the other methods available for the isolation of chemical compounds. Extraction in one of its forms can obviously be applied to almost any problem of isolation and fractionation which may be encountered. In this respect, it is in a class by itself. In addition, there are many problems for which the only practical approach available would appear to be that of extraction.

Extraction is not limited by the amounts of material involved in a particular problem. Tons of material are being fractionated daily in some of the commercial processes, notably the petroleum industry and, when only micro amounts have been available, extraction has also been applied with success on more than one occasion.[225] Extraction procedures conform more nearly to the ideal case, becoming even better when very dilute solutions are employed. Many disturbing effects disappear completely at great dilutions. It is not improbable that the future of microchemistry may well depend to a considerable extent on extraction and adsorption procedures.

Extraction can be performed in a wide range of temperature. It is thus feasible to fractionate sensitive materials under the mildest of conditions and at low temperatures. The technology of penicillin manufacture illustrates this advantage[226] as does also an extraction method for identification and proof of purity.[227,228] Large[229] and rather labile molecules, such as those of current interest in biological processes, and polymeric substances[230] can be studied with little more inconvenience than is involved with the most rugged of substances. The organic chemist is inclined to think in terms of compounds which may be either crystallized or distilled. Yet without detracting from the desirability of crystallization when possible, there may be countless substances which will not crystallize and cannot be distilled though they might become well-defined chemical individuals after the application of suitable techniques. Extraction methods offer an opportunity to broaden the experimental field. The approach often can be

[225] E. O. Titus, L. C. Craig, C. Golumbic, H. Mighton, I. Wempen, and R. C. Elderfield, *J. Org. Chem.*, **13**, 39 (1948). G. H. Hogeboom and L. C. Craig, *J. Biol. Chem.*, **162**, 363 (1946). R. L. M. Synge, *Biochem. J.*, **38**, 285 (1944). R. Consden, A. H. Gordon, and A. J. P. Martin, *ibid.*, **38**, 224 (1944).

[226] D. Rowley, H. Steiner, and E. Zimkin, *J. Soc. Chem. Ind.*, **65**, 237 (1946).

[227] L. C. Craig, G. H. Hogeboom, F. H. Carpenter, and V. du Vigneaud, *J. Biol. Chem.*, **168**, 665 (1947).

[228] G. T. Barry, Y. Sato, and L. C. Craig, *J. Biol. Chem.*, **174**, 221 (1948).

[229] J. D. Gregory and L. C. Craig, *J. Biol. Chem.*, **172**, 839 (1948).

[230] L. H. Cragg and H. Hammerschlag, *Chem. Revs.*, **39**, 79 (1946).

made just as reliable or even more so than the other conventional ones customarily applied to crystalline or volatile material.

Extraction methods vary considerably in the amount of time they require. However, after the first preliminary study, it is nearly always possible to work rapidly with few unnecessary moves and thus without loss of time. They are in this respect comparable to distillation or adsorption procedures and certainly are much more rapid than the majority of fractional recrystallization procedures. Extraction need not be an expensive operation since expensive solvents can be recovered readily.

Extraction methods are particularly valuable in biological work and in the study of polymers. They offer a direct method of proving whether or not the much used quantitative colorimetric estimations refer to a single substance. Likewise, once a biological response has been established, direct proof that the response is due to a single substance or to more than one can be obtained by extraction even though the nature of the active principle is unknown. This information can then lead logically to final isolation of the substance, if it has the required stability. Extraction is thus the most widely applicable procedure of all available for systematic investigations of unknown substances. The only requisite for its application is that the substance be capable of partition between two immiscible phases.

IX. LIQUID–LIQUID EXTRACTION FOR INCREASED QUANTITIES

Introduction

The previous sections deal with the application of liquid extraction to the purification and identification of compounds. They are primarily concerned with the isolation of small quantities of compounds for determination of physical and chemical properties. When quantities larger than those usually prepared by the previous methods are required, it is necessary to resort to equipment designed for continuous operation. The purpose of the laboratory operation may be to produce a sufficient quantity of a material for further investigation as in the preliminary clinical testing of a pharmaceutical compound. Also, the continuous laboratory operation may be employed to give preliminary data on the performance characteristics of an anticipated pilot or larger scale plant. The laboratory experience will indicate the qualitative effect of changing the operating conditions.   It will indicate the product purities obtainable by the process and may even reveal refinements in the design of the larger equipment for optimum performance.

The purpose of the following section is to describe the theoretical aspects of continuous extraction and their application to larger scale laboratory extraction operations.   In this section *continual* extraction indicates a periodic addition of uniform quantities of solvents and feed to the system. This term is distinguished from the *continuous* extraction which refers to the addition of solvents and feed to the system at a constant rate.   Continuous extraction thus represents a differential of the continual operation with respect to time, in that it results from adding infinitely small quantities at differential time cycles while maintaining these small quantities of solvents and feed at the same ratio.   The relationship between these two terms must be recognized.   In some cases the equations have been pre-

TABLE XVI

NOMENCLATURE

D = distribution coefficient = $\dfrac{\text{concentration in light phase}}{\text{concentration in heavy phase}}$

D_1 = distribution coefficient of component (1) more soluble in light phase

D_2 = distribution coefficient of component (2) more soluble in heavy phase

E = extraction factor

E_1 = extraction factor of component (1)

E_2 = extraction factor of component (2)

H = flow rate of heavy phase in continuous extraction

    = quantity of heavy phase per cycle in batchwise extraction

L = flow rate of light phase in continuous extraction

    = quantity of light solvent per cycle in batchwise extraction

m = feed stage number counting from bottom of column

n = feed stage number counting from top of column

p = fraction of a component in light solvent at equilibrium contacting between phases = $E/(E + 1)$

q = fraction of a component in heavy solvent at equilibrium contacting between phases = $1/(E + 1)$

r = tube number in batchwise extraction pattern

R = rejection ratio = $\dfrac{\text{quantity in light product phase}}{\text{quantity in heavy product phase}}$

R_1 = rejection ratio of component more soluble in light phase

R' = retention ratio = $\dfrac{\text{quantity in heavy product phase}}{\text{quantity in light product phase}}$

R_2' = retention ratio of component more soluble in heavy phase

x = concentration of solute in heavy solvent phase

y = concentration of solute in light solvent phase

β = relative distribution = D_1/D_2

ϵ = constants in equation for deviation from steady state given by equation (59)

sented on a continual basis because the differential equations defining the continuous operation have not yet been solved.

In order to be consistent with chemical engineering publications on liquid extraction, the nomenclature shown in Table XVI has been used in the expressions of the relationships in continuous liquid extraction.

2. Theory of Continuous Extraction

A. EXTRACTION FOR REMOVAL

As mentioned in Section II, the laboratory equipment for continuous extraction falls into two categories. In *single-stage* extraction the solution to be extracted is retained in a vessel and the extracting solvent is passed through it. In *countercurrent* extraction the solution and the solvent are both passed countercurrently through a contacting device.

Single-Stage Extraction with Fresh Solvent. The mathematical relationships for this type of extraction may be derived directly from the solution of the differential equation. However, the significance of the equation can be more clearly demonstrated by considering the limiting case of the extraction of a solution with a multiple number of portions of fresh solvent. If a total amount of light solvent L is used in equal portions to extract a quantity H of heavy solution, equation (11) on page 169 becomes:

$$x_n/x_0 = 1/[1 + (LD/nH)]^n \tag{35}$$

From this equation it can be found that extracting the solution with the same total amount of solvent in progressively smaller portions will give increased extraction. The limit as n approaches infinity can be shown to be:

$$x_n/x_0 = 1/e^{LD/H} = e^{-LD/H} \tag{36}$$

This equation gives the fraction unextracted after contacting H parts of heavy solution continuously with L parts of light solvent under such conditions that the heavy solution is maintained uniform while the light solvent leaving the contactor is always in equilibrium with the heavy solution.

It is not possible to conceive of a mechanical design to achieve these precise conditions. A consideration of the deviation expected in such a design shows opposing effects. The mixing of the heavy phase can never be adequate to maintain a uniform concentration; and there will always be a gradient, such that the concentration of solute at the point where the light phase disengages from the heavy will be greater than the average solute concentration. On the other hand, perfect equilibrium between the light and heavy phases cannot be attained in any continuous-flow system because of the limited time of contact.   Theoretically there will always be a difference in concentration to provide transfer of the solute, although the driving force may be immeasurably small.   The first effect will tend toward higher solute concentrations in the exit light solvent and the second effect requires lower concentrations.   Thus it is possible, by coincidence, actually to achieve the purely hypothetical concept of light solvent leaving a system continuously in equilibrium with the average composition of the

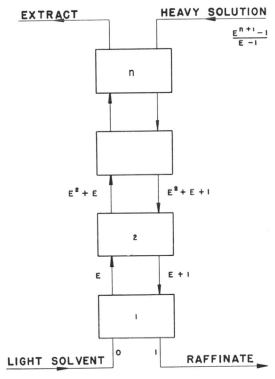

Fig. 97. Schematic diagram of multistage continuous extraction for removal.

heavy solution in the system.   Conversely, the application to a heavy solvent passing continuously through a light solution is obvious.

Continuous Countercurrent Extraction.   In the previous single-stage extractor the heavy solution could be run through at the rate of H parts in the same time required to pass L parts of light solvent.   Under these conditions it is possible, by regulating the amount of each phase retained in the contactor, to make the light solvent the dispersed phase by adjusting the liquid interface to the top of the contactor or to disperse the heavy phase by adjusting the interface to the bottom.   When the compositions

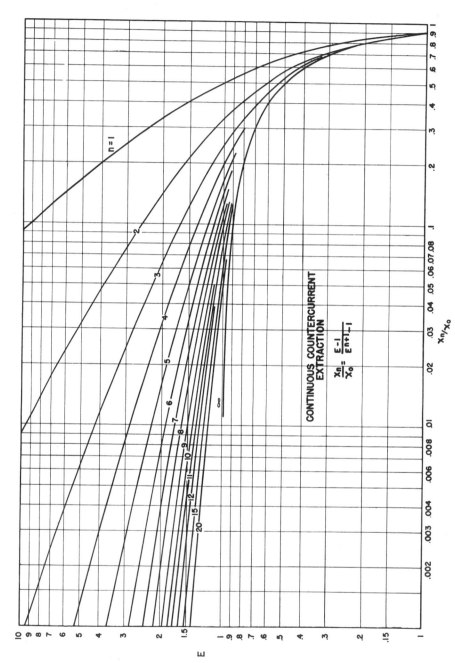

Fig. 98. Relationship between unextracted solute, extraction factor, and number of stages in continuous countercurrent extraction.

of the phases leaving the contactor are in equilibrium with each other, the extraction obtained is equal to one theoretical stage.

If the continuous phase is assumed uniformly mixed, it is not possible to reach the equilibrium concentration in the light phase at a finite rate of mass transfer.   But, similar to the discussion in the preceding section, the assumption of a concentration gradient in the continuous phase makes possible much greater extraction efficiency than is obtainable in a single stage.

It is, of course, possible to conceive of a stage in which the two phases have been sufficiently mixed so that they are in equilibrium with each other when they leave, and in practice any deviation from this condition can be adjusted by introducing an appropriate efficiency value for the particular equipment, as will be discussed in a later section.

When the solute removed in a single contacting is not sufficient for good recovery, it is possible to utilize additional stages and pass the solvents through the stages countercurrently as shown in Figure 97.   The algebraic relationships for such a multistage operation can be derived by alternate material balances and equilibrium calculations on the successive stages.

In any equilibrium stage the fraction of the total solute in the light phase is given by:

$$p = \frac{E}{E + 1} = \frac{LD/H}{(LD/H) + 1} \tag{37}$$

and the fraction in the heavy phase is given by:

$$q = \frac{1}{E + 1} = \frac{1}{(LD/H) + 1} \tag{38}$$

These relationships can be applied to the multistage column shown in Figure 97.   If the solvent feed is free of solute and the solution leaves the bottom stage of the column with a unit of solute, the total amount entering the stage in the heavy solution is $1/q$ or $E + 1$, and the amount leaving in the light solvent is E.   Similarly, the total amount in the second stage must be $1/q^2$ or $(E + 1)^2$, of which E entered with the solvent.   Thus, the difference $E^2 + E + 1$ entered with the solution from the third stage. The amount in the solvent leaving the second stage must be in equilibrium with the solution, and the same value of $E^2 + E$ could be obtained by the material balance on the stage.   In the same manner, all the values in Figure 97 can be calculated and the amount in the feed solution after n stages can be shown to be given by the general expression:

$$x_n/x_0 = (E^{n+1} - 1)/(E - 1) \tag{39}$$

and the fraction of the solute unextracted after n countercurrent stages is the reciprocal of this function or:

$$x_0/x_n = (E - 1)/(E^{n + 1} - 1) \qquad (40)$$

This equation is represented graphically in Figure 98.

The fraction of the solute extracted by the solute may also be expressed as:

$$\frac{x_n - x_0}{x_n} = 1 - \frac{E - 1}{E^{n + 1} - 1} = \frac{E^{n + 1} - E}{E^{n + 1} - 1} \qquad (41)$$

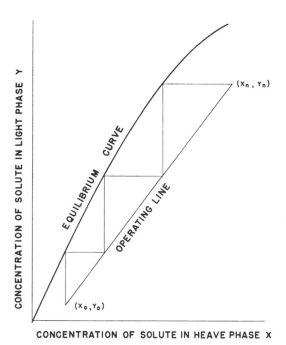

Fig. 99. Graphic equilibrium stage calculations.

But in the usual cases, where the solute removals approach completion, the equation giving the fraction unextracted lends itself more readily to slide-rule calculation.

Figure 98 demonstrates some interesting facts regarding the operation of a continuous countercurrent extraction. When the values of E are below unity, very little advantage is obtained by increasing the number of stages. On the other hand, when removal of more than 99% is desired, there is a significant advantage to increasing the number of theoretical stages. Actually, such high recoveries should not even be attempted with less than five theoretical stages.   At 99.9% removal, increasing the number of stages from five to ten will provide the same recovery with half the amount of solvent.   In this case it would probably be desirable to use even more than ten theoretical stages for this purpose.

The previous derivation has assumed a constant distribution coefficient independent of concentration.   This condition holds best in dilute solution. When concentrations become large, an appreciable variation in the distribution coefficient is usually encountered.   Where the prime purpose of

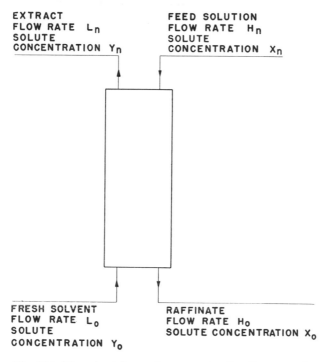

EXTRACT
FLOW RATE L_n
SOLUTE
CONCENTRATION Y_n

FEED SOLUTION
FLOW RATE H_n
SOLUTE
CONCENTRATION X_n

FRESH SOLVENT
FLOW RATE L_0
SOLUTE
CONCENTRATION Y_0

RAFFINATE
FLOW RATE H_0
SOLUTE CONCENTRATION X_0

Fig. 100.   Flow sheet for continuous extraction for removal.

the laboratory work is to obtain a sample of pure product, solute concentrations can be maintained sufficiently low that the ideal distribution law holds.   The chemical engineer, on the other hand, is always striving to obtain the maximum yield of product of acceptable purity from the particular amount of solvent and solutions handled, and this invariably leads him into the nonideal region of the distribution curve.   Where the laboratory investigator must look forward to the commercial application of his process, he should be somewhat familiar with the technique for handling nonideal mixtures in order to interpret his results properly.

When the liquids may be considered completely immiscible over the given range of solute concentrations, it is possible to evaluate the number of theoretical stages from the equilibrium diagram as shown in Figure 99. For purposes of this derivation, it will be assumed that the solvent is lighter than the original feed solution. The equations will hold for both cases if the solvent is designated L and the distribution coefficient, D, is expressed as the ratio of the concentration in the solvent phase to the concentration in the other phase. Any point on the line between the terminal concentrations of the extraction operation satisfies the material balance at this point, and this line is called the "operating line." The over-all material balance on the extraction operation shown in Figure 100 is:

$$H_n x_n + L_0 y_0 = H_0 x_0 + L_n y_n \tag{42}$$

where:
H_0 = quantity of raffinate solution per unit time
H_n = quantity of feed solution per unit time
L_0 = quantity of fresh solvent per unit time
L_n = quantity of extract solution per unit time
y_n = concentration of solute in extract after n stages
y_0 = concentration of solute in fresh solvent
x_n = concentration of solute in feed solution
x_0 = concentration of solute in final raffinate

If the values of H and L are the same at both ends of the column, this equation can be rearranged to:

$$H/L = (y_n - y_0)/(x_n - x_0) \tag{43}$$

from which it is apparent that the slope of the operating line is equal to the ratio of the quantities of heavy solution to light solution. The number of equilibrium stages necessary for a desired recovery is determined graphically by stepping off the space between the operating line and the equilibrium line as shown in Figure 99. This reproduces the usual algebraic technique of alternate equilibrium calculations and material balances previously discussed for the ideal systems.

It can also be shown by a material balance on a differential segment of a column that the ratio of H to L at any point is equal to the slope of the operating line at this point. Due to the presence of the larger amounts of solute at the upper end of the column and the variation of the mutual solubility of the solvents over the operating range of solute concentrations, this ratio will not be constant and the operating line in Figure 99 may not always be straight. Hunter and Nash[232] have devised a rigorous graphic technique for carrying out the stagewise calculations in this case by the use of a ternary diagram. The feed, raffinate, extract, and fresh solvent

[232] J. B. Hunter and A. W. Nash, *Ind. Eng. Chem.*, **27**, 836 (1935).

compositions are located at F, R_0, S_n and S_0, respectively, on the ternary diagram in Figure 101. The lines FS_n and R_0S_0 are then extended to intersect at point O. This point can be shown by geometry to lie on the line satisfying the material balance at any point in the extraction operation. The point S_1, in equilibrium with the final raffinate composition R_0, is located at the other end of the tie line, starting at R_0. A line through O and S_1 is then extended to the mutual solubility curve at R_1, which gives the

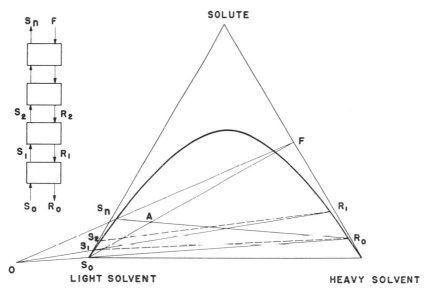

Fig. 101. Continuous countercurrent extraction calculations by method of Hunter and Nash.

raffinate composition satisfying the material balance on the first stage. The solvent concentration in equilibrium with R_1 is again located from the tie line through R_1 at S_2, and the alternate equilibrium determinations and material balances are continued until the final material balance line through S_n passes through the feed composition F or a slightly higher solute concentration along the same side of the diagram. In the latter case, the fractional amount of a theoretical stage necessary to reach the feed composition must be interpolated.

It should be noted that when the compositions of all streams have been established the ratio of solvent to feed quantities can be determined. The composition of the total amount of material introduced into the column must lie on the line between F and S_0, and the composition of the total amount leaving the column must lie on the line between R_0 and S_n. The only point satisfying both conditions is the intersection of the lines and thus the relative amounts of solvent and feed can be determined from the ratio of the distance AF to S_0A, and the relative amounts of extract and raffinate are in the ratio of the distances R_0A to AS_n.

On the other hand, the usual manner for specifying an extraction operation is to give the solvent-to-feed ratio and either the degree of extraction or raffinate concentration. In this case the total mix composition of feed and solvent is first located and the extract composition is obtained by extending the line from R_0 through this mix point to the mutual solubility curve. It is obvious that, since each of the product streams leaves the column after contacting the other phase, their compositions must lie along the mutual solubility curve.

It is also important to recognize that the other end of the tie line through S_n must lie below the line S_nF or it will not be possible to achieve the desired extraction with the given solvent quantity. The solvent quantity giving a tie line through S_n which coincides with S_nF is known as the minimum solvent quantity and will require an infinite number of stages to effect the separation. Smaller solvent quantities could not give the desired result even if the infinite number of stages could be provided.

Upon the application of the Hunter-Nash method, it becomes immediately apparent that the interpolation of the tie line data is very uncertain on the ternary diagram. Varteressian and Fenske[233] suggested a more convenient method whereby the tie line data are plotted as an equilibrium curve similar to Figure 99. The curvature of the operating line is determined by constructing a series of lines arbitrarily spaced through the point O on Figure 101 and plotting the solute concentrations at the two intersections with the mutual solubility curve as the appropriate coordinates of the graph in Figure 99. The operating line thus located is then treated as previously discussed to step off the number of theoretical stages required for the desired extraction. On this diagram the minimum solvent quantity is indicated by an intersection of the operating line and equilibrium curve at y_n. Any smaller solvent quantity will give an intersection at a smaller value of y_n, and it will not be possible to step off the number of necessary stages. The intersection of the operating line and equilibrium curve is called a "pinch," and the pinch compositions can be obtained only after infinite stages. The concept of pinch compositions proves useful in the calculation of fractional liquid extraction, which will be discussed in a later section.

The application of the theoretical stage concept to countercurrent liquid extraction equipment in which the liquids are contacted in discrete stages is obvious. Even in such cases the operating conditions may not pro-

[233] K. A. Varteressian and M. R. Fenske, *Ind. Eng. Chem.*, **28**, 928 (1936).

duce equilibrium in each stage. It may be necessary to calculate the number of theoretical stages required by the observed separation to compare it with the actual number and thus evaluate a stage efficiency. Sometimes the extraction is carried out in a unit providing continuous contacting of two phases as they flow countercurrent to each other, as in a packed or spray column. The concept of the theoretical stage can be applied to this type of equipment by calculating the number of theoretical stages in an observed separation obtained in a given height or length of fluid travel, thus evaluating the height equivalent to a theoretical stage, which is usually abbreviated as HETS. It is recognized that this stagewise variation does not accurately represent the mechanism for mass transfer in this operation, and the concept of a transfer unit[234] based on a differential change in concentrations has been derived similar to the continuous extraction with fresh solvent developed in the previous section. A thorough treatment of this concept is given by Elgin and Wynkoop[235] and by Treybal.[236]

B. FRACTIONATION BY LIQUID EXTRACTION

If the two components of a mixture possess different distribution coefficients for a pair of immiscible solvents, they will be in each solvent in a different proportion. Single-stage extraction by a continuous stream of solvent effects some degree of separation. The solute having the lower distribution remains in the original solution and the other component is removed by the solvent. The quantities of each component remaining after extraction with a given amount of solvent can be calculated from equation (40) or observed from Figure 98. It will be observed that an appreciable yield of one component in a purified state can be obtained only when the difference between the distribution coefficients is large. In distillation this would be analogous to a partial evaporation without fractionation and is obviously inefficient.

In fractional distillation the separation of the components of a mixture is always achieved through the use of a distillation column containing a predetermined number of theoretical plates. So, also, in fractional liquid extraction the desired separation is obtained through the use of an adequate number of stages through which the two solvents pass countercurrently.

Mathematics of Fractionation by Continuous Extraction.

Steady-State Conditions. The orientation of the liquid streams in the separation of two components by fractional liquid extraction is shown in

[234] T. H. Chilton and A. P. Colburn, *Ind. Eng. Chem.*, **27**, 255 (1935).

[235] J. C. Elgin and R. Wynkoop, "Solvent Extraction," in J. H. Perry, ed., *Chemical Engineers' Handbook*. McGraw-Hill, New York, 1950.

[236] R. E. Treybal, *Liquid Extractions*. McGraw-Hill, New York, 1951.

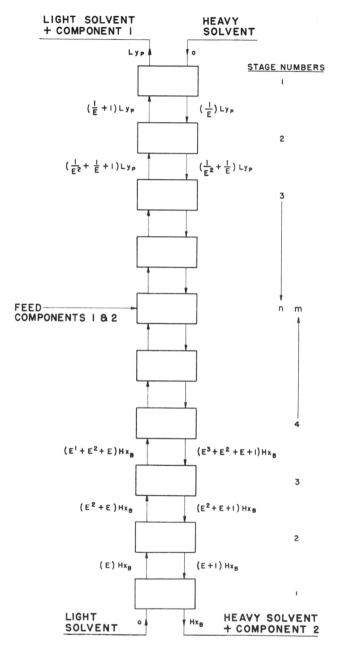

Fig. 102. Schematic diagram of multistage fractional liquid extraction

Figure 102. Component 1 is more soluble in the light solvent and component 2 is more soluble in the heavy solvent. The column may be considered as two simple extraction columns since in the section below the center feed component 1 is extracted from the heavy solution, leaving component 2 in the solution. In the section above the feed component 2 is extracted from the light solution, leaving component 1 in this solution.

The derivation for the fractionation of ideal mixtures is similar to that for the simple extraction for removal in that the expressions are developed from both top and bottom of the column and equated at the feed stage. The calculations are shown in Figure 102. If the feed stage is the nth stage from the top and the mth stage from the bottom, the quantity of solute in equilibrium with the heavy liquid leaving the stage must be equal to the quantity leaving in the light solvent from this stage.   Thus:

$$E \frac{E^m - 1}{E - 1} H x_B = \frac{(1/E^n) - 1}{(1/E) - 1} L y_P \tag{44}$$

The ratio between the quantity of a component leaving the column in the light solvent to that leaving in the heavy solvent which is called the "rejection ratio," R_1, has been derived by Bartels and Kleiman[237] as:

$$R_1 = (E_1^{n+m} - E_1^n)/(E_2^n - 1) \tag{45}$$

and:

$$R_2 = (E_2^{n+m} - E_2^n)/(E_2^n - 1) \tag{46}$$

where n is the number of stages above and including the feed stage and m is the number of stages below and including the feed stage. Since both numbers include the feed stage the total number of stages in the column is equal to $n + m - 1$.

In the above equations the value of R_2 is always less than unity because the column is operated to remove most of component 2 from the bottom of the column. For this component it is preferable to consider a "retention ratio" which is the ratio of the quantity of a component leaving at the bottom of the column to the quantity leaving at the top This ratio is the reciprocal of the rejection ratio and is designated R_2'.

When the feed is introduced into the center of the column such that $m = n$ equation (45) reduces to:

$$R_1 = E_1^n \tag{47}$$

and equation (46) in terms of retention ratio becomes:

$$R_2' = 1/R_2 = 1/E_2^n \tag{48}$$

[237] C. R. Bartels and G. Kleiman, *Chem. Eng. Prog.*, **45**, 589 (1949).

From the definition of extraction factor it can be shown that:

$$E_1 = \beta E_2 \tag{49}$$

where β = relative distribution = D_1/D_2.

If the fraction of component 1 passing overhead is equal to the fraction of component 2 passing out in the bottoms the values of E_1 and E_2 are related such that:

$$E_1 = 1/E_2 \tag{50}$$

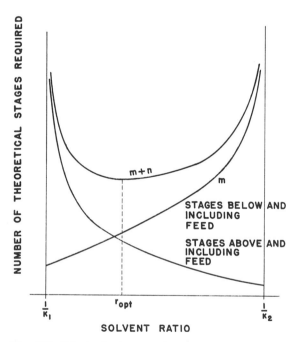

Fig. 103. Effect of solvent ratio on stages required in
continuous fractional liquid extraction.

and:

$$E_1 = \sqrt{\beta}; \qquad E_2 = 1/\sqrt{\beta} \tag{51}$$

When a given separation has been specified so that R_1 and R_2' are fixed, it is possible to select a range of solvent ratios or extraction factors which will effect this separation. In order to obtain a reasonable separation of components into products of a high degree of purity at an appreciable yield of both it is essential that both R_1 and R_2' be greater than unity. The higher the purity desired the greater the values of R_1 and R_2'.

Rearranging equation (45) gives:

$$R_1 = E_1^n[(E_1^m - 1)/(E_2^n - 1)] \tag{52}$$

and in order to give values of R_1 appreciably greater than unity it is necessary that E_1 be greater than unity. Similarly, in order for R_2' to be appreciably greater than unity it is necessary for E_2 to be less than unity. This establishes the limits for the operating range of solvent ratios and indicates that a practical separation can only be obtained when

$$D_2 < H/L < D_1$$

Figure 103 shows the general shape of the curves obtained by stagewise calculations at different solvent ratios. Rigorous consideration of equation (52) indicates that if m is appreciably greater than n it is possible to obtain a value of R_1 greater than unity even if E_1 is slightly less than unity. Thus, the curve of total stages is asymptotic to lines somewhat outside of the values of D_2 and D_1 depending upon the magnitude of the values of R_1 and R_2' for the desired separation

The curve of total stages passes through a minimum and the solvent ratio giving this minimum is called the optimum solvent ratio. Van Dijck and Schaafsma[238] suggested operating at the geometric mean of the two limiting values, namely:

$$H/L = \sqrt{D_1 D_2} \tag{53}$$

and Stene[239] showed that this optimum solvent ratio holds for $R_1 = R_2'$ and at this solvent ratio $n = m$. This situation has been called the symmetrical system and the first attempts to rationalize the performance of a fractional liquid extraction were based on this type of system.

Klinkenberg, Lauwerier, and Reman[240] developed algebraic equations to calculate the number of theoretical stages required above and below the feed to obtain a given separation at any solvent ratio. The equations could not be solved directly for n and m for all solvent ratios. However, certain particular solutions were observed which provided the data necessary to plot the curves shown in Figure 103 and the values of n and m could then be interpolated at any solvent ratio.

Klinkenberg[241] studied a large number of systems and developed an empirical correlation for the optimum solvent ratio and theoretical stages required above and below the feed, as a function of the rejection ratios of the two components. The correlations were given as families of curves.

[238] W. J. D. Van Dijck and A. Schaafsma, U. S. Pat. 2,245,945 (1941).

[239] S. Stene, Arkiv Kemi, Mineral., Geol., 18H, No. 18 (1944).

[240] A. Klinkenberg, H. A. Lauwerier, and G. H. Reman, Chem. Eng. Sci., 1, 93 (1915).

[241] A. Klinkenberg, Ind. Eng. Chem., 45, 653 (1953).

Scheibel[242] developed empirical equations to express the relationships of Klinkenberg's curves. The optimum solvent ratio can be derived from equations (45, 46, and 52) by introducing approximations holding when n and m are large. The resulting equation is:

$$\log E_1 = \frac{\log \beta}{1 + (\log R_2'/\log R_1)^{1/2}} \tag{54}$$

and this equation reproduces Klinkenberg's correlation over the range of usual separations.

The total number of theoretical stages required at the optimum solvent ratio is given as:

$$m + n = \frac{2 \log R_1 R_2'}{\log \beta}\left(1 - 0.04\left|\log\frac{R_1}{R_2'}\right|\right) \tag{55}$$

This equation without the term in the brackets on the right was observed by Klinkenberg, Lauwerier, and Reman[240] for $m = n$ and the term in the brackets was evaluated empirically to correct for nonsymmetrical extraction systems. The deviations increase as the ratio between R_1 and R_2' becomes greater but at a ratio of 1000:1 the error in the equation is only 3%. This condition is considerably outside the range of usual separations.

The feed stage at optimum solvent ratio can be located from the relationships shown in equations (56) and (57):

$$\frac{n}{m} = \left(\frac{\log R_2'}{\log R_1}\right)^{1/2}\left(1 + \frac{\log (R_1/R_2')}{R_2' \log R_1}\right) \tag{56}$$

when $R_2' < R_1$ and:

$$\frac{m}{n} = \left(\frac{\log R_1}{\log R_2'}\right)^{1/2}\left(1 + \frac{\log (R_2'/R_1)}{R_1 \log R_2'}\right) \tag{57}$$

when $R_1 < R_2'$.

These equations without the second terms in the parentheses on the right have also been derived by Klinkenberg and co-workers[240] for the symmetrical case and the terms in the parentheses have been developed empirically to fit the nonsymmetrical cases. The equations agree with the calculated distribution of stages above and below the feed at the optimum solvent ratio from equation (54) for the range of usual separations also covered by Klinkenberg's curves.

A graphic technique for the stagewise calculations in a fractional liquid extraction process was first applied by Martin and Synge[243] to an ideal

[242] E. G. Scheibel, *Ind. Eng. Chem.*, **46**, 16 (1954).
[243] A. J. P. Martin and R. L. M. Synge, *Biochem. J.*, **35**, 91–121 (1941).

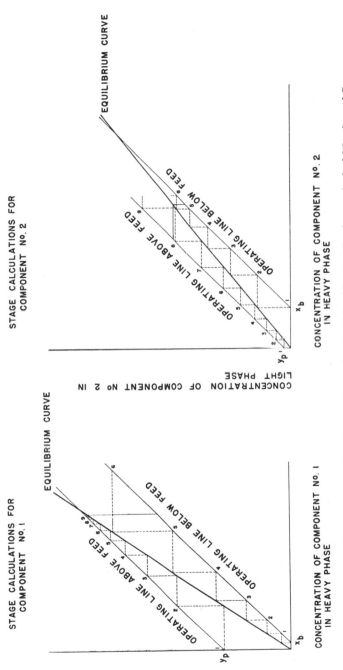

Fig. 104. Graphic stagewise calculations for continuous fractional liquid extraction by method of Martin and Synge.

system. The method consists of constructing the operating lines for the sections above and below the feed stage on the equilibrium diagrams for each of the components. If the fresh solvents are free of both components being separated, the operating lines start at the axes as shown in Figure 104. The operating lines are drawn through these points located from the over-all material balance with slopes equal to the solvent ratio, H/L for each of the sections of the column and for both components as shown in the two

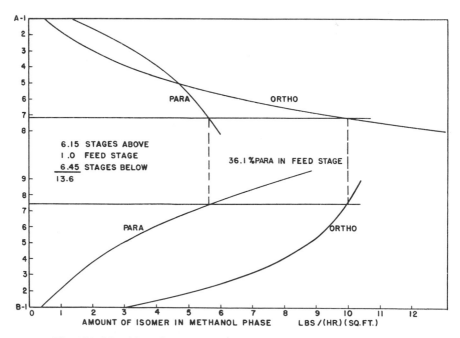

Fig. 105. Matching of components in numerical stagewise calculations.

parts of Figure 104.   The feed stage is that stage which matches the compositions at the same numbers of stages above and below the feed for each of the components and must be located by a trial-and-error technique. However, the method is fairly direct because of the existence of the pinches. Thus, for component 1 there is very little change in the stages required below the feed for more than six stages above since the stages below only increase from about 5.1 to 5.4 for stages above numbering from 6 to in-finity.   It is, therefore, immediately apparent that about five stages are required below the feed and when these are stepped off on the other section for component 2 it may be seen that they require about eight stages above the feed.   It is also apparent from this figure that a large increase in the number of stages below the feed from five to infinity only increases the stages required above from about eight to ten.   Thus, the region of the match has been accurately defined and alternate reference to the two parts of the figure rapidly establishes the complete match at 8.2 stages above the feed and 5.3 stages below.   Since these numbers both include the identical feed stage, the total number of stages required for the separation is 14.5.

Compere and Ryland[244] applied this graphic technique to a nonideal system in which the equilibrium lines were curved but in which the equilibrium curves for each of the two components were unaffected by the presence of the other so that it was possible to construct the curves shown in Figure 104.   They demonstrated the method by determining the separation obtainable in a given number of equilibrium stages and compared the calculated values with their experimentally determined data on the given system.

Scheibel[245] proposed a method for matching components at the feed stage by plotting the concentrations of each of the components in one of the phases against the stage numbers above and below the feed as shown in Figure 105.   This technique was also demonstrated on completely nonideal systems in which the distribution coefficients of each component varied with its own concentration and with that of the other component so the equilibrium data could not be represented by single lines as in Figure 104.   The methods for prediction of nonideal distribution data and the representation of the data for convenient stagewise calculations have also been described by Scheibel.[245,246]

Karr and Scheibel[247] have described a convenient method for determining the product distribution in nonideal extraction operation of a given number of stages.   They applied it to the study of the separation of 2,6-lutidine, 3-picoline, and 4-picoline in seven and nine stages.

Asselin and Comings[248] applied the graphic technique of Martin and Synge to the study of fractional liquid extraction with reflux as will be discussed in a later section.   They matched the concentration and located the feed stage by plotting the concentrations obtained in the graphic stepwise calculations against stage number as described by Scheibel.[245]

Unsteady-State Conditions.   The previous section discussed relationships between the product streams that exist when the solute concentrations in the column have reached sufficient magnitude that the sum of the solutes in the streams leaving the column equals the feed.   This condition is of prime interest in plant operation because it represents the conditions finally

[244] E. L. Compere and A. Ryland, *Ind. Eng. Chem.*, **43**, 239 (1951).
[245] E. G. Scheibel, *Chem. Eng. Prog.*, **44**, 681–690 and 771–782 (1948).
[246] E. G. Scheibel, *Ind. Eng. Chem.*, **42**, 1497 (1950).
[247] A. E. Karr and E. G. Scheibel, *Ind. Eng. Chem.*, **46**, 1583 (1954).
[248] G. F. Asselin and E. W. Comings, *Ind. Eng. Chem.*, **42**, 1198 (1950).

achieved and which will be maintained for the period of the run. On the other hand, in the laboratory the tests are run for a limited period to obtain the necessary performance data for the full-scale design. In order to interpret the laboratory data properly it is necessary to consider the approach to the ultimate steady-state conditions.

For this purpose the continual double-withdrawal pattern shown in Figure 106 can be used to develop the continuous countercurrent extraction. By introducing the same feed quantity into the center stage on alternate

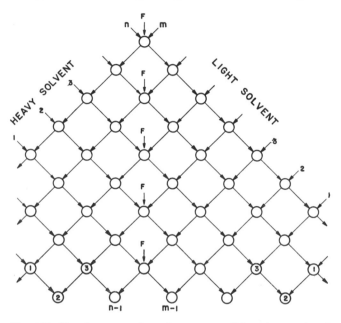

Fig. 106. Development of steady-stage conditions by continual feed in the batchwise technique.

transfers as shown in the figure, the solutes accumulate in the stages until the steady-state concentrations are finally reached. Theoretically this requires infinite cycles but practically it is achieved when quantities are constant within the limits of experimental accuracy. It was noted by Stene[249] that when the quantities in each of the product streams for a single feed introduction are expressed as a series, the quantity at any cycle for the continual feed is the sum of all the previous terms of this series. The steady-state quantity is the sum of the infinite series. Stene developed the expression for all the terms of the series when the feed is introduced into the center stage and the withdrawals are made equidistant from the center

[249] S. Stene, *Arkiv Kemi, Mineral., Geol.*, **18H**, No. 18 (1944).

stage. This is the symmetrical pattern previously mentioned. Stene concluded that the expression for the nonsymmetrical pattern of product withdrawal is hopelessly complex.

The evaluation of the sum of the terms of the series is a measure of the approach of the concentrations in the stages to the ultimate steady-state quantities. The terms were observed to approach a geometric series as their number increased and this led to a simple empirical equation for the fractional deviation of the product concentrations from the steady state.[250] This equation was found to have large errors when used for a large number of stages and a large number of cycles, and subsequently Peppard and Peppard[251] developed more complicated empirical equations, which were accurate over a greater range of values. The rigorous equation for the general case of nonsymmetrical pattern was published simultaneously by Compere and Ryland[252] and by Scheibel.[253] The former authors used a statistical method designated by Feller[254] as "gambler's ruin" to derive the equation and the latter author used a method which was observed by Compere[255] to incorporate Kelvin's "method of images." [254]

The rigorous expression for the fraction of a solute in the light solvent leaving the countercurrent fractional liquid extraction system shown in Figure 106 after t cycles is given as:

$$P_t = \left(\frac{E}{E+1}\right)^n \left\{ \epsilon_1 + \epsilon_2 \frac{E}{(E+1)^2} + \epsilon_3 \left(\frac{E}{(E+1)^2}\right)^2 + \ldots + \epsilon_t \left[\frac{E}{(E+1)^2}\right]^{t-1} \right\} \quad (58)$$

where the values of ϵ are calculated from the general equation:

$$\epsilon_t = \sum_{i=0}^{\infty} \binom{n+2t-3}{t-1-i(m+n)} - \sum_{i=0}^{m} \binom{n+2t-3}{t-2-i(m+n)} -$$

$$\sum_{i=0}^{\infty} \binom{n+2t-3}{t-m-1-i(m+n)} +$$

$$\sum_{i=0}^{\infty} \binom{n+2t-3}{t-m-2-i(m+n)} \quad (59)$$

[250] E. G. Scheibel, *Ind. Eng. Chem.*, **43**, 242 (1951).

[251] D. F. Peppard and M. A. Peppard, *Ind. Eng. Chem.*, **46**, 34 (1954).

[252] E. L. Compere and A. Ryland, *Ind. Eng. Chem.*, **46**, 24 (1954).

[253] E. G. Scheibel, *Ind. Eng. Chem.*, **46**, 43 (1954).

[254] W. Feller, *Introduction to Probability Theory and Its Application*, Vol. I, Wiley, New York, 1950.

[255] E. L. Compere, private communication.

in which the terms inside the summation designate the binomial coefficients
such that:

$$\binom{n}{r} = \frac{n!}{r!(n-r)!} \qquad \text{and} \qquad \binom{n}{0} = 1$$

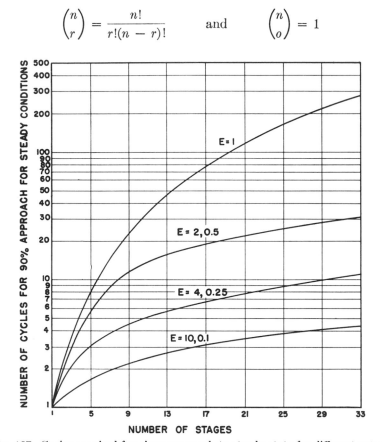

Fig. 107. Cycles required for given approach to steady state for different extraction factors and numbers of stages with uniform continual feed.

and for values of r greater than n and less than zero the terms do not exist.
This requirement thus limits the terms of the summations to relatively few
for the smaller values of t. Larger values of t approach so closely to the
steady-state conditions that it would not be possible to measure the deviation experimentally.

This equation is probably too complex for general use and for most practical purposes a graph similar to Figure 107 can be calculated and constructed for any other desired degree of approach to steady state.

It can be observed from Figure 106 that the number of stages on the
left, including the feed stage, is n, and the number on the right, also in-

cluding the feed stage, is m; the steady-state stages are numbered as indicated at the bottom of the pattern.   Thus, the total number of stages in the continuous operation is $n + m - 1$.

It is possible to derive all the relationships for the continuous operation by considering the sums of infinite series in equation (58), and the result must be the same as the direct approach made by the technique of alternate equilibrium and material balance calculations at steady state.

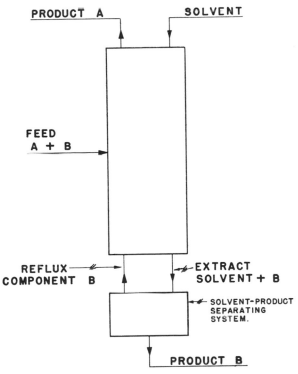

Fig. 108. Flow sheet for fractional liquid extraction using a single solvent.

For the symmetrical case the number of continuous stages required to give the separation obtained in the withdrawn solutions is thus equal to $2n - 1$ where n is also the number of stages along the bottom of the triangular pattern.   Consideration of the batchwise fractionation technique discussed in Section II.4.A indicates that the final removal of the upper and lower layers at the ends of the triangular pattern requires n transfers and it is interesting to note that the continuous operation requires about twice the number of transfers to obtain the same end products.   However, when the products are isolated from the intermediate stages to obtain a reasonable yield, it will subsequently be shown that the same separation can be achieved in a considerably smaller number of continuous stages.

Fractional Liquid Extraction with Single Solvent. The first liquid extraction process which was studied for the separation to two components employed one solvent, and depended upon the difference in the solubility of the components in the solvent. The process requires that both components being separated be only partially miscible with the solvent, and they must both be either heavier or lighter than the solvent. The component more soluble in the solvent is separated from the solvent and some of it is returned to the extraction column as the second phase, as shown in Figure 108. This is called reflux, and the ratio of the amount of this returned stream to the amount withdrawn is called the reflux ratio. As the reflux passes back through the column countercurrent to the solvent it changes in composition until it becomes a substantially pure stream of the other component. This is an exact analogy to distillation in that the solvent is equivalent to the heat required to vaporize the liquid. In this type of extraction the solvent moves the mixture to be separated through the column just as does the heat in distillation. At the end of the column the solvent is removed, and some of the product is returned, just as the heat is removed in the condenser in distillation and some of the condensation is refluxed. In addition, an identical effect is experienced in the liquid phase in distillation which passes downward through the column, and all but the amount of less volatile constituent which is withdrawn as product must be re-evaporated up the column. This analogy gives a better understanding of the factors involved in the operation of a fractionation by liquid extraction using reflux because it is apparent that sufficient solvent must be provided to dissolve all but the necessary amount of product at the bottom; doubling the reflux ratio in the extraction column increases the required solvent rate in the same manner as the increase in heat required by doubling the reflux ratio in the distillation column. This analogy is useful because the relationship between solvent rate and reflux ratio is not otherwise as apparent in extraction as the relationship between heat and reflux ratio in distillation. Varteressian and Fenske[256] studied this process as applied to the separation of *n*-heptane and methyl cyclohexane using aniline as the solvent. They derived the geometry for carrying out the stagewise calculations on a ternary diagram using experimentally determined tie lines. Their method is rigorous, but retains the inherent uncertainty, previously mentioned, in interpolating tie line data on a ternary diagram. This makes it less desirable than the method of Maloney and Schubert.[257] The latter method utilizes the Ponchon method in distillation calculations,

[256] K. S. Varteressian and M. R. Fenske, *Ind. Eng. Chem.*, **29**, 270 (1937).
[257] J. Maloney and X. Schubert, *Trans. Am. Inst. Chem. Eng.*, **36**, 741 (1940).

but replaces the heat with solvent quantity according to the analogy previously described. An application of the Maloney-Schubert method is shown in Figure 109. The upper section of the figure shows the amount of

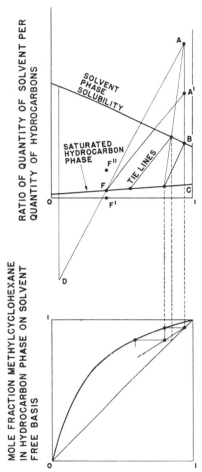

Fig. 109. Stage calculations for single-solvent fractionation by method of Maloney and Schubert.

solvent per unit quantity of mixture being separated, in this case, methylcyclohexane and n-heptane, against the fraction of methylcyclohexane on a solvent-free basis. If point A is located on the vertical line such that AB/BC is the given reflux ratio, all lines passing this point cut the two solubility curves at concentrations which satisfy the solvent balance around the bottom of the column and any point below the feed stage. Also, if the line from A through F is extended to the vertical line at D, any line through D cuts the solubility curves at concentrations which satisfy the solvent balance around the top of the column and any point above the feed stage. These relationships can be derived similar to the heat balances on the Ponchon diagram.

Equilibrium conditions are indicated by tie lines in the upper section of Figure 109, and the difficulty of interpolating these tie lines has been recognized. Maloney and Schubert have recommended obtaining the necessary equilibrium data from a curve such as that shown in the lower section of Figure 109. From this equilibrium curve, the lower end of the tie line through B is located, and the line through EA locates the point on the operating line at G which is then plotted on the equilibrium diagram. An obvious modification of this technique would be to construct the operating line by a random selection of points, and then step off the stages, as suggested by Varteressian and Fenske in applying the method of Hunter and Nash for simple extraction for removal previously discussed. When the tie line crosses the line AD the material balances are then taken through point D since the feed stage has been passed at this point in the column.

The diagram of Figure 109 also indicates an interesting technique for determining the minimum reflux ratio in this type of extraction. Similar to the distillation operation the minimum reflux ratio is obtained when the line AD coincides with the tie line through F. At this condition point A reaches the lowest possible position at which the desired separation can be obtained with infinite stages. At any lines below this position the separation is impossible even with infinite stages. Thus, the ratio of AB to BC is then the minimum reflux ratio.

In Figure 109, the feed composition corresponding to point F is saturated with solvent. For purposes of this illustration the saturated hydrocarbon line has been shown farther above the zero solvent concentration line than the actual data indicate. If the feed mixture were solvent free, it would lie on this datum line at point F'. In the Ponchon method for distillation this corresponds to subcooled feed. If some excess solvent were introduced with the saturated hydrocarbon feed, the feed point would be located at F'' which is analogous to partially vaporized feed. It can be seen that in the latter case the tie line through the feed point would be above that for the saturated feed only, and the minimum ratio would be higher. Conversely, at any possible operating reflux ratio the number of stages required when excess solvent is introduced with the feed is greater than when all the necessary solvent is introduced at the end of the column. The same effect is observed in a two-solvent fractional liquid extraction when either or both

solvents are introduced with the feed, but considerable calculation is necessary to prove it in the latter case while it can be clearly seen from the
Ponchon diagram for single-solvent fractionation.

Thus far in the discussion of fractionation by solvent extraction with
reflux no attention has been given to the method of recovering the component in the solvent stream so that it can be returned to the column for

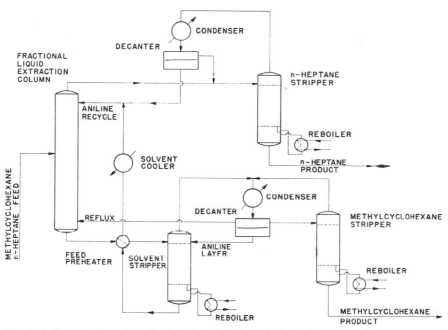

Fig. 110. Process flow sheet for fractionation of methylcyclohexane and heptane using
aniline as the solvent.

reflux.   The obvious method is by fractional distillation in which the two-
phase minimum boiling azeotrope is separated, the nonsolvent phase is removed and the necessary amount returned to the extraction column as
reflux, and the pure solvent from the bottom of the distillation column is
recycled to the extraction column.   It should be recognized that the overhead product from the distillation column is saturated with solvent, and a
further distillation is necessary to remove this solvent to give a pure solvent-free product.   Similarly, the other product from the extraction
column is saturated with solvent which must be removed.   The complete
process flow sheet for this separation as applied to the methylcyclohexane–
n-heptane fractionation with aniline is shown in Figure 110, and the complexity of the process is obvious.   Other solvents that have been used for
similar hydrocarbon separations are furfural, phenol, nitrobenzene, and

liquid SO_2 (Edleanu process). Descriptions of the application of these processes in petroleum refining complete with flow sheets are given in the Process Handbook Edition of *Petroleum Refiner*.[258]

Another method for separating the necessary reflux from the solvent consists of adding a diluent to the solvent which will decrease the solubility of the extracted product. A commercial application of this process is in the use of phenol for the fractional liquid extraction of paraffins and aromatics. Water is added to the phenol extract to precipitate the hydrocarbon. The over-all flow sheet is not noticeably simplified because the phenol and water must then be separated by fractional distillation before the phenol can be recycled, but there is an economic advantage in the operating costs when the hydrocarbons boil close to or higher than the phenol solvent. Any other additional constituent, which precipitates by chemical reaction or salts out the product from the solvent, could be used to effect the desired separation.

The third method which has been used to separate the product from the solvent takes advantage of the difference in solubility with temperature. Since this temperature change can be effected by heat transfer at the solvent end of the extraction column, an auxiliary piece of equipment is not required. The usual decrease in solubility with decreasing temperature can be utilized, but since it is generally not sufficient to produce a high reflux ratio over a practical temperature range, its application is limited. The largest commercial applications of this method of separation are based on the reverse effect encountered with propane slightly below its critical temperature. Thus, with propane and fatty acids the mixtures change from complete miscibility to almost complete immiscibility over a few degrees,[259] and this effect is utilized in the Solexol Process of M. W. Kellogg Co. for the fractionation of vegetable oils and fish oils by liquid extraction. It is also used in their propane refining of mineral oil fractions.

Relative Merits of Fractional Extraction with Reflux and Two Immiscible Solvents. It is significant that the applications of the previous section were all to the separation of similar or closely related compounds. The process requires a solvent in which both components to be separated are immiscible. When the compounds are dissimilar it may be impossible to find such a solvent. On the other hand, if two immiscible solvents are made to flow countercurrently, each has a different affinity for the two components, the degree depending upon their dissimilarity. Thus, it may be concluded that the applications of two-solvent fractionation are universal, while single-solvent fractionation is a special case with limited application.

[258] *Petroleum Refiner*, Sept. 1948, Section (2), pages 177–215.
[259] A. W. Hixson and A. H. Hixson, *Trans. Am. Inst. Chem. Eng.*, **37**, 927 (1941).

Figure 111 shows a process flow sheet for the two-solvent fractionation of a mixture, and comparison with Figure 110 shows that it contains one less distillation column.   However, unless the components being separated have volatilities widely different from the solvents, the fractional distillation is more difficult than in the previous case because the separation of a two-phase azeotrope from a mixture is always simple, requiring relatively few stripping trays to obtain a substantially pure bottom product.

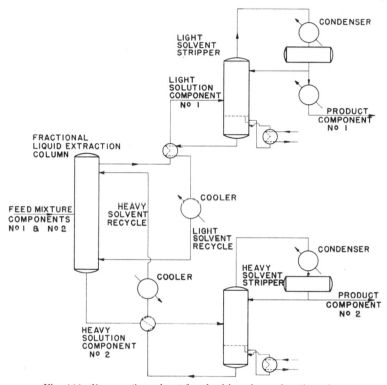

Fig. 111. Process flow sheet for double-solvent fractionation.

The commercial applications of two-solvent fractionation in petroleum refining have thus far been limited to the Duo-sol process of Max B. Miller Co. in which the light solvent is propane and the heavy solvent is a mixture of phenol and cresols.   The broader application of two-solvent fractionation merits further consideration for separation of other mixtures, particularly those which are solid at ordinary temperatures and which are unstable at the elevated temperatures necessary to liquefy them.   The development of the necessary continuous equipment to provide the large number of stages necessary for sharp separations has been progressing at an accelerating pace, and this will be discussed in the section on apparatus and procedures.

The possibility of combining the principle of reflux with a two-solvent

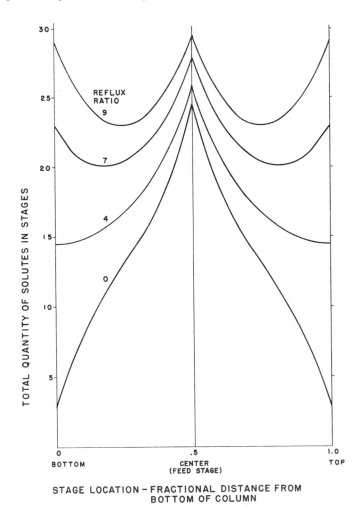

Fig. 112. Effect of reflux ratio on solute concentrations in a double-solvent fractional liquid extraction.

fractionation has been considered by Asselin and Comings.[260] At total reflux it can be shown that the solutes in the two streams passing each other in the column must be identical to satisfy the material balance.

[260] G. F. Asselin and E. W. Comings, *Ind. Eng. Chem.*, **42**, 1198 (1950).

Thus, the operating line will coincide with the $y = x$ line, as previously discussed for distillation, when the concentrations are plotted on a solvent-free basis as in Figure 109.   Since the products leave the system in different phases, a single-stage separation would be obtained by simple phase separation with no equilibrium stages in the column.   Thus, the sum of

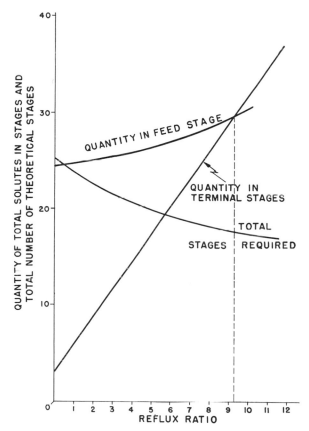

Fig. 113. Effect of reflux ratio on solute quantities and
total stages in double-solvent fractionation.

$m + n$ in equation (55) gives the number of stages in the column plus one, and for total reflux, the value of:

$$\log R_1 R_2' / \log \beta$$

gives the number of stages plus one.   By increasing the reflux ratio to infinity, it is possible to decrease the number of stages for a given separation to only about one-half.

If a two-solvent fractionation of an ideal system is operated without reflux, the maximum concentration of solute occurs at the feed stage. When reflux is returned to the column, the concentration at the feed stage increases only slightly; but as the reflux ratio is increased, the concentrations at the ends exceed that at the feed stage, and this change in the concentration pattern then begins to show a noticeable increase in the feed stage concentration, which is then no longer the point of maximum concentration. Figure 112 shows the effect of reflux ratio on total amounts

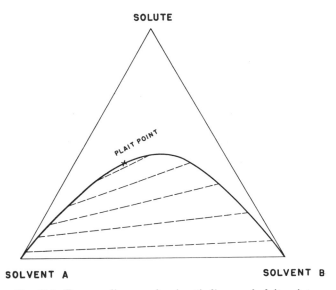

Fig. 114. Ternary diagram showing tie lines and plait point.

of solute in the stages of the extraction column. The total number of stages varies, and in order to show the amounts on a common abscissa for comparison, the quantities are plotted against the fractional location in the column expressed as per cent of the distance from the bottom. Figure 113 is a cross plot of these data at the center feed stage and at the ends. At reflux ratios above 9, the terminal concentrations are greater than the feed stage concentration.

In ideal systems, there is generally some limiting solute concentration at which the solution becomes saturated with the solute or where the system begins to deviate from ideality. It is therefore necessary to establish some maximum allowable solute concentration. It can be seen from Figure 112 that up to a reflux ratio of 9 the quantity of required solvents increases but little, and consequently the cross-sectional area of the column required is not greatly affected. However, above a reflux ratio of 9, the quantity of solvents required—and consequently the cross-sectional area of the column—increases linearly with reflux ratio.   On the other hand, Figure 113 also shows that the number of theoretical stages required de-

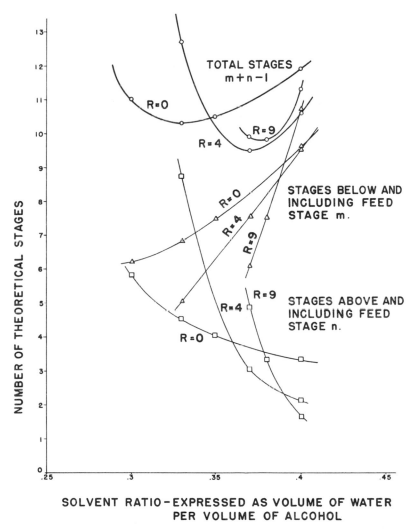

Fig. 115. Effect of reflux ratio on stages required in a nonideal double-solvent fractionation.

creases by 30% at a reflux ratio of 9, while above this ratio the curve flattens off reaching a 52% decrease in this case at total reflux or infinite column diameter.   If the optimum reflux ratio is defined as that reflux ratio which gives the most economical column to construct and operate, it is found to be below the reflux ratio of 9 in the given case. This was observed by Asselin and Comings[260] who developed a graphic technique for carrying out the stagewise calculations with reflux previously discussed. On the basis of a similar study of the concentrations in a fractional liquid extraction column, they concluded that some reflux would be advantageous in an ideal system. This subject has been studied in greater detail by Scheibel,[260a] who has derived an equation for the optimum reflux ratio at each end of a fractional liquid extraction column. The calculated reflux ratio gives the smallest volume column, but, where the cost of recovering the solute from the solvent is the controlling factor, the economic optimum reflux ratio will be less than calculated and may preclude the use of reflux entirely.

As a general rule, the relative distribution in a nonideal system decreases with concentration as can be seen from a consideration of the plait point on a ternary diagram. Figure 114 shows the mutual solubility curve and the tie lines for a ternary system. The plait point is defined as the point on the mutual solubility curve where the two liquid phases become identical. It is analogous to the critical point of a compound which occurs at the temperature and pressure conditions under which the liquid and vapor phases become identical. Similar to the concept of critical conditions for mixtures of two or more components, it is possible to consider plait points for mixtures of four or more components. At this plait point the relative distribution of the two components must be unity because their individual distribution coefficients are both equal to unity.

The possibility exists that the relative distribution of two components may increase with concentration but this could only be over a limited range because it must eventually decrease. Thus, in general, it may be considered undesirable to operate the entire column at higher concentrations. This was demonstrated by calculations on the nonideal system also investigated by Asselin and Comings.[260] Figure 115 shows the effect of the water rate on the total stages required at different reflux ratios and with a constant alcohol flow rate in the separation of oxalic and succinic acids. The optimum water rate varies so that a greater total liquid flow is required in the column at the higher reflux ratios. The total stages are decreased at the reflux ratio of 4:1 by about the same percentage as the increase in liquid flow. Above this reflux ratio the total stages actually increase due to the loss of selectivity at high solute concentrations. Thus, there is no noticeable advantage in the use of reflux in this particular system. The sharper minima obtained in the curves at the higher reflux ratios indicate that the product separation is much more sensitive to the solvent ratio than without reflux. This would make the column much

[260a] E. G. Scheibel, *Ind. Eng. Chem.*, **47**, 2290 (1955).

more difficult to control to maintain product purities. It may therefore be concluded that in this nonideal system the use of reflux has no particular merit.

3. Apparatus and Procedures for Continuous Liquid Extraction

With the exception of the single-stage extraction previously discussed, all the extractions considered in this chapter are based on countercurrent flow of the solvents regardless of whether the extraction is for removal or fractionation. An efficient apparatus provides a large amount of active contact surface between the two phases as they pass each other. The theoretical concept consists of a uniform distribution of minute droplets of a dispersed phase flowing through a uniformly moving continuous phase. Stokes' formula for spherical solids settling through a fluid indicates that the settling rate is proportional to the square of the diameter of the particles; and thus, as the droplets become smaller, their velocity relative to the other phase decreases rapidly. The capacity of such an ideal column would thus decrease as the surface of contact between the phases increases. The mechanism is complicated by the tendency of the droplets to coalesce and by the nonuniform flow of the continuous phase which produces recycles in the form of eddy currents of high local velocities. A void column, consisting of a vertical pipe through which the light liquid rises and the heavy liquid descends, has been found to give poor contacting between the phases.

In order to increase the length of path and also the time of contact with the passing liquids, columns have been filled with foreign objects and are called packed columns. Practically every reasonable shape and size of packing have been used, but the most popular are the Raschig rings and Berl saddles. These are available in the small 0.25-inch sizes for laboratory columns. The height equivalent to a theoretical stage (HETS) varies several fold even on the same system under different rates of liquid flow. The data indicate that the HETS is not constant but increases as the packed height increases so that doubling the height of packing does not necessarily double the number of theoretical stages in the column. Also, at the larger diameters the HETS is greater, and even in columns of less than 1 inch diameter the HETS is rarely less than 1 foot and is sometimes as much as 5 feet. Thus, it is apparent that these types of columns are not very efficient but they have been used when relatively few theoretical stages are required because they are so simple and inexpensive to construct.

Perforated plates, bubble cap plates, and ordinary staggered baffles have been used in the larger size columns with varying degrees of success. Many of the reported efficiencies have been less than 10% so that more than 10 plates or baffles are required for one theoretical stage. These columns cannot readily be constructed in the small sizes necessary for

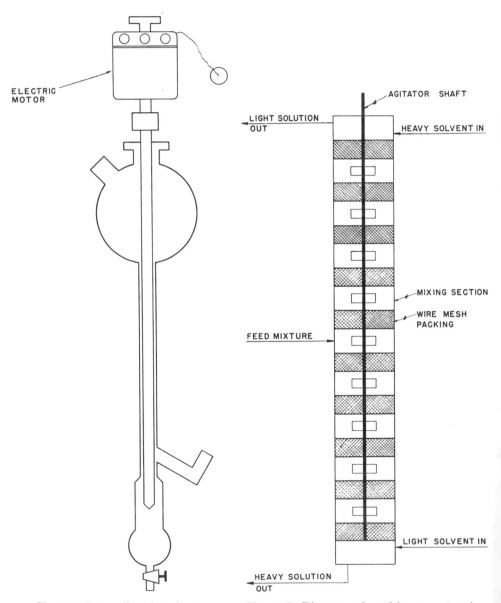

Fig. 116. Internally agitated extraction column studied by Schutze, Quebedeaux, and Lochte.

Fig. 117. Diagram of multistage extraction column studied by Scheibel.

laboratory work.   For a more complete review of the performance data on these columns and packed columns, see Elgin and Wynkoop.[261]

It has long been recognized that allowing one liquid to flow leisurely through another, even along a tortuous path through packing, does not provide intimate contacting between the phase necessary for a large number of equilibrium stages.   Most of the more successful attempts to improve the efficiency have been through the utilization of mechanical energy in various ways to break up the liquid streams into droplets and thus increase the surface of contact and simultaneously decrease the average distance of diffusion necessary to transfer the solute from one phase to the other.   The use of an agitated vessel from which the mixture of solvents flows to a settling tank where the phases separate is of course the most obvious method and is the concept used to develop the theory of continuous countercurrent extraction.   A multiplicity of such units has been used in the laboratory and commercially but they become economically impractical for more than ten stages.

The first attempt to obtain a large number of theoretical stages in a single unit by the application of mechanical action was reported by Jantzen[262] in 1932.   He used an internally stirred column and obtained a theoretical stage in 2 to 5 inches of column height.   Schutze, Quebedeaux, and Lochte[263] used an internal spinning tube to provide the agitation and a schematic drawing of their extractor is shown in Figure 116.   Ney and Lochte[264] reported HETS values varying between 6 and 10 inches and, by comparing the data with the performance of 0.25-inch Berl saddles in the same column, concluded that the spinning tube gave HETS values 75% as large as the packing.   They also stretched a wire along the outside of the spinning tube to promote turbulence but the HETS values increased to a range of 8 to 15 inches as a result of the poorer phase separation between the liquids in passing through the column.

In 1948 Scheibel[265] described a column consisting of a central rotating shaft with agitators spaced at intervals and stationary wire mesh packing between the agitators to effect the phase separation.   Details of the column are shown in Figure 117.   In effect the column consists of a vertical arrangement of mixers and settlers which effects the same operation as was used in developing the theory for continuous liquid extraction.   It was

[261] J. C. Elgin and R. Wynkoop, "Solvent Extraction," in J. H. Perry, ed., *Chemical Engineers' Handbook*.   McGraw-Hill, New York, 1950.

[262] E. Jantzen, *Das fractionierte Distillieren und das fractionierte Verteilen*.   Dechema Monographie, Vol. V, No. 48, Verlag Chemie, Berlin, 1932, p. 81.

[263] H. G. Schutze, W. A. Quebedeaux, and H. L. Lochte, *Ind. Eng. Chem., Anal. Ed.*, **10**, 675 (1938).

[264] W. O. Ney, Jr., and H. L. Lochte, *Ind. Eng. Chem.*, **33**, 825 (1941).

[265] E. G. Scheibel, *Chem. Eng. Prog.*, **44**, 681–690, 771–782 (1948).

found that each combination of mixer and settler could provide more than one theoretical stage at the proper operating conditions. This additional transfer was attributed to the countercurrent flow through the packing during phase separation and does not occur in the usual arrangement of individual mixers and settlers. The same height of packing gave different efficiencies on different systems and the optimum packing height was determined for three different pairs of solvents in the first work and two additional pairs of solvents in a later publication.[266] It was observed that insufficient packing gave incomplete phase separation and loss in efficiency while excessive packing gave no increase in efficiency and was therefore unutilized space. The optimum packing height is that height which when

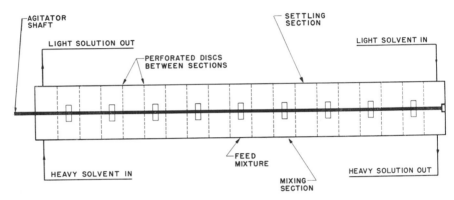

Fig. 118. Continuous multistage extractor of Van Dijck and Ruys.

combined with height of the mixing section gives the minimum height per theoretical stage. It generally occurs in the range of 90–100% total stage efficiency although there is a fairly wide range over which the height per theoretical stage does not change appreciably In the 1-inch diameter column, optimum packing height varied from 1.5 to 5 inches depending upon solvent properties.

Data were reported on a 12-inch diameter column of the same design,[267] and the optimum packing heights were about four times those of the 1-inch column with the same solvent pairs. Karr and Scheibel[268] also investigated the mixing efficiency of a single-stage device in order to determine the effect of different variables in this particular phase of column operation.

Numerous similar designs have been reported in the literature. Van

[266] E. G. Scheibel, *Ind. Eng. Chem.*, **42**, 1497 (1950).

[267] E. G. Scheibel and A. E. Karr, *Ind. Eng. Chem.*, **42**, 1048 (1950).

[268] A. E. Karr and E. G. Scheibel, *Chem. Eng. Prog., Symp. Ser.*, **50**, No. 10, 73 (1954).

Dijck and Ruys[269] described an internally stirred extractor with calming sections between the agitators isolated from the mixing sections by perforated plates on each side as shown in Figure 118. They showed their extractor lying horizontally and presumably intended to operate it in this manner so there would be no possibility of uniform countercurrent flow in the settling section as in the vertical position. Van Dijck and Schaafsma[270] reported performance data on this type of unit which indicated 50–70% stage efficiency for each mixer and settler combination.

Another compact arrangement of mixers and settlers has been described by Coplan, Davidson, and Zebroski[271] who developed the design for the liquid extraction of radioactive solutions when it was concluded that the heavy foundation necessary for the lead shielding of a vertical column was prohibitive. Each mixing section had a separate shaft upon which was mounted an impeller which drew up the heavy liquid from the bottom, mixed it with the light phase, and pumped the mixture into the settling chamber where it separated. The respective liquids passed in their appropriate directions to another mixing section. Data on the extraction of acetic acid from water with methyl isobutyl ketone gave 100% stage efficiencies in this unit.

Fenske and Long[272] also describe a device in which a pair of mixing and settling sections are in a horizontal plane but they are stacked one above the other so that a single shaft operates the agitators in each section. The agitating action in this case is obtained from a perforated plate which is attached to the agitator shaft and is given a vertical pulsating motion in the mixing chamber instead of the conventional rotating motion.

Two other types of continuous extraction equipment that have been described utilize a central rotating shaft with agitators and annular baffles fastened to the column wall and spaced intermediate between the agitators. Oldshue and Rushton[273] used flat-bladed turbines for the agitation and obtained stage efficiencies up to 86% on the extraction of acetic acid from water with methyl isobutyl ketone in a 6-inch diameter column. They also investigated the effect of baffle position by locating the agitators at the baffles instead of midway between them and found a maximum stage efficiency of only 50%.

Reman[274] reported efficiencies of 14 to 40% in a 3-inch column using a

[269] W. J. D. Van Dijck and V. D. Ruys, *Perfumery Essent. Oil Record*, **28,** 91 (1937).

[270] W. J. D. Van Dijck and A. Schaafsma, U. S. Pat. 2,245,945 (1941).

[271] B. V. Coplan, J. K. Davidson, and E. L. Zebroski, *Chem. Eng. Prog.*, **50,** 403 (1954). See also *Chem. Eng.*, **61,** No. 3, 132 (1954).

[272] M. R. Fenske and R. B. Long, paper presented at Washington meeting of American Institute of Chemical Engineers, March 1954. See also *Chem. Eng.*, **61,** No. 1, 286 (1954).

[273] J. Y. Oldshue and J. H. Rushton, *Chem. Eng. Prog.*, **48,** 297 (1952).

[274] G. H. Reman, U. S. Pat. 2,601,674 (1952).

flat, circular disc in place of the flat-bladed turbine of Oldshue and Rushton, on the same extraction system. Thus, this type of agitator appears to be less effective. Both works anticipate construction of columns of larger diameter, and no information is available on the 1- to 2-inch columns such as might be used for laboratory work.

Many reviews of extraction equipment design have appeared but the most recent comprehensive summary of the mixer-settler types is that of Davis, Hicks, and Vermeulen.[275] The patent literature also contains designs, too numerous to mention, for prolonging the path of flow of the liquids in a column and promoting contact by mechanical agitation.

Another method for promoting contact in packed or perforated plate columns is based on imparting a pulsating motion to the column contents. The principle was first mentioned by Van Dijck[276] and has received increasing attention in recent years. The pulsation causes the dispersed phase to pass back and forth through the openings in the plates or packing several times before moving on. The effect is substantially the same as moving a perforated plate up and down in a mixing section to promote mixing as in the Fenske-Long extractor. It is necessary to determine the optimum combination of amplitude and period for the pulsations. Griffith, Jasny, and Tupper[277] observed that, when operating at the optimum amplitude with 25 pulsations per minute, the height of packing required for a given extraction was decreased by about one-third; while at the optimum amplitude for 250 pulsations per minute, the height of packing could be decreased by about two-thirds. The optimum amplitude was found to vary inversely with the frequency. Weigandt and von Berg[278] have given a digest of the operating characteristics of this type of column.

In all these types of column the liquids flow countercurrent to each other by gravity. This limits the rate of flow and, in the case of mixtures which emulsify readily, it may practically prevent the countercurrent flow of the phases. An extractor which uses centrifugal force for the separation of phases has been developed by Podbielniak.[279] It is possible to operate at speeds which give centrifugal forces of up to 5000 gravities so that liquids with small density differences or which tend to emulsify can be handled at a reasonable throughput. The original design employed a long spiral path through which the two liquids flowed countercurrently, the heavy liquid along the outer wall and the light liquid along the inner wall of the compart-

[275] M. W. Davis, T. E. Hicks, and T. Vermeulen, *Chem. Eng. Prog.*, **50**, 188 (1954).

[276] W. J. D. Van Dijck, U. S. Pat. 2,011,186 (1935).

[277] W. L. Griffith, G. R. Jasny, and H. T. Tupper, Atomic Energy Commission Declassified Report AECD-3440 (1952).

[278] H. F. Wiegandt and R. L. von Berg, *Chem. Eng.*, **61**, No. 7, 183 (1954).

[279] W. J. Podbielniak, U. S. Pats. 2,044,996 (1935), 2,093,645 (1936), and 2,153,640 (1938).

ment.   Louvers were cut in the wall of the spiral so that the heavy liquid would flow outward through the light phase on the other side of the wall and the light liquid would flow inward through the heavy phase on the other side of the partition.   It was found that this latter design was more efficient because the dispersion resulting from spraying through the louvers was greater than was originally obtained in the undisturbed flow around one turn of the spiral.   The present design thus contains a series of annular spaces as previously described (see page 202).   A small laboratory model with a capacity of about 150 ml. per minute of total solvents was studied by Barson and Beyer[280] on the extraction of boric acid in both directions between the isoamyl alcohol and water.   They obtained an efficiency of 8 theoretical stages under the best set of operating conditions, but the bulk of their data was in the range of 3–5 theoretical stages and this is in agreement with the performance reported by Bartels and Kleiman[281] who estimated 4 theoretical stages in one of the larger commercial units when used for the fractionation of streptomycins.   The performance of the unit varies with the properties of the liquid, and higher efficiencies have been claimed for the laboratory model.[282]

Other centrifugal extraction devices have been described in which the stages are placed vertically on a rotating shaft as originally proposed by Coutor,[283] and a unit operating on this principle has been made commercially available under the name of Luwesta extractor.[284]

The centrifugal extractors are characterized by high throughputs per unit volume of contents so they provide a very short time of contact between the phases before extraction is complete.   For this reason the Podbielniak extractor has found extensive application in the removal of penicillin from the fermentation broth and in subsequent purification steps. The penicillin salt is acidified to the unstable acid which is immediately extracted completely from the acid solution by passing through the extractor countercurrent to the solvent.

In general, the centrifugal extractors are too expensive to be used as common laboratory equipment, but they are invaluable for studying processes requiring their special characteristics.

4. Column Operation for Preparation of Quantities of Separated Products

A. PRELIMINARY CONSIDERATIONS

The recovery of samples of purified fractions by isolation from stages of

[280] N. Barson and G. H. Beyer, *Chem. Eng. Prog.*, **49**, 243 (1953).

[281] C. R. Bartels and G. Kleiman, *Chem. Eng. Prog.*, **45**, 589 (1949).

[282] W. J. Podbielniak, *Chem. Eng. Prog.*, **49**, 252 (1953).

[283] C. Couter, U. S. Pat. 2,036,924 (1936).

[284] Luwesta Extractor, manufactured by Centrico, Inc., New York, N. Y.

maximum concentrations in the batchwise technique of fractionation was described in Section II.4.B. of this chapter. However, the quantity of material in these stages is usually a small per cent of the amount in the feed. According to equation (15) (page 173), at a value of $K = 1$ the fraction in the stage of maximum concentration is equal to $0.8/\sqrt{n}$, and if thirty transfers suffice to separate the components, 14% of a particular component is in the stage of maximum concentration, while, if 100 transfers are necessary, only 8% is in the corresponding stage. The products in the adjacent stages can be combined but the purity of the final fraction would be decreased. Scheibel[285] has derived equations for calculating the necessary number of transfers to obtain a specified yield at a given purity from a mixture of components. In order to recover 90% of component B from the following mixture as a product containing 7.5% of component A as impurity 585 transfers are required:

Component	Feed mixture	D	E
A	40	1.50	1.25
B	30	1.20	1.00
C	30	1.00	0.833
	100		

Figure 119 shows the distribution of components in the stages after 585 transfers and, in order to obtain the desired separation, the product would be recovered from all the stages above r. This would include all of component C. If the fraction were taken symmetrically about the stage of maximum concentration as between r and r' it would constitute an 80% yield of B with about 9% of A and 17% of C as impurities in the final product. On the other hand, a continuous countercurrent fractional liquid extraction operation requires two fractionations in about 40 theoretical stages to obtain the same yield and purity on an ideal system.[285] The separation can also be obtained in the continuous operation, using about one-tenth of the volume of total solvents, even if the run is of such short duration that about 50% additional solvents are required to flush out the continuous unit after introduction of the feed mixture is complete.

In an ideal system it is possible to estimate from the distribution pattern, after a given number of transfers, the number of stages required in a continuous unit to effect the same separation (see Section V, page 263). In Figure 119 the stage in which the product contains 10% of B and 90% of A is 267 and the stage which contains 90% of B and 10% of A is 287. If

[285] E. G. Scheibel, *Chem. Ing. Tech.*, **27**, 341 (1955).

these stages are considered the first and the last, respectively, of a continuous-feed, double-withdrawal operation, the number of continuous stages in the separation is 41, for reasons discussed on pages 195–197. This is in good agreement with the value calculated from equation (55) which is 42 theoretical stages.   Also, the number of continuous stages between the peaks is 67 and this would produce products of 98% A and 2% B and 97% B and 3% A on a C-free basis.

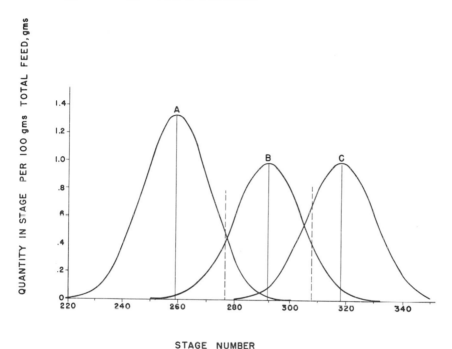

STAGE   NUMBER

Fig. 119. Calculated distribution pattern of three-component mixture after 585 transfers.

After separating components A and B, component C must be removed from the fraction containing component B; this requires a second fractionation at a solvent ratio which removes component B in the light solvent and retains component C in the heavy phase.   In order to obtain the same final product as in the center tubes of the transfer pattern 39 theoretical stages are required in this second fractionation.

In order to benefit fully from the advantages of continuous fractionation it is necessary to employ a column with the necessary number of theoretical stages.   As discussed in the previous section, a packed column is too inefficient to be used for fractional liquid extraction.   Although pulsations

considerably improve the efficiency of packed columns, it is questionable
whether this improvement is adequate, and so far no data have been reported for these columns on fractional liquid extraction. It is not possible to introduce a center feed into the conventional Podbielniak extractor
and the theoretical stages in a single unit are not sufficient to make this an
attractive proposition. Bartels and Kleiman[286] suggested the use of two
such extractors in series with the feed mixture introduced into one of the
streams between the extractors. This is an interesting application but
because of the expense of these extractors it is doubtful whether a laboratory would have two such units available for such experiments.

The internally agitated columns are generally used for continuous fractional liquid extraction. The column described by Jantzen in 1932 (see
page 369) was originally used for the fractional liquid extraction of quinoline
derivatives from a coal tar distillate. Van Dyck and Schaafsma gave fractionating performance data on their internally agitated column with perforated plates separating the mixing and settling sections (see page 371).
Scheibel also reported the performance of an internally agitated column
with wire mesh packing for the settling sections on the fractional liquid
extraction of mixtures of o- and p-chloronitrobenzene, ethyl alcohol and
isopropyl alcohol, ethyl alcohol and methyl ethyl ketone,[287] and ethyl alcohol and water.[288]

Many other investigations of continuous processes have been carried
out in discrete stages for the purpose of establishing the number of theoretical stages required by a given separation and thus demonstrate the process,
but these have been limited to less than 10 theoretical stages. For engineering purposes this is only half the information necessary because the number
of theoretical stages in a given size unit must then be ascertained in order
to complete the design of a production unit. This is done by calculating
(according to the methods previously described) the number of theoretical
stages necessary to obtain the observed separation. This number divided
into the height by the number of actual stages gives, respectively, the HETS
or the stage efficiency expressed as a fraction.

B. OPERATION OF CONTINUOUS FRACTIONAL LIQUID EXTRACTION COLUMN

In principle the most efficient method for preparing a large sample of a
purified fraction by liquid extraction of an ideal system is by the use of a
continuous column. As previously noted, the type of column usually
employed for this purpose is internally agitated. Figure 120 shows a 14-

[286] C. R. Bartels and G. Kleiman, *Chem. Eng. Prog.*, **45**, 589 (1949).

[287] E. G. Scheibel, *Chem. Eng. Prog.*, **44**, 681–690, 771–782 (1948).

[288] E. G. Scheibel, *Ind. Eng. Chem.*, **42**, 1497 (1950).

stage laboratory column, 1 inch in diameter, with wire mesh packing between the agitators for effective phase separation. With packing of sufficient height to separate the liquid phase completely stage efficiencies of over 100% have been obtained with this type of column. This height is a function of the physical properties of the system and varies with different liquids.

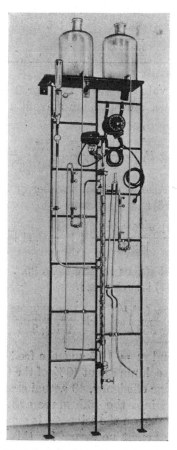

Fig. 120. Photograph of 14-stage laboratory column.

Before operating a continuous column, it is desirable to determine the optimum solvent ratio and the maximum allowable feed rate for the given solvent rates. These facts could be ascertained by adjusting the operating conditions. Since this would waste considerable time, equations have been derived to estimate these conditions directly. As an illustration, consider the separation of a two component mixture of A and B, with distribution coefficients of 3 and 2, respectively. It is desired to recover 90% of A at a purity of 99% from a feed originally containing 30 g. of A and 70 g. of B. Thus, the following material balance is desired on the column:

| | Feed, g.k. | Light solvent product | | Heavy solvent product | |
		Grams	Per cent	Grams	Per cent
A	30.3	27	99.0	3.0	4.1
B	70.2	0.27	1.0	69.73	95.9
	100	27.27		72.73	

From this table the value of R_1 is 27/3 or 9 and the value of R_2' is 69.73/0.27 or 258. Thus, the optimum solvent ratio is calculated from equation (54) as:

$$\log E_1 = \frac{\log 1.5}{1 + (\log 258/\log 9)^{1/2}}$$

whence $H/L = 0.39$. Also, the total number of theoretical stages is calculated from equation (55):

$$n + m = \frac{2 \log (9 \times 258)}{\log 1.5}\left(1 - 0.04 \log \frac{258}{9}\right) = 36$$

and the total theoretical stages required are 35. The feed stage location according to equation (57) is such that:

$$\frac{m}{n} = \left(\frac{\log 9}{\log 258}\right)^{1/2}\left[1 + \frac{\log (258/9)}{9 \log 258}\right] = 0.67$$

from which $n = 21.5$ and $m = 14.5$ and the feed stage should be located above the bottom of the column about 40% of the total column height.

Assuming an 88% stage efficiency, 40 actual stages are required and the feed may be introduced into the 16th stage above the bottom. If previous experience is available on the solvents, it may be possible to estimate in advance the packing height necessary for this stage efficiency. However, in many cases the presence of the solute has a dominant effect on the fluid properties and it is then necessary to calculate the stage efficiency from the height of packing used in the first run. At the lower values the stage efficiency is almost proportional to the packing height but the values drop off as the higher efficiencies are reached so that a maximum value is attained. Figure 121 shows a typical curve of efficiency variation with packed height. Thus, if a stage efficiency of 45% is obtained in the first run with 2 inches of packing, about 4.5 inches of packing would be required for 100% stage efficiency if the direct proportionality holds. Because of the curvature of the line, about 5 inches of packing would be preferred for the second run. Since 40 actual stages have been proposed for the present separation, an efficiency of at least 88% would give the desired separation.

It is next necessary to determine the relationship between the feed and

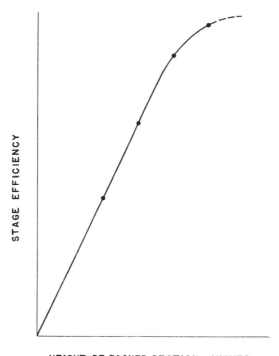

HEIGHT OF PACKED SECTION — INCHES

Fig. 121. Effect of packing height on stage efficiency.

the total solvents. The quantity of each component in the feed stage can be calculated[289] from equation (60):

$$Q = \frac{E+1}{E-1} \frac{(E^n - 1)\ (E^m - 1)}{(E^{n+m} - 1)} \qquad (60)$$

where Q is the ratio of the amount of a component in the feed stage to the amount in the feed. Thus, for the present case:

$$Q_A = \frac{1.17 + 1}{1.17 - 1} \frac{(9.72 - 1)\ (29.2 - 1)}{283 - 1} = 11.1$$

[289] C. R. Bartels and G. Kleiman, *Chem. Eng. Prog.*, **45**, 589 (1949).

$$Q_D = \frac{0.78 + 1}{0.78 - 1} \frac{(0.027 - 1)(0.005 - 1)}{(0.0001 - 1)} = 7.83$$

and the weighted average for the feed is:

$$11.1 \times 0.30 + 7.83 \times 0.70 = 8.8$$

For every gram of feed, at steady state 8.8 g. accumulate at the feed stage.

The total solvent flow capacity of the 1-inch laboratory column varies several fold with the properties of the solutions and as a preliminary test the column should be run with the solvents alone at the desired ratio to determine maximum capacity.

The 1-inch laboratory column shown in Figure 120 utilizes small ball float rotameters for flow indication and these rotameters must be calibrated for each different solvent that may be run through them because the reading varies with viscosity. For this same reason they must be calibrated at different temperatures, if temperature variations are expected during the period of the operation. More reliable devices for feeding the column, such as constant-volume pumps, can be used but rotameters are the least expensive and thus more generally available.

In some cases when the rate is large, it is possible to introduce the feed through a rotameter but usually a calibrated capillary arrangement with a constant head is required. For this purpose a small constant-volume pump has also been used to give constant feed without attention. At the other extreme, the feed has also been controlled by periodic introduction of a small portion from a buret. Since the amount in the feed stage is many times the unit quantity of feed, the column operation is not noticeably disturbed by adding the feed in small portions. However, this method, while the simplest and most precise, requires continual attention and is not desirable for prolonged periods of operation.

In the present illustrations the heavy phase is required at the greater rate so it is preferable to make it the continuous phase. Studies on the mixing efficiency of the agitated column and also on a single section indicate that this is the preferred method of operation because the centrifugal force of the agitator tends to throw the heavy liquid to the outside and return the light liquid to the center for redispersion. When the heavy phase is dispersed, it is thrown away from the agitator and settles along the walls to the next section without recycling several times to the agitator. Thus, a higher agitator speed is required for the best efficiency when the heavy phase is dispersed. Also, the maximum efficiency attainable is less although the decrease in recycling to the agitator usually allows greater solvent throughputs. The loss in efficiency is thus partially offset by an increase in capacity and this may sometimes be desirable.

In general, unless the light solvent flow rate is appreciably greater than the heavy solvent rate, it is preferable to disperse the light phase for greatest efficiency. Except for this small deviation the basic assumption still holds that it is more desirable to disperse the phase flowing at the smallest rate. This tends to maintain the residence time of the two phases in the column more nearly equal since the hold-up of dispersed phase is usually less than that of continuous phase.

The 40-stage column of the previous illustration would be started by filling the column above the top mixing section with the heavy phase and then adjusting the flow rates to the desired ratio of 0.39:1 at a low total throughput of, for example, 390 ml./hr. of light phase to 1 l./hr. of heavy phase. The agitator speed is adjusted until the maximum size droplets in the mixing section are less than about 1 mm. in diameter. The interface is maintained above the top packing bundle by adjusting the level of the over-flow of the heavy phase from the bottom of the column. On some occasions a valve in the product draw-off line has been used to regulate the interface level but this requires more attention because an interruption in the inlet flow of the solvents may cause the column to empty if it is unnoticed. When the flow rate of the heavy phase is small and the interface is maintained at the bottom of the column, the use of the valve is preferable because small changes in the column hold-up will then displace the bottom interface so far that at the slow rate of flow of the heavy phase it would take a long time to recover. Thus, periodic checks of the volume of the solvents delivered by the column would have no significance. These periodic checks are useful for indicating that the column is operating smoothly and at the proper solvent ratio.

When the agitator speed has been adjusted the flow rates of the solvents are increased slowly, maintaining the same solvent ratio, until a second interface appears at the bottom. The column is then flooding and the rates are decreased until the maximum solvent flow rates below flooding are determined. Close to flooding, one-half hour or more may be required to show the first visible signs although, if a continual change in overflow level of the heavy stream from the bottom is required to maintain the upper interface level, this constitutes an indication that a flooding condition is being approached. It may be necessary to decrease the agitator speeds at the higher throughputs because mixing becomes more intense and this produces premature flooding. Flooding can be overcome by either decreasing throughput or decreasing agitator speed but, in the latter case, care must be exercised not to lose mixing efficiency in order to gain capacity.

If the maximum capacity of the column in the present case was observed as 780 ml./hr. of light phase and 2000 ml./hr. of heavy phase, the rates should be decreased to about three-fourths of these values because, while in some rare cases the presence of the solutes increases the column capacity, the usual effect is to decrease it.   A decrease to as little as one-third the capacity of solute-free solvents has been noted, but three-fourths is an average effect.   Thus, the solvent flows will be set at 585 ml./hr. of light phase and 1500 ml./hr. of heavy phase for a total flow of 2085 ml./hr.

It is then necessary to establish, from the solubility or distribution data, the maximum concentration of solutes which may be tolerated in the column. If this is 10% of the solvents the maximum amount of solutes in the feed stage is 208 g./hr. and, since the ratio of this quantity to the feed rate is 8.8, the maximum feed rate that can be tolerated at the solvent flows is about 24 g./hr. or 0.4 g./min. at steady state.

If the purpose of the run is only to prepare a sample of purified material the feed can be introduced at this rate until the desired amount has been run in and the column can be flushed to remove as much of the product as practical.   In order to obtain performance data for engineering design purposes it is necessary to operate the column at steady state and it is, therefore, desirable to know the deviation from steady state at any time or to know when the column conditions are within 10% of steady state. Figure 107 indicates that about 200 cycles are required for a 10% approach to steady state by extrapolating the curves to 35 stages.   If the total column hold-up is 2000 ml. of liquid and the column provides the necessary 35 theoretical stages, the average hold-up per stage is 57 ml.   At a total solvent flow of 2085 ml./hr. about 1.6 minutes are required to remove the contents of one theoretical stage, which is the time for one cycle.   On this basis, over 5 hours are required for a 90% approach to steady state, which would require over 120 g. of feed.

It has been noted[290] that by introducing feed at a sufficient rate to maintain the concentration in the feed stage at the steady-state value the column can be brought to within 10% of steady state in a number of cycles equal to the number of stages; in the present case this would be in less than 1 hour.   The method for varying the feed rate has been studied and an empirical relationship has been proposed whereby the excess feed is decreased by one-half at every cycle when the values of E are close to unity. Thus, a total of 5.7 g. is introduced in the first cycle, which is about 5.0 g. of excess feed, and for the second cycle 2.5 g. of excess feed is added, etc.

If the feed capillary is adjusted to deliver the steady-state feed rate of 24 g. per hour, the excess feed can be introduced through a separate buret. Since the sum of an infinite geometric series with a ratio of 0.5 between turns is equal to the first term divided by $(1-0.5)$, the total amount in the buret would be 10 g. and it would be run into the column as shown in Figure

[290] E. G. Scheibel, <i>Ind. Eng. Chem.</i>, 44, 2942 (1952).

122. This figure is convenient because it enables the operator to introduce the excess feed periodically and keep the variation of the buret reading with time in the proper relation.   After about 15 minutes the balance of the buret contents may be run in and the feed rate then maintained constant by periodic readings of the level in the reservoir above the constant-head device.

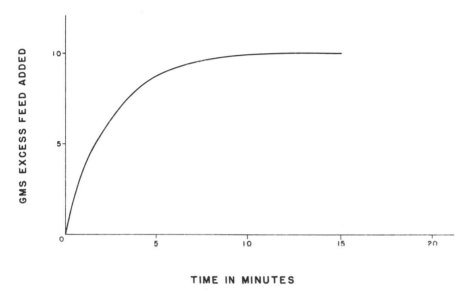

TIME IN MINUTES

Fig. 122. Illustration of the method for adding excess feed to continuous column for rapid approach to steady-state conditions.

It can be seen from the triangular pattern that no products appear at either end until the solvents from the first feed cycle reach the withdrawal ends of the pattern.   Similarly, no product can leave the extraction column until approximately one-half the column contents have been turned over and this requires about 0.5 hour.   Thus, the solvents removed from the column during this period may be recycled to the overhead reservoir and only the products collected thereafter need be saved for isolation.

After about 1 to 1.5 hours the column is at 90% of steady-state concentrations with this method of feeding.   There is another less obvious advantage in this procedure.   In general, the presence of solute in the solvents affects the rate of agitation necessary for good efficiency and where the concentration varies over a period of 5 hours a continuous adjustment of the agitator speed may be required.   With the increased rate of feed the agitator speed can be adjusted to handle the steady-state conditions after about 1 hour and reasonably uniform performance is obtained for the balance of the run.

When all the feed has been introduced the solvent flows are continued because for the same reason that 0.5 hour was required for any solute to appear in the product streams, it will then be another 0.5 hour before there is any decrease in the solute concentration in the product streams. The column should then be flushed with the solvents for another hour to reduce the residual hold-up of solute. The solute remaining in the column can be recovered and credited to the feed, or if additional runs are anticipated, the phases in the column are allowed to separate after the solvent feeds are shut off. This establishes a concentration gradient in the column which is convenient for starting up the next batch and then the initial solvent streams must not be recycled. If the column is not to be operated again for a prolonged period it is not desirable to allow the phases to stand because convection and diffusion eventually neutralize the concentration gradients and thus the initial products from the column are contaminated with the other components.

The previous discussion assumed a liquid feed which could be handled without dilution. If the feed is solid or requires dilution it should be mixed with the phase flowing at the greatest rate in the column, in this case the heavy phase. A solid which is soluble to about 10% in the heavy phase would require an additional 240 ml. of heavy solvent to allow it to be introduced as described. The fresh heavy solvent feed would be decreased by one-half this amount to 1380 ml. so that the solvent ratio would be about 0.42 above the feed and 0.36 below the feed to give the desired average. In general, the addition of solvent with the feed requires extra theoretical stages but where the quantity is small with respect to the total amount flowing the effect is negligible. This is the reason for mixing the feed with the solvent flowing at the greatest rate wherever possible. Also, in some cases the feed may be warmed to melt it so that it can be handled as a liquid to avoid the effect of the solvent in the feed.

When the run has been completed, analysis of the products permits calculation of the stage efficiency of the column. While visual inspection of the drop size in the mixing chamber allows preliminary adjustment of the agitator speed and visual inspection of the center of the packing bundle for clearness of separation allows an estimate of the necessary packing height between stages, the final conclusions can only be drawn based on the observed stage efficiency. A complete study, therefore, involves investigation of higher and lower agitator speeds as well as an investigation of higher and lower throughputs to determine the optimum set of operating conditions for the given separation. Also, as discussed in the previous section, where a fraction is to be isolated from the middle of the distribution pattern, a second fractionation must then be made at the optimum solvent ratio for this separation calculated in the same manner as just discussed.

The method of analysis of the products has not been considered in the foregoing discussions.   O'Keeffe, Dolliver, and Stiller[291] described work on the continuous fractionation of a mixture of streptomycins in which all the analyses were determined from the batchwise countercurrent-distribution pattern using 24 transfers.   This constitutes an interesting combination of the batchwise and continuous techniques.

5. Applications of Symmetrical Triangular Pattern in Interpretation of Data

A. THEORETICAL BASIS

As mentioned on page 352, the symmetrical pattern of double-product withdrawal was the subject of considerable investigation because the simpler relationships were readily recognized before the rigorous solution of the general case had been deduced.   Figure 123 shows a symmetrical triangular pattern for a 9-stage operation for which $n = 5$.   The numerical values of the successive terms expressing the quantities of solute in each of the product streams can be calculated from equation (58).   If the unit quantity of feed is introduced into each center stage as shown by the broken lines, each quantity would distribute according to the same pattern with the values displaced downward by the corresponding number of cycles. Thus, it is apparent that for the continual feed the total amount of solute in each product stream is equal to the sum of all the quantities above and including the given cycle.   It can be readily recognized that this was the basis for deriving the relationship in equation (58).

Equation (58), which gives the fraction of the unit feed appearing in the light solvent at successive cycles, becomes in this case:

$$P_t = \left(\frac{E}{E+1}\right)^5\left[1 + 5\frac{E}{(E+1)^2} + 20\frac{E^2}{(E+1)^4} + 75\frac{E^3}{(E+1)^6} + \right.$$
$$\left. 275\frac{E^4}{(E+1)^8} + \cdots + \epsilon_t\frac{E^{t-1}}{(E+1)^{2t-2}}\right]$$

The quantity in the heavy solvent at each cycle can be calculated by replacing E by $1/E$ in equation (58) and the values on the right-hand side of Figure 123 result.   A significant feature of these relationships is that the ratio between the quantity of a solute leaving in the light solvent to the quantity leaving in the heavy solvent in all cycles is $[E/(E+1)]^5$.   This

[291] A. E. O'Keeffe, M. A. Dolliver, and E. T. Stiller, *J. Am. Chem. Soc.*, **71**, 2452 (1949).

holds for both the single feed and for the continual feed and the general relationship can be shown to be $[E/(E + 1)]^n$ where n is the number of stages along one side of the initial triangular pattern and the total stages are $2n - 1$.

The extraction pattern with double withdrawal can be carried out in $2n - 1$ or, in this case, nine separatory funnels. If the feed consists of

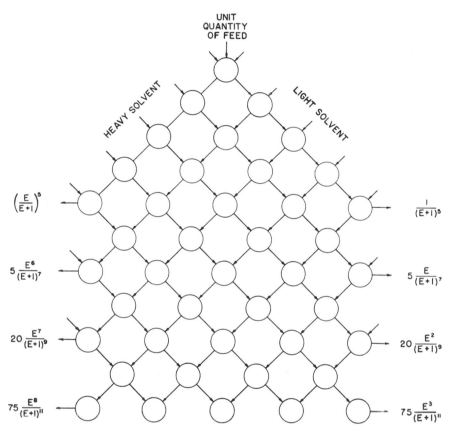

Fig. 123. Quantities in withdrawal streams of a 9-stage fractionation with single feed.

two components, component (1) being more soluble in the light solvent and component (2) more soluble in the heavy solvent, each component, therefore, distributes in the product streams in the ratio of $[E/(E + 1)]^5$ depending upon its E value. If the respective values of E are close to unity, the determination of the individual component distributions gives a more accurate evaluation of their absolute values from which the relative distribution coefficient can be more reliably ascertained.

However, it is possible to simplify the situation even further by using the optimum solvent ratio for the symmetrical system such that $E_1 = \sqrt{\beta}$ and $E_2 = 1/\sqrt{\beta}$.   In this case, it can be shown that the relative distribution of the two components can be calculated from the compositions of the solutes in the product streams on a solvent-free basis, directly as:

$$\beta^n = \frac{y_1\,x_2}{y_2\,x_1} = \frac{y_1(1 - x_1)}{x_1(1 - y_1)} \tag{61}$$

where y is the fraction of the component in the total solutes in the light solvent product stream and x is the fraction of the component in total solutes in the heavy product stream, whence $y_1 + y_2 = 1$ and $x_1 + x_2 = 1$ for a two-component feed mixture.   It would, of course, be desirable to measure the amount of total solutes in each stream to confirm that the pattern was actually operated at the optimum solvent ratio although small deviations do not significantly change the value of β calculated from equation (61).

These relationships indicate a valuable procedure for the accurate determination of small relative distributions.   Two components are distributed between two immiscible solvents.   The phases are separated and the solvents removed.   If the feed mixture was 50% of each component, and the solutes in the light phase analyzed 51% of component 1 while the solutes in the heavy phase analyzed 49% of component 1, it would appear that the relative distribution between these phases was $\frac{51}{49} \cdot \frac{51}{49}$ or 1.082.   However, if an analytical technique, such as freezing point, was used with an accuracy of 1%, the relative distribution could lie between 1.0 and 1.17. The first value makes the separation impossible and the second value places it within the realm of a possible but difficult commercial separation.

On the other hand, if this same feed mixture was introduced into the 9-stage symmetrical fractionation system shown in Figure 123 an analysis of the light solvent product of 56% component 1 and an analysis of the heavy solvent product of 44% of component 1 would establish the value of β^n as 1.62 with a variation of 0.14 for the same analytical accuracy.   Thus, the value of β must be 1.101 $\pm$ 0.019.   The use of additional stages would limit the relative distribution to a narrower range, but this accuracy is sufficiently accurate for a preliminary engineering design and can serve as the basis for a more comprehensive laboratory or pilot plant investigation. In general, the use of the particular system for the separation of components with relative distributions of the order of 1.1 would only be economically feasible if the value of the separated products could justify a high processing cost.   Relative distributions of this order of magnitude usually occur in separation of isomers.   On the other hand, the relative distribution coefficient of dissimilar compounds is usually of the order of 2 to 10, in which case the process can be applied to the more common chemicals at a reasonable cost.

By applying the techniques of the previous section, it is possible to make a completely empirical approach to a fractional liquid extraction problem. It is possible to evaluate the performance of a continuous extraction column without applying any of the calculation techniques, but the empirical method requires a greater amount of laboratory data and finds its greatest application in the separation of complex multicomponent mixtures where the isolation of only one component is desired.   In this case, it is not necessary to obtain complete data on all the other constituents of the mixture. It is only essential that a method of analysis, specific for the desired component, be available.

The first step in the empirical investigation of a multicomponent mixture is to determine the distribution coefficient for the desired component between different pairs of immiscible solvents.   Solvents giving distribution coefficients around unity are most convenient to use since it is possible to obtain extraction factors close to unity with more nearly equal volumes of solvents.   If the distribution coefficient is outside the range of 0.1 to 10, the solvent volume of one phase is less than one-tenth that of the other to give extraction factors about unity.   This makes it essential to obtain complete phase separation in all batchwise extractions since an entrainment of the smaller phase equal to 1% of the larger phase would change the net extraction by more than 10% and thus greatly distort the basic data.   It would be necessary to obtain a more complete phase separation than in the case of more nearly equal solvent ratios, and this generally increases the settling time several fold.   Another contributing factor to this longer settling time is the fact that, in order to disperse the smaller volume of solvent throughout the larger volume to obtain substantial equilibrium between the phases, a much smaller droplet size is required.   Continuous extraction columns of the internally agitated type have been found to give the same efficiencies under the optimum operating conditions at solvent ratios of 1:1 and 20:1.   Probably the only disadvantage of the high solvent ratios after the preliminary investigation lies in the larger volume of solvents handled to maintain a fixed maximum concentration in the smaller phase.

The distribution coefficients can most conveniently be obtained by using a pure sample of the desired component.   Frequently, this is not available, particularly when fractional liquid extraction is considered as the method for obtaining such a sample. In this case, a sample of the crude is distributed between the solvents and the phases separated. The products are separated from the solvent and the quantities and assays of these products allow calculation of the distribution coefficient of the desired constituent.

The feed mixture can then be subjected to a countercurrent fractional liquid extraction in a continual batchwise technique in a series of separatory funnels, as discussed in Section IX.5.A, or directly in a continuous laboratory column. The batchwise technique allows more reliable interpretation of the data, since the number of stages are known, but it requires considerably more time and effort than the continuous column. On the other hand, the efficiency of the column varies with different operating conditions, and the treatment of the separation data is subject to this uncertainty. Actually, both techniques serve to complement each other, because the batch-wise technique gives the separation obtainable in a known number of stages and comparison of these data with the separation obtained in the continuous column gives the number of theoretical stages and, therefore, the efficiency of the multistage unit.

In the isolation of pure material by fractional liquid extraction, there is a definite relationship between the extraction factor and the fractional recovery of component and the number of stages, which is given by equation (52). For the symmetrical case, $n = m$. In order to achieve 95% recovery of a component in a solvent, it can be shown that the extraction factor is related to the number of stages by the approximate relationship:

$$E = 1 + (3/n) \qquad \text{or} \qquad E = 1/[1 + (3/n)] \qquad (62)$$

where the total stages are related to n in the usual manner, namely, as $2n - 1$. This equation holds for values of n greater than 5 and is most accurate for larger values of n when the relationship may be expressed:

$$E = 1 \pm (3/n) \qquad (63)$$

Operation at extraction factors greater than unity recovers the desired component in the light solvent phase and separates it from the components soluble in the heavy phase. Operation at extraction factors less than unity recovers the desired component in the heavy phase and separates it from the components more soluble in the light phase. In the usual multicomponent mixture, both types of impurities are present, and it is necessary to fractionate the mixture twice, once at an extraction factor greater than unity and then at an extraction factor less than unity.

The purity of the final product depends upon the components having distribution coefficients close to that of the desired component. If, for example, the mixture is subjected to a 39-stage fractionation, for which $n = 20$, at extraction factors of 1.15 and 0.85 in the two steps, and no components are present having distribution coefficients such that their extraction factors are between 1.3 and 0.70 in these two operations, the desired component is obtained substantially pure and at a 90% yield. On the other hand, if some components are present which have extraction factors of unity in either one of the steps, one-half of their quantities in the feed is present in the final product. An approximate quantitative relationship can be derived for the fraction of each component removed when operating at extraction factors given by equation (63) based on the relationship between the distribution coefficient, D, of the impurity and the distribution coefficient, D_0, of the desired component. Thus, for components less soluble in the light phase, the fraction removed by operating at extraction factors greater than unity for the desired component is given by the function:

$$\frac{n}{6}\left(\frac{D_0}{D} - 1\right) \tag{64}$$

and the fraction of a component more soluble in the light phase removed at extraction factors less than unity for the desired component is given by the function:

$$\frac{n}{6}\left(\frac{D}{D_0} - 1\right) \tag{65}$$

These relationships apply only to values of the functions between 0 and 1 and would indicate complete removal at some limiting values of D. This is theoretically impossible in a finite number of stages, but the quantities of components which have distribution coefficients outside of this range and which would be retained in the final product are so small that they may be omitted from practical considerations. These expressions are most convenient for discussing the interrelation between distribution coefficients of adjacent impurities and the number of theoretical stages necessary for a high degree of purity.

In the empirical approach to fractionation, the first run must be made completely at random, and let us assume that a battery of 11 separatory funnels is an available set-up in the laboratory so that it can be readily used for the first studies. Solvents have been found for which the distribution coefficient of desired component is 2.0. In the 11-stage operation, $n = 6$, and the solvent ratio must be chosen so that $E = 1.5$ in the first step and 1/1.5 or 0.667 in the second. Thus, a solvent ratio of heavy phase to light phase of 2/1.5 or 1.33 is required in the first step. If the funnels have a 1-liter capacity, 450 ml. of heavy phase and 337 ml. of light phase can be introduced at each cycle of the triangular pattern shown in Figure 123. If the solvents can tolerate a 10% total solute concentration, 80 g.

of the feed mixture can be introduced in the first feed cycle. This allows sufficient free space in the funnel for convenient shaking. According to equation (60), the maximum accumulation occurs at the feed stage when $E = 1$ and is equal to n times the steady-state feed quantity. Other components having higher and lower extraction factors accumulate to a lesser degree and, therefore, the steady-state feed rate in this case can be greater than 13 ml.; if the feed contains a relatively small fraction of the desired component, for example, 15%, it would probably be safe to use a steady-state feed rate equal to two or more times this value. Thus, a feed rate of 30 g. would be tried and the feed for the second cycle would then be 30 + 50/2 or 55 g., the third cycle 30 + 50/4 or 42 g., the fourth cycle 36 g., and so forth, until after the seventh cycle the feed rate of 30 g. would be retained. The formation of an emulsion or a disproportionate ratio of phases in the feed funnel indicates an excessive feed rate and it must then be reduced.

If the maximum solute concentration is of the order of 1–2% of the solvents, it may be necessary to carry out a large number of cycles to obtain a sample for the next step. Also, in the final study of the data, it may frequently be observed that the over-all distribution of the desired component in the products is different from the expected 19:1 ratio. This is particularly noticeable at the higher feed rates due to deviations from ideality producing a varying distribution coefficient over the range of concentrations in the stages. The average value observed can be used to modify the solvent ratio in the next run.

The second step is then carried out on the combined products from the light solvent phases removed at the successive cycles and separated from the solvent. In this case, a solvent ratio of three parts of heavy phase to one of light is used to give a value of $E = 0.667$. In the same funnels, 600 ml. of heavy solvent and 200 ml. of light solvent would be used in each cycle with an initial feed rate of 80 g. The steady-state feed rate of 20–25 g. must be approximated since the concentration of the desired component is greater in this feed than in the original crude mixture.

If the final product isolated from the heavy phase shows a high degree of purity, the 11-stage operation is satisfactory. On the other hand, if the final product assays only 40%, it is necessary to investigate the possibility of more precise fractionation using a greater number of stages. The next step would be to process the original feed in a continuous column since the funnel operation for this separation is prohibitively tedious. If the column contains 39 theoretical stages, $n = 20$, it should be operated at extraction factors of 1.15 and 0.85 for the desired component. The average value of the distribution coefficient calculated from the funnel operation serves as a better basis for selecting the solvent ratios than the single-stage measurement previously used.   The operation of such a column has been described in Section IX.4.B.   In this operation, according to the relationship shown in equation (64), impurities with distribution coefficients less than $D_0/[1 + (6/n)]$ or about 1.5 are substantially completely eliminated in the first step while more than one-half of the components with distribution coefficients between 1.75 and 2 is retained.   Similarly, in the second step, components with distribution coefficients greater than $D_0[1 + (6/n)]$ or 2.6 will be almost completely eliminated while more than one-half of those with distribution coefficients between 2 and 2.3 is retained.

If the final product purity is not satisfactory, it may be improved by trying a greater number of stages, but, in this case, it may be possible to spread the range of the distribution coefficients of the remaining impurities by forming a chemical derivative of the desired component and fractionating the mixture by an identical procedure.   If the corresponding derivatives of the impurities cover a wider range of distribution coefficients, the purity of the final product can be significantly improved.   Crystallization of the desired product from the final concentrate is a convenient method for improving the purity although the yield by this method is poor if the concentration is not appreciably greater than 50%.

The results of the application of this empirical technique to the concentration of vitamin A have been described by Scheibel and Karr.[292]

General References

Craig, L. C., "Extraction," *Anal. Chem.*, **21**, 85 (1949); **22**, 61 (1950); **23**, 41 (1951); **24**, 66 (1952); **26**, 110 (1954).

Elgin, J. C., "Solvent Extraction," *Ind. Eng. Chem.*, **38**, 26 (1946); **39**, 23 (1947); **40**, 53 (1948); **41**, 35 (1949).   R. E. Treybal, "Solvent Extraction," *Ind. Eng. Chem.*, **43**, 79 (1951); **45**, 58 (1953).

Hunter, T. G., and H. A. Nash, "The Application of Physico-chemical Principles to the Design of Liquid-Liquid Contact Equipment, Part I.   General Theory," *J. Soc. Chem. Ind.*, **51**, T285 (1932); "Part II.   Application of Phase-Rule Graphical Methods," *ibid.*, **53**, 95 (1934); "Liquid-Liquid Extraction Systems," *Ind. Eng. Chem.*, **27**, 836 (1935).

Jantzen, E., *Das fractionierte Distillieren und das fractionierte Verteilen*.   Dechema Monographie, Vol. V, No. 48.   Verlag Chemie, Berlin, 1932, p. 81.

von Metzsch, F. A., "Extraction and Countercurrent Distribution," *Angew. Chem.*, **65**, 586 (1953).

Morton, A. A., *Laboratory Technique in Organic Chemistry*.   McGraw-Hill, New York, 1938.

Perry, J. H., *Chemical Engineer's Handbook*.   3rd ed., McGraw-Hill, New York, 1950.

---

[292] E. G. Scheibel and A. E. Karr, U. S. Pat. 2,676,903 (April 27, 1954).

Rauen, H. M., and W. Stamm, *Anleitungen für die chemische Laboratorium Praxis.* Vol. VI, Springer, Göttingen, 1953.

Sherwood, T. K., *Absorption and Extraction.* 2nd ed., McGraw-Hill, New York, 1952.

Stene, S., "A Contribution to the Theory of Systematic Extraction and other Related Convection Problems," *Arkiv Kemi Mineral. Geol.*, **A18,** No. 18 (1944).

Treybal, R. E., *Liquid Extraction.* McGraw-Hill, New York, 1951.

Varteressian, K. A., and M. R. Fenske, "Liquid-Liquid Extraction," *Ind. Eng. Chem.*, **28,** 1353 (1936).

Weisiger, J. R., "Countercurrent Distribution," in *Organic Analysis*, Vol. II. Interscience, New York-London, 1954, p. 277.

CHAPTER III

CRYSTALLIZATION AND RECRYSTALLIZATION

R. Stuart Tipson, *Mellon Institute of Industrial Research, University of Pittsburgh, Pittsburgh, Pennsylvania*

I. INTRODUCTION

When a compound crystallizes, orientation and aggregation of molecules or ions take place in such a manner as to give a particle or particles "having a fixed number of plane surfaces...inclined to one another at definite and characteristic angles,"[1] and possessing a definite geometrical form if allowed to grow freely. *Crystallization* of a compound is desirable because the crystals exhibit physical properties not possessed in the amorphous state, and the crystallographic characteristics may serve[2] to identify the compound. Many pure crystalline organic compounds have a definite melting point, and, with few exceptions, *e.g.*, a eutectic composition[3] or a special type of solid solution (see Sect. II.9), a sharp melting point unchanged by recrystallization indicates a pure substance. Moreover, an organic compound is often more stable chemically when crystalline than when amorphous. Crystallization may take place *spontaneously* or may be *induced* by the creation of conditions favorable to its occurrence. Among other objectives, the present chapter endeavors to review theories, experiences, and recommendations in the literature which may help in dealing with the problem of inducing crystallization.

The term *recrystallization* as used here refers to the melting, dissolution, or vaporization[4] of an *already* crystalline compound, followed by crystallization, in order to control the *shape and size* of the resulting crystals or to effect separation from other compounds. This process is usually highly selective because, apart from certain exceptions to be discussed later, an

[1] S. G. M. Ure, "Crystallisation," in J. F. Thorpe and M. A. Whiteley, eds., *Thorpe's Dictionary of Applied Chemistry*. 4th ed., Vol. III, Longmans, Green, New York, 1939, p. 445.

[2] A. E. H. Tutton, *Crystallography and Practical Crystal Measurement*, Macmillan, London, 1922. T. V. Barker, *Systematic Crystallography, An Essay on Crystal Description, Classification and Identification*, Murby, London, 1930. M. W. Porter and R. C. Spiller, *Nature*, **144**, 298 (1939); *The Barker Index of Crystals, a Method for the Identification of Crystalline Substances*, Heffer, Cambridge, England, 1951. R. W. G. Wyckoff, *Crystal Structures*, Interscience, New York-London, 1951 and 1953. J. Timmermans, *Les Constantes Physiques des Composés Organiques Cristallisés*, Masson, Paris, 1953. J. D. H. Donnay, W. Nowacki, and G. Donnay, *Crystal Data, Classification of Substances by Space Groups and Their Identification from Cell Dimensions*, Geological Society of America, New York, 1954. A. N. Winchell, *The Optical Properties of Organic Compounds*, 2nd ed., Academic Press, New York, 1954. See chapters by E. E. Jelley, M. A. Peacock, J. D. H. Donnay, I. Fankuchen, and L. O. Brockway in A. Weissberger, ed., *Technique of Organic Chemistry*, Vol. I, 2nd ed., Interscience, New York-London, 1949.

[3] E. L. Skau and H. Wakeham, "Determination of Melting and Freezing Temperatures," in A. Weissberger, ed., *Technique of Organic Chemistry*, Vol. I, 2nd ed., Interscience, New York-London, 1949, Chapter III, Section II.3.

[4] See chapter on sublimation by R. S. Tipson in A. Weissberger, ed., *Technique of Organic Chemistry*, Vol. IV, Interscience, New York-London, 1951, Chapter VII.

organic crystal grows only by addition of molecules or ions of the same kind. Consequently, once crystals of a compound have been obtained, their recrystallization may be an excellent means[5] for effecting *separation* from other compounds.   If only one compound is separated from its impurities, the operation is usually known as *simple recrystallization*.   If the objective is the separation of two or more pure compounds from a mixture, the process is called *fractional recrystallization*.   However, the latter term is sometimes applied if several crops of crystals of the same compound are successively collected from a mother liquor.

Crystallization and recrystallization in the *solid* state may occur, *e.g.*, in the transformation of a polymorphic modification,[6] and, under suitable conditions, the *vapor* of certain organic compounds condenses directly[4] to crystals.   However, crystallization and recrystallization from *supercooled melts* and *supersaturated solutions* are of prime interest to the organic chemist.   In the following discussion, the term *liquid* may refer to a substance which is liquid at room temperature even though, when eventually obtained crystalline, its melting point may be above room temperature.   The term *melt implies* that the substance has previously existed as crystals; it is, however, convenient to use the name to include liquids, *e.g.*, newly synthesized compounds, which have not been obtained by melting a solid. A melt containing dissolved impurity is a solution.   Supercooled melts are often called amorphous solids, glasses, resins, lacquers, etc.

The first stage of crystallization is the formation or introduction of an appropriate minute *nucleus*, also called a seed, germ, submicron, or crystallon.   Deposition of molecules or ions of the *crystallizand* on this nucleus eventually gives a visible crystal.   However, although nuclei may be present, their growth may be arrested.   Consequently, from the practical standpoint, there are three consecutive stages in the process of crystallization: removal of impurities which may retard or inhibit crystallization (see Sects. II.5 and III.1), achievement of nucleus formation (see Sect. III.2), and encouragement of growth to visible crystals (see Sect. IV.2).   Although the temperature during nucleus formation and growth must be below the melting point and, for a solution, below the saturation point of the crystallizand, sufficient freedom of motion of the molecules or ions must be permitted, *i.e.*, the viscosity of the system should not be too high.

Whenever a substance has been isolated in apparently crystalline condi-

[5] J. Berdez and M. Nencki, *Arch. exptl. Pathol. Pharmakol.*, **20**, 346 (1885–1886).

[6] See Chapters III and XV of Volume I, this series.   W. J. Pope, *J. Chem. Soc.*, **75**, 463 (1899).   K. Schaum, *Ann.*, **308**, 18 (1899).   A. Weissberger and R. Sängewald, *Z. physik. Chem.*, **B13**, 383 (1931).   E. L. Skau and H. Wakeham in Volume I (2nd ed.) of this series, Chapter III, Section III.6.   R. Smoluchowski, J. E. Mayer, and W. A. Weyl, eds., *Phase Transformations in Solids*, Wiley, New York, 1951. J. C. Fisher, J. H. Hollomon, and J. G. Leschen, *Ind. Eng. Chem.*, **44**, 1324 (1952).   R. Smoluchowski, *ibid.*, **44**, 1321 (1952).

tion, it should be examined with a simple lens or under the microscope, since amorphous materials often appear crystalline to the naked eye, or vice versa.   If the particles are not extremely small, a hand lens of magnification 20 × will usually prove adequate.   For microscopic examination, the particles may be transferred to a microscope slide without separation from the mother liquor and be covered with a cover glass to prevent access of dust or evaporation of solvent.   As an adjunct in determining crystallinity, use of the polarizing microscope[7] may prove helpful.   A method utilizing darkfield illumination and polarized light, simultaneously, has been applied[8] particularly to crystalline waxes.

II. GENERAL CONSIDERATIONS

1. Mechanism of Nucleus Formation and Crystal Growth

A. HISTORICAL

In formulating theories for crystal nucleation and growth, many empirical observations have had to be accounted for.

Supersaturated solutions of crystallizable compounds were preserved[9] in sealed tubes for 30 years without their showing any sign of spontaneous crystallization. A compound prepared for the first time is frequently difficult to obtain in crystalline form, but, when once it *has* been crystallized, crystals may separate readily in subsequent preparations without deliberate nucleation.   A compound may crystallize *spontaneously* in one laboratory, but the same substance prepared in another laboratory, in identical manner, may resist crystallization attempts until crystals from the first laboratory are used for nucleation.[10]   Likewise, a substance may consistently be obtained in one polymorphic modification in one laboratory and in another modification elsewhere, until "seed" crystals have been exchanged.   Furthermore, once an isomer has been crystallized, crystallization of another isomer may prove impossible in the same laboratory.   Thus, after α-D-mannose crystals had been obtained, the stereoisomer β-D-mannose (the anomeric form) could no longer be purified by recrystallization.[11]

Nuclei may be formed spontaneously from the crystallizand itself by orientation and aggregation of a sufficient number of molecules, in so-

[7] T. N. McVay, *Bull. Am. Ceram. Soc.*, **13**, 255 (1934).   W. Kraemer, *Z. wiss. Mikroskop.*, **44**, 476 (1927).   N. H. Hartshorne and A. Stuart, *Crystals and the Polarising Microscope*, Arnold, London, 1950.   See Chapter XV, Vol. I (2nd ed.) of this series.

[8] K. Fischer: see M. H. Bigelow, *Chem. Eng. News*, **25**, 2366 (1947).

[9] L.-C. de Coppet, *Ann. chim. et phys.*, **10**, 457 (1907).

[10] P. A. Levene and R. S. Tipson, *J. Biol. Chem.*, **93**, 631 (1931).   W. Bosshard, *Helv. Chim. Acta*, **18**, 482 (1935).

[11] P. A. Levene, *J. Biol. Chem.*, **108**, 419 (1935).

called *homogeneous nucleogenesis*.[12] It is operative in melts,[12] highly supersaturated solutions,[13] and colloids, but practically never[14] occurs in slightly supersaturated pure solutions.[15]

Homogeneous nucleogenesis is understandable in view of the discovery that, in the vicinity of the freezing point, certain liquids have a quasicrystalline structure, as shown by x-ray investigations and confirmed in many other ways. Near the freezing point, the packing of molecules may resemble that in the corresponding solids. "A liquid, near the melting point of the solid, corresponds with a polycrystalline conglomerate in which the individuals have such a large number of defects that its crystalline character is not apparent except in special tests."[16] If there is little change in molecular packing on crystallizing, as evidenced by slight change in density, specific heat, etc., the transition is termed *homeomorphous*. If there is considerable change in packing, the transition is *morphotropic*.

Even at higher temperatures, there is evidence for a temporary grouping[17] of some molecules in certain liquids into small, oriented clusters of short life, called *cybomas*. These are continually breaking apart and re-forming because of chance impact and thermal agitation, but become more stable at lower temperatures,[18] and may[19] give rise to a crystal nucleus on reaching *a critical size*.[20] The average energy per particle consisting of an oriented aggregate of small units can be calculated and it is found that theoretically, below a characteristic temperature, nucleation from outside is not necessary because such aggregates will be stable. This is supported by studies on phenyl salicylate.[21] The statistical distribution[22] of crystallization

[12] W. T. Richards, E. C. Kirkpatrick, and C. E. Hutz, *J. Am. Chem. Soc.*, **58**, 2243 (1936).

[13] M. Volmer, *Z. Elektrochem.*, **35**, 555 (1929). I. N. Stranski and R. Kaischew, *Z. physik. Chem.*, **B26**, 100 (1934). R. Kaischew and I. N. Stranski, *ibid.*, **B26**, 317 (1934). G. Tammann, *Kristallisieren und Schmelzen*, Barth, Leipzig, 1903.

[14] N. Fuks, *Uspekhi Fiz. Nauk*, **15**, 496 (1935); *C. A.*, **30**, 3703 (1936).

[15] H. Cassel and E. Landt, *Z. Ver. deut. Zucker-Ind.*, **77**, 483 (1927); *C. A.*, **22**, 178 (1928).

[16] A. R. Ubbelohde, *Ann. Repts. Progr. Chem. (Chem. Soc. London)*, **37**, 169 (1941).

[17] R. Bloch, T. Brings, and W. Kuhn, *Z. physik. Chem.*, **B12**, 415 (1931). *Cf.* N. F. Mott and R. W. Gurney, *Trans. Faraday Soc.*, **35**, 364 (1939).

[18] N. V. Tantzov, *J. Russ. Phys.-Chem. Soc.*, **58**, 947 (1926); **61**, 41 (1929); *C. A.*, **21**, 2093 (1927); **23**, 3847 (1929); *Cf.* G. Tammann, *Z. physik. Chem.*, **25**, 441 (1898); A. R. Ubbelohde, *Sci. J. Roy. Coll. Sci.*, **15**, 40 (1945).

[19] N. F. Lashko, *Trudy Inst. Khim. Kar'kov. Gosudarst. Univ.*, **5**, 191 (1940); *C. A.*, **37**, 5899 (1943).

[20] R. Bloch, T. Brings, and W. Kuhn, *Z. physik. Chem.*, **B12**, 415 (1931). F. von Göler and G. Sachs, *Z. Physik*, **77**, 281 (1932). R. F. Mehl, "The Physics of Hardenability," in *Hardenability of Alloy Steels*, Am. Soc. Metals, Cleveland, 1939, pp. 1–54. G. Tammann, *Kristallisieren und Schmelzen*, Barth, Leipzig, 1903. M. Volmer and A. Weber, *Z. physik. Chem.*, **119**, 277 (1926). M. Volmer and M. Marder, *ibid.*, **A154**, 97 (1931). L.-C. de Coppet, *Ann. chim. phys.*, **10**, 457 (1907). C. Hammer, *Ann. Physik*, **33**, 445 (1938). E. Scheil and A. Langeweise, *Arch. Eisenhüttenw.*, **11**, 93 (1937). W. Kauzmann, *Chem. Revs.*, **43**, 219 (1948).

[21] G. Kornfeld, *Monatsh.*, **37**, 609 (1916); *Ann. Physik*, **34**, 488 (1939).

[22] P. Othmer, *Z. anorg. Chem.*, **91**, 209 (1915).

in a large number of samples, over a long period of time, indicated two processes: a change in the internal energy of the molecules which renders them anisotropic, followed by arrangement of these anisotropic molecules to give a crystalline structure. When samples of compounds were heated to temperatures above the melting point and then cooled, the number of nuclei[23] decreased greatly with increase in preheating.[22,24]

In supersaturated solutions, too, a particle *of a certain size*[25] is needed before crystal growth takes place, because at very small sizes, owing to the relationship between surface free energy and volume free energy, the smaller the size, the greater the tendency to redissolve.[26] For example, for particles of 0.1μ diameter of some compounds, this tendency is almost twice that of large particles of the same substance[26,27]; hence, the higher the degree of supersaturation, the greater the probability that small particles will become crystallization nuclei and will not disaggregate[28] to molecules. According to Ostwald,[29] crystal particles containing some 10^8 to 10^{12} molecules are too small to induce crystallization in their supersaturated solutions, but it has been shown[30] that crystals containing only 10 to 10^5 molecules may still possess nucleating ability. Ostwald's upper limit is many million times too large; as little as 10^{-18} gram, *i.e.*, a cube of approximately 10^{-6} cm. or 100 Å. on edge, suffices to cause homogeneous nucleation.[31] For ionic crystals, a very small number of ions affords a nucleus.[32] Thus, the smallest nucleus for barium sulfate solutions is a unit crystal of four barium ions and four sulfate ions,[33] or this unit minus one of the ions.

Crystals can also originate[34] by *heterogeneous nucleation*[35] at an interface, *e.g.*, on the surface of suspended, insoluble particles,[36] or on the walls of the

[23] R. Marcelin, *Compt. rend.*, **148**, 631 (1909). C. N. Hinshelwood and H. Hartley, *Phil. Mag.*, **43**, 78 (1922). K. Schaum, *Z. anorg. allgem. Chem.*, **120**, 241 (1922).

[24] R. Kaishev, *Ann. Physik*, **30**, 184 (1937).

[25] W. J. Jones and J. R. Partington, *Z. physik. Chem.*, **88**, 291 (1914).

[26] G. A. Hulett, *Z. physik. Chem.*, **37**, 385 (1901); **47**, 357 (1904).

[27] H. Hartley and N. G. Thomas, *J. Chem. Soc.*, **89**, 1013 (1906). H. Hartley, B. M. Jones, and G. A. Hutchinson, *ibid.*, **93**, 825 (1908).

[28] P. V. Grushvitskiĭ, *Uchenye Zapiski Leningrad. Gosudarst. Univ.*, **1939**, No. 7 (No. 34), 24; *C. A.*, **36**, 3078 (1942). E. T. Ross, *Pacific Chem. Met. Inds.*, **2**, No. 3. 9 (1938). H. B. Caldwell. *Chem. & Met. Eng.*, **49**, 116 (May, 1942). F. Serowy. *Chem. Fabrik*, **13** [15], 257 (1940). *Cf.* W. J. Fawcett, *Trans. Roy. Soc. Can., III*. **7**, 218 (1913).

[29] W. Ostwald, *Lehrbuch der Allgemeinen Chemie*. Vol. II, 2, Engelmann, Leipzig, 1902, pp. 383 ff., 710 ff.

[30] G. Tammann and H. E. von Gronow, *Z. anorg. allgem. Chem.*, **200**, 57 (1931).

[31] D. McIntosh, *Trans. Roy. Soc. Can., III*, **13**, 265 (1919).

[32] F. R. Duke, R. J. Bever, and H. Diehl, *Iowa State Coll. J. Sci.*, **23**, 297 (1949). F. R. Duke and L. M. Brown, *J Am. Chem. Soc.*, **76**, 1443 (1954).

[33] J. A. Christiansen and A. Nielsen, *Acta Chem. Scand.*, **5**, 673 (1951). V. K. La Mer, *Ind. Eng. Chem.*, **44**, 1270 (1952).

[34] N. N. Afanas'ev, *Zhur. Tekh. Fiz.*, **7**, 2305 (1937); *C. A.*, **34**, 6153 (1940).

[35] W. T. Richards, E. C. Kirkpatrick, and C. E. Hutz. *J. Am. Chem. Soc.*, **58**, 2243 (1936).

[36] H. Cassel and E. Landt, *Z. Ver. deut. Zucker-Ind.*, **77**, 483 (1927); *C. A.*, **22**, 178 (1928).

container.   This effect of *insoluble particles*, *e.g.*, dust, has long been known. Quartz powder[37] greatly increases the number of crystal nuclei in 2-naphthyl salicylate.   Some materials are more efficient than others, *e.g.*, for the crystallization of certain compounds, active carbon is superior to ground Pyrex glass, mica, or brass filings.[38]   It has been suggested that, if not crystallographically identical with the desired crystals, some of the dust particles may be suitably isomorphic with them, or may have a specific orientation of molecules, on the surface, appropriate to initiation of crystallization.

"Spontaneous" crystallization is sometimes caused[39] by particles in the air. When the air was "sterilized" by bubbling through water, filtering through cotton, or passing through a hot tube, crystallization was not induced.   Whether the particles removed in these experiments consisted of foreign dust or of dust of the crystallizand was not clear.

It has been contended[40] that spontaneous crystallization of sucrose solutions is always caused by air-borne, microscopic *sucrose* particles.   Ultrafiltered, supersaturated solutions[41] of sucrose did not crystallize, even if kept for a year or cooled to $-192°C.$, unless a crystal of sucrose was added.   Filtration through hardened filter paper[42] does not remove the nuclei.   With supercooled melts,[43] the effect of ultrafiltration is the same.   However, nucleation from outside by the *same* material can play no part in the crystallization of newly synthesized compounds not occurring in Nature, and crystallization must come about by a homogeneous mechanism, by nucleation with a suitable isomorph (see Sect. III.2), or by a heterogeneous mechanism.   The *degree* of supercooling which may be applied without the occurrence of crystallization may often be greatly increased by filtering or centrifuging. In many cases, it is not certain whether this effect is caused by the removal of crystal nuclei of the crystallizand or of dust particles,[44] but the dependence of the number of crystal nuclei in a supercooled melt of piperonal on the temperature to

[37] G. Tammann, *Z. physik. Chem.*, **25**, 441 (1898).   *Cf.* V. J. Schaefer, *Science*, **104,** 457 (1946).   I. Langmuir, V. J. Schaefer, and B. Vonnegut, *Science News Letter*, **51,** No. 8, 127 (1947).   R. Smith-Johannsen, *Science*, **108**, 652 (1948).

[38] W. T. Richards, *J. Am. Chem. Soc.*, **54**, 479 (1932).

[39] H Loevel, *Ann. chim. phys.*, [3], **29**, 62 (1850).   C. Violette, *Compt. rend.*, 60, 831, 973 (1865).   D. Gernez, *ibid.*, **60**, 833, 1027 (1865); **61**, 71, 289 (1865).

[40] I. A. Kukharenko, *Sucr. belge*, **45**, 3 (1925); *Intern. Rev. Sci. Practice Agr.*, **3**, 1 (1925); *C. A.*, **19**, 1978 (1925).   I. A. Kukharenko and B. G. Savinov, *Nauch. Zapiski Gosudarst. Eksptl. Inst. Sakharnoĭ Prom.*, **4**, 139 (1927); *C. A.*, **21**, 2074 (1927).

[41] G. Jaffé, *Z. physik. Chem.*, **43**, 565 (1903).   I. A. Kukharenko, *Louisiana Planter*, **73**, 328 (1924).   A. Schweizer, *Rec. trav. chim.*, **52**, 678 (1933).

[42] A. Schweitzer, *Intern. Sugar J.*, **35**, 385 (1933); *C. A.*, **28**, 672 (1934).

[43] C. Füchtbauer, *Z. physik. Chem.*, **48**, 549 (1904).   J. Meyer and W. Pfaff, *Z. anorg. allgem. Chem.*, **217**, 257 (1934); **222**, 382 (1935); **224**, 305 (1935).   J. Michel, *Bull. soc. chim. Belg.*, **48**, 105 (1939).   *Cf.* N. E. Dorsey, *J. Research Natl. Bur. Standards*, 20, 799 (1938).

[44] R. Marcelin, *Compt. rend.*, **148**, 631 (1909).

which it had been preheated and on the time heated,[45] as well as the effects of ultrasonic and alternating electric fields (see Sect. III.2), indicate that the nuclei are *foreign bodies*.[46] Moreover, use of a fine dispersion of many liquid droplets[47] permitted localization of motes in only a small proportion of the droplets; on supercooling, these were heterogeneously nucleated, but the others underwent homogeneous nucleation. This work was based on very old observations that: (1) if the same volume of the same sample of a liquid, *e.g.*, water, is placed in two different containers, one may reproducibly crystallize with much less supercooling than the other; and (2) a small volume of a given liquid, *e.g.*, molten gold, may often be supercooled much more than a large volume of the same liquid before crystallization occurs. If a large number of small samples are simultaneously cooled, some may not crystallize at all. At one time, the effect[48] of suspended solid particles was thought not to be related specifically to their nature but to be governed by their number and size; this view is no longer held.

Repeated melting and crystallizing of benzophenone[49] decreases the crystallizing tendency as the number of such treatments is increased. Similarly, the longer *p*-nitrotoluene[50] is kept liquid or the higher it is heated above the melting point, the greater the difficulty of subsequent crystallization. Although the velocity of crystallization on homogeneously nucleating is unaffected,[51] spontaneous crystallization of phenyl salicylate (m.p. 48°C.) stops[52] if tubes of the material are heated ten times to 78° and cooled to below 48°, but this "sterilization" cannot be brought about merely by heating to a few degrees above the melting point. These results are compatible with the assumption of heterogeneous nucleation by air-borne organic dust particles whose activity depends on the particle size and is diminished by aging and heating. The latter conclusion was confirmed by investigations on supercooled piperonal, allocinnamic acid,[53] phenyl salicylate, phenol, and *p*-toluidine,[54]

[45] C. Hammer, *Ann. Physik*, **33**, 445 (1938).

[46] J. Meyer and W. Pfaff, *Z. anorg. allgem. Chem.*, **222**, 382 (1935); **224**, 305 (1935). W. Rix, *Z. Krist.*, **96**, 155 (1937). H. C. Hamaker, *Trans. Faraday Soc.*, **36**, 279 (1940). A. R. Ubbelohde, *ibid.*, **36**, 863 (1940). R. Y. Berlaga, *Zhur. Eksptl. i Teoret. Fiz.*, **9**, 1397 (1939); **16**, 647 (1946); *C. A.*, **35**, 5022 (1941); **41**, 326 (1947). G. E. Mikhin and S. S. Urazovs'kiĭ, *Zhur. Fiz. Khim.*, **1**, 419 (1930); *C. A.*, **28**, 955 (1934). S. S. Urazovs'kiĭ and Y. S. Rozum, *Ukrain. Khem. Zhur.*, **11**, 136 (1936); *C. A.*, **30**, 7416 (1936). *Cf.* R. Y. Berlaga and F. K. Gorskiĭ, *Zhur. Eksptl. i Teoret. Fiz.*, **4**, 527 (1934); *C. A.*, **29**, 2805 (1935).

[47] B. Vonnegut, *J. Colloid Sci.*, **3**, 563 (1948). *Cf.*, M. Volmer and H. Flood, *Z. physik. Chem.*, **A170**, 273 (1934). D. Turnbull, *J. Chem. Phys.*, **20**, 411 (1952).

[48] S. W. Young and R. J. Cross, *J. Am. Chem. Soc.*, **33**, 1375 (1911).

[49] K. Schaum, *Z. physik. Chem.*, **25**, 722 (1898).

[50] S. W. Young and W. E. Burke, *J. Am. Chem. Soc.*, **29**, 329 (1907). S. W. Young, *ibid.*, **33**, 148 (1911).

[51] H. Möller, *Physik. Ber.*, **6**, 517 (1925).

[52] D. McIntosh, *Trans. Roy. Soc. Con., III*, **13**, 265 (1919).

[53] E. Biilmann and A. Klit, *Kgl. Danske Videnskab. Selskab, Mat.-fys. Medd.*, **12**, No. 4, 51 pp. (1932); *C. A.*, **27**, 4150 (1933). S. Roginskiĭ, L. Sena, and I. Zeldovwich, *Physik. Z. Sowjetunion*, **1**, 630 (1932); *C. A.*, **26**, 5477 (1932). *Cf.*, P. Othmer, *Z. anorg. Chem.*, **91**, 209 (1915).

[54] C. N. Hinshelwood and H. Hartley, *Phil. Mag.*, [6], **43**, 78 (1922).

and by study[55] of the crystallizing propensity of added insoluble powders.   Charcoal and powdered quartz, which had the greatest effect in promoting crystallization of phenyl salicylate and benzophenone, could be heated to over 100° above the respective melting points of the organic compounds without destroying the "memory" of crystallization.   The effect was attributed to preservation of a "crystalline adsorbate" on the surface of the insoluble powders, and a theory of nucleus formation and growth and of the kinetics of crystallization has been developed[56] on these experimental findings.

Crystal growth frequently starts at the wall of the container, at the surface of a liquid, or at a liquid–liquid boundary.   Preferential crystallization at the vapor–liquid surface of supercooled melts has been attributed[57] to the greater probability of appropriate molecular orientation at the surface. The number of nuclei varies from point to point when certain melts are supercooled between two glass plates, and they are most numerous near the outer edges of the melt.[58]   A group of crystals often grow from a critical spot[59] on the surface of a container.   Its previous history,[60] e.g., whether the inner walls of a glass container have been scratched, has a great influence on the phenomenon.   The stability of supercooled films of phenyl salicylate or benzophenone depends[61] on the smoothness of the supporting surface but not on its chemical nature.   However, there are examples which show that crystallization from supersaturated solutions may start equally well on rough or on greasy surfaces.[62]

On repeated melting and crystallizing of a substance, crystallization tends to start[63] at the same spots on the container surface.   This "memory in crystallization" may be due to orientation of particles in the glass surface, or to the persistence there of minute crystals or impurities.[64]   In the crystallization of supercooled 2-

[55] W. T. Richards, J. Am. Chem. Soc., 54, 479 (1932).   W. T. Richards, E. C. Kirkpatrick, and C. E. Hutz, ibid., 58, 2243 (1936).

[56] M. Avrami, J. Chem. Phys., 7, 1103 (1939).   Cf. C. H. Desch, The Chemistry of Solids, Cornell Univ. Press, Ithaca, 1934.   J. Frenkel, J. Chem. Phys., 7, 538 (1939). J. Phys. (U. S. S. R.), 1, 315 (1939); C. A., 34, 7711 (1940).

[57] K. Söllner, Kolloid-Z., 59, 58 (1932).

[58] K. Schaum and E. Riffert, Z. anorg. allgem. Chem., 120, 241 (1922).

[59] A. Glazunov, Collection Czechoslov. Chem. Communs., 3, 76 (1931); C. A., 25, 4455 (1931).

[60] S. Roginskiĭ, L. Sena, and I. Zeldovwich, Physik. Z. Sowjetunion, 1, 630 (1932); C. A., 26, 5477 (1932).

[61] I. V. Krotov, Bull. acad. sci. U. R. S. S., Classe sci. math. nat., 1932, 817; C. A., 27, 2617 (1933).

[62] R. Fricke, Kolloid-Z., 68, 165 (1934).   Cf. M. Volmer, Z. physik. Chem., 102, 267 (1922).   M. Volmer and W. Schultze, ibid., A156, 1 (1931).

[63] K. Schaum and F. Schoenbeck, Ann. Physik, 8, 652 (1902).   K. Schaum and E. Riffert, Z. anorg. allgem. Chem., 120, 241 (1922).

[64] V. I. Danilov and V. E. Neimark, Zhur. Eksptl. i Teoret. Fiz., 7, 1161 (1937); C. A. 32, 5676 (1938).

naphthyl salicylate in thin layers between two glass plates, the critical spots may be destroyed by heating or by hydrofluoric acid[65]; the crystal nuclei then form uniformly over the whole surface and throughout the entire mass. Possibly, instead of the de-activation of existing centers, new centers may be exposed by the hydrofluoric acid. Collodion shields the active points, but a layer of lactic acid (1 γ per cm.²) causes many nuclei to form near the glass plates, presumably because the carboxyl groups are uniformly oriented toward the glass surface. It has been suggested that nucleus formation depends on surface and interfacial tension,[66] and a formula has been developed[67] for the maximum number of crystallization centers in two-dimensional crystallization which applies fairly well[68] to the crystallization of o-nitrophenol.

Certain metals increase the number of crystal nuclei formed in supercooled melts.[69] When the supporting surface is of appropriate nature, a special kind of mutually oriented overgrowth, *epitaxy*, may result. Thus, owing to the similarity of surface structure, anthraquinone[70] dissolved in benzene will crystallize on metallic antimony; hexamethylenetetramine in benzene will crystallize on gypsum crystals; and certain quinones crystallize on alkali halides. The deposit has an induced structure if the first monolayer conforms to the structure of the substrate: this depends[71] on the degree of misfit.

B. HOMOGENEOUS NUCLEOGENESIS

In any minute volume in the interior of a one-component organic liquid, very rapid, transient changes in energy, density, and orientation of the molecules, are continually occurring, even though the liquid is in complete thermodynamic equilibrium and is free from foreign particles. The same is true of homogeneous solutions, and here local fluctuations[72] in concentration also occur. As a result of these deviations from the norm, ions or molecules are continually clumping together and then separating. Fluctu-

[65] G. L. Mikhnevich and E. N. Ovchinnikova, *Acta Physicochim. U. R. S. S.*, 11, 603 (1939); *C. A.*, 34, 3147 (1940). G. L. Mikhnevich and I. F. Brovko, *Zhur. Eksptl. i Teoret. Fiz.*, 10, 349 (1940); *C. A.*, 34, 7690 (1940).

[66] M. Volmer, *Z. physik. Chem.*, 102, 267 (1922); M. Volmer and W. Schultze, *ibid.*, A156, 1 (1931); M. Volmer, *Kinetik der Phasenbildung*, Steinkopff, Dresden, 1939.

[67] F. K. Gorskiĭ, *Physik. Z. Sowjetunion*, 9, 89 (1936); *C. A.*, 30, 5477 (1936).

[68] F. K. Gorskiĭ, *Zhur Eksptl. i Teoret. Fiz.*, 6, 278 (1936); *C. A.*, 31, 16 (1937).

[69] P. Othmer, *Z. anorg. Chem.*, 91, 209 (1915).

[70] J. Willems, *Naturwissenschaften*, 31, 146, 208 (1943). H. Seifert, "Epitaxy," in R. Gomer and C. S. Smith, eds., *Structure and Properties of Solid Surfaces*. Univ. Chicago Press, Chicago, 1953, pp. 318–383.

[71] J. H. van der Merwe, *Discussions Faraday Soc.*, 5, 201 (1949).

[72] M. Smoluchowski, *Ann. Physik*, 25, 205 (1908). A. Einstein, *ibid.*, 33, 1275 (1910). R. H. Fowler and E. A. Guggenheim, *Statistical Thermodynamics*, Macmillan, New York, 1939.

ations in a stable phase are called[73] "homophase fluctuations"; their time-average values of density and energy (and concentration, for a solution) correspond to those of the bulk phase.

Cooling the melt below its melting point, or the solution below its saturation temperature, tends to lessen dissociation and to encourage stability; the same effect may result from increase in pressure. Some clusters may have a configuration approximating that of the inchoate, unborn crystal. These *heterophase* fluctuations[74] are called *embryos;* they are minute, unstable, temporary aggregations which are continually forming and disappearing. The applied conditions might be expected to favor their

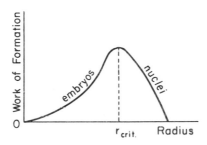

Fig. 1. Relation between work of formation and radius, of embryos and nuclei ($r_{crit.}$ = critical radius).[75]

growth, but, from examination of the formation of liquid droplets from supersaturated vapor, now believed to be a comparable phenomenon, it has been found (see Sect. II.2.A) that the energy required for growth of an embryo increases up to a critical size; when once this energy maximum has been reached and passed, the energy needed for subsequent growth falls off rapidly[75] with increasing radius (see Fig. 1). The embryo of this critical size[76] is called a three-dimensional *nucleus;* it has a 50:50 chance of growing or decreasing, and if it grows, it becomes thermodynamically stable. As soon as one or more stable nuclei have formed, crystallization proceeds more

[73] J. Frenkel, *Kinetic Theory of Liquids.* Clarendon Press, Oxford, 1946.
[74] A. R. Ubbelohde, *Trans. Faraday Soc.*, **34**, 292 (1938).
[75] V. K. La Mer, *Ind. Eng. Chem.*, **44**, 1270 (1952).
[76] M. Volmer and A. Weber, *Z. physik. Chem.*, **119**, 277 (1926). L. Farkas, *ibid.*, **125**, 236 (1927). I. N. Stranski and R. Kaischew, *ibid.*, **B26**, 317 (1934). R. Becker and W. Döring, *Ann. Physik*, **24**, 719 (1935). M. Volmer, *Kinetik der Phasenbildung*, Steinkopff, Dresden, 1939. I. N. Stranski and R. Kaishev, *Annuaire univ. Sofia II. Fac. phys.-math.*, Livre 2, **32**, 171 (1936); *C. A.*, **31**, 3365 (1937); *Uspekhi Fiz. Nauk*, **21**, 408 (1939); *C. A.*, **34**, 1232 (1940). I. N. Stranski, *Trav. congr. jubilaire Mendeléev*, **2**, 185 (1937); *C. A.*, **32**, 3682 (1938). I. N. Stranski and R. Kaischew, *Z. physik. Chem.*, **B26**, 100, 312 (1934). R. Kaischew and I. N. Stranski, *ibid.*, **B26**, 114 (1934).

or less rapidly, depending on the physical conditions of the system.   This is *spontaneous self-nucleation* and growth.

C. HETEROGENEOUS NUCLEATION

If a small, imperfect crystal of the crystallizand, larger than a critical-size crystal nucleus thereof, is added to the suitably supercooled one-component melt or the supersaturated solution, the work of passing the energy barrier has already been applied; and so crystallization will ensue at a rate dependent on the physical conditions.   This is *deliberate self-nucleation and growth.*

Similarly, if a particle of a foreign material, crystallographically very similar to the desired crystal, is introduced, it may fulfil the function of a

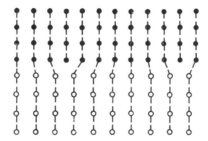

Fig. 2. Cross section of interface between two misfitting
lattices, showing regions of fairly good fit.[77]

homogeneous nucleus in initiating crystallization, presumably *via* a two-dimensional monolayer; such a particle is a *heterogeneous nucleator.*   The amount of energy needed for passing the energy barrier will then be less than in spontaneous self-nucleation but may be more than in deliberate self-nucleation; and the more closely the foreign particle resembles a self-nucleus, the less the strain in the layer of crystallizand and the closer the approach to deliberate self-nucleation—that is, the greater the likelihood that crystallization will occur.   The heterogeneous particle, to be effective, must be larger than a homogeneous nucleus.

Low-index planes of the heterogeneous particle and of the unborn crystal must be nearly congruent; a sufficient adhesive force is required, and the symmetry, lattice spacing, and atomic arrangement (packing) of the two must[77] be similar.   The greater the similarity, the more effective is the foreign particle as a nucleator (see Fig. 2); the order of effectiveness is the same as the order of the reciprocal of the disregistry (mismatch) with low-index planes of the unborn crystal.   For really effective heterogeneous nu-

[77] D. Turnbull and B. Vonnegut, *Ind. Eng. Chem.*, **44**, 1292 (1952).

cleation, the discrepancy should not exceed *ca.* 5%; but nucleation can occur up to a discrepancy of at least 15%.   Complete isomorphy, with a fit permitting a continuous series of solid solutions, is advantageous but not essential; partial isomorphy can suffice.   The latter comprises[78] two systems: (*a*) those pseudoisomorphous in three dimensions, affording anomalous solid solutions because inexact fit gives limited mutual solubility; and (*b*) di- or unidimensional isomorphous systems, which do not give solid solutions but permit oriented overgrowth (epitaxy[79]).   Epitaxy may occur if, in the two crystals, the planes and directions with the most similar atomic arrangement are parallel, and the unit-cell dimensions of the two match within a range of *ca.* 15%.   The same limitation on the mismatch applies[80] in solid-solution formation in alloys and in heterogeneous nucleation.[81] Nucleators having crystallographic properties within this range were added[81] to samples of a saturated solution in glass tubes, which were then sealed and cooled.   Crystallization always occurred on undercooling slightly; whereas, in control tubes containing no nucleator, crystallization did not supervene until the temperature of labile supersaturation was reached.   A few examples are known of effective nucleation where the mismatch considerably exceeds 15%; the effect may here be attributable to dislocations or other imperfections on the surface of the nucleator.[82]

D. CRYSTAL GROWTH

Crystals of organic compounds are composed of units, either of ions or of molecules.   In ionic crystals, the units are held together by electrostatic attraction; in molecular crystals, the units are held together by van der Waals' attractive forces, by hydrogen bonds, and, if the molecule has a dipole moment, by electrostatic forces.   In crystals of some substances, the same forces act in all three dimensions. For other compounds, "two-dimensional" layers or "one-dimensional" chains may be distinguished.   The structure unit, or *lepton*, is seldom the growth unit.   The three-dimensional nucleus is not formed by simultaneous collision of all its constituent *growth units*, because the probability of such an occurrence is small.   Instead, the nucleus must arise by a stepwise addition[83] of growth units to an embryo; then, as soon as the radius exceeds the critical radius, a nucleus has formed.   Further

[78] A. Neuhaus, *Z. Krist.*, **105**, 161 (1943).

[79] L. Royer, *Bull. soc. franç. minéral.*, **51**, 1 (1928); *Compt. rend.*, **194**, 620, 1088 (1932); **196**, 282, 552 (1933); **205**, 1418 (1937).   G. P. Thomson, *Proc. Phys. Soc. London*, **61**, 403 (1948).   J. H. van der Merwe, *Discussions Faraday Soc.*, **5**, 201 (1949). G. W. Johnson, *J. Applied Phys.*, **21**, 1057 (1950); **22**, 797 (1951).   L. G. Schulz, *Acta Cryst.*, **4**, 483 (1951).

[80] W. Hume-Rothery, *Atomic Theory for Students of Metallurgy*.   Institute of Metals, London, 1946.

[81] M. Telkes, *Ind. Eng. Chem.*, **44**, 1308 (1952).

[82] G. P. Thomson, *Proc. Phys. Soc. London*, **61**, 403 (1948).

[83] M. Volmer, *Kinetik der Phasenbildung*.   Steinkopff, Dresden, 1939.

growth continues spontaneously, under appropriate conditions, until the potential of the liquid phase equals that of the solid phase or until the liquid has completely solidified.

An imaginary, spherical nucleus, bombarded uniformly all over its surface by units, would be expected to grow as a sphere. But, with slow growth, this never occurs; instead, different facets appear. If the external conditions are constant, a freely growing crystal preserves its geometric shape from the moment it comes into view. Hence, growth proceeds[84] as a regular deposition of strata on the various faces. The rate at which a face moves outward, normal to the face, is called its *translation velocity*. Unless the crystal is a regular geometric solid, the various faces have different translation velocities. Those faces with the lowest translation velocities become[85] larger and larger; growth tends to give the minimum, surface free energy. If the over-all rate is increased, the difference in the growth rate of various faces becomes smaller. One factor determining the relative growth rates of different surfaces may be the presence or absence of certain surface imperfections. Certain types of faults may be healed over at growth rates well below the maximum.

It has been stated[86] that at the very beginning of crystal growth, instead of formation of small crystals by addition of individual molecules or ions, submicrons clump together. Traube claims[87] to have observed, under the ultramicroscope, the linking up of chains of submicrons to form certain crystals, and it has been shown[88] that, in later stages, a crystal can certainly grow by attachment of other small crystals. The attractive fields of small, discrete crystals appear to be much stronger[89] than those of the original nuclei[90] and, in further growth, molecules or ions may be attached individually. For a given degree of supercooling, minute nuclei grow much more slowly than visible particles.[91]

The forces which hold the units together inside the crystal are also operative in the surface layers[92] and cause attachment of additional units, but it appears that in crystal growth from supersaturated solution, diffusion of the substance takes

[84] R. Marcelin, *Ann. phys.*, [9], **10**, 185 (1918). H. Brandes, *Z. physik. Chem.*, **126**, 196 (1927).

[85] M. Bentivoglio, *Proc. Roy. Soc. London*, **A115**, 59 (1927). L. F. Bates, *Science Progr.*, **22**, 197 (1927). *Cf.* J. J. P. Valeton, *Z. Krist.*, **59**, 135 (1924).

[86] J. Traube and W. von Behren, *Z. physik. Chem.*, **A138**, 85 (1928).

[87] J. Traube, *Kolloid-Z.*, **47**, 45 (1929); *Z. Elektrochem.*, **35**, 626 (1929).

[88] D. Balarev, *Kolloid-Beih.*, **53**, 377 (1941).

[89] E. T. Ross, *Pacific Chem. Met. Ind.*, **2**, No. 3, 9 (1938); F. Serowy, *Chem. Fabrik*, **13**, [15], 257 (1940). D. Samuiacas, *Z. Krist.*, **85**, 474 (1933).

[90] P. V. Grushvitskiĭ, *Uchenye Zapiski Leningrad. Gosudarst. Univ.*, **1939**, No. 7 (No. 34), 24; *C. A.*, **36**, 3078 (1942). H. B. Caldwell, *Chem. Met. Eng.*, **49**, 116 (May, 1942).

[91] R. Bloch, T. Brings, and W. Kuhn, *Z. physik. Chem.*, **B12**, 415 (1931). *Cf.* L.-C. de Coppet, *Ann. chim. phys.*, **10**, 457 (1907). C. Hammer, *Ann. Physik*, **33**, 445 (1938). E. Scheil and A. Langeweise, *Arch. Eisenhüttenw.*, **11**, 93 (1937). W. Kauzmann, *Chem. Revs.*, **43**, 219 (1948).

[92] I. N. Stranski, *Z. physik. Chem.*, **136**, 259 (1928). I. N. Stranski and D. Totomanow, *ibid.*, **A163**, 399 (1933).

place through a liquid film[93] on the surface of the crystal (see Sect. II.2.D). The growth[94] of ionic and molecular crystals has been analyzed on this basis.[92,95] In some cases,[96] crystallization does not proceed uniformly along a plane surface but along a three-dimensional lattice which is filled in later. Molecules or ions arriving at the growing crystal may not become attached at the place struck,[97] but may move rather freely over the crystal surface until they become fixed.[98] This process may[99] be interfered with by adsorption and other secondary effects.[100] Growth of both micro- and macrocrystals in melts and solutions may be followed by means of cinematographic records.[101] Preliminary studies with the electron microscope have been made.[102]

The smooth faces and sharp edges bounding a crystal are the outer evidence of inner order, the lattice; and a crystal may be regarded as composed of regular sheets or layers of material. All the faces of the crystal do not necessarily contain the same arrangement of building units, and their spacing is usually different.

[93] J. W. Gibbs, *Trans. Conn. Acad. Arts Sci.*, **3**, 489 (1878). *The Scientific Papers of J. Willard Gibbs*, Vol. I, Longmans, Green, New York, 1906, pp. 221, 325. P. Curie, *Bull. soc. franç. minéral.*, **8**, 145 (1885). G. Wulff, *Z. kryst. Mineral.*, **34**, 449 (1901).

[94] W. Kossel, "Crystals and Crystal Growth," in G. Joos, ed., *Physics of Solids*, Part I (FIAT *Review of German Science 1939–1946*), Office of Military Government for Germany, Field Information Agencies Technical, Wiesbaden, 1947, pp. 15–42. G. P. Thomson, *Proc. Phys. Soc. London*, **61**, 403 (1948). W. J. Dunning, *Research*, **2**, 275 (1949). I. N. Stranski, *Discussions Faraday Soc.*, **5**, 13 (1949).

[95] P. Niggli, *Z. anorg. allgem. Chem.*, **110**, 55 (1920). J. J. P. Valeton, *Physik. Z.*, **21**, 606 (1920); *Z. Krist.*, **59**, 135, 335 (1924). K. Spangenberg, *ibid.*, **59**, 375, 383 (1924); **61**, 189 (1925). H. Brandes, *Z. physik. Chem.*, **126**, 196 (1927). W. Kossel, *Nachr. Ges. Wiss. Göttingen. Math.-physik. Klasse*, **1927**, 135; *C. A.*, **22**, 2690 (1928); *Physik. Z.*, **29**, 553 (1928); "Die molekularen Vorgänge beim Kristallwachstum," in H. Falkenhagen, ed., *Quantentheorie und Chemie*, Hirzel, Leipzig, 1928, pp. 1–46; *Naturwissenschaften*, **18**, 901 (1930); *Ann. Physik*, **21**, 457 (1934); *Handwörterbuch der Naturwiss.*, 2nd ed., **10**, 372 (1934).

[96] W. P. Davey, *Phys. Rev.*, **29**, 206 (1927).

[97] M. Volmer, *Trans. Faraday Soc.*, **28**, 359 (1932); *Ann. Physik*, **23**, 44 (1935).

[98] L. Kowarski, *J. chim. phys.*, **32**, 469 (1935). *Cf.* W. Kossel, *Naturwissenschaften*, **18**, 901 (1930). I. N. Stranski, *Z. physik. Chem.*, **136**, 259 (1928).

[99] W. Kleber, *Kolloid-Z.*, **94**, 39 (1941).

[100] I. N. Stranski and R. Kaishev. *Z. Krist.*, **78**, 373 (1931); *Ann. Physik*, **23**, 330 (1935); *Physik. Z.*, **36**, 393 (1935). M. Straumanis, *Z. physik. Chem.*, **B19**, 63 (1932); **B26**, 246 (1934); **B30**, 132 (1935). D. Balarev, *Kolloid-Z.*, **96**, 24 (1941); *Kolloid-Beih.*, **52**, 45 (1941); *Zentr. Mineral. Geol.*, **1941A**, 228; *C. A.*, **36**, 4001 (1942); *Neues Jahrb. Mineral. Geol., Abt. A*, **1943**, 86; *C. A.*, **38**, 5706 (1944).

[101] W. G. France, *Colloid Symp. Monograph*, **3**, 317 (1925). F. G. Keenan, G. W. Bennett, and W. G. France, *J. Am. Ceram. Soc.*, **10**, 435 (1927). L. Kowarski, *J. chim. phys.*, **32**, 395 (1935). H. Emmett, *J. Roy. Microscop. Soc.*, **63**, Nos. 1/2, 26 (1943). R. M. Garrels, C. L. Jones, and A. L. Howland, *Science*, **105**, 46 (1947).

[102] J. H. Blomquist and W. G. France, *J. Phys. Chem.*, **46**, 1044 (1942). E. A. Gulbransen, R. T. Phelps, and A. Langer, *Ind. Eng. Chem., Anal. Ed.*, **17**, 646 (1945).

The ease of deposition, or detachment, of building units at different portions of the surface is not the same.   A unit lying on the *surface* is attached by one face only, and is the most readily attached or removed; for a unit at a *corner* of an uncompleted step, three faces are in contact; and for a unit in a completed edge, four faces are in contact (see Fig. 3).   Thus, the tendency for firm attachment during growth is least for a single adsorbed unit on the surface and greatest at the uncompleted edge.   Any holes in the surface would be filled up first, since the evolution of energy would then be even greater.

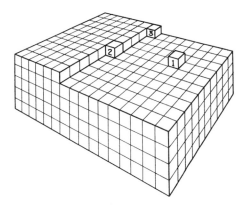

Fig. 3. Preferred sequence of addition of unit 1 (one face in contact) to the stepped surface of a potentially perfect crystal (2, three faces in contact; 3, two faces in contact).

Often, crystals increase in area at a rate much greater than would be expected on the assumption that all units hitting the surface *rebound* and that all those striking the edges *stick*, thereby increasing the area of the face. This has led to the hypothesis of adlineation or surface mobility, namely, that molecules which hit the surface may adhere by adsorption and may then travel over the surface for considerable distances before coming to rest at a place of stronger attachment.   Experiments, *e.g.*, on the migration of benzoquinone[103] or *p*-toluidine[104] on glass, confirm this idea.   Such movement requires less energy than does retransferral to the liquid phase.

Even on apparently smooth faces of a crystal, there are irregularities,[105] *e.g.*, steps, pits, vacant sites, and dislocations.   Modern theory suggests

[103] M. Volmer and G. Adhikari, *Z. physik. Chem.*, **119**, 46 (1926).   *Cf.* M. Volmer, *ibid.*, **102**, 267 (1922).

[104] L. Kowarski, *J. chim. phys.*, **32**, 303, 395, 469 (1935).

[105] *Cf.* H. W. Leverenz, *An Introduction to Luminescence of Solids*.   Wiley, New York, 1950, pp. 40–58.

that a perfect crystal, with low-index, close-packed[106] surfaces, would grow
extremely slowly in a slightly supersaturated solution; units could be adsorbed and then move over the surface of the crystal, but would also be
detached again with relative ease.   For a potentially perfect crystal having
an incomplete surface edge or high-index surfaces consisting of a series of
steps, each of molecular height, growth proceeds[107] at low supersaturation
until all the surfaces are low-index and it then ceases.   Attachment at an

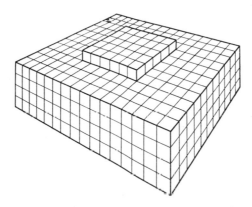

Fig. 4. Surface of a potentially perfect crystal, bearing
an island monolayer ("two-dimensional" nucleus).

uncompleted edge is called "the repeatable step." With an imperfect crystal,
if units meet a plateau, a pit, or a dislocation,[108] firm attachment is very
much more likely, since much more energy will be liberated.   There are
six primary types of crystal imperfection,[109] but only a dislocation affects
the lattice at distances greater than a few interatomic spacings.

Obviously, for *starting a new plane*, in the absence of such imperfections, a
critical-size, homogeneous, island monolayer or so-called "*two-dimensional*"
nucleus (see Fig. 4) must form on the close-packed surface[106,110]; as soon
as it is born, a sheet of units starts spreading over the surface of the facet,

[106] W. K. Burton and N. Cabrera, *Discussions Faraday Soc.*, **5**, 33 (1949).   N. Cabrera
and W. K. Burton, *ibid.*, **5**, 40 (1949).

[107] C. W. Bunn, *Discussions Faraday Soc.*, **5**, 75 (1949).

[108] W. K. Burton, N. Cabrera, and F. C. Frank, *Nature*, **163**, 398 (1949).   F. C. Frank,
Discussions Faraday Soc., **5**, 48 (1949).

[109] F. Seitz, *J. Phys. Chem.*, **57**, 737 (1953).   *Cf.* A. L. G. Rees, *Chemistry of the Defect
Solid State.*   Wiley, New York, 1954.

[110] R. Becker and W. Döring, *Ann. Physik*, **24**, 719 (1935).   *Cf.* N. F. Mott, *Nature*,
165, 295 (1950).   R. S. Bradley, *Quart. Revs. Chem. Soc. London*, **5**, 315 (1951).

at a speed proportional to the degree of supercooling or supersaturation; when this layer is completed, growth stops for the time being. Outward spreading from the center of a face may be the most common type of growth[111]; per unit area of face, more solute arrives at the center of a face than at the edges.[112] The phenomenon of growth is thus, here, inseparable from that of surface nucleation. Addition of each new layer requires prior formation of at least one fresh two-dimensional nucleus on top of the preceding layer. The time required for completion of a layer is often much less than that required for formation of a new surface nucleus, and building up of a two-dimensional nucleus of the critical size is a rare event.

The velocity of crystal growth is, therefore, dependent on the rate of two-dimensional nucleation on the crystal surface. Hence, growth occurring *via* two-dimensional nucleation is rhythmic, not continuous. If a compound has many degrees of freedom of rotation and if its crystal lattice does not permit random constellations, a unit thereof must, in order to become permanently attached, be adsorbed on the crystal long enough for a constellation, required for lattice formation, to come into being.

At a somewhat high supersaturation, before the first sheet considered has grown completely, another nucleus may form on top of this sheet and proceed to give rise to another layer. Alternatively, the nucleus on the surface may be high enough to initiate the growth of several layers, one on top of another, almost simultaneously; this gives, temporarily, a high-index surface. Continuation of growth requires maintenance of high-index surfaces. Particularly at high supersaturations and with substances which are ionic or contain strongly polar groups,[111] sheets may interlock and grow as one thick layer, visible by interference methods, as distinct from the monomolecular layers probably formed under other conditions. A series of such sheets may, *e.g.*, because of continuous fall of the degree of supersaturation, stop growing before their edges precisely coincide, affording a vicinal face at a small angle to the main face. The less the supercooling or initial supersaturation, the more regular is the crystal growth.

Heterogeneous surface nuclei can be formed, either by incorporation of foreign units in the lattice or by adsorption on the surface. These may help growth by lowering the amount of energy needed to form a critical-size surface nucleus or by setting up a kind of dislocation, or they may hinder growth at that face by interfering with adlineation of adsorbed units of crystallizand (see Sect. II.5).

According to Frank,[113] the surfaces of most crystals are imperfect and

[111] C. W. Bunn and H. Emmett, *Discussions Faraday Soc.*, **5**, 119 (1949).

[112] W. F. Berg, *Proc. Roy. Soc. London*, **A164**, 79 (1938). S. P. F. Humphreys-Owen, *Discussions Faraday Soc.*, **5**, 144 (1949).

[113] F. C. Frank, *Discussions Faraday Soc.*, **5**, 48 (1949).

contain *dislocations*[114] with a screw component,[115] terminating in the surface and causing steps which remain during growth (see Fig. 5). Two-dimensional nucleation, and growth by layers, is *unnecessary*, and spiral growth takes place continuously at each such dislocation[116] on the surface concerned. Motion pictures reveal that such growth can occur; and electron microscopy, phase-contrast microscopy, and multiple-beam interferometry have shown spiral formations on some crystal surfaces. Thus, in all cases, in order that a crystal may grow, it *must have steps on its surface;* these may already be there, as high-index steps or as screw dislocations, or they are the boundaries of the two-dimensional nuclei which are deposited.

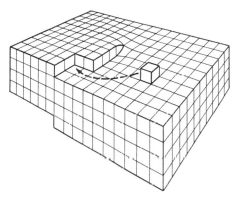

Fig. 5. The end of a screw dislocation.[114]

Occurrence of spiral markings on the surface of silicon carbide crystals has long been known,[117] and etching[118] of the surface of a macroscopic crystal by its slightly

[114] E. Orowan, *Z. Physik,* **89,** 634 (1934). M. Polanyi, *ibid.,* **89,** 660 (1934). G. I. Taylor, *Proc. Roy. Soc. London,* **A145,** 362 (1934). N. F. Mott and F. R. N. Nabarro, *The Strength of Solids,* Physical Society, London, 1948, p. 1. A. H. Cottrell, *Progress in Metal Physics,* Vol. 1, Butterworth, London, 1949, p. 77. W. Shockley, J. H. Hollomon, R. Maurer, and F. Seitz, eds., *Imperfections in Nearly Perfect Crystals,* Wiley, New York, 1952. W. T. Read, Jr., *Dislocations in Crystals,* McGraw-Hill, New York, 1953. A. R. Verma, *Crystal Growth and Dislocations,* Academic Press, New York, 1953. M. Cohen, ed., *Dislocations in Metals,* Am. Inst. Mining and Metallurgical Engrs., New York, 1954.

[115] J. M. Burgers, *Koninkl. Ned. Akad. Wetenschap. Proc.,* **42,** 293, 378 (1939).

[116] W. K. Burton, N. Cabrera, and F. C. Frank, *Nature,* **163,** 398 (1949); *Trans. Roy. Soc. London,* **A243,** 299 (1951). F. C. Frank, *Phil. Mag.,* **42,** 809 (1951); *Advances in Physics,* **1,** [11], 91 (1952); *Z. Elektrochem.,* **56,** 429 (1952). J. H. Robertson, *Ann. Repts. Progress Chem.* (Chem. Soc. London), **49,** 343 (1953).

[117] J. W. Mellor, *A Comprehensive Treatise on Inorganic and Theoretical Chemistry.* Vol. V, Longmans, Green, London, 1924, p. 879.

[118] A. P. Honess, *The Nature, Origin, and Interpretation of the Etch Figures of Crystals.* Wiley, New York, 1927.

undersaturated solution gives etch figures with minute elevations or depressions which indicate the presence of dislocations. Spiral formation has been observed on the surfaces of crystals of such long-chain compounds as n-hexatriacontane[119] ($C_{36}H_{74}$), n-nonatriacontane[120] ($C_{39}H_{80}$), n-hectane[121] ($C_{100}H_{202}$), and stearic acid[122] grown from solution. The spiral steps are not monomolecular in height. For n-paraffin and n-hectane, the step height has been measured by shadow casting and electron microscopy, and found to be the size of, or an integral multiple of, the x-ray unit cell, i.e., the length of the carbon chain. For stearic acid, the step height can equal, or be a half-integral multiple of, the x-ray unit cell; the carboxyl group at the end of one molecule can associate, through polar or ionic bonding, with that at the end of another molecule, resulting in pairs of molecules which give a double-layer structure. The x-ray structure of these long-chain organic crystals consists[123] of zigzag chains of carbon atoms packed more or less parallel in the crystals; these chains are bound laterally by weak van der Waals' forces which permit slippage resulting in dislocations.

Dislocations could arise in a number of other ways. If surface nucleation occurs simultaneously at a proper and an improper, e.g., twin, position on the same face, a dislocation will form where sheets from the two meet. During rapid growth at high supersaturation, dislocations could form and develop. Presence of incorporated or adsorbed impurity could cause development of curvature in the growing crystal, leading to stress in the surface and eventual formation of a dislocation. Mechanical stress during crystal growth, or fluctuations in temperature originating, for example, from dissipation of heat of crystallization, may also produce cracks and vacancies.[124]

2. Rate of Crystallization

The rate of crystallization is determined by the rate of nucleus formation or the rate of growth of the individual crystals, or both. Both rates depend on such factors as the nature of the crystallizand, the physical conditions, and the proportion and nature of the solvent, if any.

A. RATE OF NUCLEATION

Rate of Homogeneous, Three-Dimensional Nucleus Formation. The rate at which homogeneous nuclei are formed is identical with the rate at which embryos acquire sufficient thermodynamic potential to pass the

---

[119] I. M. Dawson and V. Vand, *Nature,* **167,** 476 (1951); *Proc. Roy. Soc. London,* **A206,** 555 (1951).

[120] N. G. Anderson and I. M. Dawson, *Proc. Roy. Soc. London,* **A218,** 255 (1953).

[121] I. M. Dawson, *Proc. Roy. Soc. London,* **A214,** 72 (1952).

[122] A. R. Verma and P. M. Reynolds, *Proc. Phys. Soc. London,* **B66,** 414 (1953). P M. Reynolds and A. R. Verma, *Nature,* **171,** 486 (1953).

[123] A. Müller, *Proc. Roy. Soc. London,* **A124,** 317 (1929); **A127,** 417 (1930).

[124] C. W. Bunn and H. Emmett, *Discussions Faraday Soc.,* **5,** 119 (1949).

energy barrier (see Fig. 1). Many years ago, Gibbs[125] realized that the work, W, of forming a critical-size particle of a new phase from another phase is given by:

$$W = \sigma A/3 \qquad (1)$$

where σ is the interfacial tension and A is the surface area of the new particle.

For a strain-free, spherical particle of radius r, the free energy ΔF associated with its formation is given by:

$$\Delta F = 4\pi r^2 \sigma + (4\pi r^3)\Delta F_v/3 \qquad (2)$$

where σ is the solid–liquid, interfacial free energy, and ΔF_v is the free-energy difference per unit volume between the two phases. Basic assumptions are that σ is independent of r, and that there is no lower-lying saddle point in the free-energy surface than that corresponding to the standard free energy of nuclei, calculated from the macroscopic thermodynamic coefficients. The free energy of particle formation is a maximum (see Fig. 1) for a particle with the critical radius r_c, given by:

$$r_c = -2\sigma/\Delta F_v \qquad (3)$$

Hence:

$$\Delta F = 4\pi r^2 \sigma + (4\pi r^3)(-2\sigma/3r_c) \qquad (4)$$

$$= 4\pi\sigma(r^2 - 2r^3/3r_c) \qquad (5)$$

Equation (5) was used for plotting ΔF as a function of r in Figure 1. ΔF is a maximum (ΔF^*, the local free-energy change on forming a critical-size nucleus) when $r = r_c$, that is:[126]

$$\Delta F^* = 4\pi\sigma r_c^2/3 \qquad (6)$$

$$= 16\pi\sigma^3/3(\Delta F_v)^2 \qquad (7)$$

Combining equation (7) with equation (3) gives equation (1).

The general rate expression is of the form:[127]

$$\text{rate} = N \exp\{-\Delta F/kT\} \qquad (8)$$

[125] J. W. Gibbs, Collected Works. Vol. I, Longmans, Green, New York, 1928.

[126] M. Volmer, Kinetik der Phasenbildung, Steinkopff, Dresden and Leipzig, 1939; Edwards Bros., Ann Arbor, Mich., 1945. J. Frenkel, Kinetic Theory of Liquids, Chapter VII, Oxford Univ. Press, Oxford, 1946. R. Smoluchowski, in R. Smoluchowski, J. E. Mayer, and W. A. Weyl, eds., Phase Transformations in Solids, Wiley, New York, 1951, pp. 156–161. V. K. La Mer, Ind. Eng. Chem., 44, 1270 (1952).

[127] S. Glasstone, K. J. Laidler, and H. Eyring, The Theory of Rate Processes. McGraw-Hill, New York, 1941.

where N is the total number of single molecules per mole in the system, k is the Boltzmann constant, and T is the absolute temperature; and Becker[128] showed that the rate of nucleation n, which is governed by the rate of diffusion of units from liquid to crystal and by the rate of deposition on the crystal, is expressed by:

$$n = K \exp \left\{ -(\Delta F^* + q)/kT \right\} \qquad (9)$$

where n is the number of critical-size nuclei formed per mole of liquid phase per second, q is the energy of activation for diffusion across the phase boundary, and K is a constant which he was unable to determine. It has since been shown[129] that:

$$n = (NkT/h) \exp \left\{ -(\Delta F^* + \Delta F_A)/kT \right\} \qquad (10)$$

where h is the Planck constant and ΔF_A is the free energy of activation for crystal growth. That is:

$$n = (NkT/h) \exp \left\{ -(4\pi\sigma r_c^2/3 + \Delta F_A)/kT \right\} \qquad (11)$$

Hence, nucleation will occur the more rapidly, the smaller is ΔF^*. According to this equation, nucleus formation will eventually take place in a supersaturated solution, no matter how low the degree of supersaturation, provided that the time allowed is long enough.

Rate of Heterogeneous Nucleation. The kinetics of nucleation on the surface of heterogeneous nucleators has been derived[130] from that of homogeneous three-dimensional nucleation, under the simplifying assumption that the free energy of nucleus formation is modified by the change in interfacial energy, compared with homogeneous nucleation. The key equation, similar to equation (10) is:

$$n = 10^{-8}A' \exp \left\{ -(\Delta F^*f(\theta) + \Delta F_A)/kT \right\} \qquad (12)$$

where n is the frequency of formation, per unit area, of crystal nuclei on the surface of the nucleator, A' is the kinetic coefficient (volume/time) for nucleation, and θ is the contact angle of the crystals on the nucleator surface. Thus, the kinetics of heterogeneous nucleation is described, in this

[128] R. Becker, *Ann. Physik*, **32**, 128 (1938); *Proc. Phys. Soc. London*, **52**, 71 (1940). *Cf.* R. Becker and W. Döring, *Ann. Physik*, **24**, 719 (1935). J. Frenkel, *Physik. Z. Sowjetunion* **1**, 498 (1932); *C. A.*, **26**, 5480 (1932).

[129] D. Turnbull and J. C. Fisher, *J. Chem. Phys.*, **17**, 71 (1949). *Cf.* J. C. Fisher, J. H. Hollomon, and D. Turnbull, *J. Applied Phys.*, **19**, 775 (1948); *Science*, **109**, 168 (1949).

[130] J. H. Hollomon, *Thermodynamics in Physical Metallurgy*, Am. Soc. Metals, Cleveland, 1949, p. 161. D. Turnbull, *ibid.*, p. 282. D. Turnbull, *J. Applied Phys.*, **21**, 1022 (1950); *J. Chem. Phys.*, **18**, 198 (1950); **20**, 411 (1952). D. Turnbull and B. Vonnegut, *Ind. Eng. Chem.*, **44**, 1292 (1952).

case, as a function of temperature by using one parameter, θ, additional to those for homogeneous nucleation.   The free energy of formation of a critical-size nucleus on the nucleator is less than for formation of a homogeneous nucleus of comparable size.   This explains the observation that less supercooling or supersaturation is needed for nucleation in the presence of effective heterogeneous nucleator than in its absence.

B. RATE OF GROWTH

Growth of a Potentially Perfect or Perfect Crystal.   In growth on a flat, low-index surface of a crystal *having an uncompleted layer* (see Fig. 6), by addition of units from the vapor, a pressure increment Δp, over the equilibrium vapor pressure p, causes the layer to grow at a speed proportional to

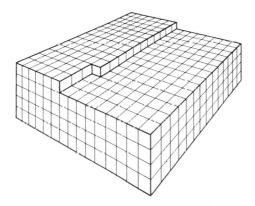

Fig. 6. Crystal surface with an uncompleted
step, below the critical temperature.

Δp until the layer has been completed.   Growth from the liquid phase is regarded as being essentially similar.   The rate of growth J at a stepped surface is a function of the number of steps per centimeter, and is given[131] by:

$$J = (\alpha - 1) \, \nu \exp \left\{ -W/kT \right\} /a^2 \tag{13}$$

where J is the number of units adsorbed per sq. cm. per second, $(\alpha - 1)$ is the supersaturation, ν is the frequency of vibration of the adsorbed atoms, W is the total evaporation energy, and a is the interatomic distance.   A stepped or a *step-free*, low-index surface, heated above a certain critical temperature, acquires[132] Frenkel "kinks," consisting of adsorbed units on

[131] N. Cabrera and W. K. Burton, *Discussions Faraday Soc.*, **5**, 40 (1949).
[132] J. Frenkel, *J. Phys.* (U. S. S. R.), **9**, 392 (1945).

some parts of the surface and holes left by these units at other places (see Fig. 7). These kinks amount to a stepped surface, and the rate of growth is given[131] by equation (13).

Below the critical temperature, as soon as each uncompleted layer has been completed, growth ceases temporarily. In order to start a new layer, units have to accumulate until a *two-dimensional nucleus of the critical size* has arisen; this is relatively slow because of low probability, and the rate

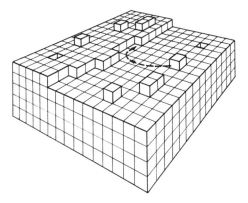

Fig. 7. Crystal surface, above the critical temperature, showing Frenkel kinks.

of the process varies[133] with Δp as exp $\{-A/\Delta p\}$, where A is a constant at a given temperature. Hence, when Δp is small enough, the rate of surface nucleation is negligibly small. The rate of formation of these island nuclei, in the absence of diffusion of adsorbed units, has been treated.[134] For a flat surface with *no steps or Frenkel kinks*, the number of units condensing per sq. cm. per second is given[131] by:

$$J = \nu \exp \left\{ -(W + U)/kT \right\} \exp \left\{ -A_c/3kT \right\}/a^2 \qquad (14)$$

where U is the activation energy for diffusion and A_c is the increase in free energy required for formation of a critical-size two-dimensional nucleus. This equation cannot account for formation of new layers at low supersaturation; here, screw dislocations must be operative.

Growth of an Imperfect Crystal. If the surface has *screw dislocations*, two-dimensional nucleus formation is not needed, and the rate of growth, for simple examples, is given[131] by:

$$J = (\alpha - 1)N^{1/2}a\nu \exp \left\{ -W/kT \right\}/\beta a^2 \qquad (15)$$

[133] N. F. Mott, *Discussions Faraday Soc.*, **5**, 11 (1949).
[134] R. Becker and W. Döring, *Ann. Physik*, **24**, 719 (1935).

where N is the number of dislocations per sq. cm., and β is the square root of the ratio of the probabilities of an adsorbed atom's *diffusing* on the surface or *evaporating*. This equation agrees with experimental results much better than does that derived assuming two-dimensional nucleation. The observed rates of growth at supersaturations below 20% are not in accord with those calculated for a perfect crystal, whereas, the rate calculated assuming dislocations is proportional to the square of the supersaturation, at low supersaturation, and to the supersaturation at higher supersaturations, in agreement with experiment.

C. CRYSTALLIZATION OF ONE-COMPONENT LIQUID

In a one-component liquid, free from homogeneous nuclei or heterogeneous nucleator, the rate of homogeneous, three-dimensional nucleus formation, at any constant pressure, is zero at the melting point.[135] At lower temperatures, crystallization proceeds after nuclei have formed[136] or been added. As the temperature is lowered, the tendency for aggregation to homogeneous nuclei is correspondingly increased. However, simultaneously, the viscosity increases exponentially, *i.e.*, the free movement of building units is diminished. Consequently, with decrease in temperature the probability of nucleus formation or the number of such nuclei formed per unit of time, *i.e.*, the *rate of homogeneous, three-dimensional nucleus formation*, smoothly increases from zero (I) to a maximum[137] (A) and then falls off, asymptotically approaching zero (II), where the liquid has become a resin or glass (see Fig. 8). Tammann found that nucleus formation obeys the laws of probability, and that the rate curve resembles the bell-shaped, ogival probability curve. Just below the melting point (I), the rate of homogeneous, three-dimensional nucleation is extremely low, but an introduced homogeneous nucleus will grow, indicating that two-dimensional self-nucleation can occur. In the rate range between zero (I) and the vicinity of maximum (A), the rate of homogeneous, two-dimensional nucleation and growth also increases from zero I, reaching a maximum (B) and then smoothly falling off to zero II; maximum (B) is not necessarily coincident with maximum (A), and is usually found at a higher temperature, that is, in the range from zero I to B, growth is nearly always faster than homogeneous, three-dimensional nucleation. The effect[138] of temperature on vis-

[135] G. Tammann, *Z. physik. Chem.*, **68**, 257 (1910). W. E. Garner, F. C. Madden, and J. E. Rushbrooke, *J. Chem. Soc.*, **1926**, 2491. A. M. King and W. E. Garner, *ibid.*, **1936**, 1368.

[136] G. Tammann, *Z. anorg. Chem.*, **87**, 248 (1914).

[137] G. Tammann, *Z. physik. Chem.*, **25**, 441 (1898); *The States of Aggregation*, translation by R. F. Mehl, Van Nostrand, New York, 1925.

[138] C. Kurylenko, *Rev. opt.*, **23**, 1 (1944).

cosity, rate of three-dimensional nucleus formation, and rate of crystal growth is shown in Figure 8. In the temperature range corresponding to B and A, there will be simultaneous three-dimensional nucleation and growth; at temperature X, where the curves cross, both speeds are appreciable.

Hence, at temperatures just below the melting point, if a homogeneous three-dimensional nucleus forms, or a self-nucleus or a particle of heterogeneous nucleator is introduced, it will grow slowly to give a well-shaped

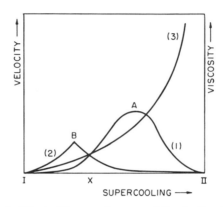

Fig. 8. Effect of temperature on: (1) velocity of three-dimensional nucleus formation, (2) velocity of crystal growth, and (3) viscosity.[138] Abscissa, $1/T$, °K.

crystal, and the formation of more than one crystal is unlikely. But, as the temperature is lowered, the chance of formation of more than one self-nucleus (per unit of time) increases, and the possibility of growing a single crystal decreases. Instead, the formation of a large number of small crystals becomes more and more likely, until the maximum rate of homogeneous, three-dimensional nucleation has been passed.

A classic example of crystallization retarded at low temperatures is[139] that of pure glycerol (m.p. 19.5°C.). In a given time, no crystals formed at −70°, few at −50°, and most at about −61°, as shown in Figure 9. On cooling below the freezing point there is a metastable zone in which spontaneous nucleogenesis is extremely slow, appreciable crystallization occurs only after nucleation, and a single nucleus develops into a single crystal[140]; this is followed by a zone in which spontaneous crystallization may take place; and, finally, there is a vitreous zone, in which

[139] G. Tammann and E. Jenckel, *Z. anorg. allgem. Chem.*, **193,** 76 (1930). M.-O. Samsoen, *Compt. rend.*, **182,** 846 (1926). S. D. Schierloh, *Chemist Analyst*, **33,** 87 (1944).

[140] H. Möller, *Physik. Ber.*, **6,** 517 (1925).

there is very slow, or no, crystallization. For many compounds,[141] the maximum probability or optimal temperature for formation of crystal nuclei in the melt is, with considerable variations,[142] about 90° below the melting point of the crystals.

In order to render the nuclei visible for counting, Tammann[139] developed them by warming the melt to a temperature at which growth was appreciable. However, some of the nuclei which form when a melt is cooled are destroyed[143] when the temperature is raised, and this impairs Tammann's results. An improved method[144] for the measurement of the frequency of formation of crystal nuclei in undercooled melts involves adiabatic compression during heating of the walls.

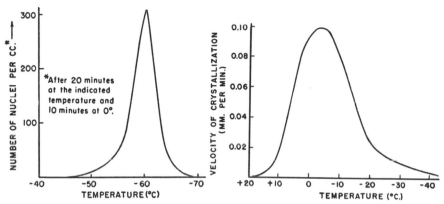

Fig. 9. Change in velocity of three-dimensional nucleus formation in glycerol, with temperature.[152]

Fig. 10. Change in velocity of crystallization of glycerol, with temperature.[152]

In the early work[145] on the rate of crystal growth, the movement of the interface between crystal and liquid in a narrow tube[146] of crystallizing melt was measured. This *linear velocity of crystallization*[147] is constant for any

[141] G. Tammann, *Z. anorg. allgem. Chem.*, **181**, 408 (1929).

[142] G. Tammann, *Kristallisieren und Schmelzen*, Barth, Leipzig, 1903. See also V. Y. Al'tberg, *Uspekhi Fiz. Nauk*, **21**, 69 (1939); *C. A.*, **33**, 4843 (1939).

[143] G. L. Mikhnevich, I. F. Brovko, and A. V. Babadshan, *Physik. Z. Sowjetunion*, **13**, 103 (1938); *C. A.*, **32**, 4849 (1938). G. L. Mikhnevich and I. F. Brovko, *ibid.*, **13**, 113 (1938); *C. A.*, **32**, 4850 (1938).

[144] I. N. Stranski, *Annuaire univ. Sofia, II, Fac. phys.-math.*, Livre 2, **34**, 303 (1937–1938); *C. A.*, **34**, 2225 (1940).

[145] D. Gernez, *Compt. rend.*, **95**, 1278 (1882).

[146] B. Moore, *Z. physik. Chem.*, **12**, 545 (1893).

[147] D. Gernez, *Compt. rend.*, **97**, 1366, 1433 (1883). O. Tumlirz, *Sitzber. Akad. Wiss. Wien*, **103**, iia, 266 (1894). J. Friedländer and G. Tammann, *Z. physik. Chem.*, **24**, 152 (1897). A. Bogojawlensky, *ibid.*, **27**, 585 (1898). E. von Pickardt, *ibid.*, **42**, 17 (1903). A. H. R. Müller, *ibid.*, **86**, 177 (1914). J. H. Walton, Jr., and R. C. Judd, *J. Phys. Chem.*, **18**, 722 (1914). R. Hartmann, *Z. anorg. Chem.*, **88**, 128 (1914). M. Hasselblatt, *ibid.*, **119**, 325 (1921). H. Freundlich and F. Oppenheimer, *Ber.*, **58**, 143 (1925).

given degree of supercooling, but becomes greater[148] as the degree of supercooling is increased, up to a certain maximum, usually found at a temperature some 20 to 30° below the melting point.   This velocity[149] remains constant over a certain temperature range; after this, further cooling decreases the velocity of crystallization, and, if the supercooling is sufficient, the velocity approaches zero at very high viscosity.[150]   Thus, for glycerol,[151] the velocity was maximal[152] at $-3.5°C$. and practically zero at $-45°$ (see Fig. 10).   The maximum linear velocity of crystallization of a supercooled melt is characteristic of the compound (see Table I), but each polymorph, e.g., of dimethyl tartrate[153] has its own linear velocity.

TABLE I

SOME MAXIMUM LINEAR VELOCITIES OF CRYSTALLIZATION

Compound	M.p., °C.	Temp. of max. velocity, °C.	Max. velocity, mm./min.
Water[a]	0	-9.1	6840
Butylphenol[b]	98	70	1117
Picric acid[c]	122	85	858
Azobenzene[b]	67	37	600
Benzil[c]	95	60	433
m-Dinitrobenzoic acid[c]	140	120	31
Piperonal[d]	36.5	16.5	6.5
Phenyl salicylate I[b]	42	20	3.46

[a] J. H. Walton, Jr., and R. C. Judd, J. Phys. Chem., 18, 722 (1914).
[b] G. Tammann, Kristallisieren nd Schmelzen. Barth, Leipzig, 1903, pp. 146–147.
[c] A. Bogojawlensky, Z. physik. Chem., 27, 585 (1898).
[d] G. Tammann and H. E. von Gronow, Z. anorg. allgem. Chem., 200, 57 (1931).

The maxima of the rate of three-dimensional nucleus formation and of the rate of crystal growth lie at different temperatures.   Crystal nuclei readily formed at a certain temperature do not necessarily grow rapidly at the same temperature, but do grow at a desirable speed if the temperature is suitably raised.   However, with many substances, the two temperatures are very close to each other and to the freezing point, so that practically no supercooling is possible or necessary.

According to Tammann[148] the maximum rate of crystallization is found when the temperature (T) of the melt is:

[148] G. Tammann, Kristallisieren und Schmelzen, Barth, Leipzig, 1903, pp. 131 et seq.; Z. physik. Chem., 81, 171 (1913).
[149] J. Frenkel, J. Phys. (U. S. S. R.), 1, 315 (1939); C. A., 34, 7711 (1940).
[150] J. Frenkel, Physik. Z. Sowjetunion, 1, 498 (1932); C. A., 26, 5480 (1932).
[151] M. Volmer and M. Marder, Z. physik. Chem., A154, 97 (1931). P. Mondain-Monval, Ann. chim., [11], 3, 5 (1935).
[152] G. Tammann and E. Jenckel, Z. anorg. allgem. Chem., 193, 76 (1930).
[153] G. Rumeau, Compt. rend., 193, 1085 (1931).

$$T = T_0 - q_0/c_m \tag{16}$$

where T_0 is the melting point, q_0 the heat of crystallization, and c_m the mean specific heat. The heat of crystallization raises the temperature of the liquid at the interface above the melting point, and the shape of the curve relating linear velocity of crystallization to degree of supercooling therefore depends largely on the rate of heat loss from the system. As the degree of supercooling is increased, the heat evolution becomes less important. In the range of constant velocity of crystallization, heat is lost just fast enough to keep the interface at the temperature of the melting point, but, at lower temperatures, the temperature of the interface is below the freezing point. In other words, near the melting point the velocity is mainly determined[154] by the rate at which heat crosses the interface separating solid from liquid; the velocity increases linearly as the temperature difference between solid and liquid is increased.[155] It has been pointed out[156] that Tammann's assumption —that the melting-point temperature prevails at the crystal surface during crystallization of undercooled melts in tubes—is only an approximation, and that the interface does not achieve uniform temperature.[157] Modifications of Tammann's theory have been suggested,[158] and have been verified by direct measurements on phenyl salicylate.[159]

Though measurement of the "linear" velocity of crystallization may have some practical value as a measure of relative crystallizability from melts, its precise physical meaning is rather obscure. Velocities of growth at a certain crystal face have been studied microscopically[160] and the results cast some doubt on certain of Tammann's interpretations. It appears that his curve depicting variation of linear velocity of crystallization with temperature is a resultant or composite of several effects. These include such factors as the energy of motion of molecules which collide with the crystal face and then rebound or become attached, and the effect of viscosity, particularly where the supercooling is great. It is claimed[161] that, if there is a relatively large linear velocity of growth of the nuclei, and growth is one-dimensional, the transformation velocity per unit volume of the initial phase is proportional to the time; in two-dimensional growth, it is proportional to the

[154] G. Tammann, *Z. physik. Chem.*, **68**, 257 (1910).

[155] J. H. Walton, Jr., and R. C. Judd, *J. Phys. Chem.*, **18**, 722 (1914). M. Volmer and M. Marder, *Z. physik. Chem.*, **A154**, 97 (1931).

[156] G. Masing, *Wiss. Veröffentl. Siemens-Konzern*, **8**, 144 (1929); *C. A.*, **24**, 2366 (1930).

[157] T. Förster, *Z. physik. Chem.*, **A175**, 177 (1936).

[158] W. Reinders, *Rec. trav. chim.*, **51**, 589 (1932). F. von Göler and G. Sachs, *Z. Physik*, **77**, 281 (1932). R. Kaishev and I. N. Stranski, *Z. physik. Chem.*, **A170**, 295 (1934). N. N. Afanas'ev, *Zhur. Tekh. Fiz.*, **7**, 2305 (1937); *C. A.*, **34**, 6153 (1940).

[159] H. Pollatschek, *Z. physik. Chem.*, **A142**, 289 (1929). *Cf.* A. N. Campbell and E. J. Pritchard, *Can. J. Research*, **B25**, 183 (1947).

[160] R. Nacken, *Centr. Mineral. Geol.*, **1917**, 191; *C. A.*, **11**, 3170 (1917); *Neues Jahrb. Mineral. Geol.*, **II**, 133 (1915); *C. A.*, **10**, 1616 (1916). W. McCrone, A. Smedal, and V. Gilpin, *Ind. Eng. Chem., Anal. Ed.*, **18**, 578 (1946). V. Gilpin, W. McCrone, A. Smedal, and H. Grant, *J. Am. Chem. Soc.*, **70**, 208 (1948).

[161] N. N. Sirota, *Compt. rend. acad. sci. U. R. S. S.*, **36**, 175 (1942); *C. A.*, **37**, 2644 (1943).

square of the time; in three-dimensional growth, to the cube of the time.   The change in linear velocity of crystallization on increasing the pressure to 1000 kg. per square centimeter has been determined[162] for a number of organic compounds.

D. CRYSTALLIZATION FROM SOLUTION

The same principles hold for crystallization from solution; but here, the point of reference for a given composition of solution, at any constant pressure, is the saturation temperature, at which the rate of homogeneous, three-dimensional nucleus formation is zero.   The *crystallization potential*[163] for any given solute and solvent

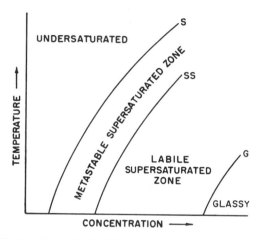

Fig. 11. Typical solubility and supersolubility curves.

depends on the degree of supersaturation; if C is the concentration of solute and C_{sat} its solubility at the given temperature, the crystallization potential is C/C_{sat}. Solutions, *e.g.*, of sucrose,[164] in sealed tubes may often be supercooled to a certain degree without the formation of crystals, but crystals appear suddenly[165] at a lower temperature (see Fig. 11).   The rate range over which homogeneous three-dimensional nucleation is negligible, but in which an introduced self-nucleus or a particle of heterogeneous nucleator will grow, has been called the "metastable zone." That rate range in which homogeneous three-dimensional nucleation is appreciable

[162] M. Hasselblatt, *Z. anorg. allgem. Chem.*, **119**, 325 (1921).

[163] W. E. Gibbs, *Trans. Inst. Chem. Engrs. London*, **8**, 38 (1930).

[164] G. Fouquet, *Compt. rend.*, **150**, 280 (1910).

[165] H. A. Miers and F. Isaac, *J. Chem. Soc.*, **89**, 413 (1906); **93**, 927 (1908); *Proc Roy. Soc. London*, **A79**, 322 (1907).   F. Isaac, *J. Chem. Soc.*, **93**, 384 (1908); *Proc. Roy. Soc. London*, **A88**, 205 (1913).   H. A. Miers, *J. Inst. Metals*, **37**, 331 (1927).   *Cf.* H Hartley and N. G. Thomas, *J. Chem. Soc.*, **89**, 1016 (1906).   H. Hartley, B. M. Jones, and G. A. Hutchinson, *ibid.*, **93**, 825 (1908).   J. Amsler and P. Scherrer, *Helv. Phys. Acta*, **14**, 318 (1941).   J. Amsler, *ibid.*, **15**, 699 (1942).   W. Ostwald, *Outlines of General Chemistry*, translation by W. W. Taylor, Macmillan, London, 1912, p. 101.

has been called the "labile zone." The extreme case, involving rapid formation of a very large number of minute crystals, is known as *"precipitation."*

In Figure 11, S is the *solubility curve*, a segment of the phase diagram (see Sect. II.9); and the boundary line, SS, between the two fields of supersaturation is termed the *supersolubility curve*. The distance between S and SS has been considered to be characteristic of the solute and influenced by the solvent. According to Young,[166] reproducible results are obtained only under constant shaking conditions. Sufficient mechanical shock may narrow or eliminate the metastable zone, and, given sufficient time, crystallization will often occur even at slight supersaturation without mechanical shock. A number of factors influence both rate ranges, including the viscosity and the types and amounts of impurities both dissolved and undissolved. Small proportions of certain additives greatly extend the metastable zone, and more supercooling is necessary to cause crystallization in solutions after ultrafiltration has removed dust particles and, perhaps, minute crystal nuclei. Even without special pretreatment, solutions may pass into the labile zone, on cooling, without ready occurrence of crystallization; but nucleus formation may often be induced by shaking or stirring. The supersolubility curve is therefore not a sharp boundary, but, rather, a zone in which nucleus formation increases rapidly with decrease in temperature; it describes a rate phenomenon. If the corresponding rates of three-dimensional nucleation are plotted against the temperature, a curve of the type shown in Figure 9 is obtained. The number of crystals obtained from a supersaturated solution, free from heterogeneous nucleator, in a given time thus depends on the relative rates of homogeneous three-dimensional nucleation and of growth.

Rate of Three-Dimensional Nucleus Formation. The rate of formation of crystal nuclei in supersaturated solutions has been measured, using a photoelectric cell[167] to reveal the nuclei. At constant temperature, the rate is proportional to the degree of supersaturation of the solution. As with melts, the rate, *e.g.*, in an aqueous lactose solution,[168] increases as undercooling is increased, to attain a maximum[169] beyond which further cooling diminishes nucleus formation, presumably because a still isotropic solution is obtained in which crystallization is practically impossible because of high viscosity. It has been claimed[170] that the rate of nucleus formation may be increased by lowering the surface tension or increasing the association of the solvent.

Rate of Crystal Growth. As with melts,[171] the temperature ideal for formation of crystal nuclei is not necessarily the best for their subsequent growth from solution. At low supersaturation, the rate of growth from a given solution is proportional to the square of the supersaturation; but, at high supersaturation, the diffusion barrier is the controlling factor, and the growth rate is proportional to the

[166] S. W. Young, *J. Am. Chem. Soc.*, **33**, 148 (1911). *Cf.* F. Serowy, *Chem. Fabrik*, **13**, [15], 257 (1940).

[167] J. Stauff, *Z. physik. Chem.*, **A187**, 107 (1940).

[168] B. L. Herrington, *J. Dairy Sci.*, **17**, 501 (1934).

[169] J. Amsler, *Helv. Phys. Acta*, **15**, 699 (1942).

[170] P. P. von Weimarn, *Z. Chem. Ind. Kolloide*, **2**, 76 (1907); *C. A.*, **3**, 393 (1909).

[171] W. Rawitzer, *Z. anorg. allgem. Chem.*, **175**, 321 (1928).

degree of supersaturation. There are two general methods for following crystallization from solution[172]: by measuring the decrease in concentration[173] of the mother liquor, while a large number of seed crystals are growing in it, or by determining the increase in size of a single crystal[174] suspended in the supersaturated solution. Much argument has centered around the question of the extent to which crystallization from supersaturated solution may be regarded as kinetically the reverse of dissolution. Berthoud[175] was probably the first to realize that the concentration of the solution at the surface of the growing crystal may be different from that in the main body of the solution. It was demonstrated[169,176] that a sheath of lesser concentration actually surrounds growing crystals. The supersaturation is not the same at all faces of the crystal if the solution is still; stirring the solution minimizes this effect. It has been postulated[177] that *dissolution* occurs by diffusion of solute from a film of saturated solution, surrounding the crystals, into the solvent, and that the dissolution rate is a function of the difference in concentration and of the diffusion constant. On the premise, reasonable at first glance but probably unjustifiable, that the process of crystallization from a solution involves the reverse mechanism, it was believed[177] that the rate of crystallization[178] is determined by the rate at which solute diffuses from the solution to the surface of the growing crystal, where the concentration in the absence of agitation is supposedly that of the saturated solution. Reaction at the interface was held to be much more rapid than the rate of diffusion, and resistance to diffusion was supposedly confined to a thin film surrounding the crystal. On this view, it was held that the velocity of crystallization (V) should fit the formula for a unimolecular mechanism. Applying Fick's law that the rate of diffusion is proportional to the concentration gradient:

$$V = -dC/dt = k(C - C_{sat}) \qquad (17)$$

where C is concentration at time t, C_{sat} is concentration of the saturated solution, and k is a constant; this was found true experimentally.[178,179] It was claimed[180] that both the velocity of dissolution and of growth from supersaturated solution can be represented by the equation:

$$V' = kA(C - J) \qquad (18)$$

where V' is rate of dissolution or deposition of substance; C is concentration of

[172] H. Schwerdtfeger, *Chem. App.*, **16**, 45, 82 (1929); *C. A.*, **23**, 3384 (1929).

[173] E. O. Whittier and S. P. Gould, *Ind. Eng. Chem.*, **23**, 670 (1931).

[174] I. A. Kukharenko, *Planter Sugar Mfr.*, **80**, 361 (1928); **81**, 2 (1928).

[175] A. Berthoud, *Bull. soc. neuchatel. sci. nat.*, **33**, 122: *C. A.*, **2**, 2202 (1908); *J. chim. phys.*, **10**, 624 (1912). G. Friedel, *Bull. soc. franç. minéral.*, **50**, 464 (1927); *C. A.*, **24**, 765 (1930).

[176] J. Amsler and P. Scherrer, *Helv. Phys. Acta*, **14**, 318 (1941).

[177] A. A. Noyes and W. R. Whitney, *Z. physik. Chem.*, **23**, 689 (1897). W. Nernst, *ibid.*, **47**, 52 (1904). E. Brunner, *ibid.*, **47**, 56 (1904).

[178] A. A. Noyes and W. R. Whitney, *J. Am. Chem. Soc.*, **19**, 930 (1897).

[179] L. Bruner and S. Tolloczko, *Z. physik. Chem.*, **35**, 283 (1900); *Z. anorg. Chem.*, **28**, 314 (1901); **35**, 23 (1903); **37**, 455 (1903).

[180] I. I. Andreev, *J. Russ. Phys.-Chem. Soc.*, **40**, 397 (1909); *C. A.*, **3**, 982 (1909).

supersaturated or unsaturated solution, respectively; k is a constant which depends on the velocity of diffusion; A is area of the crystal; and J varies with the crystallographic form.

Nernst's general theory[177] for heterogeneous reactions was applied[181] to the crystallization process. According to this, the velocity of crystallization at any moment is given by:

$$V = DA(C - C_{sat})/F \qquad (19)$$

where D is diffusion coefficient, and F is effective film thickness. *The Berthoud-Valeton theory*[182] supposes that the process of diffusion is followed by a first-order interfacial reaction and that the rate of crystallization depends on both reactions. The rate of deposition of material is given by:

$$dW/dt = kA(C_s - C_{sat}) = DA(C - C_s)/F =$$
$$A(C - C_{sat})(1/k + F/D)^{-1} \qquad (20)$$

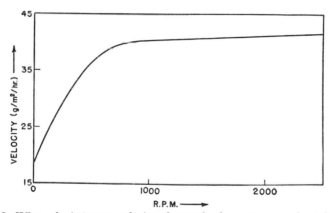

Fig. 12. Effect of stirring on velocity of growth of sucrose crystals at 30 °C.[187]

where W is weight, k is reaction constant of the interfacial reaction, and C_s is concentration of solution at the crystal surface. If k is very large compared to D, this equation is identical with that of Noyes and Whitney,[177] which has been given[183] in the form:

$$dC/dt = k'A(C_{sat} - C) \qquad (21)$$

and which resembles equation (17).

[181] P. P. von Weimarn, *Grundzüge der Dispersoidchemie*, Steinkopff, Dresden, 1911; *Zur Lehre von dem Zuständen der Materie*, Steinkopff, Dresden, 1914; *Kolloides und kristalloides Loesen und Niederschlagen*, Steinkopff, Dresden, 1925; *Chem. Revs.*, **2**, 217 (1925).

[182] A. Berthoud, *J. chim. phys.*, **10**, 625 (1912). J. J. P. Valeton, *Z. Krist.*, **59**, 335 (1924); **60**, 1 (1924).

[183] J. D. Jenkins, *J. Am. Chem. Soc.*, **47**, 903 (1925).

This expresses the observed facts that the process is dependent on the degree of supersaturation of the solution, and on the crystal surface area exposed for growth. The crystallization of naphthalene from a mechanically stirred solution in methanol at 0°C. conforms to this equation. The diffusion theory has been extended.[184]

However, diffusion is not the controlling factor in crystallization from solution, chiefly for the following reasons: (a) Some crystal faces grow faster than others[185] whereas they all dissolve at about the same speed. (b) The rate of crystallization becomes independent[186] of agitation at high rates[187, 188] of stirring (Fig. 12). Certain experiments[189] suggest that, as agitation is increased, the velocity of crystallization increases until mechanical attrition becomes appreciable. It was considered that a crystal "attracts" only those molecules in the solution which are in its immediate neighborhood, and the mechanical agitation counteracts exhaustion of these layers, resulting in improvement in rate and control of crystallization.[190] (c) Large molecules, e.g., colloids,[191] may, like dyes, retard or inhibit crystallization but have little or no effect[186] on the dissolution process; materials adsorbed[192] by the crystal can reduce the crystallization rate enormously. (d) Though it is true that the more viscous the solution, the more slowly will the solute crystallize,[193] addition of a substance which increases the viscosity does not necessarily decrease the rate of crystallization,[194] and vice versa. Moreover, it has been thought that a growing crystal is surrounded by an adsorbed layer which furnishes the particles for deposition and which is replenished from the supersaturated solution.[195] If the rate[196] at which the particles are oriented and built into the lattice is

[184] G. H. de Vries, Chem. Weekblad, 43, 83 (1947). F. H. C. Barkhuysen, ibid., 43, 234 (1947).

[185] G. Wulff, Z. Kryst. Mineral., 34, 511 (1901). R. Marc, Z. Elektrochem., 15, 679 (1909); Z. physik. Chem., 67, 470 (1909); 75, 710 (1911); 79, 71 (1912).

[186] R. Marc, Z. physik. Chem., 61, 385 (1908); 73, 685 (1910). R. Marc and W. Wenk, ibid., 68, 104 (1910).

[187] A. H. Van Hook, Ind. Eng. Chem., 37, 782 (1945).

[188] Cf. A. W. Hixson, ibid., 36, 488 (1944). R. Marc, Z. Electrochem., 15, 679 (1909); Z. physik. Chem., 67, 470, 640 (1909). B. G. Savinov, Nauch. Zapiski Sakharnoï Prom., 7, 416 (1929); C. A., 23, 3825 (1929).

[189] L. Wulff, Z. Kryst. Mineral., 11, 120 (1886); Z. Rubenzuckerind., 917 (1887); 226 (1888); 1076 (1890); Ger. Pats. 33,190 (1884); 39,957 (1885); 41,347 (1886); 95,183 (1896); B. Block, Chem. App., 12, 133 (1925).

[190] K. Kieper, Chem. App., 15, 185 (1928).

[191] W. G. France, Colloid Symposium Monograph, 3, 317 (1925).

[192] R. Marc, Z. Electrochem., 15, 679 (1909); Z. physik. Chem., 75, 710 (1911); 79, 71 (1912).

[193] J. D. Jenkins, J. Am. Chem. Soc., 47, 903 (1925). H. Cassel and E. Landt, Z. Ver. deut. Zucker-Ind., 77, 483 (1927); C. A., 22, 178 (1928). A. N. Campbell and A. J. R. Campbell, Trans. Faraday Soc, 33, 299 (1937).

[194] A. Van Hook, Ind. Eng. Chem., 37, 782 (1945).

[195] E. N. Gapon, Ukrain. Khem. Zhur., 4, Sci. pt., 161 (1929); C. A., 25, 5339 (1931). P. M. Silin, Bull. assoc. chim., 52, 265 (1935); C. A., 29, 3869 (1935). I. A. Kukharenko and I. N. Kaganov, Nauk. Zapiski Tzukrovoï Prom., 9, 492 (1930); C. A., 25, 1700 (1931). Cf. E. N. Gapon, J. Russ. Phys.-Chem. Soc., 61, 2319 (1929); C. A., 24, 5204 (1930).

high, the over-all rate is determined by the rate of replenishment,[197] which depends on diffusion.   However, in other cases, *e.g.*, sucrose,[198] the rate of orientation and building into the lattice controls[199] the rate of crystallization.[200]

If k_0 and a are constants, T is absolute temperature, η is viscosity in centipoises, and S is supersaturation $-$ 1, the rate of crystallization, V, is given[197] by:

$$V = k_0 T[S + 0.5a - \sqrt{a(S + 0.25a)}]/\eta^{2.5} \tag{22}$$

The *temperature* of crystallization from solution affects the rate of crystallization as with melts; the rate of crystallization of lactose from unagitated, supersaturated solution varies[201] with various degrees of supercooling and passes through a maximum at about 30°C.   It must be borne in mind that, in such cases as the crystallization of mutarotating sugars, the rate at which equilibrium among the isomeric forms is established may be the rate-controlling factor.   Later, the rate falls off considerably.   The temperature coefficient of the rate of crystallization of some solutions is governed[202] by the change in viscosity of the solution with temperature.   Crystallization involves heat exchange.[203]   Consequently, the temperature of the solution in immediate contact with the growing crystal may vary, resulting in an effect on the rate of growth.   Adequate stirring tends to minimize this effect.

Most workers find the process of crystallization to be of the first order.   It appears that the order may vary with the temperature.   Thus, in some solutions, the velocity at about 0° is often approximately proportional to the square of the supersaturation, but at 25° it appears to increase with the concentration.   In some cases, the order (O) of the process is given[204] by:

$$O = p/q \tag{23}$$

where p and q are characteristics of the compound in solution and in the crystal-unit cell, respectively.   It has been stated[204] that the crystallization velocity constant has a negative, or nearly zero, temperature coefficient.

The unimolecular velocity constant (k) in the Noyes-Whitney equation is given[205,206] by:

$$k = DA/FY \tag{24}$$

[196] R. Marc, *Z. Elektrochem.*, **15**, 679 (1909); *Z. physik. Chem.*, **67**, 470, 640 (1909).

[197] P. M. Silin, *Bull. assoc. chim.*, **52**, 265 (1935); *C. A.*, **29**, 3869 (1935).

[198] M. I. Nakhmanovich and I. F. Zelikman, *Nauch. Zapiski Sakharnoĭ Prom.*, **6**, 109 (1928); *C. A.*, **23**, 2593 (1929).

[199] A. N. Campbell and A. J. R. Campbell, *Trans. Faraday Soc.*, **33**, 299 (1937).

[200] W. Rawitzer, *Z. anorg. allgem. Chem.*, **175**, 321 (1928).   E. N. Gapon, *Ukrain. Khem. Zhur.*, **4**, 505 (1929); *C. A.*, **24**, 5583 (1930).

[201] B. L. Herrington, *J. Dairy Sci.*, **17**, 501 (1934).

[202] J. D. Jenkins, *J. Am. Chem. Soc.*, **47**, 903 (1925).

[203] G. Friedel, *Bull. soc. franç. minéral.*, **48**, 12 (1925); **49**, 87 (1926); *C. A.*, **20**, 1547 (1926); *C. A.*, **24**, 764 (1930).

[204] G. Birstein and M. Blumenthal, *Bull. intern. acad. polon. sci., Classe sci. math. nat.*, **1937A**, 399; *C. A.*, **32**, 1169 (1938).

[205] A. Van Hook, *Ind. Eng. Chem.*, **36**, 1042 (1944).   A. Van Hook and D. Shields, *ibid.*, **36**, 1048 (1944).

[206] A. Van Hook, *Ind. Eng. Chem.*, **37**, 782 (1945).

where Y is volume of the solution.   When A and Y are kept constant and the concentration is increased, the values of D increase and those of k decrease, for pure sucrose solutions.[206]   This means that the effective film thickness, F, should diminish as the concentration is increased, which is the opposite of what might be expected.   Hence, doubt is cast on the Noyes-Whitney equation as applied to sucrose.

More attention has been devoted to the study of the rate of crystallization of sucrose than to that of any other organic compound.   Its unidimensional and three-dimensional rates of crystallization have been ascertained.[207]   It has been shown[205,206] that the rate of growth of the crystals is proportional to the difference between the equilibrium activity at the temperature of crystallization and the thermodynamic activity of the dissolved sucrose.   The rate is usually decreased, but is sometimes increased, by presence of electrolytes and other cosolutes.   The results suggest[208] that the main factor controlling the rate of growth is a surface mechanism, not the diffusion of solute from the main solution to the crystal surface.

Independent of their initial size, all geometrically similar crystals of the same substance suspended in the same solution grow at the same rate.[209]   In measuring the rate of growth of sucrose from solution,[210] it has been assumed that:

$$dW/dt = uA \tag{25}$$

where W is average weight of a crystal during the crystallization, A is surface of the crystal, t is time, and u is a characteristic of the solution, dependent on temperature, concentration, purity, etc.   It has also been stated that the velocity of crystallization of sucrose from supersaturated solution is given[211] by:

$$V = 10^3 \cdot dW/At \tag{26}$$

Another formula derived[212] is:

$$V = kA \cdot G^2/G_0 \tag{27}$$

where G is coefficient of supersaturation at time t, and G_0 is initial coefficient of supersaturation.

A method for calculating the velocity of crystallization[213] has been developed[214];

[207] E. H. Hungerford, *Proc. Am. Soc. Sugar Beet Technol.*, **3**, 499 (1942); *Intern. Sugar J.*, **46**, 323 (1944).

[208] A. Van Hook, *Ind. Eng. Chem.*, **38**, 50 (1946); **40**, 85 (1948).   *Proc. Am. Soc. Sugar Beet Technol.*, **4**, 559 (1946).

[209] W. L. McCabe, *Ind. Eng. Chem.*, **21**, 30, 112 (1929).

[210] G. J. F. Breedveld and H. I. Waterman, *Rec. trav. chim.*, **51**, 239 (1932).

[211] I. A. Kukharenko, *III Congr. intern. tech. et chim. ind. agr.* (Paris), **1934**, 38 pp.; *Facts about Sugar*, **30**, 34 (1935); *C. A.*, **30**, 4037 (1936).

[212] K. Smoleński and A. Żelazny, *Gaz. Cukrownicza*, **74**, 303 (1934); *C. A.*, **28**, 5700 (1934).

[213] E. O. Whittier and S. P. Gould, *Ind. Eng. Chem.*, **23**, 670 (1931).   H. I. Waterman and A. J. Gentil, *Chem. Weekblad*, **23**, 345 (1926).   P. J. H. van Ginneken, *ibid.*, **16**, 1210 (1919).

[214] S. Odén and D. Werner, *Arkiv. Kemi, Mineral. Geol.*, **9**, No. 32 (1926); *C.A.*, **21**, 520 (1927).

the kinetics of the formation and growth of crystals, and the role of supersaturation have been considered mathematically[215]; and a complicated formula for the rate of crystallization has been derived.[216]   The equation describing the rate of growth of crystal nuclei is analogous[217] to that for the condensation of liquid from vapor, except that a viscosity factor must be included.

It is important to keep in mind that nucleus formation and crystal growth may be slow processes, and that their rates depend on the factors considered above.   The relation to the development, size, and number of crystals will be discussed in subsequent sections.   If the rate of separation from solution or vapor exceeds the rate of orientation and nucleus formation, amorphous precipitates will result, but slow separation with high tendency for orientation favors[218] the development of distinct crystals.

3. Mathematical Distribution of Crystal Sizes

Since embryos and nuclei, both three-dimensional and two-dimensional, originate statistically, crystallization in the labile zone is a cumulative statistical process.   Thus, crystal growth, in this zone, will normally result in a collection of crystals having a distribution of sizes that can be represented as a size–frequency curve in which the relative frequency of occurrence (a number) is plotted against the size in which they occur.   Moreover, the resulting distribution is an integral of the velocity of crystallization. However, since the largest crystals, in the tail of the frequency curve, must have been formed and started growing first, it is obvious that the rate of crystal formation is an inverse function of the derivative of the size–frequency curve.[219]   It will be noted that the equations for the rate of crystallization (Sect. II.2.Eq. 13) contain the area of the surface as a parameter, $i.e.$, the rate is proportional to the size at each moment.   A biologist[219] showed that, if that is true, the resulting size–frequency curve is of a form that can be derived as a logarithmic transformation of the Gauss law of errors.   It was then shown[220] that this is the law that applies to the size distribution of a crystalline precipitate.   It is an inherently skew distribution with a range from zero (or some small size, s_0) to infinity, thus differing from the so-called "normal" Gaussian distribution, which is

[215] S. Z. Roginskiĭ, $Trans. Faraday Soc.$, 34, 959 (1938).

[216] I. N. Stranski and R. Kaishev, $Annuaire univ. Sofia. II. Fac. phys.-math.$, Livre 2, 32, 171 (1936); $C. A.$, 31, 3365 (1937); $Uspekhi Fiz. Nauk$, 21, 408 (1939); $C. A.$, 34, 1232 (1940); see also S. Z. Roginskiĭ, $Zhur. Fiz. Khim.$, 13, 1040 (1939); $C. A.$, 34, 4632 (1940).

[217] M. L. Chepelevetskiĭ, $Zhur. Fiz. Khim.$, 13, 561 (1939); $C. A.$, 34, 1540 (1940).

[218] F. Haber, $Ber.$, 55, 1717 (1922).

[219] J. C. Kapteyn and M. J. van Uven, $Skew Frequency Curves in Biology and Statistics$, Hoitsema, Gröningen, 1916.   M. J. van Uven, $Proc. Koninkl. Ned. Akad. Wetenschap. Amsterdam$, 19, 533 (1916).

[220] R. P. Loveland and A. P. H. Trivelli, $J. Franklin Inst.$, 204, 193, 377 (1927).

symmetrical and has negative values of the variate s. This law has since been found to have very wide application and has become known as the *logarithmiconormal law* represented by the formula:

$$y = (A/s) \exp \{ -k(\log s - a)^2 \} \, ds \tag{28}$$

Here y represents the frequency, or number of crystals of each successive size, and s represents the size as measured by any appropriate attribute such as diameter, area, or weight. This unique and important property of the formula follows because it has been shown[220] that only the parameters k and a need be affected when $s = ct^n$ is substituted, and this is the only operation involved in a change of the size attribute that is measured. It has since been stated[221] that, if the crystallization results from seeding and without independent formation of nuclei, *i.e.*, in the metastable zone, the normal type of distribution may result.

In the labile zone of crystal formation, the size distribution can rarely be accurately expressed by the simple lognormal formula (28) since it is made up of several seemingly independent portions, each requiring different parameters. It has been suggested[222] that the rate of crystallization changes during the formation of the distribution. This change in rate is assumed to be caused by crystal formation on successive types of nuclei because, at each break of crystallization rate, the rate becomes lower. If the change of rate were due to the exhaustion of a material that had been adsorbing on the advancing crystal faces, the rate should increase, whereas the most efficient type of crystallization nuclei would be used and exhausted first. The analysis of particle sizes, in both homogeneous[223] and heterogeneous[224] populations, performed algebraically after appropriate study of the relevant log-probability graphs, revealed that different crystals may grow at different rates throughout the growth period, which explains the apparent discontinuity mentioned above.

It is well known that, when a crystalline precipitate is kept in its saturated solution at a constant temperature, *i.e.*, under conditions that allow so-called Ostwald ripening, the size–frequency curve, as usually plotted, changes to show growth of large crystals at the expense of small ones. However, when the distribution is plotted on log-log paper, the resulting curve is an invariant form[220] that is unchanged in shape by the ripening

[221] S. Z. Roginskiĭ and O. M. Todes, *Compt. rend. acad. sci. U. R. S. S.*, **27**, 677 (1940); *C. A.*, **35**, 1296 (1941); *Izvest. Akad. Nauk S. S. S. R.*, *Otdel. Khim. Nauk*, **1940**, No. 3, 331; *C. A.*, **35**, 5010 (1941).

[222] R. P. Loveland and A. P. H. Trivelli, *J. Phys. & Colloid Chem.*, **51**, 1004 (1947).

[223] F. Kottler, *J. Franklin Inst.*, **250**, 339, 419 (1950); **251**, 499, 617 (1951).

[224] F. Kottler, *J. Phys. Chem.*, **56**, 442 (1952).

process.   Moreover, the effects of the ripening on the average size, $\bar{s}$, of the crystals, and on the total number, N, of crystals, are expressed by:

$$\bar{s} = cu^m \tag{29}$$

$$N = c'u^{m'} \tag{30}$$

where c, c', m, and m' are constants, and u may represent time, temperature, or the degree of solvent action.   Thus, after determination of the constants, the crystal growth can be calculated.

On the other hand, other assumptions were apparently verified[225] when potassium chloride and copper sulfate crystals were grown from seeds in the metastable zone—namely, that all nucleus crystals which are geometrically similar grow at the same rate in each linear dimension regardless of their original size, and that no new nuclei are formed.   The seed crystals and also the crystals obtained when the latter were suspended in a cooled, saturated solution were analyzed for size by sieving.   Over 97% of the seed crystals were held by sieves with 0.3-mm. diameter holes.   Here, all of the crystals grew so that the integral size–frequency curve (ogive) was shifted parallel to itself and all crystals increased, statistically, by an equal increment.   A nomograph is available[226] which aids in the prediction of crystal size under such circumstances, through trial-and-error solution of the integral for crystal growth.

4. Crystal Habit

If the environment of a growing crystal affects its external shape without changing its internal structure, a different habit results.   Such alteration is caused by interference with the uniform approach of crystallizand units to faces of the crystal.   Unsymmetrical surroundings include proximity to the container walls, as in a tube or between two plates, proximity to another crystal, and a supersaturation difference on opposite sides of the crystal.   Variations in other conditions of growth[227] may cause variation[228] in crystal habit.   Such variables include the degree of supersaturation of the mother liquor, the rate of cooling, the degree of agitation of the solution, the size and number of crystals used as nuclei, the presence of impurities, the pressure, the nature of the solvent, and the constancy of conditions. Thus, if rapidly crystallized by rapid cooling, naphthalene gives thin plates from methanol or ethanol, and needles from cyclohexane, but if slowly

[225] W. L. McCabe, *Ind. Eng. Chem.*, **21**, 30, 112 (1929).

[226] I. J. Hooks and F. Kerze, Jr., *Chem. Met. Eng.*, **53**, No. 7, 140 (1946).

[227] Sir Robert Boyle, *Origin of Formes and Qualities*.   Oxford, 1666.

[228] R. Nacken, *Neues Jahrb. Mineral. Geol.*, **II**, 133 (1915); *C. A.*, **10**, 1616 (1916). U. R. Evans, *Chemistry & Industry*, **44**, 791, 812 (1925).   A. F. Wells, *Phil. Mag.*, **37**, 184, 217 (1946).

crystallized by evaporation, it gives compact crystals from either solvent. During recrystallization from any given solvent, the *degree of supersaturation* is the major factor[229] affecting the shape of the crystals and such factors as rate of cooling are effective because of their influence on the degree of supersaturation.   As supersaturation is increased, the crystal form tends to change from granular to needlelike.   A thin needle or dendrite will need to lose less heat by conduction than a thicker crystal, and so will grow faster.

The effect of supersaturation on the change in the external form is given[229] by a curve of high order which is characteristic of the substance, namely:

$$y/x = k\Delta G^n \tag{31}$$

where y/x is the ratio of length to breadth, k is a coefficient of proportionality which depends on the conditions of crystallization, especially on diffusion, G is degree of supersaturation, in moles per 1000 moles of solvent, at the moment of formation of the nuclei of crystallization, and n is a number, above unity, dependent on the crystallographic classification and chemical composition of the substance.

The form of a crystal grown from solution depends not only on the internal structure of the crystallizing compound but also on "the interaction between solute and *solvent.*"[230]   Changes in habit may often be produced and controlled by altering the solvent.   Resorcinol crystallizes from benzene in fine needles, but from butyl acetate in squat prisms; iodoform crystallizes as hexagonal bipyramids from aniline, and as prisms from cyclohexane.   During growth, solvated solvent has to be detached from the units being adsorbed by the crystal face; if the interaction between the units and the solvent is strong enough, a face may remain permanently solvated, so that its growth is entirely prevented.   If a crystal is grown slowly from a solution and then placed in a supersaturated solution in a different solvent from which it crystallizes in a different habit, it will now grow according to the habit induced by the second solvent.   An example is anthranilic acid grown first from ethanol and then from glacial acetic acid.[230]

Change in crystal habit may also be brought about[231] by variation in pH of the solution, and presence[227] of other *cosolutes or cosolvents* and adsorbable foreign ions, *e.g.*, dispersing agents and colloids.   Sodium chloride, usually cubic, is octahedral when grown in the presence of urea.[232]   Rapid growth may counteract the habit-varying influence of a cosolute.[233]   The

[229] J. Grzymek, *Przemysl Chem.*, **21**, 279 (1937); *C. A.*, **32**, 2802 (1938).

[230] A. F. Wells, *Phil. Mag.*, **37**, 184 (1946).

[231] H. B. Caldwell, *Chem. Met. Eng.*, **49**, No. 5, 116 (1942).

[232] J. B. L. de Romé de l'Isle, *Cristallographie*, 2nd ed., L'Imprimerie de Monsieur, Paris, I, 379 (1783).   A.-F., Compte de Fourcroy and L.-N. Vauquelin, *Ann. chim. phys.*, **32**, 130 (1799).

[233] F. S. Beudant, *Ann. mines*, **3**, 239, 289 (1818).

impurities affecting crystal shape may be regarded as stunting growth in certain directions, resulting in malformation. Both the amount and nature of the impurities are important. If the cosolute is strongly adsorbed[234] on certain faces, thus retarding surface nucleation and growth normal to them, these faces will become the most prominent. Adsorption at the "repeatable step" would produce the same result. For crystals having dislocations, a very small concentration of impurity adsorbed at the ledge, where the dislocation meets the crystal surface, would greatly affect the growth rate and result in habit modification. The crystal habit of many substances may be changed at will[235] by deliberate introduction of an appropriate cosolute, and there are well-defined structural relations[236] among such modifiers. Increasing use of this effect is being made in industrial practice, e.g., modification in habit of ammonium oxalate monohydrate by a variety of cations has been described.[237] Certain surfactants affect both crystal shape and size; some impurities so affect growth as to afford spherules.

The use of dyes[238] as cosolute revealed their adsorption[239] and, in some cases, the formation of solid solutions.[240] It was found[241] that dyes retard crystallization, but not dissolution. The effect of albumin and gelatin on the habit of uric acid and other compounds has been regarded[242] as physical, but changes in habit caused by selective adsorption at the various faces depend ultimately[243] on the chemical nature of the compounds involved and on the arrangement of the atoms[244] in the surface layers. According to Frondel,[238] this theory of growth and adsorption is largely at variance with observation and not valid for macroscopic crystals. Whereas submicroscopic crystals[245] are in equilibrium with their solution when their faces are those of minimum surface energy, with macroscopic crystals the differences in surface energy among different crystal faces are practically nil and have no influence on the habit development. A refutation of some of Frondel's objections are given

[234] W. G. France, *Colloid Symp. Monograph*, **7**, 59 (1930). P. P. Davis and W. G. France, *J. Phys. Chem.*, **40**, 81 (1936).

[235] J. J. P. Valeton, *Physik. Z.*, **21**, 606 (1920).

[236] L. Royer, *Compt. rend.*, **198**, 185 (1934).

[237] H. J. Kolb and J. J. Comer, *J. Am. Chem. Soc.*, **68**, 719 (1946).

[238] C. Frondel, *Am. Mineralogist*, **25**, 91 (1940).

[239] H. de Senarmont, *Ann. chim. et phys.*, [3], **41**, 319 (1854); *Compt. rend.*, **38**, 101 (1854).

[240] P. Gaubert, *Compt. rend.*, **142**, 219 (1906); **194**, 109 (1932).

[241] R. Marc *et al.*, *Z. physik. Chem.*, **61**, 385 (1908); **67**, 470, 640 (1909); **68**, 104 (1910); **73**, 685 (1910); **75**, 710 (1911); **76**, 58, 584 (1911); **79**, 71 (1912); **81**, 641 (1913).

[242] W. M. Ord, *On the Influence of Colloids upon Crystalline Form and Cohesion, With Observations on the Structure and Mode of Formation of Urinary and Other Calculi.* Stanford, London, 1879.

[243] I. Langmuir, *J. Am. Chem. Soc.*, **38**, 2221 (1916); *Phys. Rev.*, **6**, 79 (1915).

by France,[246] who concludes that adsorption of impurities by a growing crystal depends on "(a) the lattice structure of the host crystal; (b) the residual valency force fields; (c) the ionic structure of the crystal face; and (d) the presence, size, shape, position, and orientation of polar groups within the foreign molecule."

5. Impediments to Crystallization

As previously mentioned, nucleus formation and crystal growth are slowed down if the *viscosity* is high. Hence, it is often advantageous to dissolve a melt in, or to dilute a viscous solution with, a solvent of low viscosity, provided that the resulting solution will be supersaturated at the temperature chosen for crystallization.

Some *impurities* have little effect on the rate of nucleus formation and crystal growth; occasionally, we may even encounter an example in which impurities enhance crystallizability.[247] However, in many cases impurities will completely inhibit[248] nucleus formation, and greatly retard[249] the rate of growth. The maximum linear velocity of crystallization of benzil is reduced from 433 to 250 mm. per minute by the addition of 8% of benzophenone.

The relation between the velocity of crystallization and the concentration of some binary mixtures, *e.g.*, palmitic acid–stearic acid, has been studied.[250] There seems to be no simple relation between the effect of impurities and their influence on surface tension.[251] Von Pickardt developed[252] a formula for the diminution in velocity of crystallization of impure melts:

$$V - V_i = KC^{1/2} \tag{32}$$

[244] C. H. Saylor, *Colloid Symp. Monograph*, **5**, 49 (1928). P. A. Paine and W. G. France, *J. Phys. Chem.*, **39**, 425 (1935). M. D. Rigterink and W. G. France, *ibid.*, **42**, 1079 (1938). W. G. France and K. M. Wolfe, *ibid.*, **45**, 395 (1941). H. E. Buckley, *Mem. Proc. Manchester Lit. Phil. Soc.*, **83**, 31 (1938–1939). A. F. Wells, *Phil. Mag.*, **37**, 217 (1946).

[245] J. W. Gibbs, *Scientific Papers*. Vol. I, Longmans, Green, New York, 1906, pp. 321, 325.

[246] W. G. France, "Adsorption and Crystal Habit Modification," in J. Alexander, ed., *Colloid Chemistry*. Vol. 5, Reinhold, New York, 1944, pp. 443–457.

[247] G. Tammann, *The States of Aggregation*, translation by R. F. Mehl, Van Nostrand, New York, 1925, pp. 220–251. R. Marc, *Z. Elektrochem.*, **15**, 679 (1909).

[248] J. Michel, *Bull. soc. chim. Belg.*, **48**, 105 (1939). W. McCrone, A. Smedal, and V. Gilpin, *Ind. Eng. Chem., Anal. Ed.*, **18**, 578 (1946). V. Gilpin, W. McCrone, A. Smedal, and H. Grant, *J. Am. Chem. Soc.*, **70**, 208 (1948).

[249] M. Padoa and L. Mervini, *Atti accad. nazl. Lincei*, **18**, 58 (1909); *Gazz. chim. ital.*, **41**, 198 (1911). H. Freundlich, *Kapillarchemie*, 2nd ed., Akadem. Verlagsgesellschaft, Leipzig, 1922, pp. 457–466.

[250] W. Rawitzer, *Z. anorg. allgem. Chem.*. **175**, 321 (1928).

[251] R. Marc, *Z. Elektrochem.*, **15**, 679 (1909).

[252] E. von Pickardt, *Z. physik. Chem.*, **42**, 17 (1903).

where V and V_i are the crystallization velocities of the pure and impure melts, respectively, C is the concentration of dissolved impurity, and K is a constant. It was thought that the retardation is the same for equimolecular quantities of various impurities and that its measurement would be of value for the determination of molecular weights; but this holds[253] for only a few cases and the impurity exerts a specific effect depending on the relative nature of the material and the contaminant, *viz.*, on whether the latter dissolves in,[254] is adsorbed by,[255] or forms a compound with, the substance to be crystallized. Formation of solid solutions is seldom inimical to crystallization. However, an impurity may retard crystallization by "increasing the solubility" of the main solute, thus reducing the yield, and an attempt to increase the supersaturation by lowering the temperature may give too high a viscosity.

If stable adsorption complexes,[256] particularly with colloids, form on the crystal surfaces, these will interfere[257] with the orientation of the solute at such surfaces. The inhibiting effect of lyophilic colloids,[258] *e.g.*, of a small quantity of gelatin,[259] is well known. Even in the presence of crystals of the main solute, the crystallization of highly supersaturated solutions can often be greatly retarded by small amounts of a third substance.[260] Thus, a trace of collodion has a pronounced adverse effect on the rate of crystallization of naphthalene from methanol.[261] In some cases,[262] the more powerful the dyeing power of the impurity, *i.e.*, its adsorption on the crystal surface, the greater its retarding effect. On the assumption that adsorbed impurities diminish the concentration of the adsorbed layer of the crystallizand (see Sect. II.2), Freundlich[263] changed the exponent in von Pickardt's formula to $1/n$, where n depends on the crystallizand and the impurity.

The effect of such inorganic salts[264] as calcium chloride,[265] which strongly inhibit

[253] M. Padoa and D. Galeati, *Gazz. chim. ital.*, **35**, 181 (1905). F. Dreyer, *Z. physik. Chem.*, **48**, 467 (1904). G. Tammann, *ibid.*, **81**, 171 (1913). J. H. Walton, Jr., and A. Brann, *J. Am. Chem. Soc.*, **38**, 317, 1161 (1916). A. Brann, *ibid.*, **40**, 1168 (1918).

[254] M. Padoa, *Atti accad. nazl. Lincei*, **13**, 329 (1904). H. Freundlich, *Z. physik. Chem.*, **75**, 245 (1911). M. Hasselblatt, *ibid.*, **73**, 1 (1913).

[255] H. Freundlich and F. Oppenheimer, *Ber.*, **58**, 143 (1925).

[256] R. Marc, *Z. physik. Chem.*, **61**, 385 (1908); **67**, 470 (1909); **68**, 104 (1910); **73**, 685 (1910); **75**, 710 (1911).

[257] S. Kúthy, *Kolloid-Z.*, **68**, 335 (1934).

[258] H. Freundlich, *Colloid and Capillary Chemistry*. Translation by H. S. Hatfield, Methuen, London, 1926, p. 596.

[259] W. G. France, *Colloid Symposium Monograph*, **3**, 317 (1925).

[260] E. Cohen and A. L. T. Moesveld, *Z. physik. Chem.*, **94**, 482 (1920). M. Faye and R. A. Hagberg, *Chem. Inds.*, **50**, 358 (1942). S. E. Coalstad, *J. Soc. Chem. Ind. London*, **65**, 206 (1946). I. N. Kaganov and B. E. Krasilshchikov, *Nauch. Zapiski Sakharnoĭ Prom.*, **6**, 344 (1928); *C. A.*, **23**, 3825 (1929).

[261] J. D. Jenkins, *J. Am. Chem. Soc.*, **47**, 903 (1925).

[262] R. Marc, *Z. physik. Chem.*, **73**, 685 (1910).

[263] H. Freundlich, *Z. physik. Chem.*, **75**, 245 (1911).

[264] M. Amagasa and K. Nishizawa, *J. Soc. Chem. Ind., Japan*, **39**, Suppl. binding, 387 (1936).

[265] I. A. Kukharenko and A. K. Kartashev, *Nauch. Zapiski Gosudarst. Ekspll. Inst. Sakharnoĭ Prom.*, **4**, 369 (1927); *C. A.*, **21**, 3282 (1927).

crystallization of certain sugars, may be due[266] to compound formation in the solution rather than on the crystal surface. The rate of crystallization of sucrose from water at a given supersaturation is greatly affected by nonsugars.[267] The effect of mpurities is expressed approximately[268] by the equation:

$$\log (V_i/V) = kC \qquad (33)$$

where k = a constant and C = concentration of impurity in terms of molality. Sucrose containing 5% of impurity crystallizes[269] from solution about one-half as fast, and containing 10% of impurity about one-ninth as fast, as pure sucrose. Even a *small* increase in purity may *greatly* accelerate the rate of formation and raise the yield of crystals; thus, pure sucrose was found[270] to crystallize fifteen times faster than a 72%-pure sample; the latter crystallized *twice* as fast as a 70%-pure sample. The depressant action of betaine[268] on the velocity of crystallization of sucrose from aqueous solution, at pH 8 and 30°C., is shown in Figure 13.

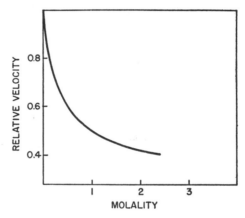

Fig. 13. Effect of betaine on velocity of crystallization of sucrose.[268]

Foreign materials in a solution often modify the crystal habit (see Sect. II.4) of the crystallizand through their effect on the rate of growth of individual faces. This effect has been used in order to change habit or modification, or to *restrain* or entirely inhibit crystallization, if the impur-

[266] B. L. Herrington, *J. Dairy Sci.*, **17**, 805 (1934). O. Wiklund, *Socker Handl.*, **2**, 65 (1946); *C. A.*, **40**, 5940 (1946).

[267] M. I. Nakhmanovich and I. F. Zelikman, *Nauch. Zapiski Sakharnoĭ Prom.*, **6**, 109 (1928); *C. A.*, **23**, 2593 (1929).

[268] A. Van Hook, *Ind. Eng. Chem.*, **38**, 50 (1946).

[269] K. Smoleński and A. Żelazny, *Gaz. Cukrownicza*, **74**, 303 (1934); *C. A.*, **28**, 5700 (1934).

[270] A. R. Nees and E. H. Hungerford, *Ind. Eng. Chem.*, **28**, 893 (1936).

ity is strongly adsorbed by all the surfaces.   Thus, the addition[271] of 1%
or more of the pour-point depressant Paraflow, a condensation product of
highly chlorinated paraffin wax and naphthalene, inhibits the crystallization of paraffin wax, e.g., in lubricating oils; if crystals *do* form, their shape
is changed from needles to small, almost equidimensional grains of approximately uniform size.   On the other hand, a foreign material strongly
adsorbed but present at extremely low concentration may become imbedded in a crystal face, thus distorting the lattice, introducing dislocations,
and speeding crystal growth at that face.

6. Polymorphism

When the *same* compound is capable of forming crystals of *different*
structures, usually indicated by different melting points, the phenomenon is
known as *polymorphism*.   Many thousands of organic compounds, including most long-chain aliphatic substances,[272] may occur in two or more different modifications having different physical properties.[273]   In such
cases,[274] the temperature and the solvent chosen for crystallization and

[271] G. H. B. Davis, U. S. Pat. 2,062,354 (Dec. 1, 1936); *Natl. Petroleum News*, **24**,
No. 52, 32 (1932).   H. Bennett, *Commercial Waxes, Natural and Synthetic*, Chemical
Publ. Co., Brooklyn, 1944, p. 50.

[272] G. M. de Boer, *Nature*, **119**, 634 (1927).   S. H. Piper, *Trans. Faraday Soc.*, **25**,
348 (1929).   *Cf.* T. F. W. Barth, *Am. J. Sci.*, **27**, 273 (1934).   M. J. Buerger, *Proc.
Natl. Acad. Sci., U. S.*, **22**, 682, 685 (1936).   M. J. Buerger and M. C. Bloom, *Z. Krist.*,
96, 182 (1937).   J. W. H. Oldham and A. R. Ubbelohde, *Proc. Roy. Soc. London*, **A176**,
50 (1940).   T. Malkin *et al.*, *J. Chem. Soc.*, **1934**, 666; **1936**, 1628; **1937**, 1409; **1939**,
103, 577, 1141.   E. S. Lutton, *J. Am. Chem. Soc.*, **67**, 524 (1945); **73**, 5595 (1951); *J.
Am. Oil Chemists' Soc.*, **27**, 276 (1950).   B. F. Daubert *et al.*, *J. Am. Chem. Soc.*, **66**,
690, 997, 1333 (1944); **67**, 1256, 2085 (1945); **68**, 167 (1946); *Oil & Soap*, **22**, 113
(1945).   M. J. Buerger, *Am. Mineralogist*, **30**, 551 (1945).   K. W. Gardiner, M. J. Buerger,
and L. B. Smith, *J. Phys. Chem.*, **49**, 417 (1945).   M. J. Buerger, L. B. Smith, F. V,
Ryer, and J. E. Spike, Jr., *Proc. Natl. Acad. Sci., U. S.*, **31**, 226 (1945).   J. C. Smith.
Ann. Repts. Progress Chem. (Chem. Soc. London), **35**, 256 (1939).   J. Timmermans and
L. Deffet, "Le Polymorphisme des Composés Organiques," Vol. 42, *Memorial des Sciences Physiques*, Gauthier-Villars, Paris, 1939.   A. E. Bailey, *Melting and Solidification
of Fats*, Interscience, New York-London, 1950.   E. S. Lutton *et al.*, *J. Am. Chem. Soc.*,
72, 4519 (1950); **73**, 4280, 5593 (1951); **74**, 4827 (1952).   C. P. Smyth *et al.*, *ibid.*, **60**,
1229 (1938); **71**, 431 (1949).

[273] E. E. Jelley, "Microscopy," Chapter XV, and E. L. Skau and H. Wakeham, "Determination of Melting and Freezing Temperatures," Chapter III, in A. Weissberger,
ed., *Technique of Organic Chemistry*.   Vol. I, 2nd ed., Interscience, New York-London,
1949.

[274] W. Ostwald, *Z. physik. Chem.*, **22**, 289 (1897).   N. V. Sidgwick, *J. Chem. Soc.*, **107**,
672 (1915).   A. R. Ubbelohde, *Trans. Faraday Soc.*, **33**, 1203 (1937).   *Ann. Repts.
Progress Chem.* (Chem. Soc. London), **37**, 170 (1941).

the rate of cooling may determine which polymorph is obtained.[275] Enantiotropic polymorphs interchange reversibly at a definite transition temperature at which they are in equilibrium; monotropic polymorphs do not. Most aliphatic, polymorphic compounds are monotropic, but dodecylammonium chloride[276] is enantiotropic, though its mono-, di-, and tri-N-methyl derivatives are monotropic. Compounds whose molecules are approximately spherical and have orientational freedom when supercooled are likely to exhibit polymorphism.[277]

The modification crystallizing from solution is sometimes determined[278] by the crystal form of the nucleating crystals. In some cases,[279] the crystal form of the surface on which crystallization takes place determines which modification is deposited. It was shown[280] that allocinnamic acid is polymorphic since the transformation from any one of its three modifications to another occurs, from the melt, only when the *existing* nuclei are destroyed by melting and nuclei of another modification are introduced. The same behavior was demonstrated[281] after removal of nuclei by careful filtration of the supercooled melt. Each polymorph of a substance has a different temperature[282] of spontaneous crystallization when mixed with a non-polymorphic substance. Tammann[283] considered that the relative ease of spontaneous nucleus formation of the metastable and stable modifications largely determines which will separate on supercooling.

[275] N. V. Tantzov, *J. Russ. Phys.-Chem. Soc.*, **55**, 342 (1924); **58**, 947 (1926); **61**, 41 (1929); *C. A.*, **19**, 2437 (1925); **21**, 2093 (1927); **23**, 3847 (1929). M. Volmer and A. Weber, *Z. physik Chem.*, **119**, 277 (1926). M. Volmer, *Z. Elektrochem.*, **35**, 555 (1929). L. Farkas, *Z. physik. Chem.*, **125**, 236 (1927). E. P. Volochneva, *J. Russ. Phys.-Chem. Soc.*, **62**, 77 (1930); *C. A.*, **24**, 4679 (1930). I. N. Stranski and D. Totomanow, *Naturwissenschaften*, **20**, 905 (1932); *Z. physik. Chem.*, **A163**, 399 (1933).

[276] F. K. Broome and H. J. Harwood, *J. Am. Chem. Soc.*, **72**, 3257 (1950). F. K. Broome, C. W. Hoerr, and H. J. Harwood, *ibid.*, **73**, 3350 (1951). C. W. Hoerr and H. J. Harwood, *ibid.*, **74**, 4290 (1952).

[277] K. K. Kelley, *J. Am. Chem. Soc.*, **51**, 1400 (1929). A. H. White and S. O. Morgan, *ibid.*, **57**, 2078 (1935). O. Hassel and A. M. Sommerfeldt, *Z. physik. Chem.*, **B40**, 391 (1938). A. van de Vloed, *Bull. soc. chim. Belg.*, **48**, 229 (1939). W. O. Baker and C. P. Smyth, *J. Am. Chem. Soc.*, **61**, 2798 (1939). A. H. White and W. S. Bishop, *ibid.*, **62**, 8 (1940). A. Turkevich and C. P. Smyth, *ibid.*, **62**, 2468 (1940). W. P. Conner and C. P. Smyth, *ibid.*, **63**, 3424 (1941). L. M. Kushner, R. W. Crowe, and C. P. Smyth, *ibid.*, **72**, 1091 (1950). R. W. Crowe and C. P. Smyth, *ibid.*, **72**, 4009 (1950); **73**, 5406 (1951).

[278] A. Serra, *Atti soc. toscana sci. nat. Pisa, Mem. Processi verbali*, **41**, 115 (1932); *C. A.*, **29**, 4987 (1935).

[279] K. Lark-Horovitz and S. E. Madigan, *Phys. Rev.*, **44**, 320 (1933). R. Pheasant, *J. Am. Chem. Soc.*, **72**, 4303 (1950).

[280] E. Biilmann and A. Klit, *Kgl. Danske Videnskab. Selskab, Mat.-fys. Medd.*, **12**, No. 4, 51 pp. (1932); *C. A.*, **27**, 4150 (1933).

[281] J. Meyer and W. Pfaff, *Z. anorg. allgem. Chem.*, **222**, 382 (1935).

[282] H. A. Miers and F. Isaac, *Proc. Roy. Soc. London*, **A82**, 184 (1909).

Sometimes a compound will crystallize in different modifications from different solvents; and often either modification can be transformed to the other by recrystallization from the proper solvent.   The effect of various solvents on the crystal modification is largely determined[284] by the dielectric properties of the solvent; in general, nonpolar solvents promote crystallization of the modification of higher melting point, whereas highly polar solvents tend to stabilize the other.[285]   If the velocity of transformation of the unstable to the stable is very small, the two modifications may crystallize together[286] from solution at an appropriate temperature.   It is therefore *extremely important* to make sure that any sample whose physical constants are to be measured is a single modification and not a *mixture* of polymorphs.[287]   Different solvents have different effects on the velocity of transformation.[288]   The velocity of transformation is increased by increase in temperature, and is greatly affected by certain kinds of impurities.[285,289]   Certain additives, *e.g.*, some surfactants, prevent deposition of the unstable modification.

Polymorphic transformations occurring *after* the isolation of a crystalline compound may be misleading or troublesome.   Thus, if enantiotropic crystals are separated at a temperature above the transition point, they may crumble to a powder of different melting point on being stored; also, the volume changes accompanying polymorphic transformation on storage may have undesirable effects.

For a compound which melts, stable polymorphs have different melting points, whereas crystals exhibiting different habits have the *same* melting point.   Normal paraffins having a chain of 25 to 38 carbon atoms undergo a polymorphic transition between the melting point and room temperature, and so can be crystallized as needles or as plates, formerly thought to be different habits; those with more than 38 carbon atoms undergo no transition[290] and give platelets.   If the compound does not melt, care must be taken to ensure that differences ascribed to polymorphism are not actually differences of crystal *habit*.   For example, two crystalline forms

[283] G. Tammann, *Z. physik. Chem.*, 25, 441 (1898).

[284] S. S. Urazovskiĭ, *Sbornik Trudov "I. V. Stalinu, Akad. Nauk Ukrain. S. S. R.,"* 1940, 465; *C. A.*, 37, 5634 (1943).

[285] P. L. Du Brow, C. W. Hoerr, and H. J. Harwood, *J. Am. Chem. Soc.*, 74, 2241 (1952).

[286] G. Tammann, *Z. physik. Chem.*, 69, 569 (1909).

[287] E. J. Cohen, *Physico-chemical Metamorphosis and Some Problems in Piezo-chemistry.*   McGraw-Hill, New York, 1926.

[288] J. H. Kastle and J. V. Reed, *Am. Chem. J.*, 27, 209 (1902).

[289] A. W. Ralston, *Fatty Acids and Their Derivatives.*   Wiley, New York, 1948, pp. 332–333.

[290] B. J. Fontana, *J. Phys. Chem.*, 57, 222 (1953).

of insulin were long thought to be polymorphs. The needle- or wedge-shaped variety was obtained[291] on crystallization from acetate buffers at pH 5.2. The more common form, consisting of flat rhombohedra,[292] was isolated from phosphate buffers at pH 6.2. X-ray study reveals[293] that the two types are *not* polymorphs but represent different habits. Although identity of x-ray powder diagrams of two samples constitutes positive evidence of their chemical identity, difference in diagrams may be ascribable to different polymorphs[294] of the same compound. Consequently, both samples should be isolated under identical conditions, *e.g.*, by recrystallization from the same solvent at the same temperature, prior to such comparison. Other methods for distinguishing between polymorphs include light microscopy,[295] electron microscopy and electron diffraction,[296] infrared spectroscopy,[297] and dilatometry.[298]

7. Molecular Structure and Crystallizability

The crystallizability of a pure compound depends on the *shape* and *size* of its molecules or ions and on the magnitude and kind of lattice forces. Thus, the type of substituent attached to a fundamental molecular skeleton can greatly influence the crystallizability. For example, certain sugars and their polymethyl ethers are very difficult to crystallize, but their polytosyl esters often crystallize with great ease. The presence of high, permanent dipole moments appears to favor crystallization. As a rule, the supercooled melt of a compound of fairly high molecular weight will, if kept quiet and free from dust, produce few nuclei, but a molten substance of low molecular weight, cooled rapidly and stirred vigorously, will give many nuclei. It was thought that "the greater the molecular weight of a compound, the greater is the difficulty of obtaining the compound in the form of crystals," and that "simple molecules will arrange themselves more readily than will heavier and more complex ones."[299] Although these statements apply to the majority of cases, it must be kept in mind that rather complicated vitamins, enzymes, hormones, viruses, bacterial toxins, anti-

[291] D. A. Scott, *Trans. Roy. Soc. Can.,* V, **26,** 275 (1932).

[292] J. J. Abel, *Proc. Natl. Acad. Sci., U. S.,* **12,** 132 (1926).

[293] D. Crowfoot, *Nature,* **140,** 149 (1937).

[294] G. Susich, *Anal. Chem.,* **22,** 425 (1950).

[295] L. Kofler, A. Kofler, and M. Brandstätter, *Mikro-Thermo-Methoden zur Kennzeichnung organischer Stoffe und Stoffgemische,* 3rd ed. Verlag Chemie, Weinheim, 1954.

[296] F. A. Hamm and E. Van Norman, *J. Applied Phys.,* **19,** 1097 (1948).

[297] D. N. Kendall, *Anal. Chem.,* **25,** 382 (1953). R. J. C. Harris, S. F. D. Orr, E. M. F. Roe, and J. F. Thomas, *J. Chem. Soc.,* **1953,** 489.

[298] W. Tan, T. A. Krieger, and J. G. Miller, *J. Am. Chem. Soc.,* **74,** 6181 (1952).

[299] D. W. MacArdle, *The Use of Solvents in Synthetic Organic Chemistry.* Van Nostrand, New York, 1925, p. 144.

biotics, and many other substances of high molecular weight[300] have been crystallized, but some relatively simple substances have not.

A relation between the structure of certain organic compounds (phenyl salicylate, benzophenone, o-chloronitrobenzene, and toluidine) and their ability to undergo supercooling has been suggested.[301]   The first two permit strong supercooling and the liquid and solid phases exhibit very different angles and periods in x-ray photographs.   The latter two display more similar x-ray pictures for solid and liquid, and they can be undercooled only slightly.

TABLE II

EFFECT OF STRUCTURE ON MAXIMUM LINEAR VELOCITY OF CRYSTALLIZATION[a]

Compound	M.p., °C.	Undercooling, °C.	Max. velocity, mm./min.
p-Dichlorobenzene........	52.9	20–35	25,000
o-Dichlorobenzene........	−17.6	19–36	2200
m-Dichlorobenzene........	−24.8	21–28	700
p-Dihydroxybenzene.	169	35–47	6300
o-Dihydroxybenzene......	104	29–59	1700
m-Dihydroxybenzene......	116	37–74	400
2-Naphthol..........	122	53	6000
1-Naphthol.............	96	44	275
2-Iodonaphthalene........	54	7	300
1-Iodonaphthalene........	4.2	11–16	1

[a] M. E. Krahl, J. Am. Chem. Soc., 54, 1256 (1932);   55, 1425 (1933).

There may be a relation[302] between the ability of supercooled melts to crystallize spontaneously and the velocity of linear crystallization. Under ideal conditions, each substance apparently has its own maximum growth rate, and, as a rule, highly soluble compounds have a high maximum rate. In general, the more symmetrical the molecule, the greater its velocity of crystallization from a melt.   Thus it is often observed that p-substituted derivatives of benzene crystallize faster than the less symmetrical o-isomers and that these crystallize faster than the m-derivatives.   The maximum linear velocities of crystallization (in millimeters per minute) of some 34 compounds of this type have been determined[303] (see Table II).   It was found that the rate of crystallization of the supercooled melt largely de-

[300] R. O. Herzog and K. Becker, Z. physiol. Chem., 112, 231 (1921).

[301] V. I. Danilov and M. A. Levashevich, Zhur. Eksptl. i Teoret. Fiz., 10, 814 (1940); C. A., 35, 5368 (1941).

[302] W. Rawitzer, Z. anorg. allgem. Chem., 175, 321 (1928).

[303] M. E. Krahl, J. Am. Chem. Soc., 54, 1256 (1932); 55, 1425 (1933).   Cf. J. Michel, Bull. soc. chim. Belg., 48, 105 (1939).

pends on the degree of symmetry of the molecule. Spherical molecules generally have a high crystallizability,[304] whereas long molecules crystallize with difficulty. Organic solids have been subdivided[305] into classes according to their relationship to their melts. *Subcrystalline* solids are supercooled melts which do not normally crystallize, *e.g.*, resins, lacquers, and glasses.[306] *Supercrystalline* solids are those, *e.g.*, starch, cellulose, and proteins, that, on heating, decompose instead of melting.

In order to investigate the relationship between the shape of the molecule and the symmetry of the crystal lattice, the readily vitrified isobutyl and isoamyl bromides, whose molecules are pear-shaped and therefore intermediate between the almost spherical *tert*-butyl halides and the rodlike long-chain compounds, have been studied.[307] It was found that such moderately unsymmetrical molecules can, with economical use of the volume, pack randomly in the liquid, thus permitting extensive undercooling. On the other hand, in the long-chain compounds, the molecules may be arranged in crystal-like groups in the liquid, so that the melts cannot be supercooled much but crystallize at or just below the melting point without forming glasses. The almost spherical, very symmetrical molecules usually cannot be supercooled; the liquid may be considered to consist of spheres, packed in an orderly manner, which require little or no rearrangement to give the crystal lattice on cooling. Molecules whose symmetry lies between the pear-shaped and the rodlike seldom give true glasses, but the degree of supercooling to which they will submit before crystallizing depends on their shape. However, it must be kept in mind that in the liquid the molecules of many compounds exist in different shapes, only one of which is that occurring in the crystal; this phenomenon may greatly lessen the crystallizability of a compound.

8. Isomorphism; Ability to Form Solid Solutions

Two compounds are *isomorphous*[308] if their crystals have "a similar arrangement of geometrically similar structural units."[309] The crystals generally have similar face developments and approximate equality of

[304] H. J. Backer, *Chem. Weekblad*, **37**, 79 (1941).

[305] D. Vorländer, *Naturwissenschaften*, **24**, 113 (1936).

[306] C. E. Hollis, *Oil Colour Trades J.*, **101**, 588 (1942).

[307] W. O. Baker and C. P. Smyth, *J. Am. Chem. Soc.*, **61**, 2063 (1939).

[308] E. Mitscherlich, *Ann. chim. phys.*, **14**, 172 (1820); **19**, 350 (1822).

[309] A. F. Wells, "Crystals," in R. E. Kirk and D. F. Othmer, eds., *Encyclopedia of Chemical Technology*. Vol. IV, Interscience Encyclopedia, New York, 1949, p. 644.

interfacial angles, and often form oriented overgrowths (see Sect. II.1.C) or solid solutions[310] with each other. In a *solid solution*,[311] some of the building units (ions or molecules) of one compound have been replaced by units of the other compound. This occurs if the units: (*a*) are similar chemically, and (*b*) have approximately the same size or unit-cell dimensions. Hence, two isomorphs can fail to give solid solutions if the sizes are sufficiently different; and formation of solid solutions is no proof of isomorphism. Units of one kind may often be replaced by those of another kind to a limited extent, even though the second compound by itself crystallizes with a different structure. Thus, miscibility may be complete or partial. For complete miscibility, close metrical correspondence of the structures is necessary. Many organic compounds form solid solutions.[312]

If a *continuous series* of solid solutions exists over the whole range of composition, no eutectic conglomerate (see Sect. II.9.A) will be formed. The proportion of the two compounds in the solid solution usually differs from, but depends on, the proportion in the parent liquid. The physical constants of solid solutions change with the composition. Just as with certain pairs of liquids, there may be a *limited range* of mutual solubility—in this case, of one solid in the other. That is to say, two compounds may give two crystallographically different solid solutions containing different proportions of the two components. It has been found that the degree of miscibility depends on such factors as similarity in molecular volumes, shapes, and external fields of the two substances. Sometimes, the proportions of the two constituents may be determined from the unit-cell dimensions of the solid solution by applying Vegard's law[313] that, in solid solutions, the cell dimensions vary linearly with the concentration of the "solute." The x-ray powder diagram of a solid solution containing a small proportion of one component may differ only slightly from that of the pure main component, as regards intensity or spacings of lines.

[310] M. J. Buerger, *Am. Mineralogist*, **19**, 53 (1934); *Proc. Natl. Acad. Sci., U. S.*, **20**, 444 (1934); **22**, 685 (1936). J. R. Partington, *An Advanced Treatise on Physical Chemistry*, Vol. III, Longmans, Green, New York, 1952, pp. 114–141.

[311] J. H. van't Hoff, *Z. physik. Chem.*, **5**, 322 (1890).

[312] F. Garelli, *Gazz. chim. ital.*, **23**, ii, 354 (1893). F. Garelli and C. Montanari, *ibid.*, **24**, ii, 229 (1894). A. Ferratini and F. Garelli, *Z. physik. Chem.*, **13**, 1 (1894). G. Bruni, *Chem. Revs.*, **1**, 345 (1925). J. Timmermans, *Bull. soc. chim. Belg.*, **36**, 179 (1937). A. D. Vinogradova and N. N. Efremov, *Ann. secteur. anal. phys. chim., Inst. chim. gén.* (U. S. S. R.), **14**, 211 (1941); *C. A.*, **40**, 2725 (1946). U. Croatto, *Chimica e industria* (Milan), **26**, 1 (1944). A. Neuhaus, *Die Chemie*, **57**, 33 (1944). J. Pirsch, *ibid.*, **57**, 40 (1944).

[313] L. Vegard, *Z. Physik*, **5**, 17 (1921).

9. Types and Behavior of Liquid Solutions

A. SYSTEMS GIVING EUTECTICS

Depending on the system,[314] the crystals separating, *e.g.*, on cooling, may be those of an essentially pure compound or of solid solutions.   In the former case, the mother liquor may, on further cooling, become super-

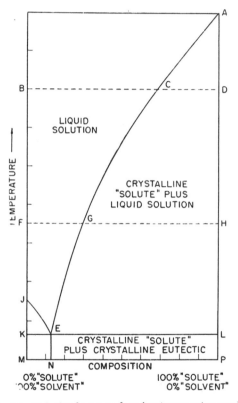

Fig. 14. Relation between freezing temperature and composition of mixtures of two components giving a eutectic only.

saturated with respect to a cosolute and this may also crystallize, forming a *eutectic conglomerate*. Although this has a definite melting point,[315]

[314] M. B. Thi, L. C. Strang, T. G. Hunter, and A. W. Nash, *J. Inst. Petroleum Technol.*, **23**, 226 (1937).

[315] E. L. Skau and H. Wakeham, in A. Weissberger, ed., *Technique of Organic Chemistry.* Vol. I, 2nd ed., Interscience, New York-London, 1949, Chapter III.

it consists of two kinds of crystals lying *side by side*. Its composition[315,316] does not bear a simple relation to the respective molecular weights of its constituents, except by chance, but it is characteristic of the system and identical with that of the solution from which it separates.

In crystallization and recrystallization from solution it is usually advantageous to choose the solvent so that (*a*) the melting point of the crystallizand is above the boiling point of the solution and (*b*) the freezing point of the solvent is far below the lower operating temperature. A typical *eutectogenic* system of this kind is depicted in Figure 14. The melting points of pure P and M are at A and J, respectively; the eutectic composition, N, and temperature, K, define E. If B is the boiling point of the solution, the concentration at C would be that of the saturated, boiling solution. If F represents room temperature, G gives the concentration of a saturated solution at room temperature. If A is below B, AE and JE record the depression in freezing point of P by M, and vice versa. *Section GC is the solubility curve of* P *between room temperature and the boiling point of a saturated solution*. On cooling a solution of any concentration between P and N from a temperature above ACGE, no crystals will separate until ACGE is reached; then, after crystallization has set in, P will separate from the solution until temperature K and composition N are reached; after that, the whole material will be a crystalline conglomerate of P plus M. The same applies to deposition of M and then eutectic, on the other branch of the diagram. The part of JE nearest J is used for cryometric molecular-weight determination. Except for arbitrary insertion of BCD and FGH, Figure 14 represents the naphthalene–benzene system.[317] The eutectic temperatures of the binary eutectics formed by a compound A with the individual members of a homologous series lie[318] on the freezing curve of A.[319]

A solution of two compounds A and B in a solvent S—compounds which do not form compounds, complexes, or solid solutions with one another— cooled to a temperature at which the system is *supersaturated with A but undersaturated with B*, and nucleated with crystalline A if necessary, deposits crystals of A until cooled to a lower temperature, at which A plus B separate, provided that nuclei of B are present. If we start with a solu-

[316] E. Kordes, *Z. anorg. allgem. Chem.*, **167**, 97 (1927).   A. E. Korvezee, P. Dingemans, and L. L. Dijkgraaf, *Rec. trav. chim.*, **66**, 383 (1947).

[317] E. W. Washburn and J. W. Read, *Proc. Natl. Acad. Sci. U. S.*, **1**, 191 (1915). H. L. Ward, *J. Phys. Chem.*, **30**, 1316 (1926); *International Critical Tables*, Vol. IV, McGraw-Hill, New York, 1928, p. 177.

[318] W. Swietoslawski, *Roczniki Chem.*, **23**, 1 (1949); *Metody rozdzielania i oczyszczania substancji*, Warsaw, 1950.

[319] T. Penkala, *Bull. intern. acad. polon. sci., Classe III*, **1**, 149 (1953). *Cf.* V. M. Kravchenko, *Zhur. Priklad. Khim.*, **22**, 491, 724 (1949).

tion containing A and B in the proportions of the eutectic composition, only this eutectic conglomerate will first crystallize on cooling. If the *solvent* crystallizes, two other binary eutectics, A with S, and B with S, and the ternary eutectic of A, B, and S, may result.[320] Cooling from a temperature at which S is saturated with neither A nor B, the order of crystallization will be: (*1*) any *one* component, if present in excess of its eutectic compositions, (*2*) any *one* binary eutectic composition, if present in excess of the ternary eutectic, and (*3*) the ternary eutectic. It might happen that, after deposition of the component in excess, the *ternary* eutectic would crystallize immediately, *without* intermediate deposition of one of the binary eutectics; this could occur when S is then present in exactly the right proportion relative to the proportions of A and B. A typical system which can give rise to three binary eutectic compositions and a ternary eutectic is a mixture of *m*-, *o*-, and *p*-xylene.[321]

On crystallizing a compound from solution by cooling or evaporation, the solution may become saturated with respect to other solutes, which separate as oil, gum, or amorphous solid and contaminate the crystals. Even prior to precipitation, such materials may be adsorbed on the growing crystals and be overgrown in further crystallization. Such contamination is common and may necessitate repeated recrystallization. Choice of a solvent which will retain impurities in solution is therefore important. The solvent should also provide a medium of sufficient fluidity that crystallization may proceed at a reasonable rate. Its melting point should be considerably lower than those of either compound A or B. The temperature and composition at which the eutectic of A and B will crystallize are given by the point of intersection of the solubility curves of A and B, respectively, in the solution of A and B in S.

If the percentage of cosolute is *high*, the amount of pure crystals obtained before cosolute starts to crystallize, as eutectic composition, may be small, and purification by other means prior to recrystallization may greatly increase the yield. Ready formation of crystals is not necessarily a criterion of purity; a binary eutectic conglomerate may crystallize with ease and no separation of the components will be achieved if their proportions in the solution are the same as in the eutectic. An illustration is found in the recrystallization of a mixture of *o*- and *m*-nitroaniline from carbon tetrachloride.[322] These form a binary eutectic[323] (m.p. 50°, composition 25.5% *m*-isomer), and, if we should happen to start with these substances mixed in the proportions of the eutectic composition, recrystallization from

[320] H. G. Deming, *J. Chem. Ed.*, **16**, 260 (1939).

[321] K. S. Pitzer and D. W. Scott, *J. Am. Chem. Soc.*, **65**, 803 (1943).

[322] R. D. Vold and M. J. Vold, in Vol. I of this series. 1st ed., p. 130.

[323] *International Critical Tables.* Vol. IV, McGraw-Hill, New York, 1928, p. 168.

carbon tetrachloride would not cause their separation, despite their great difference in *solubility* in carbon tetrachloride when *separately* dissolved in it.   Solubility is related to the respective melting points, and changing to a different solvent can have no effect on these, except as it affects association and hydrogen bonding, as with polar solvents.

The individual crystals of a eutectic conglomerate can sometimes be picked apart by hand.[324]   If they differ sufficiently in their specific gravities they may be separated by flotation.   When pentaerythritol and dipentaerythritol crystallize side by side, it will often be found that the crystals of the former are coated with very much smaller crystals of the latter, and that a fairly good mechanical separation may be achieved by scouring, rubbing, or kneading, followed by sifting or sedimentation,[325] to give coarse crystals of the *mono* compound.   Often, a better method[326] is to add a compound which forms solid solutions with one or both components of the eutectic.   Other separative methods are mentioned in Sect. III.1.   On occasion it may be possible to avoid deposition of eutectic conglomerate by nucleating with only one component, thus avoiding crystallization of the other (see Sect. IV.1.A).

Except for the last case, it has been generally assumed in the preceding paragraphs that the systems under discussion were in equilibrium.   However, owing to the manner in which solutions are often prepared for recrystallization, amounting to a process of extraction by hot or boiling solvent, the *percentage* of impurity present in the solution may not depend so much on the composition of the starting material as on the relative *rates* at which its various components dissolve.   If there is a considerable difference in these rates, a preliminary partial separation may be achieved by rapid treatment at a certain temperature with just sufficient solvent to dissolve all of the more readily soluble but as little as possible of the less readily soluble compound; the undissolved material is then filtered or centrifuged off.   In these cases, prolonged heating, until a less readily soluble impurity has been dissolved to saturation, is obviously inadvisable.   On cooling or evaporating, the filtrate will deposit the solutes according to their concentrations, *i.e.*, if the concentration of the more soluble compound is high enough, it will separate before the less-soluble component, until the eutectic composition is reached, when both compounds crystallize.

[324] L. Pasteur, *Ann. chim. et phys.*, [3], **24**, 442 (1848); [3], **28**, 56 (1850).   V. Dessaignes, *Bull. soc. chim. France*, **5**, 355 (1863).   E. Jungfleisch, *ibid.*, **18**, 201 (1872).   A. F. Holleman, *Rec. trav. chim.*, **17**, 66 (1898).

[325] Lonza-Werke Elektrochemische Fabriken, Ger. Pat. 706,617 (1941); *C. A.*, **36**, 1956 (1942); Brit. Pat. 535,399 (1942); *C. A.*, **36**, 1337 (1942).   *Cf.* J. A. Wyler, U. S. Pat. 2,270,839 (1942); *C. A.*, **36**, 3192 (1942).

[326] W. Swietoslawski and J. R. Anderson, U. S. Pat. 2,470,116 (May 17, 1949); *C. A.*, **43**, 5236 (1949).

B. SYSTEMS GIVING SOLID SOLUTIONS

If A and B do not form a compound with each other or with the solvent, if any, but form an *unbroken series of solid solutions*,[327] a separation will result if the composition of the crystals, with respect to A and B, differs from that of the liquid. This difference is represented by the horizontal distance between points a and b of equal temperature on the liquidus and

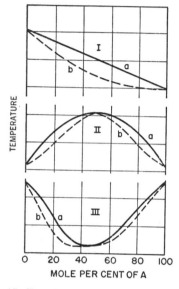

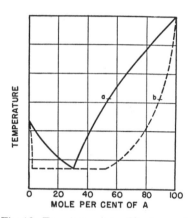

Fig. 15. Freezing points of three kinds of continuous series of solid solutions.

Fig. 16. Freezing points of broken series of solid solutions.

solidus curves of the phase diagram (see Fig. 15). The *only case* in which both A *and* B can be isolated in pure condition by repeated fractional recrystallization with or without a solvent is when the freezing point of any and every mixture of A and B *lies between their individual freezing points* (I, Fig. 15).

If there is a *maximum* in the phase diagram (II, Fig. 15), separation will end with the solid solution of maximum melting point and pure A, or pure B, depending upon the side of the maximum on which the initial composition lies. If the curve exhibits a *minimum* melting point, the separation may be carried to one or other of the pure solutes together with a liquid solution of the solid solution with the minimum melting point (III, Fig. 15).

[327] *Cf.* A. Findlay, A. N. Campbell, and N. O. Smith, *The Phase Rule and Its Applications*, 9th ed., Dover, New York, 1951, pp. 157–164. S. Glasstone, *Textbook of Physical Chemistry*, 2nd ed., Van Nostrand, New York, 1946, pp. 761–765.

If the *series of solid solutions is not continuous, i.e.,* if there are limited ranges of mutual solubility in the solid state, two types of crystals may be obtained, depending on the composition of the liquid.   The compositions of the final products of fractional recrystallization will depend upon whether the system displays a eutectic point[328] (see Fig. 16) or a transition point, and upon the side of the break on which the initial composition lies.   Temperature–concentration diagrams of various systems forming eutectics or solid solutions are discussed in Vol. I of this series.[328]

Separation of A and B by recrystallization is, of course, not possible if they form a stable compound or complex, or a dissociating compound less soluble in the solvent than A and B (see Sect. II.10).   Examples are: α-D-gulose[329] and calcium chloride ($C_6H_{12}O_6 \cdot CaCl_2 \cdot H_2O$); and p-nitrobenzoic acid and p-acetamidobenzoic acid.[330]

The binary mixtures formed by a compound with representatives of a homologous series show a gradual transition from ideal eutectics, through eutectics of solid solutions, to solid solutions having complete mutual solubility[331]; the eutectic points lie on one curve regardless of whether the solid phases are pure components or solid solutions.

It should be noted that phase diagrams and solubility curves refer to equilibrium conditions[332] and can be used for the calculation of yields only insofar as such conditions prevail.[333]   It was mentioned above that, in actual practice, this is often not the case.   Care must be taken regarding the way in which the data are presented in the literature (see Fig. 17).   Moreover, the solubility may be influenced by cosolutes.

As crystals grow, mother liquor may be included.   This source of contamination is usually greater with large crystals.   On the other hand, the same weight of very small crystals has a much larger surface and so may adsorb more impurity.   The best procedure is probably to strike a compromise between the two extremes of size.   However, more important than the absolute size of the crystals appears to be their relative size, and purification by recrystallization may be more efficient if the resulting crystals are of about the same size than if their dimensions vary over a wide range.   If the crystals are formed rapidly, the concentration of impurities in their immediate vicinity will be high, because of the withdrawal of the

[328] E. L. Skau and H. Wakeham, in A. Weissberger, ed., *Technique of Organic Chemistry.* Vol. I, 2nd ed., Interscience, New York-London, 1949, Chapter III, Section II.3.

[329] H. S. Isbell, *J. Research Natl. Bur. Standards,* **5,** 741 (1930).

[330] R. Cohn, *Z. physiol. Chem.,* **17,** 274 (1893).

[331] T. Penkala, *Bull. intern. acad. polon. sci., Classe III,* **1,** 151 (1953). *Cf.* W. F. Seyer, *J. Am. Chem. Soc.,* **60,** 827 (1938).

[332] H. L. Ward, *J. Chem. Ed.,* **7,** 2100 (1930).

[333] L. A. Dahl, *J. Phys. Chem.,* **50,** 96 (1946).

main solute, resulting in occlusion of impurity on the crystals. According to Schwab and Wichers,[334] the purest crystals will be obtained by nucleating a slightly supercooled solution and stirring it gently while maintaining a

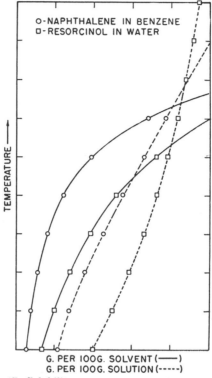

Fig. 17. Solubility curves, expressed in two ways.

low rate of cooling. The rejection of impurities during growth of a monocrystal may be extremely high[335] and this is the best way of purifying some substances (see Sect. IV.1.B), particularly if the procedure is repeated.[336]

10. Molecular Compounds and Inclusion Complexes

The crystals separating from a solution may consist of a pure component, a eutectic mixture (see Sect. II.9.A), or solid solutions (see Sect. II.9.B). Moreover, the crystals may be those of a molecular compound or of an

[334] F. W. Schwab and E. Wichers, *J. Research Natl. Bur. Standards*, **32,** 253 (1944).

[335] S. Zerfoss, L. R. Johnson, and P. H. Egli, *Discussions Faraday Soc.*, **5,** 166 (1949).

[336] W. Zimmerman, III, *Science*, **119,** 411 (1954).

inclusion complex.   Molecular compounds or inclusion complexes may contain two or more constituents; in both of them, different molecules, with completely satisfied, classical "valence forces," are deposited together as a single, new, crystalline entity.   Formation of a molecular compound or of an inclusion complex may be suspected if, by use of techniques already suggested, a eutectic mixture or a solid solution has been ruled out and yet the analytical data are inexplicable.   A nonintegral, molar ratio of constituents indicates an inclusion complex; a whole-number ratio obtains for molecular compounds and for some inclusion complexes.   In order to distinguish between the two possibilities an individual examination must be made.   Consequently, some incompletely studied "molecular compounds" may prove to be inclusion complexes.   Both types may be used in separating, identifying, or even quantitatively estimating appropriate organic compounds (see Sect. IV.1.A).

Molecular compounds[337] may be of two kinds.   In one group, van der Waals' forces are involved, as in the compounds formed by various electrophilic, polynitro compounds with aromatic hydrocarbons and their derivatives, *e.g.*, one molecule of 2,4,6-trinitrophenol (picric acid), 1,3,5-trinitrobenzene, 2,4,6-trinitroresorcinol (styphnic acid), or 2,4,7-trinitrofluorenone[338] with one, two, or sometimes more molecules of such mono-, di-, or polynuclear compounds as hexamethylbenzene, naphthalene, or phenanthrene.   Hexanitroethane gives similar molecular compounds.   Azulenes may be purified *via* their compounds[339] with 1,3,5-trinitrobenzene.   The presence of two or more nitro groups or analogs in one constituent and of an aromatic ring in the other appears[340] necessary for formation of a crystallizable compound, but the structure of each constituent can be varied considerably without preventing compound formation; steric factors are, however, important.[341]   The products, over 700 of which are

[337] P. Pfeiffer, *Organische Molekülverbindungen*, 2nd ed., Enke, Stuttgart, 1927; *Chem.-Ztg.*, **59**, 205 (1935).   G. Briegleb, *Zwischenmolekulare Kräfte und Molekülstruktur*, Enke, Stuttgart, 1937.

[338] M. Orchin and E. O. Woolfolk, *J. Am. Chem. Soc.*, **68**, 1727 (1946).   M. Orchin, L. Reggel, and E. O. Woolfolk, *ibid.*, **69**, 1225 (1947).   D. E. Laskowski, D. G. Grabar, and W. C. McCrone, *Anal. Chem.*, **25**, 1400 (1953).   D. E. Laskowski and W. C. McCrone, *ibid.*, **26**, 1497 (1954).

[339] T. Wagner-Jauregg and H. Hippchen, *Ber.*, **76**, 694 (1943).   A. Plattner, A. Fürst, and K. Jirasek, *Helv. Chim. Acta*, **29**, 730 (1946).

[340] T. Sinomiya, *Bull. Chem. Soc. Japan*, **15**, 92, 137, 259, 281 (1940).   I. Nitta, S. Seki, and H. Chihara, *J. Chem. Soc. Japan*, Pure Chem. Sect., **70**, 387 (1949).   I. Nitta, S. Seki, H. Chihara, and K. Suzuki, *Sci. Papers Osaka Univ.*, **29** (1951).   S. D. Ross, M. Bassin, M. Finkelstein, and W. A. Leach, *J. Am. Chem. Soc.*, **76**, 69 (1954).   S. D. Ross and I. Kuntz, *ibid.*, **76**, 74, 3000 (1954).   S. D. Ross, M. Bassin, and I. Kuntz, *ibid.*, **76**, 4176 (1954).

[341] M. Orchin, *J. Org. Chem.*, **16**, 1165 (1951).   B. Dale, R. Foster, and D. L. Hammick, *J. Chem. Soc.*, **1954**, 3986.

known, are usually sharp melting and highly colored; they dissociate in dilute solution. In these examples, an electrophilic compound unites with a compound having a large number of π electrons, giving[342] a "π-complex." Polarization occurs between the strongly polar, electron-poor nitro groups and the polarizable, electron-rich double bonds of the hydrocarbon involved; the nitro groups thus approach as closely as possible to the polarized double bonds, affording a compound, held together by polar forces,[343] which usually has a dipole moment less than that of the original dipolar molecule because the constituent molecules lie side by side. For the compound of carbon tetrabromide with[344] benzene, two molecules possessing no dipole moment, compound formation is attributed to reaction of the halogen atom with the π bonds of benzene, because carbon tetrabromide and carbon tetrachloride[345] do not give compounds with cyclohexane.

A molecular compound of the other class is formed by stoichiometric combination of an electron donor (Lewis base) with an appropriate electron acceptor (Lewis acid); actual protonation or charge transfer occurs, giving[346] a "σ-complex" having an intermolecular bond, as follows:

$$A + B \rightleftharpoons (AB) \leftrightarrow (A^- - B^+)$$

Many such molecular compounds have been listed[347]; they include the compounds formed by: (1) boron trifluoride with methylamine[348] ($CH_3\text{-}NH_2 \cdot BF_3$), acetonitrile[349] ($CH_3CN \cdot BF_3$), and trimethylamine[350] ($NMe_3 \cdot BF_3$); and (2) trimethylboron with[351] trimethylamine, ethylenimine, trimethylenimine, pyrrolidine, and piperidine. The compounds formed by the halides of aluminum and tin with many organic compounds are probably of the same type. The polynitro hydrocarbons give molecular compounds with phenols and aromatic amines; and phenols form molec-

[342] H. C. Brown and J. D. Brady, *J. Am. Chem. Soc.*, **74**, 350 (1952).

[343] D. L. Hammick, and R. B. M. Yule, *J. Chem. Soc.*, **1940**, 1539. W. S. Rapson, D. H. Saunder, and E. T. Stewart, *ibid.*, **1946**, 1110.

[344] A. F. Kapustinskiĭ and S. I. Drakin, *Izvest. Akad. Nauk S. S. S. R., Otdel. Khim. Nauk*, 233 (1950).

[345] J. Timmermans, *Bull. soc. chim. Belg.*, **37**, 409 (1928). M. S. Kennard and P. A. McCusker, *J. Am. Chem. Soc.*, **70**, 3375 (1948).

[346] H. C. Brown and J. D. Brady, *J. Am. Chem. Soc.*, **74**, 350 (1952).

[347] R. S. Mulliken, *J. Phys. Chem.*, **56**, 801 (1952); *J. Am. Chem. Soc.*, **72**, 600 (1950); **74**, 811 (1952); *J. Chem. Phys.*, **19**, 514 (1951). *Cf.* J. Weiss, *J. Chem. Soc.*, **1942**, 245; **1943**, 462. R. B. Woodward, *J. Am. Chem. Soc.*, **64**, 3058 (1942). K. Nakamoto, *ibid.*, **74**, 1739 (1952). W. Brackmann, *Rec. trav. chim.*, **68**, 147 (1949). L. J. Andrews, *Chem. Revs.*, **54**, 713 (1954).

[348] S. Geller and J. L. Hoard, *Acta Cryst.*, **3**, 121 (1950).

[349] J. L. Hoard, T. B. Owen, A. Buzzell, and O. N. Salmon, *Acta Cryst.*, **3**, 130 (1950).

[350] S. Geller and J. L. Hoard, *Acta Cryst.*, **4**, 399 (1951). J. L. Hoard, S. Geller, and T. B. Owen, *ibid.*, **4**, 405 (1951).

[351] H. C. Brown and M. Gerstein, *J. Am. Chem. Soc.*, **72**, 2923, 2926 (1950).

ular compounds with acridine, alkaloids, amines, and pyridine and quinoline derivatives.   Results with the rush-membrane osmometer show that
alcohols form molecular compounds with carboxylic acids[352] and with[353]
phenol, but not with *o*-nitrophenol because the latter has an intramolecular
hydrogen bond which prevents the phenolic hydrogen atom from bridging
to an alcoholic hydroxyl group.   Many other molecular compounds have
been[354] described.

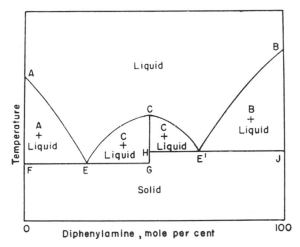

Fig. 18. Relation between freezing temperature and composition for a molecular
compound giving a eutectic with each of its constituents.[355]

If a molecular compound (A_nB) can exist as a stable solid in equilibrium
with liquid of the same composition it has a *congruent melting point*.   Should
the compound be eutectogenic with A, a phase diagram AEC resembling
Figure 14 results; if it also gives a eutectogenic system $CE'B$ with B,
another such phase diagram is obtained.   These may be placed side by
side, giving a diagram of the kind shown in Figure 18, where C, the melting
point of the compound, is the maximum lying between the eutectic points
E and E'.   Depending on the system, C may be higher or lower than A
or B, or than both.   If more than one molecular compound is formed be-

[352] A. Tkáč, *Chem. Listy*, **42**, 169 (1948).

[353] B. Stehlík, *Chem. Listy*, **42**, 171 (1948).

[354] S. Kuroyanagi, *J. Pharm. Soc. Japan*, **61**, 433 (1941).   E. Mueller, *Melliand Textil-
ber.*, **31**, 339 (1950).   R. Tsuchida, M. Kobayashi, and K. Nakamoto, *Nature*, **167**, 726
(1951).   A. W. Laubengayer and G. R. Finlay, *J. Am. Chem. Soc.*, **65**, 884 (1943).   A.
W. Laubengayer and W. C. Smith, *ibid.*, **76**, 5985 (1954).   G. Cilento, *J. Phys. & Colloid Chem.*, **55**, 716 (1951).

[355] M. Giua and F. Cherchi, *Gazz. chim. ital.*, **49**, II, 264 (1919).

tween compounds A and B, a series of curves resembling ECE' results; for each, the composition with maximum melting point is that of the particular molecular compound. Figure 18 depicts the benzophenone–diphenylamine system,[355] which affords a 1:1 compound; the 1-naphthyl-amine–phenol system[356] is similar. The sharper the maximum at C, the more stable the compound. A rather flat maximum indicates occurrence of considerable dissociation, and this is the only common system where addition of either or both of two "impurities" (A or B) causes insignificant

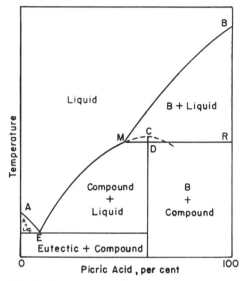

Fig. 19. Relation between freezing temperature and composition for a molecular compound having a meritectic point.[358]

change in the melting point of a compound. An example is the m-cresol phenol system which gives[357] a 2:1 compound at a flat maximum.

If a molecular compound decomposes to give a new solid phase plus a liquid at a temperature below its true, congruent melting point, it has an *incongruent melting point*. Such a system is shown in Figure 19; at the meritectic point M, the compound decomposes to pure B plus a liquid consisting of A saturated with B. Figure 19 depicts the benzene–picric acid system,[358] which affords a 1:1 compound capable of existence only at temperatures below R. At lower temperatures, the solid may consist of compound mixed with B or, at still lower temperatures, of compound plus its

[356] J. C. Philip, *J. Chem. Soc.*, **83**, 814 (1903).
[357] H. M. Dawson and C. A. Mountford, *J. Chem. Soc.*, **113**, 923 (1918).
[358] B. Kuriloff, *Z. physik. Chem.*, **23**, 676 (1897).

eutectic with A, depending on the ratio of A to B in the starting material. Unless recognized, such behavior may complicate use, *e.g.*, in identification of hydrocarbons as picrates.   Furthermore, if a series of molecular compounds is formed, some may have congruent, and others incongruent, melting points; each maximum then indicates a congruently melting compound, and each meritectic break reveals an incongruently melting compound.

Numerous molecular compounds have been discovered by microscopic examination[359] of binary melts.   In half the space between the slide and cover glass is placed a sample of the higher melting compound; this is melted, cooled, and crystallized.   The second compound is introduced and, by just melting, is caused to fill the remaining space; the temperature is now maintained at the latter melting point and the contact zone is observed.   If reaction occurs between the two compounds, complete solidification or melting may ensue; polymorphs and eutectics may also be observed.   This technique may prove useful in selecting candidate heterogeneous nucleators, since formation of a molecular compound at the interface may explain[360] some cases of epitaxy.   Other methods for detecting formation of molecular compounds have been reviewed.[361]

Various *inclusion complexes*[362] have been discovered from time to time, since early in the nineteenth century[363]; but their structures had not been elucidated until recently, and those of many complexes have yet to be established.   Inclusion complexes are of at least three general types, in all of which some form of physical entrapment[364] is involved; the constituents are usually present in constant, but not necessarily stoichiometric, proportions.   Formation of complexes or adducts derives from the respective *molecular sizes and shapes* of the constituents, and only to a small or negligible extent from the lesser attractive forces between them; it is a

[359] H. Quehenberger, *Monatsh.*, **80**, 595 (1949).   A. Kofler, *Plansee Proc.*, **1952**, 21 (1953).   *C. A.*, **47**, 10438d (1953).

[360] J. Willems, *Z. Elektrochem.*, **56**, 348 (1952).   M. Brandstätter, *Mikroskopie*, **7**, 37 (1952).

[361] L. J. Andrews, *Chem. Revs.*, **54**, 713 (1954).

[362] W. Schlenk, Jr., *Ann.*, **565**, 204 (1949).

[363] Sir Humphry Davy, *Trans. Roy. Soc. London*, **101**, 155 (1811).   F. Wöhler, *Ann.*, **69**, 297 (1849).   K. A. Hofmann and F. Höchtlen, *Ber.*, **36**, 1149 (1903).   H. Wieland and H. Sorge, *Z. physiol. Chem.*, **97**, 1 (1916).

[364] H. M. Powell, *Endeavour*, **9**, 154 (1950).   W. Schlenk, Jr., *Fortschr. chem. Forsch.*, **2**, 92 (1951).   G. Zilberstein, *Bull. soc. chim. France*, D33 (1951).   W. Schlenk, Jr., *Analyst*, **77**, 867 (1952).   F. D. Rossini, B. J. Mair, and A. J. Streiff, *Hydrocarbons From Petroleum*, Reinhold, New York, 1953, pp. 182–188.   F. Cramer, *Angew. Chem.*, **64**, 437 (1952); *Einschlussverbindungen*, Springer, Berlin, 1954.   R. L. McLaughlin, "Separation of Paraffins by Urea and Thiourea," in B. T. Brooks, C. E. Boord, S. S. Kurtz, Jr., and L. Schmerling, eds., *The Chemistry of Petroleum Hydrocarbons*, Vol. I, Reinhold, New York, 1954, pp. 241–274.

TABLE III
SOME INCLUSION COMPLEXES

Compound A	Compound B	Value of n in Complex A_nB
CHANNEL (CANAL) COMPLEXES		
Desoxycholic acid[a]	Fatty acids, normal paraffins, camphor, benzaldehyde, etc.	1, 3, 4, 6, or 8 (increasing as length of B is increased)
4,4'-Dinitrobiphenyl[b]	4,4'-Substituted biphenyls	3, 3.5, 4, or 5 (depending on length of B)
Thiourea[c]	Certain branched and cyclic compounds, e.g., paraffins	Usually increases as length of B is increased
Urea[d]	Normal paraffins, straight-chain alcohols, carboxylic acids, esters, etc.	$0.653x + 1.51$, where $x =$ number of carbon atoms in B
CLATHRATE (CAGE) COMPLEXES		
Hydroquinone[e]	Methanol, acetonitrile, etc.	3
Hydroquinone[e,f]	HBr, HCl, HCN, H_2S, SO_2, CO_2, C_2H_2, N_2, O_2, A, Kr, Xe, etc.	3 as limit, but often higher
Ammonia-nickel cyanide,[g] $NH_3 \cdot Ni(CN)_2$	Benzene, thiophene, etc., but not their homologs	1
Water[h]	Molecules giving gas hydrates, e.g., A, Cl_2, $CHCl_3$, CH_3Cl, CH_4, C_3H_8, CH_3SH, C_2H_5Cl	6 (8), or 15 (17); the larger molecules have the higher hydrating numbers

[a] H. Wieland and H. Sorge, Z. physiol Chem., 97, 1 (1916). H. Rheinboldt, Ann., 451, 258 (1927); 473, 253 (1929); J. prakt. Chem., 153, 313 (1939). Y. Go and O. Kratky, Z. physik. Chem., B26, 439 (1934). O. Kratky and G. Giacomello, Monatsh., 69, 427 (1936). G. Giacomello, Atti reale accad. nazl. Lincei, 27, 101 (1938); Gazz. chim. ital., 69, 790 (1939). H. Sobotka and S. Kahn, Biochem. J., 26, 898 (1932). H. Sobotka, Chem. Revs., 15, 358 (1934); J. Org. Chem., 1, 274 (1936). N. P. Buu-Hoï, Z. physiol. Chem., 278, 230 (1943).
[b] W. S. Rapson, D. H. Saunder, and E. T. Stewart, J. Chem. Soc., 1946, 1110. D. H. Saunder, Proc. Roy. Soc. London, A188, 31 (1946); A190, 508 (1947).
[c] B. Angla, Ann. chim., [12], 4, 693 (1949). W. Schlenk, Jr., Ann., 573, 142 (1951).
[d] W. Schlenk, Jr., Ann., 565, 204 (1949). A. E. Smith, Acta Cryst., 5, 224 (1952). O. Redlich, C. M. Gable, A. K. Dunlop, and R. W. Millar, J. Am. Chem. Soc., 72, 4153 (1950). O. Redlich, C. M. Gable, L. R. Beason, and R. W. Millar, ibid., 72, 4161 (1950).
[e] D. E. Palin and H. M. Powell, J. Chem. Soc., 1948, 815.
[f] H. M. Powell, J. Chem. Soc., 1948, 61; 1950, 298, 300, 468. D. F. Evans and R. E. Richards, Nature, 170, 246 (1952).
[g] R. F. Evans, O. Ormrod, B. B. Goalby, and L. A. K. Staveley, J. Chem. Soc., 1950, 3346. J. H. Rayner and H. M. Powell, ibid., 1952, 319. H. M. Powell and J. H. Rayner, Nature, 163, 566 (1949).
[h] M. von Stackelberg, Naturwissenschaften, 36, 327, 359 (1949). M. von Stackelberg and H. Müller, ibid., 38, 457 (1951); 39, 20 (1952). W. F. Claussen, J. Chem. Phys., 19, 259, 662 (1951). L. Pauling and R. E. Marsh, Proc. Natl. Acad. Sci. U. S., 38, 112 (1952). W. Schroeder, Die Geschichte der Gashydrate, Enke, Stuttgart, 1926. W. M. Deaton and E. M. Frost, "Gas Hydrates and Their Relation to the Operation of Natural Gas Pipe Lines," U. S. Bur. Mines Monograph, 8 (1949). A. F. Wells, Acta Cryst., 7, 545 (1954).

selective process, and can be employed for the same purposes as can molecular-compound formation (see Sect. IV.1.A).

Channel (canal) complexes comprise those in which one constituent (A) crystallizes in a framework which leaves a parallel, approximately cylindrical channel, in which molecules of the second constituent (B) are enclosed lengthwise. In such complexes, if A is kept constant, the molecules of B can be those of compounds having some structural resemblance to each other (see Table III). Examples are the adducts of *urea*[365] with relatively straight-chain, organic compounds, *e.g.*, paraffinic and olefinic hydrocarbons, alcohols, esters, aldehydes, ketones, and carboxylic acids. In channel complexes, constituent A is usually not in its customary crystalline structure. Thus, whereas pure urea crystals are tetragonal and close packed, with no channels available for the enclosure of other molecules, x-ray diffraction patterns of the urea adducts show a lattice arrangement belonging to the hexagonal system. This affords a hexagonal canal, of effective diameter 4.9 Å., into which certain other molecules can fit. Similarly, the crystal lattices of *thiourea* in its adducts[366] are completely different from those of the pure compound. The framework of molecules of A, with definite sized channels, limits the enclosed constituent to substances with molecules of a size and shape which will fit into the available space. To form an adduct with *urea*, a hydrocarbon must have a long, unbranched chain. Thus, normal, straight-chain paraffins with a chain diameter of *ca.* 3.8 by 4.2 Å. fit into the channels provided by urea, whereas the branched-chain isomers of low molecular weight cannot normally be accommodated and so do not usually form adducts with urea. However, if the branched isomer has a straight-chain component sufficiently long, formation of an adduct is possible; in certain cases of close fit, the urea lattice may be distorted to accommodate a slightly larger molecule. The formula of the complexes is A_nB, where n, usually not integral, has values of 4 or higher, increasing as the length of B increases. Generally, a simple molecular ratio of the two constituents is not found, although a 3-to-1 weight ratio of urea to the second constituent is common. The adducts of urea and thiourea have been extensively studied[367] because of

[365] F. Bengen, German Pat. Application O. Z. 12438 (March 18, 1940); U. S. Technical Oil Mission, Reel 6, frames 263–70, and Reel 143, pp. 135–139; *Angew. Chem.*, **63**, 207 (1951); German Pat., 869,070 (Feb. 3, 1953). F. Bengen and W. Schlenk, Jr., *Experientia*, **5**, 200 (1949).

[366] B. Angla, *Compt. rend.*, **224**, 402, 1166 (1947); *Ann. chim.*, [12], **4**, 693 (1949). L. C. Fetterly, Ph.D. Thesis, University of Washington, 1950; U. S. Pat. 2,499,820 (March 7, 1950). W. A. Bailey, Jr., R. A. Bannerot, L. C. Fetterly, and A. G. Smith, *Ind. Eng. Chem.*, **43**, 2125 (1951).

[367] W. Schlenk, Jr., *Ann.*, **565**, 204 (1949); **573**, 142 (1951). O. Redlich, C. M. Gable, A. K. Dunlop, and R. W. Millar, *J. Am. Chem. Soc.*, **72**, 4153 (1950). O. Redlich, C. M. Gable, L. R. Beason, and R. W. Millar, *ibid.*, **72**, 4161 (1950). W. J. Zimmerschied, R. A. Dinerstein, A. W. Weitkamp, and R. F. Marschner, *ibid.*, **71**, 2947 (1949); *Ind. Eng. Chem.*, **42**, 1300 (1950). W. J. Zimmerschied, W. S. Higley, and A. P. Lien, *Petroleum Eng.*, **22**, 7, C-43 Reference Annual (1950). R. W. Schiessler and D. J. Flitter, *J. Am. Chem. Soc.*, **74**, 1720 (1952). W. Schlenk, Jr., *Analyst*, **77**, 867 (1952). K. A. Kobe and W. G. Domask, *Petroleum Refiner*, **31**, No. 3, 106 (Mar., May. July 1952). C. Hermann and A. V. Lenné, *Naturwissenschaften*, **39**, 234 (1952).

their value for fractionation of petroleum hydrocarbons. Owing to the larger size of the sulfur atom of thiourea, resulting in a somewhat larger channel, larger molecules, *e.g.*, having some branching or cyclization, can adduct with thiourea than with urea. These "reagents" do not necessarily unite with suitable "reactants" merely by contact; certain impurities can interfere with adduction, but presence of an "activator," *e.g.*, methanol, brings it about. Use of adduction or "extractive crystallization" is described in Sect. IV.1.A.

In contrast to the molecular ratio, usually 1:1 or 1:2, in molecular compounds formed by other aromatic nitro compounds, *4,4'-dinitrobiphenyl* gives,[368] with 4- or 4,4'-substituted biphenyls, channel complexes having the ratios 1:3 for biphenyl, 4-amino-, 4-hydroxy-, and 4,4'-dihydroxy-biphenyl, 2:7 for 4-bromo- and 4-iodobiphenyl, 1:4 for 4-acetoxy-, 4,4'-diamino-, 4,4'-dimethoxy-, and *N,N,N',N'*-tetramethyl-4,4'-diaminobiphenyl, and 1:5 for 4,4'-diacetoxybiphenyl. The channels have an effective diameter of 3.7 Å., and the complexes are high melting and particularly stable.

Channel complexes, called choleic acids, are formed by *desoxycholic acid* with fatty acids,[369] with paraffins,[370] and with acenaphthene, alcohols, various alkaloids,[371] azo dyes,[372] benzaldehyde, benzanthrene, benzoic acid, camphor. carvone, cholesterol, dicarboxylic acids, ketones, naphthalene, phenanthrene, salol, and xylene. The complexes with large, ring molecules and with steroids may, however, not be channel complexes. Fatty acids having 3 to 7 carbon atoms bind 4 molecular proportions of desoxycholic acid, those with 8 to 14 bind 6, and those with 15 or more bind 8; however, for methyl arachinate (C_{26}), there is a ratio[373] of 10:1 or 12:1. This ability of desoxycholic acid to combine with water-insoluble materials is particularly important because the resulting complexes are soluble in water or aqueous alkali, and so are transportable in the body; this effect resembles the salting-in by sulfochlorinated naphthalenes and by sodium xylenesulfonate (see Sect. III.1). The choleic acids found in human bile are complexes of 8 moles of desoxycholic acid per mole of palmitic or stearic acid. Cholic acid gives[374] a blue, iodine adduct which may be a channel complex.

To date, the *cyclodextrins* are the sole representatives of a separate class of complexes in which a single, annular molecule has an enclosed hol-

[368] D. H. Saunder, *Proc. Roy. Soc. London*, **A188**, 31 (1946); **A190**, 508 (1947).

[369] H. Wieland and H. Sorge, *Z. physiol. Chem.*, **97**, 1 (1916).

[370] H. Rheinboldt, *J. prakt. Chem.*, **153**, 313 (1939).

[371] L. Fieser and M. Newman, *J. Am. Chem. Soc.*, **57**, 1602 (1935).

[372] G. Cilento, *J. Am. Chem. Soc.*, **74**, 968 (1952).

[373] G. Giacomello, *Gazz. chim. ital.*, **73**, 3 (1943).

[374] G. Bassil and R. J. Boscott, *Biochem. J.*, **48**, xlviii (1951).

low space[375] capable of holding certain other compounds. The α- and β-dextrins, formed[376] from starch by the action of an amylase from *Bacillus macerans*, and γ-dextrin[377] are rings of D-glucose residues, linked[378] as in maltose; α- has 6, β- has 7, and γ- dextrin has[379] 8 D-glucose residues. The hydrophilic dextrins form insoluble complexes with a large number of organic compounds, including lipophilic molecules, usually on simply mixing the components. Although foreign molecules can be taken up, to an extent as high as 30% by weight, there is no increase in volume, showing that the reactants enter preexisting holes. The rings of sugar residues probably are superimposed to form hollow, cylindrical channels which can accept such long-chain molecules as paraffins. Unlike the urea adducts, which acquire their hexagonal channels only when the appropriate reactant is present, the cyclodextrins already have their channels, either empty or containing water; consequently, stable complexes result even on incomplete filling thereof. Any molecule of suitable dimensions and properties can thus be adducted to any extent between zero and a certain characteristic maximum. Halogenated paraffins give cyclodextrin adducts; thus, trichloroethylene has long been used for precipitation of quite pure cyclodextrin adducts after enzymic preparation of the dextrins. The solid complexes are generally stable at 100° under diminished pressure, but dissociate in aqueous suspension at 60–70°; however, on cooling, they immediately re-form, so they can usually be recrystallized from water without decomposition. Consequently, the adducts formed by α- and β-dextrin were long regarded as independent compounds, the *r*- and *s*-dextrins. The three cyclodextrins present the remarkable phenomenon of graded, molecular sieves, useful for study of molecular sizes, because each has a different sized hole and so behaves somewhat differently from the other two. α-Dextrin, having a channel diameter of 6 Å., can only accommodate small molecules up to the size of a spatially little-substituted benzene ring; β-dextrin, with a hole diameter of 7.5 Å., can accept naphthalene derivatives; and γ-dextrin, having a hole diameter of 9–10 Å., forms few inclusion complexes, because its hole is too big for most organic molecules. Bromobenzene can be used[380] for separating α- from β-dextrin because the

[375] K. Freudenberg and M. Meyer-Delius, *Ber.*, **71**, 1596 (1938).

[376] F. Schardinger, *Z. Untersuch. Nahr. u. Genussm.*, **6**, 874 (1903).

[377] K. Freudenberg and R. Jacobi, *Ann.*, **518**, 102 (1935).

[378] K. Freudenberg and M. Meyer-Delius, *Ber.*, **71**, 1596 (1938). K. Freudenberg, E. Plankenhorn, and H. Knauber, *Ann.*, **558**, 1 (1947). K. Freudenberg and F. Cramer, *Chem. Ber.*, **93**, 296 (1950).

[379] D. French and R. E. Rundle, *J. Am. Chem. Soc.*, **64**, 1651 (1942). D. French, M. Levine, and J. Pazur, *ibid.*, **71**, 356 (1949). W. Borschert, *Z. Naturforsch.*, **3b**, 464 (1948).

[380] K. Freudenberg, E. Plankenhorn, and H. Knauber, *Ann.*, **558**, 1 (1947).

holes in α-dextrin are too small to afford a complex with it. Adducts of cyclodextrins with octanol, hexanol,[381] trichloroethylene, p-nitrophenol, nitrosophenol, and 1-isopropylazulene[382] have been studied. Like desoxycholic acid, the dextrins form inclusion complexes with[383] the higher alcohols. The solubilities of the individual dextrins in the presence of many precipitating media have been[384] determined. Nearly all lipophilic compounds of suitable molecular size and shape form insoluble adducts on admixture with the cyclodextrins, presumably because the inside of the annulus is essentially a ring of hydrogen atoms. Certain rather unstable compounds, e.g., 1-isopropylazulene or benzaldehyde, form highly stable adducts with β-cyclodextrin because the entrapped molecules are protected[385] from external influences. Thus, benzaldehyde does not then undergo autoxidation, since atmospheric oxygen cannot reach the adducted molecules; similar behavior is displayed by the adduct of desoxycholic acid with benzaldehyde.

Nearly all *macromolecular substances* exhibit the property of swelling when they are soaked in appropriate liquids; this swelling may proceed to an end point giving a still-solid product, as with cellulose plus aqueous alkali, or may end in complete dissolution, as with rubber plus ether. Swollen materials contain foreign molecules entrapped between their micelles or chains. In this category are the inclusion complexes given by cellulose, some clays, and starch, and, perhaps, by graphite and by proteins.

Cellulose, prewashed with acetone and then soaked in cyclohexane, affords a complex with cyclohexane which, after drying at 100° under diminished pressure, has[386] an elementary analysis corresponding to the inclusion of 1 molecule of cyclohexane for each 6 D-glucose residues. Carbon tetrachloride and other low-boiling, indifferent solvents are similarly included; the reactant is so tightly bound that it is not removed after being heated for several days at 80–100° under high vacuum. Presumably, the reactant is incorporated in long channels between the fibers of molecules. This idea is borne out by observations on the fastness of substantive dyes which, although they must bear certain groupings which facilitate[387] some kind of bonding to the hydroxyl groups of the cellulose, must also have a long, straight shape, as in certain benzidine derivatives, in order to be firmly held[388] in the long channels afforded by the cellulose.

[381] K. Freudenberg and F. Cramer, Z. Naturforsch., 3b, 464 (1948).

[382] F. Cramer, Ber., 84, 851 (1951).

[383] K. Freudenberg and F. Cramer, Ber., 83, 296 (1950).

[384] D. French, M. Levine, J. Pazur, and E. Norberg, J. Am. Chem. Soc., 71, 354 (1949).

[385] F. Cramer, Ber., 84, 851 (1951).

[386] H. Staudinger, Z. angew. Chem., 64, 152 (1952).

[387] H. Krzikalla and B. Eistert, J. prakt. Chem., 143, 50 (1935).

[388] H. H. Hodgson, J. Soc. Dyers Colourists, 49, 213 (1933). P. Ruggli, Kolloid-Z., 63, 129 (1933).

Zeolite[389] has channels of diameter 5–6 Å., normally filled with water, from which the water can be displaced by a variety of other compounds, *e.g.*, the members of the series methane through *n*-heptane. As with the urea adducts, the saturation values are proportional to the length of the included molecule; constant proportions are not exhibited.

Amylose, the unbranched carbohydrate constituent of potato starch, gives adducts, *e.g.*, with butanol, and may thus be separated[390] from the branched constituent, amylopectin. Whereas starch swollen with alkali has a linear arrangement[391] of the chains of D-glucose residues, the adducts with higher alcohols, cyclohexanol, fatty acids, and iodine probably have a helical[392] conformation, affording a central channel for the reception of foreign molecules.

Clathrate (cage) complexes[393] (see Table III) are those in which molecules of the included constituent fit into separate, molecular cages formed by molecules of the first constituent. With regard to determining whether or not a clathrate will form, the molecular dimensions of the second constituent are a much more critical factor than are those of the included constituent of channel complexes, but chemical similarities are not decisive. Since it is probably just as difficult for a molecule of B to enter a formed vacant site in A as to leave a filled cage, such complexes are presumably formed by simultaneous deposition of constituents.

Examples of clathrate complexes are those which the molecular compound of *nickel cyanide with ammonia*, $Ni(CN)_2 \cdot NH_3$, forms with benzene,[394,395] aniline,[395] phenol,[395] furan, pyridine, pyrrole, or thiophene.[396] These have the formula AB. In clathrates, molecules of the included constituent may be replaceable by molecules of *similar size*, but not by homologs. Thus, ammonia-nickel cyanide does not afford a clathrate with toluene or nonaromatic hydrocarbons; this permits separation of benzene from these compounds.

Normally, *hydroquinone* crystallizes as the α form of m.p. 172.3°, and by sublimation crystallizes as the γ form. However, by recrystallization

[389] R. M. Barrer, *J. Chem. Soc.*, **1948**, 127; *Trans. Faraday Soc.*, **40**, 195 (1944); *Chemistry & Industry*, **1955**, 1291. R. M. Barrer and D. W. Riley, *J. Chem. Soc.*, **1948**, 133.

[390] T. J. Schoch, *Advances in Carbohydrate Chem.*, **1**, 247 (1945).

[391] F. R. Senti and L. P. Witnauer, *J. Am. Chem. Soc.*, **70**, 1438 (1949).

[392] C. S. Hanes, *New Phytologist*, **36**, 101, 189 (1937). K. Freudenberg, E. Schaaf, G. Dumpert, and T. Ploetz, *Naturwissenschaften*, **27**, 850 (1939). R. E. Rundle, *J. Am. Chem. Soc.*, **69**, 1769 (1947).

[393] H. M. Powell, *J. Chem. Soc.*, **1948**, 61.

[394] K. A. Hofmann and F. Küspert, *Z. anorg. Chem.*, **15**, 204 (1897). H. M. Powell and J. H. Rayner, *Nature*, **163**, 566 (1949). J. H. Rayner and H. M. Powell, *J. Chem. Soc.*, **1952**, 319.

[395] K. A. Hofmann and F. Höchtlen, *Ber.*, **36**, 1149 (1903).

[396] K. A. Hofmann and H. Arnoldi, *Ber.*, **39**, 339 (1906).

from methanol, the so-called β form, a clathrate[397] consisting of three molecules of hydroquinone per molecule of "methanol of crystallization," is obtained. Hydroquinone also forms clathrates with such chemically diverse compounds as hydrogen sulfide,[398] sulfur dioxide,[399] formic acid,[400] hydrogen cyanide,[400] hydrogen chloride,[401] hydrogen bromide,[402] acetonitrile,[403] carbon dioxide,[404] and acetylene,[404] having a minimum ratio of 3 molecules of hydroquinone per molecule of other constituent; but this number is changed if all the cages in the hydrogen-bonded hydroquinone are not filled. Similar clathrates are formed with argon,[405] krypton,[406] and xenon.[407] The geometry of clathrates is so specific, however, that resorcinol cannot replace the isomer, hydroquinone, and methanol is not replaced by the larger, ethanol, or the smaller, water, molecule. Water also does not replace hydrogen sulfide, and helium does not replace the larger, argon, molecule. The clathrates with methanol and acetonitrile have the formula A_3B if they are crystallized directly from these liquids. Those with such gases as hydrogen bromide, hydrogen sulfide, or sulfur dioxide, crystallized from an indifferent solvent, have vacant cages; and the formula, though approximating A_3B, is usually deficient in B; application of pressure to increase the gas concentration is therefore advisable. The crystalline argon clathrate shows a negligible argon pressure, and argon is set free only by treatments which destroy the cage structure, such as heat or use of a solvent for hydroquinone; this indicates that the crystal structure of the clathrate involves geometric entrapment of the argon molecules rather than attraction *via* van der Waals' forces.

The first *gas hydrate*, $Cl \cdot 6H_2O$, was discovered[408] over 140 years ago; the hydrate-forming ability of many constituents of natural gas is used

[397] D. E. Palin and H. M. Powell, *Nature*, **156**, 334 (1945); *J. Chem. Soc.*, **1948,** 571.

[398] F. Wöhler, *Ann.*, **69,** 297 (1849).

[399] A. Clemm, *Ann.*, **110,** 357 (1859). D. E. Palin and H. M. Powell, *J. Chem. Soc.*, **1947, 208.**

[400] F. Mylius, *Ber.*, **19,** 999 (1886).

[401] J. Schmidlin and R. Lang, *Ber.*, **43,** 2817 (1910).

[402] M. Gomberg and L. H. Cone, *Ann.*, **376,** 238 (1910).

[403] D. E. Palin and H. M. Powell, *J. Chem. Soc.*, **1947,** 208.

[404] H. M. Powell, *Proc. Intern. Congr. Pure Applied Chem. London*, **11,** 585 (1947); *Endeavour*, **9,** 154 (1950). See also H. Murakami, *Sci. Papers Osaka Univ.*, **No. 18** (1949); J. W. Smith, *Science Progress*, **38,** 698 (1950); J. S. Dryden and R. J. Meakins, *Nature*, **169,** 324 (1952).

[405] H. M. Powell and M. Guter, *Nature*, **164,** 240 (1949). H. M. Powell, *J. Chem. Soc.*, **1950,** 298.

[406] H. M. Powell, *J. Chem. Soc.*, **1950,** 300.

[407] H. M. Powell, *J. Chem. Soc.*, **1950,** 468.

[408] Sir Humphry Davy, *Trans. Roy. Soc. London*, **101,** 155 (1811). M. Faraday, *Quart. J. Sci.*, **15,** 71 (1823). F. Wöhler, *Ann.*, **85,** 374 (1853).

industrially.[409] The hydrates of such molecules as methyl iodide, ethyl chloride, ethyl bromide, and chloroform contain 15 (or possibly 17[409a]) molecules of water per molecule of included constituent; the hydrates of smaller molecules contain 6 molecules of water, except that of methyl bromide, which contains 8. Often, presence of an activating gas is necessary for formation of the hydrates of the larger molecules to occur; argon, helium, neon, nitrogen, and oxygen can perform this function.

Layer (sandwich) complexes are formed in some instances. Thus, the *basic zinc salts of acidic organic dyes*, e.g., Naphthol Yellow S, consist[410] of layers of zinc hydroxide between layers of dye. The general formula of these complexes is:

$$4[Zn(OH)_2 \cdot Zn]^{++} \cdot dye^{--}$$

and the organic part must be a ring system having a large surface area. Between the layers, additional neutral molecules can be imbedded up to a certain saturation value; the thickness of a layer may thereby be increased as much as 50%. Compounds which can be thus incorporated include water, methanol, ethanol, ethylene glycol, glycerol, acetonitrile, and propionitrile.

Montmorillonite and *halloysite* afford[411] two types of inclusion complex. One kind is formed by such basic substances as adenine, adenosine, benzidine, brucine, codeine, guanine, guanosine, o-phenylenediamine, and piperidine; here, the base penetrates to the space between two layers of clay, displaces cations on these inner surfaces, and then the ring lies flat between the silicate layers. Nonionic complexes are also[412] known; the cations of the mineral are not replaced, but mutual electrostatic attraction between the silicate and the included constituent is set up. Whereas montmorillonite can be dehydrated at 100° and then be swollen with a suitable organic compound, halloysite crumbles on complete dehydration, and so the water must be cautiously driven out by means of the organic constituent.

The complexes formed by graphite,[413] *horse methemoglobin*,[414] and *turnip-yellow mosaic virus*[415] may be layer complexes.

[409] W. Wilcox, D. Carson, and D. Klatz, *Ind. Eng. Chem.*, **33**, 662 (1941).

[409a] A. F. Wells, *Acta Cryst.*, **7**, 545 (1954).

[410] W. Feitknecht and H. Bürki, *Experientia*, **5**, 154 (1949). W. Feitknecht and H. Weidmann, *Helv. Chim. Acta*, **26**, 1560, 1564, 1911 (1943). D. McEvan, *Trans. Faraday Soc.*, **44**, 349 (1948).

[411] J. E. Gieseking, *Soil Sci.*, **47**, 1 (1939). S. B. Hendricks, *J. Phys. Chem.*, **45**, 65 (1941). W. Schlenk, Jr., *Fortschr. chem. Forsch.*, **2**, 92 (1951). Cf. W. F. Spencer and J. E. Gieseking, *J. Phys. Chem.*, **56**, 751 (1952).

[412] W. Bradley, *J. Am. Chem. Soc.*, **67**, 975 (1945). D. McEvan, *Trans. Faraday Soc.*, **44**, 349 (1948).

[413] A. Schleede and M. Wellmann, *Z. physik. Chem.*, **B18**, 1 (1932). U. Hofmann and E. König, *Z. anorg. Chem.*, **234**, 311 (1937). O. Ruff, *Z. Elektrochem.*, **44**, 333 (1938).

[414] M. F. Perutz, *Proc. Roy. Soc. London*, **A195**, 474 (1949).

[415] J. D. Bernal and C. H. Carlisle, *Nature*, **162**, 139 (1948).

Inclusion complexes *as yet unclassified* include those formed by acetylene with inorganic salts, and by orcinol and phloroglucinol. Those formed by sulfurous acid may be clathrates; and those given by lipoproteins may be channel complexes, but the question as to whether *proteins* really give inclusion complexes is still[416] not settled. Protein molecules contain free amino and carboxyl groups and so can give both cationic and anionic salts; furthermore, acid amide groupings must be considered. In this connection, Meyer[417] points out that hemoglobin can be crystallized whereas globin cannot; this behavior resembles that of desoxycholic acid, which has not been crystallized, but which gives crystalline inclusion complexes with many substances.

The 2'-hydroxyflavan, *2'-hydroxy-2,4,4,7,4'-pentamethylflavan*,[418] forms 1:1 adducts with[419] ethers, ketones, amines, pyridines, quinolines, coniine, etc., some of which are useful in purifying the originally oily flavan. A complex with dioxane is not formed unless water is also present, giving a complex of the formula 1 dioxane:2 flavan:2 H_2O. Morpholine behaves similarly. The very unstable 2-iodopyridine, when in excess, forms a stable 1:1 complex; when recrystallized, this loses iodopyridine and gives a 3:2 complex; a 7:2 adduct has also been isolated. All three adducts have the same melting point. *2'-Hydroxy-2,4,4-trimethylflavan*[420] gives 2:1 complexes with dioxane and with morpholine; and *2'-hydroxy-2,4,4;6,5'-pentamethylflavan* affords 1:1 complexes with tetrahydrofuran, morpholine, pyridine, piperidine, and cyclohexylamine.

From certain solvents, *tri-o-thymotide*[421] crystallizes unsolvated, but it gives inclusion complexes with others. Thus, it forms a 1:2 complex with *n*-hexane which can only be freed from hexane after drying for several days at 160° at 1 mm.; 1:2 complexes are also formed with benzene, carbon tetrachloride, chloroform, dioxane, methanol, and ethanol; *m*-xylene gives a 3:4, and *p*-xylene a 1:1, complex. Many small molecules, including normal alcohols up to pentanol, active pentyl alcohol, acetone, *sec*-butyl bromide and iodide, carbon disulfide, and ethylene dibromide, give trigonal crystals with properties resembling those of channel complexes or of clathrates. Longer molecules, *e.g.*, *n*-hexane, 1-hexanol, 1-heptanol, and *sec*-octyl and cetyl bromides, afford a different kind of crystalline complex;

[416] F. Cramer, *Einschlussverbindungen*. Springer, Berlin, 1954, pp. 61–69.

[417] K. H. Meyer, *Makromolekulare Chemie*. Akadem. Verlagsgesellschaft, Leipzig, 1950, p. 728.

[418] W. Baker, R. F. Curtis, and J. McOmie, *J. Chem. Soc.*, 1951, 76.

[419] W. Baker, R. F. Curtis, and M. Edwards, *J. Chem. Soc.*, 1951, 83.

[420] W. Baker, R. F. Curtis, and J. McOmie, *J. Chem. Soc.*, 1952, 1774.

[421] R. Spallino and G. Provenzal, *Gazz. chim. ital.*, 39 II, 325 (1909). W. Baker, B. Gilbert, and W. D. Ollis, *J. Chem. Soc.*, 1952, 1443. A. Newman and H. M. Powell, *ibid.*, 1952, 3747.

and two wider molecules, acetylene tetrabromide and *sec*-butyl bromide, form 1:1 complexes, each of still different structure.

Other *anhydrides of phenolcarboxylic acids* afford adducts; thus, tetrasalicylide gives a 1:2 complex with[422] chloroform, and so does[423] tetra-*o*-cresotide; these complexes have been used for preparing very pure chloroform. Similarly, tetra-*m*- and -*p*-cresotides give 1:1 adducts with[424] benzene and so does[425] tetrathiosalicylide.

Diphenyliodonium iodide forms[426] a complex with iodoform on warming in methanol at 50 60°. *Pentaphenylantimony* yields a 2:1 adduct with[427] cyclohexane. *Conidendrin* forms complexes with[428] trichloroethylene and other organic compounds.

III. TECHNIQUES OF CRYSTALLIZATION

Depending on the crystallizand, crystallization may be effected from: (*a*) an oil or sirup containing the least possible proportion of extraneous material, or (*b*) a supersaturated solution. Preparation of the system and induction of nucleus formation usually differ from the corresponding steps in recrystallization. The steps involving growth, separation, washing, and drying of the crystals are essentially those used in recrystallization (see Sect. IV).

1. Preparation of System

Since many *impurities* retard or inhibit crystallization, it is important, prior to attempting crystallization, to remove them as far as possible by differential chemical reaction, partition (see Chapter II), volatility,[429] adsorption,[430] solubility,[431] etc., or by derivative formation[432] followed by

[422] R. Anschütz, *Ber.*, **25**, 3512 (1892).

[423] R. Anschütz, *Friedländer*, **3**, 825 (1913).

[424] W. Baker, B. Gilbert, W. D. Ollis, and T. S. Zealley, *J. Chem. Soc.*, **1951**, 209.

[425] W. Baker, A. S. El Nawawy, and W. D. Ollis, *J. Chem. Soc.*, **1952**, 3163.

[426] W. Steinkopf, J. Roch, and K. Schultz, *J. prakt. Chem.*, [2], **113**, 164 (1926).

[427] G. Wittig and K. Clauss, *Ann.*, **577**, 26 (1952).

[428] H. B. Lackey, W. W. Moyer, and W. M. Hearon, *Tappi*, **32**, 469 (1949).

[429] See *Distillation* (A. Weissberger, ed., *Technique of Organic Chemistry*, Vol. IV). Interscience, New York-London, 1951.

[430] See H. G. Cassidy, *Adsorption and Chromatography* (A. Weissberger, ed., *Technique of Organic Chemistry*, Vol. V). Interscience, New York-London, 1951.

[431] See R. D. Vold and M. J. Vold, "Determination of Solubility," in A. Weissberger, ed., *Technique of Organic Chemistry*. Vol. I, 2nd ed., Interscience, New York-London, 1949, Chapter VII.

[432] P. A. Levene and R. S. Tipson, *J. Biol. Chem.*, **115**, 731 (1936).   D. R. Stevens, *Ind. Eng. Chem.*, **35**, 655 (1943).

one of these treatments or crystallization, with subsequent regeneration. Some impurities may not affect the crystallizability appreciably, but may be adsorbed on the crystals. Thus, traces of coloring matter, too small to change the melting point, may impart color to otherwise colorless substances. In such cases, treatment of the solution by differential adsorption is a valuable procedure. Charcoal, fuller's earth, kieselguhr, silica gel, etc., are useful for this purpose.[430] It is sometimes advantageous to isolate a crop of crystals from an untreated solution. The mother liquor or its concentrate is then subjected to one or more of the above-mentioned purification procedures before an additional crop of crystals is isolated.

An excellent method for removing coloring matter and certain other impurities, particularly from aqueous solutions, is by *formation of a precipitate* in the solution. In some cases, the coloring matter unites with the added reagent to give the precipitate; in others, the precipitate formed adsorbs the coloring matter. One of the oldest of such methods is the addition of a small amount of a lead-salt solution[433] alone or preceded by a little ammonia.[434] Basic lead nitrate[435] is sometimes useful, but neutral,[436] monobasic, or dibasic[437] lead acetate, in alcoholic or aqueous solution,[438] are more extensively employed. After filtering off the resultant precipitate, excess lead is removed from the filtrate by treatment with hydrogen sulfide. Any remaining traces of coloring matter are usually adsorbed by the lead sulfide. This is filtered off, and the solution aerated or treated with inert gas to remove hydrogen sulfide. Certain aromatic amines have been decolorized by dissolution in dilute hydrochloric acid, addition of a little stannous chloride, warming to 50°C., and passing in hydrogen sulfide. If the tin sulfide does not readily precipitate, sodium chloride may be added. The sulfide is filtered off, excess hydrogen sulfide is removed, and the base is liberated by means of sodium sulfite.[439]

Mercuric nitrate, sulfate,[440] and acetate[441] are precipitants for certain

[433] H. Hlasiwetz *et al.*, *Ann.*, **127**, 353, 355 (1863); **134**, 277 (1865).

[434] C. Neuberg *et al.*, *Biochem. Z.*, **24**, 163 (1910).

[435] F. Herles, *Z. Ver. deut. Zucker-Ind.*, **59**, 782 (1909); *C. A.*, **5**, 601 (1911).

[436] C. Neuberg, *Biochem. Z.*, **24**, 427 (1910); F. L. Pyman, *J. Chem. Soc.*, **91**, 1229 (1907).

[437] E. Fischer, *Ber.*, **27**, 3195 (1894).

[438] H. Langecker, *Biochem. Z.*, **122**, 34 (1921).

[439] A. Lumière and A. Seyewetz, *Compt. rend.*, **116**, 1202 (1893). A. Weissberger and E. Strasser, *J. prakt. Chem.*, **135**, 209 (1932).

[440] G. Patein and E. Dufau, *Compt. rend.*, **128**, 375 (1899). A. C. Andersen, *Biochem. Z.*, **15**, 83 (1909). C. Neuberg, *ibid.*, **24**, 426 (1910). G. Denigès, *Ann. chim. et phys.*, **18**, 382 (1899). F. G. Hopkins and S. W. Cole, *J. Physiol.*, **27**, 418 (1901). A. Kossel and A. J. Patten, *Z. physiol. Chem.*, **38**, 39 (1903). H. Onslow, *Biochem. J.*, **15**, 383 (1921). H. O. Calvery, *J. Biol. Chem.*, **83**, 631 (1929).

[441] C. Neuberg *et al.*, *Biochem. Z.*, **24**, 173, 429 (1910); **37**, 142 (1911).

nitrogen-containing compounds. For simultaneous neutralization of acid, finely powdered silver or lead carbonate[442] may be employed. Other useful precipitants include copper oxide hydrate,[443] cadmium hydroxide,[444] and colloidal iron hydroxide.[445] The last-mentioned flocculates humic substances[446] in the presence of an electrolyte. An acid may often be decolorized by converting it, partially or completely, to the copper, lead, or barium salt, and decomposing this, *e.g.*, with hydrogen sulfide, carbon dioxide, or sulfuric acid, with formation of an insoluble salt of the metal, which then acts as the adsorbent. Precipitate formation may also be employed for the removal of finely divided, insoluble impurities which pass through ordinary filter paper. Thus tannin solutions were clarified by adding aluminum sulfate solution and then barium hydroxide solution, and filtering off the aluminum hydroxide plus barium sulfate.[447]

Melts. In *crystallizing a melt* it is important to remove all traces of solvent. After the preliminary treatment, the system is *supercooled*. If the compound is new, it may be possible to estimate its probable melting point (see Volume I of this series, Chapter III, Section II.5). In other cases a system of trial and error must be employed. The crystallization of sheets of high polymers, *e.g.*, rubber or Saran, may be followed by observing the increase in density,[448] but ordinarily it will be uncertain whether nuclei have formed until they have grown to visible crystals, and the best temperature for nucleus formation is not necessarily optimal for rapid growth[449] (see Sect. II.2). It is often advisable to cool the melt or solution intensively and then allow it to *warm up slowly* to some temperature below the melting point.[450] Thus, a sample of the liquid in a stoppered test tube may be maintained at a low temperature, *e.g.*, at $-80°C$. by means of a chloroform–dry ice mixture in a Dewar flask, for several hours or longer, and then may be permitted to warm up extremely slowly, say, to $-20°$. It may then be placed in a Dewar flask containing ice–alcohol at $-20°$ and allowed to warm up in the refrigerator, to 0 or $+5°$. In this way, it may

[442] E. Fischer and O. Piloty, *Ber.*, **24**, 4216 (1891).   P. A. Levene and W. A. Jacobs, *Ber.*, **43**, 3142 (1910).

[443] A. Stutzer, *J. Landw.*, **29**, 473 (1881).   E. Přibram, *Arch. exptl. Path. Pharmakol.*, **51**, 379 (1904).

[444] F. P. Dwyer, *J. Soc. Chem. Ind. London*, **56**, 70T (1937).

[445] P. Rona *et al.*, *Biochem. Z.*, **7**, 329 (1908); **27**, 348 (1910).   C. Neuberg, *ibid.*, **24**, 424 (1910).

[446] A. Clementi, *Arch. farmacol. sper.*, **20**, 561 (1915); *C. A.*, **10**, 1046 (1916).

[447] A. H. Schenk, *Chem.-Ztg.*, **17**, 1793 (1893); Ger. Pat., 71309 (1892); *Chem. Centr.*, I, **65**, 366 (1894).

[448] R. F. Boyer, R. S. Spencer, and R. M. Wiley, *J. Polymer Sci.*, **1**, 249 (1946).

[449] H. W. de Boer, *Chem. Weekblad*, **28**, 682 (1931).

[450] G. Tammann, *Nachr. kgl. Ges. Wiss. Göttingen*, **1914**, 110; *C. A.*, **9**, 875 (1915).

pass through a temperature optimal for formation of crystal nuclei and then through a temperature favorable to their growth. Precautions must usually be taken to avoid condensation of moisture on the sample.

Alternatively, the whole sample may be cooled and then gently warmed on one side of the receptacle, e.g., with a blast of warm air, in order to establish a heat gradient and so obtain the optimal temperature for nucleation at some point in the mass. The same effect may sometimes be produced by the addition of a few small pieces of clean dry ice to a sample of the liquid. A gradient may also be established in a tube by partial insertion[451] in dry ice–chloroform so that the upper part extends outside the coolant. At some point, crystals may eventually form. The tube is then gradually raised, and shaken occasionally, so that growth may proceed more rapidly.

The amount of heat liberated when some melts crystallize is rather startling; if the material is sensitive to heat, it is often advisable to cool the crystallizing mélange as soon as this evolution becomes noticeable. Some melts may disrupt[452] glass containers during crystallization, because of the attendant change in volume. For example, crystallization of molten 2-chloroethyl p-toluenesulfonate in glass test tubes or bottles almost invariably cracks them. If supercooling of a melt fails to cause crystallization, the procedures for inducing crystallization (see Sect. III.2) are applied or a sample is dissolved in the minimum volume of a suitable solvent.[453]

Solutions. *Crystallization from supersaturated solution* is applicable to substances decomposing at, or below, their melting points, and those whose melts are too viscous to crystallize without a solvent. Crystallization may not occur spontaneously and if attempts to induce crystallization (Sect. III.2) fail, further purification is indicated. In some cases, crystallization from the melt is necessary, e.g., glycylvaline anhydride[454] always separates in amorphous condition from solution and thus far has only been obtained crystalline from the melt.

In *selecting a solvent*. solubility data in the literature[455] should be consulted. For new compounds, data on melting points and solubilities of related substances may give valuable hints. However, the nature of the solvent may be so important that a thorough search by experiment may be rewarding even for compounds described in the literature. It is advis-

[451] Professor W. Swietoslawski, private communication.

[452] J. W. Cobb, *Trans. Am. Ceram. Soc.*, 11, 65 (1909). *Cf.* M. H. Hey, *Nature*, 158, 584 (1946).

[453] F. Dryer, *Z. physik. Chem.*, 48, 467 (1904).

[454] E. Fischer and E. Abderhalden, *Ber.*, 40, 3558 (1907).

[455] Sources of solubility data are given in Chapter VII, A. Weissberger, ed., *Technique of Organic Chemistry*, Vol. I, 2nd ed., Interscience, New York-London, 1949.

able to use solvents of high and known purity.   Some guidance on the selection of a solvent is given in Section V of this chapter.

Testing of solvents (see Table IV, Sect. V.2) may be undertaken as follows: Portions of about 0.01 g. of crystallizand are placed in several small test tubes (about 10 × 75 mm.) and, to one, 0.5 ml. or less of the solvent is added dropwise,[456] while the contents are stirred with a glass rod (about 2-mm. diameter) the ends of which have been fire-polished.   Note whether the substance dissolves appreciably at room temperature.   If it dissolves completely, the solubility is 2 g. per 100 ml. or greater.   If a suspension is obtained, it is filtered, and the filtrate allowed to evaporate to dryness on a watch glass; the amount of residue indicates the solubility at room temperature.   If a suspension is obtained at room temperature with 0.5 ml. solvent, a further portion of crystallizand suspended in the same volume is warmed, if necessary until boiling.   Should the substance now dissolve completely, the solution is cooled, with stirring, to see if the compound will crystallize.   Then the test is repeated with a smaller volume of solvent, *e.g.*, 0.25 ml., to ascertain more closely the solubility in hot solvent. If part of the crystallizand remains undissolved in the boiling solvent, the suspension is filtered hot, and the filtrate evaporated and examined as before.   If there is any suspicion that the undissolved part differs from the dissolved, the amount dissolved by increasing proportions of solvent should be ascertained.

Some temperature-solubility curves are given in Figure 20.   A solvent with a high temperature coefficient of solubility is usually desirable.   For preference, it should dissolve about five times as much of the crystallizand when hot than when cold.   However, other factors may influence the decision as to which solvent is preferable.   Thus, solvents of high boiling point may be rather difficult to remove completely from the resulting crystals; those of very low boiling point require care in manipulation to minimize loss by evaporation.   Certain sparingly soluble substances may be dissolved under pressure at temperatures above the boiling point of the solvent.   Thus, terephthalic acid[457] has been recrystallized from water at 230°C., and phenolphthalein[458] from dilute hydrochloric acid at 175°. If impurities are present in a solute to be recrystallized, the solvent should, for preference, be so chosen and its amount so regulated that it will either not appreciably dissolve them, or else dissolve them readily and retain

[456] N. D. Cheronis and J. B. Entrikin, *Semimicro Qualitative Organic Analysis*, Crowell, New York, 1947, p. 76.   N. D. Cheronis, *Micro and Semimicro Methods* (A. Weissberger, ed., *Technique of Organic Chemistry*, Vol. VI), Interscience, New York-London, 1954.

[457] C. Hell and T. Rockenbach, *Ber.*, **22**, 508 (1889).

[458] A. Baeyer, *Ann.*, **202**, 71 (1880).

them in solution when the desired solute crystallizes. A solvent satisfactory for recrystallization of a compound prepared by one reaction may be unsuitable for recrystallization of the same compound prepared by a different reaction if the impurities are different. The tendency to crystallize

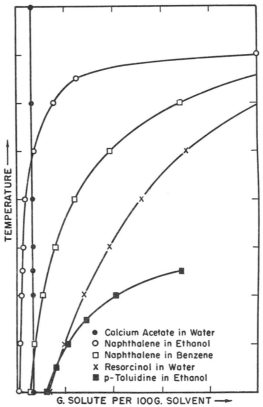

Fig. 20. Some typical temperature–solubility curves.

often depends on the solvent, and in this respect a "poor" solvent may prove better than a "good" one. Hence, a solvent satisfactory for crystallization of a substance may not be suitable for its recrystallization. If the crystallizand is very soluble in the cold or very sparingly soluble in the hot solvent, a mixture of two miscible solvents, one a "good" solvent, the other a "poor" solvent, may prove of value. Consequently, it is often important to know which solvents have low dissolving power for the crystallizand.

The addition of an *inorganic or organic salt* to water may give a solution capable of dissolving organic compounds which are insoluble or only sparingly soluble in pure water; this phenomenon, known as *hydrotropy*,[459] solubilization, or "salting in," may be used in recrystallization. Thus, purpurin was purified[460] by recrystallization from aqueous alum solution, thereby removing much of the contaminating alizarin, which was considerably less soluble. In a similar procedure, naphthalene[461] was recrystallized from aqueous soap solution by warming to 85°C. and slowly cooling the solution. Borax solution has also found use.[462] The sodium salts of benzene-, toluene-, and xylenesulfonic acids are excellent "hydrotropes."

In *preparing the solution*, it is usually desirable to dissolve the substance as rapidly as possible. To this end, a solid should be finely powdered and added to the solvent with swirling or stirring at a suitable temperature. As a rule, the minimum volume of solvent to effect dissolution is employed, and centrifuging, filtration, or hot filtration may be necessary (see Chapters IV and V). Heating with solvents should always be conducted under reflux.

Supersaturation is obtained by cooling,[463] by evaporating off solvent,[464] by adding a cosolute, or by combinations of these procedures. Depending on the nature of the system, these operations are usually effected gradually and stepwise, bearing in mind that nucleus formation and growth may be slow. Thionyldiglycolic acid[405] and certain sugars crystallize when evaporated slowly under diminished pressure. Crops of crystals should be collected periodically, dried, and examined, for example, for change in melting point. Sometimes an oil separates above the crystallization temperature, but often the temperature of the solution in which oil appears is below the melting point of the crystallizand. The first traces of oil may extract impurities from the solution and their removal frequently affords purification, enhancing crystallization of the rest of the solute.

An instructive example of the crystallization of a difficultly crystallizable substance by cooling is the crystallization of rubber hydrocarbon[466] from

[459] C. Neuberg, *Biochem. Z.*, **76**, 107 (1916). F. Boedecker, *Ber.*, **53**, 1852 (1920); H. Meyer and K. Bernhauer, *Monatsh.*, **54**, 724 (1929).

[460] E. Schunck and H. Römer, *Ber.*, **10**, 175, 550 (1877).

[461] G. Link, Ger. Pat. 35,168 (1885). *Friedlaender*, **1**, 11 (1888).

[462] R. Palm, *Z. anal. Chem.*, **22**, 324 (1883).

[463] H. Meyer and A. Hofmann, *Monatsh.*, **37**, 685 (1916). W. Hempel, *Ber.*, **31**, 2993 (1898).

[464] See Chapter II of Part II. E. W. Washburn, *J. Phys. Chem.*, **31**, 1246 (1927). C. W. Davis, *Chemist-Analyst*, **27**, 19 (1918). J. A. Reavell, Brit. Pats. 553,019 (1943); 553,200 (1943); *C. A.*, **38**, 4161, 4841 (1944); *Inst. Chem. Engrs. London* and *Soc. Chem. Ind. London Chem. Eng. Group*, Advance copy, Feb. 8, 1944, pp. 2-12. M. Déribéré, *Electricité*, **26**, 33 (1942); *Chem. Centr.*, **114**, I, 660 (1943); *C. A.*, **38**, 4474 (1944).

[465] M. Gazdar and S. Smiles, *J. Chem. Soc.*, **93**, 1833 (1908).

[466] W. H. Smith, C. P. Saylor, and H. J. Wing, *Bur. Standards J. Research*, **10**, 479 (1933).

solution. First, impurities of protein nature were removed, giving a transparent, colorless glass. Then a very dilute (0.05%) solution in ether was prepared and cooled to −65 °C. in order to assist formation of nuclei in the highly mobile solution. After nuclei had formed, the temperature was raised to −58° to enable growth to proceed at a reasonable pace, giving spherulites of thin needles.

Evaporation may simultaneously cool the solution, as in the crystallization of certain substances from liquefied butane. With other readily volatilized solvents, e.g., ether, the spontaneous cooling may not be as great, though still appreciable. Such rapid evaporation from an open vessel should be employed only if the substance to be crystallized is insensitive to water and air, and nonhygroscopic. Otherwise, it should be conducted in a vacuum desiccator or other suitable apparatus. Large adiabatic crystallizers, in which the temperature is lowered according to a rigid time schedule by automatic increase of the applied vacuum, are used industrially (see Sect. IV.2).

The amount of a compound dissolved in a definite volume of a given solvent may often be diminished by *introduction of an appropriate second solute*—solid, liquid, or gas. The addition of a soluble *solid* to a solution, usually aqueous, of an organic compound, in order to obtain a supersaturated solution from which material may crystallize, is often termed "salting out," since, as a rule, the added solute is an inorganic salt. It is a common practice in the dye industry.[467] Substances which have been used successfully include: potassium carbonate, potassium citrate, sodium chloride, sodium sulfate, sodium acetate, ammonium chloride, ammonium sulfate, ammonium oxalate, and magnesium sulfate. For example, murexide[468] may be recrystallized from water by adding ammonium chloride. Similarly, the solubility of sodium naphthalene-1,6-disulfonate is 18% in water,[469] but falls to 1% in 25% sodium chloride. Sodium and potassium salts often crystallize out on addition of sodium or potassium hydroxide to their aqueous solutions. It is sometimes possible to crystallize water-soluble substances of high molecular weight, e.g., virus proteins,[470] bacterial toxins,[471] enzymes,[472] etc., by salting out. The concentration of

[467] H. E. Fierz-David and L. Blangey, *Fundamental Processes of Dye Chemistry*, translation by P. W. Vittum. Interscience, New York-London, 1949.

[468] A. Hantzsch and R. Robison, *Ber.*, **43**, 92 (1910).

[469] N. A. Tolmachev, *Anilinokrasochnaya Prom.*, **5**, 219 (1935); *C. A.*, **30**, 7014 (1936).

[470] W. M. Stanley, *J. Phys. Chem.*, **42**, 55 (1938). W. C. Price, *Science*, **101**, 515 (1945).

[471] C. Lamanna, O. E. McElroy, and H. W. Eklund, *Science*, **103**, 613 (1946). L. Pillemer, R. Wittler, and D. B. Grossberg, *ibid.*, **103**, 615 (1946).

[472] J. H. Northrop, M. Kunitz, and R. M. Herriot, *Crystalline Enzymes*. Columbia Univ. Press, New York, 1948.

protein and salt,[472,473] and the conditions of temperature and pH must be kept within narrow limits; otherwise, amorphous instead of crystalline material may be deposited. The product is then repeatedly recrystallized in a similar manner until its solubility is constant. An application of "salting out" to microscopic identification of organic compounds has been described.[474] Addition of certain inorganic salts to solutions of various organic compounds results in the ready formation of crystals of characteristic appearances.

If, at the usual working temperatures, the crystallizand is too soluble in one solvent but too little soluble in another to permit its crystallization from either, it is often possible to crystallize it *by adding poor solvent to the solution in the good one*. This method is particularly useful for substances which decompose on treatment with hot solvent. Even when a substance can be crystallized in other ways, use of a solvent pair often proves advantageous because of the possibility of obtaining a higher yield of crystals. The two solvents need not be miscible in all proportions so long as the desired effect can be produced in the range of mutual solubility. The solubility in a mixed solvent[475] is not always a linear function of the relative concentration of the two individual solvents. For optimum yield it is often necessary to adjust the relative proportions of the two solvents quite carefully Thus, in the crystallization of digitalin,[476] the largest yield was obtained from 85% aqueous alcohol. Similarly, the gliadins are insoluble in absolute ethanol and more soluble in 75% aqueous alcohol than in water. Magnesium diphenyl is sparingly soluble in ether and insoluble in benzene but readily soluble in ether–benzene because of formation of a compound with ether which is benzene-soluble.[477] Barium choleate is practically insoluble in either ethanol or water, but readily soluble in aqueous ethanol because of hydrate formation.[478] Some compounds are more soluble[479] in aqueous pyridine or pyridine monohydrate than in either pyridine or water; cocacitrin[480] is more soluble in aqueous acetone than in acetone or water. Cinchonine is almost eight times as soluble in 23% alcohol–chloroform as in absolute alcohol,[481] and over twenty times as soluble in the mixed solvent as in chloroform alone.

[473] E. J. Cohn, I. Fankuchen, J. L. Oncley, H. B. Vickery, and B. E. Warren, *Ann. N. Y. Acad. Sci.*, 41, 77 (1941). K. Bailey, *Trans. Faraday Soc.*, 38, 186 (1942). B. Stallmann, *Arch. exptl. Path. Pharmakol.*, 185, 77 (1937); *C. A.*, 32, 5995 (1938). W. C. M. Lewis, *Chem. Revs.*, 8, 81 (1931).

[474] L. Rosenthaler, *Mikrochemie*, 16, 37 (1934–1935); 18, 50 (1935).

[475] D. Tyrer, *J. Chem. Soc.*, 97, 1778 (1910).

[476] H. Kiliani, *Arch. Pharm.*, 233, 299 (1895).

[477] S. Hilpert and G. Grüttner, *Ber.*, 46, 1680 (1913).

[478] F. Mylius, *Ber.*, 20, 1970 (1887).

[479] W. M. Dehn, *J. Am. Chem. Soc.*, 39, 1399 (1917).

[480] O. Hesse, *J. prakt. Chem.*, 66, 401 (1902).

[481] A. C. Oudemans, Jr., *Ann.*, 166, 65 (1873).

A solution, hot or cold, of crystallizand in good solvent is prepared, and, if necessary, filtered. The "poor" solvent, at about the same temperature as the solution, is now added dropwise with swirling or stirring, until crystallization begins, or a faint opalescence appears, depending on which takes place first. The flask is then stoppered. It frequently happens that, on adding the poor solvent, the degree of supersaturation attained is too high, and the resulting precipitate may be colloidal or oily; when the supersaturation is low, the product may be comprised of a few large crystals. It is therefore advisable[482] to add the poor solvent cautiously in portions. Should crystals separate, more poor solvent should be added very cautiously, e.g., 1 ml. dropwise per day, in order to maintain supersaturation. If crystallization does not occur on standing, the solution is slowly cooled. If a noncrystalline, strong opalescence or an oily layer forms, it is sometimes advisable to redissolve it by dropwise addition of good solvent, with swirling, and then to cool. At this point, scratching and other means of inducing crystallization should be applied. Occasionally it is worth while to filter the faintly opalescent solution, or to warm it slightly until the opalescence just disappears and allow to cool slowly. If an oily, uncrystallizable layer forms, the mother liquor may sometimes crystallize after filtration or decantation. In some cases it is advantageous[483] repeatedly to dissolve the crystallizand in good solvent and reprecipitate it slowly with a miscible poor solvent at a suitable temperature, while stirring vigorously. After repeating this procedure a number of times, the material often separates in very small balls or spheres which, under the microscope, are seen to be made up of minute crystals; further treatment may give individual crystals. If desired, a system of fractional precipitation may be employed. The method is useful if the impurity remains dissolved in the resulting solvent pair. It is sometimes found advisable to add poor solvent cautiously in such a manner that, owing to difference in density, two layers form. Slow diffusion may then take place, resulting in gradual achievement of supersaturation and formation of crystals. In some instances, it may prove advantageous to *reverse* the procedure, e.g., to heat the crystallizand with the poor solvent and then add the good solvent dropwise through the top of the condenser until the substance *just* dissolves.

Alcohols of low molecular weight are often used in combination with a nonpolar solvent in order to give a solvent pair suited to the polar character of the crystallizand. The importance of viscosity should be kept in mind when mixed solvents are employed, particularly in conjunction with extreme cooling. Thus, methanol may prove more suitable than ethanol

[482] P. Blackman, *J. Phys. Chem.*, **13**, 436 (1909).
[483] R. Willstätter and F. Hocheder, *Ann.*, **354**, 221, 245, 246 (1907).

or higher alcohols because of its lower viscosity; similarly, ether or ethyl acetate may be preferable to more viscous solvents having about the same dissolving power.   Since so many compounds are but sparingly soluble in petroleum ether and ligroin, these hydrocarbons are often excellent as poor solvents.   Useful combinations are: ether–pentane, chloroform–hexane, xylene–heptane, and carbon disulfide–petroleum ether.   Benzoic anhydride has been recrystallized[484] from benzene plus light petroleum, and theobromine tetra-O-acetyl-β-D-glucoside from ethyl acetate plus light petroleum.[485]   Water is often added to such solvents as methanol, ethanol, acetone, or glacial acetic acid.   Thus, the methyl carbonate of p-hydroxybenzoic acid was crystallized[486] by adding water gradually, to opalescence, to a hot solution in acetone, and cooling slowly.   Some compounds are much more soluble in methanol than in ethanol, and a combination of the two solvents is sometimes used to prepare a supersaturated solution. Thus, 6-D-glucosidogalactose was crystallized[487] by dissolving the glasslike material in boiling absolute methanol, cooling, adding ethanol, and evaporating the solution slowly in a vacuum desiccator.   6-D-Glucosidodulcitol[487] was crystallized similarly; it was recrystallized by suspending it in boiling absolute methanol, adding water dropwise until the substance just dissolved in the boiling solvent pair, and cooling.   Other solvent pairs which have been used include: ethanol plus ether, acetone, chloroform, xylene, acetic acid, or dioxane; methanol plus chloroform or glycerol; benzene plus chloroform, pyridine, or acetone; toluene plus ethanol or pyridine; xylene–phenol; nitrobenzene–aniline; chloroform plus acetone, acetic acid, ethyl acetate, or pyridine; ethyl acetate–acetic acid;   methylal–ether;   and pyridine plus ammonia or dioxane.   After preliminary purification, 2-benzyl-1-hydroxynaphthalene was recrystallized[488] from acetic acid–85% formic acid.   Mixed solvents may consist of *more than* 2 solvents.   Thus, 4-β-D-glucosidosorbitol was crystallized[489] by dissolving the sirupy material in methanol, adding ethanol to opalescence, adding a little water, and cooling.   Ascorbic acid may also be recrystallized with advantage from three solvents mixed together.[490]   In work with mixed solvents it is usually advantageous to use solvents of approximately the same boiling point, since a mixture of, say, ether and heptane might be unsatisfactory when filtering off the crystals, owing to faster evaporation of

[484] H. T. Clarke and E. J. Rahrs, *Org. Syntheses*, **3**, 21 (1923).

[485] E. Fischer and B. Helferich, *Ber.*, **47**, 210 (1914).

[486] E. Fischer, *Ber.*, **41**, 2875 (1908).

[487] P. A. Levene and R. S. Tipson, *J. Biol. Chem.*, **125**, 355 (1938).

[488] W. J. Hickinbottom, *Reactions of Organic Compounds*. 2nd ed., Longmans, Green, New York, 1948, p. 94.

[489] P. A. Levene and M. Kuna, *J. Biol. Chem.*, **127**, 49 (1939).

[490] R. W. Herbert *et al.*, *J. Chem. Soc.*, **1933**, 1270.

the ether than of the heptane and consequent deposition of oily product, or impurity on the crystals.

If, on the other hand, the crystallizand is dissolved in a mixed solvent whose poor solvent is less volatile than the good solvent, or which forms an azeotrope richer in the good solvent, evaporation leads to supersaturation and may cause crystallization. Veratrine[491] was crystallized by dissolving it in alcohol, adding water to slight turbidity, and evaporating by gentle warming. In other cases, the evaporation is conducted in an open dish at room temperature to give slower loss of solvent. Thus, many silver salts and acid amides are soluble in concentrated aqueous ammonia and crystallize well on gradual evaporation of the ammonia. On allowing hydrochloric acid to evaporate from a solution of α,α- plus β,β-dimethyladipic acid in concentrated aqueous hydrochloric acid, only the α,α-acid crystallized out.[492] Evaporation under diminished pressure is useful when the poor solvent in a nonazeotropic pair is only slightly less volatile than the good solvent or the two form an azeotrope[493] containing a preponderance of the good solvent. By appropriate choice of an absorbent it is sometimes possible to evaporate preferentially the less-volatile solvent in a vacuum desiccator. For instance, by using calcium oxide,[494] which absorbs water but not alcohol, as the desiccator absorbent, water may be removed from aqueous alcohol, leaving a more alcoholic solution in which crystals may appear. This procedure was employed[494] to crystallize materials much more soluble in water than in alcohol.

Sometimes a liquid may be added to remove some of the good solvent of a solvent pair by extraction and so produce a supersaturated solution.[495] For example, a substance which is readily soluble in benzene plus alcohol but only sparingly soluble in aqueous alcohol or benzene may be dissolved in the former mixture; on adding a little water and shaking, some alcohol is extracted into the aqueous layer and the substance may crystallize from the benzene–alcohol solution, which now contains less alcohol. Instead of *shaking* with the absorbing liquid, it may prove advantageous to add this liquid cautiously in such a manner that the two layers form *without* agitation. Slow diffusion may then occur, resulting in supersaturation. Thus, cholic acid was crystallized[496] by dissolving it in alcohol, adding water to faint opalescence, and overlaying the solution with ether.

In order to grow large crystals of certain substances, the solution, *e.g.*,

[491] E. Bosetti, *Arch. Pharm.*, [3], **21**, 81 (1883).
[492] A. W. Crossley and N. Renouf, *J. Chem. Soc.*, **89**, 1552 (1906).
[493] L. H. Horsley, *Ind. Eng. Chem., Anal. Ed.*, **19**, 508 (1947).
[494] A. Rümpler, *Ber.*, **33**, 3474 (1900).
[495] R. Willstätter and M. Benz, *Ann.*, **358**, 277 (1908).
[496] H. Bayer, *Z. physiol. Chem.*, **3**, 293 (1879).

in benzene or chloroform, is exposed to the vapors of a "poor" solvent, say, methanol. These are slowly absorbed, and slow growth of large crystals may result. Thus, by allowing an alcoholic solution of a phenyl-ammonium derivative to stand in a desiccator containing a dish of ether, crystallization was successfully induced.[497] Similarly, a solution in con-centrated sulfuric acid may be permitted to absorb water vapor slowly. The introduction of a gaseous solute in order to produce a supersaturated solution, without chemical reaction, is a procedure rather extensively employed in inorganic chemistry, but it has found little application in organic chemistry. Certain compounds may be crystallized from chloro-form, alcohol, or ether by saturation with carbon dioxide under a pressure of 3 atmospheres.[498] Aromatic sulfonic acids are conveniently crystallized by passing hydrogen chloride into the aqueous solution.[499]

Some materials may be recrystallized by chemical treatment, by dissolv-ing in an acid and reprecipitating by cautious addition of alkali, or vice versa. Cocacitrin[500] was recrystallized by dissolving the crude material in hot barium hydroxide solution, filtering, and adding to the cooled filtrate a slight excess of acetic acid. Similarly, apocupreine[501] was dissolved in sodium hydroxide solution, freed from alkali-insoluble impurities, and pre-cipitated by passing in carbon dioxide to pH 8.

2. Induction of Nucleus Formation

In order to induce a compound to crystallize, it is often necessary to subject it systematically to a variety of treatments in the hope that one of them may lead to formation of crystal nuclei; sometimes a combination of treatments is necessary. These techniques mainly involve orienting in-fluences, the effect of foreign particles and surfaces, or mechanical agitation and shock. Microchemical application of the various types of stimulus has been described.[502]

Crystallization, particularly of sirups, "amorphous solids," and gums, is often induced by *extraction* with a solvent which does not appreciably dissolve the crystallizand but which may dissolve out certain impurities,[503] give an interface effect (see Sect. II.1.A), or cause polymorphic transforma-

[497] M. S. Kharasch and L. Chalkley, Jr., *J. Am. Chem. Soc.*, **46**, 1211 (1924).

[498] C. Weitenkampf, German Pats. 57,393 (1890) and 69,884 (1892); *Ber.*, **25²**, 88 (1892); **26⁴**, 900 (1893).

[499] J. H. Kastle, *Am. Chem. J.*, **44**, 483 (1910).

[500] O. Hesse, *J. prakt. Chem.*, **66**, 401 (1902).

[501] R. S. Tipson and L. H. Cretcher, *J. Am. Chem. Soc.*, **64**, 1162 (1942).

[502] F. Amelink, *Pharm. Weekblad*, **68**, 1086 (1931); *C. A.*, **26**, 936 (1932).

[503] P. A. Levene and R. S. Tipson, *J. Biol. Chem.*, **93**, 631 (1931); **105**, 419 (1934).

tion. Treatment may consist in digestion with the boiling solvent under reflux or extraction in a Soxhlet apparatus, followed by appropriate supercooling, or in long shaking with the poor solvent in the cold.[504] Sometimes contact with the poor solvent for several days at room temperature is effective; thus, sugar acetates[505] are often crystallized by letting them stand under water to dissolve out acetic acid and other impurities. A variant of this procedure consists in the lixiviation, trituration, or "rubbing" of gums and sirups. The substance is covered with a small layer of a liquid in which it is only sparingly soluble. It is then rubbed with a stirring rod or ground with a pestle, for perhaps an hour at a time. Crystallization may set in, probably because of the effects previously mentioned, together with the extraction. Addition of a little kieselguhr,[506] silica gel, or charcoal sometimes helps in crystallization by rubbing. Another method is to extract the *solution* with a practically immiscible liquid[507] which dissolves out impurity.

Crystal nuclei often originate at surfaces, *e.g.*, the walls of the container. Scratched or roughened glass may be particularly effective, and it is desirable to choose a container of such size and shape that there is maximum "contact," *i.e.*, ratio of surface to volume.[508] Surfaces of different materials may differ in their effectiveness. A *thin film* of the liquid may be prepared by placing a few drops in a test tube and then rotating it almost horizontally. The available surface may be still further increased by introduction of a glass bead[509] which may be precooled in dry ice. A thin film may also be prepared by dissolving a small amount of crystallizand in a volatile solvent and allowing the solution to evaporate on a watch glass, or in a desiccator if hygroscopic.

However, in general, it may be advisable to set aside a thin film in a dish open to the air, at room temperature or in the refrigerator, so that *dust* effective in causing crystallization may have access to the material. Compounds which must be protected against moisture or air may be stirred with various powders, *e.g.*, active carbon, quartz powder, or kieselguhr, and then may be preserved over a desiccant in the vacuum desiccator. In many cases, nucleation with a suitable *isomorphous or partially isomorphous*

[504] F. D. Chattaway and W. J. Lambert, *J. Chem. Soc.*, **107**, 1773 (1915). E. W. Washburn, *Bull. Am. Ceram. Soc.*, **14**, 138 (1935). E. Maas, *Ber.*, **41**, 1637 (1908). O. Dimroth and K. Pfister, *ibid.*, **43**, 2763 (1910). R. Willstätter and A. Pfannenstiel, *Ann.*, **358**, 226 (1908).

[505] E. Fischer, *Ber.*, **49**, 584 (1916).

[506] W. Will, *Ber.*, **41**, 1112, 1118 (1908).

[507] D. M. Jackman, U. S. Pat. 1,801,509 (Apr. 21, 1931); *C. A.*, **25**, 3486 (1931).

[508] J. Piazza, *Anales asoc. quim. argentina*, **27**, 145 (1939); *C. A.*, **34**, 289 (1940).

[509] D. E. Kenyon and G. A. Hulett, *J. Am. Chem. Soc.*, **56**, 1649 (1934).

substance[510] (see Sections II.1.C and II.8) will induce crystallization. Compounds which may be worth trying[511] include crystalline homologs, derivatives, isomers, polymers, and those which give a *molecular compound*[512] with the crystallizand.   Thus, triphenylpropane was successfully nucleated with a trace of crystalline triphenylbutane[513]; a supercooled melt of citraconic anhydride crystallized[514] on adding a trace of itaconic anhydride; *m*-cresol,[515] previously thought to be noncrystallizable, crystallized on cooling to −18°C. and nucleating with phenol; ethyl acetanilide[515] was nucleated with methyl acetanilide; and 4-chloroquinoline crystallized on nucleating with 2-chloroquinoline.[516]   Small test samples of the supercooled liquid should be nucleated with traces of a variety of crystalline compounds.   Should crystallization then take place, a trace of the resulting crystals, as free as possible from the introduced nucleator, is employed for nucleation of the main portion.

Scratching the inner surface of the container with a glass rod is probably the most common method of inducing crystallization.   This method may be[517] particularly effective because it consists of a series of impacts.   It might also be due to roughening of the surface.   On the other hand, scratching of glass on glass produces some glass powder,[518] and it was considered that these particles serve as nuclei.   However, in some cases, a rod tipped with a rubber sheath gives[519] better results than one of bare glass and it was suggested that the effect is mainly electrostatic.   Glass particles formed by scratching are negatively charged,[520] and glass powder is ineffective[521] unless formed in the presence of the crystallizand.   In some cases, friction between metal and glass is more effective[517] than that between glass and glass.   Of the various metals examined, copper gave the best results. The tip of a glass rod used for scratching may be fire-polished to remove

[510] M. Hasselblatt, *Z. anorg. Chem.*, **89**, 53 (1914).   A. Tschermak-Seysenegg, *Mikrochemie*, **27**, 96 (1939).   P.-E. Lecoq de Boisbaudran, *Ann. chim. el phys.*, [4], **9**, 173 (1866).   D. Gernez, *Compt. rend.*, **63**, 843 (1866).   J. M. Thomson, *J. Chem. Soc.*, **35**, 196 (1879).   J. M. Thomson and W. P. Bloxam, *ibid.*, **41**, 379 (1882).   A. E. Tutton, *ibid.*, **65**, 628 (1894).

[511] C. Weygand, *Z. anorg. allgem. Chem.*, **224**, 265 (1935).

[512] M. Brandstätter, *Mikrochemie ver. Mikrochim. Acta*, **44**, 142 (1942); *Mikroscopie*, **7**, 37 (1952).   J. Willems, *Naturwissenschaften*, **36**, 373 (1949); *Discussions Faraday Soc.*, **5**, 283 (1949); *Z. Elektrochem.*, **56**, 348 (1952).

[513] M. Gomberg and L. H. Cone, *Ber.*, **39**, 2957 (1906).

[514] R. Anschütz, *Ber.*, **14**, 2788 (1881).

[515] W. Staedel, *Ber.*, **18**, 3443 (1885).

[516] Z. H. Skraup, *Monatsh.*, **10**, 730 (1889).

[517] S. W. Young, *J. Am. Chem. Soc.*, **33**, 148 (1911).

[518] R. Fricke, *Z. Elektrochem.*, **28**, 244 (1922).

[519] L. Dede, *Z. Elektrochem.*, **28**, 364 (1922).

[520] R. Fricke, *Z. Elektrochem.*, **28**, 365 (1922); *Kolloid-Z.*, **31**, 80 (1922).

[521] R. Fricke, *Z. Elektrochem.*, **29**, 44 (1923).

jagged edges and should then be lightly roughened with emery paper. Sometimes, a pine-stick applicator gives better results than a glass rod. Scratching should be repeated frequently during cooling or other operations tried for nucleus formation.

Agitation often induces crystallization. It is sometimes useful to continue the treatment over a long period of time. The speed of nucleus formation depends on the manner of agitation. Besides rocking, shaking, or stirring, agitation may be produced by bubbling gas[522] through the liquid to be crystallized. Mechanical swirling is often advantageous, since crystallization on the closure can be avoided. Other ways of agitating consist in tapping the outside of the container with a small electric hammer[523] for a prolonged period, or in filtering or forcing the liquid through a fine orifice. Water[524] could be frozen repeatedly at about 0.02° below its melting point if stimulated by the impact of a 37-g. hammer falling 11 mm. onto an anvil in the water. The degree of supercooling necessary to cause crystallization was found to decrease with increased magnitude of the impact. An impact of 20,000 atmospheres was used in some experiments.[525] "Prince Rupert's tears,"[526] prepared by allowing hot drops of glass to fall into cold water, disrupt, with a slight detonation, into a fine powder, when they are scratched or the thin tip is broken. This has been used for inducing crystallization. The effect presumably depends on the production of shock or supersonic waves and glass dust.

Finally, there may be mentioned some experiments on the induction of nucleus formation in readily crystallizable compounds which may prove of value for other crystallizands. *Ultrasonic irradiation*[527] increases the number of centers of crystal-

---

[522] J. Bock, Ger. Pat. 219,749 (1906); *C. A.*, **4**, 2187 (1910). I. G. Farbenindustrie A.-G., French Pat. 656,642 (1928); *C. A.*, **23**, 4282 (1929).

[523] S. W. Young, *J. Am. Chem. Soc.*, **33**, 148 (1911). S. W. Young and R. J. Cross, *ibid.*, **33**, 1375 (1911). S. W. Young and W. J. Van Sicklen, *ibid.*, **35**, 1067 (1913). L. M. Dennis, R. B. Corey, and R. W. Moore, *ibid.*, **46**, 657 (1924).

[524] S. W. Young and W. J. Van Sicklen, *J. Am. Chem. Soc.*, **35**, 1067 (1913). S. W. Young, *ibid.*, **33**, 148 (1911).

[525] Earl of Berkeley, *Phil. Mag.*, **24**, 254 (1912).

[526] J. Beckmann, *Beyträge zur Geschichte der Erfindungen*, Leipzig, **4**, 420 (1799); London, **2**, 241 (1846). B. DeMonconys, *Journal de Voyages*, Lyon, **2**, 162 (1666). J. C. Schulenburg, *Springende Gläser samt ihren Eigenschaften*, Göttingen, 1695. J. W. Mellor, *A Comprehensive Treatise on Inorganic and Theoretical Chemistry*, Vol. 6, Longmans, Green, London, 1925, p. 530.

[527] R. W. Wood and A. L. Loomis, *Phil. Mag.*, [7], **4**, 417 (1927). R. W. Wood, *Supersonics, The Science of Inaudible Sounds*, Brown Univ., Providence, 1939, pp. 83–84. P. N. Shablykin, *Mineral'. Syr'e*, **12**, 28 (1937); *Khim. Referat. Zhur.*, **1**, 23 (1938); *C. A.*, **33**, 6106 (1939). V. Altberg and V. Lavrov, *Acta Physicochim. U. S. S. R.*, **11**, 287 (1939); *C. A.*, **34**, 3554 (1940). See K. Sollner, *Chem. Revs.*, **34**, 371 (1944); "Sonic and Ultrasonic Waves in Colloid Chemistry" in J. Alexander, ed., *Colloid Chemistry*, Vol. 5, Reinhold, 1944, pp. 337–373. *Cf.* L. Bergmann, *Ultrasonics*, translation by H. S. Hatfield, Bell, London, 1938.

lization in supercooled organic liquids.[528] In molten piperine, undercooled some 30 to 70°, the rate of nucleus formation and the rate of crystal growth increased[529] with the intensity of the field. The rate of crystallization of supercooled molten phenyl salicylate was also greatly increased[530] by an ultrasonic field; but low-frequency elastic vibrations[531] of 256–895 hertz *decreased* the number of centers of crystallization, presumably through the destruction of oriented cybomas. *Light* is said[532] to hasten the crystallization of sugars from honey, and similar claims regarding its effect on the crystallization of other substances are scattered through the literature. *Radium emanations (β-rays)*[533] and *x-rays*[534] sometimes enhance crystallization, by increasing the number of crystal nuclei formed, *e.g.*, in supercooled piperine. *Electric and magnetic fields* may orient molecules having permanent or induced electric or magnetic moments, so that crystallization is facilitated.[535] Crystallization then begins[536] in the body of the material instead of at a containing interface. An electric field caused marked crystallization[537] in supercooled melts of such polar compounds as benzonitrile, nitrobenzene, and fenchone, but had no effect on the crystallization of nonpolar substances. In addition, sparks, gases ionized by discharges, and brush discharges may initiate[536] crystallization. Application of a high-frequency current increased[538] the number of nuclei in undercooled melts, *e.g.*, of phenyl salicylate, but decreased their size; they became arranged along the lines of force. Electric or magnetic fields increased the number of centers of crystallization in undercooled phenyl salicylate or piperine by a factor of 200, and were more effective than radiation from radium.[539] The number of nuclei formed in a given time was[540] approximately proportional to the strength of the

[528] V. I. Danilov and B. M. Teverovskiĭ, *J. Exptl. Theoret. Phys. U. S. S. R.*, 10, 1305 (1940); *C. A.*, 35, 5368 (1941). Mitsubishi Electrical Instruments Co., Jap. Pat. 155,-066 (1943); *C. A.*, 44, 9 (1950).

[529] V. I. Danilov, E. E. Pluzhnik, and B. M. Teverovskiĭ, *J. Exptl. Theoret. Phys. U. S. S. R.*, 9, 66 (1939); *C. A.*, 33, 8071 (1939).

[530] R. Y. Berlaga and K. K. Demidov, *J. Exptl. Theoret. Phys. U. S. S. R.*, 9, 889 (1939); *C. A.*, 35, 5021 (1941). R. Y. Berlaga, *ibid.*, 16, 647 (1946); *C. A.*, 41, 326 (1947).

[531] G. L. Mikhnevich and P. I. Dombrovskiĭ, *Acta Physicochim. U. R. S. S.*, 12, 437 (1940); *C. A.*, 34, 7683 (1940).

[532] E. I. Fulmer, O. W. Park, and J. C. Williams, *Iowa Agr. Expt. Sta., Rept. State Apiarist*, 62–63 (1935).

[533] L. Frischauer, *Compt. rend.*, 148, 1251 (1909). V. V. Kondoguri, *J. Russ. Phys.-Chem. Soc.*, Phys. Pt., 62, 451 (1930); *C. A.*, 26, 5236 (1932).

[534] D. Samuracas, *Compt. rend.*, 196, 418 (1933).

[535] Ternion A.-G., Brit. Pat., 417,501 (1934); *C. A.*, 29, 1178 (1935). L. Sprink and M. Sprink, French Pat. 866,491 (1941); *C. A.*, 43, 4587 (1949). J. Blandin, *Compt. rend.*, 229, 1075 (1949).

[536] K. Schaum and E. A. Scheidt, *Z. anorg. allgem. Chem.*, 188, 52 (1930).

[537] R. Swinne, *Wiss. Veröffentl. Siemens-Werken*, 15, 124 (1936); *C. A.*, 31, 4172 (1937).

[538] D. Samuracas, *Z. Krist.*, 85, 474 (1933).

[539] V. V. Kondoguri, *J. Russ. Phys.-Chem. Soc.*, Phys. Pt., 58, 279 (1926); *C. A.*, 21, 2207 (1927).

[540] V. V. Kondoguri, *Z. Physik*, 47, 589 (1928). See also, G. Foëx, *Compt. rend.*, 187, 822 (1928).

field applied; at constant field strength, the number increased with time until a constant state was attained. If the field strength was then increased, an increase in the number of nuclei again resulted until a new constant value was reached. The formation of crystal nuclei in piperine may be increased or decreased[541] by electric fields of 2000 to 4300 v. per centimeter, depending on the temperature. The untreated melt shows two maxima for number of nuclei, at 42 and 45°C., with a minimum at 43°; when the field is applied, the maxima and minimum move to lower temperatures. They are greatly increased by stronger fields. In thin layers of 2-naphthyl salicylate under an electric field, nuclei near the surface respond[542] to the field, but internal nuclei are unaffected.

For some substances, the number (N) of nuclei formed, per unit volume and time, increases[543] with *pressure*. At a given temperature, the properties of 2-naphthyl salicylate at 1 kg. per square centimeter are about the same as at 25° higher at 1000 kg. per square centimeter. With papaverine, N has a maximum at 40° at 1 kg. per square centimeter, and at 60° at 1000 kg. per square centimeter, but is not increased by further increase in pressure. The formation of new stable molecular modifications may account[544] for the change in N with pressure. If the melting point of the crystallizand increases at high pressures, supercooling may be dispensed with[545] by increasing the pressure while keeping the temperature at, or even above, the melting point displayed at atmospheric pressure. Using an apparatus[546] giving pressures up to 4000 kg. per square centimeter, it was possible to study the effect of pressure on crystallization, melting, and supercooling phenomena. Some modifications, *e.g.*, of phenol and ice, which are denser[547] than the usual crystals have been obtained. The effect of pressures of over 1000 atmospheres on the melting point of rubber,[548] and of 2995 kg. per square centimeter on those of 1-naphthylamine and *p*-azoxyanisole[549] has been ascertained. Rubber may be crystallized by application of high pressure,[550] but crystallization is inhibited[551] by very high pressure. Crystallization occurs when rubber and certain other macromolecular materials,[552]

[541] F. K. Gorskiĭ, *J. Exptl. Theoret. Phys. U. S. S. R.*, **4**, 522 (1934); *C. A.*, **29**, 2805 (1935).

[542] G. L. Mikhnevich, I. F. Brovko, and E. N. Ovchinnikova, *Acta Physicochim. U. R. S. S.*, **9**, 795 (1938); *C. A.*, **33**, 7635 (1939). G. L. Mikhnevich, I. F. Brovko, and A. V. Babadshan, *Acta Physicochim. U. R. S. S.*, **6**, 455 (1937); *C. A.*, **32**, 4403 (1938).

[543] M. Hasselblatt, *Z. anorg. allgem. Chem.*, **119**, 353 (1921).

[544] G. Tammann, *Z. physik. Chem.*, **82**, 172 (1913).

[545] I. N. Stranski, *J. Phys. Chem. U. S. S. R.*, **8**, 955 (1936); *C. A.*, **31**, 2059 (1937).

[546] W. Wahl, *Proc. Roy. Soc. London*, **A87**, 152 (1912); *Trans. Roy. Soc. London*, **A212**, 117 (1913).

[547] G. Tammann, *Z. physik. Chem.*, **69**, 569 (1909).

[548] L. A. Wood, N. Bekkedahl, and R. E. Gibson, *J. Chem. Phys.*, **13**, 475 (1945).

[549] N. A. Puschin and I. W. Grebenschtschikow, *Z. physik. Chem.*, **124**, 270 (1926).

[550] P. A. Thiessen and W. Kirsch, *Naturwissenschaften*, **26**, 387 (1938).

[551] R. B. Dow, *J. Chem. Phys.*, **7**, 201 (1939).

[552] H. Mark, *Ind. Eng. Chem.*, **34**, 449 (1942). T. Alfrey and H. Mark, *J. Phys. Chem.*, **46**, 112 (1942). W. O. Baker, C. S. Fuller, and N. R. Pape, *J. Am. Chem. Soc.*, **64**, 776 (1942). W. O. Baker, *Bell Labs. Record*, **23**, 97 (1945). *Cf.* L. A. Wood and N. Bekkedahl, *J. Applied Phys.*, **17**, 362 (1946). P. J. Flory, *J. Chem. Phys.*, **15**, 397 (1947).

e.g., plastics, are stretched. The crystalline structure usually disappears on relaxation.

Crystallization, either spontaneous or induced, *takes time*, and, consequently, patience and perseverance are often necessary. If all other methods fail, the sample should be divided into several portions, some of which are placed in stoppered containers and preserved at different temperatures, *e.g.*, at room temperature and in the refrigerator, respectively; another is placed in a dish and left open to air and dust. The samples should be kept for a long time and inspected, stirred, and scratched occasionally. A turanose sirup was kept[553] for many years before it crystallized; when once crystalline, it was readily recrystallized. Similarly, methyl D-riboside crystallized after standing for 9 months.[554] After nuclei have formed in a liquid, stirring may accelerate crystallization, presumably by distributing the nuclei throughout the liquid. Furthermore, the liquid should now be warmed somewhat[555] in order to encourage growth to visible crystals, and should be kept at this temperature until crystallization is complete.

IV. TECHNIQUES OF RECRYSTALLIZATION

Recrystallization is a repetitive process, the first cycle of which is identical with that of *crystallization* (see Sect. III) except that crystals of the substance are available for nucleation.

1. Recrystallization for Purification and Fractionation

A. PRINCIPLES

Addition of a trace[556] of crystals of the substance itself to the supercooled melt or supersaturated solution will cause crystallization at a rate in accordance with the properties and composition of the system. A scarcely detectable amount of impurity may sometimes so greatly diminish the velocity of crystallization, *e.g.*, with sugar sirups,[557] that nucleation produces no immediate effect. Sometimes, the introduced nuclei dissolve in the melt as a result of isomerization to an uncrystallizable material. Moreover, the crystallizand may be sensitive to heat and may undergo decomposition during dissolution or react with the solvent. Sometimes, if nucleation seems ineffective, it is advisable to crush the seed crystals to expose

[553] C. S. Hudson and E. Pacsu, *Science*, 69, 278 (1929).
[554] J. Minsaas, *Ann.*, 512, 286 (1934).
[555] D. Vorländer, J. Osterburg and O. Meye, *Ber.*, 56, 1139 (1923).
[556] D. McIntosh, *Trans. Roy. Soc. Can., III*, 13, 265 (1919).
[557] H. Kiliani, *Arch. Pharm.*, 254, 266 (1916).

fresh surfaces.   In addition, it must be borne in mind that there are crystal-lizable substances which have low crystallizability, and usually, a low melting point, and which separate from solution as difficultly crystallizable sirups, gums, or oils unless the solution is cooled *very slowly,* even though nucleating crystals are added.   Slow evaporation of a saturated solution may be more satisfactory.   In recrystallization for purification, an esti-mate of the effect obtained should be made after each recrystallization, preferably by two or more such criteria as melting point,[558] solubility,[559] countercurrent distribution,[560] partition chromatography,[561,562] optical activity, etc.   Recrystallization is repeated until the physical and chemical properties remain unchanged[563] on further recrystallization.

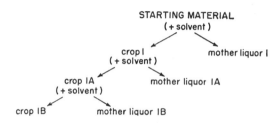

Fig. 21. Simple repeated recrystallization.

If *only one compound* in a mixture is to be isolated pure, if it *does not form solid solutions* with its contaminants, and crystallizes *first,* it will, except for adsorption and inclusion, separate pure at temperatures above that at which the eutectic composition crystallizes.   Hence, a few simple recrystallizations by cooling to a single lower temperature are usually all that is needed to give a highly pure sample.   Little attention is paid to the mother liquors, provided the percentage of impurity present is far below its proportion in its eutectic with the crystallizand.   However, with a larger proportion of impurity, still below this limit, purification will be attended by a large loss in yield if the mother liquor is discarded instead of being saved and separated into its components.

[558] See E. L. Skau and H. Wakeham, in A. Weissberger, ed., *Technique of Organic Chemistry.* Vol. I, 2nd ed., Interscience, New York-London, 1949, Chapter 3, Section II.2.

[559] H. Kiliani, *Arch. Pharm.,* **254,** 260 (1916).   E. Schmidt and R. Wilkendorf, *Ber.,* **55,** 320 (1922).   S. P. L. Sørensen and M. Høyrup, *Compt. rend. trav. lab. Carlsberg, Sér. chim.,* **12,** 213 (1917); *C. A.,* **12,** 2576 (1918).

[560] See Chapter II, this volume.

[561] A. J. P. Martin and R. L. M. Synge, *Biochem. J.,* **35,** 1358 (1941).

[562] See H. G. Cassidy, *Adsorption and Chromatography* (A. Weissberger, ed., *Technique of Organic Chemistry,* Vol. V), Interscience, New York-London, 1951.

[563] H. G. Cassidy, *J. Chem. Ed.,* **23,** 427 (1946).

If the impurity forms *solid solutions* with the desired compound, purity for the latter can be approached depending on the respective phase diagram and the initial proportion of impurity. If a very high degree of purity is desired, a large number of simple recrystallizations may be necessary. This will entail great loss of material unless fractional recrystallization is resorted to. Figure 21 shows schematically a sequence of *simple recrystallizations*. Just as in the process of repeated extraction,[560] if the proportion of impurity removed at each stage is *constant*, this series will constitute the first term of a binomial expansion. If dQ is the amount of one component separated in fraction dP of crystals, Q is the fraction of that component still remaining in the mother liquor, and P is the percentage of other solute as crystals, as a first approximation[564]:

$$dQ = kQ \, dP \quad \text{or} \quad Q_1 = e^{kP} \tag{34}$$

This has been expressed by Doerner and Hoskins[565] as:

$$dX/dY = kX/Y \quad \text{or} \quad \log (b/X) = k \log (b'/Y) \tag{35}$$

where the initial amounts of components in solution are b and b', respectively, the amounts in solution at the time of deposition on the crystal are X and Y, and k is the "partition factor." Small amounts of isomorphous impurity were found[566] to be distributed between liquid and crystals according to the Doerner-Hoskins formula in both rapid crystallization of a supersaturated solution and steady evaporation of a saturated solution.

Riehl[567] distinguishes three sets of conditions influencing distribution of *micro amounts* of impurity between crystal and solution. In slow crystallization from a slightly supersaturated solution, the ratio of impurity to main solute in each molecular layer as it separates may be *proportional* to that in the solution at that moment, so that the Doerner-Hoskins formula applies to the entire crystal. Should the impurity be concentrated in the crystal, the outer part will contain less than the inner, or vice versa if the crystal does not readily take up the impurity. In slow crystallization from a more supersaturated solution, it is assumed that, as each new molecular layer is laid down, the ratio of impurity to main component is the same as that in the solution. Hence, the ratio in the entire crystal is proportional to the ratio in the final solution, *i.e.*:

$$(X - b)/(Y - b') = kb/b' \tag{36}$$

[564] H. Schlundt, *U. S. Bur. Mines Tech. Paper*, No. **265**, 35 (1922).

[565] H. A. Doerner and W. M. Hoskins, *J. Am. Chem. Soc.*, **47**, 662 (1925).

[566] H. Käding, R. Mumbrauer, and N. Riehl, *Z. physik. Chem.*, **A161**, 362 (1932).

[567] N. Riehl, *Z. physik. Chem.*, **A177**, 224 (1936)

In rapid crystallization from supersaturated solution, it is thought that, in the presence of plenty of nuclei, there is a metastable equilibrium between crystals and solution because of the greater solubility of very small crystals; the Doerner-Hoskins formula also applies to this case, but the distribution coefficient is different.

In many cases, e.g., the higher fatty acids, purification by recrystallization is of little use until the purity has been at least raised to over 80% by some other means. Only part of the main solute should be allowed to crystallize out in each recrystallization, in order to retain impurity in the mother liquor. De Visser[568] recrystallized stearic acid 51 times and palmitic acid 36 times from alcohol, but successive use of several different solvents may often prove more efficacious; the freezing points of these acids have been raised in this way, and still further raised by distillation followed by twenty recrystallizations from various solvents.[569]

Fractional recrystallization differs from simple repeated recrystallization in that both the crystals and the mother liquor are repeatedly fractionated. In the simplest case, this may be accomplished by collecting the crystals in successive fractions, e.g., on stepwise cooling of the solution. More strictly, fractional recrystallization involves the separation of *two or more compounds*, with the objective of *isolating each in pure condition*. In the purification of a *single* compound, resort must be had to fractional recrystallization when the percentage of impurity is appreciable. If the compound and its impurities form solid solutions, elaborate fractionations may be necessary in order to obtain a pure sample without excessive loss of material.

As previously mentioned, the solubility of a substance in a solution of another solute is usually different from its solubility in the pure solvent, and the feasibility of fractionation by recrystallization depends on the phase diagram of the system (Sects. II.9–10). However, in rare cases, a solution supersaturated with two solutes may, in the absence of seed crystals of one solute, or if there is a great difference in rate of crystallization, deposit crystals of the other solute only. For example, if a mixture of two *nonisomorphous* compounds is dissolved, filtered free from insoluble impurities, allowed to cool slowly without movement, and nucleated with crystals of one solute, it sometimes happens[570] that that substance *only* crystallizes from the solution even though it is supersaturated with both compounds. A mixture of the *cis* and *trans* isomers of dinitrostilbene was dissolved[571]

[568] L. E. O. de Visser, *Rec. trav. chim.*, **17**, 182, 346 (1898).

[569] J. C. Smith, *J. Chem. Soc.*, **1931**, 802. J. B. Guy and J. C. Smith, "Fatty Acids and Other Long-chain Compounds," in *Ann. Repts. on Progr. Chem. (Chem. Soc. London)*, **35**, 254, ref. 19 (1939).

[570] H. Biltz, *Ber.*, **44**, 297 (1911).

[571] J. Thiele and O. Dimroth, *Ber.*, **28**, 1411 (1895).

in hot epichlorohydrin; on cooling, only the *trans* isomer separated. The mother liquor was evaporated to dryness and the material was dissolved in ethyl acetate. On cooling, and nucleating with a crystal of *trans* isomer, the rest of the *trans* isomer crystallized, leaving a supersaturated solution of the *cis* isomer. This was decanted and allowed to crystallize, giving the pure *cis* isomer. Similarly, the *cis* or *trans* isomers of diiodobenzalacetophenone could be crystallized at will[572] from a supersaturated solution of a mixture of the two by nucleation with one isomer or the other. Zinc ammonium DL-lactate was resolved by inoculating[573] the supersaturated aqueous solution with a crystal of the D- or the L-isomer. "Spontaneous" resolution of atropine occurs similarly.[574] Industrially, the method has been employed[575] for removing impurities by crystallization before crystallizing the desired compound.

If a solution of D-glucose or other reducing sugar is allowed to reach optical equilibrium by mutarotation, evaporated until fairly concentrated, and then nucleated with a trace of pure α-D-pyranose form, the α-D-pyranose form only will crystallize from the solution. As this crystallization proceeds, the original equilibrium is disturbed and β-form is transformed to the α-form until *all* the sugar is α-pyranose. Similarly, if the nucleating material is pure β-D-pyranose, the β-D-pyranose form only will crystallize and eventually all the sugar will be β-D-pyranose.

As mentioned above, the principles involved in *separation of solid solutions* by fractional recrystallization are identical with those of fractionation by extraction (see Chapter 11). The over-all process can be set up to follow the binomial theorem and is most efficient in terms of labor and yield when a constant proportion of crystals is collected in each recrystallization cycle. The optimum value of this proportion depends on the composition of the original mixture. If Z is the proportion which crystallizes in a single recrystallization, $1-Z$ represents the proportion in the mother liquor, and the binomial expansion is:

$$[Z + (1-Z)]^n = 1 \tag{37}$$

For a binary mixture of approximately *equal amounts*, the best separation, in terms of labor and yield, of both components requires that Z and $1-Z$ be equal, *i.e.*, that, in each recrystallization cycle, half[576] the material

[572] C. Dufraisse, *Ann. chim.*, [9], **17**, 133 (1922).

[573] T. Purdie and J. W. Walker, *J. Chem. Soc.*, **61**, 754 (1892).

[574] L. Anderson and D. W. Hill, *J. Chem. Soc.*, **1928**, 993. *Cf.* E. I. Rosenblum and W. S. Taylor, *J. Pharm. Pharmacol.*, **6**, 256 (1954).

[575] W. C. Weber, U. S. Pat. 2,091,898 (1937); *C. A.*, **31**, 7298 (1937). The Dorr Co., Inc., Brit. Pat. 431,812 (1935); *C. A.*, **30**, 5 (1936).

[576] Lord Rayleigh, *Phil. Mag.*, [5], **42**, 493 (1896). A. A. Sunier, *J. Phys. Chem.*, **33**, 577 (1929). T. W. Richards and N. F. Hall, *J. Am. Chem. Soc.*, **39**, 531 (1917). L. M. Dennis and R. W. G. Wyckoff, *ibid.*, **42**, 985 (1920). R. S. Mulliken and W. D. Harkins *ibid.*, **44**, 37 (1922).

is crystallized out and half remains in the mother liquor. If compounds A and B do not give a series of solid solutions of freezing points intermediate between those of A and B, only one of these compounds will eventually be isolated pure; the other end material is, for example, the solid solution of maximum or minimum melting point. The theory of fractional recrystallization,[577] including graphical treatment[578] and application to polycomponent systems,[579] has been evolved by mathematical analysis, and a detailed theoretical study[580] of some aspects of the subject has been made.

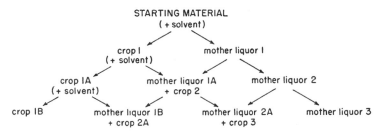

Fig. 22. "Triangular" fractional recrystallization.

The following schemes are those most commonly employed for fractional recrystallization.[581]

(a) Figure 22 shows the scheme often referred to as *"triangular recrystallization."* The starting material is dissolved in the solvent and caused to give crop 1, which is collected, dissolved in a fresh portion of the solvent, and caused to give crop 1A. For separation of a solute from a cosolute with which it forms solid solutions, enough solvent is usually taken each time to permit about half of the solid to crystallize on cooling or other treatment. The mother liquor of crop 1 is concentrated, *e.g.*, to half volume, and caused to give crop 2, which is then dissolved in the mother liquor of crop 1A, *e.g.*, by heating, and caused to give crop 2A. If their properties indicate that crop 2A is as pure as crop 1A, they are united; if not, crop 2A is recrystallized, from the mother liquor of crop 1B, if crop

[577] A. V. Rakovskii, *Trans. Inst. Pure Chem. Reagents U. S. S. R.*, No. **11**, 62 (1931); *C. A.*, **26**, 2363 (1932).

[578] E. A. Guggenheim and W. H. Campbell, *J. Soc. Chem. Ind. London*, **51**, 161T (1932).

[579] H. J. Garber and A. W. Goodman, *J. Phys. Chem.*, **45**, 573 (1941).

[580] N. L. Bowen, *Proc. Natl. Acad. Sci. U. S.*, **27**, 301 (1941); *Am. J. Sci.*, **38**, 207 (1914).

[581] R. S. Tipson, *Anal. Chem.*, **22**, 628 (1950). See also E. F. Joy and J. H. Payne, Jr., *Ind. Eng. Chem.*, **47**, 2157 (1955). M. L. Salutsky and J. G. Stites, Jr., *ibid.*, **47**, 2162 (1955).

1A had to be recrystallized. When crop 1 (A or B or C, etc.) has reached constant purity, recrystallization of it is stopped. The mother liquor becomes richer and richer in the other component(s), and, as a rule, in any impurity originally present in the solvent. As the number of recrystallizations is increased, the crystals become purer and purer, but the purer the

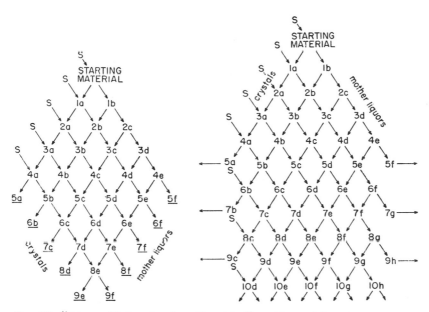

Fig. 23. "Diamond" fractional recrystallization.

Fig. 24. "Double withdrawal" fractional recrystallization.

fraction, the less its weight. Hence unless the object is the preparation of a small sample of very pure material, the simple triangular scheme may not be suitable. In order to obtain a higher yield, the "diamond" scheme of fractionation is preferred (see Fig. 23). At the nth row, when the outermost fractions have reached the desired degree of purity, they are set aside, and fractionation is continued, as shown, until all the material is obtained as crystals or final mother liquor. Enriched fractions may now be combined and again fractionally recrystallized.[582] However, this procedure is not ideal because fractions of different purities are united. If each fraction has about the same composition as the one "vertically" above it, an excellent method consists of double-withdrawal, as shown in Figure 24.

(b) When the main component is fairly soluble in the hot but only sparingly soluble in the cold solvent, and when it is desired to use as little sol-

[582] T. W. Richards and N. F. Hall, *J. Am. Chem. Soc.*, **39**, 531 (1917).

vent as possible, the following *alternative method* of *fractional recrystallization* may be employed. The same portion of solvent is, up to a point, repeatedly used. The starting material is divided into several equal parts, 1, 2, and 3, etc. (see Fig. 25). Part 1 is recrystallized from the minimum volume of hot solvent, giving crop 1A and mother liquor 1A; part 2 is then recrystallized from mother liquor 1A, yielding crop 2A and mother

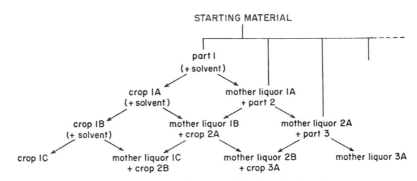

Fig. 25. Fractional recrystallization of aliquots.

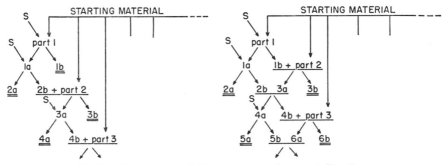

Fig. 26. Two-stage and three-stage batch recrystallizations.

liquor 2A, which is, in turn, used for the recrystallization of part 3, to give crop 3A. By this time, the mother liquor (3A) is probably about saturated with impurities, but, if not, may be used for a first recrystallization of still further portions of starting material. If not yet pure, crop 1A is recrystallized from *pure* solvent, giving crop 1B and mother liquor 1B. The latter is used for the recrystallization of crop 2A, and so on, the procedure being repeated until crop 1 (A, B, C, etc.) is pure. Then attention is devoted to the purification of crop 2 (A, B, C, etc.) in a similar manner. The final mother liquors are then combined and evaporated to yield crop 4, for example. If the ratio of the distribution constants is very large, and extreme purity is not desired, the procedure may be shortened by using a two-stage or three-stage scheme, as shown in Figure 26.   Of course, if only one component is desired, any of the foregoing schemes may often be greatly simplified by discarding highly impure fractions.[583]

The following are the principal methods employed for *fractionation by deposition of successive fractions* of crystals.   A solution of a compound and an impurity which form solid solutions with each other but not with the solvent will on *slow stepwise cooling* deposit a series of fractions of crystals, each of which may be less or more pure than the preceding crop.   Each fraction is then recrystallized, allowing only *part* of the main solute to crystallize out in each operation.   Each mother liquor may be evaporated to dryness and re-treated with a smaller volume of solvent, or may be used for redissolving an appropriate crop of crystals.   If *solid solutions are not formed*, each crop will be essentially pure main solute until the eutectic composition and temperature are reached.   Isolation of two substances in pure form by equilibrium fractional recrystallization of any one composition is here impossible, but the *most complete purification possible* for *one* compound can be obtained with such a system (see Sect. II.9).

The component glycerides of various fats and oils have been separated[584] by crystallization from acetone at -10, -20, and $-30°C$.   Saturated acids[585] were similarly separated from the acetone solutions of certain oils by crystallization at a series of temperatures down to $-40°$.   Compounds gaseous or liquid at room temperature may be purified by fractional recrystallization at very low temperatures.[586]   "Solvent dewaxing"[587] of lubricating oils is performed by dissolving the oil in a suitable solvent, *e.g.*, propane, ethylene dichloride, or benzene–acetone, and cooling to successively lower temperatures.   The wax which separates is filtered or centri-

[583] G. P. Baxter and E. E. Behrens, *J. Am. Chem. Soc.*, 54, 591 (1932).   A. A. Sunier, *J. Phys. Chem.*, 33, 577 (1929).

[584] T. P. Hilditch and L. Maddison, *J. Soc. Chem. Ind. (London)*, 61, 169 (1942)- *Cf.* T. P. Hilditch and J. P. Riley, *ibid.*, 64, 204 (1945).   F. D. Gunstone and T. P. Hilditch, *ibid.*, 65, 8 (1946).   T. P. Hilditch and J. P. Riley, *ibid.*, 65, 74 (1946).   T. P. Hilditch, M. L. Meara, and O. A. Roels, *ibid.*, 66, 284 (1947).   E. L. Jack and J. L. Henderson, *J. Dairy Sci.*, 28, 65 (1945).   E. L. Jack *et al.*, *J. Nutrition*, 30, 175 (1945). W. S. Singleton, M. G. Lambou, and A. E. Bailey, *Oil & Soap*, 22, 168 (1945).   F. A. Smith and J. B. Brown, *ibid.*, 22, 277 (1945).   D. Swern, H. B. Knight, J. T. Scanlan, and W. C. Ault, *ibid.*, 22, 302 (1945).   R. W. Riemenschneider, F. E. Luddy, M. L. Swain, and W. C. Ault, *ibid.*, 23, 276 (1946).

[585] D. S. Anthony, F. W. Quackenbush, and H. Steenbock, *Oil & Soap*, 20, 53 (1943).

[586] A. Thiel and E. Caspar, *Z. physik. Chem.*, 86, 257 (1914).   M. M. Hicks, *Bur. Standards J. Research*, 2, 483 (1929).   E. W. Washburn, *Ind. Eng. Chem.*, 25, 891 (1933).   R. T. Leslie and S. T. Schicktanz, *Bur. Standards J. Research*, 6, 377 (1931).

[587] B. J. Mair, S. T. Schicktanz, and F. W. Rose, Jr., *J. Research Natl. Bur. Standards*, 15, 557 (1935).   V. A. Kalichevsky, *Modern Methods of Refining Lubricating Oils*, Reinhold, New York, 1938.

fuged off. A variant of the procedure is illustrated by a purification method for sulfamic acid.[588] A sample of the crude acid was dissolved in water preheated to 70°, cooled slightly, and the suspension filtered. Slight cooling, followed by filtration, was repeated twice more, and the three crops of crystals were discarded. The *final* filtrate was then cooled rapidly in ice–salt and the crystals which separated were filtered off.

A series of fractions of crystals is sometimes obtainable by *stepwise addition of a third solute, e.g.,* a miscible "poor" solvent in which one of the solutes is less soluble, at a suitable temperature. The fractions are removed when, after each addition, equilibrium has been reached. Thus, water may be added to ethanol or acetone solutions, and pentane to ether solutions, etc. (see Section III.1). Care must be taken that neither solute forms solid solutions with the added component of this now quaternary system, and the possibilities of deposition of binary, ternary, and quaternary eutectics, particularly on extreme cooling, must be borne in mind. The method is useful for compounds which decompose on heating.

The solution may be *evaporated* slowly at room temperature in a covered beaker. After some crystals have formed, the mother liquor may be decanted into another beaker and decantation repeated from time to time, as judged by the amount and appearance of the crystals. If the evaporation is to be performed in the absence of air, it may be carried out in a desiccator over a suitable absorbent, or in the usual apparatus for evaporation under diminished pressure. In working with certain stable, highly crystallizable compounds it may be advisable to effect evaporation until crystals just appear at the boiling point of the solution. The suspension is then cooled, filtered, the mother liquor further evaporated, and the procedure repeated. This technique avoids the formation of crusts, often encountered in evaporation by other methods.

An example of the use of *molecular compounds* (see Sect. II.10) for purification is the separation[589] of *p*-cresol, b.p. 202.0°C., from *m*-cresol, b.p. 202.4°C., not separable by azeotropic or extractive distillation, by adding benzidine, which forms a molecular compound with both; the *para* compound crystallizes out at 110° and is filtered off. The xylenes have been separated[589a] by compound formation with carbon tetrachloride.

Purification by use of *inclusion complexes* (see Sect. II.10) depends on the fact that, in formation of the complex, molecules of one kind are fitted into spaces between molecules of a different kind. The spaces are usually of

[588] M. J. Butler, G. F. Smith, and L. F. Audrieth, *Ind. Eng. Chem., Anal. Ed.,* 10, 690 (1938).

[589] W. H. Bentley and B. Catlow, U. S. Pat. 1,980,901 (1934); *C. A.,* 29, 476 (1935). S. A. Savitt and D. F. Othmer, *Ind. Eng. Chem.,* 44, 2428 (1952).

[589a] C. J. Egan and R. V. Luthy, *Ind. Eng. Chem.,* 47, 250 (1955).

fixed shape and size and so will only accommodate certain molecules; thus, molecules of one kind may be taken up from a mixture, leaving other molecules behind.   *Clathrates* are therefore useful for separation of certain homologs; that of ammonia-nickel cyanide with benzene has been employed[590] for the preparation in high yield of 99.992% pure benzene.   On the other hand, homologs are not separable *via channel complexes*, but branched compounds may often be separated from straight-chain isomers; *cis* and *trans* isomers may also be separated.

Complex formation between two compounds that normally afford a complex is sometimes prevented by the presence of a compound which does not give a complex.[591]   Furthermore, a molecule may be unable to enter the channels of urea or thiourea unless accompanied by an "activator," *e.g.*, methanol, which enters readily.   Hence, for "extractive crystallization," *e.g.*, with urea adducts (see Sect. II.10), the reactant is preferably dissolved in an inert, liquid hydrocarbon, the activator is added, and this solution is mixed with the reagent, *e.g.*, urea.   The resulting crystalline complex is filtered off, and may then be decomposed, *e.g.*, by treatment with water, or by heating, to liberate the purified reactant.

Variation of the reaction conditions often greatly affects the reaction rate, the equilibrium, and the efficiency of the separation.   As a rule, as much material as possible is first precipitated as the adduct; this is then fractionally readducted, *e.g.*, by use of insufficient urea or thiourea, by reprecipitation at a different temperature or with a different ratio of reagent to reactant, or by a combination of these techniques.   Thus, insufficient urea was added[592] to an isooctane solution of equimolar amounts of *n*-decane and *n*-hexadecane.   The hydrocarbon mixture from the resulting adduct contained much more *n*-hexadecane than *n*-decane, and only a small proportion of the latter had been removed from the initial solution.

When urea is added to a mixture of hydrocarbons, it reacts preferentially with the *n*-paraffins, next with the slightly branched isoparaffins, and then with the more highly branched isoparaffins and cyclic structures.   In some cases, fractional distillation, after decomposition of the adduct, is satisfactory.   *Selective decomposition* of the adduct may also be employed; this involves extraction with a solvent of relatively low dissociating power, whereby the least stable adducts dissociate first.   In *selective replacement*, the hydrocarbons in the less stable adducts are slowly replaced by more stable reagents, in a process resembling elution.   *Selective dissociation* by

[590] R. F. Evans, O. Ormrod, B. B. Goalby, and L. A. K. Staveley, *J. Chem. Soc.*, 1950, 3346.
[591] R. P. Linstead and M. Whalley, *J. Chem. Soc.*, 1950, 2987.
[592] C. E. Adams and R. A. Dinerstein, U. S. Pat. 2,588,602 (March 11, 1952).

cautious heating is applicable to the less stable adducts of volatile compounds.

Optical resolution of racemates may be partially effected by means of inclusion complexes. Windaus and co-workers[593] observed that digitonin forms compounds or complexes, of different solubilities, with certain *dextro* and *levo* isomers; they thus partially resolved *dl*-α-terpineol.

The *channel complexes* of *desoxycholic acid* with *d*- and *l*-camphor are different and can be[594] partially separated; decomposition of the choleic acid then gives a 12% optically active camphor. Racemates, *e.g.*, of 2-chlorooctane, have also been partially resolved by means of *urea* adducts,[595] despite the fact that urea is optically inactive. The optically active *β-cyclodextrin* has been used[596] for partial resolution of racemates, *e.g.*, of mandelic acid esters; here, the hole, having optically active walls of D-glucose residues, presumably effects the resolution. The separation may resemble the resolution obtainable by chromatography using[597] a column of optically active material, where there occurs optically specific adsorption.

Racemic *tri-o-thymotide*, dissolved in adductible, optically inactive solvents, *e.g.*, benzene, and nucleated with a crystal of the *dextro* form of the adduct, deposits[598] only the *dextro* form, the dissolved *levo* form racemizing rapidly to provide more *dextro* form. Conversely, if a nucleating crystal of the *levo* form of adduct is used, all the material can be obtained as the *levo* form. Furthermore, if the solvent[599] is itself a racemate, *e.g.*, *sec*-butyl bromide, the complex crystallizes out with the D or L form of the solvent. The optical rotation of the resolved bromide is in the same direction as that of the tri-*o*-thymotide which separated with it.

B. EXAMPLES OF EQUIPMENT

Melts. *Partial Freezing.* Impure, crystallizable liquids, *e.g.*, acetic acid or benzene, may be purified by slow fractional freezing. If the major component *does not form solid solutions* with the dissolved impurity, the latter will, in the absence of such secondary phenomena as adsorption, accumulate in the portion crystallizing last, and so the crystallization is stopped while part of the material is still liquid, namely, above the eutectic temperature (see section JE, Fig. 14). The material is stirred, cooled to just below the freezing point, and nucleated, if necessary.

[593] A. Windaus, F. Klänhard, and R. Weinhold, *Z. physiol. Chem.*, 126, 308 (1923).

[594] H. Sobotka and A. Goldberg, *Biochem. J.*, 26, 905 (1932).

[595] W. Schlenk, Jr., *Experientia*, 8, 337 (1952).

[596] F. Cramer, *Z. angew. Chem.*, 64, 136 (1952).

[597] C. E. Dalgleish, *J. Chem. Soc.*, 1952, 3940.

[598] H. M. Powell, *Nature*, 170, 155 (1952); *J. Chem. Soc.*, 1954, 2658.

[599] A. Newman and H. M. Powell, *J. Chem. Soc.*, 1952, 3747.

Stirring with slow cooling is continued until a suspension of crystals in liquid is formed.   The solid is collected, remelted, and the process repeated until a product of constant melting point results.   By re-treating the liquids, one may obtain more of the component in excess relative to the eutectic composition and, finally, the eutectic composition.   This method of frac-

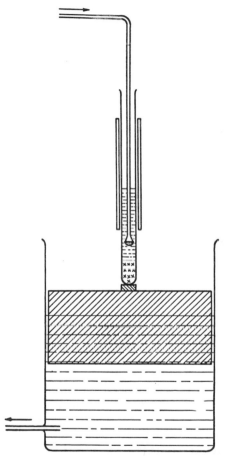

Fig. 27. Apparatus for slow fractional freezing.[605]

tionation has been applied to the separation of low-melting paraffins[600] and to the purification of acetic acid, benzene, o-nitrotoluene,[601] anthracene,[602]

[600] M. M. Hicks, *Bur. Standards J. Research*, **2**, 483 (1929).

[601] J. M. Bell, E. B. Cordon, F. H. Spry, and W. White, *J. Ind. Eng. Chem.*, **13**, 59 (1921).

[602] L. Scholvien, French Pat. 335,013 (1903).   A. Winther, *Zusammenst. Patente*, **3**, 433 (1910).

and benzoic acid.[603] The purity of the benzoic acid obtained in this way exceeded 99.999%. Practical details for crystallization from a melt, with subsequent centrifuging, have been given.[604]

Two very useful devices for purifying substances by *slow fractional freezing* have been described.[605] A cylindrical tube (Fig. 27) containing the melt rests on a float and is slowly lowered through a heating coil as the water supporting the float runs out during, say, 16 to 20 hours. As the

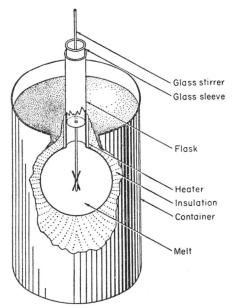

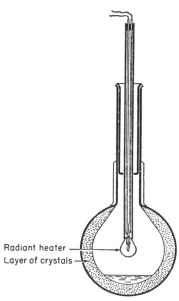

Fig. 28. Large-scale apparatus for slow fractional freezing.[605]

Fig. 29. Melting the innermost layer after slow freezing.[605]

bottom emerges from the coil, crystallization begins there and progresses upward. The melt is kept stirred by means of nitrogen dispersed through a bubbler. When the whole of the melt has crystallized, the tube plus contents is cut into fractions for further examination.

In the second method, useful for the purification of larger samples, the melt is introduced into a spherical flask (see Fig. 28) the neck of which, insulated by means of a glass sleeve, is heated. The flask is then gradually cooled, with stirring, so that crystallization starts at the flask walls and proceeds inward. After part of the melt has crystallized, the remaining liquid is siphoned out. A point-source, radiant heater is now introduced

[603] F. W. Schwab and E. Wichers, *J. Research Natl. Bur. Standards*, 25, 747 (1940).

[604] L. Ramberg, *Svensk Kem. Tid.*, 49, 134 (1937); *C. A.*, 31, 5622 (1937).

[605] F. W. Schwab and E. Wichers, *J. Research Natl. Bur. Standards*, 32, 253 (1944).

(see Fig. 29), the innermost layer of crystals is melted, and the melt removed in fractions. Benzoic acid was more rapidly purified by this method than by recrystallization from solvents. The method was also applied to purification of acetanilide. If the components of the melt form *solid solutions*, fractionation may be effected by repeated alternate freezing and thawing with intermediate removal of crystals, subject to the conditions discussed in Section II.9.

In crystallization of low-melting or very reactive compounds it is often necessary to *protect the material from condensation of moisture or interaction with atmospheric components*. Four types of enclosed apparatus suitable

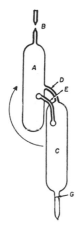

Fig. 30. Enclosed apparatus for fractionation of melt by gravitational drainage after partial crystallization.[606]

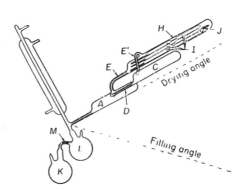

Fig. 31. Enclosed apparatus for fractionation of melt by gravitational drainage after partial crystallization.[606]

for laboratory recrystallization of melts have been described.[606] The melt is partially crystallized at a selected temperature in one chamber and the remaining liquid drained or centrifuged off into a second chamber. The crystals are then melted and the process repeated as many times as desired, at temperatures closer and closer to the melting point of the pure compound. The liquid is introduced into *A* (Fig. 30) through a narrow neck, which is then sealed off at *B*. The apparatus is now so tilted that the liquid flows through capillary *D* into chamber *C*. The whole apparatus is cooled in a constant-temperature bath until the desired amount of crystallization has occurred, after which it is inverted, while still in the bath, so that unfrozen material flows through *D* into *A*. Capillary *E* serves as a

[606] J. D. Piper and N. A. Kerstein, *Ind. Eng. Chem., Anal. Ed.*, **9**, 403 (1937).

pressure equalizer. After draining is complete, the apparatus is inverted by clockwise rotation. In repeating the melting and partial-crystallization cycle, the apparatus is inverted in counterclockwise direction so that, when once liquid has collected in A, it cannot return to C. After the final recrystallization, D and E are sealed off and C may be sealed onto another apparatus and its contents emptied out by breaking G from the inside.

Figure 31 shows a modification of this apparatus, used under greatly diminished pressure, for filling a number of sample tubes (I) with purified

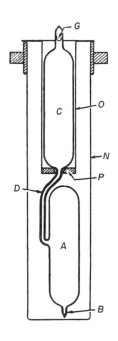

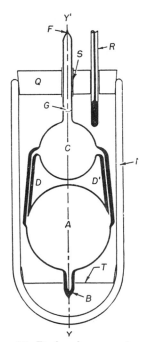

Fig. 32. Enclosed apparatus for fractionation of melt by centrifuging after partial crystallization.[606]

Fig. 33. Enclosed apparatus for fractionation of melt by centrifuging after partial crystallization.[606]

material. These tubes are contained in chamber H and have open capillary ends. The liquid is placed in K, dried over a suitable desiccant, and distilled into L. Capillary M is then sealed off and the liquid in L is distilled into A, the apparatus being tilted at the "filling angle." Fractional recrystallization is now performed as described above, and the purified material isolated in C by sealing off capillaries D and E; it is now transferred to H by alternately warming and cooling the two compartments. Capillary E' is now sealed off and the sample tubes, tips downward, are filled by slowly introducing dry nitrogen through capillary J. H is now carefully broken, and tubes I are removed and sealed off.   If the unfrozen material does not readily drain off the crystals, it may be removed by gentle centrifuging, using the apparatus shown in Figure 32.   The operations are as previously described except that, during the centrifugation, the apparatus is surrounded by a bath in the centrifuge cup, N, and is held in position by means of a split clamp, O, having a split rubber collar, P.

For centrifuging materials of low melting point, the apparatus shown in Figure 33 may be employed.   After the sample has been partially crystallized in the lower half of chamber C, the liquid is discharged through tubes D and D', into A, by rotating the apparatus around axis YY' using a motor attached at F.   The apparatus is contained in Dewar flask N, closed by stopper Q through which pass brass bearings S and thermometer R. T is a bearing consisting of a metal plate in which is bored a hole large enough to accept tip B.   The outer edges of T are bent up to fit the Dewar flask and hold by friction.   The whole apparatus may be cooled by means of acetone–dry ice contained in N.

A differential cryometer, used for the purification of benzene and of p-xylene,[607] is shown in Figure 34; the melting temperature is observed as purification proceeds.   The tube containing the liquid is cooled in dry ice, with shaking, until crystals start to form, and is then cautiously warmed until only a few crystals remain.   It is next placed in a bath at a constant temperature somewhat below the freezing point of the liquid. A cylindrical solid phase forms on the inner surface of the outer walls; this should be continuous and about 0.5 mm. thick.   The tube is now immersed in a bath at a temperature slightly above the melting point, in order to form a thin outer layer of liquid between the walls and the cylinder of crystals.   The tube is next inserted in a larger tube, held in position by means of a rubber stopper, and kept for about 20 minutes in a bath at the freezing point of the liquid.   The liquid phase in the middle of the apparatus is now in equilibrium with the cylindrical solid phase which, together with the outer liquid layer, protects the inner liquid from losing or gaining heat. The freezing temperature of the liquid is now determined by means of a thermocouple, one contact of which is inserted into the innermost tube. The tube is next immersed in a bath below the freezing point, and held there until about 90% of the liquid has frozen.   The remaining liquid, which contains the contaminant, is transferred to the other chamber by tilting the apparatus, and its freezing temperature is determined as described above.   The crystals in the first chamber are now heated until almost all have melted, a cylinder of crystals is formed as before, and the cycle is repeated until the freezing temperature of the material in this chamber is constant.   The material *may* then be pure.   Four partial

[607] W. Swietoslawski, *J. Phys. Chem.*, **47**, 590 (1943).

freezings and transfers sufficed to give very pure samples of *p*-xylene or benzene.

Partial Melting.   Nonhygroscopic materials, not affected by air, may be treated as follows: The melt to be purified is put into a wide-mouth vessel[608] and completely crystallized by cooling, while it is stirred to prevent

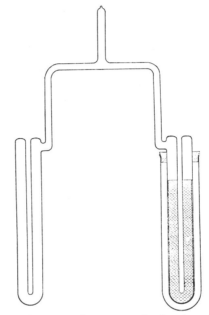

Fig. 34. Differential cryometer for fractionation
of melt by partial crystallization.[607]

formation of a single lump.   The crystals are transferred to an elongated funnel surrounded by a bath a few degrees above the melting point of the material being purified, a thermometer is inserted, and the material is allowed to warm up slowly so that only *part* of it melts.   The liquid formed is allowed to drain off and the crystals are pressed or centrifuged in the funnel.   A further portion of the crystals is then melted, and the resulting liquid collected separately, and so on.   Cyclohexane, *n*-heptane, and other hydrocarbons have thus[609] been purified.   In purifying *p*-xylene by this method, the crystals formed at $-90°$ to $-110°$F. were removed[610] by centrifuging at -30 to $40°$F.

     [608] J. Timmermans, *Chemical Species*, translation by R. E. Oesper, Chem. Pub. Co., New York, 1940, pp. 82–83.
     [609] J. G. Aston and S. V. R. Mastrangelo, *Anal. Chem.*, **22**, 636 (1950).   S. V. R. Mastrangelo and J. G. Aston, *ibid.*, **26**, 764 (1954).
     [610] J. D. Booker, U. S. Pat. 2,651,665 (1953); *C. A.*, **48**, 8821 (1954).

Figure 35 shows a useful apparatus[611] for fractional melting and filtration, in which the temperature and rate of flow of the heating liquid may be regulated. Funnel *B*, provided with a sintered-glass filter plate, is surrounded by jacket *A*, which may be detachable or sealed on. Through *A* is circulated steam, introduced at *M*, or hot liquid, introduced at *N*. Funnel *B* may be removed to permit weighing of the crystals. A modification, useful for making a series of separations by filtration at various temperatures, was also described.[611]

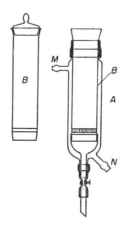

Fig. 35. Apparatus for fractionation by partial melting at single temperature.[611]

Alternate Melting and Freezing. Superior results are achieved by slow, equilibrium freezing, often to a monocrystal, followed by slow, equilibrium melting; fractions are collected and the process is repeated. *Zone melting*,[612] which resembles zone sublimation,[613] may be performed in a horizontal or vertical tube containing melt or crystals, by means of an annular cooler or heater moved slowly along the tube. As the crystalline or molten zone progresses along the tube, purer material tends to crystallize and impurities move with the melted zone; the precise results achieved[614]

[611] A. G. Kul'man, *Zhur. Priklad. Khim.*, 11, 557 (1938).

[612] W. G. Pfann, *J. Metals*, 4, 747, 861 (1952). C. H. L. Goodman, *Research (London)*, 7, No. 5, 168 (1954). *Cf.* E. N. da C. Andrade and R. Roscoe, *Proc. Phys. Soc. London*, 49, 152 (1937); W. G. Pfann and K. M. Olsen, *Phys. Rev.*, 89, 322 (1953). W. Heywang and H. Henker, *Z. Elektrochem.*, 58, 283 (1954). R. G. Pohl, *J. Appl. Phys.*, 25, 1170 (1954).

[613] R. S. Tipson, in A. Weissberger, ed., *Technique of Organic Chemistry.* Vol. IV, Interscience, New York-London, 1951, p. 636.

[614] C. H. L. Goodman, *Research (London)*, 7, No. 5, 168 (1954).

depend on whether the components are eutectogenic or form solid solutions,
molecular compounds, or inclusion complexes. The process is applicable
to any solid which is stable at the melting point and to some incongruently
melting substances. Several repetitions may give very pure material at
one end and much impurity at the other. Naphthalene has thus been
freed[614a] from a very small proportion of anthracene. In one device,[615] a

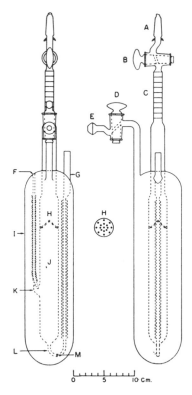

Fig. 36. Tube for fractional freezing and fractional melting.[616]

vertical column, packed, *e.g.*, with sand, is jacketed with a suitable liquid
coolant, below $T°$, on which floats an annular heater, slightly above $T°$.
The melt, containing desired material of m.p. $= T°$, is placed in the top
of the column and starts to percolate down; then the jacket is slowly
drained so that crystals formed are slowly remelted, and fractions are collected below.

    [614a] H. C. Wolf and H. P. Deutsch, *Naturwissenschaften*, 41, 425 (1954).
    [615] J. R. Bowman (to Gulf Research and Development Co.), U. S. Pat. 2,427,042
(Sept. 9, 1947).

Figure 36 shows a closed apparatus,[616] useful for toxic or sensitive compounds. The sample of impure melt is placed in tube *J*, which is surrounded by tube *I* having silvered, inner surfaces; heat transfer between *I* and *J* is controllable by stopcock *D* which regulates the degree of evacuation, permitted in the enclosed space, which is afforded by a high-vacuum system connected at spherical joint *E*. The temperature of the sample at

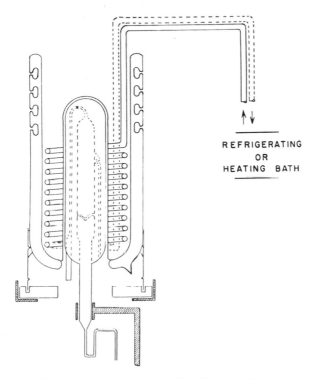

REFRIGERATING
OR
HEATING BATH

Fig. 37. Apparatus for slow fractional melting.[616]

K is measured with a thermocouple inserted in well *F*, which is then filled with a high-melting wax to a point several inches above the thermocouple junction. Tube *I* is now placed in a constant-temperature, cooling bath, usually held some 10 to 20° below the freezing point, and is cooled to just below its freezing point; then a small amount at *L*, beyond glass barrier *M*, is caused to crystallize by introduction of a coolant at *G*; powdered dry ice is used for substances freezing above −50°C., and liquid nitrogen, after evacuation of *G*, for those freezing below −50°C. Tubes *F* and *G* have glass expansion bellows to compensate for unequal expansions. Space *IJ* is

[616] A. R. Glasgow, Jr., and G. Ross, Sr., *J. Research Natl. Bur. Standards*, in press.

now suitably evacuated; the rate of heat removal is so adjusted, with *D*, that the temperature of the liquid falls about 1° in 10 to 15 minutes; for liquids needing considerable undercooling, high vacuum is used, to provide very slow crystallization. The crystals grow slowly upward, so that those near the bottom are purest and the impurities tend to concentrate near the top. After crystallization is complete (*ca.* 16 hours for 100 ml.), the tube is *inverted*, and the sample is very slowly melted, during 6 to 7 hours, by holding the walls of *I* at a temperature just above the melting point of the

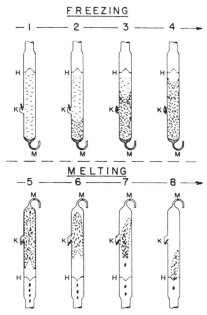

Fig. 38. Stages in fractional freezing and fractional melting of 2,5-dichlorostyrene.[616]

pure compound, using a special Dewar flask, shown in Figure 37, containing coils through which flows liquid from a constant-temperature bath. In this way, the most impure material is melted first and the purest is melted last; freshly formed melt continually bathes the crystals remaining and displaces less pure melt. The perforated, conical, glass disc *H* directs the liquid into the calibrated receiver *C*, and then, by opening *B*, the melt is collected in fractions by means of an "udder" fraction collector attached at joint *A* or sealed on (see Fig. 37); recovery is practically quantitative. The progress of freezing, in ice plus water, and of melting, in air at room temperature, of a sample of 2,5-dichlorostyrene, of f.p. 8.058°C. and original purity of 98.68 mole per cent, is shown in Figure 38. A series of 10-ml.

fractions of melt was collected; the total amount of impurity present and removed is shown in Figure 39, and the percentage removed at the various stages is shown in Figure 40; 73.6% of the total impurity was removed in the first 20% melted.

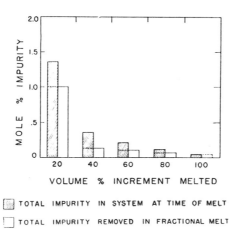

TOTAL IMPURITY IN SYSTEM AT TIME OF MELT

TOTAL IMPURITY REMOVED IN FRACTIONAL MELT

Fig. 39. Total amount of impurity present and removed in fractional melting of 2,5-dichlorostyrene.[616]

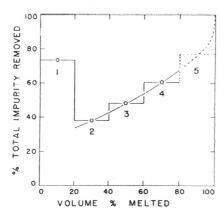

Fig. 40. Per cent removed, of total impurity present, at various stages of melting of 2,5-dichlorostyrene.[616]

Growth of large monocrystals from the melt, followed by fractional melting, has been employed for the purification of benzoic acid, dimethyl oxalate, and stilbene.[617]   The glass tube (see Fig. 41), attached at A to a

[617] A. T. Horton and A. R. Glasgow, Jr., *J. Research Natl. Bur. Standards,* in press.

transfer device, is evacuated, the melt is introduced under its own vapor
pressure, and the tube is sealed at S_1. The tube is now centered in the
bath (see Fig. 42), weighted by a guide weight GW attached at E, and suspended by cable C, attached at one end to E_1 and at the other end to an
automatic lowering device. *The bath*[617] *contains* *two immiscible liquids,*
L-1 and L-2; these are electrically heated by resistance-wire heaters H-1

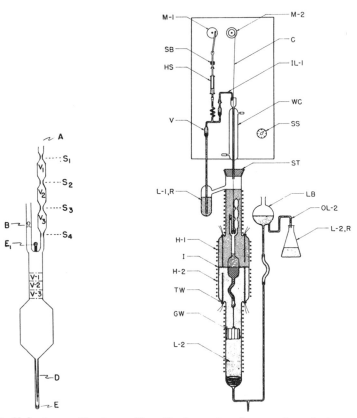

Fig. 41. Tube for purification   Fig. 42. Apparatus for growing single crystal
by slow recrystallization and   at boundary of two immiscible liquids.[617]
slow melting.[617]

and H-2, affording two distinct temperature zones having a *plane, tempera-*
ture boundary at interface I. Often, the temperature of L-1 is held at 25°
above, and of L-2 at 25° below, the freezing point of the compound;
the temperature on each side of I is measured with thermocouples, inserted
in six wells TW spaced at 0, 0.5, and 1.5 inches above and below I, and
connected with selector switch SS. Using a silicone oil (Dow-Corning

No. 500) above and ethylene glycol below, typical temperatures at these wells were: above, 143.34°, 154.34°, and 156.84°C.; below, 109.86°, 99.82°, and 97.56°C. A crystal is started by cooling—or, on melting, a crystal is left—in the bottom of the long capillary D, which is now placed just below I; and the tube is lowered through I at a rate of 0.5 to 1.5 inches per day, by means of the synchronous clock motor M-2 moving 1 revolution per day, causing growth of a large monocrystal from the melt. I is initially adjusted by means of the levelling bulb LB and is kept at a constant height automatically; as the sample tube leaves L-1, input of

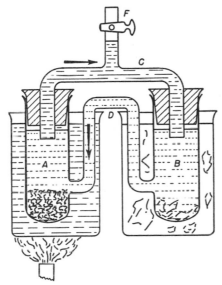

Fig. 43. Apparatus for recrystallization by heating and cooling.[618]

liquid from reservoir L-1,R compensates for the change by action of a graduated pumping system consisting of the synchronous, clock motor M-1 moving 1 revolution per minute, sleeve bearing SB, hypodermic syringe HS, glass check valve V, inlet IL-1, and water condenser WC passing through stopper ST. The pump also recycles excess L-1. Changes in the volume of L-2 are compensated for by overflow through OL-2 to reservoir L-2,R. Complete formation of the monocrystal, with all of the sample, e.g., 475 ml., reaching L-2, takes about 7 days; L-2 is then very gradually warmed to room temperature to prevent fractures in the crystal. The tube is now *inverted* and fractional melting is performed, e.g., by so adjusting the electrical heaters that L-1 is below and L-2 is just above the melting point of the compound. Thus, rejected impurity V_1 is melted, passes into bulb V_1, and this bulb is sealed at S_2 and removed. The sample, minus impurities V_1, is now remelted, again caused to give a single crystal, and volume V_2 of impurity is removed; and so on. B is a break-off bulb for transfer of material, under vacuum, after the final purification.

Solutions. In any of the various modifications of the procedure, there are essentially seven steps in each cycle: (*1*) dissolution of the crude substance in the solvent, and removal of insoluble impurities, if any; (*2*) changing the conditions to effect supersaturation; (*3*) nucleating; (*4*) growing the crystals; (*5*) separation of the crystals from the mother liquor; (*6*) washing; and (*7*) drying the crystals. The cycle is then repeated as many times as is found necessary. These steps are customarily carried out using the usual laboratory equipment. However, some special devices have been elaborated to meet specific needs.

The apparatus[618] shown in Figure 43 is used for automatic recrystallizations. There is a very large choice of solvents since even "poor" solvents may be employed. Thus, many organic compounds only slightly soluble in water may be recrystallized from water in this apparatus. The procedure is essentially a continuous extraction and very little solvent is needed, but the impurities accumulate in the mother liquor and care must be taken that their concentration does not become excessively high. A and B are containers connected below through tube D, and above through tube C. The crude material is placed in A, the saturated solution is put into A and B, and solution is drawn into C by suction at F. If A is now warmed and B is cooled, and if the crystallizand has a positive temperature coefficient of solubility, some of it in A dissolves and is deposited in B. If the solubility is low, warm solution rises and the cold, denser solution falls, so that circulation proceeds in the direction $A \rightarrow C \rightarrow B \rightarrow D \rightarrow A$. On the other hand, if the solubility and its temperature coefficient are great, the warm, saturated solution in A is denser than that in B, which has given up material, so the cycle is in the direction $A \rightarrow D \rightarrow B \rightarrow C \rightarrow A$. In either case, compound is transferred from A to B. For very soluble compounds, it is better not to place the crude material on the bottom of A, since a stagnant, saturated solution soon forms there; instead, it is placed in a perforated vessel, suspended in A. The velocity of crystallization is controlled by the difference in temperature of A and B; if large crystals are desired, this temperature difference should be small. An exchangeable insert may be placed in B for reception of crystals, and this may be withdrawn carefully from time to time.

In a different device,[619] a *vertical* column is packed with a filter bed, *e.g.*,

[618] H. Danneel, *Chem. App.*, **14**, 193 (1927). D. von Klobusitzky, *Monatsh.*, **81**, 129 (1950). D. McLachlan and C. J. Christensen, *Rev. Sci. Instruments*, **23**, 306 (1952).

[619] J. R. Bowman (to Gulf Research and Development Co.), U. S. Pat. 2,427,042 (Sept. 9, 1947).

of sand, and jacketed with a coolant. The crude crystals are placed at the top of the column and solvent is added there; the coolant is then very slowly drained away, the top of the column is suitably warmed, and ma-

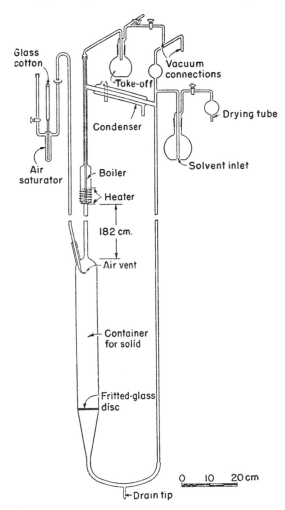

Fig. 44. Apparatus for continuous extraction and recrystallization.[623]

terial which dissolves at the top crystallizes out again lower down, affording multiple redissolution and recrystallization. Crystals may also[620] be grown in an ascending current of solution in a vertical column containing constrictions of progressively larger size, giving size classification. In a

620 J. W. Ridsdale, Brit. Pat. 624,125 (May 27, 1949).

modification,[621] successively higher zones are heated to redissolve some crystals as they pass upward. A *horizontal* tube, having a horizontal temperature gradient, has been applied[622] to solid solutions and eutectogenic mixtures. A solution thereof enters in the middle and leaves at the ends, and a rotating, horizontal helix impels crystals toward one end.

Partial evaporation may be employed for materials affected by heat or hot solvent, when the solubility in hot solvent is only a little greater than that in the cold, when the substance is very soluble in all solvents even when cold, or if the solubility increases on cooling. In the apparatus for continuous recrystallization[623] shown in Figure 44, part of the solvent is evaporated from the saturated solution. It is an adaptation, for solid material, of the Fenske reflux extractor.[624] The upper ends of a U-tube 10 ft. high are connected by a condenser. The crystals are placed on a fritted-glass disc sealed into the wide arm of the U-tube, near the bottom. The solvent is introduced into the narrow arm, by suction, from the solvent inlet; it circulates by the action of gravity. The solvent is saturated at room temperature by percolating through the disc; as solute dissolves, undissolved solute is caused to fall by gentle tapping. Sufficient solvent is added to bring it to the desired level in the boiler, which is then electrically heated. Solvent distils off through the condenser into the narrow arm; and crystals separate in or below the boiler, fall through the saturated solution, and settle on the crystals on the disc. During this procedure, dry air saturated with the solvent vapor is passed in through the air vent to agitate the crystals and avert clogging. It may be necessary to operate the apparatus under diminished pressure; in recrystallizing benzoic acid from benzene, it functioned satisfactorily at 215 mm. of Hg. A receiver is connected to the upper end of the boiler; after all of the batch of solute has been dissolved and recrystallized, part of the solution is removed from the boiler. In this way, a batch may be divided into as many fractions as desired; each is cooled until crystals appear and these are filtered off. The separation obtained per single recrystallization is not as efficient as with simple repeated recrystallization, presumably because of diffusion and channelling in the apparatus.

2. Growth of Crystals of Controlled Size

It has been mentioned in Section II.4 that, with some compounds, the *shape* of the crystals depends on the conditions of their growth. Probably

[621] R. L. Macklin, U. S. Pat. 2,620,263 (Dec. 2, 1952).

[622] R. A. Findlay, U. S. Pat. 2,617,273 (Nov. 11, 1952); *C. A.*, **47**, 362a (1953).

[623] F. W. Schwab and E. Wichers, *J. Research Natl. Bur. Standards*, **25**, 747 (1940).

[624] M. R. Cannon and M. R. Fenske, *Ind. Eng. Chem.*, **28**, 1035 (1936).

more important from the practical point of view is the production of crystals of a certain specified *size* by control of the conditions of growth. Recrystallization from the melt[625] or from solution may be used for obtaining *large, single crystals.* If a *batch* of crystals of one specified size[626] is desired, recrystallization *from the melt* may be employed if the heat of crystallization is dissipated through the melt[627]; the desired number of nuclei of about the same size are added, heat is slowly withdrawn through the walls of the containing vessel, and the suspension is gently stirred to prevent the crystals from forming a layer on the bottom.

However, recrystallization *from solution* is usually employed. If the initial and final concentrations of the solution are fixed, and no nuclei are introduced from outside, the number, and hence the *size*, of the crystals is determined by the rate of nucleus formation, the rate of growth of the crystals, and the relation between these rates. If new nuclei form continuously, a batch of crystals of various sizes will be obtained. However, if many nuclei are formed or added, and these grow uniformly without the appearance of new nuclei, a crop of uniform crystals will result; hence, the labile zone of supersaturation must be avoided. *Precipitation*[628] is an extreme case of crystallization from solution, in which a very large number of very small crystals form practically simultaneously with complete removal of supersaturation, so that further growth, except by Ostwald ripening (see Sect. II.3), is impossible. The principles of fractional precipitation[629] are the same as those of fractional recrystallization.

As mentioned in Section II.2, the degree of supersaturation or supercooling giving the maximum rate of nucleus formation usually differs from that for maximum rate of growth. Although growth can proceed even with very slight undercooling or supersaturation, three-dimensional nucleus formation becomes marked only at higher supersaturation or undercooling. Hence, many nucleated, undercooled melts or supersaturated solutions can be kept long enough to permit the added crystal or nuclei to grow to the desired size without the spontaneous formation of new three-dimensional nuclei. In the crystallization of *sucrose*, sudden cooling resulting in sudden increase in supersaturation may give crystal nuclei almost immediately; then, by slight warming, just sufficient supersaturation may be maintained so that new nuclei do not form while the first nuclei are growing. With

[625] C. Weygand, *Z. anorg. allgem. Chem.*, **224**, 265 (1935).

[626] H. Griffiths, *Chem. Trade J.*, **75**, 486, 516 (1924).

[627] G. Masing and R. Reinbach, *Atti X° congr. intern. chim.*, **3**, 594 (1939); *C. A.*, **33**, 8465 (1939).

[628] F. R. Duke, R. J. Bever, and H. Diehl, *Iowa State Coll. J. Sci.*, **23**, 297, 300 (1949). F. R. Duke and L. M. Brown, *J. Am. Chem. Soc.*, **76**, 1443 (1954).

[629] M. L. Salutsky, J. G. Stites, Jr., and A. W. Martin, *Anal. Chem.*, **25**, 1677 (1953). V. K. La Mer, *Ind. Eng. Chem.*, **44**, 1270 (1952).

other compounds, new nuclei often form even at slight supersaturation, while the crystals are growing, making cultivation of well-shaped monocrystals difficult.   However, certain additives[630] greatly extend the metastable zone, by restraining formation of these unwanted nuclei, thereby enhancing production of monocrystals.   The metastable supersaturated zone of Figure 11 is rather narrow for most inorganic compounds but is usually much wider for organic compounds, solutions of which can often be supercooled as much as 30°C. before spontaneous deposition of crystals sets in, thus permitting growth of good monocrystals.

Spontaneous crystallization from strongly supercooled solutions frequently yields a "shower" of small crystals of extreme habit, *e.g.*, dendritic needles, bearing little resemblance to the well developed macrocrystals obtained at moderate supersaturation.   It is, as a rule, not possible to predict whether or not a given set of conditions will yield euhedral crystals of satisfactory size, and the experimental details must be worked out in each case.   With organic compounds having a relatively large solubility–temperature gradient, fluctuations in temperature may result in redissolution of crystals or deposition of dendritic crystals on those which have partially developed, giving crystals with blurred edges and corroded or dulled faces, often bearing tiny "parasitic" crystals.   On the other hand, with care, monocrystals of readily soluble compounds are usually grown with ease, and those of slightly soluble compounds, with difficulty.   The state of association of the solute may be important; an increased association may favor formation of a well-shaped monocrystal.   For example, good growth of a monocrystal of benzil[631] is difficult from every solvent tried except benzene.

A. LARGE MONOCRYSTALS

Large, flawless crystals are now needed in many applications; these include use in spectroscopy, for piezoelectric measurements, and in the electrical industry.   In contrast to recrystallization for purification, a small amount of suitable impurity[632] is often deliberately added; thus, good monocrystals of sodium chloride cannot be grown from pure solution, but addition of a trace of lead ion gives excellent monocrystals.   On the other hand, monocrystals are now grown as a purification procedure, since they are often purer than the same weight of smaller crystals.

    [630] V. K. Semenchenko and L. P. Shikhobalova, *Zhur. Fiz. Khim.*, **21**, 613 (1947). S. Zerfoss, *Ceram. Age*, **54**, 293 (1949).
    [631] P. H. Egli and S. Zerfoss, *Discussions Faraday Soc.*, **5**, 61 (1949).
    [632] S. Zerfoss, *Ceram. Age*, **54**, 293 (1949).
    [633] See P. Walden, *Chem.-Ztg.*, **55**, 373 (1931).   E. O. von Lippmann, *ibid.*, **55**, 257 (1931).   P. H. Egli, *Sci. Monthly*, **68**, No. 4, 270 (1949).

The first step in growing monocrystals[633] is to acquire a well-shaped seed crystal. It may be selected from the crystals obtained in a preliminary growth experiment, or a crystal may be cut[634] parallel to a major crystallographic face and then used as a seed. A method has been described [635] of growing a single crystal from a melt in contact with a cleavage surface of mica, which acts as a "seed" and orients the resulting crystal. Since a crystal confined on one or more sides can grow only in those directions exposed to the melt or solution, the seed is often freely suspended to avoid malformation.

Local variations in temperature and concentration, and unwanted nucleation must, of course, be carefully avoided, and, except for deliberate addition of impurity or surfactant, chemicals should be pure. Freedom from dust and nuclei is important, and it is often advisable to subject the melt or solution to filtration, ultrafiltration, or ultracentrifuging, or, if the compound is sufficiently stable, to vigorous heating. The surface of the vessel should be smooth and clean, and the ratio of surface area to volume, the minimum.[636] Freed and Spedding[637] cleaned all glassware with hot chromic acid and dried it in a dust-free electric oven; the solution was filtered through a Jena-glass filter prior to nucleation. It is now customary to grow monocrystals in apparatus in a laboratory equipped with stainless-steel furniture and provided with filtered air. Precise details have been given[638] for ensuring extremely slow growth in order to obtain relatively large crystals from solution; useful instrumentation has been described.[639] With slow growth, internal imperfections, e.g., inclusions, are usually avoided. Addition of certain surfactants sometimes prevents incorporation of liquor or gas bubbles. A growth rate of two inches per month is often considered excellent.

As the size of a surface increases, the maximum or critical rate at which good growth can be obtained decreases[640]; this means that there is a practical limit on the size to which a good monocrystal of any compound can be grown, although at an infinitely low growth rate there would be no limit on the size attainable. The critical growth rate from solution increases as the temperature is raised.

There are three main procedures[641] for growing large, organic mono-

[634] N. N. Sheftal, U. S. S. R. Pat. 66,668 (1946); C. A., 41, 1778 (1947).

[635] C. D. West, J. Optical Soc. Am., 35, 26 (1945).

[636] J. Piazza, Anales asoc. quim. argentina, 27, 145 (1939); C. A., 34, 289 (1940).

[637] S. Freed and F. H. Spedding, Phys. Rev., 34, 945 (1929).

[638] L. C. Baker, New Zealand J. Sci. Technol., 25B, 62 (1943).

[639] S. A. Hluchan, Instruments, 24, 585 (1951).

[640] T. Yamamoto, Sci. Papers Inst. Phys. Chem. Research Tokyo, 35, 228 (1939). P. H. Egli and S. Zerfoss, Discussions Faraday Soc., 5, 61 (1949).

[641] R. I. Taylor, Chem. Inds., 55, 906 (1944). S. Zerfoss, Ceram. Age, 56, No. 5, 20 (1950).

crystals from a *melt*.[642] In the apparatus[643] shown in Figure 45, a seed
crystal is fastened to, or started at, the end of a copper rod which is then
immersed in the melt.   The other end of the copper rod is cooled, causing

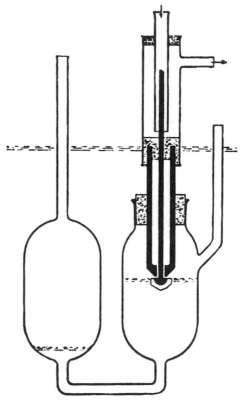

Fig. 45. Apparatus for growth of monocrystal from melt.[643]

cooling of the crystal.   The melt is maintained at, or even slightly above,
its freezing point, by immersion in a thermostat.   Spontaneous nucleation
is thereby prevented and only a single crystal grows.   A phenyl salicylate
crystal of 2.5-cm. diameter was obtained in 3 hours.   In a modification,[644]
the cooled monocrystal, kept just in contact with the melt, is slowly withdrawn.   Another method[642] involves simultaneous cooling from below and

    [642] F. Stöber, *Z. Krist.*, **61,** 299 (1925).
    [643] P. Nacken, *Neues. Jahrb. Mineral., Geol.*, **2,** 133 (1915).   *Z. Instrumentenk.*, **26,**
12 (1916).   J. M. Adams and W. Lewis, *Rev. Sci. Instruments*, **5,** 400 (1934).
    [644] S. Kyropolous, *Z. anorg. Chem.*, **154,** 308 (1926); *Z. Physik*, **63,** 849 (1930).   K.
Chamberlain, *Rev. Sci. Instruments*, **9,** 322 (1938).   A. C. Menzies and J. Skinner,
Discussions Faraday Soc., **5,** 306 (1949).

heating from above in such a manner as to eliminate convection currents (see Fig. 46).   There is an orientation according to the direction of greatest thermal conductivity, so a crystal started at the bottom of the melt can be caused to grow up through it.   Monocrystals have thus been grown[645] at −100°.   Thirdly, a crystal may be grown by slowly lowering a melt through a diminishing temperature gradient; the melt may be contained[646] in a cylinder having a cone-shaped bottom with a constriction just above the apex. Polycrystals may form at the tip, but a monocrystal may originate at the constriction.

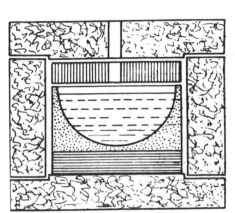

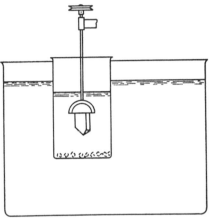

Fig. 46. Apparatus for growth of mono-   Fig. 47. Growth of monocrystal by slow
crystal from bottom of melt.[642]   evaporation of solvent.[643,647]

For growth of large monocrystals from *solution*, precise control of the degree of supersaturation is essential.   This degree should be the maximum consistent with absence of spontaneous nucleation or of misorientation to yield flaws.   Perhaps the simplest laboratory method of maintaining slight supersaturation is to allow the solution to *evaporate* extremely slowly. This is the preferred procedure for compounds with a slight or positive change in solubility on cooling.   A beaker containing the solution may be placed[647] in a thermostat (see Fig. 47), and the seed crystal is suspended and slowly rotated to keep the solution free from concentration currents. Difficulties encountered include the ingress of dust and crystal nuclei, and the formation of crystalline crusts on the inner walls of the beaker near the surface of the solution.   Suppression of undesirable crystal growth by

[645] L. Bouttier, *Compt. rend.*, **228**, 1419 (1949).

[646] P. W. Bridgman, *Proc. Am. Acad. Arts Sci.*, **60**, 305 (1925).   D. C. Stockbarger *Rev. Sci. Instruments*, **7**, 133 (1936).   R. F. Leininger, *ibid.*, **23**, 127 (1952).

[647] A. Johnsen, *Centr. Mineral. Geol.*, **1915**, 235.   (Fig. 47 from Nacken, *loc. cit.*).

keeping the surface of the solution slightly warmer than the main solution, *e.g.*, by irradiation, has been suggested.[648] Dust may be excluded by conducting the evaporation in a closed chamber. In order to maintain a precise rate of evaporation of the solution, the temperature and pressure are carefully controlled. For example, after introducing a selected seed crystal, evaporation was conducted[649] in a vacuum desiccator connected, through a capillary of about 0.001-mm. diameter, to a vacuum pump. Alternatively, evaporated solvent may be[650] condensed, passed through a sintered-glass receptacle containing feed crystals, and the resulting solution returned to the crystallizer. Evaporation of the good solvent from a *solvent pair* provides a useful modification of this technique. An excellent method of obtaining large crystals is to allow a poor solvent to mix very slowly with the solution in a good solvent, by diffusion,[651] at an appropriate temperature. Incidentally, fairly large crystals of sparingly soluble salts may sometimes be prepared in pure condition by a diffusion method involving slow mixing of the appropriate ions.[652]

Application of "*salting out*" methods to the preparation of large protein crystals has been described.[653] In salting out, use may be made of pH and temperature effects. The rate of deposition may be controlled by slow evaporation or by dialysis against slightly more concentrated salt solution. In other cases, a solubilizing salt may be slowly removed by dialysis. Crystals may appear on cooling or warming, depending on whether the solubility of the crystallizand falls or rises with decrease in temperature. A four-component system may be formed by adding alcohol or other miscible solvent or solute, *e.g.*, a gas, in which salt and crystallizand are not very soluble.

Another method of maintaining slight supersaturation is by the *dropwise addition of supersaturated solution*, with constant agitation, at constant temperature. This method is preferred for compounds with a flat solubility curve or where the temperature range is limited by instability of the solution or by transition to an undesired crystal form or habit. Alternatively, one may circulate[654] the mother liquor, no longer supersaturated, into another vessel in which it is warmed with more solute. It is then returned to the crystallizing vessel[655] in a continuous process (see Fig. 48).

[648] P. Pfundt, Ger. Pat. 738,978 (1943); *C. A.*, **39**, 5137 (1945).

[649] S. Freed and F. H. Spedding, *Phys. Rev.*, **34**, 945 (1929).

[650] J. Chappelle, *Compt. rend.*, **229**, 61 (1949).

[651] J. Johnston, *J. Am. Chem. Soc.*, **36**, 16 (1914).

[652] W. C. Fernelius and K. D. Detling, *J. Chem. Ed.*, **11**, 176 (1934).

[653] K. Bailey, *Trans. Faraday Soc.*, **38**, 186 (1942).

[654] J. C. Hostetter, *J. Wash. Acad. Sci.*, **9**, 85 (1919).

[655] F. Krüger and W. Finke, Ger. Pat. 228,246 (Feb. 1, 1908). (Fig. 48 from Nacken, *loc. cit.*)

The compound dissolves slowly from a bag suspended in the solution in one vessel, which is electrically heated, and passes through a condenser into the other vessel containing the crystal.   The liquid returns from this vessel to the first vessel through the upper tube.   The two vessels are, preferably, heated and cooled, respectively, in two thermostats (cf. Fig. 43).[656]   The gradient in refractive index near a monocrystal in a solution may be used[657] for determining the degree of supersaturation and the saturation temperature of the solution.

An improved apparatus[643] for such growth is shown in Figure 49.   The central vessel is that in which material is dissolved; the upper one contains the growing crystal.   The solution passes up a tube from the central to the upper vessel, which is surrounded by a Liebig condenser for cooling, and then down the central tube in the bottom of the upper vessel.   Both these

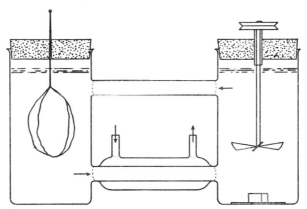

Fig. 48. Growth of monocrystal by addition of supersaturated solution.[643,655]

tubes are provided with glass ball-and-socket valves and when one is open the other is closed.   The center chamber has two side arms, one of which is closed by a rubber tube and pinchcock, the other with a rubber bulb. Solute is placed on the bottom of the center chamber and the center tube is perforated in this vicinity.   Solution is introduced and forced to the levels shown in the upper chambers by air pressure exerted with the rubber bulb. Solute is also placed on the bottom of the third chamber and saturated solution may be added through the side arm on this chamber, which is then closed with a rubber tube and pinchcock.   The two lower chambers are placed in a thermostat and a saturated solution is formed; this is then forced into the top chamber.   Solution is periodically forced into the crys-

[656] J. J. P. Valeton, Ber. Verhandl. K. sächs. Ges. Wiss., 67, 4 (1915); C. A., 10, 1615 (1916).

[657] L. A. Dauncey and J. E. Still, J. Applied Chem. London, 2, 399 (1952).

tallizing chamber by means of the rubber bulb; the chamber must be closed to prevent evaporation.

It is possible to maintain a slight supersaturation by *dissolving* extremely fine particles[658] of the crystalline material in the mother liquor, held at

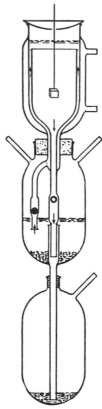

Fig. 49. Growth of mono-crystal by addition of super-saturated solution.[643]

constant temperature. Large crystals will grow still larger by diminution or disappearance of the very small ones in contact with the same mother liquor. This phenomenon is known[659] as "Ostwald ripening" (see Sect. II.3); it occurs because units in the surface of a large crystal are more tightly bound than those on a small crystal.

[658] G. L. Clark, *Cold Spring Harbor Symposia Quant. Biol.*, **2**, 6 (1934). F. B. Dehn, Brit. Pat. 579, 330 (1946); *C. A.*, **41**, 1898 (1947).

[659] J. M. Anscheles, *Z. Krist.*, **95**, 150 (1936). *Cf.* E. S. Federov, *Bull. Russ. Imp. Acad. Sci.*, **1916**, 435; *C. A.*, **12**, 8 (1918). I. M. Kolthoff, *Science*, **84**, 376 (1936).

In order to obtain large, well-developed crystals of compounds whose solubility decreases on cooling, slow *cooling* of a solution is usually preferable to slow evaporation; at one time it was thought that there should be no jarring, vibration, or other agitation. A filtered, almost saturated solution is cooled almost to the saturation temperature, which should be known accurately, the seed crystal is added, and the system is then cooled 0.1° per day until there is a noticeable increase in size and a good crystal has formed. After that, the temperature may be allowed to fall 0.2° per day, and finally 0.3° per day. Since the rate of fall in temperature must be carefully controlled,[660] an accurately regulated thermostat should be employed.[661] However, it is sometimes satisfactory to surround the receptacle containing the warm solution with a large volume of water at the same temperature, contained in a Dewar flask or in a bath lagged with a heat-insulating material. Spontaneous cooling may be sufficiently slow to permit the formation of large, well-shaped crystals. Periodical removal of imperfect crystals is advisable.

For many organic compounds, a hot, almost saturated solution may be prepared at a temperature just below the boiling point, filtered, and cooled at such a rate that, after 3 or 4 hours, its temperature is several degrees above room temperature. If deposition of a "shower" of crystals has occurred (see Fig. 11), the mother liquor is carefully decanted or filtered off, giving a solution from which an excellent macrocrystal may often be obtained after nucleation with a single small crystal of the pure substance and further slow cooling. The solubility–temperature gradients of organic compounds are usually fairly large; this often permits the preparation of relatively large, euhedral crystals in a comparatively short deposition time. However, solvents which are ideal in recrystallization for purification may be unsatisfactory for production of isolated macrocrystals. If the temperature–solubility gradient is large, moderate cooling will usually give a dendritic "shower" in high yield, but, lacking highly precise temperature control, such a solvent may be unsuitable for growing macrocrystals, since the solution is too sensitive to small changes in temperature.

With the development of equipment for constant agitation over long periods of time, *slow cooling with agitation* has largely replaced the methods discussed above, particularly in industry. Thus, in the growth of large crystals of Rochelle salt,[662] "seed" rods are cut from large crystals and placed in rubber trays containing a supersaturated solution of the salt. These trays are kept in constant, even motion in a room whose temperature,

[660] J. M. Blake, *Am. J. Sci.*, **39**, 567 (1915). *Cf.* A. De Bretteville, Jr., and F. V. Ryer, *J. Phys. Chem.*, **48**, 154 (1944).

[661] R. W. Moore, *J. Am. Chem. Soc.*, **41**, 1060 (1919).

[662] *Life*, **21**, 131–135 (1946).

starting at about 38 °C., is lowered a fraction of a degree per day.   After it
has grown for about a month, the crystal is removed and the attached seed
rod is ground off.   Large ethylenediamine tartrate monocrystals, weighing
about 1 lb. and measuring about 6 × 2 × 3 in., are grown commercially
during 3 months.[663]

A simple apparatus[664] for growing large crystals is shown in Figure 50.
It consists of a large cylinder which can be turned on a horizontal axis.   In
the center of this cylinder is placed the crystal, surrounded by saturated

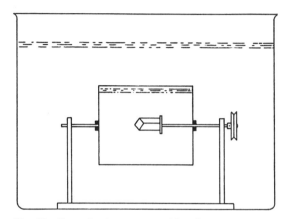

Fig. 50. Growth of monocrystal by slow cooling.[643,664]

solution.   The temperature of the thermostat is then very slowly lowered,
causing the crystal to grow, while the cylinder is slowly rotated.   Movement of the crystal in an otherwise unagitated solution is preferable; a re-
ciprocating rotary crystallizer, in which seed crystals are moved about a
vertical axis in a stationary tank, has been used[665]; a modification[666] employs constant temperature with replenishment of depleted solution.
Sonic and supersonic waves have also been used[667] for providing agitation.

B. SIMULTANEOUS GROWTH OF MANY CRYSTALS OF CONTROLLED SIZE

The first systematic attempts to obtain large numbers of crystals con-

[663] Science News Letter, 52, 198 (1947).   Electronics, 20, No. 11, 144 (1947).   Cf.
W. P. Mason, Proc. Inst. Radio Engrs., 35, 1005 (1947).

[664] G. Wulff, Z. Kryst. Mineral., 50, 17 (1912).   (Fig. 50 from P. Nacken, Z. Instrumentenk., 26, 12 (1916).)

[665] A. C. Walker, Bell Labs. Record, 25, 357 (1947); J. Franklin Inst., 250, 481 (1950).
A. N. Holden, Discussions Faraday Soc., 5, 312 (1949); U. S. Pat. 2,484,829 (1949).

[666] C. J. Christensen and A. C. Walker, U. S. Pat. 2,459,869 (Jan. 25, 1949).

[667] Mitsubishi Electrical Instruments Co., Japan. Pat. 155,066 (Feb. 19, 1943); C. A.,
44, 9c (1950).

sistently having a certain, nearly identical size and shape were made in the sugar industry.   A similar trend has since been noticeable[668] in other branches of industrial chemistry, e.g., quinine sulfate, which used to be supplied in small, granular crystals, is now often prepared in long, thin needles. After the same number of recrystallizations, crystals of constant, fairly uniform size are usually *purer* and show less tendency to cake than those comprising a wider range of sizes.   In the absence of deliquescence or sublimation, that shape which gives minimum contact between the granules has the least such tendency.   Crystal shape often determines the rate of filtration of suspensions, the bulk density and ease of flow of powders, and the stability of tablets made of compressed powders.   It is therefore important to choose the most suitable crystal shape and to ensure constancy of habit from batch to batch.   Small crystals of uniform size dissolve more speedily than the same weight of large ones.   If of uniform size, different samples may be expected to dissolve at the same speed—a consideration of importance in routine preparation of solutions.   If the crystals are small and uniform, powdering may often be dispensed with.   Detonating mixtures for explosives must be composed[669] of crystals of definite size and shape.   The crystalline particles of explosives should be as nearly spherical as possible.   The size and the degree of uniformity of silver halide crystals are of prime importance in their effect on the characteristics of photographic emulsion.   Control of particle size is also important in manufacturing materials for certain plastics.

As a consequence, attention has been devoted in the past three decades to the problem of accurate control of crystal size during recrystallization. This has entailed study of the theory of nucleus formation and crystal growth (see Sects. II.1 and II.2), the effect of additives, e.g., surfactants, and the design for industrial purposes of crystallizers which permit the required control.   Although similar equipment for laboratory use is, with the possible exception of small models of industrial crystallizers, still unavailable, the principles involved may prove valuable for work in the laboratory, and a brief description of the most important industrial crystallizers is therefore given below.

The following methods are sometimes of value in the *laboratory* for the preparation of batches of uniform crystals.   A hot, almost saturated solution is cooled a few degrees fairly rapidly, so that deposition of a "shower" occurs.   On further *slow* cooling or evaporation, each of these tiny crystals acts as a nucleus, resulting in the formation of a large number of fairly small, uniform crystals.   Their number can be reduced by carefully decanting the mother liquor from the first "shower" and thus limiting the number

[668] H. B. Caldwell, *Chem. Inds.*, **57**, 852 (1945).

[669] W. Cullen, *Trans. Inst. Chem. Engrs.*, **17**, 11 (1939).

of nuclei to those suspended in the liquor.   The number of crystals can also
be regulated by warming the decanted liquor to destroy the nuclei and,
after recooling to the previous temperature, seeding with a limited number
of crystals obtained from the first "shower." These methods can easily
be varied further.   If the speed at which the solution is made more supersaturated much exceeds the speed at which the crystals grow, new nuclei
will be formed, giving a crop of variously sized crystals.   Hence, it is
important to maintain only a slight supersaturation.

   Equipment for recrystallization may be designed for either discontinuous
(batch) or continuous operation.   In either case, crystallization may be
caused to proceed with or without agitation, and cooling may be provided
by the atmosphere, by a liquid, or by diminishing the pressure, i.e., adiabatic evaporation.   Evaporation without significant cooling may also be
employed.   The crystallizer may be designed to discharge the crystals
after they have reached a certain size (classifying crystallizer).   If uniform
crystals are desired in a *batch* process,[670] as many crystals as possible should
be formed at the same time.   In a *continuous*[671] process, the number of
nuclei formed per second should be uniform and equal to the number of
crystals removed per second from the crystallizer.   In the Swenson-
Walker continuous crystallizer, the nuclei are formed in one part of the
crystallizer, so that they will all grow for the same length of time while being
carried through the apparatus.   In the continuous vacuum crystallizer,
the crystals are classified in the crystallizer so that smaller crystals are
retained until they have grown to be large enough to be removed.   Isaachsen[672] appears to have been the first to patent a practical apparatus and
method for crystallization using the principles evolved by Miers; the Oslo
crystallizer is also based on them.

   In *sucrose crystallization,* unwanted nucleation or "false graining" occurs at high
supersaturation and high temperature, with rapid agitation,[673] thus increasing the
rate of crystallization.[674]   In the zone of false graining, said[675] to be in the vicinity
of the supersolubility curve, addition of "seeds" causes formation of new "seeds,"
probably because of disintegration of fragments from the crystals added.   Hence,
to prevent formation of extra nucleating crystals, those used should be free from
dust, particularly from dust of the crystallizand, and too vigorous stirring should be

   [670] G. E. Seavoy and H. B. Caldwell, *Ind. Eng. Chem.*, **32**, 633 (1940).
   [671] J. A. Platte and G. H. De Vries, *Indische Mercuur*, **60**, 291 (1937); *C. A.*, **31**, 7278
(1937).
   [672] I. Isaachsen, U. S. Pat. 1,478,337 (1923); *Chem. Centr.*, I, **95**, 1573 (1924).
   [673] J. D. Jenkins, *J. Am. Chem. Soc.*, **47**, 903 (1925).   S. W. Young and W. J. Van
Sicklen, *ibid.*, **35**, 1067 (1913).
   [674] J. G. Thieme, *Arch. Suikerind. Nederland en Ned. Indië*, **41**, 17 (1933); *C. A.*, **27**,
3101 (1933).
   [675] A. L. Webre, *Proc. 11th Ann. Conf., Asoc. técnicos azucar. Cuba*, 9–16 (1937).

avoided.   For some compounds,[676] there are *two* supersolubility curves, depending
on rate of cooling, speed of stirring, and size and number of crystal nuclei.   The
criteria for successful control of crystal size have been summarized[677] as follows:
"(1) The solution must not be supersaturated beyond its metastable limit...   (2)
To prevent excessive supersaturation and still render possible a high rate of production, a large total crystal surface is required and its efficient utilization must be
secured by exposing the crystals to fresh solution supersaturated to the maximum
degree.   (3) The crystals must be kept in constant motion to prevent their growing
together, but this motion must not be so violent that too large a number of new
crystals will be formed by attrition.   (4) In order to secure even crystal size, the
formation of new crystals or nuclei should equal the number of full-grown crystals
produced and removed" from the equipment in a continuous process.

As the crystals grow, the surface available for deposition of further
molecules or ions increases, but the rate of crystallization decreases because
of the fall in concentration of the solution.   Hence, the rate of cooling or
the rate of evaporation, or both, must be suitably accelerated, in order to
maintain constant the rate of deposition of material on the crystal faces and
give uniform crystals.   In the sugar industry, an instrument known as the
"tarphometer" or Cuitometer continuously measures the electrical conductivity of the sugar solution, and registers the supersaturation.   Other devices, such as the Brasmoscope, have been used.[678]

Open vats or crystallizing pans have been used for centuries for crystallization
by cooling or evaporation, or both, and are still employed to some extent, *e.g.*, for
naphthalene.   Heat is removed through the vat walls and the surface of the solution only, and as soon as a coating of crystals has formed on the walls, loss of heat
becomes very slow;   the supply of supersaturated solution to the surface of the
crystals takes place only through diffusion and convection currents.   Although
large crystals can be produced if the vats are not agitated, their size is uneven, and
it is often necessary to crush and screen the product.   Any dirt present settles to
the bottom, contaminating the crystals, and the crystals may clump into agglom-
erates occluding impurities and mother liquor.   One of the first advances[679] was
to blow air over the surface of the solution;   then, where slow cooling was desired,
it was found advisable to surround the tank with lagging;   if it was desired to increase the rate of cooling, the tank sides were sloped or the tank was supported on
piers so that the air might circulate freely on every side.

At one time, great care was taken to form crystals in quiescent solutions,
but Wulff[680] succeeded in obtaining crystals of approximately one desired

[676] H. H. Ting and W. L. McCabe, *Ind. Eng. Chem.*, **26**, 1201 (1934).

[677] F. Jeremiassen and H. Svanoe, *Chem. & Met. Eng.*, **39**, 594 (1932).

[678] A. L. Holven, *Ind. Eng. Chem.*, **34**, 1234 (1942).

[679] H. B. Caldwell, *Chem. & Met. Eng.*, **42**, 213 (1935).

[680] L. Wulff, *Z. Kryst. Mineral.*, **11**, 120 (1886); *Z. Rübenzuckerind.*, 917 (1887); 226
(1888); 1076 (1890); Ger. Pats., 33,190 (1884); 39,957 (1885); 41,347 (1886); 95,183
(1896).

size by means of shaking under closely controlled temperature conditions. He considered that shaking is preferable to stirring, since, with the latter, the danger of crystal attrition by mechanical attack is greater. In the *agitated batch* crystallizer, the solution is cooled at a controllable rate, by means of coils through which cold water or refrigerated brine is circulated, and is rocked or stirred, giving a batch of fine but fairly uniform crystals; however, crystals rapidly coat the cooling coils and the crystallizer must be cleaned frequently.

Crystallizers employing *evaporation without appreciable cooling* resemble evaporators in design. In the simplest form, the hot solution is kept supersaturated by evaporation; nuclei develop at the liquid–vapor surface and grow there until heavy enough to fall to the bottom of the vessel. In crystallizing sucrose in the *vacuum* evaporator, the sirup is concentrated to a specified density, nucleated, and then crystallized without formation of new nuclei. The process is controlled by regulating the steam heat and the vacuum applied. The batch vacuum crystallizer consists of a lagged, cylindrical vessel, tapered at its lower end to a cone whose apex is provided with a dump valve. Its advantage is the absence of a heat-transfer surface which would tend to "salt-up."

Many of the disadvantages of batch methods are eliminated by *continuous* crystallization; the first such device was the Wulff-Bock rocking crystallizer[681]— a slightly inclined trough which could be rocked on rollers, and whose contents were *air-cooled* by convection or by blowing air over the surface of the solution by means of a fan. The crystallizing solution flows zigzag from the higher to the lower end of the trough because of the insertion, at intervals, of partitions part way across the trough. It is useful for growing large, uniform crystals. A rotating-tube, continuous crystallizer through which air may be blown for cooling has also been developed. The *liquid-cooled* continuous crystallizer (Swenson-Walker) consists essentially of a long, semicylindrical trough, into which the hot, concentrated solution flows, cooled by a countercurrent water or brine jacket, and agitated by means of a low-speed, long-pitched spiral agitator which almost touches the bottom of the trough. Its great advantage is that the cooling surface is kept free of crystal accumulations and the crystals are continuously scattered through the solution by the agitator, which also serves to convey them from one end to the other. It gives true continuous crystallization, resulting in well shaped, uniform crystals. The *Howard crystallizer* is a conical vessel, wider at the top, through which the solution is forced upward. The lower part is surrounded by a cooling water jacket, and is also cooled internally by a "finger"-type condenser. Crystals formed in the solution must grow to a certain size before they can sink, against the current, to the

[681] See H. Griffiths, *J. Soc. Chem. Ind. London*, **44**, 7T (1925).

apex and into a collecting vessel; their size is controlled by regulating the flow of the solution.   Since this velocity is low, the smaller crystals do not escape in the overflow of mother liquor at the top of the cone. The crystals are thus classified.   In the *double-pipe crystallizer*,[682] the crystallizing solution is forced through a pipe containing helices, surrounded by a cooling jacket through which coolant flows in the opposite direction. The helices are used for scraping crystals off the crystallizer walls.

In *adiabatic crystallizers*, cooling at a controlled rate is effected by evaporation under diminished pressure.   The procedure is useful for compounds whose solubility is moderately decreased by cooling.   The amount of evaporation depends on the vacuum, heat of crystallization, amount of crystals formed, specific heats of initial solution, crystals, and mother liquor, as well as on the point of initial crystallization, the rate of crystallization, and the heat lost by radiation.   Since the lowest temperature would normally be at the surface of the liquid, it is important to ensure that all parts of the liquid are brought to the surface.   The vacuum crystallizer is probably the most satisfactory apparatus for accurate control of crystal size and uniformity.   In *batch* operations, the filtered solution is placed in a closed, insulated kettle and nucleated by addition of crystals or by briefly cooling to the labile zone of supersaturation by diminishing the pressure.   The solution is vigorously stirred and the rate of cooling is regulated by the rate of evaporation.   If the vacuum over the solution is increased, evaporation and cooling proceed faster; if the vacuum is diminished, the system cools less rapidly or even warms up, because of the heat of crystallization[683] liberated.   The temperature is regulated in accordance with the temperature–solubility curve of the system in such a way that the crystals grow uniformly and no new nuclei form.   In *continuous* vacuum crystallizers, the incoming solution is freed of any nuclei, cooled to the metastable zone of supersaturation, and passed through a chamber containing crystals so that only part of the supersaturation is removed in one cycle unless the cycling rate is very low; the mother liquor is then separated from the suspension, is again rendered supersaturated to the previous degree, and the cycle is repeated.   In the Oslo (Jeremiassen or Krystal classifying) crystallizer,[684] the warm solution is concentrated and cooled under diminished pressure to a point within the metastable region of supersaturation. It is then allowed to sink into a conical crystallizing vessel, containing

[682] G. E. Seavoy and H. B. Caldwell, *Ind. Eng. Chem.*, **32**, 627 (1940).

[683] F. Bošnjaković, *Z. ges. Kälte-Ind.*, **39**, 182 (1932).   W. L. McCabe, *Trans. Am. Inst. Chem. Engrs.*, **31**, 129 (1934–1935).

[684] H. B. Caldwell, *Chem. & Met. Eng.*, **39**, 133 (1932); *Chem. Inds.*, **65**, 526 (1949). F. Jeremiassen and H. Svanoe, *Chem. & Met. Eng.*, **39**, 594 (1932); **40**, 258 (1933). H. Svanoe, *Ind. Eng. Chem.*, **32**, 636 (1940).   A. W. Bamforth, *Ind. Chemist*, **25**, No. 289, 81 (1949).

crystal nuclei, from which it flows upward through a perforated plate, a large number of crystals being maintained in suspension as it rises.   After the crystals have grown, the solution, no longer supersaturated, leaves the crystallizer and is pumped back into the evaporator, while crystals are removed continuously from the crystallization chamber.   If fine crystals are desired, the solution is kept in the labile zone of supersaturation during the crystallization.

A fairly large number of different types of apparatus, including vacuum and mechanical (e.g., Swenson-Walker) crystallizers,[682] have been devised for automatic control of industrial crystallizations.   They all embody[685] one or more of the principles already discussed.   The crystallizers are often made of highly polished stainless steel and may have a neoprene lining. To prevent formation of crusts on the walls, increase of the contact angle between wall and liquid by at least 25% is often achievable[686] with an inner coating of bitumen, chromium, or paraffin.   It is believed[687] that the Ross theory[688] of crystallization offers a practical approach to the design of crystallizers for the production of crystals of a desired size.   Calculation of particle trajectories, of value in designing crystallization chambers, has been developed,[689] and a method for calculating the heat-transfer coefficient of crystallizers has been described.[690]   Finally, it may be mentioned that extremely fine crystals may be obtained by spraying[691] a solution into a large volume of cold air in such a way as to cause almost instantaneous chilling.

3. Separation of Crystals from Mother Liquor

The two chief methods for separation of crystals from mother liquor, by centrifuging or filtering, are treated in Chapters IV and V, respec-

[685] V. Dehon, French Pat. 819,851 (1937); C. A., 32, 2789 (1938).   J. A. Courbis, Trans. Chem. Eng. Congr. World Power Conf., II, 453 (1937).   H. Griffiths, Chem. Age London, 37, 521 (1937).   P. J. Bar, ibid., 38, 125 (1938).   S. G. M. Ure, "Crystallisation," in J. F. Thorpe and M. A. Whiteley, eds., Thorpe's Dictionary of Applied Chemistry, 4th ed., Vol. III, Longmans, Green, New York, 1939, pp. 445–455.   H. Svanoe, Ind. Eng. Chem., 32, 636 (1940).   T. R. Olive, Chem. & Met. Eng., 52, 125 (March, 1945).   N. R. Mukherjee, J. Imp. Coll. Chem. Eng. Soc., 2, 68 (1946).   P. Miller and W. C. Saeman, Chem. Eng. Progress, 43, 667 (1947).   H. Svanoe, J. Chem. Ed., 27, 549 (1950).   A. R. Thompson, Chem. Eng., 57, No. 10, 125 (1950).

[686] Werkspoor N. V., Dutch Pat. 69,392 (Jan. 15, 1952); C. A., 46, 6877a (1952).

[687] H. B. Caldwell, Chem. & Met. Eng., 49, 116 (May, 1942).

[688] E. T. Ross, Pacific Chem. Met. Inds., 2, [3], 9 (1938).

[689] C. E. Lapple and C. B. Shepherd, Ind. Eng. Chem., 32, 605 (1940).

[690] I. G. Golomshtok, Groznenskiĭ Neftyanik, 6, No. 5, 51 (1936); C. A., 31, 2798 (1937).

[691] F. Jeremiassen, U. S. Pat. 2,375,922 (1945).   C. P. Davis, U. S. Pat. 2,396,689 (1946).   Corn Products Refining Co., Brit. Pat. 596,951 (1947).

tively. The following presentation of special equipment and methods for recrystallization supplements those discussions.

In *preliminary isolation* of crystals from a viscous mother liquor it may be advisable to smear the suspension on a plate of unglazed porcelain. Most of the adhering sirup usually drains away and penetrates the pores, leaving fairly pure crystals which may be scraped off and recrystallized. The process may be slow, and it is sometimes advisable to precool the plate and let the absorption proceed in a desiccator in the refrigerator. The plate and contents may be later extracted with a solvent. The procedure is an excellent method for isolating a small sample of crystals for preliminary tests, *e.g.*, rough melting-point determination, and for use as seeds. *After crystals have been obtained, a sample of them should be set aside;* cases are known in which a substance has been obtained crystalline, has all been melted or dissolved for recrystallization, and has then refused to crystallize again.   It is often advisable to add dropwise to the main portion of a sirupy suspension of crystals, while stirring, a solvent which dissolves the sirup but not much of the crystalline material, and then remove the thinned sirup as described subsequently.

Hardened filter paper is recommended for filtration under suction or pressure because of its greater mechanical strength and because the solid can usually be scraped off without contamination by paper fibers. Silk fabric is also useful. Sintered-glass, ceramic, and other rigid filter septa (see Chapter V, Sect. IV) serve the same purpose, but particles of them may be detached when the crystals are scraped off, leading to contamination. Nonhygroscopic crystals are often removable by blowing suddenly into the stem of the inverted funnel while its wide end rests on a watch glass or dish.   In filtering saturated solutions, care must be taken to avoid appreciable evaporation of solvent in, or cooling of, the septum; both may lead to blocking of its pores through deposition of crystals. It is often advisable to diminish the suction by "bleeding" inert gas into the vacuum system, for example, by means of a needle valve. Evaporation is, of course, obviated in pressure filtration (see Chapter V, Sects. III.5 and VI.2) and greatly reduced in centrifuging and centrifuge filtration.

Many substances not normally very hygroscopic may collect moisture when moist with a volatile or hygroscopic solvent. In these cases, and with truly hygroscopic compounds, suction filtration under a rubber dam[692] (see Chapter V, Sect. VI.7) may prove satisfactory. However, for *filtration in a dry, inert atmosphere*, special apparatus must be used (see Chapter V, Sect. VI.3). Such an apparatus for *suction filtration* is shown in Figure 51. The substance is recrystallized[693] in flask *A* and the

[692] R. A. Gortner, *J. Am. Chem. Soc.*, **36**, 1967 (1914).

[693] J. Houben and H. Kauffmann, *Ber.*, **46**, 2821 (1913).

suspension then drawn into filter B by applying suction at b.   It is filtered by applying suction to the side arm of the suction flask, while admitting dry, inert gas at a.   Wash solvent may now be introduced at a and drawn over the crystals.   Finally, dry, inert gas may be admitted at b in order to dry the crystals on the filter.

A related device[694] for filtering off and washing crystals in a dry, inert atmosphere (Fig. 52) has been adapted[695] for performing, in uninterrupted sequence, preparation of the solution, filtration of insoluble impurity, crystallization, and filtration, washing, and drying of the crystals—all in

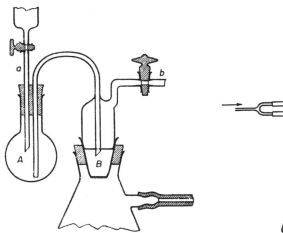

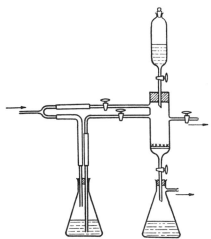

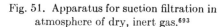

Fig. 51. Apparatus for suction filtration in   Fig. 52. Apparatus for filtering off and
atmosphere of dry, inert gas.[693]   washing crystals in inert atmosphere.[694]

the presence of an inert gas (Fig. 53).   The compound to be recrystallized is placed in flask A, stopcock h is closed, and the whole apparatus is evacuated and then filled with the inert gas from both ends of the system; this procedure is repeated once more.   Then stopcock b is closed and the whole apparatus to the left is kept under pressure from the gas generator, while a constant stream of gas is passed through the right-hand part and out through a and the bulbs at C, which contain liquid to exclude air.   Solvent is now dropped into A from B, and the solution is prepared; this is then freed from insoluble impurity by filtration through Gooch crucible D into flask E, by closing a and d and applying suction at i.   Stopcock e is now closed and the filtrate in E is cooled until the desired amount of crystals has been deposited.   After closing c, the contents of flask E are filtered through

[694] E. Beckmann and T. Paul, *Ann.*, **266**, 1 (1891).
[695] W. Steinkopf, *Ber.*, **40**, 400 (1907).

Gooch crucible F, by opening d and e and applying suction at i. The crystals in F may now be washed with solvent from H, after closing e. In order to dry the product, f is closed and flask J, containing concentrated sulfuric acid, is evacuated after opening g; g is closed and J is filled with gas from the left-hand gas source, and again evacuated. The crystals are then left in the apparatus until dry.

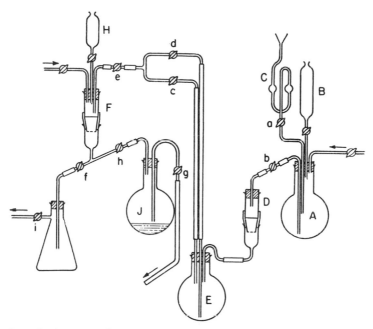

Fig. 53. Apparatus for one recrystallization cycle in inert atmosphere.[695]

The all-glass apparatus[696] shown in Figure 54 for *filter-stick filtration* is useful if the volume of solvent is large. It may be employed for repeated recrystallizations from hot solutions in volatile liquids, even if they are corrosive. For example, by its use, various paraffin hydrocarbons were recrystallized from glacial acetic acid as many as twenty times. The substance to be purified is dissolved in the solvent and poured into flask 2 through condenser G, with application of suction at A through C; alternatively, the solvent is placed in flask 2, the solute is introduced through G, and the mixture is heated under reflux until solution is complete. Flask 2 is now cooled until crystals have formed. F is packed with clean glass wool, which provides the filter plug. Stopcocks A and C are closed and suction is applied at B through D. In this way the crystals are collected

[696] J. L Keays, *Ind. Eng. Chem., Anal. Ed.*, **15**, 391 (1943).

on filter stick F and the filtrate passes into flask 1. Stopcocks B and D are now closed, C is opened, and flask 1 is heated so that some of the solvent distils into flask 2. The cycle is now repeated. The material in flask

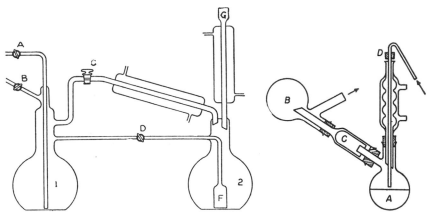

Fig. 54. Enclosed apparatus for filter-stick filtration after recrystallization.[696]

Fig. 55. Recrystallization and gravity filtration in dry, inert atmosphere.[697]

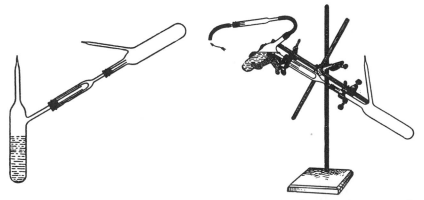

Fig. 56. Enclosed glass apparatus for recrystallization and gravity filtration.[698]

Fig. 57. Device for inverting recrystallization apparatus.[698]

2 becomes purer and purer; more and more impurity is collected in flask 1. Samples may be withdrawn periodically from flask 2 by means of a long glass tube inserted through condenser G. When the compound has been purified sufficiently, C and D are closed and the mother liquor in flask 1 is discharged through A by applying pressure at B. Flask 1 is now thoroughly

[697] J. Schmidlin, *Ber.*, **41**, 423 (1908)

washed with solvent and the final solution in flask 2 is drawn into flask 1 and discharged through A into a clean receiver, where it is crystallized.

Recrystallization and *gravity filtration* in an inert atmosphere may be performed[697] in the apparatus shown in Figure 55. For instance, a reaction may be conducted in flask A, while an inert gas is passed into flask B, in direction $B \rightarrow C \rightarrow A \rightarrow D$, with stopper D raised. After the reaction is complete, the inert gas is passed in the direction $D \rightarrow A \rightarrow C \rightarrow B$, with

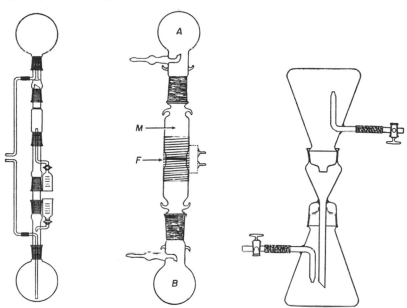

Fig. 58. Conant's re-crystallization apparatus with sintered-glass fil-ter.[699]

Fig. 59. Recrystalliza-tion apparatus with sin-tered-glass filter.[700]

Fig. 60. Enclosed recrystallization ap-paratus.[701]

stopper D inserted, and the apparatus is slowly inverted counterclockwise, so that the suspension in A is filtered through filter C and the filtrate col-lects in B. If a crop of crystals is formed in B by cooling, B may be sub-stituted for A, a clean receiver and filter placed in position, and this second crop filtered off. If the solvent is readily volatilized, the crystals may be dried on the filter by passing a stream of anhydrous, inert gas over them in the apparatus.

In a similar apparatus[698] (see Fig. 56), the substance is crystallized from

[698] W. Schlenk and A. Thal, *Ber.*, **46**, 2840 (1913).
[699] J. B. Conant; see F. Friedrichs, *Chem. Fabrik*, **4**, 318 (1931).
[700] H. Ulich, *Chem. Fabrik*, **4**, 278 (1931).
[701] P. Dickens, *Chem. Fabrik*, **1**, 323 (1928).

solvent in one tube and then the apparatus is tilted so that the suspension passes onto the filter, and the filtrate is collected in the other tube. A simple device for inverting such units is shown in Figure 57.

These devices for recrystallizing and filtering in the absence of air were improved by employing a sintered-glass filter plate instead of a Soxhlet thimble for filtration. That of Conant[699] (see Fig. 58) is very similar to that described by Ulich[700] for compounds sensitive to moisture, carbon dioxide, or oxygen. Ulich's apparatus (see Fig. 59) is a modification of Dickens' device[701] (Fig. 60) and permits the processes—dissolution of the substance, filtering of insoluble impurities, crystallization, collecting on a filter plate, washing, and drying by electric heating—to be conducted in the one apparatus with complete exclusion of air. The apparatus consists of two round-bottom flasks, A and B, carrying side arms and connected through ground-glass joints to a tube M in the middle of which is a filter plate, F. Surrounding F and M is an electric heating coil. A, B, and M are held tightly together by means of metal springs, so that the whole apparatus may be supported with a single clamp around M. The apparatus is filled through the side tubes with an inert gas, e.g., dry air, nitrogen, or hydrogen, which can also be passed in during operation of the apparatus. Overpressure from a gas cylinder or underpressure from a water pump may be employed. The substance to be recrystallized is placed in flask B, and the solvent is added. After part or all of the material has dissolved, the whole apparatus is inverted by turning the clamp through 180°. The suspension or solution now lies on the filter plate, and any undissolved material is collected on the side of the filter plate nearer B; the solution is collected in A. If the solution is hot and the compound crystallizes on slight cooling, the filter plate is heated, either electrically or by means of the hot vapor obtained by boiling the solution in B before inverting the apparatus. In order to filter the suspension, suitable over- or underpressure is applied at the side tubes. The solution in flask A is now caused to crystallize by cooling, by evaporating off part of the solvent through the side tube on A, or by introducing a poor solvent through this side tube, with suction. The apparatus is again inverted and the crystals are collected on the side of the filter plate nearer A; the mother liquor is collected in B. The crystals may now be washed by introducing wash liquid through the side tube on A. They are dried by careful electric heating and by passing an inert gas through the side tube on A. After drying, A and B are detached from M, and the crystals are removed, passing in inert gas from the other end of tube M if necessary. A modification, useful for fractionation by fractional melting under vacuum, has been described.[702]

[702] H. A. Scheraga and M. Manes, Anal. Chem., 21, 1581 (1949).

Figure 61 illustrates an enclosed apparatus[703] for repeated recrystallization from a volatile solvent.   It is shown here in the filling position, in which
it had served as receiver in a vacuum distillation of the material to be
recrystallized.   A flask containing solvent is then sealed on, as shown in
Figure 62, and the space between the two glass partitions is evacuated.
The partitions are now broken with the "hammer" enclosed in the flask
of solvent, and the apparatus is cautiously inverted so that the solvent

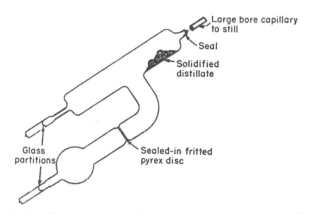

Fig. 61. Enclosed recrystallization—introduction of solute.[703]

all flows into the tube containing the substance; the large-bore capillary
is sealed off and at the same time the solvent flask is removed.   The
compound is now dissolved; if necessary, by warming the whole apparatus.
The apparatus is then tilted and inverted so that the solution passes through
the filter into the bulb, which is cooled until the desired amount of crystals
has formed (Fig. 63).   Any insoluble impurities are held back by the filter
plate.   To filter off the crystals, the apparatus is again inverted and the
mother liquor allowed to drain out of the bulb (see Fig. 64).   The apparatus
is then cautiously inverted clockwise, and part of the solvent is distilled
back into the crystallizer bulb by heating the mother liquor (see Fig. 65)
or by cooling the bulb, or both.   The crystals are redissolved and recrystallized and the apparatus is inverted counterclockwise.   The cycle is
repeated as many times as desired.   The apparatus may also be used for
repeated recrystallization from a melt.

In filtering off crystals *below room temperature*,[704] it is usually important

[703] J. D. Piper, N. A. Kerstein, and A. G. Fleiger, *Ind. Eng. Chem., Anal. Ed.*, 14, 738
(1942).
[704] R. Willstätter and J. Piccard, *Ber.*, 42, 1905 (1909).   R. Willstätter and T. Wirth,
ibid., 42, 1913, 1915 (1909).   P. Karrer and K. Schöpp, *Helv. Chim. Acta*, 17, 693 (1934).
See also Chapter V, Section III.7, this volume.

to prevent ingress or condensation of moisture. A simple method[705] is to employ a cylindrical glass funnel with sintered-glass filter plate and to attach a drying tube to the mouth of the funnel. The funnel may be surrounded by a cooling bath, contained, for example, in an inverted flask from which the bottom has been removed. The funnel and contents should then be rapidly placed in a precooled vacuum desiccator which is immediately evacuated, and cooled in the refrigerator. Alternatively, a cooled filter stick may be employed or the operations may be conducted[706] in a constant-temperature room, e.g., at −20°C.

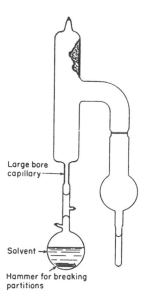

Fig. 62. Enclosed recrystallization—introduction of solvent.[703]

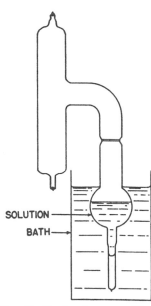

Fig. 63. Enclosed recrystallization—cooling the solution.[703]

Crystallization and filtration at temperatures as low as −75° C. may be performed[707] in an apparatus enclosed in a well-insulated chamber provided with external controls (see Fig. 66). This chamber has three compartments: A, for crystallizing and filtering; B, for collecting and removing mother liquor; and C, a reservoir. It is provided with a triple-glazed observation window. The crystallization flask and Büchner funnel are

[705] See, for example, P. A. Levene and R. S. Tipson, J. Biol. Chem., 115, 731 (1936). B. B. Elsner and P. F. M. Paul, J. Chem Soc., 1951, 893.

[706] J. B. Brown and G. G. Stoner, J. Am. Chem. Soc., 59, 3 (1937). N. L. Matthews, W. R. Brode, and J. B. Brown, ibid., 63, 1064 (1941).

[707] F. W. Quackenbush and H. Steenbock, Ind. Eng. Chem., Anal. Ed., 14, 736 (1942).

partly submerged in compartment A, which contains cooling liquid and is provided with a mechanical stirrer and chute F through which dry ice is introduced. The solution is introduced through tube D into the crystallizing flask; this tube also serves for introduction of a thermometer, and of dry air during the filtration. Tube E is a glass bearing for a mechanical glass stirrer and also serves for conveyance of the flask contents to the Büchner funnel. Compartment B contains the stem of the Büchner funnel, leading into a receiving flask to which suction may be applied by means of

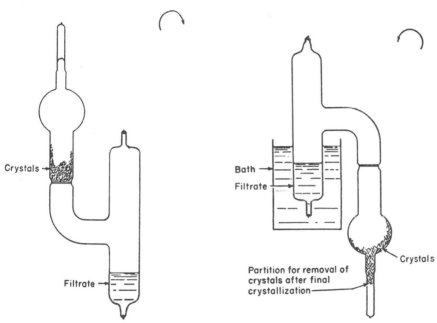

Fig. 64. Enclosed recrystallization —after filtration.[703]

Fig. 65. Enclosed recrystallization —distillation of solvent.[703]

tube I. This compartment is accessible through a door at the side. Compartment C is a gas-tight reservoir for holding coolant from A during removal of crystals from the funnel. A tube at the left of C extends from the bottom of A to within half an inch of the bottom of C. Glass tube H in the top of C is connected to a compressed-air line and permits introduction or removal of air for transferring coolant from one compartment to the other. Warm solvent for dissolving crystals on the funnel may be introduced through G. For operation, H is closed and enough alcohol is introduced into A to reach the neck of the crystallizing flask. A filter paper is placed in the funnel and the lid is put on the chamber. The solution is now admitted into the crystallizer through D, which is then closed by means

of a thermometer.   The stirrers are started and dry ice is added through
F until the desired temperature is reached.   To filter the suspension of
crystals, the thermometer is removed and a rubber bulb attached at D.
Application of pressure at D then forces the suspension into the funnel, and
suction at I carries the filtrate into the receiving flask.   The precipitate

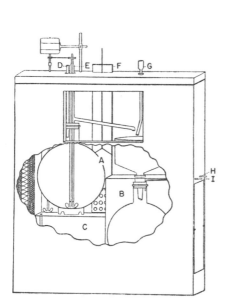

Fig. 66. Refrigerated recrystallization
apparatus.[707]

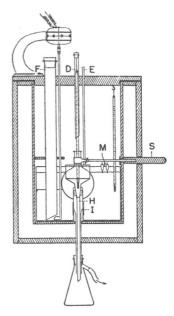

Fig. 67. Refrigerated recrystallization
apparatus.[707]

may be washed by running into the crystallizer a little solvent, cooling it,
and forcing it over into the funnel.   H is now opened, and the bath liquid
run into C.   To repeat the cycle, the flask of filtrate is removed and replaced by a clean flask.   Warm solvent is introduced through G to dissolve
the crystals on the funnel and carry the solution into the receiver.   The
solution is then returned through D into the crystallization flask.   The
coolant in C is returned to A, and sufficient dry ice added to give the correct temperature for the second crystallization.   The original filtrate
may also be returned to the crystallizer if a second crop is desired.

   In a somewhat similar but smaller unit, the crystallizer, held on a supporting shaft, S, extending outside the chamber, is inverted by hand (see
Figure 67).   The melting point may be determined, during operation of
the chamber, by means of capillary-tube holders, M.   Tube D leads to the
crystallizer, E to the funnel, and F to the bottom of the tank.   Tube H

extends the Büchner stem through tube I to the receiver under the chamber.   Operation of the apparatus is similar to that of the larger unit.

In low-temperature fractional recrystallization of fats from solvents, an apparatus (see Figure 68) resembling those previously described (see Figs. 56–65) has been used.[708]   It may be completely immersed in a constant-temperature bath, so that equilibration and filtration may be conducted at one temperature.   The solution is placed in C, and stirred by means of an iron coil in C and an external electromagnet, operating every 5 seconds, which lifts the coil and allows it to fall.   To the neck of C is

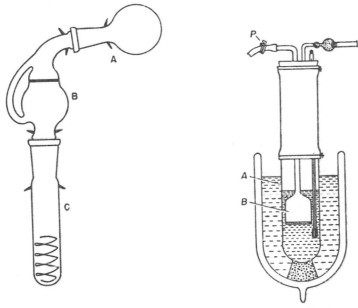

Fig. 68. Apparatus for recrystallization at   Fig. 69. Filter-stick filtration after low-
low temperatures.[708]   temperature recrystallization.[709]

attached part B, into which is sealed a sintered filter plate, by-passed by a pressure-equalizing tube.   The material to be crystallized and the solvent are weighed into C; then parts B and A are attached and held in place with spring coils.   Tube C is heated until the material has dissolved; then the whole apparatus is cooled to 20° below the equilibration temperature, and stirred electromagnetically at the same time.   The apparatus is now kept overnight in the constant-temperature bath and is then inverted clockwise, while still in the bath, so that the suspension passes into

[708] A. E. Bailey, W. S. Singleton, and R. O. Feuge, *Oil & Soap*, **23**, 201 (1946).
[709] R. Padmanabhan, *J. Indian Chem. Soc.*, **12**, 197 (1935).

B. It is then filtered *by gravity*, the crystals collecting on the filter plate and the mother liquor passing into flask A.

Filtration below room temperature may also be performed[709] by means of a *filter stick* in the apparatus in Figure 69. The melt or solution is placed in a wide tube, A, to the top of which is attached a length of wide, stout-walled rubber tubing closed by a stopper through which are inserted a thermometer, a drying tube, and the stem of a filter stick, B. The upper end of the filter stick is connected at P to a source of inert gas, and this is gently bubbled through to provide agitation, while crystallization occurs by cooling A. After the desired amount of crystals has formed, suction is applied at P, the filter stick being lowered as liquid is withdrawn from A. When all the mother liquor has been filtered off, the pinchcock at P is closed. Tube A may now be allowed to warm up to room temperature, so that the crystals may be removed without condensation of moisture.

A device for fractional recrystallization[710] by *pressure filtration* (see Chapter V, Section III.5) is shown in Figure 70. The solution is introduced into the bulb and prevented from flowing through the sintered-glass plate by means of a slow current of dry air passed through the apparatus and up through the plate. The whole apparatus is then immersed in a freezing mixture, *e.g.*, dry ice–acetone, contained in a large Dewar flask. After the desired amount of crystallization has occurred, the direction of the pressure of dry air is reversed and the mother liquor is forced through the filter plate and into the receptacle. The apparatus is now removed from the bath, the bulb is detached at the ground joint, and the crystals are allowed to melt. The resulting liquid is redissolved and recrystallized in the same manner, the cycle being repeated as many times as desired. The three xylene isomers have been recrystallized from acetone and methanol in this manner.

Techniques for micro- and semimicrofiltrations are described in the book by Cheronis in this series (Vol. VI).

If the crystals are compact and settle readily, it may be advisable, instead of filtering them off, to *decant* as much as possible of the mother liquor from them. If not very soluble, the crystals may be washed several times by swirling with a small amount of pure solvent, letting settle, and decanting; they may then be dried as usual (see Chapter VI). The relative efficiency of simple gravitational drainage of crystals as compared to centrifugal draining has been considered mathematically.[711] In some cases, simple gravitational drainage appears to be as satisfactory as centrifuging, but, as a rule, *centrifuging* is much superior[711a] as regards yield for the

[710] K. S. Pitzer and D. W. Scott, *J. Am. Chem. Soc.*, **65**, 803 (1943).

[711] N. F. Hall, *J. Am. Chem. Soc.*, **39**, 1148 (1917).

[711a] T. W. Richards, *J. Am. Chem. Soc.*, **27**, 104 (1905); **30**, 285 (1908).   *Ber.*, **40**, 2771 (1907). See also Chapter IV, Section III, this volume.

same degree of purity, and saving of time and labor. The efficiency depends on the intensity of the centrifuging and on the difference in specific gravity of crystals and mother liquor. The centrifuge tube may be provided with a septum; centrifuging forces the liquid through its pores and the crystals are retained on its surface.

When unenclosed centrifuge tubes are employed and the solvent evaporates appreciably during centrifuging at room temperature, a *refrigerated centrifuge* must be employed, to avoid deposition of impurities on the crystals. Use of such a centrifuge is essential for unstable compounds and for crystals which melt, or redissolve in the mother liquor, at room temperature. Purification of hydrocarbons by crystallizing from liquid propane–methane mixture involves[712] use of the low-temperature centrifuge.

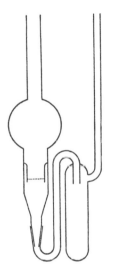

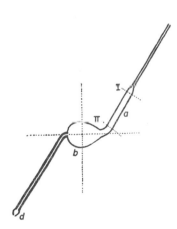

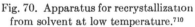

Fig. 70. Apparatus for recrystallization from solvent at low temperature.[710]

Fig. 71. Apparatus for microrecrystallization with centrifuging.[712a]

Semimicrorecrystallization with ordinary centrifuging may be employed for repeated recrystallization of readily crystallizable substances. The material is dissolved in the solvent by warming in a small centrifuge tube, cooled, crystallized, and centrifuged; the mother liquor is decanted or pipetted off. The crystals may be dried *in the centrifuge tube*, in a current of clean, dry air admitted through a fine jet, with warming of the tube in a bath if necessary.

By using capillary tubes, *e.g.*, of 2- to 3-mm. diameter, it is possible to

[712] R. T. Leslie, *Bur. Standards J. Research*, **10**, 609 (1933).
[712a] T. Kato, *J. Pharm. Soc. Japan*, **60**, 228 (1940); *C. A.*, **36**, 2182 (1942).

recrystallize a few milligrams of substance a number of times. The substance is put in the capillary tube and tapped or centrifuged down to the closed end; the solvent is introduced with a capillary pipet and the tube again centrifuged. The tube may now be sealed if desired. The mixture is heated until the crystals have dissolved; it is then cooled until crystals reappear, and centrifuged. If the crystals adhere to the glass walls, they may be disengaged by stirring with a fine-capillary stirring rod. They may be dried as described above.

Another apparatus[712a] for the recrystallization of a small amount of substance, e.g., of 50 mg. from a few drops of solvent, is shown in Figure 71 An undersaturated, hot solution is prepared in a small test tube. Charcoal may be added if necessary. A piece of filter paper is placed on d and the solution is drawn into bulb b of the apparatus by suction applied at the other end. Excess solvent may now be evaporated off by drawing a current of dry air through the apparatus while warming the solution. The bulb b is now cooled until the compound has crystallized. Tube a is then sealed off at I and the apparatus is inverted clockwise, so that the suspension passes into a. Finally, tube a is cut off at II and centrifuged.

When the centrifuge tube is *provided with a filter septum*, centrifuging resembles application of pressure (see Chapter V, Sect. III.5) for forcing the liquid through the septum. This technique is superior to other methods of filtration or centrifuging. Since practically no mother liquid adheres to the crystals, washing is seldom necessary. If the solid is not very fine, a perforated centrifuge basket[713] may often be used without other filter medium, particularly if the crystals are needle-shaped. Methylcyclohexane and heptane[714] were purified by partial freezing followed by centrifuging through *fine linen* on a rotating drum surrounded by dry ice. Using *an enclosed tube*, there is no evaporation during centrifuging, ingress of dust and moisture is prevented, and the hazard of blowing gas through, encountered in pressure filtration, is avoided. If a suitable centrifuge is employed, centrifuge filtration is simple and quantitative, and is performed as readily at −100°C. as at room temperature. It is of particular value for hygroscopic substances and for semimicro- and microfiltrations. In recrystallization of small amounts involving ordinary filtration, it may be necessary to use a solvent in which the material is not very soluble, in order that the volume of solution may be large enough to handle, but centrifuge filtration permits manipulation of very small volumes of liquid.

Tubes designed for *centrifuge filtration through paper*[715] are depicted in

[713] G. P. Baxter, *J. Am. Chem. Soc.*, **30**, 286 (1908).

[714] M. M. Hicks-Bruun and J. H. Bruun, *Bur. Standards J. Research*, **8**, 525 (1932).

[715] E. L. Skau, *J. Phys. Chem.*, **33**, 951 (1929); E. L. Skau and L. F. Rowe, *Ind. Eng. Chem., Anal. Ed.*, **3**, 147 (1931); E. L. Skau and W. Bergmann, *J. Org. Chem.*, **3**, 166 (1938).

Figure 72. In 72*a* a perforated, glazed porcelain disc, C, rests on a slight constriction, B, in a 25–40 mm. heavy Pyrex tube, A. On C is placed a filter paper. The solute and enough solvent to dissolve it at the higher temperature are introduced, stopper D is inserted, and the tube inverted, warmed in a bath until dissolution is complete, cooled to the desired temperature until crystallization is complete, and reinverted. It is now balanced against a similar tube of the same weight in the opposite cup, and centrifuged. The mother liquor collects below C and the crystals on C. C and crystals may be lifted out by means of E, a stiff Nichrome wire.

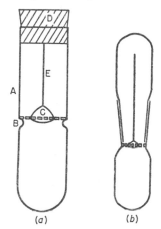
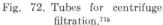

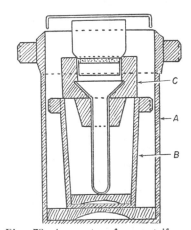

Fig. 72. Tubes for centrifuge filtration.[715]

Fig. 73. Apparatus for centrifuge filtration.[717]

In variations, the apparatus is divided into two chambers by incorporation of a ground-glass joint above C (as in Fig. 72*b*) or below C. In the latter unit, a short, wide test tube rests on C, with its closed end touching D, and E is omitted; since the solution is in this tube until the suspension is centrifuged, there is no contact with D. A modification[716] dispenses with the ground-glass joint by connecting the two chambers with a glass sleeve, passing through and resting on a rubber stopper closing the lower chamber.

The centrifuge apparatus[717] shown in Figure 73 employs filtration through *sintered glass*. After recrystallization, the suspension of crystals is placed in a sintered-glass funnel supported on a Gooch filter funnel, C, the lower end of which is sealed off. This assembly is placed inside cup *B*, which rests inside a larger centrifuge cup, *A*. A microapparatus,[718] a modification

[716] E. B. Hershberg, in A. A. Morton, *Laboratory Technique in Organic Chemistry.* McGraw-Hill, New York, 1938, p. 178.

[717] G. F. Smith, *Chemist-Analyst*, 18, No. 6, 22 (1929).

[718] *Cf.* H. R. Ing and M. Bergmann, *J. Biol. Chem.*, 129, 603 (1939). S. Moore and W. H. Stein, *ibid.*, 150, 113 (1943).

of the Skau tube, is shown in Figure 74.   In this case, the solution is
placed in A by means of a pipet with a rubber bulb, and cooled until the
substance crystallizes; alternatively, the *suspension* of crystals is introduced directly.   Then B is placed on top of A, and C on top of B.   The

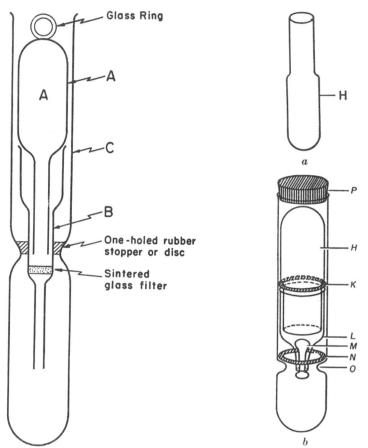

Fig. 74. Apparatus for centrifuge   Fig. 75. Apparatus for
filtration.   centrifuge filtration.[719]

unit is now inverted, inserted in a centrifuge tube in a precooled centrifuge
cup and balanced against a similar, empty assembly, by adding liquid to the
"blank."   It is then centrifuged gently for about 5 minutes, and A plus B
are dried in the vacuum desiccator.
   Sintered filters may retain mother liquor, and are not always easy to
clean.   Furthermore, when crystals are being scraped off, particles of glass

[719] L. C. Craig, *Ind. Eng. Chem., Anal. Ed.*, **12,** 773 (1940).

may simultaneously be removed.   Hence, *glass filter plugs* have been introduced to obviate these difficulties; they are smooth and readily cleaned.
The principle on which they operate resembles that of the sintered filter
except that the pores which effect filtration are confined to the wall surface.
After the crystals have formed in the crystallizer H (see Figure 75a)
they may be separated in the apparatus[719] shown in Figure 75b.   The
shoulder of H, inverted in the diagram, rests on a lead collar *K*, which
in turn rests on the rim of filter *L*, the lower end of which is closed by glass

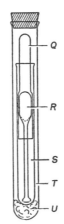

Fig. 76. Apparatus for centri-   Fig. 77. Apparatus for centrifuge filtration.[719]   fuge filtration.[720]

plug *M*.   *L* is supported by a lead collar, *N*, which rests on shoulder *O*,
formed in a test tube which collects the filtrate.   This test tube is closed
by stopper *P*.   While the apparatus is being assembled, its position is the
inverse of that shown.   The whole apparatus is cooled by immersion in a
cooling bath until crystals have formed; it is then inverted and centrifuged
quickly.   For handling smaller amounts of material, the simpler apparatus
shown in Figure 76 may be used.   The crystallizer, *Q*, is a test tube
of diameter 6 mm. or less, having a symmetrical mouth.   *R* is a *glass filter
rod* the upper end of which is a ball slightly larger than the mouth of *Q*.
These are placed inside test tube *S*, which rests inside a still larger test
tube, closed with a rubber stopper, which fits the centrifuge cup.   On
centrifuging, the crystals collect at the mouth of *Q*; *Q* and *R* are then
removed by means of forceps and the mother liquor remains in *S*.   Another
form of this apparatus is recommended[720] for routine fractional recrystallization of small amounts of material.   It rests on a plug of cotton, *U*, inside a larger test tube, *T* (see Figure 77).

[720] L. C. Craig and O. W. Post, *Ind. Eng. Chem., Anal. Ed.*, **16,** 413 (1944).

Instead of plugs M or R in Figures 75–77, a plug of the type B depicted in Figure 78 may be employed.   It is shaped as shown and then ground so that, when inserted in funnel A, the surfaces at C will remove fine charcoal from aqueous suspension.   This assemblage is used in the apparatus shown in Figure 79, in which E is a flexible wire spring and D is a tin collar.   Further improvements on these designs, employing standard-taper, rough-ground surfaces for filtration have been described.[721]   In the modification[722] shown in Figure 80, end C of capillary tube B is constricted to 0.1 mm. and sealed to tube A; the Teflon plug F is ground to fit the

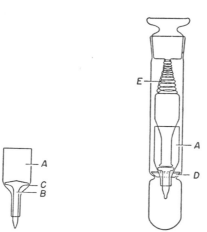

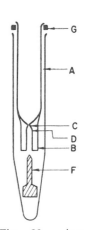

Fig. 78. Glass plug for centrifuge filtration.[720]

Fig. 79. Apparatus for centrifuge filtration.[720]

Fig. 80.   Apparatus with Teflon plug, for centrifuge filtration.[722]

ground conical surface D, and A rests on rubber gasket G on the rim of a centrifuge tube.   With F in place, material is recrystallized in A; then F is removed and the assemblage is centrifuged; F may now be replaced and the crystals recrystallized in the same way.

For work not strictly quantitative, other materials,[723] *e.g.*, paper pulp, cotton, asbestos, or linen, may be used for the filter plug.   An inexpensive tube for centrifuge filtration of 200–500 mg. of crystals has been developed[724]; it is a tube constricted in the middle to permit formation of a filtering plug of paper pulp (see Fig. 81).   A convenient size is 120 mm. × 14-mm. diameter with the constriction of 2-mm. diameter; one end of

[721] J. English, Jr., *Ind. Eng. Chem., Anal. Ed.*, 16, 478 (1944).   M. T. Bush, *ibid.*, 18, 584 (1946).

[722] C. E. Blades and W. Schöniger, *Anal. Chem.*, 26, 1256 (1954).

[723] E. Beckmann and A. Stock, *Z. physik. Chem.*, 17, 122 (1895).

[724] N. D. Cheronis, *J. Chem. Ed.*, 16, 28 (1939).

the tube is flared to permit insertion of a rubber stopper.   A small plug of paper pulp, *e.g.*, from filter paper, is molded to a tapered shape, placed on the constriction, moistened with a few drops of solvent, pressed out with a glass rod, and then centrifuged for 15 seconds.   After removing the excess solvent, the tube is ready for use.   The suspension of crystals in solvent is placed in one tube and balanced against a similar tube containing solvent only.   After centrifuging for about 2 minutes the stopper is cautiously removed and the filtrate collected in a test tube.   If desired, the crystals may be washed several times by centrifuging with small

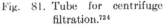
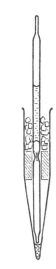

Fig. 81. Tube for centrifuge   Fig. 82. Centrifuge filtration in
filtration.[724]   a microtube.[725]

portions of fresh solvent; and, if the solvent is very volatile, the crystals may often be dried merely by centrifuging for 2 or 3 minutes more after all wash solvent has been drained off.

A technique of microrecrystallization in melting-point tubing has been described.[725]   An asbestos plug is introduced into a capillary tube, 7 to 8 cm. long, and is held in place by a constriction.   Then 0.03 to 0.05 ml. solution is drawn into the tube in such a manner that the plug is not wetted, and the other end is sealed off.   The sealed end is now cooled, causing the liquid to draw away from the open end, and this is then sealed off.   The end containing the solution is now cooled until crystallization takes place, and the tube inverted, placed on a cotton wad in a small centrifuge tube, and centrifuged.   The mother liquor is thus filtered off and the crystals

725 F. Emich *et al.*, *Monatsh.*, **53–54**, 312 (1929).

remain on the plug. If desired, the capillary may be held in position in the centrifuge tube by means of a bored stopper and may be cooled as shown (see Fig. 82). The tube is now cut at a point midway between the surface of the mother liquor and the plug. The mother liquor may then be withdrawn by means of a capillary pipet. Finally, the part of the tube containing the crystals is cut above the surface of the crystals. A similar method, using a plug of silk or linen, has been employed[726] for the recrystallization of small samples for microscopic examination.

Two microrecrystallizations from a melt may be made in a tube having two constrictions, the upper one holding an asbestos plug. The liquid is introduced into the upper bulb and the two ends of the tube are sealed off as previously described. The liquid is then partly crystallized and centrifuged so that the mother liquor is collected at the far end, where it is removed by sealing off at this constriction. The crystals are now melted, cooled until partly crystallized, and the tube again centrifuged.[725]

4. Washing the Crystals

Whether or not the crystals should be washed depends on the system, the method of removal, and the end in view. If the substance being purified does not form solid solutions with the impurity, and the crystallization temperature is above that at which the eutectic separates, the crystals deposited are pure save for mother liquor retained within or impurity adsorbed on the crystals. Ordinary centrifuging reduces adhering mother liquor to some 2 to 5% of the weight of the crystals. The minimum proportion of mother liquor is adsorbed by large, uniform crystals deposited from a mother liquor of low viscosity. Nonuniform, small crystals deposited from a viscous solution retain much more mother liquor. Liquid still adhering after pressing or centrifuging the crystals may be removed by washing. Washing on the filter (Chapter V, Section VI.7) is inadvisable since channelling may occur and some crystals may not come in contact with the solvent. If the yield is unimportant, these difficulties are overcome by using plenty of solvent and stirring on the filter. Removal of the crystals and agitation with the solvent, followed by filtering or centrifuging, usually gives better results. Repeated washing with small amounts is more effective than fewer washings with the same total volume of solvent (see Chapter II).

If it is necessary to recrystallize from a solvent of relatively high boiling point, not readily volatilized on "drying," e.g., glacial acetic acid or nitrobenzene, the crystals may be washed with a second solvent of lower boiling point in which the first solvent is soluble and the solute is very sparingly

[726] M. Perutz, Z. Krist., 96, 328 (1937).

soluble or insoluble. Thus, water may be used to remove acetic acid, and ether, alcohol, or benzene to remove other high-boiling organic solvents. In order to minimize precipitation of impurities by the second solvent, the crystals should first be washed with a mixture of the two solvents, and then with the pure second solvent. The *drying of crystals* is discussed in Chapter VI.

V. SOLVENTS FOR CRYSTALLIZATION AND RECRYSTALLIZATION

The prime requirement of the solvent is obviously that it should dissolve the compound to be crystallized or recrystallized, and that this solute should then crystallize from it by cooling, evaporation, or other treatment. No all-embracing rule predicts whether or not one compound will dissolve another. Some *general rules of solubility* have been summarized[727] as follows: "(1) Chemically similar substances are usually mutually soluble, and chemically dissimilar substances are usually but slightly soluble in each other." This is the old rule, *similia similibus solvuntur* (like dissolves like). In practice, it often implies that a solvent too closely resembling the crystallizand is to be avoided as a medium for crystallization, because of too great a solubility. "(2) Homologs are mutually soluble. (3) Stereoisomers are mutually soluble. (4) Polysubstituted products are mutually soluble. (5) The most fusible isomeric substances are the most soluble." (Hildebrand[728] expresses this rule thus: "A solid having a higher melting point is" generally "less soluble at a given temperature than one having a lower melting point.") "(6) The most fusible isomeric acids are the most soluble; the solubilities of their salts are in the same order. (7) The order of solubility of isomeric compounds is the same in all solvents. (8) The ratio of solubility of two isomers in any given solvent is nearly constant and is independent of the nature of the solvent." Rules

[727] W. M. Dehn, *J. Am. Chem. Soc.*, **39**, 1399 (1917). See also, D. W. MacArdle, *The Use of Solvents in Synthetic Organic Chemistry*, Van Nostrand, New York, 1925, pp. 4–5. S. L. Bigelow, *Theoretical and Physical Chemistry*, Century, New York, 1919, p. 335. I. Ostromysslensky, *J. prakt. Chem.*, **76**, 264 (1907). T. Carnelley and A. Thomson, *J. Chem. Soc.*, **53**, 782 (1888). J. A. Riddick and E. E. Toops, Jr., *Organic Solvents* (based on 1st ed. by A. Weissberger and E. Proskauer), 2nd ed. (*Technique of Organic Chemistry*, Vol. VII) Interscience, New York-London, 1955. O. Jordan, *The Technology of Solvents*, translation by A. D. Whitehead, Hill, London, 1938. T. H. Durrans, *Solvents*, Chapman & Hall, London, 1950. I. Mellan, *Industrial Solvents*, Reinhold, New York, 1950. L. Scheflan and M. B. Jacobs, *The Handbook of Solvents*, Van Nostrand, New York, 1953. C. Marsden, *Solvents Manual*, Elsevier, New York, 1954. A. K. Doolittle, "Industrial Solvents," in *Elsevier's Encyclopedia of Chem. Technol.*, **12**, 654 (1954).

[728] J. H. Hildebrand and R. L. Scott, *Solubility of Non-Electrolytes*. 3rd ed., Reinhold, New York, 1950, p. 28.

2, 3, and 4 are obviously special cases of rule 1, and rule 6 is a special case of 5. Another specialization of rule 1 is that a polar compound is usually more soluble in a polar than in a nonpolar solvent, and vice versa.

Theories correlating solubility and solvent power with other properties and with the chemical constitution of compounds have been put forward by Walden, Debye, Langmuir and Hildebrand, K. H. Meyer, Staudinger, Fajans, and others. Solvents may be grouped into polar and nonpolar compounds. The latter, *e.g.*, the aliphatic hydrocarbons, do not contain atoms or groups imparting marked dipole moment to the molecule, but toluene has a small, finite dipole moment. Polar solvents usually contain nitrogen, halogens, oxygen, etc. Nonpolar solvents have lower boiling points than polar solvents of similar molecular weight because of association of the latter solvents.

The forces responsible for association of polar-solvent molecules also cause loose bonding with suitable solutes and increase their solubility; hydrogen bonds and other co-ordinate links are of particular importance. The mutual solubility of substances has therefore been used as a measure of the extent of interaction between molecules (see Chapter VII in Volume I, part I, page 303, of this series). "In homologous series of polar solvents, the solubility for polar materials decreases with increasing molecular weight or increasing proportion of hydrocarbon residue"[729] but the solubility of nonpolar compounds increases with increasing paraffinic nature of the solvent. A special case is constituted by those compounds which, though containing polar groups, have little or no dipole moment because of symmetrical arrangement of the groups, *e.g.*, carbon tetrachloride, *p*-dichlorobenzene, and dioxane. The last has a negligible dipole moment but readily dissolves polar compounds, even water, with which it is miscible and with which it can form complexes through hydrogen bonds.

A few *specific observations* are: Substances which are but slightly soluble in other common solvents are often fairly soluble in glacial acetic acid or pyridine. Substances soluble in glacial acetic acid are usually less soluble in alcohol. Ether and benzene often have similar dissolving power. At atmospheric pressure, boiling pentane dissolves materials dissolved by boiling heptane or hexane, but to a lesser extent, because of its lower boiling point. Substances readily soluble in petroleum ethers or ligroin are usually only very sparingly soluble in water. Substances having hydroxyl groups are often quite soluble in water or methanol, but less soluble in ethanol and the higher alcohols. The presence of several hydroxyl groups often increases the solubility in water. Sulfonic and carboxylic acid groups may impart water solubility. Many substances readily soluble in chloroform (dipole

---

[729] K. B. Lehmann and F. Flury, *Toxicology and Hygiene of Industrial Solvents*. Translation by E. King and H. F. Smyth, Jr., Williams & Wilkins, Baltimore, 1943, p. 4.

moment, 1.1×10^{-18} e.s.u.) are but sparingly soluble in carbon tetrachloride (dipole moment, zero).

The solvent *must not react chemically* with the crystallizand, beyond the formation of loose complexes. In crystallization from chemically reactive solvents, *e.g.*, acetic acid, the compound is often unchanged on working with small amounts over a short time, but a longer heating period or the presence of catalysts may cause reaction, *e.g.*, acetylation. Readily reduced compounds may undergo reduction by such solvents as formic acid. It should also be noted that isomerization of solute by solvent is encountered. Thus, digitogenic acid is isomerized by recrystallization from acetic acid[730]; α-D-glucose is transformed to β-D-glucose by pyridine[731]; reducing sugars and aldonic acids are epimerized by boiling pyridine. Although the solvent may not actually react with the solute, many substances undergo decomposition in boiling solvents of high boiling point; such reactions may be influenced by the chemical nature of the solvent, *e.g.*, decarboxylation is often facilitated by quinoline and similar bases. Other compounds may be oxidized while being dissolved in boiling solvents of high boiling point; this may be avoided by passing inert gas through the boiling suspension, or, in certain cases, by addition of sulfurous acid. Sensitive acid chlorides may sometimes be protected by addition of a little phosphorus pentachloride.

The solvent should be *pure*[732] or of known composition. Relatively small amounts of common impurities, particularly water, may greatly change the behavior of the system. For example, the solubility of many sugars and glycosides in alcohol and other solvents is greatly increased by traces of water. The solubility of salicylic acid in benzene at 30°C. is increased 10% by 0.07 part of water.[733]

Often the resulting crystals contain *"solvent of crystallization"* (Sect. II.10). Sometimes two solvents are retained together, *e.g.*, conchairamine crystals contain[734] both alcohol and water of crystallization. Other combinations are water and benzene, and acetic acid and benzene. Retention of solvent often facilitates crystallization, but removal of the solvent usually leads to collapse of the crystal lattice, *e.g.*, certain sulfonic acids and some crystalline proteins become amorphous on drying. Tri-*O*-benzoyl-"γ"-D-glucose crystallizes from carbon tetrachloride with one mole of CCl_4 per mole,[735]

[730] H. Kiliani and J. Schweissinger, *Ber.*, **37**, 1215 (1904).

[731] R. Behrend, *Ann.*, **353**, 106 (1907); **377**, 220 (1910).

[732] J. Timmermans, *Bull. soc. chim. Belg.*, **24**, 244 (1910).

[733] E. Cohen and W. D. J. van Dobbenburgh, *Verslag Gewone Vergader. Afdeel. Natuurk. Nederland. Akad. Wetenschap.*, **34**, 518 (1925); *Z. physik. Chem.*, **118**, 37 (1925). E. Cohen and S. Miyake, *ibid.*, **119**, 247 (1926).

[734] O. Hesse, *Ann.*, **225**, 247 (1884).

[735] E. Fischer and C. Rund, *Ber.*, **49**, 88 (1916).

but on removal of the CCl_4 it reverts to the sirupy state. It is noteworthy that solvents are often retained with great tenacity. Thus, one mole of apocupreine[736] crystallizes with "1.5 moles of water of crystallization. One mole of water is lost on drying at 110° (20 mm.) for sixteen to twenty hours." The remaining half mole can only be removed by drying at 140° (20 mm.) during a further 24 hours. Even ether, methanol, ethanol, and benzene of crystallization may be difficult to expel. Acetic acid of crystallization is sometimes removable by dissolving the crystals in a high-boiling hydrocarbon and distilling. The number of moles of solvent of crystallization associated with a mole of the compound is usually 1, 2, 3, or more moles, but 0.25, 0.5, 0.6 mole, or 1.5 or 2.5 moles may be encountered. The number sometimes depends on the conditions of crystallization, e.g., the presence of different impurities, the velocity and temperature of crystallization, and the solvent employed. Thus, tetrahydropapaverine[737] crystallizes without solvent of crystallization from absolute methanol, but with methanol of crystallization from aqueous methanol. Some substances, e.g., D-glucose,[738] may crystallize from water in either the anhydrous or the hydrated form, depending on which type of nucleating crystal is added or forms.

Except for its presence as solvent of crystallization, the solvent should be *readily removable* from the crystallized substance by washing and drying. Its boiling point, vapor pressure at room temperature, volatility, and solubility in more volatile solvents should therefore be appropriate. Such properties as inflammability, flash point, temperature of spontaneous ignition, explosive limits and potentialities, odor, toxicity, availability, and cost should also receive attention. For a discussion of solvents for *extraction*, see Chapter II.

1. Inorganic Solvents

Water. Water readily dissolves many hydroxylic substances, including sugars and some phenols, and such compounds as benzohydrazide, p-nitrosophenol, 6-nitro-m-cresol, and pinacone. Many carboxylic acids —e.g., cinnamic, sorbic, and benzoic acids, and some of their inorganic salts, e.g., calcium D-gluconate—may be crystallized from water. It should be noted that many compounds, e.g., esters, the diazobenzenesulfonic acids, and aloin, though sensitive to boiling water, are readily crystallized from warm water. Sulfurous acid[739] or hydrogen sulfide

[736] R. S. Tipson and L. H. Cretcher, *J. Am. Chem. Soc.*, **64**, 1162 (1942).

[737] G. Goldschmiedt, *Monatsh.*, **9**, 327 (1888).

[738] A. Behr, *J. Am. Chem. Soc.*, **4**, 11 (1882).

[739] A. Baeyer, *Ann.*, **183**, 6 (1876). M. Guggenheim, *Z. physiol. Chem.*, **88**, 279 (1913).

may sometimes be added to the solution for protection against oxidation by atmospheric oxygen. *Hydrogen peroxide* has also been used as a solvent for crystallization.[740]

Addition of some *acid or base* is frequently recommended in crystallization from water. Amino acid amides[741] often crystallize well from *aqueous ammonia*,[742] and certain nitrogen-containing sulfonates are readily recrystallized from boiling, dilute aqueous *sodium hydroxide* solution. Many sulfonic acids are best recrystallized from *dilute sulfuric acid*,[743] certain pyridine derivatives from *dilute nitric or hydrochloric acid*,[744] and some anthocyanins from 7% sulfuric acid or 2% hydrochloric acid.[745] It often happens that the solute is too soluble in dilute acid or alkali, but an increase in concentration of the acid or alkali may give an excellent solvent for recrystallization. Thus cystine nitrate is readily soluble in dilute nitric acid and decomposed by concentrated acid, but is recrystallizable from 30 to 45% acid.[746]

Concentrated Sulfuric Acid.[747] Some compounds, relatively insoluble in water, dissolve in concentrated sulfuric acid unharmed. The substance may be cautiously warmed with the acid until dissolved, the solution cooled, placed in a desiccator containing a dish of water, and allowed to absorb water gradually.[748] Chlorohydurilic acid was dissolved[749] in concentrated sulfuric acid and precipitated in crystalline form by cautious dilution with water. Trinitrotoluene[750] and certain aromatic sulfonic acids may be recrystallized and purified similarly.

Concentrated Nitric Acid. This acid is sometimes of value in the recrystallization of aromatic nitro compounds.[751] Thus tetranitronaphthalene[752] may be recrystallized by dissolving it in the concentrated acid and

[740] M. Bamberger and J. Nussbaum, *Monatsh.*, **40**, 411 (1919). *Cf.* H. Stoltzenberg, *Ber.*, **49**, 1545 (1916).

[741] E. Fischer, *Ber.*, **35**, 1102 (1902).

[742] E. Posen, *Ann.*, **195**, 144 (1879). F. Tiemann, *Ber.*, **13**, 384 (1880). L. Spiegel, *ibid.*, **37**, 1763 (1904).

[743] H. Lönnies, *Ber.*, **13**, 704 (1880).

[744] H. Weidel and J. Herzig, *Monatsh.*, **1**, 5 (1880). C. A. Bischoff, *Ann.*, **251**, 377 (1889).

[745] R. Willstätter and E. K. Bolton, *Ann.*, **412**, 129, 135 (1917). R. Willstätter and E. H. Zollinger, *ibid.*, **412**, 173 (1917).

[746] C. T. Mörner, *Z. physiol. Chem.*, **93**, 203 (1914).

[747] G. Schroeter, *Ann.*, **426**, 44 (1922). S. von Niementowski, *J. prakt. Chem.*, **40**, 22 (1889); A. Schleicher, *ibid.*, **105**, 358 (1923).

[748] F. Kaufler, *Ber.*, **36**, 931 (1903).

[749] A. Baeyer, *Ann.*, **127**, 1 (1863).

[750] V. Vender, Brit. Pat. 18,281 (1909); French Pat. 405,812 (1909).

[751] S. N. Dhar, *J. Chem. Soc.*, **117**, 1001 (1920). H. Decker, *J. prakt. Chem.*, **64**, 99 (1901).

[752] W. Will, *Ber.*, **28**, 367 (1895).

diluting with water; and 3,4-dinitrotoluene[753] was first crystallized from hot nitric acid.   Caryophyllic acid can only be crystallized from nitric acid.[754]

Hydrochloric Acid and Other Hydrogen Halides.   Hydrohalide acids alone, or subsequently diluted with water, have been used for crystallization of many organic compounds.   Thus, concentrated hydrochloric acid was the only solvent from which crude 2-bromo-3-nitrophenol[755] could be crystallized; thymoquinone dioxime was recrystallized from concentrated hydrochloric acid by adding water[756]; naphthalene-2-sulfonic acid has been recrystallized by dissolving its trihydrate in half its weight of water at 70°C., adding about one-sixth of its weight of concentrated hydrochloric acid, and cooling.[757] α,α- and β,β-Dimethyladipic acid[758] may be separated from one another because the former can be crystallized from concentrated hydrochloric acid, whereas the latter remains in solution.   *Hydrofluoric acid* is suitable for recrystallization of diazobenzenesulfonic acid.[759]   Even *aqua regia,*[760] and *perchloric acid*[761] have found use as solvents for recrystallization.

Concentrated Alkalis.   These are often useful for the recrystallization of alkali salts of carboxylic and sulfonic acids.   Concentrated *potassium hydroxide* was employed[762] for the recrystallization of potassium nitroacetate.

Liquefied Gases.[763]   Liquid *ammonia,*[764] *sulfur dioxide, hydrogen chloride, hydrogen bromide,* and *hydrogen sulfide,* for example, often display remarkable solvent properties for organic compounds but do not appear to have been extensively used for their crystallization, though liquid *sulfur dioxide* has been employed[765] for recrystallization of theine, anthracene, anthraquinone, and triphenylmethylcarbinol derivatives.[766]

[753] O. L. Brady and P. N. Williams, *J. Chem. Soc.*, **117**, 1137 (1920).

[754] E. Mylius, *Ber.*, **6**, 1053 (1873).

[755] F. W. Schlieper, *Ber.*, **25**, 552 (1892).

[756] F. Kehrmann and J. Messinger, *Ber.*, **23**, 3557 (1890).

[757] O. N. Witt, *Ber.*, **48**, 743 (1915).

[758] A. W. Crossley and N. Renouf, *J. Chem. Soc.*, **89**, 1553 (1906).

[759] W. Lenz, *Ber.*, **12**, 580 (1879).

[760] R. Kempf and H. Moehrke, Ger. Pat. 256,034 (1913); *Chem. Centr.*, *I*, **84**, 758 (1913).

[761] F. Arndt and L. Lorenz, *Ber.*, **63**, 3129 (1930).

[762] W. Steinkopf, *Ber.*, **42**, 2027 (1909).

[763] F. Friedrichs, *Z. angew. Chem.*, **26**, 201 (1913).

[764] T. Welton, Ger. Pat. 113,291 (1900).   J. Bronn, *Verflüssigtes Ammoniak als Lösungsmittel*, Springer, Berlin, 1905.

[765] P. Walden, *Z. physik. Chem.*, **43**, 457 (1903).   M. Gomberg *et al.*, *Ber.*, **35**, 2405 (1902); **37**, 2043 (1904).   I. Moore, J. C. Morrell, and G. Egloff, *Petroleum Z.*, **16**, 425, 461 (1920).

[766] W. Schlenk, T. Weickel, and A. Herzenstein, *Ann.*, **372**, 4, 9 (1910).

Phosphorus Trichloride and Phosphorus Oxychloride. These substances are often excellent solvents for the crystallization of aromatic nitro hydrocarbons.[767] *Aluminum bromide* has been employed for the crystallization of dibromobenzene and dimethylpyrone,[768] and *thionyl chloride* has been used for recrystallization of certain acid anhydrides.[769]

2. Organic Solvents

A number of the most useful common solvents are listed in Table IV. It should be noted that some of them may freeze in the refrigerator or in dry ice, that *most of them are inflammable*, and that some, particularly chloroform, carbon tetrachloride, and benzene, are *toxic*[770] if absorbed through the skin or if their vapors are inhaled over a prolonged period of time.

TABLE IV

SOME COMMON SOLVENTS FOR CRYSTALLIZATION OF ORGANIC COMPOUNDS

Solvent	F.p., °C.	B.p., °C.
Acetone.....................	−94	56
Chloroform[a, b]...............	−63.5	61
Methanol[b]....................	−98	64.5
Ethanol......................	−117	78.5
Water[a]......................	0	100
Pyridine.....................	−42	115
Glacial acetic acid[b]...........	+16.5	118
Ether.......................	−116	34.5
Ethyl acetate................	−84	77
Pentane (fraction)...........	Below −100	30–40
Hexane (fraction)...........	Below −95	60–70
Carbon tetrachloride[a, b].......	−23	76
Benzene[b]....................	+5.5	80
Heptane (fraction)...........	Below −90	90–100

[a] Not inflammable.
[b] Toxic.

Alcohols. The lower alcohols are soluble in water, the higher ones are insoluble; many substances not very soluble in water show progres-

[767] A. Oppenheim, *Ber.*, **2**, 54 (1869).

[768] B. A. Izbekov and W. A. Plotnikov, *J. Russ. Phys.-Chem. Soc.*, **43**, 18 (1911); *Z. anorg. Chem.*, **71**, 328 (1911).

[769] W. Steinkopf, *Ber.*, **42**, 3927 (1909).

[770] E. Browning, *Toxic Solvents*, Arnold, London, 1953. K. B. Lehmann and F. Flury, *Toxicology and Hygiene of Industrial Solvents*, translation by E. King and H. F. Smyth, Jr., Williams & Wilkins, Baltimore, 1943. F. A. Patty, ed., *Industrial Hygiene and Toxicology*. Interscience, New York-London, 1948.

sively increasing solubility in the alcohols as the alkyl group is lengthened. Moreover, the boiling point becomes higher with increasing chain length, permitting the preparation, at atmospheric pressure, of saturated solutions at higher temperatures. In addition, the higher alcohols are less hygroscopic than ethanol and are easier to dehydrate. The alcohols often react with the solute, *e.g.*, forming esters. Difficultly esterified acids may be separated, during recrystallization, from easily esterified impurities by treatment with ethanol containing a trace of sulfuric acid.[771] Ethers may be formed with tertiary alcohols, and alcoholysis, especially in the presence of a trace of acid or alkali, may occur. Replacement of an acetyl group by the ethyl group is occasionally observed.

Methanol[772] as a solvent is usually intermediate[773] between water and ethanol. Some substances which refused to crystallize from ethanol have been crystallized from methanol, for example, bebeerine[774] from Indian mallow. Many heat-sensitive substances may be recrystallized from hot or boiling methanol but not from boiling ethanol. As a rule, the methanol should be freed from water and acetone. *Ethanol* is a good solvent for many organic compounds. It forms a binary azeotrope with water. Sometimes, aqueous alcohol of precise concentration must be employed; thus digitonin[775] crystallizes from 85% ethanol. It is usually advisable to recrystallize salts of organic bases from ethanol containing some of the free acid. Amino acids often crystallize well from ethanol containing ammonia. Methanol,[776] *propanol,*[776] and *isopropyl alcohol*[777] have been used more and more in recent years. 1-*Butanol* is a good solvent for the recrystallization of many compounds, including anthraquinone dyes, and picrolonates[778]; and *isobutyl alcohol* has been used for indanones,[779] anthocyanins,[780] and hydrocarbons[781] of high molecular weight. *Allyl alcohol* has found occasional use.[782] *Amyl alcohol* has proved especially suitable for the recrystallization of certain hydrochlorides.[783] *2-Phenylethanol* has also been employed.

[771] J. J. Sudborough and E. R. Thomas, *J. Chem. Soc.*, **99**, 2307 (1911).

[772] C. A. Lobry de Bruyn, *Rec. trav. chim.*, **11**, 112 (1892); *Z. physik. Chem.*, **10**, 782 (1892); *Ber.*, **26**, 268 (1893).

[773] J.-B. Dumas and E.-M. Péligot, *Ann. chim. et phys.*, **58**, 5 (1835).

[774] M. Scholtz, *Arch. Pharm.*, **236**, 530 (1898); **237**, 199 (1899).

[775] H. Kiliani, *Ber.*, **24**, 339 (1891).

[776] H. S. Isbell, *J. Research Natl. Bur. Standards*, **26**, 47 (1941).

[777] R. C. Elderfield, *J. Biol. Chem.*, **115**, 247 (1936).

[778] A. Skita, F. Keil, and E. Baesler, *Ber.*, **66**, 858 (1933).

[779] F. Mayer and P. Müller, *Ber.*, **60**, 2283 (1927).

[780] O. Rosenheim, *Biochem. J.*, **14**, 73 (1920).

[781] F. Krafft, *Ber.*, **40**, 4782 (1907).

[782] F. Mylius, *Ber.*, **19**, 373 (1886). R. Kremann, *Monatsh.*, **26**, 786 (1905); **29**, 23 (1908).

[783] W. Küster, *Ber.*, **27**, 573 (1894).

Phenol has been used as a solvent for the crystallization of many sub-stances, more, perhaps, industrially than in the laboratory.   Phenol mono-hydrate is sometimes preferable as the solvent since it remains liquid at room temperature.   Phenol adhering to the resulting crystals can often be washed off with alcohol or with dilute aqueous alkali.   *Cyclohexanol, m-cresol,* cresol mixtures, and *2-naphthol* have also been used as solvents for recrystallization.

The polyhydric alcohols, *ethylene glycol* and *glycerol,* are often good sol-vents for recrystallizations, although their high viscosity is a drawback. Fluidity may be increased by the addition of a miscible second solvent, *e.g.,* methanol,[784] or water.

Esters.   Like the alcohols, esters are polar solvents which are proton acceptors, for example, in formation of hydrogen bonds, but, unlike the alcohols, are not proton donors;   only the lower members are water-soluble.   *Methyl, ethyl,* and *isopropyl acetate* and *benzoate* find use as solvents for crystallization, and *ethyl lactate,*[785] having one hydroxyl group per molecule, is superior to ethyl acetate for the crystallization of some glycosides and sugars.   As a rule, these esters should be anhydrous and free from the alcohol;   some substances are very much more soluble in the moist ester.   Some esters, *e.g.,* ethyl benzoate, may act as acylating agents.[786]   Readily hydrolyzed esters must be used with discretion if there is any possibility that the solute might be affected by their hydrolysis prod-ucts.   Useful esters include *methyl formate, cyclohexyl formate, ethyl oxalate, propyl, butyl,* and *amyl acetates, triacetylglycerol, olive oil, methyl* and *ethyl chloroacetates, benzyl benzoate* and *cyanide,* neutral *esters of phthalic acid,* and *ethyl acetoacetate.*   Liquid *methyl*[787] and *ethyl chloride, methyl* and *ethyl iodide, ethyl* and *amyl bromide, dimethyl sulfate,* and *ethyl nitrite* are sometimes valuable solvents for recrystallization.

Organic acids.   These are powerful proton donors.   *Formic acid* is often superior, as a solvent, to acetic acid.   Such compounds as uric acid and alizarin, difficultly soluble in other solvents, dissolve readily in formic acid.   Both the anhydrous and the 95% acid find use; occasionally, 85% acid is preferable.   Thus, phenylaminoacetic acid was recrystallized[788] from aqueous formic acid.   It may also be used in admixture with acetic acid.   It esterifies alcohols and phenols, often in the cold, decomposes some

[784] H. Erdmann, *Ann.,* **275, 255** (1893).

[785] C. S. Hudson, *Advances in Carbohydrate Chem.,* 1, 24 (1945).

[786] F. Kehrmann and H. Bürgin, *Ber.,* 29, 1248 (1896).

[787] C. Harries and R. Koetschau, *Ber.,* 42, 3305 (1909); C. Harries, *Ann.,* 390, 239 (1912).

[788] W. J. Hickinbottom, *Reactions of Organic Compounds.* 2nd ed., Longmans, Green. New York, 1948, p. 151.

compounds, and isomerizes others.[789] Readily reduced substances should not be heated with formic acid. *Acetic acid* is often a valuable solvent[790] for crystallization, but may act as an acetylating agent. It has been used for the separation of isomeric acids.[791] Its use is limited to some extent by its melting point. If the glacial acid proves unsuitable, appropriate addition of water may often facilitate crystallization. Certain other organic acids, *e.g.*, aqueous *oxalic acid* solution,[792] have found some use in crystallizing organic compounds.

Acetic anhydride can, of course, cause acetylation and dehydration; it is useful for the recrystallization of acetates, acid anhydrides, and hydrocarbons of high molecular weight. It has been employed for the fractional crystallization of some phytosterol acetates.[793] Contaminating acetic acid may be removed by careful fractionation. Acetic anhydride may also be used in combination with acetic acid, to depress the freezing point of the latter, in cases where addition of water would be undesirable. *Acetyl chloride* and *acetyl bromide* act as acetylating, dehydrating, and halogenating agents. Preferably after removing any free hydrogen halide contained, they may be used for the recrystallization of certain acid anhydrides and acid halides. Sensitive acid chlorides may be recrystallized from *benzoyl chloride*.[794] *Formamide* and *acetamide* readily dissolve albumins, peptones, and certain polysaccharides. Formamide and *N-methylformamide* find considerable use as solvents for recrystallization of anthraquinone dyes, and *dimethylformamide* is widely used.

Ethers. The ethers are not very polar but are powerful proton acceptors as evidenced by their ability to form oxonium salts. *Diethyl ether* dissolves many polar and nonpolar compounds. As a rule, it should be dry and free from alcohol. Explosion of peroxides formed by the ether sometimes occurs on evaporation of ether solutions.[795] *Isopropyl ether* finds occasional use[796]: it, too, may give rise to explosions.[797] *Tetrahydrofuran* is an excellent solvent for a wide variety of compounds.

[789] L. Ruzicka and J. R. Hosking, *Helv. Chim. Acta,* **13,** 1419 (1930).

[790] A. Wernicke and W. Pfitzinger, Ger. Pat. 20,595 (1882); U. S. Pat. 260,340 (1882); *Ber.,* **15,** 3105 (1882). C. S. Hudson and H. L. Sawyer, *J. Am. Chem. Soc.,* **39,** 470 (1917). P. A. Levene, *J. Biol. Chem.,* **108,** 419 (1935). C. S. Hudson and J. K. Dale, *J. Am. Chem. Soc.,* **39,** 320 (1917). T. S. Harding, *ibid.,* **44,** 1765 (1922).

[791] J. Bougault, *Bull. soc. chim. France,* [4], **21,** 172 (1917).

[792] E. Noelting and W. Wortmann, *Ber.,* **39,** 638 (1906).

[793] F. W. Heyl, *J. Am. Chem. Soc.,* **44,** 2283 (1922).

[794] A. Pongratz, *Monatsh.,* **52,** 9 (1929).

[795] P. T. Cleve, *Proc. Chem. Soc.,* **7,** 15 (1891); *Ber.,* **25³,** 745 (1892). H. Ditz, *ibid.,* **38,** 1409 (1905). E. Schär, *Arch. Pharm.,* **25,** 623 (1887).

[796] C. E. Wilson and H. J. Lucas, *J. Am. Chem. Soc.,* **58,** 2396 (1936).

[797] R. Robertson, *Chemistry & Industry,* **11,** 274 (1933). *Cf.* W. Hunter and J. Downing, *J. Soc. Chem. Ind.,* **68,** 362 (1949).

Anisole[798] is a superior solvent for the recrystallization of glucosazone. *Phenetole, cyclohexanol methyl ether*, and *naphthol ethers* are sometimes useful. The *glycol monoethers* contain both ether groups *and* free hydroxyl groups. *2-Methoxyethanol* is an excellent solvent for crystallizing sugars.[799] *2-Ethoxyethanol* and its acetate, and *2-methoxyethanol acetate* may also have some uses for crystallization. *Dioxane*, which is miscible with water, is a valuable solvent for many compounds[800] and has been used[801] for preparing crystalline D-gluconic acid; owing to formation of peroxides it has explosive potentialities.

Ketones and Aldehydes. The carbonyl group of *ketones* is a proton acceptor and, if enolized, functions also as a proton donor. The lower ketones are water-soluble and dissolve certain compounds containing hydroxyl groups. *Acetone*[802] is used frequently. However, it reacts with many compounds. *Ethyl methyl ketone*[803] has a higher boiling point than acetone and is sometimes preferable[804] in crystallizations; *butyl ethyl ketone, dibutyl ketone, cyclohexanone*, and *methylcyclohexanone* may also have some value where a more paraffinic solvent is desired.

Methylal is extremely useful, and *acetal, paraldehyde, benzaldehyde, furfural*, and *chloral* are occasionally employed. Chloral hydrate is sometimes preferable, and its aqueous solution has been used for the crystallization of sparingly soluble semicarbazones.[805]

Organic Bases. The principal organic bases employed as solvents are *pyridine, quinoline*, and *aniline*. However, aniline has a tendency to form addition compounds.[806] Traces of the bases can be removed from the resulting crystals by washing with certain organic solvents, or with dilute acid; pyridine can also be washed out with water. Pyridine is sometimes suitable for the recrystallization of compounds which are very sparingly soluble in other common solvents. The solvent power of pyridine is often dependent on its dryness. Thus certain hydrocarbons of high molecular weight, soluble in dry pyridine, are but sparingly soluble in the moist base. A study of the solubility of a large number of organic compounds in pyridine, water, and aqueous pyridine has been made.[807] The latter, or pyridine plus methanol, may be preferable for certain recrystallizations.

[798] L. Hugounenq, *J. pharm. chim.*, **4**, 447 (1896).
[799] C. S. Hudson, *Advances in Carbohydrate Chem.*, **1**, 24 (1945).
[800] L. Anschütz and W. Broeker, *Ber.*, **59**, 2844 (1926).
[801] H. S. Isbell and H. L. Frush, *Bur. Standards J. Research*, **11**, 649 (1933).
[802] R. S. Tipson, *J. Biol. Chem.*, **125**, 341 (1938).
[803] O. Diels and E. Abderhalden, *Ber.*, **36**, 3179 (1903).
[804] S. L. Langedijk, *Vernici*, **18**, 401 (1940); *C. A.*, **36**, 3975 (1942).
[805] R. Mauch, *Arch. Pharm.*, **240**, 113, 166 (1902).
[806] C. Schraube, *Ber.*, **8**, 616 (1875).
[807] W. M. Dehn, *J. Am. Chem. Soc.*, **39**, 1399 (1917). *Cf.* C. Neuberg, *Ber.*, **32**, 3384 (1899).

Other organic bases which have found occasional use for crystallization include *phenylhydrazine, dimethylaniline, diethylaniline, diphenylamine, methyldiphenylamine, hydrazine hydrate, methylamine, picoline, lutidine,* and *quinaldine.*

Hydrocarbons. Hydrocarbons are largely nonpolar, usually dissolve hydrocarbons and other nonpolar or slightly polar compounds, and are valuable solvents for crystallization of many substances. As a rule, the aromatic hydrocarbons are better solvents than the aliphatic hydrocarbons. *Pentane,*[808] *hexane, heptane,* and *cyclohexane* are particularly useful for crystallization since many organic compounds are soluble in them when hot but only sparingly soluble in the cold. Use of poorly fractionated samples of solvent may give misleading results if solutions are not prepared under reflux, since the more volatile solvent constituents may evaporate, leaving the less volatile hydrocarbons in which the solute may be more soluble and from which it may not crystallize out. Presence of a trace of alcohol sometimes greatly increases the solubility in ligroin.[809] *Benzene* should be free from carbon disulfide, thiophene, and water. Many substances sparingly soluble in boiling benzene dissolve readily in its homologs, *e.g.,* toluene, *m*-xylene, or *pseudo*-cumene. *Tetralin* is a valuable aliphatic–aromatic hydrocarbon. Such compounds as *methylcyclohexane, naphthalene, decalin, cumene, p-cymene, thiophene, and turpentine (d-pinene)* have found occasional use for crystallization.

Compared to their parent hydrocarbons, the *halogenated hydrocarbons,* most of which are polar, usually possess a more general solvent power and are less inflammable or noninflammable, but many of them are *highly toxic.*[770] *Chloroform* usually contains about 1% of ethanol; it may prove desirable to remove this. Certain acids, and such basic substances as hydrazones and hydrazides, decompose chloroform, particularly on heating. *Carbon tetrachloride* is an excellent solvent for recrystallization, *e.g.,* of certain acid anhydrides, acid chlorides, esters of 3,5-dinitrobenzoic acid,[810] and paraffins. It should be noted that carbon tetrachloride reacts with such substances as phenylhydrazine and aniline. *Di-, tri-,* and *tetrachloroethylene,* and *tetra-* and *pentachloroethane* are cheap, stable, unreactive, noninflammable solvents. Some chlorinated hydrocarbons tend to lose hydrogen chloride in the presence of moisture or metals, or by the action of light. It is said that all organic compounds containing no more than one hydroxyl or carboxyl group[811] are soluble in trichloroethylene. Other useful

[808] S. Fachini and G. Dorta, *Chem.-Ztg.,* **34,** 324 (1910). H. Meyer and A. Hofmann, *Monatsh.,* **37,** 685 (1916).

[809] R. Willstätter and M. Isler, *Ann.,* **390,** 329 (1912).

[810] H. W. Underwood, Jr., G. C. Baril, and O. L. Toone, *J. Am. Chem. Soc.,* **52,** 4087 (1930).

[811] L. Gowing-Scopes, *Analyst,* **35,** 238 (1910).

solvents include *ethylene dibromide, ethylene diiodide, epichlorohydrin,* and *dichlorohydrin.* The *halogenated benzenes* are usually higher-boiling and possess greater solvent power than benzene. *Chlorobenzene* and *o-dichlorobenzene* are particularly useful. *Mono-* and *p-di-bromobenzene, p-di-, 1,2,4-tri-, tetra-,* and *hexachlorobenzene,* and *1-chloro-* and *1-bromonaphthalene* have also found occasional use. As with other high-boiling solvents, oxidation of solute may occur during dissolution in the presence of air.

Nitrobenzene and the *nitroparaffins* are useful solvents for recrystallization, *e.g.,* of vat dyes; *azobenzene, benzonitrile,* and *acetonitrile* are sometimes employed. The last is miscible with water.

Carbon disulfide is usually avoided as a solvent for crystallization because of its objectionable odor and its inflammability.

General References

J. G. Aston and H. L. Fink, "Application of Low Temperatures to Chemical Research," *Chem. Revs.,* **39,** 357 (1946).

L. F. Audrieth and J. Kleinberg, *Non-aqueous Solvents.* Wiley, New York, 1953.

A. E. Bailey, *Melting and Solidification of Fats.* Interscience, New York-London, 1950.

T. V. Barker, *Systematic Crystallography, An Essay on Crystal Description, Classification, and Identification.* Murby, London, 1930.

S. T. Bowden, *The Phase Rule and Phase Reactions.* Macmillan, London, 1945.

J. B. Brown, "Low-Temperature Crystallization of the Fatty Acids and Glycerides," *Chem. Revs.,* **29,** 333 (1941).

H. E. Buckley, *Crystal Growth.* Wiley, New York, 1951.

C. W. Bunn, *Chemical Crystallography.* Oxford Univ. Press, London, 1945.

F. Cramer, *Einschlussverbindungen.* Springer, Berlin, 1954.

L. Deffet, *Répertoire des composés organiques polymorphes.* Desoer, Liège, 1942.

A. Findlay, *The Phase Rule and Its Applications.* 9th ed., by A. N. Campbell and N. O. Smith, Dover, New York, 1952.

J. Frenkel, *Kinetic Theory of Liquids.* Clarendon Press, Oxford, 1946.

R. Gomer and C. S. Smith, eds., *Structure and Properties of Solid Surfaces.* Univ. Chicago Press, Chicago, Ill., 1953.

C. S. Grove, Jr., and J. B. Gray, "Crystallization," *Ind. Eng. Chem.,* **40,** 11 (1948); **41,** 22 (1949); **42,** 28 (1950); **43,** 58 (1951); **44,** 41 (1952); **45,** 34 (1953).

C. S. Grove, Jr., H. M. Schoen, and J. A. Palermo, "Crystallization," *Ind. Eng. Chem.,* **46,** 75 (1954); **47,** 520 (1955).

W. Kauzmann, "The Nature of the Glassy State and the Behavior of Liquids at Low Temperatures," *Chem. Revs.,* **43,** 219 (1948).

L. Kofler, A. Kofler, and M. Brandstätter, *Thermo-Micro-Methoden zur Kennzeichnung organischer Stoffe und Stoffgemische.* 3rd ed., Verlag Chemie, Weinheim, 1954.

D. W. MacArdle, *The Use of Solvents in Synthetic Organic Chemistry.* Van Nostrand, New York, 1925.

G. Masing, *Ternary Systems, Introduction to the Theory of Three-Component Systems*. Translation by B. A. Rogers, Reinhold, New York, 1944.

W. L. McCabe, "Crystallization," *Ind. Eng. Chem.*, **38**, 18 (1946); "Crystallization," in J. H. Perry, ed., *Chemical Engineers' Handbook*, 3rd ed., McGraw-Hill, New York, 1950, pp. 1050–1072.

J. H. Northrop, M. Kunitz, and R. M. Herriot, *Crystalline Enzymes*. 2nd ed., Columbia Univ. Press, New York, 1948.

M. W. Porter and R. C. Spiller, *The Barker Index of Crystals, A Method for the Identification of Crystalline Substances*. Heffer, Cambridge, 1951.

J. E. Ricci, *The Phase Rule and Heterogeneous Equilibrium*. Van Nostrand, New York, 1951.

E. K. Rideal, "How Crystals Grow," *Nature*, **164**, 303 (1949).

J. A. Riddick and E. E. Toops, Jr., *Organic Solvents* (based on 1st ed. by A. Weissberger and E. S. Proskauer), 2nd ed. (*Technique of Organic Chemistry*, Vol. VII), Interscience, New York-London, 1955.

T. B. Smith, "Supersaturation and Crystallisation," in *Analytical Processes*. 2nd ed., Arnold, London, 1940, pp. 335–371.

C. W. Stillwell, *Crystal Chemistry*. McGraw-Hill, New York, 1938.

G. Tammann, *Kristallisieren und Schmelzen*, Barth, Leipzig, 1903; *The States of Aggregation*, translation by R. F. Mehl, Van Nostrand, New York, 1925.

R. Vogel, "Die Heterogenen Gleichgewichte," in G. Masing, ed., *Handbuch der Metallphysik*. Vol. II, Akadem. Verlagsgesellschaft, Leipzig, 1937; lithoprinted by Edwards, Ann Arbor, 1944.

A. F. Wells, *Structural Inorganic Chemistry*, Oxford Univ. Press, London, 1945; "Crystal Growth," in *Ann. Repts. on Progr. Chem. (Chem. Soc. London)*, **43**, 62 (1947).

F. E. W. Wetmore and D. J. LeRoy, *Principles of Phase Equilibria*. McGraw-Hill, New York, 1950.

CHAPTER IV

CENTRIFUGING

CHARLES M. AMBLER AND FREDERICK W. KEITH, JR., *The Sharples Corporation, Philadelphia, Pennsylvania*

I. INTRODUCTION. DEFINITIONS

Centrifugal force is the force, $F = ma$, that tends to impel a mass, or parts of it, outward from a center of rotation.

Centrifuge, in the broadest sense, is a device designed to utilize centrifugal force. By custom this has been narrowed to indicate a device for resolving multicomponent systems, at least one phase of which is fluid, by centrifugal force.

Centrifuging is the operation of performing such a separation in a centrifugal field.

The result of centrifugal force is similar to the result of the force of gravity except that centrifugal force: (1) may be many times greater, by a factor of 10⁵ and in some cases even more; and (2) is applied along lines radiating from a center of rotation. The lines of force in a centrifugal field diverge from a center of rotation, those in the gravitational field converge toward the center of the earth and are, for all practical purposes, parallel.

There are two basic types of centrifuges, and a third that may be considered as a combination of the first two.

(1) *Solid wall* centrifuges, in which separation or concentration is by subsidence or flotation.

(2) *Perforate wall* centrifuges, centrifugal filters, in which the solid phase is supported on a permeable surface through which the fluid phase is free to pass.

(3) *Combinations* of the two in which the primary concentration is effected by subsidence followed by drainage of the liquid phase away from the solid phase.

The sedimentation type of centrifuge is used to increase the settling rate of the dispersed phase and permit the attainment of equilibrium conditions more quickly than is possible by gravity settling. The higher field of force of the centrifuge overcomes the diffusion effects of small particles and permits the attainment of higher solid phase concentrations with sharply defined and stable boundaries. Because of this, the use of sedimentation-type centrifuges under controlled conditions of time and rotational speed is specified for many analytical procedures.

The centrifuge is used frequently where the customary means of separation by filtration are not applicable because of the gummy or gelatinous nature of the solid phase. It is used for the rapid and complete separation of immiscible liquids and the resolution of emulsions that are formed during extraction procedures. It is particularly useful for the concentration, and washing by decantation, of labile systems such as proteins or easily oxidized inorganic precipitates that are subject to deterioration by exposure to air or other change in environment.

As will be shown later in the section entitled "Theory," the sedimentation type of centrifuge has the same restriction to its use as has gravitational force, *i.e.*, a difference must exist between the densities of the continuous and discontinuous phases for any separation to occur. The perforate wall centrifuge is used for the removal of surplus liquid from crystalloid solids. Drainage is more rapid and complete, and washing, when required, is more effective than on the gravity or vacuum filter. The analytical ultracentrifuge is a particular type of sedimentation centrifuge in which the rate of subsidence and the attainment of concentration equilibrium can be observed and accurately measured. It is used for the determination of the molecular weight of proteins and similar purposes.   The ultracentrifuge is also supplied with rotors for the concentration and purification of samples preparatory to such analyses.

II. THEORY

1. Centrifugal Force

The force on a particle restrained to move in a circular path results from its acceleration toward the axis of rotation, or the rate of change of velocity away from the linear path tangent to the circle of rotation that it would normally tend to follow, Newton's first law of motion.   In the c.g.s. system:

$$F = ma = m\omega^2 r \tag{1}$$

where F = force on particle in dynes, m = mass of particle in grams, ω = angular velocity of rotation in radians per second, and r = radial distance of particle from axis of rotation in centimeters.   In its elemental form this is illustrated by whirling around a weight that is tied on the end of a string.   Centrifugal force is the outward pull of this weight, and centripetal force is the pull that must be exerted on the other end of the string to keep the weight in a circular path.

Equation (1) is more easily handled when force is expressed in grams, in which case:

$$F' = m\omega^2 r/g \tag{2}$$

where F' = centrifugal force in grams and g = gravitational constant 980.7 cm./sec.^{2}.   By proper substitution this assumes the more usable form.

$$F' = 0.00001117 mrN^2 \tag{3}$$

where N = speed of rotation in r.p.m.   Equation (3) gives the total centrifugal force and forms the basis for the design of centrifugal equipment.   For the centrifuge user another index that is much more useful, particularly for making comparisons, is relative centrifugal force, RCF. This may be defined as the force acting on a given particle in a centrifugal field in terms of multiples of its weight in the earth's gravitational field, and:

$$RCF = \omega^2 r/g \tag{4}$$

or by substitution:

$$RCF = 0.00001117 rN^2 \tag{5}$$

It is never adequate to report results in such terms as "the separation was effected by centrifuging at 3000 r.p.m. in an eight-place head using 50-ml. tubes for 20 minutes." Since the radius and depth of liquid used with different types of centrifuges will vary over wide limits the work done can more adequately be defined by reporting "the separation was effected by centrifuging in 50-ml. tubes for 20 minutes, at a speed that gave a relative centrifugal force of 1980 × G at the tip and 960 × G at the free surface of the liquid."

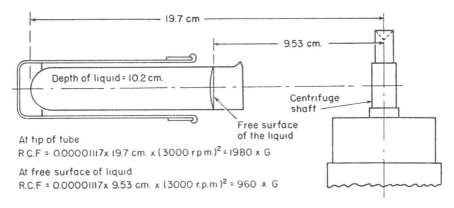

Fig. 1. Determination of relative centrifugal force.

By taking the measurements indicated in Figure 1 and applying equation (5) the above values are obtained and the results are made more definitive. By measuring the radius to the tip of the glass tube of his centrifuge any other investigator can calculate the rotational speed and liquid depth that he must use to attain the same result, the liquid depth being obtained from the expression:

$$\text{liquid depth} = \frac{(\text{RCF at tip} - \text{RCF at surface})}{(\text{RCF at tip})}(\text{radius at tip}) \qquad (6)$$

In this manner the force at the liquid surface required to effect the particular separation and the time and force at the tips of the tubes to concentrate the heavy phase to the required degree are completely defined.

If the axis of rotation is vertical, as it is in the laboratory centrifuge, the effect of the pull of gravity on the rotating parts, which of course always acts downward, becomes insignificant when the RCF reaches 25 G or more. Figure 2 shows that under such conditions the resultant vector G' is 25.02 G, an error of less than 0.1% which becomes progressively less as the RCF increases. It should also be noted that at the specified condition, the angle that this vector G' makes with the horizontal is 2.3° which decreases to 0.11° as the RCF increases to 500 G.   The vector effect of the force of gravity produces this same angle between the free surface of the liquid and the axis of rotation at the corresponding RCF (see Fig. 1) and its effect in influencing the liquid depth in the tube is also negligible.

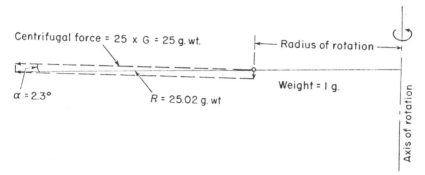

Fig. 2. Resultant of gravity and centrifugal force.

2. Sedimentation

The force acting on a particle in a centrifugal field (Eq. 1) must be corrected for the mass of the continuous phase fluid displaced by the particle.

$$F = (m - m_l)\omega^2 r \tag{7}$$

where m = mass of particle in grams, m_l = mass of fluid it displaces in grams, ω = angular velocity about axis of rotation in radians per second, r = distance of particle from axis of rotation in centimeters, and F = force in dynes.   If the particle is a sphere:

$$F = (\pi/6)D^3 \Delta\rho\omega^2 r \tag{8}$$

where D = diameter of particle and $\Delta\rho = (\rho - \rho_l)$ = difference between the density of the particle and that of the fluid in which it is suspended. This is the force that is available to move the particle through the fluid medium.

For a small particle moving not too rapidly, the viscous resistance to its motion is expressed by Stokes' law:

$$F = 3\pi\eta D v_s \tag{9}$$

where η = viscosity of fluid phase and v_s = velocity of particle moving through the fluid phase.

Stokes law does not apply when the particle size and velocity are relatively large so that its Reynolds number, $Dv_s\rho/\eta$, exceeds the order of unity. In this case the viscous resistance becomes negligible compared to the turbulent resistance, which is proportional to the square of the velocity of sedimentation. Stokes law is also subject to a lower limit of particle size. When the particle diameter approaches the mean free path of the fluid molecules, the velocity tends to increase. Small particles are also subject to Brownian movement due to the unbalanced impact of the fluid molecules. This random movement superimposed on the settling velocity may limit the concentration to which small particles will settle in a given field of centrifugal force.

Subject to these limitations the settling velocity, or rising velocity if $\Delta\rho$ is negative, reaches a constant value when the forces creating and those resisting the motion are in equilibrium, and from equations (8) and (9):

$$F = (\pi/6)D^3\Delta\rho\omega^2r = 3\pi\eta Dv_s \tag{10}$$

and:

$$v_s = \Delta\rho D^2\omega^2r/18\eta \tag{11}$$

From this basic equation, the velocity of the particle at any distance from the axis of rotation can be calculated.

In the gravitational field the sedimenting velocity of the particle is:

$$v_g = \Delta\rho D^2g/18\eta \tag{12}$$

The simplest form of a centrifuge in which the fluid flow is continuous is a cylinder rotating about its longitudinal axis and provided with end caps, and with means for being fed fluid at one end and discharging it at the other. In such a device v_s is the velocity with which the particles approach the bowl wall (or if $\Delta\rho$ is negative, the liquid surface). If the thickness, s, of the liquid layer is small compared to the inside radius of the cylinder then v_s will be approximately constant across the liquid layer and the distance a given particle will settle during the time, t, that the liquid in which it is suspended is in the bowl:

$$x = v_st = (\Delta\rho D^2\omega^2r/18\eta)(V/Q) \tag{13}$$

where V = volume of liquid in the bowl in cubic centimeters, $V = \pi l(r_2^2 - r_1^2)$, for a hollow cylinder, and Q = rate of flow through the bowl in cubic centimeters per second.

If x is greater than the initial distance of the given particle from the wall of such a rotor, it will be deposited against the wall and removed from the fluid phase. In an ideal system, when $x = s/2$, one-half of the particles of diameter D will be removed from suspension and one-half will not. This condition will be considered as the "cut-off point." At the "cut-off point," by substituting and rearranging equation (13):

$$Q = (\Delta \rho D^2/9\eta)(V\omega^2 r/s) \tag{14}$$

Since from equation (12):

$$\Delta \rho D^2/9\eta = 2v_g/g$$

this may be rewritten as:

$$Q = 2v_g \Sigma \tag{15}$$

in which:

$$\Sigma = V\omega^2 r/gs \tag{16}$$

In these expressions it will be noted that v_g is defined entirely by the parameters of the disperse system being examined, while Σ contains only factors relating to the centrifuge. For centrifuges in which the liquid layer thickness is not small with respect to the radius so that the centrifugal force varies appreciably across the liquid layer, the same relationship applies provided that the effective average or integrated values r_e and s_e are used.

This concept of Σ value is a very important one, since when r_e and s_e are properly developed for a given type of centrifuge, it permits a direct comparison of the performance of various types of centrifuges. In terms of gravity, Σ is the area of a settling tank in which the same throughput of liquid can be clarified to the same degree as in the centrifuge to which it applies. As with the area of a settling tank, the larger the Σ value of a centrifuge, the greater is its theoretical ability to do useful work. Furthermore, it will be noted that for a given amount of work done on a given system:

$$Q/\Sigma = 2v_g = \text{constant} \tag{17}$$

and therefore:

$$Q/\Sigma = Q_1/\Sigma_1 = Q_n/\Sigma_n \tag{18}$$

and this equation sets the basis for comparing the performance of different centrifuges.

3. Hydrostatic Pressure

The hydrostatic pressure exerted on a filled glass container in the laboratory bottle centrifuge, operating at even normal conditions, reaches a comparatively high value. In the gravitational field, given a container filled with liquid, *e.g.*, a glass beaker on the laboratory bench, at a distance *h* below the liquid-atmosphere interface, the hydrostatic pressure is equal to:

$$P = \rho_l h \qquad (19)$$

where P = pressure in grams per square centimeter. In the centrifugal field, since centrifugal force varies with the distance from the axis of rotation:

$$P = \int_{r_1}^{r_2} \rho_l(\omega^2 r/g) \, dr \qquad (20)$$

and:

$$P = \rho_l \omega^2(r_2^2 - r_1^2)/2g \qquad (21)$$

It will be noted that the general form is:

$$P = \int_{h_1}^{h_2} \rho_l f(h) \, dh$$

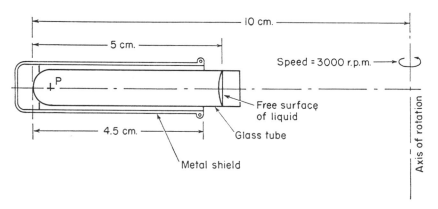

Fig. 3. Fluid pressure from centrifugal force.

and that equation (19) is only valid because the difference in the force of the gravitational field between level $h = 0$ and $h = h$ is negligible.

As an example of the magnitude of this hydrostatic pressure on the container, consider a glass tube filled with human blood, $\rho_l = 1.07$, Figure 3. If the bottom of this tube is 10 cm. from the axis of rotation, the liquid column is 5 cm. high, and the rotational speed is 3000 r.p.m., $\omega = 314$, from equation (21), the hydrostatic pressure at the bottom of the tube is:

$$P = \frac{1.07 \times 314^2 \times (100 - 25)}{2 \times 980.7} = 4030 \text{ g./cm.}^2$$

It is obvious that hydrostatic pressures can readily be reached that will rupture glass containers. This internal fluid pressure can be offset to a considerable degree by filling the space between the glass tube and the metal cup with water or some other liquid. For example, consider the case when the space between the glass tube and the metal cup of Figure 3 is filled with water. The depth of the water annulus to the bottom of the glass tube would be 4.5 cm. and at this point its hydrostatic pressure would be:

$$P = \frac{1.00 \times (314)^2 \times (100 - 30.2)}{2 \times 980.7} = 3510 \text{ g./cm.}^2$$

The net pressure at the bottom of the tube is therefore 4030 − 3510 = 520 g./cm.², a pressure which most glassware should withstand satisfactorily. By proper selection of the surrounding liquid it should be possible to balance exactly the glass tube and its contents in the metal shield so that there is no net internal or external pressure on the glass tube. This is the ideal condition to prevent glassware breakage during centrifuging, but only noncorrosive liquids that will not attack the metal shield should be used. For general purposes glycerine and ethylene glycol are quite satisfactory. However, the example indicates that surrounding the glass tube with water is sufficient in many cases.

When operating at high rotational speeds, semielastic containers, for example, polyethylene, may be used. These deform under pressure sufficiently without rupture so that the hydrostatic pressure is carried directly on the wall of the metal shield. As an alternative, containers of metal such as aluminum may be used when the possibility of their contaminating the product is not a factor.

4. Stresses

While the subject matter of this heading may seem of greater importance to the designer of the centrifuge than to the user, an understanding of the basic principles involved will point out the hazards of overloading or improper loading and the dangers that may result from operating damaged or corroded equipment. All rotating parts of the centrifuge are subject to the stresses created by centrifugal force. It is important to realize the limitations that these stresses impose upon the permissible speed of the centrifuge. In all cases the manufacturer's recommendations of allowable maximum speed, under various load conditions, should be strictly followed.

Motor armatures for normal service are wound with copper wire and have copper bar commutators. The standard construction of these parts permits a safe maximum speed of about 6000 r.p.m. Above this speed continuous operation may result in rupture of the windings and commutator.

In a bottle centrifuge the trunnions on the rings that support the metal shields carrying the glass tubes must withstand the total pull exerted by the trunnion rings themselves, the metal shields, and the glass tubes and their contents while under centrifugal force. This pull will equal the combined weight of these parts multiplied by the relative centrifugal force existing at the radial distance of the center of gravity of the assembly from the axis of rotation.

As an example of the magnitude of this force, consider a 100-ml. glass tube filled with water and placed in a 100-ml. metal shield supported in an appropriate trunnion ring. The combined weight is 383 g. If this assembly is placed in a rotor that gives a radial distance to its center of gravity of 17.5 cm. when the tube is swung outward to a horizontal position, and is rotated at 2200 r.p.m., the relative centrifugal force is 947 times that of gravity. The pull on the trunnions is therefore 947 $\times$ 383 g., a total of 363 kg.

This example indicates the magnitude of the forces involved and the potential danger from overstressing the moving parts. Since these forces increase as the square of the rotative speed, it can be seen how important it is not to exceed the speed limits specified by the manufacturer for any given equipment. While most centrifuges have a protecting guard to insure the safety of the operator in case of breakage, the rotating parts are usually so badly damaged that expensive repair is required.

The mechanical pull on the trunnions of the bottle-type centrifuge may be defined mathematically as:

$$F = Wr\omega^2/g \tag{22}$$

where F = force imposed on the trunnions by the rotating load in grams, W = weight of the rotating load in grams, r = radial distance of the center of gravity of the load from the axis of rotation in centimeters, ω = rotational speed in radians per second, and g = gravitational constant, 980.7 centimeters per square second.

The stress on the ring section of a bowl-type centrifuge is the sum of two factors:

(*1*) The self stress in the rotor itself:

$$\gamma_r = \rho_r r^2 \omega^2/g \tag{23}$$

where γ_r = self stress in grams per square centimeter, ρ_r = density of wall material in grams per cubic centimeter, and r = mean radius of wall section in centimeters.

(*2*) The stress due to the liquid load:

$$\gamma_l = \rho_l r_2 \omega^2 (r_2^2 - r_1^2)/2gz \tag{24}$$

where γ_l = liquid load stress in grams per square centimeter, ρ_l = density of liquid in grams per cubic centimeter, r_2 = outer radius of liquid layer in centimeters, r_1 = inner radius of liquid layer in centimeters, z = radial thickness of bowl wall in centimeters, and the total stress is:

$$\gamma_t = \gamma_r + \gamma_l$$

III. EQUIPMENT

In the laboratory, centrifuges may perform one or more functions: to meet the specifications of standard analytical procedures, to effect separations during bench-scale experimentation, to facilitate small-batch or continuous pilot-plant production, or to yield the bench-scale or pilot-plant data necessary for scaling equipment up to plant size.   The purpose and scale of the work as well as the type of system being treated determine the centrifuge to be used and the degree to which theory must be applied to the operation.

1. Bottle Centrifuges

A bottle centrifuge consists of a motor-driven, vertical spindle on which various heads or rotors can be mounted.   The rotors are arranged to carry metal containers into which fit glass tubes or bottles of many sizes and shapes.   The heads may carry from two to sixteen bottles at a time, but for the larger bottles the number is usually four.   Since the largest bottle normally used holds about one liter, the capacity of these machines is limited to about one gallon for a single batch.   The time, speed, and temperature of centrifuging can be closely controlled, so that bottle centrifuges are particularly useful for analytical methods and for batch separations in bench-scale experimentation.

A bench-top bottle centrifuge is shown in Figure 4.   It is driven directly by a vertical electric motor with a speed-regulating rheostat mounted in the base.   The motor shaft, which projects through the top part of the base for mounting the various rotors, is enclosed by a metal guard bowl with a cover in order to protect the operator against glassware breakage or failure of the rotating metal parts.

Bottle centrifuges can be equipped with three different kinds of rotors, the most common being the horizontal, swinging-tube type shown in Figure 4.   The glass tubes are set into metal shields on a rubber cushion and the shields or containers are supported in trunnion rings which are set in slots in the rotor head.   Since the center of gravity of the assembly is below the trunnions, the tubes hang vertically while at rest, but as the rotor starts to turn they gradually swing out to a horizontal position where they remain as long as the head is rotating. When stopped, they return to the vertical position. With the tubes horizontal, sedimenting particles travel

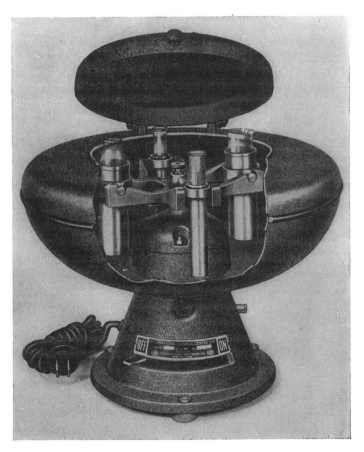

Fig. 4. Bench-top centrifuge with swinging tube rotor.

radially from the axis of rotation and are deposited on the bottom of the tube. Two disadvantages of this type of rotor are: (a) the path of travel is the full length of the tube for some of the particles, and (b) hindered settling occurs as the particles are concentrated near the bottom. Both increased speed and time of centrifuging overcome these disadvantages. On the other hand, the long radial path of travel and the normality of the sedimented surface to the axis of the tube are distinct advantages in effecting fractional sedimentation, in applying theory to the bottle centrifuge, and in reading relative volumes of supernatant liquid and sedimented solid.

Another rotor in common use is the angle or conical type. This is usually made in the form of a truncated cone with holes drilled at an angle as shown in Figure 5. The glass tubes are set into metal shields and these are inserted in the holes in the rotor where they are held at a fixed angle, usually about 45°, both at rest and in rotation. Due to the streamlined contour, higher speeds are possible with this type of rotor than with the horizontal tube type and higher rates of sedimentation are attainable. Moreover, the particles travel in free sedimentation only a distance equal to no more than the diameter of the tube multiplied by the secant of the

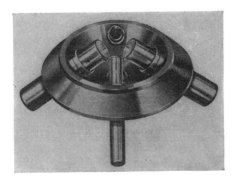

Fig. 5. Angle-type rotor.

angle of inclination from the vertical (see Fig. 6). The particles of most solids, on striking the glass wall of the tube, tend to aggregate and slide to the bottom of the tube. Since the cake is deposited at an angle, this type of rotor is suitable only for liquid–liquid separations or where measurement of the volume of the sediment is not required.

A basket type of centrifuge bowl can be mounted on some rotors but discussion of this equipment will be deferred to a later section.

As mentioned previously, the fundamental equation for centrifugal force is equation (1): $F = mr\omega^2$. In making comparisons of centrifuging conditions, it is generally more convenient to consider the force of the centrifugal field without regard to the physical characteristics of a particle or its ambient fluid; this force is termed the relative centrifugal force: equation (4), RCF $= \omega^2 r/g$. It expresses the centrifugal force as a number of multiples of the normal gravitational force. It is apparent that for a centrifuge tube in a horizontal position in a bottle centrifuge, as illustrated in Figure 7, the relative centrifugal force differs at the surface of the liquid

(r_1) and at the bottom of the tube (r_2). For example, if $r_1 = 9.53$ cm. and the tube is rotating at 3000 r.p.m., then at the surface of the liquid:

$$RCF_1 = 1.117 \times 10^{-5} \times 9.53 \times 3000^2 = 960 \times \text{gravity}$$

while at the bottom of the tube, if $r_2 = 19.7$ cm.:

$$RCF_2 = 1.117 \times 10^{-5} \times 19.7 \times 3000^2 = 1980 \times \text{gravity}$$

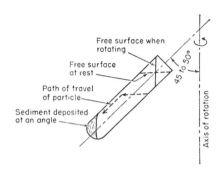

Fig. 6. Sedimentation in angle-type rotor.

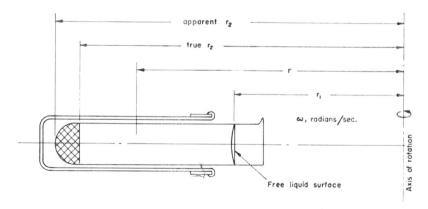

Fig. 7. Centrifugal settling.

A particle travelling from r_1 to r_2 is necessarily subjected to a constantly changing centrifugal field varying from F_1 to F_2. In the general case, these forces also depend on the rotational speed of the centrifuge. In addition to these factors, for any particular suspension, the proportion of the particles sedimented depends on the time of exposure to the centrifugal field. Thus, it is seen that comparison of centrifuging conditions requires the proper relation of speed, bottle size, centrifuge dimensions, and centrifuging time. It is difficult to duplicate centrifuging conditions without using identical equipment unless these variables are properly combined as in a Q/Σ function where Σ defines the physical parameters of the centrifuge as discussed previously for the general case.

In considering sedimentation in a bottle centrifuge, the radius at the surface of the final cake is important because any particle reaching that point at any time during the test has been removed from the final supernatant liquid and this should be considered the real r_2 for the centrifuge in a particular test. Therefore, from equations (11) and (12), the rate of sedimentation of some particle at radius r between r_1 and r_2 is defined as:

$$v_s = dr/dt = v_g(\omega^2 r/g) \tag{25}$$

Separating the variables and integrating for a particle that just reaches r_2 in total centrifuging time t:

$$\int_r^{r_2} dr/r = \int_0^t (v_g\omega^2/g)\, dt \tag{26}$$

which yields the result:

$$\ln (r_2/r) = v_g\omega^2 t/g \tag{27}$$

Then, considering particles of diameter D, one-half of the particles are sedimented at the 50% cut-off point in a tube of cross section A if:

$$A(r - r_1) = A(r_2 - r)$$

so that:

$$r_{50\%} = (r_1 + r_2)/2 \tag{28}$$

Substituting equation (28) in equation (27) and solving for v_g gives:

$$v_g = \frac{g}{\omega^2 t} \ln \left(\frac{2r_2}{r_1 + r_2}\right) \tag{29}$$

Since the general development of Σ functions showed previously (Eq. 17) that $Q/\Sigma = 2v_g$, it is apparent that for the bottle centrifuge:

$$\frac{Q}{\Sigma} = \frac{4.6g}{\omega^2 t} \log \left(\frac{2r_2}{r_1 + r_2}\right) \tag{30}$$

From the derivation it is seen in this case that:

$$\Sigma = \frac{\omega^2 V}{4.6g \log [2r_2/(r_1 + r_2)]} \tag{31}$$

where V = the liquid volume in the tube.

Q alone, however, has no real meaning as a "flow rate" in a bottle, but it does incorporate the time factor. Therefore, by matching Q/Σ through any convenient combination of the parameters of equation (30), centrifuging conditions can be matched between different bottle centrifuges, and for a given suspension the same degree of sedimentation can be obtained. It is obviously necessary to use cylindrical centrifuge tubes to eliminate the abnormal sedimentation that results from particles striking and settling along the wall of tapered tubes.

As an example of the calculations, consider an International bottle centrifuge, Size 1, Type C, with 100-ml. cylindrical tubes turning at 2000 r.p.m. When the sample volume is 100 ml., the liquid surface is approximately at $r_1 = 5.0$ cm.; assuming a sedimented cake about 1 cm. thick, $r_2 = 18.5$ cm. In this case:

$$\Sigma = \frac{(2\pi \times 2000/60)^2 \times 100}{4.6 \times 980 \times \log\,[2 \times 18.5/(5.0 + 18.5)]} = 0.049 \times 10^5 \text{ cm.}^2$$

For this system Q/Σ for a centrifuging time of 10 minutes becomes:

$$\frac{Q}{\Sigma} = \frac{4.6 \times 980}{(2\pi \times 2000/60)^2 \times 10 \times 60} \log\left(\frac{2 \times 18.5}{5.0 + 18.5}\right) =$$

$$0.338 \times 10^{-4} \text{ cm./sec.}$$

Certain emulsions constitute an exception to the behavior defined by equation (30). For these cases, t and ω^2 are not interchangeable because a threshold of centrifugal force must be exceeded before an appreciable breaking of the emulsion occurs regardless of the time of centrifuging.

Occasionally it is necessary to duplicate sedimentation conditions at a very low Q/Σ value or to accomplish a fractional sedimentation or to determine a Q/Σ versus percentage sedimented curve where some particles are of large size or high density. In this case the acceleration and deceleration periods of the rotor become an appreciable portion of the time. For example, in the International bottle centrifuge of the example above with two 100-ml. tubes it requires 20 to 30 seconds to approach final speed. A stopping time of less than 10 seconds is unfeasible because of the possibility of disturbing the sedimented solids; even longer stopping times are necessary with solids that do not pack. Experiment shows that the rotational speed is roughly proportional to the time from start-up and that a linear function over the first 20 seconds after start-up is sufficiently accurate to account for the value of Q/Σ during that period.

In this case, if it is assumed that $\omega = kt$, then equation (26) can be revised:

$$\int_r^{r_2} \frac{dr}{r} = \int_0^{t_1} \frac{v_g k_1^2 t^2}{g}\,dt + \int_{t_1}^{t+t_1} \frac{v_g \omega^2}{g}\,dt + \int_{t+t_1}^{t_T} \frac{v_g k_2^2 t^2}{g}\,dt \qquad (32)$$

where k_1 = slope of ω versus t plot while starting $= \omega/t_1$, k_2 = slope of ω

versus t plot while stopping $= \omega/t_2$, $t_1 =$ time to reach full speed by linear approximation, $t_2 = t_T - (t + t_1) =$ time needed to stop rotor, $t_T =$ total centrifuging time from start to stop, and $t =$ centrifuging time at full speed $= t_T - (t_1 + t_2)$.   This equation can be resolved to give:

$$\frac{Q}{\Sigma} = \frac{4.6g}{\omega^2 t + \frac{1}{3}(k_1^2 t_1^3 + k_2^2 t_2^3)} \log \left(\frac{2r_2}{r_1 + r_2}\right) \tag{33}$$

In general, equation (33) need be used instead of equation (30) only for centrifuging times of less than three minutes at which point the correction is about 5% for the time values of the example given above.

If the bottle centrifuge is used for fractional sedimentation separations, it is necessary to calculate the time needed to sediment all particles of diameter D or greater.   In this case, equation (26) is integrated between the limits of r_1 and r_2 so that:

$$\ln (r_2/r_1) = v_g \omega^2 t/g \tag{34}$$

Most of the particles encountered in centrifugal sedimentation are sufficiently small to settle according to Stokes law.   Equation (12), derived from Stokes law as applied to spherical particles, may be rewritten in the form:

$$v_g = (gD^2 \, \Delta\rho/4\eta)K \tag{35}$$

where K is a shape factor relating the shape and surface roughness of a particle to the frictional resistance to passage of the particle through the liquid.   For spheres $K = \frac{2}{9} = 0.222$ and this factor applies equally well to all particles approaching sphericity.   If the particles are nonspherical, then their size is usually defined by the equivalent spherical diameter which is the diameter of a sphere of the same material as the particle that would settle at the same rate as the irregularly shaped particle under the same conditions.   A number of shape factors for the Stokes law range have been reported: K for cubes $= 0.206$,[1] for discs $= 0.19$,[2] for tetrahedrons $= 0.188$,[1] for natural phosphate rock particles $= 0.154$,[3] for cylinders $= 0.03$ to 0.06.[2]   If equations (34) and (35) are combined and the appropriate value of K is inserted, then the desired cut-off time for particles of diameter D is found from:

$$t_D = 4\eta \ln (r_2/r_1)/\omega^2 D^2 \, \Delta\rho \, K \tag{36}$$

[1] E. S. Pettyjohn and E. B. Christianson, *Chem. Eng. Progress*, **44**, 157 (1948).

[2] J. H. Perry, *Chemical Engineer's Handbook*.   3rd ed., McGraw-Hill, New York, 1950, p. 1018.

[3] L. T. Alexander and K. D. Jacob, "Mechanical Analysis of Finely Divided Natural Phosphates," *U. S. Tech. Bull.*, 212.

It is possible to remove many of the fines of diameters less than that desired by reslurrying the sedimented solids in a clean portion of liquid and re-centrifuging with the same time limit as before.   It is frequently necessary to use dispersing agents to prevent aggregation of the solid particles during fractional sedimentation or when determining a particle size distribution.

It is convenient to determine the proportion of particles sedimented

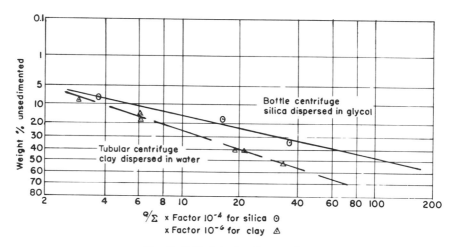

Fig. 8. Q/Σ plot of sedimentation.

from a given suspension at several values of Q/Σ by varying either centri-fuging time or speed or both in the bottle centrifuge. As a basis, one or more samples of the suspension is centrifuged for a sufficient time to give a completely clear supernatant liquid; this volume of sediment is the maximum that can be obtained from the corresponding volume of sample. At larger values of Q/Σ, smaller quantities of solids are sedimented. If the sediment amounts to more than about 75% of the maximum, it is generally inaccurate to obtain the quantity of the unsedimented material by difference.   The value can be obtained directly by decanting the super-nate and recentrifuging it for an extended time to obtain the volume of sediment in the total volume of supernate.   These data then permit con-struction of a curve of Q/Σ versus percentage sedimented or unsedimented, depending on convenience.

Such a graph is shown in Figure 8 for silica particles sedimented in ethylene glycol.   On logarithmic probability paper, Q/Σ plots for solids following the normal probability distribution are linear within the limits of experimental error and can therefore be drawn from relatively few points and can be extrapolated over short ranges.   Thus, extrapolation indicates that Q/Σ at the 50% cut-off point is 126×10^{-4} cm./sec. Combining equations (17) and (35) gives the form for calculating the equivalent spherical particle diameter:

$$D = \left(\frac{2\eta}{g \, \Delta\rho \, K} \frac{Q/\Sigma}{E} \right)^{1/2} \qquad (37)$$

where E is the fractional estimated centrifugal efficiency for the system and the centrifuge. E is generally assumed at 1.0 for bottle sedimentation. Then for $\eta = 0.17$ poise and $\Delta\rho = 1.1$ g./cc. with an estimated shape factor $K = 0.17$, the particle size at the 50% point is found to be 49 microns; this agrees well with the mean value of 54 microns indicated by the manufacturer of the silica.

It is often possible to determine a Q/Σ curve on the basis of the sedimented volumes, but in most cases it is more accurate to use a weight basis. This can be done either by preparing a weight–volume correlation or by decanting the supernate and drying and weighing the solids. The Q/Σ relationship is useful for calculating particle sizes and particularly particle size distributions. The width of the distribution is indicated by the slope of the curve, a wide distribution showing a relatively small change in percentage unsedimented for a large change in Q/Σ as in Figure 8. A suspension of uniform particles gives a curve sloping sharply toward the Q/Σ axis. With appropriate correction factors based on experience, bottle centrifuge Q/Σ curves can be used to predict the operation of continuous centrifuges on a given material. In theory and practice the Q/Σ curves from different types of centrifuges operating on the same material differ only by the different operating efficiencies of the centrifuge types.

The flexibility of a bottle centrifuge in the laboratory is increased by the large variety of tubes and bottles available. Some of these include graduated and plain tubes of 10- to 100-ml. capacity with round or conical bottoms, 10-ml. Hoskins tubes that are reduced in size at the bottom to a stem graduated for 0.05 ml., 100-ml. pear-shaped oil tubes with graduated stems of 1.0-, 1.5-, and 3.0-ml. capacity, 100-ml. Goetz phosphorus test pear-shaped tubes with a stem calibrated for 0.2 ml., 150-ml. Squibbs separatory funnels with a stopcock at the bottom, and various bottles of 2-oz. to 1000-ml. capacity. The plain cylindrical tubes are particularly suitable for Q/Σ tests while the pear-shaped oil and Goetz tubes are good for measuring small solids volumes.

Special refrigerated bottle centrifuges (Fig. 9) are available for working with low-melting compounds or with biochemical materials which must be kept cool to inhibit enzyme action and bacterial growth. Fractional separation by differential solubility also may require cooling as, for example, in the removal of certain proteins from blood serum. Adjustable temperature control is obtained on these units by using a direct expansion-compression refrigerating system with the evaporation coil installed inside the centrifuge guard bowl along with a thermostat unit.

Fig. 9. Refrigerated centrifuge.

Heated centrifuges are also required for some work such as Babcock tests for butterfat in milk and cream. Temperatures of 25° to 70°C. are obtainable if thermostatically controlled electric units are located in the guard bowl and plugged into the same circuit as the centrifuge motor. When such a unit is not at hand, it is convenient in the laboratory to operate at temperatures up to 110°C. by insulating the guard bowl and introducing into it a stream of air heated as required by passing through a coil over a gas burner.

2. Tubular Centrifuges

A number of laboratory-size continuous centrifuges are available for separation or clarification of a larger amount of material than is feasible in a bottle centrifuge.   If the aim of the work is to obtain data for scaling to

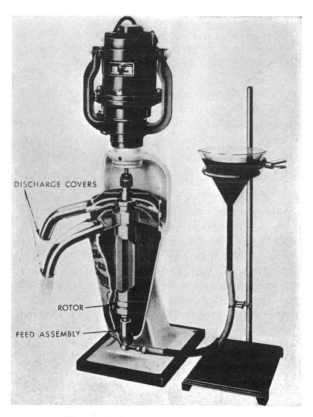

Fig. 10. Laboratory supercentrifuge.

plant size, selection of the type of centrifuge ultimately to be used must be made, if possible, in time to use the same type for test work.   Smith and Hebb[4] have discussed many of the factors leading to a choice between tu-

[4] M. H. Hebb and F. H. Smith, "Centrifugal Separation,"in R. E. Kirk and D. F. Othmer, eds., *Encyclopedia of Chemical Technology*.   Vol. III, Interscience, New York London, 1949.

bular, disc, perforate or imperforate basket, and conveyor-discharge centrifuges or combinations thereof.

The laboratory tubular centrifuge (Fig. 10) is a flexible unit for continuous treatment of a liquid–solid suspension or a liquid–liquid mixture where the solid content is low and the particles are medium to fine in size. It is convenient for handling batches of four liters or more or for pilot-plant production at feed rates up to four liters per minute depending on the system. It consists of a relatively long hollow cylindrical bowl of small diameter suspended from a flexible spindle at the top and guided at the bottom by a loose-fitting bushing. With standard motor drive it operates at 22,000 r.p.m. The turbine-driven design can be run at any speed up to 50,000 r.p.m. at which the RCF = 62,400 G. Inside the bowl is an accelerating device whose function is to insure rotation of the liquid at bowl speed.

Feed is jetted into the bottom of the bowl through a hole in the guide bushing and is thrown outward to the wall where it forms a layer of controlled thickness. Clarification or separation is effected during the time the feed passes up the length of the bowl. In a clarifier bowl, solid particles of density greater than the liquid are deposited as a packed cake on the bowl wall while the clarified liquid is discharged by overflowing a dam at the top of the bowl at a radius somewhat greater than that of the bottom feed hole. When the cake has built up sufficiently to interfere with clarification, the bowl is stopped and cleaned out.

In a separator bowl for resolving liquid–liquid mixtures, the heavier liquid settles to the bowl wall to form a continuous layer on which floats a layer of the lighter liquid. Unresolved emulsion remains at the interface until broken; premature discharge of interface material is prevented by an annular dam near the top of the bowl. Light liquid continuously overflows the inner circumference of the annular dam and is discharged into a cover through radial holes in the bowl. Heavy liquid passes outside the annular dam and is discharged over the inner circumference of a second dam which maintains the heavy liquid layer at the desired depth inside the bowl. The heavy liquid is discharged into a separate cover from the light effluent. Heavy solids introduced with the emulsion are also sedimented as a cake in the separator bowl.

Development of Σ theory for tubular centrifuges is reported by Ambler,[5] so only its application will be covered. In a continuous centrifuge, the term Q denotes the volumetric flow rate through the bowl and provides the necessary time parameter. The physical dimensions of a clarifier bowl are expressed by:

$$\Sigma = \frac{2\pi l \omega^2}{g} \left(\frac{3}{4} r_2^2 + \frac{1}{4} r_1^2 \right) \tag{38}$$

[5] C. M. Ambler, Meeting of New Jersey Section, Am. Inst. Chem. Engrs., Newark, N. J., May, 1951.

where l = length of the bowl, r_1 = inner radius of liquid layer = radius of the liquid discharge dam, and r_2 = outer radius of liquid layer = inner radius of the bowl wall.   As cake builds up at the bowl wall, r_2 is reduced and hold-up time is also reduced so that clarification efficiency is decreased. Until the bowl is too full of cake, the loss in efficiency can be temporarily compensated for by a reduction in the throughput, Q.

The Σ value for any clarifier bowl can be readily computed from equation (38) if the bowl dimensions and operating speed are known.   The data for a bowl with a specific overflow diameter are, for example: l = 18.7 cm., r_1 = 0.71 cm., r_2 = 2.22 cm., and r.p.m. − 20,000.

$$\Sigma = \frac{2\pi \times 18.7 \times (2\pi \times 20000/60)^2}{980} (0.75 \times 2.22^2 + 0.25 \times 0.71^2)$$

$$= 18.8 \times 10^5 \text{ cm.}^2$$

At 50,000 r.p.m., as attained with a turbine driven model, Σ becomes 117 $\times 10^5$ cm.^{2}.

If the bottle centrifuge example calculated previously is assumed to give satisfactory clarification on a particular material, then the theoretical throughput rate can be calculated for the laboratory tubular centrifuge to give the same degree of clarification.   Assume that the tubular operates at 20,000 r.p.m. with Σ = 18.8 $\times 10^5$ cm.^{2} as above and that Q/Σ = 0.338 $\times$ 10^{-4} cm./sec. as for the bottle machine; then Q for the tubular bowl theoretically equals 0.338 $\times 10^{-4} \times 18.8 \times 10^5$ = 63.5 cc./sec.   In practice, the actual tubular centrifuge feed rate for the required degree of clarity may vary from 20% to nearly 100% of theoretical depending on the system.   Hard, nonaggregated solids result in high efficiency but flocculent, agglomerated feeds may suffer considerable dispersion as a result of the shear forces imposed during acceleration to the speed of the bowl.   For scaling up centrifuging data from a laboratory-sized tubular bowl to a production-sized tubular, tests on the former should be made at approximately the same rotational speed as for the latter to avoid this kind of variation of the efficiency factor.

The clarifier bowl of the tubular centrifuge is readily used to determine Q/Σ curves for estimating particle size distribution or mean particle size if the shape factor K can be estimated and the centrifuge efficiency for the system is known.   Also, by comparison with bottle centrifuge Q/Σ data, the efficiency of the tubular bowl for the particular system can be approximated.   In Figure 8 is shown a set of Q/Σ data for the laboratory tubular centrifuge on a suspension of clay particles in water with Tamol NNO as a dispersant.   For this system the centrifugal efficiency is assumed to be 80% and K can be estimated at 0.18; the density difference is 1.64 g./cc.

and the viscosity 0.89 cp. Q/Σ at 50% sedimented is 31.7×10^{-6} cm./sec., so that from equation (38) the calculated mean equivalent spherical diameter of the clay particles is 0.49 micron. A particle size distribution curve provided by the manufacturer shows a size of 0.55 micron at the 50% weight point, a very reasonable correlation.

In a separator bowl, Σ values can be calculated for each layer, that is, r_1 and r_2 correspond to the inner and outer radii, respectively, of each layer. This requires knowledge of the radius of the interface. This factor can be approximated from equation (21) together with the known overflow dam sizes since the pressure at the interface exerted by the light and heavy phases will be equal. In simplified form:

$$\frac{\rho \text{ (heavy phase)}}{\rho \text{ (light phase)}} = \frac{r_I^2 - r_L^2}{r_I^2 - r_H^2} \tag{39}$$

where r_I = radial distance interface line from axis, r_L = radial distance light phase discharge from axis, and r_H = radial distance heavy phase discharge from axis. More exact data are found by a study of the interface mark usually left on the accelerator device during an experimental run. The Σ value of the phases can be varied inversely by adjusting the diameter of the discharge dam.

Many variations are possible in tubular centrifuges to meet special conditions. Work with solvents requires a vapor-tight housing; for operation at elevated temperatures the frame can be jacketed. Light solids that float on a heavier liquid can be discharged as in the case of wax from lube oil. Highly viscous fluids such as soap or soapstock can be discharged in a frame hopper instead of the more restricted space of a cover and spout. Refrigerated frames are used for biochemical operations requiring low temperatures. Completely closed bowls can be used for treatment at high centrifugal force of 250-ml. batches.

3. Disc Centrifuges

Disc centrifuges are units for effecting on a continuous basis: (1) the clarification of suspensions in which the particles are fine and the concentrations relatively low, (2) the separation of liquid mixtures with or without a solids content, or (3) the concentration into a relatively small stream of the solids existing at low concentrations in the feed. The first two functions are similar to those of the tubular centrifuge although in commercial sizes the latter is generally smaller in size, lower in cost, and of lower capacity than the disc machine. The last function is unique with the disc centrifuge and provides its largest field of application.

The distinct feature of the design is a stack of concentric metal cones separated by spacers and so arranged in the bowl that feed must pass through the narrow spaces between discs before leaving the bowl. The purpose of the discs is to reduce the settling distance from the full depth of liquid in the bowl to the radial distance of separation of adjacent conical

Fig. 11. Centrico laboratory disc centrifuge (courtesy Centrico Inc.).

surfaces.   The angle of the cones with the vertical axis is sufficiently large that solids or liquid layers deposited on their surfaces move to the inner or outer edge of the stack under the centrifugal field.   In general, the bowl is underdriven and is supported on a spindle, as shown in Figure 11.   The feed is usually introduced at the top center of a clarifier bowl, passes down through the center post, and under the disc stack to the periphery of the bowl.   Here it is distributed up the height of the stack and passes through the parallel disc spaces.   Clarified feed is discharged over a dam or through orifices whose radial location can be varied to maintain the proper submergence of the disc stack.

Heavy solids are deposited on the underside of the disc and, after aggregating, slide down the surface to the periphery of the disc and are thence settled to the outer wall of the bowl.   In cases where the total volume of solids to be collected is very small, the bowl wall is solid and cake builds up in the space outside the discs.   When cake builds into the disc stack, the stack loses efficiency and the bowl must be cleaned.   When the proportion of solids is large, the bowl wall is sloped so that the solids slide to discharge ports around the periphery where they may be continuously discharged from the bowl in a stream of liquid.   The volume of the solids concentrate stream is controlled by the number of discharge ports and the size of the nozzles used in the ports.   There are two limitations on the discharge ports that may prevent obtaining as concentrated a solids stream as desired: (1) an even number of ports should be used to maintain bowl cake symmetry so that two ports is the minimum number; and (2) the nozzles should be at least twice the diameter of the largest solids particle present. In addition, the solids must be of such a nature that they will flow or be extruded through the nozzles at the pressures available and that their angle of repose must be sufficiently low so that the cake between discharge ports does not build up to the disc stack before it reaches the ports.   Some commercial-size disc machines utilize valved ports to permit greater concentration of solids before discharge, but these are not available in laboratory-size machines.

The Σ value for a disc machine involves disc angle and the number of discs as well as the parameters previously introduced; Ambler[5] has discussed the derivation of the formula and the factors affecting it.   For a clarifier bowl the Σ value is given by:

$$\Sigma = 2\pi n \ \omega^2 \ (r_2{}^3 - r_1{}^3)/3gC \tan \Theta \tag{40}$$

where n = number of spaces between discs, r_1 = radius of inner periphery of disc slope, r_2 = radius of outer periphery of disc slope, C = factor for fluid flow pattern between discs, generally assumed at unity, and Θ = angle of the disc from the vertical.

The disc centrifuge of Figure 11 is a flexible laboratory unit in that a solid-wall clarifier bowl, a nozzle discharge solids concentrator, and a liquid–liquid separator bowl can be mounted interchangeably on the same frame.   The design characteristics of the nozzle discharge bowl are as follows: n = 25, r_1 = 2.1 cm., r_2 = 3.6 cm., Θ = 45°, and rotational speed = 12,000 r.p.m.   With these data it is possible to calculate a Σ value, thus:

$$\Sigma = \frac{2\pi \times 25 \ (2\pi \times 12000/60)^2 \ (3.6^3 - 2.1^3)}{3 \times 980 \times 1.0 \times \tan 45°} = 31.6 \times 10^5 \ \text{cm.}^2$$

Again using the system previously computed for the bottle centrifuge example where $Q/\Sigma = 0.338 \times 10^{-4}$ cm./sec. for satisfactory clarity, the theoretical throughput for this disc machine clarifier bowl is: $Q = 0.338 \times 10^{-4} \times 31.6 \times 10^{5} = 107$ cc./sec. Experimental tests have shown that the efficiency of a disc machine as a clarifier seldom exceeds 55% and is considerably lower for solids subject to dispersion by shearing stresses or for those that do not aggregate readily. The practical feed rate for the desired clarity in this example is then probably not over 60 cc./sec.

Nozzle discharge in disc machines may be either "peripheral," that is, at the full radius of the bowl, or "return," in which solids are withdrawn at the full radius of the bowl but are returned toward the center of the bowl in an internal channel and discharged at some radius R where $r_2 > R > r_1$. There is little difference in the two types except that the return nozzle gives a smaller flow rate for a given nozzle size due to the lower pressure head at the smaller radius. The laboratory machine discussed above uses return nozzles with a minimum orifice size of 0.3 mm. Two such nozzles give a flow rate of the order of 3 cc./sec., so that for the example above the maximum concentration ratio is roughly 20 to 1.

In some solid-wall clarifier bowls, the disc stack is replaced by two concentric chambers, the outer of the radius of the bowl wall and the inner one of smaller radius. Feed enters the inner chamber first and then the outer chamber before discharge. Because of the depth of the liquid layer the efficiency of this type of bowl is lower than that of a disc stack or tubular centrifuge. The Σ value may be estimated as the sum of the Σ values for the two chambers where each is computed from equation (38).

The design of the liquid–liquid separator differs in two respects from a clarifier bowl. Since each layer must be clarified, the feed enters the disc stack from the bottom through a ring of holes piercing the discs and forming feed channels vertically through the stack. The liquid streams are discharged at the top of the bowl into separate covers. Solids, if any are present, form a cake at the bowl wall. For maximum efficiency the interface should be maintained at the radius of the center line of the holes by proper selection of the heavy phase discharge dam. In disc machines designed for a specific separating problem the radius of the location of the disc holes is selected to give the required separation in the phase representing the more difficult problem. In an all-purpose laboratory machine the holes are usually located at from one-half to two-thirds of the disc width. In the centrifuge of Figure 11 the holes are halfway out; other dimensions for the separator bowl are: $n = 25$, inner radius of discs = 2.4 cm., radius of the center line of the holes = 3.5 cm., outer radius of discs = 4.6 cm., $\Theta = 45°$, and speed = 12,000 r.p.m.

In evaluating separator bowls, a Σ value is computed separately for each layer by equation (40); the light phase is assumed to fill the stack inward from the center line of the holes and the heavy layer extends outward from that radius. Thus, for the dimensions of the bowl above: for the light layer $r_1 = 2.4$ cm., and $r_2 = 3.5$ cm., so that $\Sigma_L = 24.6 \times 10^5$ cm.²; for the heavy layer, $r_1 = 3.5$ cm. and $r_2 = 4.6$ cm., so that $\Sigma_H = 45.9 \times 10^5$ cm.². Throughput data are determined for the phase of greater importance. In general, the total capacity for the separator above is reported to be not over 70 cc./sec.

4. Conveyor-Discharge Centrifuges

The conveyor-discharge machine is designed for the removal and drying of relatively coarse solids above 2 microns in diameter in fairly large volumes on a continuous basis. The feed may contain solids at high or low concentrations and the effluent carries with it most of the fines. Consequently,

Fig. 12. Sharples P-4 Super-D-Canter.

this centrifuge is used more for pilot-plant work or as a test model for scaling up than for bench-scale laboratory clarification. Industrially, it is generally followed by a disc or tubular centrifuge to effect satisfactory clarity of the effluent.

The centrifuge is shown in Figure 12 and a diagram of its operation is given in Figure 13. The bowl is in the form of a truncated cone rotating about a horizontal axis. Feed is introduced through the hollow shaft and reaches the liquid layer near the large end. Solids are sedimented to the bowl wall where they are picked up and carried to the smaller end of the bowl by a helical scroll which turns at a speed slightly different from that of the bowl itself. Liquid is discharged at the larger end of the bowl through overflow ports that are adjustable with respect to their distance from the axis of rotation. A liquid layer exists only at the larger end of the bowl; as a result, solids approaching the small end of the bowl leave the liquid layer and are given an opportunity to drain freely under centrifugal force before being discharged. The lower the liquid level in the bowl, the longer the drying period for the solids, but the shorter the hold-up time and poorer the clarity of the effluent. The rate of solids discharge often determines the capacity of this centrifuge; for the laboratory model illustrated, the maximum solids rate is 1 to 4 lb./min., depending on the desired dryness of the solids and their density. Also, the solids must be scrollable,

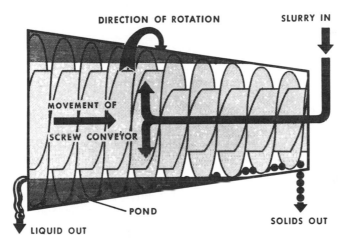

Fig. 13. Diagram of conveyor-discharge centrifuge

that is, they must have a high angle of repose and in general be movable by a standard screw conveyor.

The theoretical Σ value for this type of centrifuge is given by the equation:

$$\Sigma = \frac{2\pi\omega^2 l}{g} \left(\frac{r_2^2 + 3r_1r_2 + 4r_1^2}{8} \right) \tag{41}$$

where l = length of liquid layer measured at its surface, r_1 = radius of liquid surface, and r_2 = outermost radius of liquid layer. A correction must be made to the Σ of equation (41) to allow for the volume of the liquid pond actually occupied by the metal of the scroll. This value varies somewhat with overflow dam setting and is generally rather high for small centrifuges. For the model above, the corrected theoretical Σ is about 82% of that given by the equation.

The dimensions of the laboratory unit illustrated are as follows: $l = 10.8$ cm., $r_1 = 3.5$ cm., $r_2 = 5.1$ cm., and speed up to 6000 r.p.m. The theoretical Σ from equation (41) is 5.50×10^5 cm.^{2}. If it is assumed that the solids of the system used for the bottle centrifuge example given previously are scrollable, then for $Q/\Sigma = 0.338 \times 10^{-4}$ cm./sec., and with Σ corrected for the scroll volume, the corrected theoretical capacity of this laboratory unit is 15.3 cc./sec. Industrial size conveyor-discharge centrifuges have efficiencies ranging from about 62% on clay down to 20% on other solids. Turbulence due to scrolling is more important in the small model so that efficiencies of 15 to 50% are probable and the practical value of capacity is closer to 8 cc./sec. in the example above. This assumes that the solids load is not the controlling factor.

5. Basket Centrifuges

As mentioned previously, perforate or imperforate basket rotors with suitable collecting chambers may be mounted on the spindle of a bottle centrifuge. Laboratory-size basket centrifuges are also available as separate units (Fig. 14). The basket consists of a cylindrical bowl with a lip at the top and usually a solid bottom. The bowl diameter is generally larger than its depth.

In the perforate type, which is extensively used for separation of crystals or fibrous materials from their mother liquor, the wall of the bowl has numerous large perforations to permit free escape of the liquid. The basket is enclosed in a collecting chamber with a drain for removing the filtrate continuously. The solids are retained on a liner consisting of a fine screen, cloth, or filter paper backed by a coarse screen; the filter medium must have holes large enough to allow free drainage but small enough not to be plugged by solids. The drainage rate and packing characteristics of the cake determine the time required to spin the solids to the desired dryness. Ambler[5] indicates that a laboratory perforated basket with a diameter of about 12 inches can provide satisfactory data for scaling up to commercial sizes.

Suspensions containing solids of small size or gummy or gelatinous nature cannot be clarified readily in a perforate basket due to rapid clogging of the pores of the filter medium. A solid bowl basket is satisfactory for such mixtures but does not give a dry cake. The size of the lip at the top of the basket determines the volume of hold-up in the bowl; sometimes an adjustable scoop dipping into the liquid layer is used to remove clarified liquid so that the hold-up volume can be varied. Baffles are necessary to keep the liquid mass rotating at bowl speed. Feed is introduced through a tube extending to the bottom of the bowl near the center and it flows outward along the bottom to the liquid level.   Since solids sediment through the liquid layer as it moves to the top of the bowl, the physical picture is much the same as for the clarifier bowl of the tubular centrifuge and the same theory applies.   The Σ value for a solid basket is thus given by equation (38) where r_1 is the inner radius of the lip of the bowl and r_2 is the

Fig. 14. Laboratory centrifuge with perforated basket.

radius of the bowl wall; as the run progresses and cake builds up, r_2 becomes the radius of the surface of the cake.   The advantage of an imperforate basket over a tubular clarifier centrifuge is that the former generally has a much larger solids-holding capacity than the latter, and the lower speeds impose less shear stress on the particles of the entering feed.   The disadvantages of the basket, however, are several: (1) it is hard to introduce feed exactly at the bottom so that a portion of the relatively short length is lost; (2) the relatively large depth of the liquid layer necessitates long sedimentation times and permits large-scale turbulence; and (3) a portion of the feed probably moves along the inner surface of the liquid to the overflow point so that the full liquid volume is not utilized for holdup.

The Σ values of two sizes of laboratory solid basket centrifuges can be computed for dimensions as in Table I.

TABLE I

Dimension	Small size[6]	Large size
Vertical height $= l$, cm................	6.0	15.2
Inner radius of lip $= r_1$, cm............	4.5	10.5
Bowl wall radius $= r_3$, cm............	6.5	15.2
Rotational Speed, r.p.m..............	4800	2100
Σ, cm.²...........................	3.6×10^5	8.2×10^5

The Σ values are seen to be roughly 20 to 50% of that of the tubular centrifuge when it is operated at 20,000 r.p.m. Again using the sedimentation conditions of the bottle centrifuge example, that is, satisfactory clarity at $Q/\Sigma = 0.338 \times 10^{-4}$ cm./sec., the theoretical throughputs for the basket centrifuges at this same clarity are found to be 12.2 cc./sec. for the smaller machine and 27.7 cc./sec. for the larger. The efficiency factor for solid basket centrifuges probably ranges from 50 to 80% of theoretical so that these feed rates would be reduced to this extent in practice.

6. Analytical Ultracentrifuges

In the development of the theory of centrifugal sedimentation it was assumed that no interfering forces, other than viscous resistance to particle motion, were present. In a dilute suspension of similar particles, assuming the absence of convection and electrical forces, the sedimentation velocity of all particles is equal and the movement of the particles originally on the surface of the suspension, or at the bottom of the container if $\Delta\rho$ is negative, forms a well-defined and moving boundary between the suspension and the fluid phase.

In a polydisperse system, multiple boundaries are formed that become further separated with time. The relative concentration of each dispersed component in the mixture is indicated by the change in concentration across its boundary. Although usually well defined, these boundaries are not infinitely sharp because of the Brownian movement of the particles. In general, the smaller the particles, and the slower the sedimentation rate, the greater the extent to which this boundary diffusion occurs.

Between the diffused boundary layer and the bottom of the container, in the case of a monodisperse system, or between adjacent boundary layers, in the case of polydisperse systems, a plateau region of uniform concentration exists.   Sedimentation rates can still be measured because it is known from the nature of the diffusion process that the true position that the boundary would have had in the absence of diffusion is the point at which the concentration in the diffused layer is one-half that which exists in the adjacent plateau region.   However, the sharper this boundary layer, the more accurately can its rate of motion be measured.

Fig. 15 Spinco ultracentrifuge (courtesy Spinco Division, Beckman Instruments Corp. Belmont, Calif.).

As a special case, the sedimentation rate for a given system may be kept low enough in comparison with the diffusion rate so that an equilibrium is established between the forces of sedimentation and diffusion.   An analysis of the concentration gradient established in such a system permits the determination of particle mass or molecular weight independent of particle shape.   Sedimentation velocity can be increased and diffusion effects minimized by increasing the applied centrifugal force.   At high rotational speeds, the windage of the rotor produces appreciable thermal effects that set up convection currents in the system.   These in turn interfere with the precise determination of the true sedimentation velocity unless adequately taken care of in the design of the ultracentrifuge.

⁶ H. B. Golding, "Centrifuging," in A. Weissberger, ed., *Technique of Organic Chemistry*.   Vol. III, 1st ed., Interscience, New York-London, 1950.

The basic requirements of the analytical ultracentrifuge are: (*1*) a rotor strong enough to withstand the stresses imposed with a transparent cell in which the sedimentation rate and concentration gradient of the

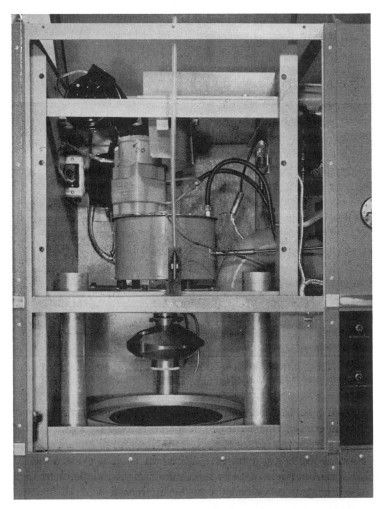

Fig. 16. Ultracentrifuge drive compartment and rotor, vacuum chamber lowered (courtesy Spinco Division, Beckman Instruments Corp., Belmont, Calif.).

sample under centrifugal force can be progressively observed through a suitable optical system; (*2*) a means for driving the rotor to attain quickly and maintain accurately and measure the usually required high speed;

(3) a method for avoiding temperature gradients and consequent undesirable convection disturbances in the sample; and (4) a means for accurately measuring and preferably accurately controlling the temperature.

Analytical ultracentrifuges (Figs. 15 and 16) incorporating these features are commercially available.   The rotor containing the sample cell is of the self-balancing type flexibly suspended from a vertical shaft and driven by an electric motor.   The rotor is housed in an armored chamber for safety with temperature and vacuum control.   The optical system is of the Philpot-Svensson refractive-index type that records automatically, at prescribed intervals, the refractive-index gradient along the column of fluid being centrifuged.   The sedimentation rate is measured by the change in position of the refractive-index gradients existing in the region of the sedimentation boundaries.   The standard reference work on this subject is *The Ultracentrifuge* by Svedberg and Pederson.[7]   Recent advances in the mathematics, practices, and techniques employed are described in *Determinations with the Ultracentrifuge* by Nichols and Bailey[8] and by Pickels[9] and others.   Analysis by the ultracentrifuge is one of the few basic methods available for determination of the molecular weight of labile compounds and of the size of very small particles in their natural environment.

IV. USES OF CENTRIFUGES

Many of the techniques of preparative and analytical chemistry are based on centrifuges.   Their use is often a matter of convenience and sav-

TABLE II

BOTTLE CENTRIFUGE IN A.S.T.M. STANDARD PETROLEUM TESTS

Type of test	A.S.T.M. designation
Precipitation number of lubricating oils..................	D91-52
Water and sediment by means of centrifuge..............	D96-52T
Fuel oils: water and sediment.........................	D396-48T
Unsulfonated residue of petroleum plant spray oils.........	D483-52T
Stoddard solvent: sulfuric acid absorption test............	D484-52
Olefins and aromatics in petroleum distillation............	D875-46T
Normal pentane and benzene insolubles in used lubricating oil.......................................	D893-52T

[7] T. Svedberg and K. O. Pedersen, *The Ultracentrifuge.*   Clarendon Press, Oxford, 1940.

[8] J. B. Nichols and E. D. Bailey, "Determinations with the Ultracentrifuge," in A. Weissberger, ed., *Technique of Organic Chemistry.*   Vol. I, Part I, 2nd ed., Interscience, New York-London, 1954.

[9] E. G. Pickels, "Ultracentrifugation," in Corcoran, ed., *Methods of Medical Research.* Vol. V, Year Book Publ., Chicago, 1951.

TABLE III

USES OF CENTRIFUGES

IN ANALYTICAL METHODS

Moisture Equivalent of Subgrade Soils: A.S.T.M. Designation D425-35T; AASHO Test T94-42.
Soil Analyses: Truog *et al.*, *Proc. Soil Sci. Soc. Am.*, **1**, 101 (1936).
Determination of Bitumen in Surfacing Mixtures: AASHO Standard Method T58-37.
Determination of Unsaturated Hydrocarbons: U. S. Bur. Mines Method 550.1.
Phosphorous Determination by Goetz Method: *Ind. Eng. Chem.*, **17**, 908 (1925).
Determination of Metals: *J. Am. Chem. Soc.*, **44**, 132 (1922).
Potash Analysis: *Ind. Eng. Chem.*, **13**, 227 (1921).
Pycnometric Method of Gravimetric Analysis: *Ind. Eng. Chem.*, *Anal. Ed.*, **9**, 592 (1937).

CLINICAL AND PUBLIC HEALTH APPLICATIONS

OF BOTTLE, TUBULAR, AND ULTRACENTRIFUGES

Fat Content of Milk and Cream by Babcock Test: *Official and Tentative Methods of Analysis of the AOAC.*
Concentration of Influenza Virus: Taylor *et al.*, *J. Immunol.*, **50**, 291 (1945).
Concentration of Tobacco Mosaic and Influenza Viruses: Stanley, *ibid.*, **53**, 179 (1946).
Lipoproteins and Atherosclerosis: Gofman *et al.*, *J. Gerontol.*, **6**, 105 (1951).
Blood Fractionation: Strong, in Kirk and Othmer, eds., *Encyclopedia of Chemical Technology*, Vol. II, Interscience, New York-London, 1948.
Relative Blood Corpuscle Volume: *Am. J. Med. Sci.*, **180**, 58 (1933).
Platelet Content of Blood: *J. Lab. Clin. Med.*, **12**, 282 (1926).
Recovery of Dust and Bacteria from Air: Supl. *Am. J. Pub. Health*, **29**, 64 (1939).
Urinary Sediment Determinations: *Arch. Internal Med.*, **32**, 222 (1923).

TUBULAR CENTRIFUGE IN PARTICLE SIZE DETERMINATION

Hauser, *et al.*, *J. Phys. Chem.*, **40**, 1169 (1936); **44**, 584 (1940); *Ind. Eng. Chem.*, **32**, 659 (1940).
Analysis of Oil Well Drilling Muds: Oliphant *et al.*, *Tech. Publ.* 1530 and 1531, Am. Inst. Mining Metallurgical Engrs.

---

ing of time, but in other cases, such as the concentration of nonfilterable material, the centrifuge is a necessity. Some applications of centrifuges in the fields of petroleum, general analysis, medicine and public health, and particle size determination are listed in Tables II-III.

In practice the techniques involved in these tests are frequently applied in commercial installations. Pilot plant and laboratory tests provide the basic information necessary for the transition to full-scale operation.

V. OPERATION AND MAINTENANCE

1. Balancing

Every rotating body tends to vibrate at certain speeds regardless of how carefully it has been balanced. These critical speeds occur when the rotational speed reaches the naturally occurring frequency of the assembly about the desired or some other axis.   Above its critical speed the rotating body tends to revolve about its own center of mass which may be offset from its geometric axis by stress distortion, errors in loading, and normal manufacturing tolerances.

In terms of analytical dynamics, the rotating body has an ellipsoid of inertia.   The greater the ratio of the major to the minor axis of this ellipse, the greater the stability of the rotating assembly when operating above its critical speed.   In the design of centrifuges that are intended to be run above their critical speed this factor is considered and commercial centrifuges are either large in diameter with respect to height, such as the laboratory bottle centrifuge, or small in diameter with respect to length, such as the tubular bowl centrifuge.   Both are inherently stable forms.   When the ellipsoid of inertia becomes a circle due to the proportions or loading of the rotor, the centrifuge becomes unstable at all speeds above its critical speed.

In order to permit centrifuges to pass freely through their critical speeds some degree of flexibility in their mounting must be provided.   In addition, this flexibility permits the rotating body to find its desired axis of rotation about its center of mass, which, as noted above, may differ from its geometric axis.   The energy absorbed by a fixed mount without such flexibility would be greater than the driving power normally provided and the assembly would not reach its rated speed.   Various systems are used to provide this required flexibility.   In the small sizes of laboratory centrifuge the entire machine may be mounted on rubber (Fig. 14).   In the larger sizes only the rotating parts may be spring or rubber mounted.   In the suspended-type tubular bowl Supercentrifuge the flexibility is provided by the combination of the cushioned mounting of the drive and the flexibility of the spindle.   In this type the frame is rigidly mounted on the laboratory bench or other working surface which should be as free as possible from extraneous vibrations.

The disc centrifuge is usually underdriven, the weight being carried on a fixed thrust bearing at the lower end of the drive spindle and the required flexibility provided by a radial bearing.   This is either spring or rubber cushioned and located immediately below the bowl assembly.   The smaller sizes of disc centrifuges are also rigidly mounted on the working surface. Larger disc centrifuges are usually mounted on flexible base cushions to provide supplementary flexibility.[10]   Centrifuges such as the conveyor-discharge type (Fig. 12) are commonly designed to be operated below their critical speed and thin rubber base cushions provide the required absorption

[10] A. E. Flowers, "Centrifuges," in J. H. Perry, ed., *Chemical Engineer's Handbook*, 3rd ed., McGraw-Hill, New York, 1950, pp. 992–1013.

of extraneous vibrations. Continuous centrifuges are essentially self-balancing under normal operating conditions provided that reasonable care is exercised in avoiding mechanical damage that would result in too wide a separation of the center of mass from the geometric axis.

Certain precautions, however, must be observed in loading the laboratory bottle centrifuge. For tubes with a capacity of 20 ml. or less it is adequate to fill them to the same height by visual inspection. Tubes carrying similar loads should be placed 180° apart in the rotor head. After the tubes have been placed in their respective metal shields, the space around them should be filled with water or other suitable liquid if the centrifuge is to be operated at a speed of 2000 r.p.m. or higher. For lower speeds this precaution is usually not necessary. Tubes of 50-ml. capacity or over should be balanced more carefully. Tubes that are to be placed opposite each other in the rotor should be balanced to within 0.25 gram. The recommended procedure is to place the glass tube in the metal shield and use the trunnion ring to support them on the balance, one assembly on each balance pan, for loading the glass tubes with equal weights of sample. With the larger tubes it is always advisable to fill the space between them and the shields with a supporting fluid regardless of the proposed operating speed since the liquid pressure results in a stress in the glass that is directly proportional to the diameter of the tube. The loaded and balanced assemblies should now be placed in the rotor head in such a manner that each balanced pair is at opposite ends of a common diameter.

Similar precautions should be observed in loading angle centrifuge heads and in the case of the preparatory head of the ultracentrifuge, with its high speed, extreme care should be exercised in balancing diametrically opposite tubes.

2. Operation

The subject of balancing laboratory centrifuges was discussed in the preceding section. After the rotor head is properly loaded, the cover should be closed and latched. For centrifuges equipped with temperature control devices the preliminary adjustment should have been made prior to this time and the final adjustment is made now. The rheostat or speed controller is brought to the zero or lowest speed position and the power is turned on. The speed control handle can then be advanced slowly until the desired speed is attained.

There are two reasons for this procedure:

(1)   To limit the current inrush to the motor at the start.

(2)   To prevent the swinging tubes from oscillating violently and possibly expelling their contents or even breaking.

Larger centrifuges of this type are frequently equipped with a built-in relay to prevent their being started unless the controller handle is in the zero position. They are also frequently equipped with a tachometer to provide visual indication of the operating speed. This is a precise but somewhat delicate instrument and the manufacturer's recommendations regarding its use should be carefully followed.

While many centrifuge rotor assemblies can be operated at the full speed of the centrifuge, others, because of stress considerations (see Section II.4) cannot, and the manufacturer's recommendation of permissible speeds at various loadings should be carefully adhered to if damage to the equipment is to be avoided.

The manner in which the centrifuge should be stopped depends on the nature of the sedimented phase. Considerable agitation at the interface occurs when the acceleration or deceleration is rapid. This usually does no harm during starting up, since the dispersion of the original sample is usually fairly complete. During stopping, however, considerable remixing may occur, particularly if the sediment is a relatively light flocculent material that does not pack well. In such a case it is necessary to stop the centrifuge very slowly. Some centrifuges are equipped with belt tension releases and other devices to take as much drag off the shaft as possible during this period. If the sediment packs down as a hard layer such precautions are unnecessary and the centrifuge may be braked to a stop, if equipped with such a device.

The basket-type centrifuge is handled somewhat differently. The perforate basket should be lined with an appropriate filter medium supported on a coarser screen to permit transverse drainage between the perforations in the shell. Unless it is equipped with locking rings or grooves to seal the filter medium in place, it should be rotated at a slow speed and thoroughly wetted with some of the slurry to set the filter medium in place. The speed can then be increased and the suspension added at a rate that will not cause it to overflow the lip ring. The solids are retained in the basket and the filtrate passes to the outer casing from which it can be caught in a container placed under the spout. When the sample has been loaded or the basket approximately filled with solids, the feed is stopped and the collected solids allowed to drain at maximum centrifugal force. When washing of the cake is desired the wash medium should be distributed as accurately as possible over the entire surface of the cake. The wash may be introduced in any convenient manner such as a perforated spray pipe or manually controlled single spray or nozzle. In the small centrifuges, a wash bottle suitably manipulated can be used for this purpose. For maximum washing efficiency the rinse should be started before the mother liquor has left the cake. Otherwise, the cake may crack and offer a convenient channel for the passage of the wash liquor without its doing any useful work.   The formation of a smooth cake of uniform thickness throughout the basket promotes the efficiency of the rinsing operation.   This can usually be accomplished by control of the centrifuge speed and manipulation of the slurry feed during the loading operation.   After spinning off the mother liquor or rinse liquor the centrifuge is stopped and the basket unloaded.

A solid basket with vanes is first brought up to the desired speed and the feed slurry is slowly poured in as close to the bottom as possible.   The bowl gradually fills up and the clarified supernatant liquor overflows the lip ring into the outer chamber.   For successful operation the feed should enter the bottom of the bowl at such a rate that the desired separation has been completed when the liquid reaches the top and starts to overflow.   At the completion of the run the centrifuge is stopped and the bowl unloaded. Similar considerations apply to the operation of the disc-type centrifuge except that the assembly makes provision for the introduction of the feed stream to the proper point in the rotor.   The tubular bowl centrifuge is also always brought to the desired operating speed before the feed is introduced.   Its operation differs in one very important particular.   In operating the two centrifuges noted above the size of the feed nozzle is not of critical importance.   However, the tubular bowl is fed from the bottom and, since there is no mechanical connection between the feed nozzle and the rotor, the feed must leave the nozzle with sufficient velocity upward to jet into the accelerating blades with which this type of bowl is equipped. In general, a feed nozzle size must be selected that will provide a standing jet at least 15 cm. high at the desired operating rate, Q.

Centrifuges of the tubular bowl type that are to be used for the separation of immiscible liquids are equipped with "ring dams" for direct control of the depth of the heavy phase liquid within the bowl, and indirectly for control of the depth of the light phase liquid since the total liquid depth is a fixed value of the bowl itself.   The larger the opening (the higher the number) of the ring dam, the less is the depth of the heavy phase liquid layer and the lower the Σ value of the bowl with respect to it.   Since the total Σ value of the bowl remains constant for a given rotational speed this means that the larger the ring dam the greater the Σ value of that portion of the bowl that is working on the lighter phase.   When the feed mixture or emulsion contains less than 50 volume per cent of the heavier liquid phase, the bowl should be primed with 125 ml. of the heavy phase to seal off the outer annulus, before continuous separation is attempted.   Disc-type centrifugal separators may be equipped with either ring dam control of the heavy phase or screw plug control of the light phase.   In either case it is essential that the adjustment be made so that the interfacial line falls within the holes in the disc stack for maximum efficiency.   The conveyor-discharge centrifuge should also be brought to the desired operating speed before the feed is introduced. For all continuous liquid flow centrifuges the coarse adjustment of the feed rate should be made by adjustment of the feed head and nozzle size, with the final adjustment by means of a pinch clamp or petcock in the feed line.

3. Motors and Other Types of Drives

Most centrifuges are now driven by electric motors. The principal exception to this generality is that certain models of the tubular bowl supercentrifuge are air or steam turbine driven at speeds up to 50,000 r.p.m., RCF = 62400 G. For the latter, air or steam at 40 p.s.i.g. is required and their speed may be adjusted to any lower limit desired by controlling the air or steam pressure to a corresponding lower value.

Speed regulation during start-up and speed control during operation are desirable for most motor-driven laboratory centrifuges. For centrifuges requiring not over 0.75 horsepower, universal series or compound wound motors are usually supplied. The speed of these may be regulated by a variable rheostat connected on one side of the line or by a Variac transformer for alternating current only. In either case the speed regulation is accomplished by reducing the line voltage to give the voltage across the motor that corresponds to the desired speed. These universal motors can be used with direct current or any cycle alternating current. Since their speed is a function of the applied voltage, care should be taken that the line voltage corresponds to the name plate reading of the motor.

For direct-current motors, larger than 0.75 horsepower, rheostat control of the speed is also used. For single-phase motors in sizes larger than 0.75 horsepower either the brush-shifting repulsion type, in which the speed is regulated by adjusting the brushes, or the capacitor type with autotransformer control in the primary circuit is satisfactory. Many continuous centrifuges that are normally driven at some fixed speed can be regulated to some extent by varying the ratio of the driving to the driven pulley, or by interposing a variable-speed belt drive between the two. The use of polyphase alternating current motors on laboratory or pilot plant centrifuges is comparatively infrequent. When speed adjustment of this type is required the same method is also applicable.

4. Care of Centrifuges

Most centrifuge troubles are connected with (1) improper lubrication; (2) unbalance of the rotating parts due to mechanical damage and distortion, excessive corrosion, poorly balanced loads, and improper cleaning of the rotor; (*3*) poor condition of the mounting and drive, particularly with respect to bearings, bushings, and rubber cushions; and (*4*) poor condition of the motor, particularly with respect to bearings, brushes, and commutator. Lubrication troubles more frequently arise from too much than from too little lubrication. If the bearings are allowed to run dry, excessive wear and possible damage to adjacent parts from overheating result and replacement of the damaged parts may be required. Overlubrication is likely to result in seepage of the excess oil or grease into the motor, the surrounding working area, and in the case of continuous centrifuges into the product itself. Oil on the motor parts collects dust that may cause the motor to "ground" or the oil may insulate the commutator and render the motor unoperable. In time, oil accumulated on the motor windings causes them to deteriorate, necessitating a rewinding job. It is always advisable to follow exactly the manufacturer's recommendations on lubrication and clean up any surplus lubricant that may appear.

The proper balancing of the working load was discussed in Section V.1. Even minor mechanical damage may create sufficient unbalance in the rotating system to interfere with quantitative results and may cause sufficient vibration to damage the centrifuge further. When damage has occurred, the equipment should be returned to the supplier, who has proper facilities for this kind of work, for repair and rebalancing.

Continuous centrifuge rotors must always be thoroughly cleaned after each use. Leaving a 1-g. undistributed mass of dirt in the tubular bowl results in an eccentric load on the rotor of over 60 kg. when it is revolving at full speed. The bushings, bearings, and belts of all centrifuges should be periodically inspected for wear and corrosion. This is particularly true when the centrifuge is used intermittently and the desired oil film on the bearings may have been replaced with dust or condensed moisture. These parts should be replaced before they have completely worn out, not afterward. It is false economy to risk the results of a valuable experiment in the hope that the wearing parts will last "just one more run."

Centrifuges equipped with rubber base pads, cushions, or vibration isolators should have these parts inspected periodically to be sure they have not deteriorated from the action of oil, solvent, or age. When this does occur the worn parts should be replaced promptly to insure that vibration from the centrifuge does not interfere with the use of other laboratory instruments such as balances. Most laboratory centrifuge motors are of the universal type and have brushes and commutators. Commutators should have smooth, cylindrical surfaces free from scratches and grooves. If they do become roughened, scratched, or grooved they should be put in good condition as follows: If the commutator is not too badly roughened, fine sandpaper No. 0 or 00, but not emery cloth, may be used to smooth and polish it while the centrifuge runs at low speed.   If the commutator is markedly cut or grooved, the armature should be removed from the machine and trued up and polished in a lathe.   Only the kind of brushes recommended or furnished by the manufacturer should be used.   When a new set is installed the brushes should be properly seated with a brush-seating stone while the centrifuge runs at low speed.   They should also be checked periodically, so that they can be replaced when appreciably worn down. If the motor is not of the commutator type only a periodic checking for loose connections need be made.   This should be done for all motors.

Perhaps the most important factor in the care and maintenance of centrifuges is overlooked most often.   Like all other pieces of mechanical equipment, they must be kept clean.   Broken glass, spilled samples, and surplus lubricant and dust should be removed on a regular preventive maintenance program before they have a chance to do any damage. When glass breakage has occurred in the laboratory centrifuge, the rubber cushions should always be removed from the metal shields and thoroughly cleaned or replaced.   Otherwise, the embedded glass particles may create point stress on succeeding glass tubes and cause them to fail.   The highly stressed parts of most centrifuges are of metal construction.   Uses that cause the corrosion of these metal parts should be avoided.   When this is impossible the stressed parts should be carefully inspected after each use and replaced whenever weakness is suspected.

VI. LIST OF SYMBOLS

(Most terms are defined for convenience in the C.G.S. system)

a, acceleration, cm./sec.^{2}.
A, cross-sectional area of centrifuge tube, cm.^{2}.
C, factor for fluid flow pattern between discs, dimensionless.
D, diameter of spherical particle or equivalent spherical diameter of nonspherical particle, cm.
E, experimental centrifuge efficiency, dimensionless.
F, force, usually force on a particle, dynes.
F', centrifugal force, grams.
g, gravitational constant, cm./sec.^{2}.
G, unit of gravitational force.
h, liquid depth, cm.
k, slope of ω versus time plot for bottle centrifuge, ω/t, radians/sec.^{2}.
K, shape factor of sedimenting particle, dimensionless.
l, length of liquid flow path in centrifuge, cm.
m, mass of a particle, grams.
m_l, mass of fluid displaced by particle, grams.
n, number of spaces between discs.

N,   speed of rotation, r.p.m.

P,   hydrostatic pressure, g./cm.^{2}.

Q,   volumetric rate of liquid phase flow through centrifuge bowl, cm.^{3}/sec.

r,   radial distance of particle from axis of rotation, cm.

r_1,   radius of inner surface of liquid layer, cm.

r_2,   radius of outer surface of liquid layer, cm.

r_e,   effective average radius of centrifugal force in liquid layer, cm.

r_H,   radial distance of heavy discharge from axis, cm.

r_I,   radial distance of interface from axis, cm.

r_L,   radial distance of light discharge from axis, cm.

r_w,   mean radius of wall section of rotor, cm.

RCF,   relative centrifugal force, multiples of gravity.

s,   radial thickness of liquid layer, cm.

s_e,   effective radial thickness of thick liquid layer, cm.

t,   residence time of particle in centrifugal field, sec.

t_D,   time required to sediment all particles of diameter D, sec.

v_g,   velocity of particle relative to fluid phase in gravitational field, cm./sec.

v_s,   velocity of particle relative to fluid phase in centrifugal field, cm./sec.

V,   volume of liquid phase in bowl or bottle, cm.^{3}.

W,   weight of rotating load, grams.

x,   radial distance travelled by particle during sedimentation, cm.

z,   radial thickness of wall of rotor, cm.

γ_l,   liquid load stress on rotor, g./cm.^{2}.

γ_r,   self stress of rotor, g./cm.^{2}.

γ_T,   total stress on rotor, g./cm.^{2}.

$\Delta\rho$, $|\rho - \rho_l|$, g./cm.^{3}.

η,   viscosity of fluid, poises.

Θ,   angle of disc from vertical, degrees.

ρ,   density of a particle, g./cm.^{3}.

ρ_l,   density of fluid, g./cm.^{3}.

Σ,   factor relating physical dimensions of centrifuge design to theoretical capability of centrifuge, cm.^{2}.

Σ_H, Σ for heavy liquid phase, cm.^{2}.

Σ_L, Σ for light liquid phase, cm.^{2}.

ω,   angular velocity of rotation, radians/sec.

General References

E. R. Riegel, *Chemical Process Machinery*, Reinhold, New York, 1953.

J. O. Maloney, "Centrifugation," *Ind. Eng. Chem.*, **46**, 72–74 (1954) and **47**, 517–19 (1955).

H. Trawinski, "Zentrifugen," *Chem.-Ing.-Tech.* No. 4, 189–204 (1954).

Y. Oyama and I. Inoue "On the Characteristics of the Disc Type Centrifuge," *J. Sci. Research Inst. (Tokyo)*, **47**, 205–15 (1953).

J. F. Jupp, "Industrial Centrifuges," *Can. Chem. Processing*, 34–38 (1953).

J. E. Flood, "Centrifugals," *Chem. Eng.*, **62**, 217–27 (1955).

J. C. Smith, "Centrifuges," *Chem. Ind.*, **65**, 357-64 (1949).

CHAPTER V

FILTRATION

Arthur B. Cummins and Francis B. Hutto, Jr., *Johns-Manville Research
Center, Manville, New Jersey*

CONTENTS (*Continued*)

I. INTRODUCTION

1. General

The requirement of separating solids from liquids is common in practical organic chemistry. Filtration, perhaps the most widely used method for these separations, is applied in many different ways; apparatus and techniques vary with the objectives and with the nature and the amounts of materials to be filtered. A chapter on laboratory techniques of filtration must, therefore, cover a wide field, and the treatment must necessarily be restricted. Rather than cover the field exhaustively, an attempt has been made to present the subject in a suggestive manner, with specific examples illustrating principles or types of problems. The general outline is designed to point out the objectives of filtration, to sketch the elements of filtration theory, to describe representative types of filtering apparatus and media, to present the principles of filtration testing, and to give examples of techniques and procedures used in the filtration of the different types of materials commonly met in organic chemistry.

Filtration involves not only a sequence of physical operations employing apparatus, but also numerous physicochemical phenomena,[1-3] such as adsorption and other surface effects. It is one of the laboratory arts, in which experience and ingenuity are important; some filtrations are quite simple, employing commonly known apparatus and methods, but other filtrations may present difficult problems and require special apparatus or techniques. While the advances in filtering apparatus and methods during the past few decades have not been as spectacular as in some other laboratory techniques, there have been many significant improvements and refinements.

Speed or convenience of a filtration method may be important, but the success of a filtration is judged by the properties of the retained solid or of the liquid which has been freed of suspended solid particles. While filtration includes the separation of all types of solids from fluids, and while the separation of some organosols from gases is of great importance, this chapter is concerned solely with liquid–solid systems.

The practice of filtration is of great antiquity. The earliest records refer to the treatment of waters, beverages, and common liquids. Various practices in these early arts of filtration have been referred to in the writings of the Egyptians, Greeks, and Arabs.[4-13] Descriptions of the use of filter paper with glass funnels, of

[1] A. Meyer, *Fette u. Seifen,* **49,** 525 (1942).

[2] F. A. Friedel, *Chem.-Ing.-Tech.,* **21,** 382 (1949).

[3] L. G. Sillen, *Arkiv Kemi,* **2,** 477 (1950); **3,** 499 (1951).

[4] Raymundus Lullius, *Arbor scientiae venerabilis et coelitus, liber ad omnes scientias utilissimus.* Lugdum, 1515.

[5] Geber, *Summa perfectionis magisterii in sui natura, Venetiis.* Petrum Schaeffer Germanum, Maguntinum, 1542.

[6] Geber, *Geberi philosophi ac alchimistae maximi, de alchimia libri tres.* Johannis Grieninger, 1529. Also English translation from Arabian by Richard Russell, 1678.

[7] Libavius, *Alchymia.* N. Hoffman, Frankofurti, 1606.

[8] Nicholas Lemery, *Cours de chimie.* Estienne Michallet, Paris, 1675.

[9] M. Berthelot, *Les origines de l'alchemie.* Georges Steinheil, Paris, 1885.

various textile cloths used in different ways, of horsehair sieves for pulpy materials, etc., were given in some later medieval treatises.[14]

Lavoisier[15] defined a filter as a "species of a very fine sieve, which is permeable to the particles of fluids, but through which the particles of the finest powdered solids are incapable of passing; hence, its use in separating fine powders from suspension in fluids." Plates in the work cited show a small conical filter fitted with a woolen cloth, a filtering bag stretched upon a wooden stand, a supported paper filter, and several glass filters. Lavoisier described the use of clarifying aids, such as albumin, for filtration, and he referred to the use of sand filters and porous filter stones. The importance of filtration was also recognized by other chemists at the beginning of the modern era.[16,17] Bunsen[18] was perhaps the first to suggest the use of pumice as a filter plate and the value of asbestos as a filtering material in glass tubes.

2. Nomenclature

A popular definition states that filtration is the separation of solids from liquids. Somewhat more broadly filtration is the separation of suspended particles from a fluid by a difference of pressure on a pervious septum. The fluid passes through the openings in the septum, and the solids are deposited thereon. However, the residue retains some liquid by sorption and some particles usually pass along with the liquid into or entirely through the voids of the septum for varying periods of time. Each of these two phenomena has important practical implications.

Any device for effecting a filtration is a *filter*. The essential parts of a filter are: (*1*) the pervious *filter medium* or *septum*, (*2*) its *support*, frequently referred to as the filter *base*, and (*3*) a suitable housing for the assembly. The required conditions for filtration are the maintenance of a pressure differential on the two sides of the septum, the delivery of suspension to the high-pressure side, and the removal of filtrate from the low-pressure side.

The usual filtration is a nonstatic operation. The first step involves the formation of the *filtering layer;* the second is the *filtration proper*, during

---

[10] H. Kopp, *Geschichte der Chemie*. Braunschweig, 1844.

[11] V. Lippman, *Geschichte des Zuckers*. 2nd ed., Berlin, 1929.

[12] H. Bechhold, *Z. Physik. Chem.*, **60**, 257 (1907).

[13] H. C. Bolton, "Nine Notes on Literature of Chemistry," *Popular Sci. Monthly*, Feb., 1880.

[14] Johannes Juncken, *Conspectus Chemiae Theoretico-Practicae*. Halae, Magdeburgicae, 1730.

[15] A. L. Lavoisier, *Traité élémentaire de Chimie*. Cuchet, Paris, 1789.

[16] M. Faraday, *Chemical Manipulation*. W. Phillips, London, 1827.

[17] J. J. Berzelius, *Lehrbuch der Chemie*. 4th ed., Arnoldischen Buchhandlung, Dresden, 1835.

[18] R. Bunsen, *Ann. Chem., Justus Liebigs*, **148**, 269 (1868).

which the solid particles are more or less completely retained. Thus, there is a continually changing set of relationships between the rate of passage of the liquid through the accumulating layer of solids on the filter member and the characteristics of the filtrate.

The solids retained on a filter are referred to as the *residue* or more commonly in chemical technology as the *cake*. The filtered liquid is known as the *filtrate* or in larger scale operations as the *effluent*. The material to be filtered may be referred to as a *dispersion, influent, prefilt, suspension,* or *liquor*. Frequently there is much dissolved material in the liquid, giving solutions of considerable viscosity. Clarification refers to filtrations in which the removal of particles from the liquid has been effected to a high degree. Usually, but not always, clarification filtrations are made on suspensions of low solids content. *Clarity* is a term employed to signify the condition of a filtrate from which suspended particles have been removed completely or to a high degree. The *filterability* of a material refers to the ease or difficulty of filtering it. This is a relative term: in one connotation, "filterability" is applied to the ease with which the liquid passes through the filter member and cake; in the other, it refers to the degree to which the system can be clarified or freed of the dispersed phase.

Ultrafiltration is the separation of intermicellar liquid from solids by the application of pressure on a semipermeable membrane. *Electroultrafiltration* is an operation wherein an electrical potential difference aids in directing particles through the membrane.

Straining or *screening* are operations in which a perforated septum serves to retain and separate particles larger than the openings. As all particles smaller than the openings pass through, this operation differs from filtration in which there is cake formation. In screening no fixed residue or cake is built up. It is prevented from forming by agitation or by other means. Coarse screens are employed for the removal of pulpy, fibrous, or granular particles. The membranes for ultrafilters as usually employed function as infinitely fine screens with openings of submicroscopic or colloidal dimensions.

Permeability is the ability of a cake or membrane to pass liquids. *Porosity* is the ratio of void volume to the total cake volume. *Dead void volume* is the term used to designate the volume of voids which is unavailable to fluid flow, *e.g.*, openings extending into particles but not passing entirely through.

The so-called *"filter effect"* is the gradual increase in filtration resistance which often is observed when pure liquid is passed through a filter cake. *Blocking* is said to occur when individual particles plug the pores of the filter septum, thus reducing the open area available to fluid flow. *Bridging* occurs when several particles "bridge over" a pore in the filter septum, thus preserving the maximum open area and assuring optimum performance of the septum.

3. Objectives of Filtration

The aims of filtration in organic chemistry are many. It is well to consider *a priori* the exact requirements before apparatus and techniques are selected. The following objectives of filtration may be outlined:

(a) *To Obtain the Liquid or Solution Free of Solids.* This is perhaps the most common objective of filtration. The procedure to be adopted depends upon whether the solids are also of interest and whether it is important to recover most or only a portion of the liquid.

(b) *To Secure the Solids Free of Liquid.* This is a common requirement in preparative chemistry. The product of a reaction may be obtained as the precipitate from a solution. Moreover, a common method of purifying compounds is to dissolve the material in a suitable solvent, filter, and crystallize from the solution. Precipitates of many kinds are collected by filtration.

(c) *To Remove Excess Liquid from Solids.* Pressure or vacuum filtrations may be helpful in reducing the amount of water or other liquid held by solids. This is a preliminary step in the drying of many materials.

(d) *Purification of Solids.* Filtering techniques are convenient for washing or leaching solids. This may be accomplished by digestion of a solid in a solvent in which it is sparingly soluble—but in which the impurities are more soluble—and then filtering, and repeating the operation one or more times. Similarly, the usual filter is a satisfactory device for the repeated washing of the solids while on the filter itself.

(e) *To Obtain Both Liquid and Solvent.* The requirements here are usually more restricted than when only one component is desired. For example, wash liquid for the solids cannot be collected with the original filtrate if it is necessary to maintain the original concentration of the latter. On the other hand, the liquid may be of great value and in this case the solids would be washed thoroughly.

(f) *To Change the Liquid Phase.* Filtration is a satisfactory means of transferring solids from one liquid to another. Thus, crystals from aqueous suspension may be filtered, drained as dry as possible, and then treated with alcohol, or other water-miscible liquid. The acetone-replacement technique of changing from aqueous to nonaqueous liquid and vice versa is readily carried out when the solids are supported on a filter. Other cosolvents for polar and nonpolar liquids such as isopropyl alcohol, dioxane, and β-ethoxyethanol may be used. The solution of solids by acids or other solvents is a common operation carried out with filtration apparatus.

(*g*) *For Clarification.* To obtain highly clarified and brilliant filtrates it is usually necessary to refilter the first portions of the filtrate. With some suspensions it is essential to carry out the filtration with care to avoid any irregularities in the filtering procedure which might cause turbidity in the filtrate. When the amount of finely divided, suspended material is low, it is frequently difficult or impossible to clarify the liquid adequately. In these cases, a suitable filter aid, such as diatomaceous silica or cellulose pulp, is helpful. In the filtration of colloidal materials of high concentration it is frequently difficult to obtain adequate clarity, and when satisfactory clarity is obtained at a later stage of the operation the rate of filtration may have decreased greatly. In these cases a suitable filter aid is also useful. Frequently it is necessary to treat the unfiltered liquid by special means to assist in filtration and clarification. In all clarification filtrations, the required degree of clarity determines the treatment and the apparatus employed.

(*h*) *To Remove Large Particles, Foreign Matter, Dirt, Fibers, etc.* In many preparations and mixtures, the only objectionable impurity is a small amount of extraneous matter, which may be due to contamination. Such materials may be large particles, metallic scale, dirt, fibers, etc. Usually these are readily removed and a condition is selected which will permit rapid filtration with adequate removal of the undesired particles.

(*i*) *To Remove Processing Materials.* Liquids which have been treated with adsorbents or decolorizing agents such as carbons or clays must be freed of these solid materials. Filtrations for this purpose frequently have special requirements, as described in Section VI.9.

(*j*) *For Analytical Purposes.* The special requirements for analytical procedures are: (*1*) care to ensure extreme purity of precipitates, (*2*) prevention of any losses of material, and (*3*) employment of small quantities of material. Filtering techniques and apparatus for qualitative and quantitative analytical purposes have been highly developed and are adequately described in textbooks and references.

(*k*) *To Condition Solids or Liquids for Other Laboratory Operations.* This is an important function of many filtrations and one of the most difficult to define. For cases in which the solids are drained dry on a filter to facilitate drying, or when the precipitate is prepared for subsequent solution in a solvent, for ignition or similar purpose, the objective is clear. However, there are cases, of which the following are examples, in which the objectives are definite, but the reasons for the effect cannot be readily explained. Some examples are: (*1*) The stability of liquids may be improved by removal of trace impurities. (*2*) Some emulsions can be broken by removal of the emulsifying agent or by some electrokinetic effect. (*3*) Odorous bodies may be removed. (*4*) Opalescence or fluorescence may be removed or changed. (5) Filtration removes components which make later treatment with adsorbents, chemicals, or other processes more effective; examples are decolorizing and ion-exchange treatments. (6) Filtering of liquids prior to evaporation, crystallization, or distillation is frequently highly beneficial; particles in the filtrate may cause false graining, frothing, etc.

4. Kinds of Materials To Be Filtered

In organic chemistry we are concerned not only with the filtration of laboratory preparations, organic chemicals, dyestuffs, solvents, etc., but also with biological preparations, protein and enzyme materials, vaccines and serums, foodstuffs, gums, fats and waxes, cellulose derivatives, fermentation products, reaction mixtures of all kinds, and many others. The filtering behavior of these materials varies greatly and each class accordingly presents a different filtration problem.

Attempts have been made to classify materials with regard to filtration, but no scientific scheme of general applicability has been proposed. However, it is helpful to consider materials by classes, since experience with a given material may be applied to similar products. Table I lists some of the filtering characteristics of various kinds of materials of interest in organic chemistry.

Coarse, crystalline, or incompressible particles generally are relatively easy to filter out. Well-flocculated or coagulated materials also usually filter quite readily and yield clear filtrates. On the other hand, exceedingly fine rigid particles may be quite difficult to remove, particularly if the dispersion is one of low concentration. There are few, if any, extremely fine colloid systems in organic chemistry which are quite like the inorganic or metallic sols, but some organic materials behave similarly during filtration.

The nature and amount of the suspended or dispersed particles in a material determine its filtering qualities much more than the inherent nature of the liquid phase *per se*. The only direct effect of the latter is its viscosity, although it must be recognized that the liquid frequently may modify to a large extent particle properties such as degree of solvation or interfacial and surface characteristics. Thus, some particles act quite differently in polar and nonpolar liquids.

The shape of the particles, their inherent compressibility or lack of resistance to deformation, degree of hydration, and other factors, such as the relative proportions of particles of different sizes, shapes, and properties, all have effects on the behavior of a liquid in a filtering operation. Thus, a useful classification of materials for filtration may be based on the apparent or surmised *physical structure of the particles*, particularly with regard to

TABLE I

SOME TYPES OF MATERIALS FOR FILTRATION

Description	Examples	Usual filtration behavior
Organic solvents, nonpolar liquids, etc.	Alcohols, benzol, etc.	Ordinarily not too difficult to filter
Organic compounds and mixtures which are solid at room temperatures	Fats, waxes, and resins	When heated above melting points may be filtered like other liquids
Coarse, granular, or crystalline particles	Organic crystals. Starch granules. Dry colors. Many organic and inorganic compounds	Readily filterable. Good clarification. Rapid filter rate
Extremely fine particles, particularly at low concentrations	Many organic preparations. Sugar, oil, and fruit products	Difficult to clarify. May clog filters. Readily filterable with filter aids
Rigid colloidal particles	Carbon hazes, colloidal sulfur, metallic sols	Not usually clarified, except by adsorptive action or chemical treatment
Pulps; tissues; films; skins; flat, lamellar particles	Fruit pressings, animal and vegetable extracts. Reaction mixtures of cellulose	Sometimes exceedingly difficult to filter. Preliminary screening or coarse filtration frequently desirable
Fats, waxes, etc., at temps. below melting point	Wax emulsions, milk, plant and animal extracts	Frequently difficult. Heating above m.p. satisfactory if melted product desired in filtrate
High-viscosity materials	Pectin, algin products, viscose, cellulose products	Low filter rates. Pressing operations sometimes used. High-pressure filtrations helpful
Microorganisms, bacteria, etc.	Culture media. Food products, biological materials, pharmaceuticals	Many filtrations remove some organisms, but complete sterilization more difficult
Serums, vaccines, etc.	Antitoxins, and serums of many types	Generally filtered through fine-pored, rigid media
Animal extracts and biological preparations	Glandular and flesh extracts. Blood preparations, some hormone and vitamin extracts	May be difficult. Changes must be avoided in treatment. High values justify special techniques
Gums, pectinous materials	Hydrolyzates of fruit and vegetable matter	Like other high-viscosity materials, much affected by pH
Tarry mixtures	Residues from many organic reactions	Frequently difficult
Protein sols and gels	Glues, gelatins, cereal mixtures, etc.	Usually sensitive to pH, heat, and electrolytes
Saccharine products	Malt sugar and glucose from cereal grains, raw cane sugar	Contain colloidal material. Filter aids widely used

compressibility or deformation under stress. Here the types of particles have been classed as rigid, semicompressible, and compressible. It has been stated that finely divided particles, particularly when suspended in and wetted by liquids, may all possess some degree of compressibility. Crystals and granular particles, however, are deformed or distorted so little under the conditions prevailing in most filtrations that they may be considered as essentially rigid. When such particles build up to form a cake on a filter member, the cake has a high degree of permeability and there is little tendency for the particles to clog the filter by being forced into the openings of the pervious filter septum. Systems made up largely of rigid particles are thus the easiest to filter and also the easiest to analyze and treat mathematically as indicated in Section II.2.

Compressible particles deform on the application of pressure. They may thus be forced through the openings of the filter member or through the pore spaces of the filter cake to give turbid filtrates. There is the tendency at the same time to plug or fill the interstices of the filter septum and thus greatly increase the resistance of this member to the passage of liquid. Some compressible solids have a notable characteristic of flattening out at the point of arrested movement and their effect is similar to that of a film, which has a retarding action on filtration. Most colloidal or highly hydrated particles are more or less compressible. Gelatinous and slimy precipitates, and waxy, tarry, and amorphous mixtures, and many materials of organic nature are of colloidal or semicolloidal character such that particular attention in filtration must be given to matter in these states.

The term "colloidal" is widely used in filtering terminology to include slimy, gelatinous, and amorphous solids. In many cases the particles are truly in the colloidal state, and then there are others that may be more nearly semicolloidal; and, of course, there are mixtures of both, with or without rigid or fibrous particles of many sizes and shapes. Colloid science recognizes that the conventional boundaries between dispersed systems are not fixed and nothing is to be gained from the filtration standpoint in attempting to fit materials into rigorous colloid classifications. However, since the materials that are usually hardest to filter belong to or border on the field of colloid science, it is proper to employ colloid terms in the filtration field and certainly to take every advantage that colloid science can offer toward better understanding of the filtering characteristics of materials.[19-21]

[19] H. Freundlich, *Kapillarchemie.* 2 volumes, 4th ed., Akadem. Verlagsgesellschaft, Leipzig, 1930–32. Also *Colloid Chemistry,* trans. by H. S. Hatfield, Dutton, New York, 1926.

[20] E. J. W. Verwey and J. T. G. Overbeeck, *Theory of the Stability of Lyophobic Colloids.* Elsevier, New York, 1948.

[21] J. W. McBain, *Colloid Science.* Reinhold, New York, 1950.

The general classification of colloid systems into lyophobic and lyophilic[22,23,26] is quite helpful in the consideration of filtration problems. These terms correspond to the earlier classification of suspensoids and emulsoids.[24,25] These classifications are based mainly on the absence,

TABLE II

PROPERTIES OF COLLOIDAL MATERIALS OF FILTRATION INTEREST

Lyophilic (emulsoids)	Lyophobic (suspensoids)
Compounds mostly of high molecular weight types	Compounds of medium or low molecular weights
Properties different from those of dispersion medium, surface tension often lower than that of medium	Properties like those of dispersion medium, particularly surface tension
Pronounced viscosity	Viscosity similar to medium
Diffuse Tyndall cone. Refractive indices of particles and medium nearly same	Very pronounced and bright Tyndall cone. Resembles fluorescence. Scattered light is polarized
Particles not readily detected in ultramicroscope	Particles easily studied in ultramicroscope
Not easily flocculated	Flocculated by electrolytes, (small quantities)
Flocculation reversible	Flocculation irreversible
Maximum concentration for reasonable stability usually rather small	Concentrations may be high
Electric charge variable	Electric charge usually fixed
Stability depends on electric charge and degree of hydration	Stability depends on electric charge
In cataphoresis, particle may not migrate at all, or may go in either direction	In cataphoresis, particles go in one direction
Do not flocculate when deprived of electric charge	Flocculate when deprived of electric charge
Highly hydrated	Not so highly hydrated
Usually filter slowly. Degree of clarification depends on formation of filter cake and its thickness	May filter rapidly, but clarification generally difficult and sometimes impossible unless particles are flocculated
Filter aids of help in increasing filter rate and prolonging filtration	Filter aids assist in clarification
Examples:	Examples:
Gums Rubber	Metals
Starches Chitin	Sulfur
Proteins Pectin	Ag halides
Soaps Synthetic	
Celluloses macromolecules	

[22] J. Perrin, *J. chim. phys.*, **3**, 84 (1905).
[23] H. R. Kruyt, ed., *Colloid Science.* 2 volumes, Elsevier, New York, 1949–52.
[24] W. Ostwald, *Kleines practicum der Kolloidchemie.* Steinkopff, Dresden, 1918.
[25] H. R. Kruyt, *Colloids.* Translated by H. S. von Klooster, Wiley, New York, 1927.

presence, or degree of the attractive forces between the dispersed phase and the dispersing medium. Thus, for lyophobes it is assumed that electric double layers are responsible for the stability of most hydrosols in the absence of protective colloids. On the other hand, with lyophiles it is presumed that interaction of the electric fields of adjacent molecules of the colloid and an "active" solvent leads to mutual attractions and orientations that prevent the dispersed particles from approaching so closely as to adhere. When lyophobic particles combine with (or "adsorb") the particles of a solvated colloid without loss of the solvated condition, the aggregate shows the stability of a lyophilic colloid. This is the basis of "protective action."

An understanding of colloid principles is important not only in consideration of systems prior to filtration, but also in the filtration process itself because internal and surface effects are prominent in the minute openings and passages of the filter cake. The classifications based on the thermodynamic stability of the colloidal system (intrinsic colloids and nonintrinsic colloids)[26] appear not to have any advantage over the simpler classifications when considering filtration. Table II lists some of the properties of these two major colloid classes, with some comments on their filtration behavior. The properties of colloids as given are suggestive of methods for conditioning or altering the properties of such materials preparatory to filtration. Since colloidal systems are stabilized by electric charges on the particles, flocculation occurs when particles are deprived of the charges, *i.e.*, at the *isoelectric point*. It is not necessary for all of the charge to be removed. A lowering of the potential at the interface to a critical value is all that is required. Many organic preparations contain mixtures of various colloids, frequently of both the lyophobic and lyophilic types. Also, colloidal phenomena such as "protective action" and peptization may be expected with mixtures.

Since lyophobic colloids are sensitive to flocculation by electrolytes, they can be "protected" therefrom by adding a second colloid having an electric charge of the same sign. The lyophobic colloid is adsorbed on the surface of the lyophilic colloid. This "protects" from the action of the electrolyte. The complexities present in a nonhomogeneous system may be indicated by a material such as a sugar juice or sirup prepared therefrom which contains variable amounts of gums, waxes, minute organisms, inorganic solids, fibers, coloring matter, proteinaceous compounds, and traces of many other materials. This is an example of a complex mixture of both hydrophilic and hydrophobic colloids.

[26] E. O. Kraemer, J. W. Williams, and R. A. Alberty, "The Colloidal State and Surface Chemistry," in H. S. Taylor and S. Glasstone, eds., *A Treatise on Physical Chemistry*. Vol. II, 3rd ed., Van Nostrand, New York, 1951. pp. 509–692.

II. THEORY

1. General Considerations

The theories of filtration have been developed from simple laws governing the flow of liquids through porous bodies. Empirical filtration equations, based on data obtained from simple suspensions of rigid particles, are generally satisfactory for idealized systems. The constants for these equations result from measurements made in controlled experiments, and are usually of limited applicability. Further, most materials of interest in organic chemistry contain compressible particles for which the theoretical treatment is more complicated. It may be said that up to the present there has been developed no consistent or generally accepted theory of filtration that is satisfactory for all or even many conditions. The main reason is that filtration embodies a number of physical operations, in which a system that is made up of dispersed particles and a liquid dispersing medium is subjected to conditions wherein surface action and colloidal and electric effects all play a part.[27-31] Thus, filtration in its broadest aspects can hardly be expected to be expressible in simple mathematical terms.

Langmuir[32] has recently presented a mathematical treatment of the mechanism of filtration which was developed for aerosols and smokes but appears to be of broader applicability. Many difficulties are present in the application of the theory for the filtration of liquids, but the principles are suggestive for a somewhat new approach to the general theory of filtration.

Basically, filtration theory deals with the state of balance between a driving force, the pressure, and the resistances to the passage of liquid through a pervious structure. The resistances, while complex, are in the nature of frictional drag on the liquid as it passes through the solid particles. All of the theories advanced are attempts to explain and express this relationship for the manifold types of materials of filtration interest. The fundamental premises consider the passage of liquids through porous bodies. Since this subject is of great importance in many fields, including the earth sciences, civil and hydraulic engineering, and petroleum geology, some of the basic concepts of filtration theory have come from studies that

[27] E. Hatschek, *J. Soc. Chem. Ind.*, **27**, 538 (1908).

[28] A. Simon and W. Neth, *Z. anorg. Chem.*, **168**, 221 (1927).

[29] G. F. Hüttig and M. Nette, *Z. anal. Chem.*, **65**, 385 (1925).

[30] B. F. Ruth, *Ind. Eng. Chem.*, **38**, 564 (1946).

[31] S. Nitzsche, *Naturwissenschaften*, **37**, 428 (1950).

[32] I. Langmuir, "Theory of Filtration," in W. H. Rodebush, I. Langmuir, and V. K. LaMer, *Filtration of Aerosols and the Development of Filter Materials*, OSRD Report 865 (PB99669), Sept. 4, 1942. Pt. 4, pp. 23-70.

may appear far afield, but which are significantly analogous. Some aspects are referred to hereinafter.

Further, it must be recognized that the body of filtration theory, particularly its mathematical aspects and the filtration equations, have been developed in applied chemistry and/or chemical engineering. Thus, the filtrations which have been most rigorously investigated usually have been carried out over considerable time periods, and ordinarily with effective control of process variables. In the laboratory, the same conditions may occur, but in general to a lesser degree. Many laboratory filtrations involve short periods and are made solely for the purpose of obtaining only a small amount of either residue or filtrate. In these cases surface and adsorption effects are frequently more significant than in longer filtrations.

In the treatment to follow we shall consider first the general phenomenology of filtration and then briefly the mathematical theory of filtration involving incompressible and compressible particles. Finally the applications and limitations of filtration theory are discussed. The chronological sequence in the development of filtration theory which was presented in the first edition of this chapter is not followed here and numerous literature references given in the earlier edition have been deleted. Further, since the treatment is necessarily confined to a rather condensed outline, the general references at the end of this chapter have been presented in annotated form and may thus serve as a supplement to this section. The references prior to 1949 are not intended to be comprehensive and have been critically selected to provide only the more original or basic sources of information on the passage of liquids through porous bodies and the development of filtration theory. From 1950 on, the list of references given is more complete.

Materials to be filtered consist of solid particles of different sizes and shapes, and frequently also of different composition, which are dispersed in a liquid. When placed in the filter, the system comes in contact with the filter septum which is supported on the filter base. A pressure differential on the two sides of the septum forces liquid through the latter while some of the coarser particles are retained on the surface of the septum. These particles form a "bridge" structure over the openings which reduces their size but does not block them completely.[33-36] Depending upon the particular conditions, anywhere from a few seconds to several minutes may be re-

[33] A. Hixon, L. Work, and J. Odell, *Trans. Am. Inst. Mining Met. Engrs.*, **73**, 225 (1926).

[34] P. H. Hermans and H. L. Breedee, *Rec. trav. chim.*, **43**, 680 (1935); *J. Soc. Chem. Ind.*, **55**, 1T (1936).

[35] P. M. Heertjes and H.v.d. Haas, *Rec. trav. chim.*, **68**, 361 (1949).

[36] P. M. Heertjes, *Research*, **3**, 254 (1950).

quired to build up the *true filtering layer*. The liquid then passing through becomes more clear or relatively free of solid particles. The filtration proper may only then be considered as having started. As solids accumulate on the septum, a residue or cake builds up, the character of which depends upon the size, shape, and physical nature of the particles. In most filtrations there is *no sharp boundary between the cake and the filtering septum*. The resistance to the passage of additional liquid through the deposit of solids increases as the thickness of the cake increases. The rate of flow drops or must be maintained by an increase of pressure. In gravity filtrations, most vacuum filtrations, and some pressure filtrations, the pressure is substantially constant, and the main variable is the changing resistance.

During filtration the liquid passes through the deposit of solids by following the interstices and voids between the particles. Friction resisting the passage of liquid through the fine openings more or less balances the driving force of the pressure differential. The pressure from the unfiltered suspension, and any additional pressure applied, is transmitted to the supporting filter base through the septum, the porous structure of the cake, and the liquid in the interstices. The pressure of the liquid thus varies from ΔP, the total pressure differential at the liquid face of the cake, to "zero" at the filtrate outlet, whereas the reverse is true for the skeleton structure of solid particles, *i.e.*, "zero" pressure at the face and the full value of ΔP at the filter base.

This condition may be visualized when it is realized that the filter cake is nonuniform in solids content, porosity, and resistance, and that it is constantly changing in many respects as filtration progresses. There has been no better expression of this problem than that given by Ruth and co-authors[37] more than twenty years ago:

"It would appear that a considerable portion of the increase in resistance per unit volume of filtrate arises, not from the addition of new solids to the surface of the cake, but from a contraction in the pore volume of the solids, already deposited. Since the amount of this contraction will be proportional to the deforming stress or pressure exerted at any particular point in the cake, the question arises as to how the deforming stress varies throughout the cake.

"It would seem that the filtration pressure itself can have no effect upon the shape of individual particles. This is easily visualized by imagining the effect of an increasing hydrostatic pressure upon a freely suspended sponge. It is only when this pressure becomes unbalanced that deformation of the sponge can take place. In the filtration process an unbalanced pressure results from the movement of liquid relative to the suspended solids, and this occurs only when the latter are suddenly arrested in their free motion with the liquid by impinging upon the filter medium.

[37] B. F. Ruth, G. H. Montillon, and R. E. Montonna, *Ind. Eng. Chem.*, **25**, 76 (1933).

"The magnitude of this unbalanced pressure is equal to the kinetic energy lost by a column of water of equal area, when the column is deflected from its course by the arrested particle. At the surface of the cake this is small, and serves only to hold the particle in place against the material previously deposited. In the layers of particles immediately below it, a greater amount of kinetic energy is given up by the capillary streams, since flow must become faster in order for the same quantity of liquid to pass through the smaller openings. Thus each particle is acted upon by an unbalanced force equal to the cumulative thrust of all particles in the column above it, and opposed by an equal force transmitted from the supporting septum upwards through the column of particles below it. If the particles are deformable, they tend to fill up the voids. This in turn requires adjacent capillary streams of liquid to travel with still higher velocity. It is apparent therefore that the magnitude of this viscous drag rapidly increases in the layers near the cloth. If we try to picture the deforming stress or pressure in terms of cake thickness, we obtain a curve which begins with almost zero pressure at the deposition zone, increases but slightly as the center region of the cake is approached, and then may start to increase with exponential rapidity through the layer adjoining the cloth until it reached the full filtration pressure at the support behind the cloth."

2. Mathematical Treatment of Incompressible Particles

Incompressible particles are defined as those that do not undergo any substantial change in volume, shape, or physical properties when subjected to reasonable pressures. Filter cakes composed of such particles do not show a significant change in average specific resistance with variation in filtration pressure. It is doubtful if any particles are absolutely incompressible, but many are nearly so for all practical purposes. However, it is recognized that there is often a condition of "retarded packing compressibility" in which the first layers of cake do not compress initially but do so after a critical cake thickness or pressure has been reached.[38,39] In this case, the theoretical treatment more nearly comes within the scope of compressible particles as considered later.

Filtration theory may be best approached by consideration of *simple systems* comprising rigid, incompressible particles of stable nature. If it is assumed that the *interstices* of the cake correspond to a *multiplicity of capillary tubes*, the flow of liquids through these may be expressed by Poiseuille's law[40] as indicated by the equation:

$$V = (\Delta P \pi r^4)/(8\mu l) \tag{1}$$

where V is the volume of liquid which will flow in unit time through a capillary of length l and radius r, μ is the coefficient of internal friction or vis-

[38] M. M. Haruni and J. A. Storrow, *Chem. Eng. Sci.*, **1**, 154 (1952).

[39] K. Rietema, *Chem. Eng. Sci.*, **2**, 88 (1953).

[40] J. L. Poiseuille, *Compt. rend.*, **15**, 1167 (1842).

cosity, and ΔP is the total pressure drop. (Definitions of the terms used in the equations are given in the symbol index on page 632.)

In a filter cake the *interstices between particles* may be considered to correspond to N capillaries per unit area, with lengths L, corresponding to the cake thickness. Then:

$$V = (N \ \Delta P \pi r^4)/(8\mu L) \qquad (2)$$

Equation (2) assumes that the length of the capillaries is the same as the thickness of the cake, which is of course far from being true, since the interstices and passages in a filter cake are tortuous and of variable shape and cross section. Furthermore, N and r are usually not known, and can rarely be estimated. However, if for a given set of conditions, N, r, and μ remain constant, the rate of flow is, as a first approximation, directly proportional to pressure and inversely proportional to thickness. Poiseuille's expression has therefore served as the starting point for the mathematical treatment of filtration behavior and the filtration equations have been modified in the main to account for deviations from Poiseuille's law. In practical filtration the law of Poiseuille is not adequate, particularly for heterogeneous, very fine, and compressible solids. The reasons are usually found in the resistance factor and its variable character, and particularly in the assumptions of rigidity and absence of surface forces made above. It should be recognized that the total resistance during filtration is made up of: (*1*) resistance of the filter base, drainage channels, and filtrate outlets; (*2*) resistance of the *filter medium;* and (*3*) resistance of the collected *solids or cake.*

The resistances mentioned under (*1*) are usually small and relatively constant, and may be ignored for most laboratory purposes. The resistance of the filter medium frequently changes rapidly for the reasons previously given, and in the mathematical treatment of filtration the resistance of the filter septum is generally taken as the value which is attained somewhat after the start of the filtration when the interstices of the medium are partially plugged and formation of the cake has started. However, even after this point the resistance of the medium is variable depending on the type of solids, the velocity of flow, the total pressure and how it is applied, the nature of the medium itself, and possibly other factors. The resistance of the cake obviously varies with increase of thickness (time of filtration), but only for entirely rigid, noncompressible solids does the resistance increase proportionally with thickness. The same conditions which cause a variation in the resistance of the partially throttled medium bring about changes in the resistance of the cake and frequently much more so than with the medium. Among the reasons for this behavior are the rearrangement and packing of very fine particles among larger particles under prolonged pressure and the deformation or distortion of soft compressible particles, which always tends to increase resistance. Moreover, *hydration effects, surface adsorption,* and *electrokinetic phenomena* may play important parts in altering resistances.

More direct application of Poiseuille's law to the actual passage of liquids through porous and permeable masses, as modified by d'Arcy,[41] is expressed in the equation:

$$u = V/A\theta = (K \ \Delta P)/L \tag{3}$$

where u is linear velocity (*i.e.*, volume V flowing in time θ past a cross section of area A) and K is a coefficient the value of which depends upon the porosity and permeability of the bed which may be made up of particles of various shapes, sizes, and nature. Many studies on the movement of ground waters have given abundant evidence of the validity of d'Arcy's law for these phenomena and have supplied in addition reasonable explanations for the packing of particles.

In an application of d'Arcy's equation to filtration, experimental results obtained with a chromium hydroxide slurry[42] led to the conclusion that the rate of flow is not directly proportional to the pressure and inversely proportional to the cake thickness, but that the relationship may be shown by the equation:

$$Q = (K'' \ \Delta P^s)/V^n \tag{4}$$

where K'', s and n are constants which must be evaluated experimentally. An equation with so many empirical constants was far from satisfactory, but at such an early date it was a step in the right direction. For incompressible cakes, s has a value of 1.0 while values of less than 1.0 indicate cake compressibility.

It has been generally accepted that fluid flow through granular beds follows an inverse relationship with viscosity such that:

$$u = dV/(A \ d\theta) = K'(\Delta P/\mu L) \quad \text{(modified} \atop \text{d'Arcy equation)} \tag{5}$$

where K' is the permeability coefficient. Rearranged, we have the usual form of the equation employed for interpreting permeability data:

$$K' = (\mu L/\Delta P \ A)(dV/d\theta) \tag{6}$$

In honor of the early investigator, the usual unit of permeability is the d'Arcy unit which equals a permeability of 1 ml. per sec. per sq. cm. at

[41] H. P. G. d'Arcy, *Les fontaines publiques de la ville de Dijon.* Victor Dalmont, Paris, 1856.

[42] C. Almy and W. K. Lewis, *Ind. Eng. Chem.*, 4, 528 (1912).

unit viscosity (centipoises) through a cake 1 cm. thick at 1 atmosphere pressure.

That permeability and filtration data may be correlated was shown by Ruth[30] and later confirmed by Hoffing and Lockhart,[43] Grace,[44] and others.[45,46]

As generally used for filtration purposes, the modified d'Arcy equation is written:

$$dV/d\theta = K'(A \ \Delta P/\mu L) = 1/\alpha(A \ \Delta P/\mu L)$$

or:

$$\alpha = (A \ \Delta P/\mu L)(d\theta/dV) \tag{7}$$

where α is the average specific cake resistance.

If we assume that each successive layer of cake as deposited is identical to the one before, then L may be replaced as follows:

$$\text{cake volume} = LA = vV \qquad \text{and} \qquad L = vV/A$$

Therefore, substituting in equation (6) we get:

$$\alpha = (A^2 \ \Delta P/\mu v V)(d\theta/dV) \tag{8}$$

where v is the volume of cake deposited per unit volume of filtrate.

To evaluate α in a constant-pressure filtration, we may integrate equation (7) to obtain:

$$\theta = (\alpha \mu v)/(2\Delta P \ A^2)V^2 \tag{9}$$

which is the equation for a parabola. Thus the data might be handled by plotting log θ vs. log V, θ vs. V^2, or θ/V vs. V. Of these three, only the third method[47] gives consistent results. As put by Carman:[48]

"The reason for the failure of the first two methods of plotting was first realized by Sperry[49] in 1916. It arises from neglect of the initial resistance in deriving equation (6). If the total filtration pressure, ΔP, is made up of a part, ΔP_c, which overcomes cake resistance, and a part, $\Delta P_i = (\Delta P - \Delta P_c)$, which overcomes initial resistance, then, if the latter also obeys d'Arcy's law:

$$u = \frac{1}{A}\frac{dV}{d\theta} = \frac{\Delta P_c}{\alpha \mu L} = \frac{\Delta P_i}{\mu R_m} = \frac{\Delta P}{\mu(\alpha L + R_m)} \tag{10}$$

[43] E. H. Hoffing and F. J. Lockhart, *Chem. Eng. Progress*, **47**, 3 (1951).

[44] H. P. Grace, *Chem. Eng. Progress*, **49**, 303, 367 (1953).

[45] W. L. Ingmanson, *Tappi*, **35**, 439 (1952).

[46] W. L. Ingmanson, *Chem. Eng. Progress*, **49**, 577 (1953).

[47] A. J. V. Underwood, *Trans. Inst. Chem. Engrs. London*, **4**, 19 (1926).

[48] P. C. Carman, *Trans. Inst. Chem. Engrs. London*, **16**, 168 (1938).

[49] D. R. Sperry, *Chem. Met. Eng.*, **15**, 198 (1916); **17**, 161 (1917).

where R_m is the initial resistance per unit area for a liquid of unit viscosity. Then, since $L = vV/A$:

$$Q = \frac{dV}{d\theta} = \frac{\Delta P A^2}{\mu(\alpha v V + R_m A)} \quad \text{(Sperry filtration rate equation)} \tag{11}$$

and integration at constant pressure gives:

$$\theta = \frac{\mu \alpha v}{2\Delta P \, A^2} V^2 + \frac{\mu R_m}{\Delta P \, A} V \tag{12}$$

or:

$$\frac{\theta}{V} = \frac{\mu \alpha v}{2\Delta P \, A^2} V + \frac{\mu R_m}{\Delta P \, A} \tag{13}$$

Equation (12) gives a straight line when θ/V is plotted against V, with a gradient, $m = (\mu \alpha v)/(2\Delta P \, A^2)$, and conversely, from this gradient, α is obtained by substitution in:

$$\alpha = (2m \, \Delta P \, A^2)/(uv) \tag{14}$$

In any experimental determination of α, it is well to note that θ and V should not be measured from the beginning of the filtration. The primary layer of the cake should be deposited at low velocity, i.e., at low pressure, since otherwise the cloth may become plugged, thus making initial resistance unduly high. The filtration pressure is raised slowly and steadily to its full value, and only when it reaches constancy are simultaneous readings of θ and V begun. It is clear that while values of the initial resistance can be obtained from such experiments, they will not be very accurate. This is of minor importance since the main function of this term in equation (10) is to suggest the correct mode of plotting to obtain accurate and consistent values of α."

From this point the advance in filtration theory has been largely based on considerations of the structure and properties of porous beds, which depend to large degree upon the size and shape of the particles of which they are composed. A substantial number of practical and theoretical studies[50-54] which have been made in other fields have a bearing on filtration theory. More specifically, studies on the packing of particles which have been interpreted from the standpoint of filtration were summarized by Siegel.[55] The field of fluid dynamics to the extent of its consideration

[50] W. G. Smith, D. D. Foote, and P. F. Busang, *Phys. Rev.*, **34**, 1271 (1929).

[51] E. Manegold, R. Hofmann, and K. Solf, *Kolloid-Z.*, **56**, 142 (1931).

[52] E. Manegold and W. Engelhardt, *Kolloid-Z.*, **62**, 285 (1933); **63**, 12, 149 (1933).

[53] L. C. Graton and H. J. Fraser, *J. Geol.*, **43**, 785 (1935).

[54] H. J. Fraser, *J. Geol.*, **43**, 910 (1935).

[55] W. Siegel, "Filtration," in A. Euchen and M. Jacob, eds., *Der Chemi-Ingenieur.* Vol. I, Part 12, Akadem. Verlagsgesellschaft, Leipzig, 1933, Chap. XI, pp. 191–307.

of viscous flow, flow of suspensions, and passage through porous media is pertinent to filtration theory.[56]   As an example, Ferrandon[57] in a study of the flow of water through porous structures has attempted an analysis of the hydrodynamic flow of a perfect fluid through porous masses.   Starting with Poiseuille's law, the tensorial nature of the physical coefficient upon which the velocity depends is correlated with the hydrodynamic action of the flow on the solid particles of the filters, thus indicating the general laws controlling both fields.   It is concluded that it is difficult indeed to correlate the permeability and wetted surfaces of the porous layer with the properties of a given system.

Brinkman[58] postulated that the force on a particle retained within a porous medium is larger than that acting on an isolated particle according to Stokes' law, as expressed by the author:

"In order to describe the flow of fluids through swarms of particles it is proposed to extend the equation of hydrodynamics with a damping term proportional to the mean rate of flow.   A survey is given of various problems related to the hydrodynamic properties of swarms of particles and of macromolecules which can be treated by this method."

This constitutes a modification of d'Arcy's law for fluid flow through porous bodies.   Experimental confirmation of Brinkman's theory has been given by Verschoor.[59]

A study in the flow of fluids through porous beds directed particularly to the shape of particles and voids in streamline flow shows that the Blake equation[60] represents the flow to within $\pm 25\%$, but that the Kozeny constant varies with the particle shape and the voids in a granular bed.[61]

Most important for filtration theory has been the application by Carman[62] of the studies of Kozeny[63] on porous beds to filter cakes.   In the theory as developed the analogy between the flow of liquid through solids and the flow through capillary tubes was abandoned.   He demonstrated that flow through permeable beds may be expressed in terms of *particle surfaces*, and the bed considered as a single passage, the size of which, the *"hydraulic diameter,"* corresponds to the volume and surface of the voids in the bed.   Thus, he advocates the use of the *specific surface*, S_0, of the

[56] T. Baron and A. K. Oppenheim, *Ind. Eng. Chem.*, **45,** 941 (1953).

[57] J. Ferrandon, *Genié Civil*, **125,** 24 (1948).

[58] H. C. Brinkman, *Research*, **2,** 190 (1949).

[59] H. Verschoor, *Applied Sci. Research*, **A2,** No. 2, 155 (1950).

[60] F. C. Blake, *Trans. Am. Inst. Chem. Engrs.*, **14,** 415 (1922).

[61] J. M. Coulson, *Trans. Inst. Chem. Engrs. London*, **27,** 237 (1949).

[62] P. C. Carman, *Trans. Inst. Chem. Engrs. London*, **15,** 150 (1937).

[63] J. Kozeny, *Sitzber. Akad. Wiss. Wein, Math. Naturw. Klasse, Abt. IIa*, **136,** 271 (1927); *Wasserkraft u. Wasserwirtsch.*, **22,** 67, 86 (1927).

particles instead of the postulated "equivalent capillary diameters" previously used.   As a basis for this theory, it is assumed that for any fluid in uniform streamline flow past a solid surface, the surface in contact determines the resistance.   The surface per unit volume of pore space is given by:

$$\frac{S}{\epsilon} = \frac{S_0(1 - \epsilon)}{\epsilon} \tag{15}$$

and the passage of liquid by:

$$u = \frac{\epsilon^3}{kS^2} \frac{\Delta P\, g}{\mu L} = \frac{\epsilon^3}{(1 - \epsilon)^2\, kS_0^2} \frac{\Delta P\, g}{\mu L} \quad \text{(Kozeny-Carman equation)} \tag{16}$$

where u = linear rate of flow (cm./sec.), S_0 = specific surface of particles (cm.^{2}/cm.^{3}), and S = surface per unit volume of granular bed (cm.^{2}/cm.^{3}). Thus, $S = (1 - \epsilon)S_0$, k = a constant (usually about 5.0), ϵ = porosity (cm.^{3} of pore space per cubic centimeter of granular bed), μ = viscosity of the liquid (in poises), ΔP = pressure difference across bed (g./cm.^{2}), L = thickness of bed (cm.), and g = acceleration due to gravity (980 cm./sec.^{2}).

Thus, with a knowledge of the surface area of the material being filtered, we should be able to predict the flow rate.   Comparison with the modified d'Arcy equation reveals that:

$$\alpha = 5S_0^2(1 - \epsilon)^2/g\epsilon^3 \tag{17}$$

This relation has been confirmed by several investigators for *cakes of incompressible solids.*

Walas[64] used the Kozeny-Carman equation (15) as the basis for his relation:

$$\alpha = 9.3 \times 10^6(1 - \epsilon)/\epsilon^3\rho_s(10^6d)^{1.02} \tag{18}$$

in which ρ_s is density of solids in pounds per cubic foot and d is the harmonic mean particle diameter as determined by Oden's[65] sedimentation method. The simplicity of the treatment is attractive, but there is some doubt as to whether or not a satisfactory particle diameter may be assigned from sedimentation data, particularly for solids with a wide range of particle size.

Another approach is that of Brownell and Katz[66] which involves a correlation of "friction factor" with Reynolds number, with modifying terms based on sphericity and roughness of particles together with bed porosity. Although several empirical constants are involved, results check surpris-

[64] S. M. Walas, *Trans. Am. Inst. Chem. Engrs.*, **42**, 783 (1946).

[65] S. Oden, in J. Alexander, ed., *Colloid Chemistry, Pure and Applied.*   Vol. I Chemical Catalog Co., New York, 1926, p. 861.

[66] L. E. Brownell and D. L. Katz, *Chem. Eng. Progress*, **43**, 537 (1947).

ingly well. A second paper[67] by the same authors makes a unique contribution in dealing with the simultaneous flow of two homogeneous immiscible fluids through porous media.

3. Mathematical Treatment of Compressible Particles

A cake composed of compressible particles, which are deformed or rearranged under pressure, exhibits a marked decrease in permeability when the filtration pressure is increased. The reason for the magnitude of this permeability decrease is easily understood when it is realized that the Kozeny porosity function, $\epsilon^3/(1 - \epsilon)^2$, increases tenfold when the porosity is raised from 0.57 to 0.78—an increase of only 37%.

Since most particles and filter cakes are at least *slightly* compressible and since many are *very* compressible, the most needed aspect of filtration theory has to do with compressible cakes. Unfortunately, this is the most difficult phase to express mathematically.

The problem has been approached from a number of different angles but the most common method is to treat α, the average specific cake resistance (see Eq. 6), as a function of pressure. To date, no one has succeeded fully in deriving such a function from fundamentals, but rather the solutions have been efforts to fit experimental data into a mathematical pattern. At an early date Lewis and co-workers[68,69] formulated the relationship:

$$\alpha = \alpha' P^s \tag{19}$$

in which α' and s are constants. A similar expression was used by Ruth:[70]

$$\alpha = \alpha_0 + \gamma \, \Delta P^s \tag{20}$$

Although both relationships are useful in the interpretation of laboratory data, neither is valid over a wide range of compressibility.

Tiller[71] took a somewhat different approach in relating porosity to pressure. Since compressibility is actually manifested in shrinking of the voids, such an approach would seem logical. The expression:

$$\epsilon = \epsilon_0 p_t^{-e} \tag{21}$$

was found to fit most data except those on very compressible materials like Solka Floc and polystyrene latex. The term ϵ_0 represents the porosity at

[67] L. E. Brownell and D. L. Katz, *Chem. Eng. Progress*, **43**, 601 (1947).

[68] C. Almy and W. K. Lewis, *Ind. Eng. Chem.*, **4**, 528 (1912).

[69] W. K. Lewis and others, *Chem. Met. Eng.*, **27**, 594 (1922).

[70] B. F. Ruth, *Ind. Eng. Chem.*, **27**, 708 (1935).

[71] F. M. Tiller, *Liquid Flow Through Compressible Solids.* Manuscript, Oct. 12, 1953.

1 p.s.i. Values of e varied 0 to 0.06 for the 29 substances investigated.[72] The re.ation is said to hold true over the pressure range 0.1–100 p.s i.

None of the above relations are convenient to use and all involve considerable experimental work and computation. A more useful approach is the *compression-permeability method* which relates average cake resistance to the entire range of filtration pressures, all in a single run. This idea was advanced by Ruth[73] in 1946. Later experiments by Grace[74] were made with a cylinder having a porous drainage area in its base and a matching piston with a porous end. A cake was built up by adding slurry to the cylinder and then a uniform pressure stress was imparted to the cake by inserting the piston. Weights were placed on the piston to give moderately high pressures or a Carver hydraulic press was used to apply pressures up to several thousand pounds per square inch. At each particular pressure, the permeability of the cake was determined by passing water through at a measured hydrostatic head. With this information Grace found it possible to predict filtration behavior of a given prefilt under almost any condition of operation. In addition, he published specific calculations for predicting from compression-permeability data the filtration behavior of a particular prefilt when filtered through a horizontally oriented flat filter, a vertical flat filter, or a vertical cylindrical filter for either inside-out or outside-in filtration.

4. Applications and Limitations of Theory

The practical laboratory worker has not often made much use of filtration theory and may have been inclined to ignore mathematical formulas for such an elusive problem as filtration. It has been pointed out that formulas which have been deduced to fit results are not of much value except in an empirical way and that it is possible, by employing appropriate constants and indices, to make almost any series of experimental results fit an equation. Others have considered that there is no such thing as "filtration theory" and that it is all "mathematical gymnastics" which is at best semi-theoretical.

Bryden[75] has expressed the viewpoint of the practical filtration man in this way: "As different solids deposit and retard the progress of filtration differently, no definite or even fairly accurate filtration formulae can be devised for all cases." Alliott[76] long ago concluded that anything more

[72] F. M. Tiller, *Chem. Eng. Progress*, **51**, 282 (1955).

[73] B. F. Ruth, *Ind. Eng. Chem.*, **38**, 564 (1946).

[74] H. P. Grace, *Chem. Eng. Progress*, **49**, 303 (1953).

[75] C. L. Bryden, "Filtration," in J. C. Olsen, ed., *Unit. Processes and Principles of Chemical Engineering.* Van Nostrand, New York, 1932, Chap. VII, pp. 218–243.

[76] E. A. Alliott, *J. Soc. Chem. Ind.*, **39**, 261T (1920).

complex than Sperry's equation (see Eq. 10) is not suitable for ordinary use. On the other hand, the view that filtration has reached the status of an exact science[77] is perhaps somewhat optimistic.   Numerous experimenters have applied some aspect of filtration theory to a particular set of conditions, and have made generalizations for broad applicability which are not warranted by the data, and which are not valid for other conditions. ˙No one is more aware of the limitations of filtration theory than the considerable number of capable workers who have contributed to building up an adequate theory.

Heertjes[78] comments on some of the inadequacies of the present state of knowledge and points out the need for further study of the fundamentals of cake structure and compactibility.   The importance of considering more fully the structural arrangement of the impurities in the cake has been stressed by Meyer.[79]   Miller,[80] in discussing filtration as a phenomenon of unsteady-state fluid dynamics in which the resistance is variable and the flow rate need not be constant, states: "as a consequence of these complex conditions, a general and rigorous description does not exist."   These opinions are typical of the attitude of most workers in the field of theoretical filtration.

However, the broad outlines of filtration theory are rather well established and are at present adequate enough to be useful.   The basic principles of fluid dynamics and flow through porous bodies certainly apply to filtration.   The present filtration equations do express the relationships in simple systems.   The modern concepts of the nature of filtration resistances have given much more precise definition of this major factor in the filtration operation.   The breakdown of the complex resistance effects in terms of particle shape and size, and specific surface, have now been clearly analyzed and are capable of mathematical expression.   Recognition of other effects, such as those which are electrical, electrokinetic, or physicochemical, has led to the concepts of void volumes or something related thereto, which have been expressed in formulas and which have clarified many hitherto unexplained phenomena.

As for the practical application of theory in the laboratory it is believed that if the worker has a clear picture of the simpler theories, then he can visualize better what is going on when carrying out a filtration, and that he may be guided thereby in the selection of apparatus and techniques in the solution of his particular problem.   Thus, the mathematical expressions

[77] "Filtration Approaching Status of Exact Science," *Chem. Eng. News,* **29,** 2048 (1951).
[78] P. M. Heertjes, *Chem. Weekblad,* **48e,** 573 (1952).
[79] K. S. Meyer, *Ind. Chemist,* **25,** 5 (1949).
[80] S. A. Miller, *Chem. Eng. Progress,* **47,** 497 (1951).

show the relationships between the several variables, and, even if this can be applied only qualitatively in many cases, the principles hold and may be useful in many ways.

The main deficiency of present filtration theory is that it does not generally evaluate the factor of "filtrate quality." The organic chemist who is struggling to clarify a given material properly is less interested in precise theory than he is in obtaining a solid or a liquid that has the properties which he is seeking. Even if the filtrate obtained may have resulted from an operation in which the conditions obey the filtration "laws" completely, there has been no filtration at all so far as he is concerned if the liquid is not adequately clarified or does not meet the requirements of the job. In such a typical requirement, the volume of filtrate V might be further defined as that portion of the total filtrate volume which meets the requirements for which the filtration is performed. Since the criteria by which the products of a filtration are evaluated can usually be established only by experts in the various fields, it is perhaps beyond the scope of theoretical filtration to attempt this further difficult differentiation of filtrate volume in terms of its properties. Nevertheless, this remains the greatest limitation in the practical application of filtration theory.

5. Symbol Index

A = area of filtering surface

e = empirical constant

g = gravitational constant

K = empirical constant

K' = permeability coefficient

K'' = empirical constant

k = Kozeny's constant ($5 \pm 10\%$)

L = cake thickness

l = capillary length

m = slope of line on graph

N = number of capillaries per unit area of cake

n = empirical constant

ΔP = total pressure drop across filter

ΔP_c = pressure drop across filter cake

ΔP_i = pressure drop across initial resistance

Q = flow rate in volume per unit time

R_m = resistance of filter medium

r = capillary radius

S = surface per unit volume of bed

S_0 = surface per unit volume of solids

s = empirical constant

u = superficial flow velocity in volume per unit time per unit area

V = volume of filtrate

v = volume of cake deposited per unit volume of filtrate

α = average specific cake resistance

α' = empirical constant

α_0 = empirical constant

γ = empirical constant

ϵ = porosity, specific void volume

ϵ_0 = constant equal to porosity at 1 p.s.i.

θ = time

μ = viscosity

π = pi = 3.1416

ρ_s = density of solids

III. APPARATUS

1. Types of Filters

In the descriptions to follow filtering apparatus of the types most commonly used in organic chemistry laboratories are treated without regard to any rigid classification. For a review, however, it is useful to have some general groupings. A method frequently used is based on the force applied to effect the filtration, such as gravity, suction, or pressure. Another classification considers the amount of material to be handled. Thus, filters may be regarded as: (*1*) general laboratory size, (*2*) micro or semimicro, and (*3*) large-scale or pilot-plant size. A further classification might emphasize the type of filter medium employed, such as paper, cloth, metal screen, fibrous material, rigid porous member, loose powder, or permeable membrane. Still another classification would be based on the main objective of the filtration, *i.e.*, whether to recover the residue or filtrate, to obtain extreme clarification, as for the purposes of washing or purifying, or for other reasons as outlined in Section I.3. In large-scale laboratory work it is customary to distinguish between batch and continuous operations.

Filtrations in the laboratory usually involve combinations of the items indicated in the above classifications; hence, it is not possible to cover all conditions. The plan followed here is to describe in this section the various types of laboratory filters of bench size. Filter media are covered in Section IV, and in Section VI some special techniques of interest in organic chemistry are discussed. Microfiltration is included in Section III.9. The subject of larger scale laboratory filtrations is considered separately in Section VIII. In general, the handling of larger quantities of material involves no new principles but does involve the selection of suitable equipment, which may differ in some respects from that of smaller scale operations.

For many details on ordinary laboratory filtration, it will be necessary to consult standard references. Considerable information on the types of common laboratory filter apparatus is contained in some review chapters and articles.[81,82] A number of laboratory manuals and practical organic handbooks which include material on filtration for laboratories are included in the general references. Many research papers on the preparation and study of organic and biological compounds contain important details on various specific filtrations. Some of the books on filtration which are

[81] Lassar Cohn, *Organic Laboratory Methods*. Trans. by R. E. Oesper, Williams & Wilkins, Baltimore, 1928, Chap. XI, pp. 211–230.
[82] A. C. Villanova, *Rev. quim. e farm. Rio de Janiero*, **15**, 287 (1950).

included in the general references contain important chapters on laboratory filtering apparatus as well as larger scale laboratory filters. The filtration reviews and bibliographies also given therein may be consulted for many angles of interest. (See also Chapter III in this volume.)

2. Screens and Strainers

Screens and strainers of metal, cloth, or other materials are useful for the removal of larger particles by straining operations and may also serve as *coarse filters*. The removal of coarse particles, extraneous matters, tissues, unreacted residues, etc., is sometimes an important and frequently the only treatment necessary for a liquid. In other cases, the separation of the coarser particles from a mixture is a desirable initial step before the final filtration for purposes of clarification. Metal devices, such as colanders, strainers, and receptacles with bottom screens, are applicable for many purposes in the laboratory. Strainers and screen filters may be fabricated in various sizes and shapes to meet specific requirements. For metallic strainers perforated metal or woven wire screens may be used. Figure 1 illustrates some types of filter screening devices.

When a screen or sieve serves as a relatively coarse filter septum, so that the solids are allowed to build up on the screen in a more or less undisturbed condition, the method differs in no sense from a typical filtration with a finer filter medium. However, when the screen is agitated during the screening operation or the solids are otherwise prevented from forming a cake or sediment, the openings of the screen become the true separating medium and the size of these openings determines the size of particles held back. Thus, the action of coarse screening is analogous to that of some fine, porous ceramic filters and ultrafilters, in which the openings in the septa serve to separate the solids from the liquid.

Standard testing sieves, circular in form, are convenient for laboratory work. These are available in sizes ranging from 2 to 8 or 12 in. in diameter with mesh sizes from 4 mesh (4760 μ openings, A.S.T.M. designation) down to 325 mesh (44 μ openings, A.S.T.M. designation). Screens made of *cloth fabrics* of open texture have the advantage of being readily and cheaply adaptable for the simplest possible assembly. Thus, cheesecloth or a somewhat stronger fabric (muslin, felt, or flannel) spread over a receptacle, such as an ordinary funnel, suffices for straining many materials.[83] It may also be handled in the manner of the housewife's "jelly bag" for expulsion of the liquid by hand pressure or by twisting in opposite directions with stick supports which may be inserted through the bag.

[83] A. A. Hopkins, "Chemical Manipulation," *Scientific American Cyclopedia of Formulas*. Scientific American Pub. Co., New York, 1924, Appendix II, pp. 979–1044.

Screening operations may be conducted under suction or pressure, but the usual procedure employs gravity.   The operation may be quiescent or with agitation, as by manual or mechanical stirring or shaking.   As an example, in the filtration of some tars, suspended particles are particularly troublesome.   A satisfactory separation procedure consists in the use of a stainless-steel screening cloth which is vibrated at a high frequency but very

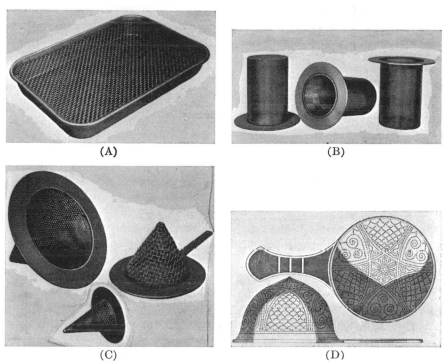

(A)   (B)

(C)   (D)

Fig. 1. Simple screening devices: (A) tray screen filter; (B) hat filter, fine screen; (C) conical sieves; (D) ancient Herculanean wine strainer.   (A, B, and C courtesy Multi-Metal Wire Cloth Co., Inc.; D courtesy *House Beautiful* Magazine.)

small amplitude.   The screen is supported in a nearly horizontal position and the solid material retained on the screen may be brushed off or removed by a spatula or equivalent.[84]   In this case, the vibration completely prevents "blinding" of the screen.

The mechanical straining out of impurities from pigmented enamels and paints is a special type of problem.   Here the requirement is to remove the coarse foreign particles but not the fine particles of the pigments.[85]   An

[84] "Tar Filtration," *Chem. & Process Eng.*, **35**, 152 (1954).
[85] A. C. Kracklauer, *Finish*, **7**, No. 4, 24 (1950).

instance wherein metal screens were found useful in the filtration of tissue residues is given by Herfurth.[86] As another example, in the isolation of chymotrypsin and trypsin from beef pancreas, the tissue is minced, contacted with sulfuric acid, and then strained through gauze before subsequent treatment.[87]

The recent development of metal screens[88] made by electroforming processes has made available smooth-surfaced perforated sheets in various thicknesses and sizes of openings (mesh equivalent from 25 to 400 openings per inch). These sheets mostly serve purposes lying between those served by perforated metals and woven wire screens. They are available in nickel, copper, and nickel on a core of copper. The sheets are easily fabricated and permit the shaping of various types of laboratory-size screening assemblies. The fine-size sheets normally would be supported on a backing of coarser and stronger mesh material. The openings in these electroformed screens are not uniform in bore, but are tapered. This feature is especially favorable when the screen is to be washed or backwashed from the side of the larger taper opening.

3. Gravity Filters

Simple gravity filters are useful in organic chemical operations since in many cases it is only necessary to obtain a small quantity of either residue or filtrate. Thus, there is frequently no necessity for setting up a vacuum or pressure filtration apparatus. In other cases, gravity filtration may actually be more effective than any other method. This occurs with some materials containing highly compressible solids, which tend to "seal" or "blind" the filter medium even under low pressures.

The descriptions under this heading refer to apparatus adapted primarily for gravity filtrations, but in addition much of the apparatus referred to in Section III.4 for vacuum filtration may be employed advantageously with gravity only. Thus, Büchner- and Hirsch-type funnels, filter tubes, etc., are quite satisfactory in many cases when used without vacuum. A simple gravity or percolation filter and decanter device, which permits collection of the filtrate directly in the receiver with allowance for the escape of displaced air is attributed to Schlumbohm.[89] A subsequent improvement is embodied as a type of filter pot.[90]

The so-called filter beaker[91] is a device suitable for various laboratory

[86] O. R. Herfurth, *Zellwolle, Kunstseide, Seide*, **47**, 2 (1942).

[87] M. Kunitz and J. H. Northrup, *J. Gen. Physiol.*, **18**, 433 (1935); **19**, 991 (1936).

[88] Trade literature, C. O. Jelliff Mfg. Corp., Southport, Conn.

[89] P. Schlumbohm, U. S. Pat. 2,359,943 (Oct. 10, 1944).

[90] P. Schlumbohm, U. S. Pat. 2,681,154 (June 15, 1954).

[91] E. Schwarz-Bergkampf, *Z. anal. Chem.*, **59**, 337 (1927).

operations in which a sequence of steps involving precipitations, gravity filtrations, and additions of various reagents and washing liquids is followed. This is usually a micro-size filter but the same type can be used for larger scale work.

A filtering apparatus, especially suitable for volumetric control of the filtrate (especially small quantities) consists of a glass tube constricted on the upper end, into which a removable filter diaphragm is fitted.[92] Gravity filters of the types that are frequently used in the preparation of organic chemicals, pharmaceuticals, etc., should have considerable filtering area because the filtration rates obtained with these types of filters are often quite slow. Some reference to larger size gravity filters is made in Section VIII.1.

A. FUNNELS

The filtering funnel, in its many variations, is one of the oldest and simplest of all laboratory filter devices, and may be made of glass, rubber, metal, enamel, or plastic. Stainless-steel funnels, with or without air vents, are produced in sizes from 2.5 in. to 7 in. or more in diameter. While relatively expensive in initial cost, they may be used for years. Recently, polyethylene funnels have become available. These will not shatter, chip, or lose shape, and are chemically inert for nearly all conditions of organic chemistry. Temperature resistance is slightly above 219°F. Some polyethylene funnels are molded with a filter "step" design which is said to increase the speed and completeness of filtration. Sizes of filter funnels range from minute microfunnels to 24 in. or more in diameter, although 10 in. is a large size for laboratory use. Filter paper is generally used with funnels, but a plug of fibrous material may also be employed.

For analytical purposes, precision-molded funnels with long stems, usually 150 mm. in length, uniform in diameter, and ground off at an angle, are employed. Usually the rims are ground for efficient covering with watch glasses. Variations consist of fluting on the lower portion of the inner cone, beveled edges, or constricted necks. It is considered good practice to employ only top-quality funnels of good manufacture in laboratory work, since their greater ease in operation and durability more than pay for their slight additional cost. For elementary techniques in the use of funnels for analytical purposes, standard texts[93,94] may be consulted. For further references on filter paper, see Section IV.2. Folding of filter papers

---

[92] A. Leschnik, Italian Pat. 445,739 (March 13, 1950).

[93] F. P. Treadwell and W. T. Hall, *Analytical Chemistry*. Vol. II, *Quantitative Analysis*, Wiley, New York, 1942.

[94] F. Müller in Böttger, ed., *Physikalische Methoden der analytischen Chemie*. Akadem. Verlagsgesellschaft, Leipzig, 1939.

at an angle of 93–98° to fit the usual 60° funnel has been advocated to accelerate filtration.[95]   While the details of fitting a circular filter paper to the 60° funnel vary slightly, the essential requirements are tight fit of the paper throughout the upper points of attachment with the upper periphery of the funnel and the stem of the funnel completely filled with liquid. Simple instructions are:

First, fold the paper as usual into halves.   Make the next fold (into quarters) about $1/8$ in. *short*.   Make a triangular tear angling to the edge of the *short* quarter. Fold the torn section on around the *larger* quarter.   Open the *larger* quarter and insert into the funnel.   Then add a liberal amount of distilled water or organic solvent to wet the paper.   Press the filter firmly to the funnel side with the finger, and gradually work out trapped air bubbles all around the filter.   Tearing the corner has eliminated the air-leaking "bump" at the top.   Now, on filtration, a solid column of filtrate should appear without a break to add its effective head to pulling more filtrate down behind it.

The "58 degree" filtering funnel was developed to obviate the necessity of special preparation of the filter paper to make the most effective fit. Thus, a paper folded simply in halves and then quarters fits a 58° funnel quickly and easily.   Only a narrow band at the top of the paper is sealed tightly to the bowl, thus providing a maximum filtering area.

For many ordinary funnel filtrations in the organic laboratory, it is preferable to employ medium- or short-stem funnels.   These have the advantage of less tendency toward plugging due to crystallization of solids in the neck.   Fluted funnels, particularly in the larger sizes, are widely used since they permit rapid drainage under the paper.   The insertion of a wire gauze between the paper and a smooth-wall funnel is also favorable for free drainage.   Fluted or ribbed funnels of large size, up to 8000 ml. capacity, are used for laboratory preparations.   Some have air vents to adapt them conveniently for gravity filtration into bottles or carboys.   Funnels with narrow tops, which may be covered with a watch glass, board, or fabric tied in place—to diminish evaporation—are desirable for some highly volatile liquids.   The gravity filter funnel is frequently useful not only for the filtering step itself, but also for purposes of isolation, washing, solution, and/or purification of preparations, examples of which are the determination of sodium in biological fluids[96] and the estimation of calcium in urine.[97] A method for testing the speed of simple gravity filtrations, specifically funnel filtrations with paper, by an electric timing device has been described by Kroeger and DeKay.[98]

[95] A. Parlow, *Chem.-Ztg.*, **54**, 183 (1930).
[96] W. Mizuta, *Igaku to Seibutsugaku* (*Medicine and Biology*), **29**, 222 (1953).
[97] K. Murate, *Igaku to Seibutsugaku* (*Medicine and Biology*), **29**, 36 (1953).
[98] R. M. Kroger and H. G. DeKay, *J. Am. Pharm. Assoc.*, **40**, 213 (1951).

Funnels adapted for hot or cold filtrations are referred to in Sections III.6 and III.7.   Ordinary funnels may be adapted for suction or pressure filtrations as described in Section III.4.B.   Stands and supports for funnels are convenient and essential for the satisfactory manipulation of several simultaneous filtrations.   Various types are described in the catalogs of laboratory supply houses and in handbooks.   A convenient adjunct for the drainage and storage of cleaned funnels is the Dworecki Funnel Stackrack,[99] which is a portable device accommodating up to 40 funnels within the sizes of 1.5 to 3 in. diameters.

B.   PERCOLATORS

Percolators are used principally for the extraction of soluble components from solid materials.   Their use for this purpose in pharmacy and in the preparation of plant and animal extracts is well known.   For a few laboratory filtrations, the conventional glass percolators are applicable, in which case the bottom tube is covered with a fibrous material, such as cotton, glass wool, or a fabric.   Either the conical or Oldberg type (cylindrical walls) is suitable.   These usually come with reinforced rims and ground tops to permit a tight closure.   Sizes range from 1 liter capacity to 8 liters or more.   The small U.S.P. percolator (200 ml. capacity) has a widely flared top and a two-way glass stopcock.   This is used for the complete extraction of drugs for assay purposes.   Percolators are advantageous for slow filtering operations.   Once assembled they require little attention. Percolators require supports and may be assembled in batteries of several units.   It is obvious that other types of simple filtering apparatus may be considered the equivalent of the conventional percolator.   Thus, a filtering tube or a column may be an equivalent in miniature, and contrariwise, a percolation tower is essentially the same on a larger scale.

C.   OTHER TYPES

Tray filters are frequently used for pharmaceutical and biological preparations as well as for organic chemicals.   They are best adapted for slow, difficult filtrations and for exceptionally soft or fine-grained precipitates which clog under the slightest pressure or pass through the openings of a cloth.   Tray filters of paper are quite convenient and cheap.   They are usually discarded after use.   More permanent types, with frames, and with or without removable and exchangeable bottoms, may be constructed in the laboratory shop.   Such flat-bottom filters may be fitted with sievelike bottoms, or may be lined with filter fabric.   A wooden frame filter

[99] Standard Scientific Supply Co., New York.

of this type has been utilized for filtering fruit juices and vinegar.[100]   A homemade muslin tube filter for similar purposes has also been described.[101]

Filter bags for laboratory use are of fabric arranged into a more or less baglike form.   They are usually mounted to permit slow gravity filtration or may be adapted for squeezing either by hand or by press.   The *hat filter* is a somewhat more permanent form of a filter device, which has been widely used for the filtration of paints and varnishes, as well as for other laboratory preparations.   Conical-shaped bags supported on hoops on a similar frame are useful with oils, stearin, and similar materials.   Cleland's original bag filter consisted of a cylindrical bag tied to the stem of a funnel. The Schroder bag filter has a folded bag within a cylindrical outer bag. Bag filters have been employed for many large-scale filtrations.   The Taylor bag filter[102] for sugar liquors is an example.

False-bottom vessels or small tanks may be constructed of a variety of materials—wood, metal, ceramic ware, etc.   The bottoms may be permanent or removable and are usually lined with the filter medium before use. Similar types of filters serve frequently in vacuum filtrations.   Larger sizes used for preparative work are referred to further in Section VIII.1. Small drainage or *cage filters* may be assembled by lining a suitable perforated frame with cloth or fabric.   These filters are useful for *free-draining* materials.

Gravity filtration, in any convenient device, with *glass beads* or *sand* may be advantageously employed in some organic preparations, particularly when a liquid is to be freed from gelatinous precipitates, but it can also be used for the recovery of solids.   Filtrations of this type can be expedited by gently stirring the upper surface of the sand, thus breaking up any impermeable layer of precipitate.   The uncertainty of securing adequate clarification with these types of filters has restricted their use in the laboratory to certain operations in which experience has shown them to be satisfactory.

4. Suction Filters

A. ASSEMBLIES

Suction filters of various types are widely used in the laboratory.   Their advantages are faster filtration rates and comparative simplicity in operation.   The common apparatus, used for many years, has been a filtering funnel, crucible, or tube, adapted to a suction flask, the side tube of which is fitted with rubber tubing to a water aspirator pump.

[100] M. G. Weber, *Fruit Products J.*, **5**, 17 (1926).

[101] R. B. Hickok and R. E. Marshall, *Mich. Agr. Exp. Sta. Quart.*, **15**, No. 3, 191 (1933).

[102] F. A. Buhler, *Filters and Filter Presses*.   Rodgers, London, 1914, pp. 123–125.

Some modern improvements consist of: (*1*) convenient adapters of rubber to accommodate different sizes of filter apparatus to the receiver; (*2*) assemblies with all-glass connections; (*3*) filter bells or the equivalent

Fig. 2. Simple suction filter with ordinary filter flask and Büchner funnel.

Fig. 3. Suction flask with stopcock on side outlet and fitted with filter crucible.

Fig. 4. All-glass suction filter assembly, with fritted glass filter. (Courtesy Corning Glass Works.)

Fig. 5. Witt suction filter assembly. (Courtesy Fisher Scientific Co.)

for the collection of filtrate in receptacles; (*4*) convenient small mechanical pumps for supplying vacuum; (*5*) glass stopcocks, valves, or the equivalent.

which are inserted between the receptacle and the vacuum line for convenience in breaking the vacuum at the end of the filtration; (6) filter flasks with a "stepped" tubulation, which makes possible the use of a wide variety of rubber tubing sizes with equal ease; and (7) filter flasks with graduations

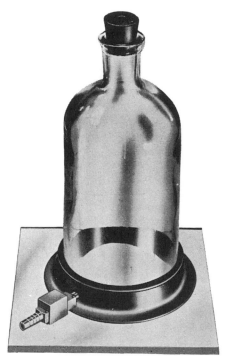

Fig. 6. Fisher Filtrator.   (Courtesy   Fig. 7. Nylab filter bell.   (Courtesy New
Fisher Scientific Co.)   York Laboratory Supply Co., Inc.)

for rough quantitative work.   Figures 2–4 show different suction filter assemblies.

Ordinary glass filter flasks should be used for medium vacuum only. Pyrex glass flasks have heavier walls, are more rugged, and are usually worth their somewhat higher cost.   Specifications have been given[103] for the shapes, vacuum connections, neck, dimensions, and tolerances for eight sizes of borosilicate glass filtering flasks, with capacities from 100 ml. to 20 liters.

The suction filter flask is not well suited for the collection of filtrate when this is of limited volume, or when it must be collected quantitatively.   A means for meeting this requirement is to employ a bell jar with outlets for

[103] "Filter Flasks," British Standard 1739, British Standards Inst., London, 1951.

the suction.   In this case, a beaker, graduated cylinder or other container receives the filtrate.   An early modification of this set-up is the Witt filter apparatus,[104] which is shown in Figure 5.   The Fisher Filtrator,[105] shown in Figure 6, employs a rubber pad located on top of a metal base, with control valve and vacuum connections, thus providing an air-tight seal.   A glass bell is placed on the pad.   The funnel or other filter is adapted to the neck of the bell with a one-hole rubber stopper.   The Nylab filter bell[106] consists of a bell jar resting on a glass plate or simply on the laboratory bench with a vacuum-tight closure assured by a soft rubber gasket acting thereon.   A slide valve permits application or release of vacuum in the jar while retaining the vacuum in other parts of the filtration system.   This device accommodates as the filtrate receiver either a beaker up to 400 ml. capacity or an Erlenmeyer flask up to 300 ml. capacity. Figure 7 shows this apparatus.

Some recent examples of vacuum filtration techniques and apparatus have been selected as suggestive for wider application.   In one of these details are given for the filtration of small volumes of acetic acid solutions in the analysis for phenanthrene in coal tar products.[107]   A suction filtration assembly for the critical filtration of aqueous dextran solutions involves filtration with a bell jar through sintered glass or porcelain filters directly into glass cells suitable for examination in a light-scattering apparatus.[108]   Means, as described, of collecting small amounts of filtrate in a simple suction filter[109] and the collection of filtrates at desired time intervals,[110] should have numerous applications.   A helpful qualitative study of various factors affecting the rate of suction filtering was given by two Japanese authors.[111]   An example of the value of simple laboratory vacuum filtration apparatus employing ordinary filtration flasks is an investigation of the relationship of the fine structure and orientation of fibers in hydrocellulose suspensions.[112]   A highly flexible and cleverly designed vacuum apparatus, which is adaptable for a variety of filtration uses, consists of a cone soldered on to a cylindrical tube fitted with a side arm which is connected to the vacuum pump.   The cone is fitted on the inside with a rubber washer, which, because of its inverted conical shape, permits it to fit on a

[104] O. N. Witt, *Chem. Inds.*, **18**, 510 (1899).

[105] Fisher Scientific Co., Pittsburgh, Pa.

[106] N. Y. Laboratory Supply Co., Inc., N. Y.

[107] L. Blom and W. J. Vranken, *Anal. Chem.*, **26**, 404 (1954).

[108] J. A. Riddick, E. E. Toops, Jr., R. L. Wieman, and R. H. Cundiff, *Anal. Chem.*, **26**, 1149 (1954).

[109] J. Gut and L. Sedivy, *Chem. Listy*, **45**, 284 (1951).

[110] E. Fest, German Pat. 683,028 (Oct. 30, 1939).

[111] T. Kato and Y. Murakoshi, *Benseki to Shiyaku*, **3**, 86 (1949).

[112] O. A. Battista. J. A. Howsmon, and S. Coppick, *Ind. Eng. Chem.*, **45**, 2107 (1953).

variety of receivers of capacities from 50 cc. to 1 liter or more. The filter may be a crucible type or funnel.[113]

The *Shaw filtering flask,*[114] shown in Figure 8, is convenient when the filtrate is to be transferred to another container and especially when the filtrate is removed at intervals. The flask is similar in shape to a Squibb separatory funnel but has a suction tube at the side top. It may be washed readily for quantitative work. Filter funnels, Gooch crucibles, porous

Fig. 8. Shaw filtering flask. (Courtesy Fisher Scientific Co.)

Fig. 9. Desiccator adapted for use as a receiver, the filtrate to be collected in fractions. (Courtesy Johns-Manville Corp.)

filter crucibles, fritted glass crucibles, and similar filters may be used. A special support stand is convenient for use with a battery of these flasks. Another useful apparatus for the collection of the filtrate in fractions is the Bruehl distilling receiver. A method for collecting samples of filtrates during the course of filtration without interrupting the suction has been described.[115] Assemblies of the apparatus may be made with rubber tubing connections or of all-glass construction.

Vacuum filtration may be carried out with common laboratory apparatus other than filter flasks. For example, some types of desiccators are suitable, and other vessels may be improvised. Thus, any vessel with its upper edges ground to receive a ground-glass plate may be used. The

[113] A. S. Thom, *Pharm. J.,* 164, 225 (1950).
[114] J. Shaw, *Ind. Eng. Chem.,* 9, 793 (1917).
[115] M. S. Telang, *Ind. Eng. Chem., Anal. Ed.,* 17, 271 (1945).

filter funnel or equivalent is inserted through a hole in the plate. Such an apparatus, provided with a depression around the upper edge of the stem to retain a small quantity of wash water for testing, appears useful for some

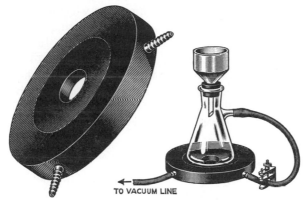

Fig. 10. Vac-U-Mat vacuum filtering accessory.
(Courtesy New York Laboratory Supply Co., Inc.)

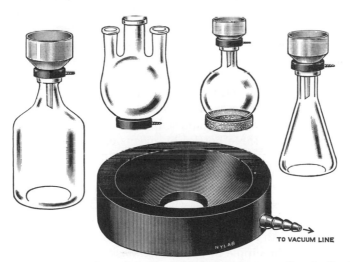

Fig. 11. Nylab filter grip. (Courtesy New York Laboratory Supply Co., Inc.)

purposes. This type of apparatus avoids contamination from the stoppers generally employed.[116] The use of an ordinary desiccator for the collection of separate fractions of filtrate from a vacuum filtration is shown in Figure 9.

[116] P. Longuet, *Rev. matériaux construction et trav. publ.*, **B. 400,** 13 (1949).

A convenient device for vacuum filtrations is the Vac-U-Mat[117] (see Fig. 10). This consists of a flat, circular rubber mat 5 in. in diameter and 0.75 in. thick. A cylindrical hollow on the underside serves as a vacuum chamber and communicates with the upper surface through an orifice. Two brass tubulatures on the side connect the vacuum chamber with the vacuum line and the filtering flask. Before starting the filtration, the flask is connected and placed on the Vac-U-Mat, the tube leading to the flask being closed by a screw clamp. Vacuum is applied to secure the flask. When the Büchner funnel, or other filter, is in place on the flask and the filtration is to be started, the screw clamp is opened to give the desired evacuation within the flask. A similar device (Fig. 11) allows the use of a Büchner funnel without the customary filter flask.

B. FUNNELS AND TUBES

The ordinary conical filter funnel is best adapted for suction filtrations by the use of some supporting device for the paper to prevent rupture thereof when the vacuum is applied. Small cones which fit snugly in the tip of a 60° funnel have been commonly employed. Such cones may be porcelain, platinum, plastic, or porous textile material. Thick, reinforced, or hardened filter papers may serve without cones, but the filtering rates through such papers are low. The use of filter funnels which are fitted with sintered glass plates is now common. These funnels are better for many purposes than perforated porcelain. Multiple suction filter assemblies permit the use of several funnels, which may be fitted into a single stand, with connectors by which the filtrates from all may be collected jointly. Marshall[118] shows such an assembly for six funnels in which the combined filtrate may be collected in any of three bottles by means of a two-way or three-way stopcock.

Büchner-type funnels are among the most widely used laboratory filtering devices for nearly all purposes aside from analytical work. The original Büchner funnel[119] was of porcelain with a fixed, perforated flat bottom and straight sides. Paper or cloth circular discs are fitted in the funnel as the filtering medium. An early modification of the Büchner funnel provided a glass stopcock on the nipple of the suction flask.[120] Many improvements and modifications have been made over the years in Büchner-type funnels. Among these have been the following:

(1) "Slit-sieve" perforations which are uniformly spaced and provide a larger filtering area. The elongated narrow shape of these openings combined with the plane surface of the filter prevents tearing of the filter paper.

[117] N. Y. Laboratory Supply Co., Inc., N. Y.
[118] C. V. Marshall, *Chemist-Analyst*, **41**, 68 (1952).

(*2*) Jacketed or double-wall funnels for hot or cold filtrations (see Sect. III.6 and III.7).

(*3*) Funnels with filtering surfaces of sintered glass or sintered metal.

(*4*) Two-piece construction, permitting ready disassembly for cleaning and inspection (example: Coors-Rogers funnel, Federal Specification S.S.C. 181A).

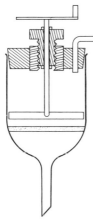

Fig. 12. Büchner funnel attachment for use in handling very difficultly filterable materials. (After Barnard.[123])

Fig. 13. Büchner funnel, common type with fixed perforated plate. (Courtesy Central Scientific Co.)

(*5*) Lightweight filters made of polyethylene.

(*6*) All-metal funnels—particularly stainless steel.

(*7*) All-glass funnels which are transparent and chemically resistant, and which may have perforated or sintered glass plates integrally attached.

(*8*) Table models which require no accessories for assembly, and which are convenient in operation and are not easily broken or damaged.   These usually have a separate removable plate which facilitates cleaning.   The plates and seats are accurately ground for good fit.   Dimensions are such that the over-all height of the filter is low, thus providing stability.   The receivers for these filters are separate and may be of any size and interchangeable.   Suction is applied to the receiver and in turn to the funnel itself.[121]

A two-piece filter funnel developed for the filtration of the acid digest of fiber in foodstuffs, consists of an upper section, a flanged ring which serves as a reservoir, and a flanged lower conical section which supports the filter septum.   The contacting surfaces of each component are ground to insure a leak-tight fit.   In use, a filter paper having the diameter as the full width

[119] E. Büchner, *Chem.-Ztg.*, **12**, 1277 (1888); **13**, 95 (1889).

[120] A. R. Wahl, *Chem.-Ztg.*, **21**, 415 (1897).

[121] "A New Büchner Funnel," *The Laboratory* (Fisher Scientific Co.), **13**, 79 (1942); **20**, 22 (1950).

of the funnel is fitted in a wetted condition. The flanged ring is then placed on the paper. The particles of fiber are localized on a circular patch in the middle of the paper, leaving a clear margin of uncontaminated paper, which facilitates its handling. Removal of the fiber is simple and the base of the filter need not be washed for subsequent use.[122]

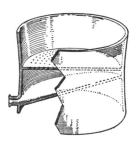

Fig. 14. Büchner funnel with removable plate. (Courtesy Coors Porcelain Co.)

Fig. 15. Büchner funnel, table type, one-piece. (Courtesy Emil Greiner Co.)

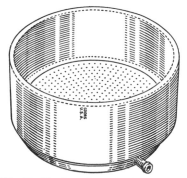

Fig. 16. Büchner funnel, table type with removable plate. (Courtesy Coors Porcelain Co.)

Fig. 17. Büchner funnel, all glass with perforated glass plate. (Courtesy Corning Glass Works.)

A simple but useful device[123] for filtering very difficultly filterable solutions is shown in Figure 12. In use, a heavy precoat of filter aid is built up in the funnel by suction before adding the slurry. When the cake seals over, the scraper blade is rotated to remove the surface of the cake. When

[122] A. W. Hartley, *Analyst*, **77**, 53 (1952).
[123] R. L. Barnard, private communication, General Electric Co., Schenectady, N. Y.

the cake seals over again, the blade is advanced and rotated to expose
another new, clean, filtering surface. By repeating this operation, some
of the most difficultly filtered materials may be successfully handled. A

Fig. 18. Büchner funnel, all metal with sintered
metal plate. (Courtesy E. Machlett and Sons.)

similar larger scale device for use with either a table-top or stoneware
Büchner funnel has been described.[124] This apparatus has been employed
to expedite the filtration of alkaline dispersions of proteins extracted from
peanut or cottonseed meals.

Fig. 19. Hirsch funnel, porcelain with
fixed plate. (Courtesy Central Scientific
Co.)

Fig. 20. Hirsch-type funnel, all glass,
with fritted glass disc. (Courtesy Corning
Glass Works.)

Various types of Büchner funnels are shown in Figures 13–18. Some
types of suction filter tubes are in reality modifications of the basic Büchner
design. Similarly, some of the larger suction filters, which are made of
ceramic ware, are essentially of the Büchner type (see Sect. VIII.1).

The *Hirsch funnel*[125] (Fig. 19) differs from the Büchner mainly in having
sloping sides. It facilitates the collection of small amounts of solids, but

[124] R. S. Burnett and A. L. Merrifield, *Ind. Eng. Chem., Anal. Ed.*, **16**, 365 (1944).
[125] R. Hirsch, *Chem.-Ztg.*, **12**, 340 (1888).

has less active filtering area.   The Witt filter plate,[126] a perforated disc of porcelain or sintered glass, provides the equivalent of a Hirsch funnel by placing the plate in an ordinary funnel.   A glass funnel with an integrally fused sintered glass plate is shown in Figure 20.   The use of the Witt plate and the Hirsch funnel is typified by the method for collecting the silver salts of propionic and butyric acids in the separation of these two fatty acids from mixtures resulting from the oxidation of ketones.[127]

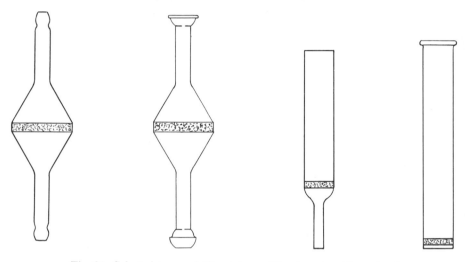

Fig. 21. Selected types of filter tubes.   (Courtesy Ace Glass, Inc.)

Filter tubes for suction use are of various sizes and shapes, and may be adapted to suction flasks or receivers by different methods.   Some of these are shown in Figure 21.   Ordinarily, fibrous materials, screens, or perforated plates are used as the filter medium or support, but affixed sintered glass plates are convenient for all-glass tubes.   The plates come in a range of permeabilities.   The technique of fabricating filter tubes with attached discs of sintered glass strands, to obtain controlled porosities, is exacting and ingenious.[128]   While the suction filter tube is of early origin,[129] the designs of recent years have greatly extended their use in the laboratory. The Zopfchen[130] tube is representative of types for small quantities of material.   For special purposes, a carefully controlled vacuum may be ob-

[126] O. N. Witt, *Ber.*, **19**, 918 (1886).

[127] W. A. Noyes, *Organic Chemistry for the Laboratory*.   5th ed., Chemical Pub. Co., Easton, 1926, pp. 137–139.

[128] W. O. Luertzing, U. S. Pat. 2,136,170 (Nov. 8, 1938).

[129] F. Allihn, *J. prakt. Chem.*, **22**, 56 (1880).

[130] H. Zopfchen, *Chem.-Ztg.*, **25**, 1008 (1901).

tained by use of a micrometer plunger with filter paper in an ordinary funnel.[131]

C. FILTERING CRUCIBLES

The original Gooch crucible, with perforated bottom and employing a mat of purified *asbestos* as the filter medium, was first described in 1878.[132] This device has been widely used particularly for analytical work, with either asbestos or other filter medium such as platinum sponge.[133] The Koenig porcelain filter crucible has a bottom of porous, heat-stable material and does not require the use of any separate filtering substance.[134]

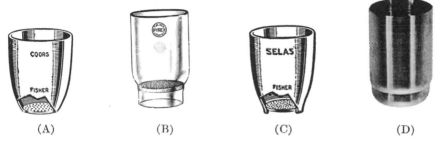

(A)   (B)   (C)   (D)

Fig. 22. Selected filter crucibles: (A) Gooch type (courtesy Coors Porcelain Co.) (B) with fritted glass disc (courtesy Corning Glass Works); (C) with porous porcelain disc (courtesy Selas Corporation of America); (D) stainless steel with porous stainless steel disc (courtesy E. Machlett and Sons).

As of 1955, porcelain crucibles of this type are produced in different porosities, with important differences in filtering rates. Fritted glass crucibles (Pyrex or Jena) are also popular for general laboratory and bacterial filtrations.[135]

Thin-wall sintered alumina crucibles are not widely used in organic chemistry, but may be advantageous when the residue must be subsequently heated under reducing conditions. Porous clay crucibles of excellent quality for filtering purposes are now produced by several American companies. These may be used with or without a loose filtering mat.

---

[131] P. M. Isakov, *J. Gen. Chem. (U. S. S. R.)*, **18**, 151 (1948).

[132] F. A. Gooch, *Proc. Am. Acad. Arts Sci.*, **13**, 342 (1878); *Chem. News*, **37**, 181 (1878).

[133] C. E. Munroe, *J. Anal. Applied Chem.*, **2**, 241 (1888).

[134] A. Konig, U. S. Pat. 1,567,654 (Dec. 29, 1925); *Z. anal. Chem.*, **64**, 224 (1924); *Chem.-Ztg.*, **50**, 326 (1926).

[135] H. Knöll, *Kolloid-Z.*, **86**, 1 (1939); *Ergeb. Hyg. Bakt. Immunitätsforsch. Exptl. Therap.*, **24**, 266 (1941).

Types of filter crucibles are shown in Figure 22. Gooch crucibles or the like are usually adapted to a suction filter flask by means of a filter tube, which is fitted into the flask as shown in Figure 3. The Bailey-type adapter (Fig. 23A) permits the use of the Gooch crucible with the ordinary filter funnel, whereas the Walter-type adapter fits directly in the mouth of the usual suction filter flask (Fig. 23B). A so-called "three-in-one" crucible holder[136] consists of a bung, funnel, and cone in one unit. The tapered rubber bung adapts this for varying neck sizes of the flask. The glass

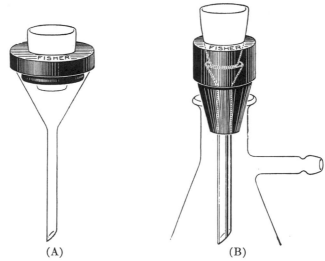

(A)　　　　　　　　　　(B)

Fig. 23. Adapters for filter crucibles: (A) Bailey type; (B) Walter type. (Courtesy Fisher Scientific Co.)

funnel which fits into the holder extends below the side arm of the filter flask.

The use of glass or silica fibers in the form of discs, mats, or paper has been advocated for filter crucible use. The principal advantages seem to be *chemical* inertness and simplicity in use.[137-140] The use of sintered glass filters of carefully controlled porosity, tailored to give a flow rate within prescribed limits for a hydrocellulose water flow number, is an example of the application of such filters to the requirements of the cellulosic fiber field.[141] A technique frequently used in Gooch crucible filtration is to

[136] Jencons (Scientific) Ltd., Rosebank Way, Acton, England.
[137] C. Duval, *Anal. Chem.*, **23**, 1271 (1951).
[138] W. W. Russell and J. H. A. Harley, Jr., *Ind. Eng. Chem., Anal. Ed.*, **11**, 168 (1939).
[139] M. J. O'Leary *et al.*, *Tappi*, **35**, 289 (1952).
[140] T. S. Ma and A. A. Benedetti-Pichler, *Anal. Chem.*, **25**, 999 (1953).
[141] O. A. Battista, J. A. Howsmon, and S. Coppick, *Ind. Eng. Chem.*, **45**, 2107 (1953).

place a layer of a good filter aid such as diatomaceous silica on top of the asbestos mat that has been prepared in the usual manner.[142]

D. CONES AND DISHES

Cones, dishes, and similar shapes made of porous materials, such as clay or aluminum oxide, are convenient for some gravity filtrations as well as for suction or pressure work. Filtration takes place through the pores of the filter device itself and requires no paper or other medium. The varied uses of Alundum laboratory ware for filtration and other purposes were first reported in 1912.[143] Other studies[144,145] bring out many advantages of these types of porous apparatus. Alundum filter cones and dishes, as examples, come in various porosities. In these vessels the entire surfaces are porous and are convenient for the collection of solids for study or for analytical purposes. Alundum and other small ceramic filters are cleaned by solvents or by ignition and may be used repeatedly. Perforated cones may be fabricated from various sheet materials and used with or without filter media—fabric, fiber, or powder. Extraction thimbles of paper or organic membranes are sometimes employed for filtrations as well as for extractions.

E. IMMERSION LEAF FILTERS AND FILTER STICKS

Immersion or suction leaf filters[146] are widely used in laboratories today and will become more so as their simplicity and advantages become more generally recognized. The filtering member in this type of filter may be of any size. Thus, the commercial types of immersion leaf filters are useful for larger scale laboratory preparations and smaller sizes are equally useful for bench work. Minute "filter sticks" for microchemical manipulations are referred to in Section III.9.

Immersion leaf filters may be fitted with different filter septa—cloth, filter screen, sintered glass or metal, porous stone, or ceramic compositions. Sintered, stainless-steel discs come in average pore sizes from 5 to 65 microns. In operation these filters are *inserted directly* into the material to be filtered, which is contained in a beaker or other receptacle. The filtrate is collected in a vacuum receiver vessel. The solids are collected on the filter member itself, and may be removed after filtration; or the steps of washing, dissolving, etc., may be accomplished by removing the filter mem-

[142] W. Eisenman, *Chemist-Analyst*, 21, 18 (1932).
[143] M. A. Williamson and P. A. Boeck, *Ind. Eng. Chem.*, 4, 672 (1912).
[144] R. C. Benner and W. H. Ross, *J. Am. Chem. Soc.*, 34, 51 (1912).
[145] J. C. Hostetter and R. B. Sosman, *J. Am. Chem. Soc.*, 38, 1188 (1916).
[146] T. M. Drown, *Tech. Quart.*, 20, 552 (1891).

ber plus adhering solids, still under suction, and placing them in another receptacle for washing with solvent.

The use of an immersion filter is shown in Figure 24.   Figure 25 illustrates filter leaves of various types and shapes.   Figure 25A shows a frame covered with fabric, 25B shows a metal drum covered by a screen which may serve as a support for filter paper or another filter medium, and 25C

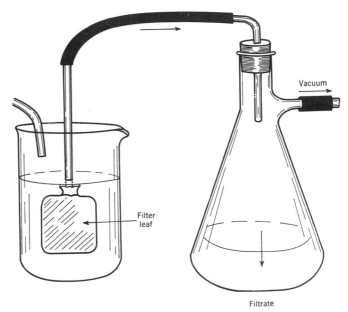

Fig. 24. Immersion leaf filter showing manner of use.

and 25D show filters made of porous stone and sintered metal, respectively.

Immersion filter tubes, often referred to as "filter sticks,"[147-152] are simply small immersion filters for small-scale operations, examples of which are shown in Figure 26.   They may be fitted with sintered glass, filter paper, asbestos, or other filter medium.   On the filter (Fig. 26C), paper or cloth is held over the end of the tube with a rubber band, adhesive tape, wire or string.   Small funnels, with paper or fabric or a fibrous plug, may also be used as immersion filters.   The ceramic Pukall cell[153] offers a larger filter-

147 P. Casamajor, Chem. News, 32, 45 (1875).
148 F. Emich, Lehrbuch der Mikrochemie.   2nd ed., Bergmann, Munich, 1926.
149 E. Schwarz-Bergkampf, Z. anal. Chem., 69, 321 (1926).
150 V. Pristoupil, Chem. Obzor, 6, 1 (1931).
151 L. Kaufman, Chem. Fabrik, 5, 163 (1932).
152 P. H. Prausnitz, Kolloid-Z., 50, 77, 167 (1930).
153 W. Pukall, Ber., 26, 1159 (1893).

ing surface than the filter sticks and can also be used as an immersion filter.

The ingenious use of filter sticks in small all-glass, ground-joint filters for use in centrifugal filtrations has been the subject of several papers.[154-156]

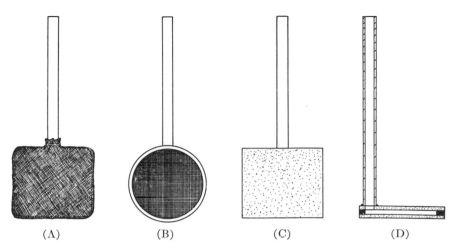

(A)   (B)   (C)   (D)

Fig. 25. Various kinds of laboratory immersion leaf filters: (A) cloth; (B) metal fabric; (C) porous stone; (D) sintered metal.

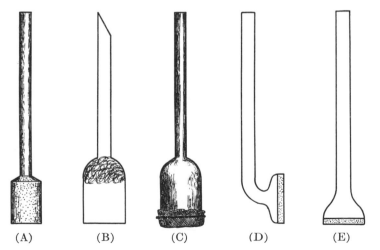

(A)   (B)   (C)   (D)   (E)

Fig. 26. Some different types of filter sticks: (A) porous stone; (B) glass wool, asbestos, etc.; (C) paper, cloth, or other fabric; (D) fritted glass; (E) fritted glass.

[154] L. C. Craig and O. W. Post, *Ind. Eng. Chem., Anal. Ed.*, **16**, 413 (1944).

[155] M. T. Bush, H. L. Dickison, C. B. Ward, and R. C. Avery, *J. Pharmacol.*, **85**, 241 (1946).

[156] M. T. Bush, *Ind. Eng. Chem., Anal. Ed.*, **18**, 584 (1946).

Instructions for the laboratory preparation of a small inexpensive filter tube from a pipet which is cut and into which a sintered glass wool layer is formed, together with suggestions for the use of such an apparatus, are given by Hahn.[157]

5. Pressure Filters

The use of pressure to *accelerate* filtration is much desired in handling larger quantities of material.   There are also some liquids which can be filtered only with difficulty by gravity or by suction.   Examples are very

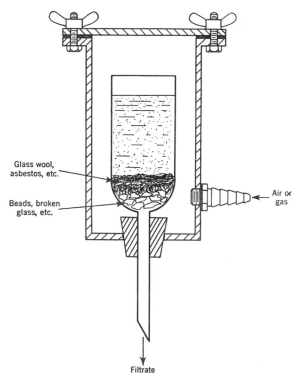

Fig. 27. Simple laboratory pressure filter.

viscous liquids or those with high vapor pressures or with a considerable amount of dissolved gas.   Small laboratory pressure filters have not been used as widely as have gravity or suction filters, but the use of pressure filters in the laboratory has increased substantially in recent years, and this trend will continue, since there are now available a number of satisfactory

[157] F. L. Hahn, *Anal. Chim. Acta*, **7**, 430 (1952).

designs for small pressure filters.   Gravity filters sometimes may be operated with increased liquid head by locating the filter several feet below the
liquid supply.   Generally, however, such an arrangement is inconvenient.

The requirements for a pressure filter are a *suitable housing* for the filter
itself and a *means of supplying pressure* with the degree of accuracy and

Fig. 28. Laboratory pressure leaf filter. (Courtesy Johns-Manville Corp.)

control necessary.   For continuous operation, the liquid must be delivered
to the apparatus and the filtrate removed.

Most types of filter elements may be easily adapted for *intermittent or
batch* filter operations, since this in principle only involves placing the filter
assembly in a closed chamber and applying pressure.   An example of a
small pressure filter is shown in Figure 27.   Filter elements for pressure
filters may be of the leaf type, "filter stick" type, tubes, or edge filters;
or they may be made of paper, fibrous material, etc.   A type of general-
utility pressure filter for laboratory use, employing a small vertical leaf

filter element, is shown in Figure 28.   The transparent housing permits observations of the cake during progress of the filtration.

A pressure filter improvised from 6 in. diameter pipe for use with Seitz pads is useful for the filtration and sterilization of protein solutions.[158] Another pressure filter has been recommended[159] for cellulose dopes, solutions of high-polymer compounds, varnishes, gelatin, glue, pectin, and other high-viscosity materials.

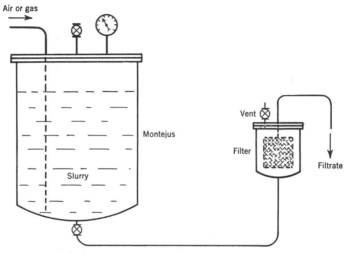

Fig. 29. Laboratory pressure filter for montejus operation.

A small pressure filter of a simulated plate and frame type utilizes filtering layers of 20 × 20 cm. size.   Supplied as a complete unit this is adapt · able for the requirements of chemical and pharmaceutical laboratories as well as for the filtration of food materials, distilled liquors, etc.[160]   Another small filtering unit, employing Metafilter or disc filter elements, while described for electroplating solutions, is adaptable for operations in organic chemistry.[161]   A research-type laboratory pressure filter[162] particularly developed for the sugar industry provides for pressure regulation, temperature control, precoating with filter aid, and maintenance of constant filter area with changing cake thickness.   It is reported that good correlations in results are obtained with this filter as compared with full-scale refinery operations.

[158] E. A. Brown and N. Benotti, *Science*, **93**, 23 (1941).
[159] K. Bratring, *Nitrocellulose*, **14**, 21 (1943).
[160] W. Kramer, *Pharm. Ind.*, **12**, 44 (1950).
[161] G. T. Colegate, *Electroplating*, **6**, 11 (1953).
[162] E. C. Gillett and R. F. Black, *Intern. Sugar J.*, **56**, 307 (1954).

As a source of pressure, air or nitrogen may be used for laboratory filtrations. For intermittent operations the compressed gas is directly connected to the filter housing and replaces the liquid as it is filtered. Various small, laboratory air pressure filters have been described.[163-165] For more

Fig. 30. Use of filter stick for pressure filtration.

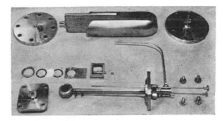

Fig. 31. Stainless steel high-pressure filtration unit. (Courtesy Johns-Manville Corp.)

continuous operation, the *montejus principle* shown schematically in Figure 29 may be employed. Pumps are widely used in industry for pressure filtrations, and today may be employed advantageously for many laboratory filtrations, since miniature rotary gear pumps, midget centrifugal-type pumps, and some other suitable types are now available. These pumps give excellent performance and are simple to operate (see further in Sect. VIII and Table X). Caution should be used, however, in that

163 H. L. Kauffman and J. B. Mull, *Chemist-Analyst*, **18**, 20 (1929).
164 E. H. Hoffing and F. J. Lockhart, *Chem. Eng. Progress*, **47**, 3 (1951).
165 H. P. Grace, *Chem. Eng. Progress*, **49**, 367 (1953).

considerable attrition may take place when these pumps are used for prefilts containing highly flocculated or friable solids.

Horizontal plate filters[166] have advantages for conditions where uninterrupted filter cake formation is desirable since the solids rest on a supported surface. This is a desirable feature for intermittent operations, particularly with filter aids. A simple pressure leaf filter, used for semicontinuous small-scale production of gluconic acid from the fermentation of glucose solution, can be easily constructed.[167] This unit has a filtering area of 346 sq. cm. and a wet cake capacity of 0.69 liter. Laboratory pressure filters have also been constructed in automatically controlled multiple units,[168]

Fig. 32. Small commercial high-pressure filter. (Courtesy Micro Metallic Corp.)

and a small filter which is satisfactory for pressures up to 2 atmospheres has been described.[169]

For the pressure filtration of *small amounts* of materials, the filter medium may be mounted in a filter tube or equivalent, the liquid poured in, and pressure applied to the upper surface of the liquid. For micro work this may be accomplished with capillary or larger tubing, or with an adaptation from a medicine dropper. Somewhat larger tubes may be fitted with a rubber pressure bulb, hand blower, or foot blower. The use of filter sticks for pressure filtration work is illustrated in Figure 30. Other simple pres-

[166] "Diatomaceous Earth Filter," *Ind. Eng. Chem., News Ed.*, **16**, 496 (1938).

[167] T. F. Clark, N. Porges, and S. I. Aronovsky, *Ind. Eng. Chem., Anal. Ed.*, **12**, 755 (1940).

[168] A. B. Cummins and L. E. Weymouth, *Ind. Eng. Chem.*, **34**, 392 (1942).

[169] W. Scheidt, *Pharmazie*, **2**, 15 (1947).

sure filters adaptable for the filtration of small quantities of liquid may be improvised from available laboratory apparatus.[170]

A number of laboratory-size filters are obtainable for operation at pressures of 500 p.s.i. and above. In general, these filters are most useful for handling highly viscous materials such as bitumens and viscose, or for filtering pulps. Filters for *high-pressure* operation fall into two categories: (*1*) *leaf filters* and (*2*) *press types.*

It is not difficult to provide a simple leaf filter for *high-pressure filtrations*, the major requirement being to construct the walls and removable closure of the vessel of such materials and thicknesses as to withstand the required pressures. A stainless-steel filter test unit for pressures up to 500 p.s.i., designed and used in the Johns-Manville Filtration Laboratories, is shown in Figure 31. A relatively recent development, the use of porous metal filters, offers new possibilities for high-pressure filtration. Standard units are available for pressures as high as 10,000 p.s.i. and even higher pressure units are available on special order. Figure 32 shows a type JS filter for use at pressures in the 2000–10,000 p.s.i. range. Some of the filter companies make small-size, extra-heavy, plate and frame type filters which may be used at several hundred pounds pressure.

Small screw or hydraulic presses may be adapted for laboratory use in the expression of liquids from solids, such as crystals, pulps, etc. In some cases these are simple pressing or extraction operations, but when pulps are forced through various pervious media, the procedure may be considered a type of high-pressure filtration. Fruits, vegetables, flesh, and many other materials are pressed for their juice (and pulp) in what is actually a high-pressure filtration. The Shoyu sauce industry of Japan depends on this method of juice extraction. Figure 33 shows a Carver laboratory filter press. This versatile piece of equipment may be used to exert a force of 10 tons, or, on a cake 3.5 in. in diameter, a pressure of 2080 p.s.i. A 20 ton model is also available. Another Carver laboratory device is a combination plate and frame filter and filter press. In operation the slurry is filtered at several hundred p.s.i. Then the cake is pressed dry and automatically discharged (Fig. 34).

6. Heated Filters

Many liquids must be maintained at *higher temperatures* during filtration to prevent the formation of crystals. Fats, waxes, etc., can be filtered only at temperatures above their melting points, and hot, saturated solutions

---

[170] A. Wexler, *J. Chem. Ed.*, **18**, 167 (1941).

Fig. 33. Carver Laboratory Press, adapted for filter pressing. (Courtesy Fred S. Carver, Inc.)

Fig. 34. Carver plate and frame filter and filter press combination. (Courtesy Fred S. Carver, Inc.)

are filtered for the common recrystallizations.[172-174] An equally important aspect of high-temperature filtration is the greatly *increased filter rate*, due primarily to decrease in the viscosity of liquids with temperature. For some purposes the filter can be heated in an oven or in a flame before use and will retain enough heat during a short filtration to avoid difficulties. It is possible in some cases to place the entire filter assembly in an oven or heated enclosure, although it is not convenient to replace the liquid in an operation of this kind, which, moreover, may be dangerous when organic solvents are used.

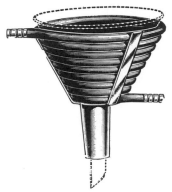

Fig. 35. Funnel heater, coiled lead tubing type, for hot or cold filtration. (Courtesy Fisher Scientific Co.)

Fig. 36. Double-wall Büchner funnel. (Courtesy Fisher Scientific Co.)

The importance of having a heated funnel for filtration was recognized by Robert Ware[175] who invented such a filter in the early 1820's. The Koch funnel heater, which was an improvement, is still used despite its disadvantages. With this device heat is applied to a handlelike projection. In the single-wall type the funnel comes in direct contact with the hot water. The metal double-wall type is more convenient. Coil heaters, in which the coils are wound on a 60° cone, may be connected with water or low-pressure steam. Figure 35 illustrates such a coil heater. Two steam-heated filters of simple design are described by Kleiss.[176]

[172] W. A. Noyes, *Organic Chemistry for the Laboratory*. 5th ed., Chemical Pub. Co., Easton, 1926, p. 207.

[173] R. E. Dodd and P. L. Robinson, *Experimental Inorganic Chemistry*. Elsevier, Amsterdam, 1954.

[174] See also Chapter III in this volume.

[175] R. Ware, Description of a part of the apparatus used in the chemical course of the University of Pennsylvania, Philadelphia, 1826.

[176] E. Kleiss, *Mikrokosmos*, **38**, 180 (1949).

The temperature of double-wall, Büchner-type, porcelain funnels may be controlled by the circulation of hot or cold water, steam, or brine in the outer jacket.   Figure 36 depicts such a funnel.   A jacketed Büchner-type funnel[177] constructed of stainless steel has several advantages, one of the most important being the rapid heat-transfer characteristics of the metal. This filter may be heated by steam or by plugging the lower side tube and filling the jacket with water which may be heated by a burner.   A float device is also described which indicates the liquid level in the filter.

Fig. 37. Electric funnel heater and accessories. (Courtesy Central Scientific Co.)

A funnel heater, based on the principles of a domestic hot-water heater, may be assembled from the usual laboratory facilities.[178]   An *electric coil heater* is wrapped on the circulating water line.   In another arrangement with a filter funnel, the solution and not the funnel is heated.[179]   This apparatus is also adapted for continuous automatic use.

Electric heaters for funnels, employing no liquid transfer media, offer some advantages.   Details for the construction of such a heater with provision for heating the stem of standard-length funnels have been given.[180] Numerous types of electric funnel heaters are now listed by laboratory supply houses.   The heaters may have variable degrees of heat control, by steps or by continuous resistance changes.[181]   One such heater is shown in Figure 37.   Electrically heated *pads or mantles* are a modern improvement for funnel heating.   They are available in various sizes for

[177] J. Erdos, *Ciencia (Mexico)*, **10**, 102 (1950).
[178] J. R. Caldwell, *Ind. Eng. Chem., Anal. Ed.*, **7**, 76 (1935).
[179] G. R. Yohe, *Ind. Eng. Chem., Anal. Ed.*, **7**, 206 (1935).
[180] B. A. Fiekers, *Chemist-Analyst*, **35**, 93 (1946).
[181] See "Heating and Cooling," Chapter II of Part II.

both cone and straight-side filters, and are now being used widely because of convenience in operation. Figure 38 shows a type of mantle heater for a Büchner funnel. The corresponding mantle for ordinary funnels is similar. For maximum safety aluminum housing type electric heating mantles are recommended.[182] These mantles are designed so that the heat input is applied only where it is most essential.

An alternate for fabricated mantles is the use of electrothermal heating tapes, which may be wrapped in the manner desired on any type of filtering

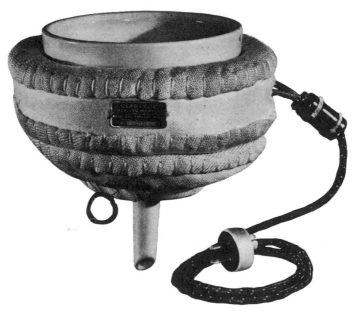

Fig. 38. Electric mantle heater for Büchner funnel. (Courtesy Glas-Col Apparatus Co.)

apparatus. These tapes may be uninsulated, thus permitting full view of the material being heated, or may be insulated on one side, which is somewhat more efficient in heat conservation.

The filtration of hot, saturated solutions in volatile solvents, such as alcohol or benzene, is accomplished by pouring the liquid through a folded filter paper on a funnel fitted to a flask in which the filtrate is boiling just vigorously enough to surround the paper with solvent vapor.[183] Occasionally there is a requirement for a filtration at some specified constant temperature. In this case it is best to employ a jacketed filter and circu-

---

[182] Glas-Col Apparatus Co., Inc., Terre Haute, Ind.
[183] Lassar Cohn, *Organic Laboratory Methods*. Williams and Wilkins, Baltimore, 1928.

late through it, by means of a pump, a liquid drawn from a thermostatically controlled reservoir.[184] A special problem in the filtration of superheated alcoholic solutions coming from autoclaves at about 110°C. was solved by filtering through a Büchner funnel fitted with a splash cover made from copper sheeting in the form of a truncated cone. Triangular outlets were cut in the cone base so that the cake would spread evenly. A reflux trap condensed the alcohol which evaporated in the filter flask.[185]

The use of an electrically heated funnel by the following procedure is an improvement over Fiekers:[186]

The tip of the funnel is capped. The stem and cone are then filled with the hot solution to be filtered, and this is brought to gentle boiling. By removing the cap from the funnel tip, the filtrate is then allowed to flow. For the cap, a well of suitable size is drilled halfway into a cork or rubber stopper, which can then be fitted over the tip of the funnel. A handle made of wire or other material is attached to the cap so that it can readily be disengaged from the funnel tip and withdrawn from the receiver.

In handling volatile and flammable liquids, loss of solvent occurs in the use of a preheated Büchner funnel. This is a disadvantage of some earlier heated filters.[187,188] A simple and convenient hot filter, well suited for recrystallization with organic solvents, is attributed to Shiba.[189] A modified Pregl microfiltration apparatus for hot filtrations employs a ground-glass joint in which the filter stick is heated with the vapors of the solvent.[190]

In *temporary installations* or where cost is a consideration, filtering apparatus of many sorts may be insulated with strips of felted insulating materials, and thus retain enough heat in the hot liquid to permit satisfactory operation. Strips of asbestos paper may also be employed. If the strips are applied wet, they may be formed around most shapes. When dry, the asbestos adheres to itself and to the glass so that a neat and durable semi-insulating job may be done with a minimum of effort. If the apparatus is of such complexity that asbestos tape is difficult to apply, wet asbestos pulp or insulating cements may be used. Some larger scale laboratory and pilot-plant filters, many of which are small models after commercial equipment, are designed for heating with hot liquids, steam, or electricity.

[184] H. Furst, *Chem. Tech. (Berlin)*, **5**, 79 (1953).

[185] A. W. Billitzer, *Ind. Eng. Chem.*, **44**, 2417 (1952).

[186] R. K. Himmelsbach, *Chemist-Analyst*, **41**, 35, 38 (1952).

[187] T. Paul, *Ber.*, **25**, 2209 (1892).

[188] J. Houben, *Die Methoden der organischen Chemie.* Vol. I, 3rd ed., Thieme, Leipzig, 1925, pp. 435–438.

[189] H. Shiba, *Anal. Chem.*, **26**, 943 (1954).

[190] V. Horak, *Chem. Listy*, **48**, 616 (1954).

7. Cooled Filters

A common problem in filtrations below room temperatures is the removal of *low-melting crystals* or *amorphous solids* from a solvent.   In some cases the liquid must be maintained constantly at a low temperature to prevent chemical or biological changes.   Ordinary funnels may be packed with cracked ice or freezing mixtures and serve satisfactorily for many purposes. Cold water or brine may be circulated through jacketed funnels or other filters in the same manner as employed for hot water or steam in hot filtrations.   If refrigerator rooms are available, the entire filter assembly may be set up and operated at the lower temperature maintained there.   Some materials may be chilled in a refrigerator or otherwise and then filtered in the laboratory at room temperature without too great a temperature rise, particularly if the funnel has also been chilled.

The filter stick or vacuum leaf filter is useful for the filtration of cold liquids.   In this technique the liquid is cooled in a container with ice, solid carbon dioxide, cooling coil, or other means.   Thus, filtration may be from a Dewar flask,[191] a beaker, or other receptacle.   *Solid carbon dioxide* may be used effectively in filtrations with a Büchner funnel,[192] and has also been employed for the filtration of a halibut oil concentrate in the preparation of vitamins.[193]

For the low-temperature filtration of hydrocarbon polymers, for example, when isobutane is polymerized in liquid phase at -70 to $-130°C$. the resulting rubberlike polymer may be easily filtered by the addition of finely divided ice or solid carbon dioxide particles, any excess of which is removed later by warming or steaming.[194]

Temperatures as low as $-75°C$. may be obtained with an apparatus[195] shown in Chapter III.   The Skau tube[196,197] is a type of centrifugal filter tube especially useful for the rapid filtration of small amounts of nongummy compounds.   This device was employed for filtering low-boiling liquids such as pentane, which can be frozen at liquid-air temperatures.   Centrifuge filtration is described in Chapter IV.

[191] C. Dufraisse, *Ann. chim.*, **17**, 165 (1922).

[192] P. Karrer and K. Schopp, *Helv. Chim. Acta*, **17**, 693 (1934).

[193] H. M. Holmes, H. Cassidy, R. S. Manley, and E. R. Harzler, *J. Am. Chem. Soc.*, **57**, 1990 (1935).

[194] A. B. Hersberger, U. S. Pat. 2,537,759 (Jan. 9, 1951).

[195] F. W. Quackenbush and H. Steenbock, *Ind. Eng. Chem., Anal. Ed.*, **14**, 736 (1942).

[196] E. L. Skau, *J. Phys. Chem.*, **33**, 951 (1929).

[197] E. L. Skau and L. F. Rowe, *Ind. Eng. Chem., Anal. Ed.*, **3**, 147 (1931).   See also Chapter IV, Section III.5, of this volume.

8. Continuous Filtration

The replacement of liquids in a funnel during a fairly rapid filtration requires almost constant attention and is time-consuming when large quantities of material are to be handled or when prolonged washing of the solids is necessary.   Numerous *siphoning arrangements* have been employed for continuous filtration without attention of the operator.   A simple

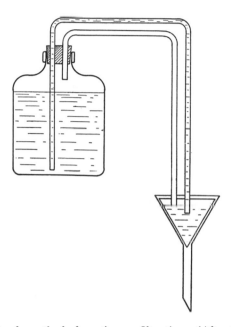

Fig. 39. Simple method of continuous filtration.   (After Vorhies.[198])

device[198] is shown in Figure 39.   Essentially the same device is used by Rhoad.[199]   Numerous other arrangements are described in the literature.[200,201]   Dodd and Robinson[202] describe a method for the continuous transfer of suspensions to a filter plate in a vacuum filtration.   Morton's text[203] also has descriptions of a number of set-ups for continuous filtration.

[198] A. Vorhies, *Chemist-Analyst*, **18**, 18 (1929).

[199] F. N. Rhoad, *Chemist-Analyst*, **40**, 23 (1951).

[200] G. Génin, *La filtration industrielle.*   Dunod, Paris, 1934, pp. 430–432.

[201] J. V. Dubsky, *Selbsttätige Filtrations Apparate.*   Thieme, Leipzig, 1931.

[202] R. E. Dodd, and P. L. Robinson, *Experimental Inorganic Chemistry.*   Elsevier, Amsterdam, 1954, p. 22.

[203] A. A. Morton, *Laboratory Technique in Organic Chemistry.*   McGraw-Hill, New York, 1938, pp. 173–174.

A very simple apparatus for continuous filtration[204] consists of an Erlenmeyer-type flask with large stopcock at the bottom. With the cock open, the liquid to be filtered is siphoned from the flask onto the filter. The level of liquid on the filter is determined by the position of a glass tube inserted through a rubber stopper which seals the flask. Operation is *automatic* and is satisfactory for slow filtrations.

Fig. 40. Multiple unit for continuous pressure filtrations. (Courtesy Johns-Manville Corp.)

Three suggestive apparatus assemblies have been described[205] for the uninterrupted filtration of pharmaceutical preparations. An experimental study on the dewaxing of butanol–benzol mixtures[206] gives information on continuous filtration and working on a little larger scale. A device[207] for filtering solutions directly into reagent bottles or equivalent utilizes vacuum to supply the solution automatically to the fritted disc filter member. Once started, the system requires no attention.

A filtering apparatus[208] developed for the almost continuous filtration of considerable volumes of parenteral solutions with provision for scrupulous rinsing of containers employs large aspirator bottles equipped with bottom stopcock outlets as alternate receivers. Appropriate cocks are provided for convenient operation. Various other types of continuous or automatic

[204] W. Frost, *Chem.-Ztg.*, **64,** 60 (1940).
[205] K. Pockel, *Deut. Apoth. Ztg.*, **92,** 251 (1952).
[206] H. Mondria, *Chem. Eng. Sci.*, **1,** 20 (1951).
[207] C. W. Fleetwood, *Anal. Chem.*, **22,** 1462 (1950).
[208] W. C. Gosby and J. C. H. Hanson, *Pharm. J.*, **165,** 417 (1950).

apparatus have been described[209-211] and a filter apparatus adapted for continuous use in blood and plasma transfusions appears applicable for more general use.[212]

An apparatus used in the authors' laboratory for multiple long-cycle pressure filtration testing[213] is depicted in Figure 40. Large quantities of liquor in a single container may be filtered continuously with suction leaf filters by replacing the filter leaf when the filter rate drops or the cake becomes too thick. If suitable multiple-stopcock connections are provided, the changeover may be effected without interruption of the vacuum. The montejus method for pressure filtration is continuous up to the amount of liquid contained in the reserve pressure supply tank. By the use of alternate tanks and suitable valve connections, montejus filtrations may be carried out continuously for an indefinite period.

In long-continued filtrations there is frequently the problem of collecting filtrate fractions at desired time intervals. Usually this may be accomplished satisfactorily by the attention of an operator. However, when high accuracy is essential, or when repeated tests warrant automatic collection of samples as an economy, various fraction collectors, developed mostly for other purposes, may be applied for the collection of filtrates.[214-218]

9. Microfilters

No distinction is made here between micro- and semimicrofiltrations since essentially the same apparatus and techniques are used for both. Much of the apparatus employed for microfiltrations is of the same shape as that previously described in this section. Thus, there are miniature 60° glass funnels, filter tubes, Büchner and Hirsch funnels, vacuum filter flasks, etc. There are, however, many special types of filtering apparatus, ingenious filter assemblies, etc., which have been developed specifically for micromanipulation and which have no counterpart in the usual apparatus for larger quantities of materials. Since details on microfiltration apparatus are given in Volume VI of this series,[219] descriptions and illustrations of

[209] L. G. Doke, *Chemist-Analyst*, **18**, 18 (1929).

[210] R. Ashworth, *Chemist-Analyst*, **18**, 17 (1929).

[211] R. W. Tarara, *Chemist-Analyst*, **35**, 18 (1946).

[212] H. Sildentopf and M. Levine, *Science*, **96**, 303 (1942).

[213] A. B. Cummins and L. E. Weymouth, *Ind. Eng. Chem.*, **34**, 392 (1942).

[214] C. Mader, *Anal. Chem.*, **25**, 1423 (1953).

[215] E. Schram and E. J. Bigwood, *Anal. Chem.*, **25**, 1424 (1953).

[216] J. L. Hickson and R. L. Whistler, *Anal. Chem.*, **25**, 1425 (1953).

[217] W. J. Wingo and I. Browning, *Anal. Chem.*, **25**, 1426 (1953).

[218] R. J. Dimler and others, *Anal. Chem.*, **25**, 1428 (1953).

[219] N. D. Cheronis, in A. Weissberger, ed., *Micro and Semimicro Methods* (Vol. VI, *Technique of Organic Chemistry*). Interscience, New York-London, 1954.

apparatus and techniques are not emphasized here, but some references to recent work which illustrate specific points are given.

A few representative types of micro- and semimicrofiltration apparatus are illustrated in Figure 41. A very simple filter suitable for quantities a little greater than the usual microfilters, and which may be made up with usual laboratory apparatus, is described by Goerdeler.[220] An interesting

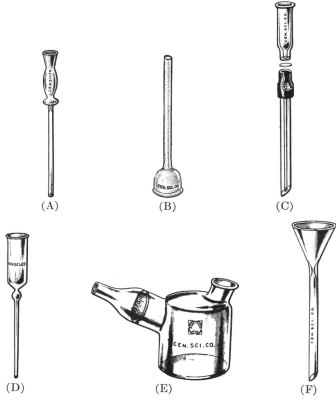

(A)   (B)   (C)

(D)   (E)   (F)

Fig. 41. Micro and semimicro filtering apparatus. (Courtesy Central Scientific Co.)

microfilter having two filter elements[221] has been described. One layer is a prefilter and the second removes the finer material that escapes the first. No. 1 is lighter and more easily removed while No. 2 remains intact after many filtrations. Cotton wool or sand is satisfactory for No. 1, while cellulose powder or asbestos is used for No. 2. Both filter layers are housed in a Pregl filter tube. In another semimicro apparatus a siphon is hung on the

[220] H. Goerdeler, *Chem.-Ing.-Tech.*, **22**, 378 (1950).
[221] G. Kainz, *Mikrochim. Acta*, **1953**, 119.

lip of the beaker with the downward outlet tube directed to a receiver for the filtrate. The inlet consists of an enlarged downward-pointing capillary tube covered with a filter paper disc.[222] An apparatus designed for the preparation of about 2 g. of solid and 4 ml. of liquid organic compounds includes figures for two filters of the reaction tube type, employing "glass nails" as supports for filter paper discs.[223] An apparatus useful in studies of fiber sections, starch granules, and the like consists of a glass cylinder 18 mm. × 12 mm. I.D., with lower edge beveled, and fitted with a lead ring about the upper end. By resting on a slide or cover glass, it provides a cylindrical reaction microvessel from which liquid can be removed by pressure or gentle tilting, leaving a single layer deposit of any material suspended in the liquid phase.[224]

An inexpensive new accessory for the filtration of small samples of precipitates in an ordinary funnel is provided by E. H. Sargent and Co., Chicago. The support is made of stainless steel and has a head with two slots. The support rests in a common 65 mm. analytical funnel and a piece of filter paper is placed on top of the head of the support. Suction may be applied to the funnel stem to speed up removal of solvent, yet sufficient support is given to the filter paper to keep it from pulling through, even under high vacuum. The precipitate is collected at one point and is easily recoverable without loss by simply punching the support out or shaking it out into a receiving vessel, paper and all.

A study wherein microfiltration techniques, some of them new, were applied in the application of the general filtration laws to the filtration of viscose led to the conclusion that the "clogging value" is dependent on the specific filter resistance and not on the initial filtering rate.[225]

The Schwinger micro vacuum filter apparatus consists of a funnel-shaped glass top with a polished lower edge. The lower tube is ground at 45° at one end and is polished at the other. Between these polished surfaces, a small circle of the desired grade of felted paper is inserted and held in place by a short length of rubber tubing. For cutting the small paper discs, it is convenient to employ a well-sharpened cork borer of the correct size or the ordinary office paper punch. Discs prepared in these ways may be used for a confined spot filtration apparatus as described by Lambert et al.[226] as well as for other methods of carrying out spot tests.

Miniature laboratory filtration apparatus must be especially well made to be useful and thus should meet exacting specifications. The Committee

[222] I. L. Teodorovich, *Zavodskaya Lab.*, **16**, 1132 (1950).
[223] P. A. Claret, *Chemist & Industry*, **1952**, 1147.
[224] N. Iwanow, *Bull. inst. textile France*, No. 37, 7 (1953).
[225] H. L. Vosters, *Svensk Papperstidn.*, **54**, 539 (1951).
[226] J. B. Lambert, T. E. Moore, and P. Arthur, *Anal. Chem.*, **23**, 1193 (1951).

for the Standardization of Microchemical Apparatus, Division of Analytical Chemistry, American Chemical Society, has helped greatly in providing detailed specifications based on the recommendations of leading practical workers in micromethods.[227] The British Standards Institution is also issuing a series of standards for microchemical apparatus (B.S. 1428). A report of a subcommittee of the B.S.I. on filter crucibles points out the deficiencies of some types of filtering crucibles and sticks when subjected to heating and acid-treatment tests.[228]

A number of commercial houses specialize in the fabrication of microapparatus, and their catalogs, as well as laboratory supply house catalogs, some of which feature microapparatus, may be helpful in keeping up to date on new items. General treatises on microchemistry, some of which are listed among the "General References" for this chapter describe earlier apparatus and techniques.

IV. FILTER MEDIA

1. General

The term filter media is used to include all materials which may serve as a filter member or septum as defined in Section I.2. The selection of a filter medium best suited for a given purpose is frequently the main factor in obtaining satisfactory filter performance. While it is correct to consider the filter medium as serving usually only to support the collected solids which function as the actual filtering layer, the requirements of organic laboratory work are so varied that filter media are often employed for other uses, such as for *screening*, for *absorption*, and for *clarification* by membrane action. Thus, the filter medium is frequently more important in laboratory filtrations than in larger scale operations.

The selection of a filter medium depends upon the purpose of the filtration, the quantity of material to be filtered, and the apparatus available for the assembly of the filter. As a first requirement the medium must be inert in the liquid to be filtered, thus being insoluble therein and undergoing little physical change, such as swelling, shrinking, or distortion. Adsorption effects should be negligible for most purposes. The filter medium is usually selected so as to permit the maximum passage of liquid consistent with positive retention of the solids to the degree necessary for the particular requirement. There are exceptions to this general rule, such as when only a small quantity of clarified liquid is required. In this case it is time-saving to employ a very "tight" medium which passes no

[227] G. L. Royer (Chairman) and others, *Ind. Eng. Chem., Anal. Ed.*, **15**, 230 (1943).
[228] C. Whalley and G. H. Wyatt, *Analyst*, **77**, 39 (1952).

turbidity or only a small amount for a short time. When retained solids are to be washed, it is best to select the most open-textured medium possible. Media for vacuum and pressure filtrations must be sufficiently strong to hold up without distortion under the pressure differential. Some open-textured media are unsuited for pressure filtrations, since fine particles of solids may enter the openings and, by plugging, make the filtering surface almost impermeable. The types and varieties of filter media which are of importance for organic laboratory filtrations are described in this section to assist in the selection of the best medium for a given purpose. The references given to illustrate particular applications should be consulted for further details.

2. Paper and Pulps

The use of paper for filtering is reputed to have been known in China during the Han dynasty and is attributed to the Chinese Tsai-Lun.[229] A scholarly sketch of the early history and later development of filter paper has been prepared by Grüne.[230] Some aspects of filter paper manufacture and other information on paper are given in two earlier references.[231,232]

Filter paper in one form or another is perhaps the most commonly used medium for laboratory filtrations. Paper in circular form may be used folded, fluted, or flat depending upon the type of filter used. Paper thimbles, trays, etc., are also useful. Papers are prepared in various textures, thicknesses, degrees of purity, etc., for different uses. Some of these papers are quite specialized in their application, and it will well repay the laboratory worker to study and become familar with the many grades and types of filter papers available. The practice of referring in the literature to the exact filter paper employed, with mention of grade or catalog number of the manufacturer, is to be commended. This detail is observed by many of the most careful workers in reporting researches or in describing procedures, since it is recognized that such detail is often important for the duplication of results.

The more important manufacturers of filter papers have for many years not only maintained high standards in the production of filter papers, but have also been alert in providing special papers for new requirements and in supplying technical information and data on the properties of and uses for the various grades of their papers. Most of these producers provide bro-

[229] A. Kufferath, *Filtration und Filter.* 2nd ed., Chemisch-technischer Verlag. Dr. Bodenbender, Berlin, 1952.

[230] A. Grüne, *Filtrierpapiere und Filtrieren.* Schleicher & Schuell, Einbeck/Hans, 1951.

[231] E. Child, *The Tools of the Chemist.* Reinhold, New York, 1940, pp. 118–122.

[232] C. J. West, *Paper Trade J.*, **71**, 34 (1920).

chures and compilations of information, which merit the attention of the laboratory technician.

Laboratory filter papers come in a variety of *forms:* circles for funnels (diameter 1 to 30 in.), folded filters for funnels, sheets and rolls for cutting to size, extraction thimbles, diffusion shells, and trays. *Textures* are: very "soft" (loosely fitted), medium-porosity grades, dense grades, and hardened. Parchment or hardened papers are supplied in different finishes: plain, antique, crinkled, embossed, and creped. The purity of filter paper is generally specified as: crude, refined, "ash-free" (acid-washed), fat-free, starch-free, etc. Some specialty papers such as lintless grades, reinforced papers, colored papers, and papers with parchmentized points are useful for particular requirements. Filter papers are made in various *thicknesses*, and, in general, it is better to employ a thicker paper of more open texture than to select a thinner, more dense paper. Dense papers of greater strength must be used, however, when they are employed with suction or pressure. The chemically resistant hard papers are all characterized by relatively high density and slow filtering. For many organic filtrations the use of two or more open-texture papers or thinner papers is preferable to a single dense or thick paper.

Highly refined analytical-grade papers,[233] which are washed with hydrochloric and hydrofluoric acids and with distilled water, are generally neither required nor desirable for most operations of the organic laboratory. Selection of papers should be made from the more open-texture papers. These give faster filtering rates and are substantially cheaper. An American development has been the preparation of high wet strength filter papers and filter tissues through the use of melamine. Such papers are useful for suction filtrations and for preparing folded filters, since the wet strength is sufficiently high practically to eliminate the danger of breaking the apex of the paper cone under the weight of liquid.

The selection of a filter paper for a particular purpose requires consideration of the qualities of a paper which have been enumerated as follows:[234]

Rapidity is shown as the quantity of liquid that passes through a single small disc of the paper under a standardized set of conditions. Rapidity is also an inexact but nonetheless definite indicator of *retentivity*, and because of this double significance is one of the major control items during manufacture. With papers of equal weight, the slower paper will be the more retentive; and with papers of equal rapidity, the heavier will be the more retentive. It is often necessary, in order to accomplish desired results, to employ two or more laminations of a single grade, or a laminated combination of several grades.

[233] R. Fresenius, *Z. anal. Chem.*, 22, 241 (1883).

[234] Eaton-Dikeman Co., *Filter Paper for Laboratory and Industry*. Mt. Holly Springs, Pa., 1954.

As yet, there is no generally accepted method for exact grading of filter paper for retentivity—as, for instance, on the minimum particle size retained. A general distinction is made for laboratory grades, however, on the basis of ability to retain residue from certain standard solutions—barium sulfate for fine particles, lead sulfate for medium, and ferric hydroxide for coarse or gelatinous materials.

Of the three *surface* finishes—smooth, embossed, and creped—the first two are considered one, inasmuch as embossing is chiefly for identification purposes. Creping, however, completely changes the characteristics by greatly increasing rapidity, somewhat reducing retentivity, and imparting the ability to handle gelatinous or voluminous residues that would quickly block or "blind" a smooth-surfaced paper.

Texture is a result of the kind and treatment of the pulp beforehand and of the processing upon the paper machine. The gradations of texture from very hard to very soft are part and parcel with other controls in producing the individual filtering characteristics of the various grades.

Wet strength is determined, following the rapidity tests, by measuring the height of the water column needed to break the standard test specimen. Certain grades are especially treated to impart a high wet strength, which may be as much as twenty times that of the untreated paper. This treatment also hardens the paper and renders it essentially lintless, but does not degrade its purity or neutrality.

Further information on the properties and uses of filter papers may be obtained from several references.[235-239] Specifications and methods of testing for filter papers by earlier European standards were given by Herzberg.[240] Studies at the U. S. Bureau of Standards[241,242] have also been reported and further methods for testing filter papers are given.[243] A later apparatus and method for determining the filtration speed of filter papers is said to approximate the normal filtration process.[244]

A procedure based on the retention of a finely divided dispersion is used by one manufacturer of filter papers to give numerical test values to different grades.[245] A detailed description of the method of *folding a fluted filter* from circular paper is given by Mann and Saunders.[246] Filter papers

[235] G. Fornstedt, *Revue ingénieur et index tech.*, **21**, 725 (1913); *J. Franklin Inst.*, **176**, 344 (1913).

[236] Schleicher und Schuell-Filtrier Papier, *Chem. Fabrik.*, **6**, Suppl. 2 (1933).

[237] "Laboratory Filter Papers," *Chem. Age*, **28**, 392 (1933).

[238] J. B. Green, *Chem. Age*, **32**, 370 (1935).

[239] "Manufacture and Use of Filter Paper," *Paper Ind.*, **24**, 1176 (1943).

[240] W. Herzberg, *Papierprüfung*. 7th ed., rev., Springer, Berlin, 1932.

[241] H. Bogarty and F. T. Carson, *J. Research Natl. Bur. Standards*, **33**, 353 (1944).

[242] B. W. Scribner and W. K. Wilson, *J. Research Natl. Bur. Standards*, **34**, 453 (1945); **39**, 21 (1947).

[243] "Testing Analytical Filter Papers," *Paper Trade J.*, **122**, 57 (1946).

[244] R. Kroeger and H. G. DeKay, *J. Am. Pharm. Assoc.*, **40**, 213 (1951).

[245] Carl Schleicher and Schuell Co., New York.

[246] F. G. Mann and B. C. Saunders, *Practical Organic Chemistry*. 2nd ed., Longmans, Green, London, 1938.

sometimes are attached to cardboard bases for special applications.[247]   A neoprene-treated filter paper with high wet strength and good chemical resistance is a low-cost "throw-away" filter medium of interest mostly for larger operations, but should be useful for laboratory purposes.[248,249] Filter papers made from borosilicate glass fibers,[250,251] as developed by the U. S. Bureau of Standards, are recommended for use with filter crucibles and other filtering apparatus.   Glass papers as made commercially in 1955[252] are said to contain no binder and to be suitable for use up to 520°C. The use of a black or colored filter paper is of considerable value in the collection and subsequent examination of light-colored particles.[253]

Recent developments in the practical fabrication of felts and/or papers from some of the modern synthetic fibers are of significance for filtration possibilities.   The ultimate success of this development would be of much importance for filter paper uses, since it would extend the applications of paper to higher temperatures, to many corrosive liquids, and, in addition, the synthetic fiber papers would have greater wet strengths and lower liquid retentions.[254,255]

Paper or cellulose pulps may be used as *plugs* or *mats* for gravity filter use, or they may be employed to form *filtering layers* for suction filters. Pulps are frequently useful as filtration accelerators for difficultly filterable materials, in which case the disintegrated pulp is stirred into the material to be filtered.[256,257]   A technique sometimes followed is to add the pulp to the solution before precipitation by the addition of a reagent or a change in temperature.   Paper pulp is supplied as a loose, *fluffy powder* or in the form of compressed *pellets* or *tablets*.   It is not difficult to prepare a satisfactory filtering pulp from paper by disintegrating the same with an efficient laboratory agitator or stirrer, *e.g.*, a high-speed Waring Blendor.[258,259] High-quality filter paper pulp sold in a moist dispersed condition is diluted with water and used.   Also available is a dry-dispersed, ash-free, analytical filter pulp, which may be more convenient to use than tablets or moist pulp.

[247] A. Grüne, *Allgem. Papier-Rundschau*, No. 12, 585 (1950).
[248] F. O'Shaughnessy, *Chem. Eng.*, **52**, No. 6, 169 (1952).
[249] "A Throw-Away Filter Medium," *Canadian Chem. Proc.*, **36**, 50 (1922).
[250] M. J. O'Leary and others, *Tappi*, **35**, 289 (1952).
[251] T. S. Ma and A. A. Benedetti-Pichler, *Anal. Chem.*, **25**, 999 (1953).
[252] H. Reeve Angel and Co., New York.
[253] M. E. Schulz and E. Warnecke, *Milchwissenschaft*, 11, 385 (1951).
[254] Synthetic Fibers, *Chem. Eng.*, **62**, No. 3, 138 (1955).
[255] "Paper from Synthetic Fibers," *Chem. Eng. News*, **33**, 956 (1955).
[256] M. Dittrich, *Ber.*, **37**, 1840 (1904).
[257] E. Bornemann, *Chem.-Ztg.*, **32**, 275 (1908).
[258] F. M. Biffen, *Chemist-Analyst*, **35**, 70 (1946).
[259] S. H. Simonsen, *Chemist-Analyst*, **40**, 21 (1951).

Examples of commercial cellulose pulps suitable for filtration purposes are the Solka-Floc products of Brown Co., Berlin, N. H., and the Filter-masse of Umbach Filtermasse G.m.b.H. of Gernsbach (Baden). Others of equal quality are available. *Prepared pads* and *discs* of paper pulp are commonly used with some types of filters which are useful in laboratory sizes. Pulp filters are used in industry as clarification and "polish" filters functioning frequently as *trap filters* to remove temporary hazes in continuous filtrations or to remove minute traces of very fine turbidity. The efficacy of pulp filtrations for these purposes depends frequently on the adsorptive capacity of cellulose fibers, which varies with the nature of the material being filtered and the character of the fine particles. Paper pulps and pads are sometimes combined with asbestos or other fibers for particular uses.

3. Textiles

Cloths and fabrics woven from many different fibrous materials are useful as filter supports and media. They are much more widely employed with industrial filters than with laboratory equipment, but have numerous advantages for many laboratory filtrations.[260-263] Some further references are given which may be consulted for suggestions from industrial use.[264-268] At times, fabrics are used in laboratory filtrations as a back-up for other media, such as paper or filter powder, and in cases where the open texture of the cloth is desired. In general, a fabric is stronger than paper, and may be washed and re-used. For occasional and general use, almost any type of woven filter fabric may serve, provided that it is chemically resistant to the material being handled, but for more extensive uses and for particular requirements, intelligent selection of the kind and type of cloth is necessary.

The *filtering characteristics* of a filter fabric are determined by the fiber from which it is fabricated, the weight of the cloth, the thread count (strands per inch), the style of weave, and other factors. Smith[267] has discussed in detail the physical properties of fabric filter media in an endeavor to correlate these with filter action. On the basis of this reasoning, new fabric constructions, particularly high-twist yarns, are recommended.[269]

[260] R. Frühling and J. Schuz, *Z. anal. Chem.*, **13**, 146 (1874).

[261] A. Mulhaus, *Kolloid-Z.*, **39**, 37 (1926).

[262] M. Daumas, *Chimie & industrie*, **52**, 10 (1944).

[263] A. J. Gibson, *Bull. Am. Soc. Hosp. Pharm.*, **2**, 68 (1945).

[264] A. A. Campbell, *J. Ind. Eng. Chem.*, **13**, 982 (1921).

[265] A. Wright, *J. Ind. Eng. Chem.*, **13**, 984 (1921).

[266] R. O. Prior and R. G. Walker, *Chem. Met. Eng.*, **45**, 250 (1938).

[267] E. G. Smith, *Chem. Eng. Progress*, **47**, 545 (1951).

[268] M. Dumas, *Ind. Textile*, **62**, 165 (1945).

[269] *A New Slant on Filter Fabrics*, Equipment Development Co., Montclair, N. J., 1952.

Where solids are to be filtered on a fabric in successive cycles, the solids themselves must bridge the apertures of the fabric and form the filtering medium if the fabric is to remain pervious to flow.   In most cloth constructions, nearly all of the fluid flow goes through the yarn itself—only a small part through the apertures.   A study of liquid flow through textile filter media[270] suggests that the flow resistance of felted materials may be expressed by a modification of d'Arcy's law (see Sect. II.2) and by a similar modification for woven fabrics, which follow the viscous flow equation at low velocities.   A "liquid resistance meter" based on an earlier Bureau of Standards apparatus[271] is useful for testing filter media.

Microscopic techniques developed for studying the filtration characteristics of wool and cotton fabrics[272] should also be applicable for other fabrics. Procedures developed for evaluating open-weave fabrics, both textile and metallic wire, may be based on measurements of air permeability.[273]   Cloths from natural fibers, such as cotton, wool, jute, etc., are tighter for comparable weaves than are synthetic fibers or glass cloth because the natural fibers are not smooth, but have finely fibrous surfaces and ends, and frequently are wavy rather than straight.

The weave of a textile determines to an important extent the porosity and flow capacity for filtration.   The principal style weaves are plain, twill, and chain.   For cloths with the same diameter threads and an equal number of strands, the chain weave has the highest porosity, followed by twill weave with medium porosity, and plain weave with minimum porosity. The closeness and thickness of threads in all weaves can be varied within limits by the method of manufacture.   There is a definite distinction between the porosity and permeability of filter fabrics.[274]

The *nonwoven* or *continuous cloths*, which may be considered types of felts, may be made from cotton, rayon, or other fibers and have interesting possibilities for filtration uses.   These materials are insoluble in many organic solvents, have high wet strength, are lintless, and may be sewed.[275]

Cotton and other yarns of soft or open texture may be fabricated into *pads or tubes* which have advantages for the filtration of oils, petroleum products, fruit juices, milk, pharmaceutical products, etc.   Felted yarns may be lightly impregnated with resins or reinforced with fabric backing. The *Fulflo* filter element is made by a special spiral winding of cotton yarn upon a metal supporting core.

[270] G. E. Cunningham, G. Broughton, and R. R. Kraybill, *Ind. Eng. Chem.*, **46,** 1196 (1954).

[271] H. F. Schiefer and P. M. Boyland, *J. Research Natl. Bur. Standards*, **28,** 637 (1942)

[272] C. A. Rodman and A. W. Pansey, *Textile Research J.*, **20,** 873 (1950).

[273] A. F. Robertson, *Textile Research J.*, **20,** 838 (1950).

[274] M. A. Sieminski and G. H. Hotte, *Rayon Textile Monthly*, **25,** 608 (1944).

[275] J. Alibert, *Chimie & industrie*, **58,** 341 (1947).

The *natural fiber* fabrics sometimes swell when wetted. Repeated usage frequently tends to accentuate this, and tight-textured cloths may become very slow in filtering. Cloths selected for use with filter aids or with free-filtering solids should be of medium open texture. Shrinkage of cloths upon drying is a troublesome characteristic, and it is best to preshrink before laboratory use. Commercial cloths are sometimes preshrunk by the manufacturer. Some types of fabric filter media are shown in Figure 42.

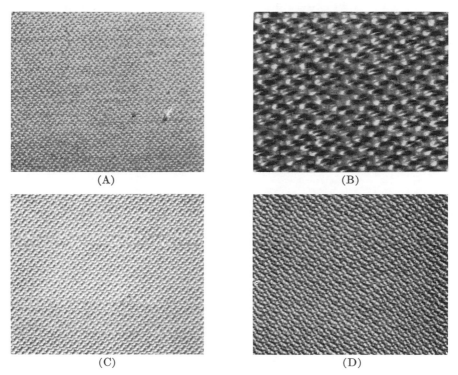

(A)   (B)

(C)   (D)

Fig. 42. Some types of filter fabrics: (A) cotton; (B) woven glass; (C) Vinyon; (D) Orlon. (Courtesy National Filter Media Corp.)

Several different types of synthetic textile materials have been established to have much value as filter media, and new types will undoubtedly continue to be developed. These include rayon, polyvinyl chloride, Vinyon, Orlon, Saran, Perlon, Terylene, polyethylene, and nylon. The advantages in the use of these for filtration are indicated by Williams.[276] A more detailed review[277] classifies available fibers as hydrophilic and hydrophobic

[276] A. W. Williams, *Rayon Synthetic Textiles*, **32**, 119 (1951).
[277] R. Bouvet, *Ind. Eng. Chem.*, **44**, 2125 (1952).

TABLE III. PROPERTIES OF FILTER FABRICS[a]

Classification and trade designation	Resistance to chemicals	Temperature limitations, °F.	Tensile strength of fiber, p.s.i.	Special characteristics
Vinyl fibers (incl. acrylics)				
Orlon.........	Good for most mineral acids, questionable for organic acids. Suitable for weak alkalis, most organic solvents	275 heat stiffens	High 60,000–75,000	Good abrasion resistance and flexural strength
Vinyon N.....	Good for most acids, alkalis, and org. solvents but not for ketones, phenol, and some conc. acids	250	Good	Good abrasion resistance. Continuous filament fabric
Dynel........	Same as Vinyon N	250	Fair	Good abrasion resistance. Spun-staple type fabric, otherwise same as Vinyon N
Saran........	Good for most acids, alkalis, and organic solvents but not for ammonia or conc. H_2SO_4	200	Low	Low abrasion resistance
Acrilan......	Similar to Orlon	275	High	Good abrasion resistance and flexural strength
X-51.........	Similar to Orlon	275	High	Good abrasion resistance and flexural strength
Polyamides				
Nylon........	Good for alkalis, most org. acids and solvents but not for mineral acids or oxidizing agents	250 Yellows and heat stiffens	High 65,000–117,000	Highest abrasion resistance, tough and durable
Perlon L.....	Similar to nylon	250	High	Highest abrasion resistance, tough and durable
Enkalon......	Similar to nylon	250		
Polyesters				
Dacron.......	Good for moderate strength acids and alkalis and for most org. solvents	300	High 78,000–116,000	High abrasion resistance, next to nylon
Terylene.....	Same as Dacron	300	High	High abrasion resistance, next to nylon
Polyethylene				
Reevon polyethylene....	Good for most acids, alkalis, and oxidizing agents and for some org. solvents	180	Low 11,000–30,000	
Tetrafluorethylene				
Teflon.......	Highly inert to most chemicals even at elevated temperatures	450	Fair 50,000–61,000	Good abrasion resistance and flexural strength

Material	Chemical resistance	Temp.	Strength	Other properties
Fluorocarbon Kel-F	Approximately the same as Teflon	350		
Metal — Stainless steel	Good for alkalis and org. acids but not for most mineral acids	1400		
Monel	Good for most acids and alkalis, but not HNO_3 or conc. H_2SO_4	1400		
Cellulose — Cotton	Good for cold dil. alkalis, fair for cold dil. acids, good for many org. solvents, not for strong acids, oxidizing agents, or alkalis	250 weakened by heat	High 59,000–124,000	Favorable for cake formation and pre-coating. Good abrasion resistance
Viscose rayon	Similar to cotton	250	Fair Low wet strength	Fair abrasion resistance
Acetate	Similar to cotton except less resistant to alkalis	250	Fair Fair wet strength	Low abrasion resistance
Arnel	Similar to cotton except less resistant to alkalis	250	Fair Fair wet strength	Low abrasion resistance
Asbestos — Chrysotile	Good for approximately neutral solutions or org. liquids, not for acids or alkalis	750	Low	Good abrasion resistance
Blue fiber	Good for acids and for dil. alkalis	1000	Low	Good abrasion resistance
Protein — Wool	Fair resistance to most acids even when hot but not suitable for alkalis. Fairly good for oxidizing agents	300	Low dry and wet strength	High abrasion resistance and flexural strength
Vicara	Fair resistance to most acids even when hot, fairly good for dil. alkalis and oxidizing agents	300	Low dry and wet strength	Good flexural strength
Glass	Highly resistant to most acids, chemicals, and heat, but only fair resistance to alkalis	600	Highest 200,000	Low flexibility and abrasion resistance, requires careful handling

ᵃ References for the above information include National Filter Media Corp. data sheets; Eimco Corp. filter media literature; T. Shriver and Co., Filter Facts, 4, No. 2; "Symposium on Textile Fibers," Ind. Eng. Chem., 44, 2101–2186 (1952); R. Bouvet, Ind. Eng. Chem., 44, 2125 (1952); "Synthetic-Fiber Table," Textile World, 1954 revision.

and endeavors to correlate fiber–fabric relationships on the basis of the physical properties of the fiber, such as tensile strength, length and diameter of the fibers, moisture absorption, dimensional stability, and stress–strain properties. Some articles describing filter cloths made up of different synthetic fibers are: Vinyon,[278] Saran,[279] Vinyon N,[280] and Dynel.[281]

Synthetic fiber textiles are generally resistant to the action of corrosive chemicals and solvents, but they differ in this respect, depending on composition. Some of these synthetics may be used at temperatures well above the maximum permissible for any natural fiber material. The synthetic fibers have less tendency for swelling or shrinking, are practically free from abrading of minute fiber elements, and are smooth in surface, thus favoring ready removal of solids therefrom. They are also easily washed and cleaned.

Satisfactory filter cloths of woven *glass* have now become commercialized and have numerous applications and advantages. Glass fabric is resistant to acids of all concentrations, is stable at higher temperatures, and is satisfactory for use with most chemicals and solvents with the exception of strong and hot alkalis and hydrogen fluoride. A photograph of a glass filter cloth is shown in Figure 42B. The applicability of glass fabrics as filter cloths depends to a considerable extent upon the method of manufacture.[282]

Asbestos filter fabrics are used where high temperatures must be maintained or where the adsorptive and clarifying capacity of asbestos is desired. Asbestos papers, now available in thicknesses down to 10 mils, are useful for some specialty filtrations. Further reference to asbestos as a filtering medium is made in Section IV.5.

Table III lists some of the various types of filter fabrics and other media of laboratory interest, with some data on properties of importance. The third edition of Ullmann's Encyclopedia[283] contains considerable information on filter fabrics of European manufacture.

4. Metallic Cloths

Woven wire and metallic fabrics are employed for screening, sifting, and straining operations, as referred to in Section III.2. They are also used in the construction of filter elements as support and drainage members and in

[278] A. J. Hall, *Textile Colorist*, **66**, 277 (1944).

[279] E. C. Fetter, *Chem. Eng.*, **54**, 129 (Feb. 1947).

[280] E. W. Rugeley, T. A. Field, and G. H. Fremon, *Ind. Eng. Chem.*, **40**, 1724 (1948).

[281] A. W. Williams, *Am. Dyestuff Reptr.*, **40**, 456 (1951).

[282] E. W. Rugeley, U. S. Pat. 2,355,822 (Aug. 15, 1944).

[283] F. Ullmann, *Encyklopädie der technischen Chemie*. 3rd ed., Urban & Schwarzenburg, Berlin, 1951.

the finer mesh sizes as the filter support itself. The making of good-quality filter screens is part of a highly specialized and well-developed metal fabric industry. *Metal filter screens* are rugged, may be cleaned readily, and can be used repeatedly. They are advantageous for use with all-metal filters. Laboratory usage of metal screens is minor compared to their employment in industrial filters. They are sometimes necessary for large laboratory and pilot-plant filters and may be advantageous for some types of laboratory apparatus.

Filter cloths are manufactured from many metals and alloys—copper, bronze, brass, mild steel, stainless steels, aluminum, nickel, Monel, silver, platinum, etc. Metallic fabrics do not have fine hairlike filaments like natural fibers, and thus are not as readily suited for immediate clarification. On the other hand, the collected solids are more easily removed from a metallic cloth, particularly if fibrous particles are to be removed. The general distinction between metallic fabrics in the trade is based on major usages. *Wire cloth* commonly refers to a group of meshes with visible square or rectangular openings between parallel wires. The weave may be plain or twilled. In metallic fabrics referred to as *filter cloths*, either the shute wires or both warp and shute wires are adjacent, and there are no square or hexagonal openings. Common weaves for filter cloth fabrics are plain Dutch, twilled Dutch, or braided. The more complicated weaves of the metallic filter cloths permit greater permeability than corresponding wire cloth weaves. The latter are best suited for screening and straining.

It is difficult to generalize on the metallic cloth mesh sizes which are best adapted for various purposes because the size required varies with different weaves, the character of the solids, and the purposes of the filtration. Some mesh sizes commonly used without filter aid are 70 × 70, and 12 × 64 (Dutch); and with filter aid, 70 × 80, 80 × 80, 24 × 110 (Dutch), and 30 × 150 (Dutch). In these designations the first number designates the number of warp strands per lineal inch, and the second number the corresponding number of filler strands.

Some weaves and sizes of metallic wire and filter cloths are shown in Figure 43. It is difficult to show the inherent permeability of the filter cloth structure by the usual photograph. This is shown somewhat better by shadowgraphs. For further information on metallic filter cloths certain references may be consulted.[284-286] The producers of metal wire screens supply samples and provide rather complete technical information about their products. Practical tests are sometimes necessary in the selection of the type best suited for a given purpose.

[284] "Use of Metallic Filter Cloth," *Chem. Met. Eng.*, **45,** 253 (1938).

[285] F. J. Van Antwerpen, *Ind. Eng. Chem.*, **32,** 1580 (1940).

[286] G. D. Dickey and C. L. Bryden, *Theory and Practice of Filtration.* Reinhold, New York, 1946.

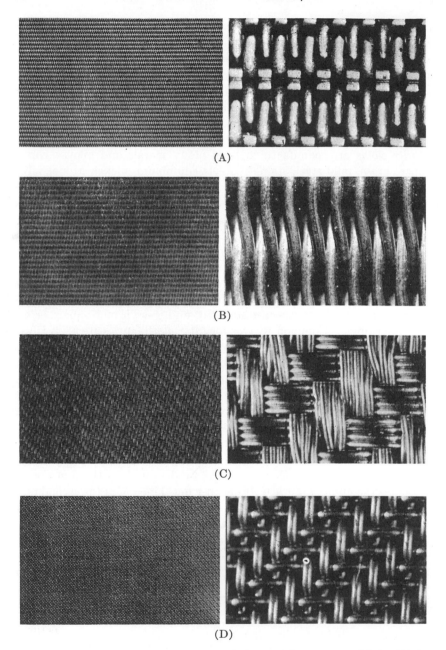

(A)

(B)

(C)

(D)

Fig. 43. Metallic-wire filter cloths (natural size on left; 10× on right): (A) 24 x 110 plain Dutch; (B) 20 x 250 twilled Dutch; (C) AU "Multibraid"; (D) 60 mesh twilled, 0.011 in. wire. (Courtesy Multi-Metal Wire Cloth Co., Inc.)

Metal screens made not from wire but by electroforming processes[287,288] offer the advantages of great mesh uniformity and controlled hole sizes. These screens serve most effectively the purpose lying between those served by perforated metals and woven wire.   These screens are available in nickel, copper, and other pure metals, or in metal combinations—core of one metal surrounded by another.   Sizes are in the mesh equivalents of "25" to "400."   The surfaces of these screens are smooth and they may be easily fabricated in the laboratory shop to provide accurate shapings for filter leaves and apparatus of different shapes and sizes.   The holes in electroformed screen are not straight bore, but are tapered, thus facilitating washing by back-pressure or otherwise.

5. Loose, Fibrous Materials

Cotton, wool, and other organic fibers are of limited use as plugs or mats for gravity and suction filters.[289]   Cotton batting has been used for straining and filtering but has the disadvantage of packing when wetted and subjected to pressure.   Cotton linter matting and sheeting in combination have been employed in the filtration of cellulose acetate.[290]   A useful filter composition[291] consists in the bonding of cotton wadding with polyvinyl alcohol or the like, which provides some rigidity for the mass and which, in addition, may be backed for additional reinforcement with fabric netting or gauze.   Prepared in the forms of discs, pads, or sheets, this type of unwoven cotton is particularly adapted for the filtration of viscous materials, solutions of resins, and emulsions, such as milk.   Other masses of fibrous organic material, jute, shavings, sponge, etc., may be used for some special purposes.

Glass wool is well adapted for use as a nonsorptive, loosely fibrous filtering medium and has been used in the laboratory for many years for funnel and tube filtrations and for other types of apparatus.[292,293]   Glass pipe spools packed with loose glass wool have been reported satisfactory for the filtration of toluene and for chlorine in hydrochloric acid recovery.[294]

The great rigidity of glass filaments provides an advantage over cotton, wool, etc., for many purposes.   The chemical resistance of glass wool made

---

[287] Mykro-Pore of Multi-Metal Wire Cloth Co., New York.

[288] Lekromesh of C. O. Jelliff Mfg. Corp., Southport, Conn.

[289] A. B. Clemence, *J. Anal. Applied Chem.*, **1**, 273 (1887).

[290] L. A. Cox and W. K. Mohney, *Ind. Eng. Chem.*, **45**, 1798 (1953).

[291] G. A. Cruickshank, *U. S. Pat.* 2,32⁻,250 (Aug. 17, 1943).

[292] F. Stolba, *Z. anal. Chem.*, **17**, 79 (1878).

[293] F. Muck, *Z. anal. Chem.*, **19**, 140 (1880).

[294] W. H. Shearon, Jr., H. E. Hall, and J. E. Stevens, Jr., *Modern Chemical Processes*. Vol. I, Reinhold, New York, 1950, pp. 47–55.

this for many years almost the only medium of loose, fibrous nature which could be used with acids. Early types of glass wool, however, were not particularly stable because of a tendency to devitrify, and deterioration in storage was common. Pyrex glass wool is stable, however, and is particularly resistant to heat and chemicals. It is now supplied for laboratory use in convenient rolls from which pads, etc. may be prepared. Long-length glass fibers may be made up into various types of pads or mats, with or without binders and backing. Such compositions are quite useful for many laboratory filtrations, and may be adapted for the screening of liquids, gases, and vapors. Filter mats made from glass fibers have also been employed for some thermobalance studies.[295]

Improved glass fiber filters have found fairly wide application in gas and air filters. Fibers of very fine diameters have been found effective in retaining aerosols. Wider use for laboratory liquid filtration and in colloid and biochemical fields has been predicted.[296] Metallic filaments such as steel, copper, and various alloys may be used as filling for loose fibrous filters or may be utilized in the form of pads.

When loose fibrous materials are employed to make filtering mats or beds it is usual to form the mat from a slurry of the fiber in a liquid. When so doing it is best to pour the slurry onto the filter which has been filled with solvent or liquid to a level above the perforation. The pulp is allowed to settle for a few seconds, and as the excess liquid drains away an even felt is deposited upon the perforated surface. The felt may be adjusted to any thickness and, if suction is employed, a range of porosities is possible.

Loose *asbestos* fiber is a valuable filtering medium for laboratory use.[297-302] For quantitative analysis, such as for Gooch crucible use, the *tremolite* or *amphibole* variety is used. Fiber for Gooch crucible and similar use must be prepared from selected crude of high purity, adequate fiber length, and some flexibility. Acid-washed and ignited grades may also be purchased from laboratory supply dealers or may be prepared in the laboratory.[303,304] Asbestos fiber may be used, loose or in pads, for the filtration and clarifica-

[295] C. Duval, *Anal. Chem.*, **23**, 1271 (1951).

[296] C. A. Smucker and W. C. Marlow, Jr., *Ind. Eng. Chem.*, **46**, 176 (1954).

[297] H. Rodewald and B. Tollens, *Ber.*, **11**, 2076 (1878).

[298] F. A. Gooch, *Chem. News*, **37**, 181 (1878–1879); *Z. anal. Chem.*, **19**, 333 (1880).

[299] F. Allihn, *J. prakt. Chem.*, **22**, 46 (1880).

[300] P. Casamajor, *J. Am. Chem. Soc.*, **3–4**, 248 (1881–1882).

[301] W. P. Barba, *Eng. Mining J.*, **53**, 305 (1892); *J. Anal. Applied Chem.*, **6**, 35 (1892); *Chem. News (London)*, **65**, 101 (1892).

[302] O. Lohse, *Ber.*, **32**, 2142 (1899).

[303] W. F. Hillebrand and G. E. F. Lundell, *Applied Inorganic Analysis*. Wiley, New York, 1929, p. 91.

[304] B. Kaspin, *Ind. Eng. Chem., Anal. Ed.*, **12**, 517 (1940).

tion of organic preparations. Here clean pure *chrysotile* asbestos, which is peculiarly surface active and possesses a definite adsorptive and clarifying capacity, is preferably employed. For exacting requirements the filtering fiber selected must be free or nearly free of reactive iron, calcium, and other impurities. Chrysotile asbestos of high purity from Arizona and some other localities is preferred. Figure 44 shows an amphibole fiber in the preferred condition for Gooch crucible use. A fine grade of chrysotile fiber as prepared for the clarification and "polish" filtration of liquids, or for the fabrication of pads to be used for similar purposes, is shown in Figure 45.

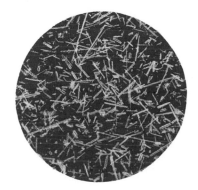 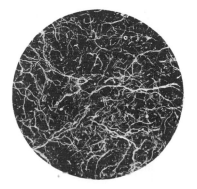

Fig. 44. Amphibole asbestos, prepared for Gooch crucible use (magnification 25×). (Courtesy Johns-Manville Corp.)

Fig. 45. Chrysotile asbestos, as used for filter discs (magnification 25×). (Courtesy Johns-Manville Corp.)

Asbestos may also be used in combination with other fibrous materials, such as cellulose, for the purification and clarification of many organic liquids, biologicals, and laboratory preparations. It has been claimed[305] that dyes, wine, blood serum, strychnine, and other electrically charged substances may be separated from dilute or colloidal solutions by adjusting the pH of the solution to minimum solubility and then filtering through asbestos and kaolin, diatomaceous earth, or other material such as cotton.

Small quantities of material may be filtered in the tube filters described above or with many other types of filtering apparatus. Diatomaceous filter aid powder may be used to advantage as a filtering layer on an asbestos pad.[306,307]

[305] H. Fink, Brit. Pat. 439,251 (Dec. 3, 1935).
[306] J. Grossfeld, *Z. Untersuch. Nahr. u. Genussm.*, **29**, 67 (1915).
[307] H. Bruns, *Gas- u. wasserfach*, **80**, 502 (1937).

TABLE IV. PORE SIZES OF FILTER MEDIA

Material	Grade	Average pore size, μ	Reference
Micro-porous porcelain[a]	XF	50	G. V. Jordan, Jr., Selas Corp. Mech. Eng., 75, 559–63, 566 (1953)
	XFF	20	
	10	4.4	
	015	1.4	
	03	0.60	
	05	0.34	
Porous Teflon filters	CPS-40	Retains 40 μ and larger	Porous Plastic Filter Co., Glen Cove, New York
	CPS-25	Retains 25 μ and larger	
Filter papers	—	Pore size 9 μ	Carl Schleicher & Schuell Co., Keene, New Hampshire
	S & S 604	4.5	
	595	4	
	597	3	
	602	2.2	
	576	1.5	
Membrane and Cella filters	Coarse	3–0.75	Carl Schleicher & Schuell Co., Keene, New Hampshire
	Medium	0.75–0.5	
	Dense	0.5–0.2	
	Very dense	Below 0.2	
Ultrafine and Ultra Cella filters	Coarse	0.2–0.08	Carl Schleicher & Schuell Co., Keene, New Hampshire
	Medium	0.08–0.05	
	Dense	0.05–0.01	
	Very dense	0.01–0.005	
	Super dense	Below 0.005	
18-8 stainless-steel filter elements (porous)	C	165	Micro Metallic Corp. Brooklyn, New York
	D	65	
	E	35	
	F	20	
	G	10	
	H	5	
Porous stainless-steel filter plates	5	6.5	Metal and Plastics Compacts, Ltd., Birmingham, England
	10	12	
	20	18	
	50	33	
	100	46	
	250	70	
Carbon	Fine	20 40	Filtros, Inc., East Rochester, New York

Material	Type/Grade	Pore size	Manufacturer / Source
Calcined refractory clay Type B	Medium	70–100	Filtros, Inc., East Rochester, New York
	Coarse	100–200	
Thermoplastic porous media (German Flexolith)	Plates and sheets	15	
Fused diatomite filter candles	Diaphragms	8	Berkefeld-Filter G.m.b.H., Celle, Germany
	N	3.4	
			Prausnitz, *Glas und keramische Filter im Laboratorium für Filtration, Gasverteilung, Dialyse, Extraction.* Akadem. Verlagsgesellschaft, Leipzig, 1933
	W	9.9	Wilhelm Schuler G.m.b.H., Eisenberg, Germany
	V		
Filterstones, quartz, pantel, carbon, chamotte	10	15–20	
	20	20–40	
	50	50–70	
	100	100–150	
	130	100–200	
Quartz filter plates	Superfix	10	Corning Glass Works, Corning, New York
Pyrex fritted glass filters	Extra-coarse	170–220	
	Coarse	40–60	
	Medium	10–15	
	Fine	4–5.5	
	Ultra-fine	0.9–1.4	
Metal cloths Mykro-Pore (can be supplied with openings from 30 μ up in pure Ni or other metals such as Fe and Cu which can be electrodeposited)	Class EL	30	Multi-Metal Wire Cloth Co., New York
Plain Dutch	24 × 110	245	
Twilled	20 × 250	100	
	30 × 250	65	
	50 × 600	70	
	100 × 1000	50	
Standard testing sieves	100 × 100	149	Newark Wire Cloth Co., Newark, New Jersey
	140 × 140	105	
	200 × 200	74	
	325 × 325	44	
	400 × 400	37	
Sintered fiber glass filters	A	145–175	Ace Glass, Inc., Vineland, New Jersey
	B	70–100	
	C	25–50	
	D	10–20	
	E	4–8	

[a] Pore size determined by bubbling pressure.

6. Rigid Filter Media

The uses for rigid porous filter bodies and septa are based mostly on the durability of such media and their adaptability for various types of filtering apparatus. The term "rigid filter medium" as used here includes porous materials and compositions, the openings of which are finer than those of perforated plates or discs, fabrics, or screens. The extreme in minute pore size is found in the types of filter elements used for bacteriological and sterilization filtrations, which are referred to in Section VI.4. The coarser pore size media are filter stones and discs, as used mostly for percolation filters. Intermediate in pore size are a considerable number of filter media which are described in categories of composition.

Originally most rigid filters were made of carbon or of various ceramic compositions, both of which are highly resistant to chemicals. Later developments resulted in the use of satisfactory rigid filter members made from sintered metals, alumina, glass, and finally various chemically resistant organic materials, granules of which are also sintered to give porous bodies.

Among the advantages of rigid filters are high strength, simplicity in use, positive action in clarifying and long life. A disadvantage in the use of rigid filters is difficulty in cleaning. This is so troublesome with some types of organic mixtures which plug and fill the pores that the filters must be discarded after one or at most a few uses. In other cases, scrubbing, washing, solvent treatment, or calcination solves the cleaning problem satisfactorily. Another difficulty with rigid filters is usually a low rate of filtration or a relatively short filtration cycle unless the liquids concerned are quite free-filtering. Another characteristic of rigid filters is their variable adsorptive effect, particularly with the finer pored filters. Thus, the filtrate composition may be quite different at the start of a filtration from that at the later stages. The porosity and permeability of rigid filters determines their suitability for different purposes. Methods for determining these properties have been given.[308-311]

Standards adopted for eight grades of sintered disc filters for laboratory use specify the maximum pore sizes and uniformities permissible for such filters made of sintered glass, silica, unglazed ceramic materials, and metals.[312] Table IV gives the characteristics of some rigid porous filters.

[308] A. Einstein and H. Mühas, *Deut. med. Wochschr.*, **49**, 1012 (1923).

[309] S. Mudd, "Filters and Filtration," in Rivers, ed., *Filterable Viruses*. Williams & Wilkins, Baltimore, 1928, pp. 55–94.

[310] H. Ruoss, *Kolloid-Z.*, **74**, 221 (1936).

[311] H. Knöll, *Z. Hyg. Infektionskrankh.*, **121** (3), 298 (1938).

[312] Brit. Standard 1752, British Standards Inst., London, 1952.

The values for pore sizes are approximate since methods for determining this property are not always the same.

A. ALUMINA AND CARBON

Aluminum oxide filter discs, cones, dishes, thimbles, and crucibles are noteworthy because of extreme chemical resistance and heat stability. Ranges in degree of pore size are claimed to be from 0.1 to 30.0 microns. *Alundum* filter members of many shapes and sizes are fabricated from alumina granules fused in the electric furnace with a small proportion of an alumina glass which is used as a bond.   With *Aloxite*, crystalline grains of aluminum oxide are bonded with a suitable ceramic flux and converted to a substantially glassy state by high-temperature firing.   Some details of the properties and techniques used in preparing sintered alumina for filtration purposes have been given.[313]

Porous carbon ware is provided in the forms of round discs, tubes, cylinders, and plates, either plain or grooved.   Acids (including hydrofluoric) in all concentrations and at any temperature are safely handled.   These carbons are resistant to thermal shock and have good mechanical and abrasion-resistant properties.   Grades range from fine to coarse—20 micron to 200 micron pore sizes—with corresponding permeabilities.   In the fabrication of porous carbon ware mixtures of carbon of graphitic nature and granular carbons are bonded with small amounts of inert bonding agents.

B. METALLIC SEPTA

Rigid metallic filter members may consist of discs or plates with fine perforations, edge or disc elements, wound-wire cylinders, or plates of sintered metals or alloys.

Finely Perforated.   Small filter septa made from perforated metal plate are useful in the laboratory mostly for high-pressure filtrations or as backing for some more flexible medium.   Metallic filtering webs and sheets have been developed for the paper industry and some of these are adaptable for laboratory purposes.   Openings may be circular or elongated slits.

Edge or Disc Elements.   Edge or disc filter elements consist of a series of thin discs, with open center spaces, mounted in a support or frame which permits variable pressure to be applied to the assembly.   Filtration takes place through the thin spaces between adjacent discs toward the core, which serves as the filtrate collector and outlet.   Coarse and relatively fine filtrations may be carried out with filters of this type.   They are suitable for either pressure or suction use.   Discs may be of paper, fabric, plastics, and

[313] D. L. Deadmore, *Ceram. Age*, **56**, 15, 23 (1951).

other materials, as well as of metals. *Edge filters* were invented by Danchell in 1889 and have been improved subsequently in many different ways.[314,315] Numerous small edge filters, completely assembled, are available from different manufacturers (Metal Edge Filter Corp., Cuno Engineering Co., Steam-Line Filter, Skinner Purifiers, Inc., and others). Figure 46A shows a filter for pressure use and 46B one for suction.[316] The *Metafilter* is a type of edge filter with wedge-shaped openings, which adapt this filter well for use with filter aids.[317] The structure of this type of filter element, as well as that of other modified Metafilters, consists of a column of scalloped rings, which comprise, in effect, a cylinder with a plurality of circumferential slits of precise dimensions. The gaps separating

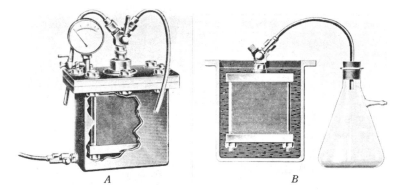

A   *B*

Fig. 46. Edge filters: (A) for pressure use; (B) for vacuum use. (After Pickard.[316])

the edges of consecutive rings determine the space dimension that is effective in the filtering action. Metafilters are provided with permanent, metallic rings or with disposable discs of cellulosic nature.

Wound Wire. Metallic wires wound on a *cylindrical support* make an efficient filter medium for both vacuum and pressure filters. The spaces between adjacent windings permit the passage of liquid and hold back the solids. These elements are best suited for use with a filter aid or with free-filtering solids. A commercial element suitable for laboratory filters is used in the *Stellar* filter. The cylindrical Pur-O-Cel filter element has spun stainless-steel metal bands of trapezoidal cross section, the spacing be-

[314] H. S. Hele-Shaw and J. A. Pickard, U. S. Pat. 1,744,510 (January 21, 1930); also Brit. Pats. 210,101, 210,376, and 227,890.

[315] J. W. Hinchley, *J. Soc. Chem. Ind.*, **44**, 117T (1925).

[316] J. A. Pickard, *Filtration and Filters*. Benn, London, 1929.

[317] J. A. Pickard, *Ind. Chemist*, **4**, 505 (1928); *J. Soc. Chem. Ind.*, **49**, 260T (1930); "Metafiltration," in J. Alexander, ed., *Colloid Chemistry, Theoretical and Applied*, Vol. III, Chemical Catalog Co., New York, 1931, pp. 215–224.

tween which can be regulated.[318] Metallic, wound filter elements have been used extensively during the past few years for water filtration,[319,320] but are equally adaptable in the smaller sizes for many filtrations in the organic laboratory.

Sintered Metals. The techniques of powder metallurgy and related arts have resulted in a variety of porous plates and septa of sintered metals and alloys. For use as filter media, such compositions are strong, have high porosity and high temperature resistance, and are chemically inert.[321,322] Materials used include stainless steel, Monel, nickel, stellite, bronze, and others. The method of manufacture has been described in considerable detail.[323-326]

Sintered stainless steel filter apparatus includes crucibles, Büchner funnels, immersion tubes, beaker filters, and other forms.[327] They are suitable for all alkalis—hot or cold—and for most salt solutions and organic liquids, but cannot be used for hydrochloric acid, hot dilute sulfuric acid, or hot concentrated nitric acid. Monel and Hastelloy B and C alloy elements are also fabricated. Sintered metal filter elements have graded porosities, varying from coarse to superfine. Many grades of stainless-steel or bronze filter plates, ranging in approximate mean pore size from 5 to 165 microns are available commercially. They are now being marketed in various forms (cylindrical, bayonet-type, star-type, and others) for laboratory and commercial filters of several types. Filter assemblies, complete with fixtures, are available. The development of sintered metal filter media constitutes an important advance in filter technology.

C. ORGANIC MATERIALS

Hard rubber has numerous advantages for use as a rigid filter me-

[318] *Pur-O-Cel Pressure Filter*, Bulletin 1550, Proportioneers, Inc., Providence, R. I., 1947.

[319] G. R. Bell, "Filter Aid Filtration of Water," in *Proceedings of the 14th Annual Water Conference*, Engineers' Society of Western Pennsylvania, Pittsburgh, Pa., October 19, 1953.

[320] G. R. Bell, *Report of the Symposium on Advance Base Water Supply and Sanitation*, U. S. Naval Civil Engineering Research and Evaluation Laboratory, Port Hueneme, Cal., Oct. 8, 1953.

[321] L. Schlecht and G. Trageser, *Chem. Fabrik*, **12**, (19/20), 243 (1939).

[322] *Announcing a New Filter Medium*, Micro Metallic Co., Forest Hills, N. Y., 1946.

[323] E. W. Reinsch, *Product Eng.*, **15**, 769 (1944).

[324] P. Schwarzkopf, *Product Eng.*, **17**, 268 (1946).

[325] M. J. Viode, *Les metaux poreux filtrants*. Presses Documentaires, Paris, 1951.

[326] C. E. Sinclair, Symposium on Powder Metallurgy, Iron and Steel Inst. (London), Spec. Report No. 3B, 105 (1947).

[327] A. J. Langhammer and P. Glick, *Product Eng.*, **24**, 179 (1953).

dium.[328-330]   In addition to perforated pieces made mechanically, micro-porous rubber sheets, plates, discs, etc., are made by a special process with openings of minute size.   The pores are formed when the natural latex is processed into sheet form.   Pore diameters range from 0.003 to 0.012 inch. Rubber filter media have less tendency toward blinding than do media fabricated from natural fibers.   Solids collected on smooth rubber surfaces are readily removed either mechanically or by washing and are free from fibrous contamination.   A review of porous rubber for filter use has been published,[331] and a general description of different processes for their fabrication is also available.[332]

Synthetic rubbers, high polymers, thermosetting resins, and other organic compounds which may be processed or cured to provide hard, porous compositions have possibilities for use as filter members.   "Brandolstein" filter elements, in the form of plates, cylinders, etc., are made with cresol-formaldehyde resins as the bonding agent.   Filter plates made of sintered plastics were developed in Germany and used widely during the war instead of filter cloths.

Porous Teflon (du Pont) or Kel-F (M. W. Kellogg Co.) filter discs in sizes up to 15 inch diameter are nonabsorbent, have no strength reduction when wetted, and are stable up to 450°C.   In the preparation of Kel-F discs powdered polytrifluorochloroethylene is cold molded at high pressures and then comminuted to obtain a 30 to 300 mesh fraction, which particles are again cold molded and sintered at a temperature below 250°C.[333,334] Pore sizes of these fluorothene filter elements are stated to be from 9 to 15 microns.   Chemical resistance is great although some swelling occurs with highly halogenated organic solvents and some aromatics.[335]

D. CERAMIC COMPOSITIONS

Natural porous siliceous stones have been used from early times for filtering,[336,337] but are not of much interest for present-day laboratory use.

[328] M. Wilderman, *Chemistry & Industry*, **46**, 51 (1927).

[329] H. Danneel, *Korrosion*, **6**, 33 (1931).

[330] H. Beckmann, *Elecktrotech. Z.*, **51**, 1605 (1930); *Chem. Fabrik*, **4**, 322 (1931); *Z. angew. Chem.*, **44**, 568 (1931); *Kautschuk*, **7**, 149 (1931).

[331] E. Vossen, "Filterkörper aus porösem Hartgummi," *Dechema Monographien*. Vol. 4, No. 40, Verlag Chemie, Berlin, 1932, pp. 41–48.

[332] F. J. Van Antwerpen, *Ind. Eng. Chem.*, **32**, 1580 (1940).

[333] M. A. Coler, U. S. Pat. 2,573,639 (Oct. 31, 1951).

[334] W. H. Reysen, D. S. Napolitan, W. T. Daniel, and R. H. Lafferty, Jr., *Modern Plastics*, **28**, 102 (1951).

[335] J. A. Jupa, *Chem. Eng.*, **61**, 272 (June 1954).

[336] P. Bolley, *Ann. Chem.-u. Pharm.*, **91**, 116 (1855).

[337] R. Bunsen, *Ann.*, **148**, 269 (1868).

Buddeus in 1905 proposed the replacement of Witt porcelain filter pads by stone discs, fitted with an asbestos ring.[338] Fabricated silica filters, on the other hand, have been used rather extensively for many years in Europe, both industrially and in the laboratory.[339-343] In the preparation of siliceous filter stones, graded sand is bonded with a ceramic flux and fired at high temperatures. Manegold et al.[344] have listed the properties of these filter media in comparison to porous rubber and other filter materials.

A siliceous filter material, Filtros, is composed of high-purity quartz sand, carefully graded and bonded with a vitreous silicate. Filtros filter plates, discs, cylinders, and tubes have relatively large pore structure (55 to 300 microns) but this structure is uniform and the permeability is high.[345] A method for determining the pressure drop in porous quartz filters is based on air permeability.[346]

Diatomaceous earth is the base material for Berkefeld[347-349] filter candles, widely used for more than 50 years. These filter elements are mostly used as vacuum and pressure filter elements for the filtration of bacteriological and biological materials and are referred to further in Sections VI.4 and VI.5. Rigid diatomite filters are also widely used for water filtration. They are supplied in different porosities and types. Allen Filter Co., Toledo, Ohio, produces the *Mandler* filter, which is commonly used in America.[350] An example of the use of the Mandler filter is in the preparation of autoclaved pectin solutions to be used as a blood plasma extender.[351]

Clay and Porcelain. High mechanical strength, resistance to abrasion, and variable but controlled degrees of fine porosities are among the advantages of clay and porcelain products as filter media.

In 1884, a "porcelain" or rigid clay filter was developed[352] in the form of

[338] Lassar Cohn, *Organic Laboratory Methods*. Williams & Wilkins, Baltimore, 1928.

[339] M. Buddeus, *Z. angew. Chem.*, **17**, 1953 (1904).

[340] W. Kill, *Chem.-Ztg.*, **43**, 262 (1919).

[341] W. Stollenwerk, *Z. angew. Chem.*, **40**, 203 (1927).

[342] H. Schmidt, *Chem. Apparatur*, **18**, 222, 233 (1931).

[343] H. Rudolf, *Chem. Fabrik*, **5**, 137 (1932); *Brennstoff-Chem.*, **13**, 95 (1932); *Chem.-Ztg.*, **60**, 235 (1936).

[344] E. Manegold, R. Hoffman, and K. Solf, *Kolloid-Z.*, **56**, 267 (1931); **57**, 23 (1931).

[345] *Filtros Porous Ceramic Media*, Catalog No. 10, Filtros Inc., 1952.

[346] H. Keller, *Schweiz. Bauz.*, **72**, 617 (1954).

[347] G. W. Reye, *Wagner's Jahresber. Fortschrift Chem. Tech.*, **26**, 201, 209, 210, 529 (1880).

[348] H. Nordtmeyer, *Z. Hyg. Infektionskrankh.*, **10**, 145 (1891).

[349] H. Bitter, *Z. Hyg. Infektionskrankh.*, **10**, 155 (1891).

[350] L. W. Shull, U. S. Pat. 1,336,591 (April 13, 1920).

[351] T. H. Schultz, H. Lotzkar, H. S. Owens, and W. D. Maclay, *J. Am. Pharm. Assoc.*, **41**, 251 (1952).

[352] C. Chamberland, Compt. rend., **99**, 247 (1884).

a hollow, unglazed candle closed at one end and fitted at the other end with a glazed porcelain enamel nipple to permit collection of the filtrate. While originally described for the preparation of bacteriologically pure water, these types of filters rapidly found use for bacteriological filtrations of many kinds and became known as Pasteur-Chamberland filters (Société Anonyme Filtre, Chamberland Système Pasteur, Paris). They are a convenient and useful type of filter for many laboratory purposes. Further details on these filters and their use are given in Section VI.4. The Pukall filter[353] is an early porous clay filter of another type. Similar filter elements and complete filters are produced by Coors Porcelain Co. and Selas Corp. in America, by Doulton & Co. in England, by Maassen and Polenske, Reichsgesundheitsamt, in Berlin, and others.

Ceramic filter elements are made up of mixtures of finely ground kaolin and quartz, calcined at temperatures sufficient to bond the mass but not so high as to sinter the particles excessively. Different degrees of porosity are obtained by controlling the fineness of the ingredients, the moisture content of the mix, and the degree of firing. Finely divided organic matter which is burned out may be added for greater porosity. The pore size and particle-retaining characteristics of ceramic filters have been the subject of various investigations.[354]

In a refinement the ceramic composition containing carbon constituents is first fired in an inert atmosphere at a temperature sufficient to sinter the ceramic components, but the carbon matter is not fully oxidized. In this manner pore spaces are occupied by the carbonaceous particles. In a second firing at a lower temperature, but in an oxidizing atmosphere, the carbon is burned out, leaving the final porous composition.[355]

Sintered Glass. Fritted, porous glass compositions have become one of the most versatile filter media for laboratory use. Plates, discs, and similar shapes are fitted into crucibles, funnels, dishes, etc., thus making these convenient forms of filtering apparatus available for use without paper, cloth, or other media. The permeability of the glass septa may be varied within a wide range. A high degree of uniformity is also obtained.

Porous glass diaphragms were initially developed in about 1920 for use in voltmeter cells for electric meters.[356] During 1923 and 1924, sintered glass compositions were adapted and modified for use in laboratory

[353] W. Pukall, *Ber.*, **26**, 1159 (1893).

[354] S. Mudd, "Filters and Filtration," in T. M. Rivers, ed., *Filterable Viruses*. Williams and Wilkins, Baltimore, 1928, pp. 55–94.

[355] E. Blaha, U. S. Pat. 2,360,929 (Oct. 24, 1944).

[356] M. Grossman, German Pat. 389,763; U. S. Pat. 1,557,931 (Oct. 20, 1925).

filters,[357] and the advantages of this type of apparatus were quickly appreciated.[358-362]

In the preparation of sintered glass filter septa, high-quality laboratory glass of low expansion coefficient and negligible solubility such as Pyrex and Jena glasses (or quartz) is finely ground, and sifted to desired grain sizes, and the powder is formed in suitable molds, after which the desired degree of sintering is produced by careful firing. The porous discs are sealed to the glass apparatus by fusing with the blowpipe or with mechanical equipment.[363] Methods for preparing sintered glass filters in the laboratory have been described.[364-366]

The porosity of sintered glass filter septa depends on the size of glass grains selected and the degree of heating. The porosities available range from average pore sizes as determined by Bechhold's method[367] of 200 or more microns down to less than 2 microns.

The development of porous, sintered glass septa has permitted the fabrication of numerous new and convenient laboratory devices for filtration, dialysis, extraction, etc. For laboratory manipulations the *integral sealing* of porous glass diaphragms to glass apparatus may be considered one of the more important advances in apparatus design since the turn of the century. The *transparency* of all-glass apparatus can be a great advantage, permitting filtration behavior and formation of the solid layer to be observed continuously. The chemical resistance of glass makes this type of apparatus suitable for nearly all solutions and solvents. Many types of filter apparatus embodying sintered glass septa have been produced and are now included as standard items in chemical supply catalogs. These include tubes, crucibles, dishes, funnels, filter sticks, plates, and numerous specialized items for microfiltration. Figure 47 illustrates various pieces of laboratory apparatus fitted with sintered glass filter members. Prausnitz[368-370]

[357] P. H. Prausnitz, *Chem.-Ztg.*, **48**, 109 (1924); *Ind. Eng. Chem.*, **16**, 370 (1924); *Analyst*, **50**, 440 (1925); German Pat. 407,769; U. S. Pat. 1,620,815 (March 15, 1927).

[358] G. F. Huttig and M. Nette, *Z. anal. Chem.*, **65**, 385 (1925).

[359] E. F. Skinner, *Brit. Med. J.*, **1925**, *II*, 516.

[360] A. Heiduschka and A. Muth, *Pharm.-Ztg.*, **72**, 1614 (1927).

[361] P. Schugt, *Apoth.-Ztg.*, **45**, 393 (1930).

[362] A. J. Schattenstein, *J. Chem. Ind. (U. S. S. R.)*, **6**, 1800 (1929).

[363] W. F. Bruce and H. E. Bent, *J. Am. Chem. Soc.*, **53**, 990 (1931).

[364] P. L. Kirk, R. Craig, and R. S. Rosenfels, *Ind. Eng. Chem., Anal. Ed.*, **6**, 154 (1934).

[365] P. L. Kirk, *Ind. Eng. Chem., Anal. Ed.*, **7**, 135 (1935).

[366] R. D. Cool and J. D. Graham, *Ind. Eng. Chem., Anal. Ed.*, **6**, 479 (1934).

[367] H. Bechhold, *Z. physik. Chem.*, **64**, 328 (1908).

[368] P. H. Prausnitz, *Kolloid-Z.*, **50**, 77, 167 (1930).

[369] P. H. Prausnitz, "Praktische Erfahrungen über Filbration mit Glasfiltergeräten," *Dechema Monographien.* Vol. 4, No. 38, Verlag Chemie, Berlin, 1932, pp. 7–30.

[370] P. H. Prausnitz, *Glas-und Keramische Filter im Laboratorium für Filtration, Gasverteilung, Dialyse, Extraktion.* Akadem. Verlagsgesellschaft, Leipzig, 1933.

has given detailed accounts of glass and ceramic filters for laboratory uses. Fritted glass fiber discs are also used in many types of laboratory apparatus.[371] The manufacturers of this medium claim several advantages over ordinary fritted glass.

A convenient, small-scale laboratory filter unit suitable for ultrafine filtrations is improvised from a Pyrex UF 30 sintered glass filter fitted by

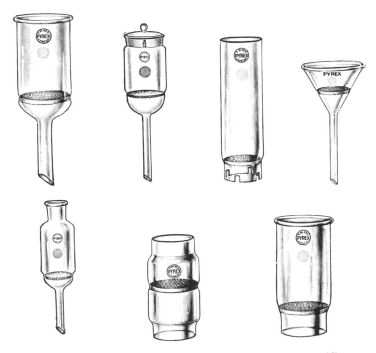

Fig. 47. Laboratory filter apparatus fitted with sintered glass septa. (Courtesy Corning Glass Works.)

rubber tubing onto a condenser coupling and a test tube.[372] Many reported uses of sintered glass filters in organic chemistry should suggest similar applications. Only a few examples can be given here. When azobenzene in alcoholic solution is filtered through glass filters it is freed from insoluble active impurities which tend to prevent good crystallization.[373] Sintered glass filters of the pipeline type are reported useful for the bulk filtration of parenteral solutions.[374]

[371] W. O. Luertzing (Ace Glass, Inc.), U. S. Pat. 2,136,170 (Nov. 8, 1938).
[372] I. N. Asheshov, *Science*, **112**, 402 (1950).
[373] V. I. Danilov and D. S. Kamenetskaya, *Zhur. Eksptl. Teort. Fiz.*, **18**, 313 (1948).
[374] W. C. Gosby and J. C. H. Hanson, *Pharm. J.*, **165**, 417 (1950).

Experiments show that filtration through sintered glass does not lower appreciably the concentration of strychnine hydrochloride solutions in the concentrations used for injection.[375]   An example of the use of a sintered glass disc in the preparation of radioactive precipitates is suggestive.[376] In a study on the stability of thiamine hydrochloride injection solutions as affected by filtration techniques, it was concluded that a Pyrex fritted glass candle-type filter is most satisfactory.[377]   Fritted glass filters are reported satisfactory for the filtration of carbon tetrachloride solutions or extracts of oil-containing refinery effluents.[378]

7. Filter Aids

A. GENERAL

When difficulties are encountered in laboratory filtrations, either in obtaining adequate throughput of filtrate or in the degree of clarity of the same, it is customary to employ a filter aid.   Selection of the proper filter aid may substantially increase the rate of filtration, or provide the desired degree of clarification, or both.   Various materials, such as rigid granular precipitates, mineral powders, some organic products, including fibers, paper pulp, sawdust, etc., and particularly diatomaceous silica, have merit for use as filter aids.[379]

The main function of a filter aid is to build up a *porous permeable*, and *rigid lattice structure* which can retain the solid particles and allow the liquid to pass through the numerous interstices and channels.   The effect is a spacing of the impurities which prevents the sliming over and plugging of the filtering surface.   The rigidity of the filter aid matrix minimizes the compressibility of the collected solids, which would be detrimental to a satisfactory filtering rate.   The action of filter aids thus tends to counteract the unfavorable characteristics of badly filtering materials.   In practice, filter aids are usually added directly to the suspension to be filtered and thus a complex filter cake is formed of both filter aid particles and the solids to be removed.   Adsorption effects may play a part in filtrations with some filter aids[380,381] and with some materials, but in general the action is physical and dependent on the porous lattice structure.   Characteristics of importance for filter aids are: (1) structure which permits formation of a per-

[375] R. G. Taylor, *Australasian J. Pharm.*, **32**, 118 (1951).

[376] J. J. Pinajian and J. M. Cross, *Anal. Chem.*, **23**, 1056 (1951).

[377] A. Taub and S. Paikoff, *J. Am. Pharm. Assoc.*, **41**, 248 (1952).

[378] W. S. Levine, G. S. Mapes, and M. J. Roddy, *Anal. Chem.*, **25**, 1840 (1953).

[379] T. Shriver and Co., *Filter Facts*, **5**, 3 (1954).

[380] H. L. Olin, F. V. Morrison, J. S. Rogers, and G. H. Nelson, *Trans. Am. Inst. Chem. Engrs.*, **18**, 379 (1926).

[381] H. L. Olin, N. A. Skow, and L. Zapf, *Trans. Am. Inst. Chem. Engrs.*, **20**, 251 (1927).

vious cake; (*2*) fineness suitable for the retention of solids as required;
(*3*) ability to remain suspended in the liquid; (*4*) freedom from impurities; (*5*) inertness in the liquid; and (*6*) freedom from moisture in cases
where it is undesirable.

B. DIATOMACEOUS SILICA

Diatomaceous silica has properties peculiarly suited for its use as a
filter aid. Specially prepared diatomaceous products for laboratory and
pilot-plant use are now stocked by nearly all laboratory supply houses and
are familiar to most laboratory workers.

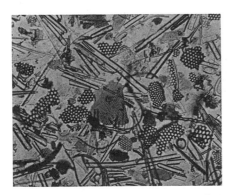

Fig. 48. Celite Analytical Filter Aid
(magnification 300×). (Courtesy Johns-
Manville Corp.)

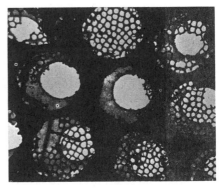

Fig. 49. Electron micrograph of diatomaceous filter aid (magnification 6000×).
(Courtesy Johns-Manville Corp.)

Naturally occurring diatomaceous earth varies greatly in its properties
and only the best qualities are selected for the preparation of filter aids.
Some of the qualities for pharmaceutical use,[382,383] for serums,[384] and for
general uses[385–389] are well established. While many of the grades of commercial filter aids (Filter-Cel, Standard Super-Cel, Hyflo Super-Cel,
Superaid, Speedplus, and Speed Flow) are used for laboratory purposes, a
more highly refined product such as Celite Analytical Filter Aid is required

[382] J. Moss, *Yearbook of Pharmacy*, with *Trans. Brit. Pharm. Conference*, **1898**, pp.
337–345; Abstract, *Proc. Am. Pharm. Assoc.*, **47**, 612 (1899).

[383] N. I. Hendey, *Chemist & Druggist*, **113**, 123 (1930); *Pharm. J.*, **125**, 97 (1930).

[384] G. E. Ewe, *J. Lab. Clin. Med.*, **5**, 538 (1920).

[385] C. P. Derleth, *J. Ind. Eng. Chem.*, **13**, 989 (1921).

[386] J. H. Lorenzen, *Apoth.-Ztg.*, **43**, 1035 (1928).

[387] A. B. Cummins, *Ind. Eng. Chem.*, **34**, 403 (1942).

[388] J. Ferenyi, *Die Filtration mit aktivierten Kieselguren.* Enke, Stuttgart, 1941.

[389] E. D. Stewart, M. W. Brenner, and M. J. Mayer, *Am. Brewer*, **85**, 29 (1952).

for many laboratory uses.[390]   A photomicrograph of this product at a magnification of 300 diameters (Fig. 48) shows the general distribution of diatom particles.   Figure 49 is an electron micrograph at a magnification of 6000×.   This shows the intricate structure and fine pore openings in the particles.   Many references describe the use of Celite Analytical Filter Aid in standardized test procedures and in preparative work.[391-396]

Celite 521[397,398] is another type of calcined and acid-purified product used particularly for the filtration of biological and pharmaceutical preparations, drugs, fine chemicals, and distilled spirits.   Laboratory Standard Filter-Cel is a carefully standardized natural diatomaceous filter aid and is used widely as a standard reference material in evaluating the refining qualities of raw sugars[399] and for testing filter aids themselves.

Sorbo-Cel is an activated filter aid with electropositive characteristics[400] which has unusual capacity for the sorption and removal of traces of oils from waters, extracts, and other liquid mixtures.[401-404]   Filter aids coated with oligodynamic silver[405] have been recommended for sterilization filtrations.   Examples of the use of diatomaceous silica filter aids in the laboratory, with detail on the techniques employed are numerous.   A few references to illustrate different types of uses are: for preparation of sugar liquors and sirups for color determination;[406,407] for clarifying olive oil;[408] in the filtration of cat tissues for the determination of free amino

[390] *Celite Analytical Filter Aid*, Cenco News Chat No. 64, Central Scientific Co. Chicago, 1949.

[391] F. W. Zerban, *J. Assoc. Official Agr. Chemists,* **35,** 636 (1952); **36,** 250 (1953); **37,** 292 (1954).

[392] T. R. Gillett and others, Subject No. 3, *Report for the 11th Session International Commission for Uniform Methods of Sugar Analysis,* Paris, June, 1954.

[393] F. W. Zerban, L. Sattler, and J. Martin, *Anal. Chem.,* **23,** 308 (1951).

[394] K. T. Williams, A. Benvenue, and B. Washauer, *J. Assoc. Official Agr. Chemists,* **33,** 986 (1950).

[395] L. E. Tufts and others, *J. Assoc. Official Agr. Chemists,* **33,** 976 (1950).

[396] K. T. Williams, E. F. Potter, A. Benvenue, and W. R. Scurzi, *J. Assoc. Official Agr. Chemists,* **32,** 698 (1949).

[397] "New Chemicals of Commerce," *Chem. Industries,* **37,** 555 (1935).

[398] Trade literature, Johns-Manville Corp., New York.

[399] H. I. Knowles, *Intern. Sugar J.,* **52,** 195 (1950).

[400] *Chem. Met. Eng.,* **51,** 142 (1944).

[401] I. L. Plummer and J. H. Peebles, *Power,* **95,** 75 (1951).

[402] Bulletin FA-46A, Johns-Manville Corp., New York, Oct., 1953.

[403] A. B. Cummins, U. S. Pat. 2,036,258 (April 7, 1936).

[404] M. Dobier, *Pulp Paper Mag. Can.,* **53,** 175 (Sept., 1952).

[405] A. Goetz, U. S. Pat. 2,508,602 (May 23, 1950).

[406] P. F. Meads and T. R. Gillett, *Anal. Chem.,* **21,** 1494 (1949).

[407] H. C. S. De Whalley, *Proc. Intern. Comm. Uniform Methods Sugar Analysis,* 10th Session, Brussels, 1949.

[408] D. A. Benfield and R. S. Young, *Chemist-Analyst,* **41,** 94 (1952).

acids therein;[409] for treatment of honey;[410] for procedures in measuring the retention of polysaccharide beater additives;[411] for preparation of amylose from starch;[412] and for isolation of enzymes.[413]

When diatomaceous silica is used for long-time filtrations, standardized grades of the material in powder form are commonly employed in two ways: (1) as a "precoat" or thin clean layer, about $1/16$ in. thick, which is applied directly on the filter medium; (2) as an "addition" in amounts varying from less than 0.01% to as much as 4% or more in weight of the liquid to be filtered. The purpose of the precoat is to provide a clarifying layer which acts immediately to remove particles at the start of the filtration. The filter medium is also kept clean by the precoat and the filter cake may be removed readily therefrom at the conclusion of the filtration. In the laboratory the equivalents of these two important procedures may be followed. Since costs are not paramount in laboratory work, the liberal use of filter powder is usually advantageous; but care must be taken not to employ too large an excess, otherwise the advantage of using the filter aid may be defeated. With this reservation there are few limitations to the use of filter aids in the laboratory and much time and trouble may be saved by adding filter powders to most materials which give trouble in filtering. It is important to keep in mind that filter aids are available in a wide range of particle sizes and porosities and that when the usage becomes a regular procedure, it is well worthwhile to select the grade best suited for a particular purpose. For maximum filter rate the principle is to use the coarsest particle size filter aid that will give the necessary clarity. A guide for selection of filter aids for laboratory use is included as Table V.

Diatomaceous filters have been used advantageously in the laboratory for the clarification of turbid urine,[414] vegetable extracts,[415] pharmaceutical preparations,[416,417] and fruit juices,[418,419] and for many other laboratory

[409] H. H. Tallan, S. Moore, and W. H. Stein, J. Biol. Chem., 206, 927 (1954).

[410] J. W. White, Jr., and G. P. Walton, U. S. Dept. Agr., Bur. Agr. Ind. Chem., AIC-272, 11 pp., May, 1950.

[411] "Methods for Measuring Retention of Polysaccharide Beater Additives," Research Bull. Inst. Paper Chem., March, 1950, pp. 155–169.

[412] R. M. McCready and W. Z. Hassid, J. Am. Chem. Soc., 65, 1154 (1943).

[413] J. H. Northrop, Crystalline Enzymes. Rev. ed., Columbia Univ. Press, New York, 1948.

[414] A. Jolles, Z. anal. Chem., 29, 407 (1894).

[415] A. Gunn, Pharm. J., 1, 495 (1895).

[416] J. Moss, Yearbook of Pharmacy, with Trans. Brit. Pharm. Conference, 1898, p. 337.

[417] H. C. Blair, Am. J. Pharm., 84, 300 (1912).

[418] E. M. Chase, Calif. Citrograph, 5, 264 (1920).

[419] W. V. Cruess, Univ. Calif. Agr. Expt. Sta. Circ., 220 (1920).

TABLE V

SOME PROPERTIES OF DIATOMACEOUS FILTER AIDS
FOR LABORATORY USE

Product	Dominant particle size range, μ	Relative and nominal filtering rate	Relative clarifying capacity	Water permeability, darcies	Specific gravity in organic solvents
Filter-Cel Laboratory Std....	1–12	1	Best	0.05	2.0
Celite Analytical Filter Aid..	2–16	2	Medium	0.2	2.2
Celite 521..................	2–16	2	Medium	0.2	2.2
Hyflo Super-Cel............	4–20	5		1	2.30
Celite 535.................	8–38	10		5	2.32
Celite 545.................	12–45	20		10	2.33
			Decreases		

purposes.[420–424] Modified methods of using diatomaceous earth are also suggestive. Thus, a mat of kieselguhr[425] was proposed in lieu of other materials for Soxhlet extractors in the determination of butterfat in milk. The extraction of amorphous petroleum wax is facilitated with filter aid.[426] Techniques and examples have been given for various biological materials such as for enzymes,[427] pancreatic preparations,[428] tobacco mosaic virus,[429] yeast extracts,[430] and culture mixtures of *Mycobacterium tuberculosis*.[431] Simple muslin tubes may be used for filtering fruit juices with *Hyflo Super-Cel*,[432] a processed filter aid. Some other examples are in the filtering of sugar and caramel solutions for color measurements,[433,434] viscose,[435] and catalysts from laboratory-scale hydrogenation reaction mixtures.[436]

[420] G. E. Ewe, *J. Lab. Clin. Med.*, **5**, 538 (1920).

[421] G. Bruhns, *Z. angew. Chem.*, **34**, 242 (1921); **34**, 438 (1921).

[422] K. Brauer, *Z. angew. Chem.*, **34**, 412 (1921).

[423] O. T. Zinkeisen, *Z. angew. Chem.*, **34**, 356 (1921).

[424] J. Grossfeld, *Z. angew. Chem.*, **24**, 411 (1921).

[425] E. Murmann, *Oesterr. Chem.-Ztg.*, **27**, 129 (1924).

[426] J. S. Weir, *Natl. Petroleum News*, **20**, 59 (1928).

[427] J. H. Lorenzen, *Apoth.-Ztg.*, **43**, 1035 (1928).

[428] M. L. Anson, *J. Gen. Physiol.*, **20**, 663, 777, 781 (1937).

[429] H. H. Thornberry, *Science*, **87**, 91 (1938).

[430] F. M. Strong, R. E. Feeney, and A. Earle, *Ind. Eng. Chem., Anal. Ed.*, **13**, 566 (1941).

[431] R. C. Mills, G. M. Briggs, Jr., T. A. Luckey, and C. A. Elvehjem, *Proc. Soc. Exptl. Biol. Med.*, **56**, 240 (1944).

[432] R. B. Hickok and R. E. Marshall, *Mich. Agr. Expt. Sta. Quart.*, **15**, 191 (1933).

[433] H. H. Peters and E. F. Phelps, *U. S. Natl. Bur. Standards, Tech. Papers*, **21**, 261 (1927).

[434] W. R. Fetzer, *Ind. Eng. Chem., Anal. Ed.*, **10**, 349 (1938).

[435] A. Marschall, *Kunstseide u. Zellwolle*, **24**, 188 (1942).

[436] F. Kipnis, *Ind. Eng. Chem., Anal. Ed.*, **16**, 637 (1944).

Filter aid is specified for prefiltration in a test method for the color of cottonseed oil.[437]   A lower boiling organic solvent can be separated from water by a filtration technique employing a short tube containing a mixture of equal parts of diatomaceous earth and anhydrous sodium sulfate held in place by fibrous wadding.[438]   The method is used in determining the fat content of foods.   Some practical trade notes on filter aid filtration present ideas on precoating, etc.[439]

The use of a diatomaceous layer on filter paper as employed in a centrifugal filtration has helped to solve a troublesome problem in the separation of amylose and amylopectin in potato starch.[440]   The starch paste is steeped at 60° to 70°C. to dissolve the amylose from the granules.   The starch solution is then cooled, and centrifuged, and the supernatant liquid is decanted from the gelatinous deposit of crude amylopectin.   The centrifuged solution is then filtered with suction on a No. 1 filter paper precoated with Hyflo Super-Cel.   A diatomaceous precoat filtration has been recommended for the filtration of dirty ethanolamine fluid that has been used to remove hydrogen sulfide and carbon dioxide, which is suggestive for similar laboratory uses.[441]

An important and recognized use of diatomaceous filter aids in the laboratory is for the evaluation of the filterability of materials.   The procedure is to determine, under prescribed test conditions, the amount of filter aid necessary to give a definite filtration performance, or to measure the amount of clarified filtrate resulting from the use of a constant weight of filter aid. Further consideration of filterability is included in Section VII.1.

In many cases chromatographic adsorption operations may be accelerated by the use of suitable grades of diatomaceous filter aids in combination with active adsorbents.   The usual method is to fill the adsorption tubes with mixtures of diatomaceous earth and adsorbent materials.   Strain[442] summarized the principles of this technique and later[443] provided an article listing various adsorbents, different grades of diatomaceous filter aids, and adsorption sequences for a number of solvents and complex mixtures of organic compounds.   The subject of these uses of diatomaceous silica in

[437] American Oil Chemists' Society, Report of Uniform Methods Comm., *J. Am. Oil Chemists Soc.*, **24**, 44 (1947).

[438] E. Bohm, *Z. Lebensm.-Untersuch. u. Forsch.*, **86**, 64 (1943).

[439] T. Shriver and Co., *Filter Facts*, **3**, 1 (1952).

[440] R. M. McCready and W. Z. Hassid, *J. Am. Chem. Soc.*, **65**, 1154 (1943).

[441] R. A. Feagan, H. L. Lawler, and M. H. Rahmes, *Petroleum Refiner*, **33**, 167 (June 1954).

[442] H. H. Strain, *Chromatographic Adsorption Analysis.*   Interscience, New York-London, 1945.

[443] H. H. Strain, *Ind. Eng. Chem., Anal. Ed.*, **18**, 605 (1946).

chromatographic and adsorption techniques has been covered by Cassidy, in Volume V of this series,[444] and is not discussed further here.

C. ORGANIC PRODUCTS

Organic materials are used to assist in filtrations somewhat differently from mineral powders. *Carbons* are employed as powders and fine granules; but cotton, paper pulps, etc., are used in a finely fibrous condition. Carbons, while generally used for decolorization and purification by adsorption, frequently serve as filter aids, particularly with nonpolar liquids. Filtration with decolorizing carbons and other adsorbents is discussed in Section VI.9. A carbonaceous filter aid (Anthra Aid) is prepared from anthracite coal fines. It is recommended for the filtration of hot alkaline solutions, and for uses in brewing, food, petroleum, pharmaceutical, and water filtrations. This material has low moisture retention, is combustible (permitting recovery of filter cake solids), and for some purposes its black color may be an advantage.[445,446] Another new type of carbonaceous filter aid, Nerofil, is produced from petroleum coke by a high-temperature furnace operation.[447]

Paper pulp may be used as a filter aid as well as for the formation of a primary filter septum as described in Section IV.2. In preparing the pulp for filter aid use, it is beaten up finely and added directly to the suspension prior to filtration. The use of paper pulp as an aid for laboratory filtrations has been practiced for a long time.[448,449] A finely divided wood cellulose product is designated as Solka-Floc.[450]

Advantages in the use of fibrous materials such as cotton, ramie, jute, or finely divided wood pulp in filtering solubles or organic derivatives of cellulose have been pointed out.[451] The fibers are added to the solution prior to filtration in the amount of about 0.05% by weight of the solution. *Organic crystals* have not been used widely either as filter aids or as filter media despite early discovery of the advantages of anthracene crystals.[452] A revival of interest in the technique of using naphthalene crystals is indicated for use in collecting lanthanum fluoride precipitates and radioactive

[444] H. G. Cassidy, in A. Weissberger, ed., *Adsorption and Chromatography* (Vol. V, *Technique of Organic Chemistry*). Interscience, New York-London, 1951.

[445] R. C. Johnson, *Trans. 11th Ann. Anthracite Conf. Lehigh Univ.*, **11**, 67 (1953).

[446] D. Simpson and P. F. Whelan, *Chem. Trade J.*, **130**, 1461 (1952).

[447] "Carbon Cohort for Diatoms," *Ind. Eng. Chem.*, **45**, 15A (Dec., 1953).

[448] M. Dittrich, *Ber.*, **37**, 1840 (1904).

[449] E. Bornemann, *Chem.-Ztg.*, **32**, 275 (1908).

[450] E. T. Thompson, ed., *Chem. Eng.*, **61**, 148 (April, 1954).

[451] C. I. Haney, U. S. Pat. 2,330,211 (Sept. 28, 1943).

[452] F. A. Gooch, *Proc. Am. Acad. Arts Sci.*, **20**, 390 (1885).

silver iodide.[453] Tetrachloronaphthalene has been employed for the preparation of a "soluble filter paper."[454] It would appear that the long, needlelike crystals of this compound, with an average diameter of 5–10 μ, should have value as a filter aid. These crystals are soluble in benzene or toluene and may be volatilized at 300°C. Pitch particles from crude petroleum are claimed to be useful for the filtration steps involved in the dewaxing of petroleum oils.[455] An unusual adaptation is the use of a modified starch as a precoat material in the filtration of milk.[456]

A recent patent[457] describes the use of frozen droplets of benzene (or other suitable organic liquid) as a filter aid. The benzene is sprayed into the slurry which is at a temperature below the freezing point of benzene, thus producing a filter aid *in situ*. When the filtration is complete, the benzene may be separated from the solids by warming to a temperature above the melting point of benzene and decanting. It is necessary of course that the solids being filtered be insoluble in benzene. The scheme would also work by spraying water into an organic liquid system at a temperature below 0°C.

D. OTHER FILTER AIDS

Materials such as calcium carbonate, sodium chloride, calcium sulfate, calcium phosphate and other granular rigid crystalline salts may be used, under certain conditions, for the filtration of many organic materials in the laboratory. Precipitated magnesium carbonate and magnesium oxides have been widely used in pharmacy for filtering extracts and solutions in organic solvents. Finely powdered glass[458] has been used for handling gelatinous precipitates. Many types of finely divided or granular mineral materials have been recommended for filtration. Among these are tripoli, brick dust, fuller's earth, clays, talc, and activated bentonite. Several others are included in a recent trade listing of filtering media.[459] The use of bleaching earths, asbestos, diatomite, etc., appears attractive for filtering fruit juices.[460] It has been pointed out that acid treatment of talc before use better suits this material for the filtration of aromatic elixirs and some drugs such as phenobarbital and choral hydrate.[461]

[453] G. R. Martin, *Chemistry & Industry*, No. 6, 131 (Feb. 9, 1952).

[454] A. Avy and J. Raillere, *Mém. services chim. état Paris*, **31**, 74–82 (1944); *Chimie & industrie*, **55**, 194 (1946).

[455] J. L. Tiedje, U. S. Pat. 2,608,517 (Aug. 26, 1952).

[456] H. Inglesent and J. A. Storrow, *Food*, **19**, 25 (1950).

[457] P. L. Gomory, U. S. Pat. 2,696,306 (Dec. 7, 1954).

[458] H. N. Warren, *Chem. News*, **61**, 63 (1890).

[459] *Oil, Paint, Drug Reptr.*, **127**, 56 (1935).

[460] E. Lehmann, *Deut. Mineralwasser Ztg.*, **42**, 810 (1938); *Allgem. Oel.-u. Fett-Ztg.*, **38**, 443 (1941).

[461] E. P. Guth, *Drug Standards*, **20**, 5 (1952).

8. Pads, Cartridges, and Discs

Pads, cylinders, cartridges, and discs are convenient forms of prefabricated filter elements.   Such forms are usually made up of fibrous materials which are more or less compressed to the density desired.   Paper pulp and asbestos, or mixtures of the two, are the most widely used materials for the fabrication of filter pads.   The fibers are selected and processed for particular filtering requirements, and the pads may be made to comprise *successive layers* made up of fibers of different lengths and characteristics. Pads and discs are made for a range of filtering requirements, from coarser screening filters down to fine *"polish"* and *"sterilizing"* grades.   In a sense, pads may be termed "adsorption filters."   Pure cellulose and the grades of asbestos employed are surface-active fibers and have definite effects on the removal of certain types of particles from liquids.   Pads are convenient to use in laboratory filtrations and are usually discarded after a single use.   They are of most value for "trap" or "polish" filtrations, in which small quantities of material are to be handled or when specific adsorption effects are desired.   They are not so well suited for filtering large quantities of difficultly filterable liquids, particularly if the amount of solids is high, or when adsorptive effects are not desired.   There may also be uncertainty as to the length of effective performance by a pad filter.

Pad and disc filter elements are usually employed in filters of special design (see Sect. VI.4).   The Uhlenhuth type[462] is of greater capacity than the simpler filter of Manteufel.[463]   Seitz filter pads were in general use in 1918[464] at which time they were advocated for water filtration as well as for bacteriological use.   For these public health uses[465] selection may be made between pad and rigid diatomite filters as conditions may require. In Europe[466,467] the use of pad filters was established earlier than in America but the well-designed American-made pad filters of the Ertel type are now well established.   Suitable commercial filters for use with pads are referred to in Section VIII.1.   However, pads or discs may be used with simple apparatus of the pressure type[468] or filter paper discs may be used with Gooch crucibles.[469]   Asbestos filter pads have considerable capacity for removal of bacteria and a method for testing this capacity, particularly for food products, has recently become available.[470]

[462] P. Uhlenhuth, *Centr. Bakt. Parasitenk., Abt. 1*, **89** (suppl.), 204 (1922).

[463] P. Manteufel, *Centr. Bakt. Parasitenk., Abt. 1*, **93** (suppl.), 259 (1924).

[464] J. Kister, *Gesundh.-Ing.*, **41**, 161 (1918).

[465] N. W. Larkum, *Am. J. Pub. Health*, **19**, 670 (1929).

[466] K. Keller, *Z. angew. Chem.*, **42**, 47 (1929); *Oesterr. Chem.-Ztg.*, **32**, 60 (1929).

[467] J. Kister, *Chem. App.*, **18**, 205 (1931).

[468] E. A. Brown and N. Benotti, *Science*, **93**, 23 (1941).

[469] J. M. Fultz, *Ind. Eng. Chem., Anal. Ed.*, **15**, 767 (1943).

[470] S. S. Epstein, *Food Industries*, **19**, 1070 (1947).

Prefabricated cylinders of filtering materials similar to those in pad or disc form have their advantages for some uses. The Metafilters consist essentially of a multiplicity of scalloped rings assembled in a cylindrical form. These rings have permanent use and may be readily cleaned. Another type of Metafilter employs cellulose base discs (Metafibre) which are changed at intervals. Cuno Micro-Klean cartridges (grades from 10 to 50 micron densities) are fitted in compact housings, complete with fittings, etc. Many small filters, employing similar filtering elements, find wide applications in laboratories and small-scale operations.

Another type of filter cartridge is fabricated from a cleaned cotton which is first spun into a roving and then wound to form a cylinder traversed radially by a network of diamond-shaped passages. In this way a fringe of cotton fibers is partially drawn from each layer of roving across each of the passages and the free ends are anchored by the succeeding layer.[471] These cartridges are inserted in a housing. Because of their small size, these filter assemblies are suited for laboratory uses with aqueous or nonaqueous fluids.

9. Granular Materials

The use of *loose sand* packed in tubes, cylinders, and larger vessels is a technique sometimes employed effectively for the filtration of flocculent and difficultly filterable materials.[472] There is an extensive literature on the use of sand, coke, and other granular filters for industrial purposes, but these have been considered of limited interest for the laboratory. However, the effective use of small filters has been reported[473] for some analytical purposes such as for the determination of starch in sausages and cellulose in polluted waters, in which "sand" layers are used as a support for other filtering media and as the filtration medium proper. Aluminum oxide granules are stated to be especially satisfactory.

Granular charcoals and carbons serve for some filtrations, particularly when a combined decolorizing and filtration treatment is required.[474] Alundum grains in 60 and 90 mesh sizes are satisfactory for small-scale bed filtrations. These granules may be readily purified for re-use by chemical or heat treatment. Thus, a granular bed filter of graded Aloxite[473] is reported as useful for materials which clog paper.

[471] *"Fulflo" Filters*, Bull. 402, Commercial Filters Corp., Melrose, Mass.

[472] H. N. Warren, *Chem. News*, 61, 63 (1890).

[473] S. Stene, *Anal. Chem.*, 19, 937 (1947).

[474] V. R. Deitz, *Bibliography of Solid Adsorbents, 1900–1942*, U. S. Cane Sugar Refiners, Bone Char Manufacturers, and National Bureau of Standards, Washington, D. C., 1944. Also New Edition, 1943 to 1953, *Natl. Bur. Standards, Circ.*, No. 566 (1956).

Graded granules of calcined and uncalcined fuller's earth may be employed for laboratory uses, when a filtering action is desired, together with some sorption of impurities and coloring matter (see further in Sect. VI.9). Many techniques and apparatus of chromatography may be employed in setting up small filtration units for filtration with granular materials or powder filter aids, or combinations of both.

10. Membranes

Some natural and fabricated membranes are used for special laboratory filtrations. The use of parchments and skins for filtering is of great antiquity. Animal parchments are rarely used today, but *paper parchment* is employed to a minor extent. Special membranes of nitrocellulose and similar compounds are widely used in dialysis and ultrafiltrations and are referred to in Chapter I.3 of this volume, and in Section V of this chapter. Chamois skin and similar leathers are occasionally used for the filtration of hydrocarbons and other organic liquids, mostly for the positive removal of rigid foreign particles. The rates of filtration of various liquids through animal membranes varies considerably.[475] A nylon filter has been useful for blood and plasma.[476] Porous Teflon[477] and Kel-F have also been advocated as suitable for use as filter frits for the most rigorous requirements of hot acid and alkaline solutions as well as for nearly all organic liquids. Further, this material is manufactured as molded sheet stock suitable for cutting into membranes of the desired size, and also as extruded films or sheets.[478]

V. ULTRAFILTRATION AND MEMBRANE FILTERS

1. General

Ultrafiltration is the method of *filtration* through a "semipermeable" membrane. This constitutes a relatively rapid means for the separation of colloidal particles (size 1 μ to 2 Å.) from solutions of ions and low molecular weight compounds. In ultrafiltration the pressure, either suction or positive, is greater that that of osmotic pressure, so that a flow of liquid from the dispersion—with consequent concentration of the solute—results. Thus, in true ultrafiltration the phenomenon of flow through the membrane is due in great part to the applied pressure rather than to diffusion effects which are predominant in dialysis or electroultrafiltration.

[475] W. Schmidt, *Ann. physik. Chem.*, **99**, 337 (1856).
[476] E. Glaser, *Science*, **98**, 570 (1943).
[477] J. Alfthan, U. S. Pat, 2,400,091 (May 14, 1946).
[478] J. A. Jupa, *Chem. Eng.*, **61**, 272 (June, 1954).

The behavior and action of ultrafilters is far from well understood at this time, but it is generally believed that the primary function of the membrane is to act as a submicroscopic sieve. However, because of the high internal surface areas of the membranes, a certain amount of sorption occurs. It is considered that the amount of sorption depends upon the surface forces in the membrane and the surfaces of the colloidal particles to be filtered. Mechanical blocking of pores can also occur under certain conditions.

The subject of ultrafiltration is so extensive that it is possible in this section only to touch upon some of the uses to which ultrafilters may be applied in organic chemistry, to illustrate some types of ultrafilter apparatus that are of general applicability, to indicate the characteristics of membranes that have been developed, and to list a few of the major references. A number of specific applications that are illustrative of possibilities in specific problems of organic chemistry are also given. Fortunately, there are available several adequate reviews and bibliographies of ultrafiltration. Some of these are referred to here[479-484] and others are included in the general references.

Sanarelli,[485] in 1891, used collodion membranes for the separation of bacteria from their toxins. Early use of membrane filtrations at considerable pressures is recorded by Martin.[486] However, Bechhold[487] is more frequently credited with the development of modern techniques. Zsigmondy and Bachmann[488] later developed cellulose derivative membranes and applied them to fundamental studies in colloid chemistry.[489]

In a sense the results of ultrafiltration are similar to those of dialysis or electrodialysis but ultrafiltration often has the advantage of *greater speed in*

[479] W. J. Elford, *J. Roy. Microscop. Soc.*, **48**, 36 (1928).

[480] J. D. Ferry, *Chem. Revs.*, **18**, 373 (1936).

[481] M. Amat, *Rev. real. acad. cienc. exact., fiss. y nat. (Madrid)*, **35**, 251 (1941).

[482] W. Bachmann, *Chem.-Ztg.*, **110**, 595 (1919).

[483] A. E. Alexander and P. Johnson, *Colloid Science*. Vol. II, Oxford Univ. Press, London, 1949.

[484] J. W. McBain, *Colloid Science*. Heath, Boston, 1950.

[485] G. Sanarelli, *Zentr. Bakt. Parasitenk., Abt. 1*, **9**, 467 (1891).

[486] C. J. Martin, *J. Physiol.*, **20**, 364 (1896); *Brit. Med. J.*, **4**, 300 (1900).

[487] H. Bechhold, *Z. Elektrochem.*, **12**, 777 (1906); *Z. physik. Chem.*, **60**, 257 (1907); *Kolloid-Z.*, **23**, 33 (1907); *Z. physik. Chem.*, **64**, 328 (1908); *Kolloide in Biologie und Medizin*, 3rd ed., Steinkopff, Dresden-Leipzig, 1920; "Ultrafiltration and Electro-Ultrafiltration," in J. Alexander, ed., *Colloid Chemistry*, Vol. I (*Theory and Methods*), Chemical Catalog Co., New York, 1920, pp. 820–837; "Ultrafiltration," in E. Abderhalden, ed., *Handbuch der biologischen Arbeitsmethoden*, Vol. III, Part B, Urban & Schwarzenberg, Berlin, 1922, p. 333.

[488] R. Zsigmondy and W. Bachmann, German Pats. 329,060 (May 9, 1916) and 329, 117 (August 22, 1916).

[489] R. Zsigmondy and W. Bachmann, *Z. anorg. Chem.*, **103**, 119 (1918); *J. Soc. Chem. Ind.*, **37**, 453A (1918).

operation. This, in itself, is time saving but is of greater importance in minimizing chemical and biological changes.   On the other hand, the application of pressure to a semipermeable membrane may to some extent alter the capacity for the selective separation of dispersed particles.   Care must be employed in interpreting the results of ultrafiltrations, particularly when higher pressures are employed.   The partial retention of dissolved crystalloids on an ultrafiltration membrane has been suggested.[490]

Ultrafilters extend the possibilities for *superlatively fine filtrations* beyond those attained with the finest pored ceramic filters, or any other type of filter septum, approaching in this respect naturally occurring membranes and tissues in living plants and animals.   In many respects, the *action of ultrafiltration* differs from those of ordinary filtrations in which retained solids serve as the true filtering membrane, and also differs from adsorption filters which are dependent mostly on surface reactions, because in ultrafiltration the semipermeable membrane itself is the means for the separation of the particles of different size.   The surfaces of ultrafilters are smooth or "glazed" and it is presumed that it is the pore openings themselves that determine the retention of particles.   Thus, there is a genuine molecular sieve action if substantial cake formation on the membrane surface is avoided.   If solids are permitted to build up to any large degree on the semipermeable membrane, these solids begin to function as the separating medium and the pore characteristics of the ultrafilter membrane may no longer be the sole or even the principal factor in the filtration.   For this reason, agitation or disturbance of the solids to prevent cake formation can be desirable.   In many cases, however, the percentage of solid particles in systems being ultrafiltered is relatively low and the effects of cake formation may be ignored.

2. Membranes

The theories of semipermeable membranes and their action are discussed by Stauffer in Chapter I.3 of this volume.   The theory of membranes as applied to dialysis holds for many ultrafiltrations, but in others the nature of the membrane, the size of the pore openings, and possible capillary adsorption effects must be considered in the rapid, high-pressure filtration of soft and compressible particles.   The effect of pressure in accelerating the passage of liquid through the pores of a membrane thus does modify to some extent the conditions theoretically obtained when osmosis and dialysis predominate.

For the preparation of ultrafilter membranes, cellulose and derivatives of cellulose are the most commonly employed materials.   Animal and plant

[490] S. Trautmann, *Compt. rend. soc. biol.*, **140**, 889 (1946).

membranes have been found useful for certain experiments. Gelatin, alginic acid, copper ferrocyanide, rubber, and silicic acid have all been employed as membranes but these latter materials have disadvantages with respect to uniformity and ease of manipulation. More recently discussions have appeared on the advantages as membranes of such high-polymer films as the polyacrylates, polymethacrylates, polystyrene, polyethylene, nylons, and organosilicon polymers. Because it is necessary that membranes have uniform thickness and pore size, many of the membranes previously used have not been found as applicable as some of the more recently improved molecular filters of cellulose and its derivatives.

However, up to the present membranes prepared from cellulose and such derivatives as nitrocellulose, cellulose acetate, and ethyl cellulose are most widely used. Particularly, collodion (nitrocellulose), parchment paper, and cellophane (regenerated viscose) have been applied to the ultrafiltration of bacteria and protein solutions for many years. Collodion membranes have been found superior for most purposes. Beginning in approximately 1930, Elford[491] and his co-workers began developing nitrocellulose membranes under controlled conditions which, like those of Zsigmondy, had graded and uniform pore sizes. These membranes have been widely used in biological work since then and are known as "gradocol" membranes. In France during the same period, Grabar[492] prepared membranes similar to the "gradocol."

Collodion membranes have been formed[493,494] by putting nitrocellulose (gun cotton, pyroxylin) into solution in ether–alcohol mixtures or glacial acetic acid, casting a film on a flat surface or test tube, and then adding water to the membrane to form the aggregates. In the case of the ether–alcohol solutions, it is first necessary to allow the cast film to lose a certain amount of solvent before adding water. By varying the concentration of nitrocellulose, the ether–alcohol ratio, the alcohol, the aggregating agents, the degree of drying, and the temperature and humidity of drying conditions, it has been found possible to vary the pore sizes of the membranes from 50 Å. to 3 μ with uniformity in both thickness and pore size. These membranes can then be dried and stored in the absence of solvents. The superior, graded membranes are made with organic solvents rather than glacial acetic acid. With the latter solvent, it has apparently not been found possible to make entirely reproducible membranes.

[491] W. J. Elford, *Proc. Roy. Soc. London*, **B105**, 216 (1930); *J. Path. Bact.*, **34**, 505 (1931); *Trans. Faraday Soc.*, **33**, 1094 (1937).

[492] P. Grabar, *Trans. Faraday Soc.*, **33**, 1104 (1937).

[493] E. Hatschek, *Laboratory Manual of Elementary Colloid Chemistry*. Blakiston, Philadelphia, 1920.

[494] L. C. Clark, *J. Lab. Clin. Med.*, **37**, 481 (1951).

In Elford's[491] technique four solvents are employed: ether, ethanol, acetone, and amyl alcohol. Ether and ethanol (or propanol) swell the cellulose and separate the polymer chains. Acetone and amyl alcohol cause aggregation and high porosity. Similarly, water may be added to the organic solvents to increase the aggregation tendency. Good solvents like acetone or ethylene glycol–monoethyl ether suppress aggregation and produce impermeable films.

Cellophane membranes are readily available commercially and are still being used in ultrafiltration.[484] These membranes are composed of pure cellulose and varying amounts of glycerol and water. By replacing the water in steps with mutually miscible solvents, McBain and Kistler[495] were able to make membranes resistant to organic solvents. The porosity of commercial membranes has been increased by swelling them with sodium hydroxide or zinc chloride.[484]

The average pore size of membranes has been determined by several methods involving the rate of water flow through a membrane, the pressure of air required to blow bubbles through the wet membrane, the ability of membranes to pass solutes of known sizes, and other methods.

Ferry[480] has discussed the theory and practice of the calibration of membranes. In order to determine pore sizes, the following items must be determined experimentally: (1) the thickness of the membranes which may be determined either by direct measurement with a micrometer gage, an optical lever, or by interferometry; (2) the amount of water, S, which fills the pores of the membrane can be measured by several procedures; and (3) the rate at which water flows, F, as defined by Elford[491] in terms which lead to the formulation:

$$F = (K_1 V \delta)/(ATP) \tag{22}$$

where K_1 is a constant, δ is the membrane thickness, V is the volume of water which flows through an area A of the membrane in time T, under a pressure P. Finally, with S and F known, the pore diameter J can be calculated from the expression:

$$J = K_2(F/S)^{1/2} \tag{23}$$

where K_2 is an empirical constant.

Knöll[496] has described the method of determining a pore diameter (not absolute) by observing the pressure required to blow bubbles through a wet membrane. Another method developed by Krueger and Ritter[497] involved the measurement of the amount of solute of known particle size which passes through the membrane. Other discussions may be found in recent literature.[498,499]

[495] J. W. McBain and S. S. Kistler, *J. Gen. Physiol.*, **12**, 187 (1928).

[496] H. Knöll, *Kolloid-Z.*, **90**, 189 (1940).

[497] A. P. Krueger and R. C. Ritter, *J. Gen. Physiol.*, **13**, 409 (1930).

[498] D. L. Mauld and R. L. M. Synge, *Analyst*, **77**, 964 (1952).

[499] A. Polson and T. I. Madsen, *Biochim. et Biophys. Acta*, **12**, 584 (1953).

By more direct techniques of microscopy, attempts have been made to study membrane structures. Elford[491] examined nitrocellulose membranes by means of the ultramicroscope. The microgel nature of the structures was found by this technique. More recently, the electron microscope has been employed to measure pore sizes and to determine the pore structure of membranes. Electron micrographs[500] of Zsigmondy-type collodion membranes in dried form reveal a net structure of the surface. The pore size within each net cell ranges from 0.15 to 1 μ and at the cell boundaries, between 0.04 and 0.05 μ. A technique[501] for observing the internal "cavity" system of membrane filters consists of filling the pores with insoluble precipitates such as calcium oxalate, barium sulfate, or silver chloride by means of counterdiffusion, and then preparing ultramicrotome sections of the fixed membranes. With the electron microscope it is possible to examine the nature of the filled pores. Another study[502] by the electron microscope and by surface-tension and adsorption techniques, indicates the existence of vacuoles with perforated walls. The position of particles retained in the membrane shows that the wall perforations are of major importance in ultrafiltration. The studies of Helmcke[503] may be expected to cast light on the mechanism of ultrafiltration. The properties of some commercially available filter membranes of cellophane, nitrocellulose, mixed esters of cellulose, and pure cellulose are listed in Table VI.

Much information has recently appeared on the commercial Millipore filters.[504] Originally designed for the analysis of bacteria in water,[505] they are being used for many other purposes by biologists and colloid chemists. A bibliography on these membranes is given in a publication of the manufacturer.[504] These membranes can be obtained with several pore sizes. The 0.5 μ pore size filters have been reported to hold the majority of particles at 0.2–0.3 μ.

Since ultrafilter membranes must be thin and are usually subjected to a pressure differential, it is necessary to use supporting structures.[480,484] Filter media are prepared either as films or impregnated directly into porous media. Silicic acid gels and copper ferrocyanide have been impregnated into porous inorganic structures. Collodion has been impregnated into many structures: filter paper,[493,494] cloth,[506] glass fabrics, or metal gauzes.[483]

[500] G. Hansmann and H. Pietsch, *Naturwissenschaften*, **36**, 250 (1949).

[501] H. Spandau and U. E. Zapp, *Kolloid-Z.*, **137**, 29 (1954).

[502] K. H. Maier and H. Beutelspacher, *Naturwissenschaften*, **40**, 605 (1953); *Kolloid-Z.*, **135**, 10 (1954); **137**, 31 (1954).

[503] J. G. Helmcke, *Optik*, **10**, 147 (1953); *Kolloid-Z.*, **135**, 29, 101, 106 (1954).

[504] *Millipore Filters*. Millipore Filter Co., Watertown, Mass., 1954.

[505] A. Goetz and N. Tsuneishi, *J. Am. Water Works Assoc.*, **43**, 943 (1951).

[506] S. G. Mokrushin and V. I. Borisikhina, *Zhur. Priklad. Khim.*, **25**, 1182 (1952).

TABLE VI

ULTRAFILTER MEMBRANES

Trade name	Supplier	Chemical composition	Pore diameter
Cellophane			
Sylphrap..........	Sylvania Division American Viscose Corp.	Cellulose, glycerine, water	50 mμ
Cellophane........	Visking Corp.		
Cellophane........	du Pont Chem. Co.		
Cellophane........	Kapcello Factory, Copenhagen		
Molecular			
1. Millipore.......	Millipore Filter Co.	Mixture of cellulose esters	0.5–0.8 μ
2. Membrane (dry) (aqueous solns.)...	Schleicher & Schuell Co., or Membranfilter G.m.b.H.	Cellulose nitrates	0.2–3 μ graded
3. Ultrafine (moist).........	" "	Cellulose nitrates	50 Å. 0.2 μ graded
4. Cella (moist).....	" "	Cellulose	0.2–3 μ graded
5. Ultra Cella (moist).........	" "	Cellulose	50 Å–0.2 μ graded

More recently, the nitrocellulose or cellophane films have been supported on porous carbon discs,[504] sintered brass powders,[507] stainless steel screens,[508] silver screens,[509] glazed porcelain, sintered glass, porous earthenware,[484] and nylon tubes.[510] Natural membranes have not been used much in recent years for ultrafiltrations, although they are still used to some extent for qualitative work in dialysis. There would appear to be many advantages in the use of uniform and standard animal and vegetable materials particularly in biological and medical research. It is believed that standardized animal membranes could be provided, similar to the way in which carefully controlled surgical sutures are prepared commercially from animal tissues.

Porous glass, i.e., unfired Vycor, has been found to have an average hole size of 30 Å.[511] This glass is semipermeable to polymer solutions in that

[507] A. Albert and D. A. Rogers, J. Lab. Clin. Med., 37, 485 (1951).
[508] I. W. Coleman, Can. J. Med. Sci., 30, 246 (1952).
[509] H. O. Nicholas, J. Biol. Chem., 97, 457 (1932).
[510] M. R. Malinow and W. Korzon, J. Lab. Clin. Med., 32, 461 (1947).
[511] P. J. Debye, private communication, Cornell University, March 29, 1955.

pure solvent may be "squeezed out" under pressure. Because of the inherent strength, durability, and workability of glass, ultrafilters of high quality eventually might be developed from this medium.

3. Ultrafilter Assemblies

An ultrafilter consists of an ultrafilter membrane, a membrane support, and a housing which has either vacuum or pressure outlets. Membrane supports are necessary because of the required thinness of membranes and the considerable pressures to which they may be subjected in some filters. Some of the classical types of ultrafilters were shown in the first edition of this chapter and are not duplicated here.

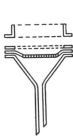

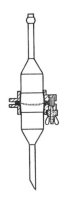

Fig. 50. Zsigmondy porcelain funnel ultrafilter. (Courtesy Pfaltz and Bauer, Inc.)

Fig. 51. Thiessen apparatus for vacuum or pressure use. (Courtesy Pfaltz and Bauer, Inc.)

Various types of ultrafilters have been made to be used with pressure, vacuum, or the centrifuge. Frequently, the apparatus must withstand high pressures or be sterilized for bacteriological studies and therefore special materials are necessary. Usually the membrane and its support are clamped between rubber or cellophane washers in an inert or metallic casing. Several types of available commercial ultrafilter apparatus are shown in Figures 50 to 53.

Some recent examples of the uses of different ultrafilter apparatus are suggestive for other applications. An apparatus[512] designed for the preparation of small amounts of protein-free biological fluid filtrates consists of a Lucite filtering chamber (3 cm. in diameter, 75 ml. in capacity) which is inserted into a brass pressure jacket. Two per cent aqueous solutions of

[512] I. W. Coleman, *Can. J. Med. Sci.*, **30**, 246 (1952).

plasma albumin, lactalbumin, casein, and egg albumen were quantitatively cleared of protein at rates of 1.5 to 2 ml. per hour under a constant pressure of 60 p.s.i. Recovery of glycine added to bovine plasma albumin solution and passed through the apparatus was 98 to 100%. An apparatus which ultrafilters in a closed sterile system features circulation achieved by a gravity system utilizing the higher specific gravity of the concentrate.[513]

A small, Plexiglass-lined apparatus is suspended from an electric vibrator and a thin flexible tongue is fastened just above the filter membrane. The

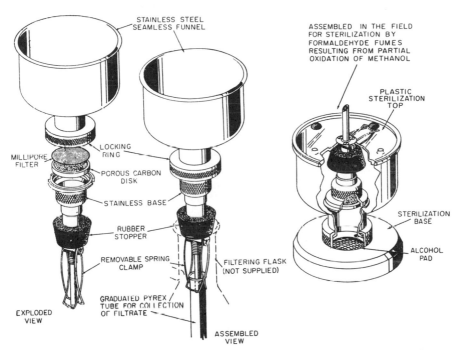

Fig. 52. Membrane filter with stainless steel holder. (Courtesy Millipore Filter Corp.)

vibratory motion retards clogging of the membrane. Filtration is at pressures up to 100 atmospheres.[514] A larger high-pressure ultrafilter has been designed for the rapid concentration of bacterial toxins, but should be useful for proteins.[515] The capacity of this filter is 15 liters, filter area 400 sq. cm. It operates at nitrogen gas pressures up to 300 p.s.i. As an example of use, 1200 ml. of papain extract broth was reduced to 10 ml. in 2.25 hours.[515] An ultrafilter for use in the clinical bioassay of urinary

[513] E. H. Baxter, *Australasian J. Med. Tech.*, **2**, 19 (1953).
[514] P. G. Waser, *Helv. Physiol. Pharmacol. Acta*, **11**, C44 (1953).
[515] J. J. Bullen, C. Thurlbourn, and P. Brown, *Nature*, **173**, 254 (1954).

gonadotropin[516] consists of a stainless-steel tank, the filter-retaining element, and a clamp. The filter-retaining element is a porous disc of sintered brass, over which is placed a filter paper, which in turn supports a cellophane membrane as prepared by Gorbman.[517]

An apparatus which may be constructed from usual laboratory materials employs cellophane sheets, which are combined with a rayon-base paper and a series of rubber gaskets. This construction permits the use of the

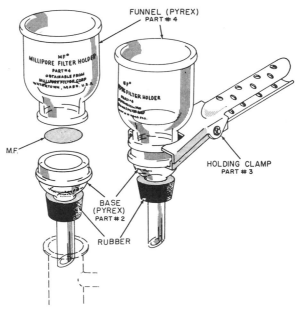

Fig. 53. Membrane filter with glass holder. (Courtesy Millipore Filter Corp.)

relatively fragile cellophane membranes in a filter of such size as to provide considerable volume of ultrafiltrates for biological work. The fluid is led into the lumens of alternate gaskets through 15-gage needles and the ultrafiltrate is led out through similar needles. Filtration rate at 1 atmosphere pressure is reported as about 75 ml. per hour per 1000 sq. cm. of area.[518] A small ultrafilter designed for blood serum work may be used with membranes of various porosities and may be adapted for many laboratory filtrations.[519] This unit produces about 20 ml. of protein-free ultrafiltrate

[516] A. Albert and D. A. Rogers, *J. Lab. Clin. Med.*, **37**, 485 (1951).

[517] A. Gorbman, *Endocrinology*, **37**, 177 (1945).

[518] L. C. Clark, Jr., *J. Lab. Clin. Med.*, **37**, 481 (1951).

[519] A. C. Kuyper, E. B. Andrews, and G. Eidt, *Rev. Sci. Instruments*, **22**, 218 (1951).

from 25 ml. of serum during 8 hours of operation at 5°C. and a pressure of 100 p.s.i. The unit is placed on a tripod and oscillates about its vertical axis by means of an eccentric drive.

A Swinny hypodermic adapter[520] may be employed with a Millipore filter membrane to effect sterilization and purification of small quantities of liquid. Figure 54 shows the construction of this adapter.

Rehberg,[521] in 1943, employed a centrifuge procedure for filtering solutions through cellophane membranes. This technique has been applied

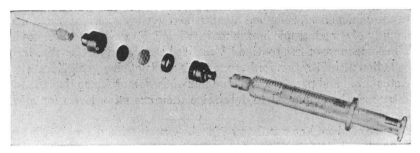

Fig. 54. Swinny hypodermic adapter for use with Millipore filter membrane.
(Courtesy Millipore Filter Corp.)

by Clegg[522] who collected the filtrate in nylon bags which were placed over the cellophane filter sacs. Collodion sacs have also been found practical for filtration in the ultracentrifuge.[523]

4. Applications

Ultrafiltration has been a powerful tool for research in colloid science, biochemistry, medicine, and bacteriology, and in other fields where the isolation or removal of colloidal size particles is necessary. Use of ultra-filtration techniques is also made in the commercial isolation and produc-tion of biological preparations, hormones, enzymes, etc. A review of the uses of ultrafilters up to 1935 has been made by Ferry.[480] Two recent bibliographies of the applications of ultrafilters and membrane filters are quite comprehensive.[504,524]

Biochemists have known for many years that proteins will not pass through membranes with fine pores. Many uses have been made of this

[520] B. Swinny, *J. Lab. Clin. Med.*, **23**, 1098 (1938).

[521] P. B. Rehberg, *Acta Physiol. Scand.*, **5**, 305 (1943).

[522] R. E. Clegg, *Chemist-Analyst*, **38**, 87 (1949).

[523] L. C. Grandjean, *Acta Physiol Scand.*, **24**, 192 (1951).

[524] *Literaturverzeichnis über Veröffentlichungen auf dem Gebiet der Ultrafiltration zusam-mengestellt bis Ende 1953.* Membranfilter Gesellschaft, Göttingen, 1954.

phenomenon. Because of the monodisperse character of proteins, it is possible to determine their size or separate them from colloids of larger or smaller sizes by the proper use of graded filter membranes. The study of viruses, enzymes, toxins, antitoxins, sera, etc., has been greatly facilitated by this technique. Thus, cerebrospinal fluids have been ultrafiltered prior to electrophoretic separation on paper.[525] Elford and his collaborators[526] were able to determine the sizes of various species of virus and bacteriophage by means of the ultrafilter and corroborated their results with measurements made with ultramicroscopy, ultracentrifugation, and diffusion.

In the clinical field, collodion membranes have been used for the isolation and study of gonadotropic hormones in urine[527–529] and the techniques have now become more or less routine.[530] It has been shown further that the use of collodion ultrafiltration for human urine does not change significantly the 17-ketosteroid and pregnanediol contents of these steroids so that the ultrafiltrates may be employed to determine their excretion levels for medical diagnosis.[531]

The use of ultrafilter membranes for the examination of bacteria in water was employed during World War II by the Russians and Germans.[532] After the war Goetz and his co-workers[505] adopted and further developed the method, and today it is fairly widely employed.[504] In this procedure the bacteria are first isolated on the filter and then filter disc is placed on an absorbent pad saturated with broth. After incubation the colonies are examined. A review of the use of Millipore membranes for the study of bacteria, pollens, and yeasts, has been prepared by the producers of these membranes.[504]

In analytical and bacteriological work, it is often of much importance to remove without contamination the material that is retained on the ultrafilter membrane so that it can be subjected to further study. This easy collection of residue is not usually possible with the adsorption-type filter.

Light-scattering methods are used for the estimation of the molecular weights of macromolecules. It is frequently difficult to remove from such systems all traces of extraneous particles or suspended impurities. Ordinary filtrations with sintered discs, cellulose pulp pads, and high-speed centrifugation sometimes do not adequately remove all traces of such par-

[525] H. Esser and F. Heinzler, *Klin. Wochschr.*, **30**, 600 (1952).

[526] W. J. Elford, *Proc. Roy. Soc. London*, **B112**, 405 (1933).

[527] H. M. Evans and A. Gorbman, *Proc. Soc. Exptl. Biol. Med.*, **49**, 674 (1942).

[528] A. Gorbman, *Endocrinology*, **37**, 177 (1945).

[529] E. C. Jungck, W. O. Maddock, and C. G. Heller, *J. Clin. Endocrinol.*, **7**, 1 (1947).

[530] C. A. Carcamo, *Rev. asoc. med. argentina*, **64**, 316 (1950).

[531] I. Rothchild, B. Greene, and L. Wilkening, *Endocrinology*, **52**, 238 (1953).

[532] G. Mueller, *Z. Hyg. Infectionskrankh.*, **127**, 3 (1947).

ticles. The problem was solved in the preparation of solutions of serum, albumin, and seed globulin by simple ultrafiltration techniques. Membranes were prepared by pouring a suitable nitrocellulose solution evenly over a rotating test tube shape mold. Each coat was dried without heat before the next was applied. Other cases in which ultrafiltration techniques have been employed in light-scattering studies have been reported.[533,534] Centrifugal ultrafiltration and electroultrafiltration are not considered in this section since they are covered elsewhere in this series.

VI. SPECIAL TECHNIQUES AND APPLICATIONS

1. Conditioning Materials for Filtration

Many materials present a filtration problem which cannot be readily solved by any ordinary combination of filtering apparatus, filter media, or techniques in carrying out the filtration itself. Examples are many extracts of biological origin, viscous colloidal preparations, and suspensions of extremely finely divided particles particularly at high dilution. In some cases the difficulty lies in inability to obtain any satisfactory quantity of filtrate, in others the rate of filtration starts off well but drops rapidly, and in others the trouble is in not being able to attain satisfactory clarification. Some materials in the condition as first obtained are practically nonfilterable. In other cases, the filter rate may be satisfactory, and the clarity appear good, yet the filtrate may contain components which are detrimental to the purposes for which the filtrate is to be used. In all of these cases, when the resources of selecting the proper filtering medium and techniques have been exhausted, the only recourse is to modify or change the unfiltered material so that it may be more amenable to filtration. This is referred to here as "conditioning" the material.

There are no general or universal rules for improving the filterability of materials. Each case must be considered with due regard to the nature of the material, its suspended particles, and the properties of either residue or filtrate or both, all with careful consideration of whether these properties may be altered to any appreciable or detrimental degree by conditioning or pretreatment of the material. Obviously, the more complete the knowledge of the material to be filtered, the better is one able to develop an effective and harmless procedure for conditioning.

An analysis of means for improving filtration and filtration rates by chemical and mechanical preparation of slurries concludes that the factors

[533] S. Greenberg and D. Sinclair, *J. Phys. Chem.*, **59**, 435 (1955).

[534] D. A. I. Goring and P. Johnson, *J. Chem. Soc.*, **1952**, 33.

of temperature, slurry concentration, viscosity, particle size, pH, and desliming are important.[537]

Following are some suggestions on principles which, in the experience of the authors, warrant consideration. The practice of precipitating in hot solution or of prolonged digestion at higher temperatures is well recognized as a means of making many organic and inorganic materials more readily filterable. Heat is often one of the most effective means of accelerating or improving filtration. The effect is primarily threefold: (1) the decrease in viscosity of the liquid with increase in temperature; (2) the coagulating effect of temperature; and (3) the promotion of increase in particle size. In Table VII the viscosities of some common liquids are shown at different

TABLE VII
VISCOSITIES OF LIQUIDS AT DIFFERENT TEMPERATURES

Liquid	Viscosity (centipoises) at temperatures of					
	0	10	20	40	70	100°C.
Water................	1.79	1.31	1.01	0.65	0.41	0.28
Ethyl alcohol..........	1.79	1.75	1.72	1.65	1.55	—
Ethyl ether...........	0.28	—	0.23	0.20	—	—
Octane...............	0.71	—	0.54	0.43	—	—
Benzene..............	0.91	0.76	0.65	0.50	0.36	—
Castor oil.............	—	2420	986	231	—	16.9
Olive oil..............	—	138	84	36	12.4	—
60% sucrose solution....	238	110	56	21	7.1	3.3
Glacial acetic acid.......	—	—	1.26	0.92	0.64	—
Glycerol..............	—	4000	1499	294	50	15
15% cellulose acetate[535] .	—	11,000	7800	3650	—	—
3% carboxymethyl starch[536]						
High-viscosity type...	—	1500	1300	1050	820	600
Medium-viscosity type	—	410	360	300	220	150
Low-viscosity type....	—	31	27	22	14	10

temperatures. The reduction in viscosity with increase in temperature is very great for some liquids and appreciable for nearly all. Since the viscosity bears a positive relationship to rate of flow, as shown by equation (5) in Section II, the advantage of filtering at the higher temperatures is obvious. Of course, there are many cases in which the temperature cannot be increased because of detrimental effects produced by heat. Also, some materials swell or disperse on heating and any such treatment would be ruinous. Many proteinaceous and other organic mixtures coagulate or otherwise agglomerate so as to become readily filterable after heating

[535] L. A. Cox and W. K. Mohney, *Ind. Eng. Chem.*, **45**, 1798 (1953).

[536] B. Fader, *Chem. Processing*, **18**, 208 (Feb. 1955).

[537] C. Fuhrmeister, Jr., *Chem. Eng. Progress*, **47**, 550 (1951).

Heating may be carried out with various degrees of agitation or aeration, with subsequent separation of the froth, after which the filtration of the liquid may be carried out.

Another expedient to reduce viscosity is dilution with an appropriate liquid. A report of conditions wherein a viscous liquid may be diluted with a low-viscosity solvent includes empirical equations which are developed to express the viscosity of filtrate as a function of solvent dilution.[538] A similar study[539] provides an equation and nomograph which are valid for a mineral oil–diluent system. An effort to establish the economic dilutions of viscous liquids by addition of solvent may also be applied for reduction of time in laboratory work.[540]

Mixtures containing solids of different types and sizes may frequently be filtered best after first removing a portion or all of the coarser material. Cellulose acetate preparations, as an example, may contain partially reacted cellulose particles which make filtration in a single operation difficult; yet, if these large particles are removed by a screening or coarse filtration, the strained liquid may be filtered much more readily. Infusions or tinctures of benzoin and similar preparations frequently contain coarse gummy particles which should be removed first by straining through an open-mesh cloth or a wire screen. Vegetable extracts should generally be strained before filtering. Tissue pulps may readily plug or cover the pores and openings of filter septa. Thus, there have been reported advantages in first filtering out the coarser particles from extracts of malignant tissue growths.[541]

When the amount of solids is high, it is frequently good practice to separate out a portion of the solids by simple sedimentation, and filter only the supernatant liquid. There are cases, on the other hand, in which the removal of solids makes more difficult good clarification of the remaining liquid. Examination and study of the material to be handled determine what it is advantageous to remove prior to filtration.

Centrifuging is a useful technique in combination with filter operations.[542] With some slurries time may be saved by quickly removing some of the solids with the centrifuge. As an example, in the isolation of dicalcium magnesium aconitate from cane sugar molasses, the precipitate as first formed by dilution and heating is a slimy, amorphous, highly hydrated solid which clogs filter paper or cloth almost instantly. This precipitate can be removed by centrifuging. It is then suspended in water and centrifuged a second time, after which it is dried. It then does not rehydrate to the

[538] E. J. Reeves, *Ind. Eng. Chem.*, **39**, 203 (1947).

[539] A. F. Orlicek and A. Schmidt, *Chem.-Ing.-Tech.*, **24**, 457 (1952).

[540] G. H. Gottner, *Erdöl u. Kohle*, **7**, 286 (1954).

[541] W. E. Gye, *Lancet*, **2**, 109 (1925).

[542] J. Richards, *J. Am. Chem. Soc.*, **27**, 104 (1905); **30**, 285 (1908).

original slimy condition and is readily filterable. The centrifuging has thrown out most of the aconitate but not the slimy material that caused the original difficulty in filtering.[543]

In a problem in the filtration of chick embryo extract, it was found that the difficult filterability was due to finely divided particulate material which could be thrown out of suspension by ultracentrifugation. The presence of hyaluronic acid and related compounds also caused trouble; these could be eliminated by treatment with the enzyme hyaluronidase for short periods. On the basis of these two techniques, a satisfactory procedure was developed for the preparation of large quantities of chick embryo extract for use in cancerous tissue cultures.[544]

The centrifuge is also useful in the preliminary examination and testing of materials to determine the filtration technique to follow. Thus, an estimate can be made of the amount of solids in a suspension by centrifuging a sample. The nature of the more finely divided particles can be checked by examining liquids prepared by centrifuging with different times and speeds. Centrifugal techniques and apparatus are described in Chapter IV by Ambler and Keith.

The use of *fining agents* is effective as a prefiltration procedure in making some materials more readily filterable. White of egg and isinglass were used as aids in the clarification of wines centuries ago. Filtration shortly after fining is frequently as effective as sedimenting for weeks or months. Tannic acid, blood, casein, agar, etc., are recognized as valuable aids in clarifying and in the pretreatment of liquors. It has been suggested that, in general, wines should be clarified to some degree prior to the final polish filtration. Gelatin, casein, and bentonite are recommended.[545]

Settling aids function by entrapping impurities and suspended particles which collect as a sediment. Decantation of the supernatant liquid permits its filtration with many impurities already removed. Gelatinous precipitates such as aluminum hydroxide are well recognized as effective for this purpose. Earthy materials, fuller's earth, and bentonite are similarly employed. Freshly precipitated calcium phosphate appears to be effective in some fermented substrates.[546] Fluid extracts of glycyrrhiza U.S.P. present unusual filtration difficulties. The drug is first extracted by hot water percolation. Upon being made ammoniacal the complex colloidal system containing starch and pectic substances becomes almost unfilterable. While enzyme treatment and filter aids are useful in handling

[543] H. W. Haines and L. G. Joyner, *Ind. Eng. Chem.*, **47**, 178 (1955).

[544] J. C. Bryant, W. R. Earle, and E. V. Peppers, *J. Natl. Cancer Inst.*, **14**, 189 (1953)

[545] J. Fessler, *Wines and Vines*, **31**, 48 (1950); **32**, 16 (1951).

[546] M. Skrivanek, *Chemie (Prague)*, **4**, 227 (1948).

this material, it has been reported[547] that the use of bentonite as a settling aid is most effective.

With some materials, violent stirring or agitation conditions for more satisfactory filtering behavior. On the other hand, some precipitates of gelatinous nature should not be agitated before filtration and should be so handled that breaking up of the floccules[548] is avoided. Some suspensions of waxes or other amorphous solids may be chilled before filtration, making the particles more rigid. The same particles at room temperature might be unfilterable.

Double or multiple filtrations, often with different media, may solve a filtration problem more effectively than any other method. *Adjustment of pH* is one of the effective means of altering the filtering characteristics of many materials. At their isoelectric points many dispersions filter most rapidly. With complex mixtures successive filtrations at two or more isoelectric points may be indicated. An application of this principle in the treatment of sugar juices calls for the addition of lime to bring the sirup to a pH of about 10.5, followed by a quick filtration and a subsequent treatment with sulfur dioxide to produce a substantially lower pH.[549] The effect of the reaction of the medium in the filtration of malt diastase has been shown to be considerable.[550] The importance of pH in changing the filterability of biological materials has been further demonstrated[551] in electroendosmosis studies with membranes.

Any means for effecting flocculation of suspended solids should be favorable to improve filterability. The addition of electrolytes is sometimes effective, but may be objectionable for other reasons. Numerous so-called addition agents may be employed to alter the physical properties of precipitates,[552] but at this stage of the art applicability must be determined by experiment. An unusual case is the use of a uranyl salt as a precipitating agent for sodium carboxymethyl cellulose in its analysis for active agent content and degree of substitution.[553] The use of small amounts of uranyl nitrate reagent modifies the precipitate so that it may be easily filtered and washed.

It would seem that the coprecipitation of anionic and cationic polyelectrolytes may be applied to the flocculation of some suspensions. Polyelectrolytes have a pronounced effect on colloidal properties of solid sus-

[547] N. A. Hall, *Am. J. Pharm.*, **124**, 43 (1952).
[548] A. B. Cummins, *Ind. Eng. Chem.*, **34**, 398 (1942).
[549] J. M. Saha and N. S. Jain, *Sugar*, **46**, 32 (1951).
[550] M. Holderer, *Compt. rend.*, **150**, 285 (1910).
[551] S. Mudd, *J. Gen. Physiol.*, **7**, 389 (1924–1925).
[552] R. B. Fischer and T. B. Rhinehammer, *Anal. Chem.*, **26**, 244 (1954).
[553] C. V. Francis, *Anal. Chem.*, **25**, 941 (1953).

pensions, and thus may improve rates of flocculation, sedimentation, and filtration. The polyelectrolyte, a long-chain molecule, sorbs on the solid particles and binds them together. The use of suitable surface-active agents may also lower the moisture content and alter the compactness of filter cakes. Some of the principles applied in the practice of flocculating mineral suspensions with coprecipitated polyelectrolytes, as followed in recent mineral beneficiation processes, should be applicable for many fields of organic chemistry. It is said that a hydrophilic colloid, Konnyaku flour, prepared from the tubers of a Japanese plant, is effective as an electrolytic stabilizer to increase filtration rates.

Claims are made that Aerosol-OT,[554] Separan 2610 (Dow Chemical Co.), and similar surface-active agents frequently can be used to speed filtration and washing. The agent can be included in the reaction mixture to encourage the formation of larger particles. This technique has yielded a readily filterable product instead of a slime that only clogs the filter. Or, the agent can be added to the mixture just before filtration, to reduce surface tension and aid in wetting the filter.[555]

Foams and emulsions frequently complicate filtrations and may be controlled or minimized by the judicious addition of some surfactants. Silicone defoaming agents (Dow-Corning Anti-Foam A or General Electric Anti-Foam 60) are said to break foams when added in amounts of only 0.1 to 1 p.p.m. Application may be with a small aerosol bomb. Duncan and Earle[556] evaluate the effectiveness of various surfactants which improve the filterability of vegetable extractions by breaking up the troublesome emulsion condition. These agents are classified as anionic, cationic, and nonionic. Further reference to handling emulsions is made in Section VI.6.

The concentration of solids in a slurry or liquid determines considerably its filterability. In some cases concentration of the solids by evaporation of the liquid is the most effective means of improving filterability. This is usual when the solids are of such nature as to "bridge" properly on the filter membrane. Thus, such materials clarify quite readily with a high concentration of solids, whereas at low concentrations complete clarification is nearly impossible. There are perhaps many more conditions when dilution is the preferred practice. It is frequently more time-saving to dilute and filter, and later concentrate, than to attempt filtration at the original higher concentration.

The filtration characteristics of colloids may be greatly altered by the addition of other colloids. Agar-agar in very small amounts greatly im-

[554] *Aerosol Surface Active Agents*, American Cyanamid Company, New York, 1954.

[555] A. M. Schwartz and J. W. Perry, *Surface Active Agents.* Interscience, New York-London, 1949.

[556] C. L. Duncan and R. H. Earle, Jr., *Anal. Chem.*, **26**, 1099 (1954).

proved the filterability of colloidal calcium sulfate.[557]   Electrolytes, protective colloids, coagulation, adsorption by filter paper, etc., must all be considered in applying the principles of colloid chemistry to the purification, filtration, and washing of precipitates.[558]   The successful treatment of sewage sludges before filtration is based on the application of adsorption, coagulation, and flocculation principles[559] which can be applied to the solution of filtration problems in other fields.   (See Taylor's text[560] for further treatment on the coagulation or flocculation of colloids.)   Thus, the lowering of temperature flocculates hydrosols of gelatin or agar, freezing tends to alter lyophilic sols, and physical actions such as mechanical stirring or exposure to electrical fields have effects on suspensions and emulsions making them more readily filterable.

In a careful laboratory study to control the filterability of a difficult material, the conclusion was reached that a compromise must be made between the best filterability and the properties most desired in the final product prepared from the filtrate.[561]   Lignin from the waste liquors of the alkaline process for the manufacture of wood pulp is a good reinforcing agent for rubber when master-batched or coprecipitated with the rubber. When coprecipitated, filtration of the latex mixture is necessary and this is difficult.   It is shown that the physical properties and filtering behavior of the mixture are influenced by premixing, agitation, pH, temperature, etc. These laboratory studies were made with filter paper on Büchner funnels and are considered applicable for commercial operations.

2. Handling Volatile Materials

In filtering volatile liquids, ether, acetone, alcohol, etc., losses due to evaporation may be excessive, resulting in precipitation of components from solution.   This may be minimized in gravity filtrations by keeping funnels and other types of filters covered.   Filtrate receivers should be narrow mouthed, covered, or partially plugged.

Vacuum filtrations are troublesome and ineffective with highly volatile liquids.   It is helpful to work at low temperatures, or a condenser may be

[557] E. M. Losee, *Can. Chem. Process Industries*, **30**, 90 (1946).

[558] H. Bassett, "Colloid Problems in Analytical Chemistry," in *Fourth Report on Colloid Chemistry*, Brit. Assoc. Advancement Sci., H. M. Stationery Office, London, 1922. Also a revised article in J. Alexander, ed., *Colloid Chemistry*, Vol. I, Chemical Catalog Co., New York, 1926.

[559] A. L. Genter, *Sewage Works J.*, **6**, 689 (1934); **9**, 285 (1937).

[560] H. S. Taylor and H. A. Taylor, *Elementary Physical Chemistry*. 3rd ed., Van Nostrand, New York, 1942.

[561] J. J. Keilen, W. K. Doughtery, and W. R. Cook, *India Rubber World*, **124, 178** (1951).

installed in the vacuum line. Pressure filters, on the other hand, are usually preferable. In the filtration of some volatile or toxic liquids, porcelain, stoneware, or glass containers fitted with a porous filter member may be placed in a pressure vessel and the filtration carried out with air or gas pressure. If the receiver is also held under some pressure, the pressure differential maintained will still be adequate for the filtration, but will prevent excessive evaporation of the solvent. Most volatile liquids have high solvent action and gaskets for pressure filters must be properly selected to prevent swelling, leakage, etc. An assembly of an enclosed laboratory apparatus for filtrations with volatile liquids[562] is illustrated in Chapter III of this volume. A device for filtering and dispersing solutions in a closed system filters, weighs, and transfers solutions with a minimum loss of solvent and exposure to the atmosphere. The apparatus consists of a sintered glass filter and a weight buret.[563]

3. Filtering in Inert Atmospheres

Some filtrations must be carried out in inert atmospheres to avoid oxidation of materials, to lessen the fire hazard, or for other reasons. In the various types of pressure filters described which employ gas pressure, carbon dioxide or nitrogen from cylinders may be substituted for air. Hydrocarbon gases may also be used. For gravity filtration it is sufficient to pass small streams of the inert gas into and out of nearly tight enclosures around the material being filtered and in the receiving vessel, after first displacing the air from the apparatus.

Lumps of solid carbon dioxide may be placed directly in the material being filtered if there are no complications due to the presence of carbon dioxide in the liquid, or due to the resulting lower temperature. Vacuum filtration is not effective in cases in which a large amount of gas is generated unless a large-capacity vacuum system is available. Schmidlin's method[564] for filtration in an inert gas atmosphere is illustrated in Chapter III. The Ziegler-Schnell[565] apparatus was designed for special reactions which must be carried out in an atmosphere of the solvent involved. Separation of reactants is effected by filtration through a plug of fibrous material held in a connecting tube between the two arms of an all-glass reaction vessel.

Suitable modification of the various, more common filter assemblies will adapt these for most laboratory filtrations requiring an inert atmosphere.

[562] J. D. Piper, N. A. Kersteim, and A. G. Fleiger, *Ind. Eng. Chem., Anal. Ed.*, **14**, 738 (1942).
[563] S. Rothman, *Anal. Chem.*, **22**, 367 (1950).
[564] J. Schmidlin, *Ber.*, **41**, 423 (1908).
[565] K. Ziegler and B. Schnell, *Ann.*, **445**, 266 (1925).

Small quantities of labile liquids which must be filtered under *sterile conditions* may be handled with an apparatus developed for the suction filtration of liquids for hypodermic injection.[566] Other apparatus effects filtration in a stream of inert gas[567] and in the atmosphere of a boiling solvent.[568] In order to reduce dust contamination pressure reduction may be used to transfer the suspension from the vessel in which it has been precipitated.[569] A somewhat elaborate apparatus assembly is also shown by Dodd and Robinson for precipitation and filtration in a nitrogen atmosphere. A simpler set-up employing a vacuum desiccator is also described by the same authors. Postis has described a small all-glass apparatus suited for laboratory filtrations in the absence of air.[570] An apparatus which has been found useful in cases where slow filtration of small quantities of materials is to be handled by centrifugal filtration, but in which the solution must be protected from atmospheric moisture or oxygen, may be fabricated of available glass tubes and parts.[571]

4. Sterilization and Bacteriological Filtrations

Filtrations involving the removal of microorganisms have requirements which have called for the development of rather specialized filter apparatus. In this field there are needs for the clarification of culture media, vaccines, serums, biological extracts, etc., and for solutions to be used in pharmaceutical, biological, and medical research. The extent to which sterilization must be accomplished varies considerably and the types of filtering media and apparatus are adapted to requirements as indicated hereinafter.

Culture media, prepared from biological extracts, gelatin, agar, etc., frequently require clarification prior to sterilization. Straining through fabrics or mats of fibrous materials is sufficient for some purposes. In other cases paper, pulp, or other tighter textured media are required. Some of the apparatus, techniques, and media described in Sections III and IV are adaptable for preliminary treatment in handling biological and bacteriological preparations. Many types of culture media are best filtered hot.

Sterilization filters are usually of four types: (*a*) those with rigid filter media of very fine pore openings; (*b*) those relying on a pad of fibrous material with adsorptive capacity; (*c*) those with membranes; and (*d*) those having fine-pored sintered glass discs. Rigid, porous filter media are made

[566] G. Barattini, *Boll. chim. farm.*, **69**, 1029 (1930).

[567] N. I. Stognii, *Zavodskaya Lab.*, **9**, 236 (1940).

[568] J. W. Dawson and W. M. Dehn, *Ind. Eng. Chem., Anal. Ed.*, **12**, 317 (1940).

[569] R. E. Dodd and P. L. Robinson, *Experimental Inorganic Chemistry*. Elsevier, Amsterdam, 1954.

[570] J. Postis, *Bull. soc. chim.*, **1952**, 283.

[571] F. J. Reithel, *Chemist-Analyst*, **40**, 23 (1951).

of ceramic compositions, clay, porcelain, diatomite, or mixtures of the same. The filter members may be in the form of the familiar bacteriological filter candle, or as cylinders, discs, etc. The filters in which these elements are used must be designed to meet different requirements of size, freedom from contamination, etc.

The original Pasteur-Chamberland bacterial filter[572,573] was and is still made of unglazed porcelain. The Selas filters of American manufacture[574] have a composition designated as a microporous porcelain made by a technique attributed to Blaha[575] as referred to in Section IV.6.D. Selas filter candles, as of early 1955, were supplied in four types, each in eight sizes and seven different porosities. These porosity grades have characteristics as shown in Table VIII. The Berkefeld[577,578] and Mandler[579] filters

TABLE VIII

CHARACTERISTICS OF SELAS BACTERIOLOGICAL FILTER CANDLES

Grade designation	Maximum pore size radius, μ	Bubbling pressure, p.s.i. [576]	Comparative initial flow rate (with H_2O)
XF.............	50	0.45	800
XFF..........	20	1.0	270
10.............	4.4	5	30
01.............	3	7	15
015...........	1.4	15	5
02.............	0.85	25	2
03.............	0.60	35	1.2
06.............	0.30	—	—

employ diatomaceous filter candles. The Berkefeld candles and cylinders[580] are supplied in three degrees of porosity, in various sizes and shapes with porcelain, metallic, or other fittings. Improvised laboratory set-ups employing the Berkefeld candle and sintered glass funnels for the "cold sterilization" of pharmaceutical preparations have been described in adequate detail by Hagelstein.[581] These are suited for small batch filtrations. Filter candles containing oligodynamic silver for sterilization are also produced by

[572] C. Chamberland, *Compt. rend.*, 99, 247 (1884).
[573] M. Schloesing, *Compt. rend.*, 101, 1398 (1895).
[574] G. V. Jordan, Jr., *Mech. Eng.*, 75, 559 (1953).
[575] E. Blaha, U. S. Pat. 2,360,929 (Oct. 24, 1944).
[576] A. Einstein and H. Muhas, *Deut. Med. Wochschr.*, 49, 1012 (1923).
[577] H. Nordtmeyer, *Z. Hyg. Infektionskrankh.*, 10, 145 (1891).
[578] H. Bitter, *Z. Hyg. Infektionskrankh.*, 10, 155 (1891).
[579] Allen Filter Co.
[580] Berkefeld-Filter Gesellschaft u. Celler Filterwerke G.m.b.H., Celle, Hannover.
[581] F. Hagelstein, *Pharm. Ztg. Nachr.*, 88, 770 (1952).

Berkefeld.   In addition, these diatomite filter elements are used in small gravity drip filters, of either glass or enameled iron construction.   These are effective for treating easily sterilized liquids.   In India a type of diatomite ceramic filter element is understood to be produced with the addition of Hyflo Super-Cel, a processed filter powder.[582]   Porcelain and diatomite filter elements for bacteriological uses are also produced in Japan.[583]

Operating assemblies for three small laboratory filter units suitable for sterilization filtrations are shown in Figure 55.   Figure 55A consists of a

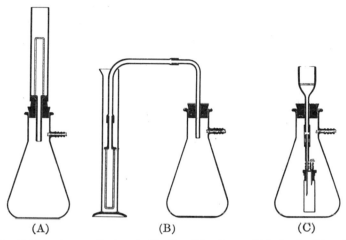

(A)   (B)   (C)

Fig. 55. Small laboratory units for sterilization filtrations: (A) simple filter element for vacuum; (B) sealed unit; (C) micro-Büchner unit.   (Courtesy Selas Corporation of America.)

Selas-type FPS filter element cylinder, and a rubber adapter which accommodates a standard Pyrex vacuum flask.   This set-up is adaptable to laboratory filtrations including the clarification, polishing and sterilization of allergenic extracts, biologicals, and serums.   Bacteriological filtrations can be efficiently and rapidly performed.   The entire set-up can be safely autoclaved.   The assembly shown in Figure 55B also employs a Selas-type FPS filter element but the porcelain connector is glazed to the filter element thus producing a single unit.   It is generally utilized where it is convenient to filter from a holding vessel through a rubber hose directly to a receiving vessel under vacuum conditions.   Figure 55C shows a set-up using a micro-Büchner funnel which is connected with the vacuum flask as shown.   This assembly is used for the cold sterilization of small volumes of preparations under aseptic conditions.

[582] B. S. R. Lastry, *Trans. Indian Ceram. Soc.*, **6**, 51 (1947).
[583] Y. Shiraki and C. Kawashima, *J. Japan. Ceram. Assoc.*, **51**, 385 (1943).

An all-glass vacuum bacterial filter employing an ultrafine sintered glass filter disc, developed by Morton,[584] is depicted in Figure 4, page 641.   This type of filter has no rubber stopper to sterilize and contamination is prevented by an inverted ground joint which may employ a cotton plug to further seal the unit.   A pressure filter apparatus[585] (Fig. 56), also employing an ultrafine filter disc, has been designed to reduce evaporation of filtrate, and in bacteriological filtrations facilitates sterile conditions.   This filter is useful for handling materials which have a tendency to foam.   The Gibson pressure filter[586] is well adapted for the filtration of small quantities

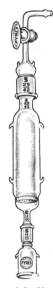

Fig. 56. Bush bacterial filter, all glass, pressure type. (Courtesy Corning Glass Works.)

of serums, vaccines, parenteral solutions, and biologicals.   Another filter apparatus[587] for filtration through bacterial filters permits control of pressure and volume and sampling of filtrate at any stage of the filtration.   The filtrate-measuring cylinder is fitted with a manometer to indicate pressure and with a delivery tube and protective apron to collect the filtrate.   Another small candle filter unit operates in an evacuated chamber.[588]

The filtering effects which occur in the filtration of the usual bacteriological and biological liquids through porous rigid filter media are still not

[584] H. E. Morton, *J. Bact.*, **47,** 379 (1944).
[585] M. T. Bush, *J. Bact.*, **51,** 4 (1946).
[586] R. B. Gibson and C. Estes, *J. Biol. Chem.*, **6,** 349 (1909).
[587] S. Mudd, *Proc. Soc. Exptl. Biol. Med.*, **25,** 60 (1927).
[588] A. Sutcliffe and E. Armitage, *Pharm. J.*, **159,** 393 (1947).

fully understood.   Mudd,[589] in 1922, observed: "The contact surface of the pores of a Berkefeld filter and the fluid bathing them is the site of an electrical potential difference, an ordinary Helmholtz double layer, the solid walls carrying a negative and the liquid a positive charge." This investigator recognized further adsorption phenomena of some sort, which are influenced by pH and affect the passage of viruses through filter candles of the Berkefeld type.

Recognition that the walls of the capillary pores of porous porcelain filters carry a negative charge, and thus retain effectively particles carrying a positive charge, accounts in part for some filtering characteristics of the usual bacteriological filters[590,591]; but since most particles to be removed from biological materials are electronegative, it is not apparent just how important this electrical charge effect may be.

An analysis of the effects occurring when biological materials are filtered through porous ceramic media indicates that the physical retention of particles is more important in prolonged filtrations than either electrical effects or adsorption, although these are factors to be considered.   Jordan[592] has concluded in part:

"Because of the variable influences that the phenomena of adsorption, particle retention, and electrical charges exert on filtration efficiencies, it is rather difficult to state a definite relationship between the size of the maximum opening present in a filter element and the size of the particles retained.   For example, in bacteriological filtrations several types of organisms of much greater size than the maximum opening of the micro-porous porcelain element will readily pass through because of their extreme flexibility.   Conversely, on the polishing of solutions for molecular weight determinations through light scattering techniques investigators have indicated the complete removal of all particles down to 1 millimicron by utilizing a micro-porous porcelain element.   However, numerous observations in the use of grades of micro-porous porcelain have indicated generally that the size of the smallest particle retained is approximately one-third the size of the maximum opening present in the filter element.   In the case of the finer grades the size of the smallest particle retained is approximately one-fourth the size of the maximum opening present.   This general relationship demands that the grades of filter elements be designated on the basis of the maximum opening rather than on the basis of other general characteristics, such as the size of the average opening and initial flow rate, which have little or no bearing on filtration efficiencies.   Specifying grades on basis of the maximum openings enables quick and convenient selection of the proper grades in relation to the degree of filtration to be accomplished."

[589] S. Mudd, Am. J. Physiol., 63, 429 (1922).

[590] H. H. Thornberry, Phytopathology, 25, 601 (1935).

[591] H. Zinsser and S. Bayne-Jones, Textbook of Bacteriology.   8th ed.   Appleton-Century, New York, 1939.

[592] G. V. Jordan, Jr., Mech. Eng., 75, 559 (1953)

Filters employing adsorptive pads made of specially selected grades of cellulose and asbestos fibers or mixtures thereof are useful for the filtration of many bacteriological and biological materials.   Under certain conditions filters of this type are effective for the removal of organisms from liquids and for sterilization, as well as for clarification.   *Seitz* filters are made in small as well as larger sizes, many of which are especially adapted for laboratory use.   A representative number of these are illustrated in Figure 57. Figure 57A represents a small filter, 10 ml. in capacity, developed for the vacuum filtration of blood; B is a small filter designed for the high-pressure

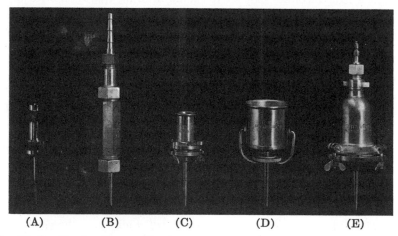

   (A)   (B)   (C)   (D)   (E)

Fig. 57. Sterilization filters, with adsorbent filter pads: (A) micro-blood filter, 10 ml. capacity; (B) micro-pressure filter, 10 ml. capacity; (C) Seitz-EK, vacuum Manteufel type, 30 ml. capacity; (D) Seitz-EK, vacuum Manteufel type, 100 ml. capacity; (E) Seitz-EK, vacuum or pressure Ulenhuth type, 100 ml. capacity. (Courtesy Seitz-Werke, G.m.b.H., Kreuznach, Rheinland.)

filtration of small amounts of bacteriological materials; C represents the classical, vacuum Manteufel-type filter, 30 ml. in capacity; D, also Monteufel, has a somewhat larger capacity (100 ml.); whereas E is the Uhlenhuth type for either vacuum or pressure filtration.[593]   All of these Seitz filters employ soft, sterilized filtering discs, which are usually discarded after one use.   The effectiveness of sorptive pad filters for the removal of pyrogenic substances from water[594] and from solutions intended for intravenous injections[595] has been recognized.

An Alsop laboratory filter which also employs absorbent filter discs for

[593] H. Wilke, *Deut. Apoth. Ztg.*, **13**, 214 (1953).

[594] H. Wilke, *Pharm. Ind.*, **15**, 224 (1953).

[595] H. Wilke and H. E. Voss, *Arzneimittel-Forsch.*, **4**, 8 (1954).

sterilization filtrations is shown in Figure 58. Another absorptive pad filter employs two pyrogen and bacterial retentive filter sheets separated by a collecting ring. In the model shown in Figure 59[596] the discs are 4 in. in diameter. Uses for this type of filter have been recorded in medical research records. Products of sterilization interest that are reported to be satisfactorily handled by Ertel absorptive pad filters include blood plasma, antibiotics, cod liver oils, medicinal preparations, cosmetic products, fruit juices, vegetable oils, and extracts.

Some membrane filters are suited for sterilization and bacteriological filtrations. An example is the MF Millipore filter membrane[597] which is

Fig. 58. Alsop multiple pad adsorptive filter. (Courtesy Alsop Engineering Corp.)

fabricated in sheets of about 150 micron thickness. These cellulose ester membranes may be considered a type of ultrafilter, and are used as previously referred to in Section V. However, numerous applications may properly come under this section, since these membranes are suited for many of the same uses as ceramic filter candles and fibrous pads. The MF filter of the HA type has a calculated pore size of about 0.45 micron. This type is used in aqueous media, but is not suited for many organic solvents—alcohols, ethers, esters, or ketones. Temperature limit is about 125°C. The low flash point, about 200°C., is a disadvantage for some uses. Various applications have been found for modified membrane filters in bacteriology

[596] Ertel Engineering Corp., Kingston, N. Y.
[597] Millipore Filter Corp., Watertown, Mass.

(colony cultivation, transfer, isolation, and counting) and also in the sterility testing of antibiotics, pharmaceuticals, food products, etc.[598−601]

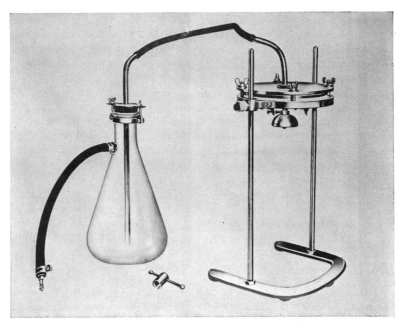

Fig. 59. Ertel laboratory sterilization filter. (Courtesy Ertel Engineering Corp.)

5. Treatment of Pulps and Biological Tissues

Many chemical products, enzymes, hormones, etc., are prepared from extracts of vegetable and animal matter. Usually the tissues are macerated prior to treatment. These pulps are generally difficult to filter because of the presence of flat or platy particles, skins, proteins, gums, waxes, and lipides. In many cases it is essential that the filtration be conducted as rapidly as possible in order to minimize changes due to chemical, enzyme, or bacterial action. Further, some materials must be handled in the cold or in the absence of air. One or more of the various expedients mentioned in Section VI.1 may be employed for handling the extracts of tissues and pulps, but in many cases some of these techniques are not permissible.

[598] *Millipore Filters, Supplemental Technical Information Regarding Bacteriological and Other Analytical Procedures.* Millipore Filter Corp., Watertown, Mass. 1954.

[599] H. F. Clark and others, *Pub. Health Repts.*, 66, 951 (1951).

[600] J. H. Bush, *Sci. Monthly*, 75, 303 (1952).

[601] A. Dickman, *Bull. Natl. Assoc. Clin. Labs.*, 4, 91 (1952).

Thus, heat, change of pH, alteration of osmotic pressure, etc., may affect or ruin the very material that is to be extracted.

As a general rule, it is best first to screen out the coarser pulp particles, skin, or fiber, and to follow the initial coarse straining by a fine filtration. On the other hand, with some materials it is better to handle the entire mass as it is and not to remove the coarse suspended solids, since these may sometimes serve as a spacing agent and thus facilitate filtration.

In many vegetable extractions filtration is aggravated by the formation of troublesome emulsions. The use of surface-active agents was recommended for controlling the foam, which was found to improve the filtering properties of potato, pea, and peeled orange extracts.[602] For preparing plant and fruit extracts for analysis, a mixture of zinc sulfate and potassium ferrocyanide may be used as a clearing aid. The complex zinc ferrocyanide is formed as a gel which collects the troublesome suspended particles. In subsequent filtration the gel functions somewhat as a filtering aid.[603] In the manufacture of essences, after removal of pulp from the extracted mass when a proportion of fruit juices is incorporated, the final blend may be cloudy due to the precipitation of pectins and/or tannins. Removal of these trace impurities may be effected by pad or sintered glass filters as referred to in Section IV.

Some "tricks" in preparing tissue extracts for filtration are suggestive. In the preparation of carboxypeptidase[604] it has been observed:

"The turbidity of the fluid which exudes when frozen pancreas is thawed is due to a small amount of dark, slimy material, which at the pH of the fluid cannot be readily removed by filtration. If the fluid is acidified (green to bromcresol green) and warmed, the dark slimy material clots and can then readily be filtered off. The filtrate on dilution with water yields a precipitate which contains most of the carboxypeptidase and most of the proteinase of the original fluid."

In the isolation of bacteriophages from bacterial material, lysed solutions of staphylococcus, for example, cannot be precipitated with neutral salts or by the usual methods of protein separation. This circumstance is also found for most dilute solutions, especially if they contain mucin. Some of the mucin can be removed with lead acetate, with subsequent concentration *in vacuo*, but decolorizing carbon and Filter-Cel are then used in subsequent filtrations.[605]

The addition of powdered filter aid materials to pulps is a recommended technique for many biological preparations. Thus, with vegetable materials such as digested citrus pulps for the extraction of pectin, for prune

[602] C. L. Dunn and R. H. Earle, Jr., *Anal. Chem.*, **26**, 1099 (1954).

[603] S. N. Lutokhin and A. N. Byushikh, *Zhur. Anal. Khim.*, **5**, 239 (1950).

[604] M. L. Anson, *Science*, **81**, 467 (1935); *J. Gen. Physiol.*, **20**, 663 (1937).

[605] J. H. Northrop, *J. Gen. Physiol.*, **21**, 335 (1938).

pulps, and many others, the addition of a considerable amount (1 to 10%) of a suitable coarse particle size diatomaceous filter aid accelerates the filtration rate and gives a higher yield of filtrate, even though an appreciable amount of liquid is sorbed and retained by the filter aid. The use of diatomaceous silica is effective for pulps if they are fluid enough to filter through gravity, vacuum, or pressure filters. Filter aids may also be added to pulps prior to pressing or squeezing operations. Alternate layers of paper pulp and diatomaceous silica have been used in the filtering of fruit juices and plant extracts on large Büchner funnels.[606] The successful filtration of unfermented peach pulp has been accomplished with filter aid.[607] The use of filter aids in the treatment of animal tissues for isolation of pure enzymes has been described in considerable detail.[608-610]

Thus, for a general procedure employed in protein separation and purification from biological tissues it is stated (ref. 608, pp. 127-8):

"In regard to experimental procedure, the most important point is thorough and complete filtration. For this reason, large funnels must be used so that the filter cake is not more than 1-5 mm. thick. The cake must be pressed with a spatula as cracks appear, until no further foam or liquid is drawn through. The vacuum must be removed before the cake dries, since drying is injurious to all proteins and completely denatures some of them. A filter cake prepared even under the above conditions still contains 30-60 per cent mother liquor while one which is several cm. thick may contain 50-80 per cent and sediment obtained in the centrifuge or a precipitate filtered without suction contains 90 per cent or more mother liquor. One careful filtration with suction is therefore as efficient as several centrifugalizations or filtrations without suction.

"The most troublesome impurity to be contended with is a mucin-like material. This substance will completely prevent crystallization even when present in very small amount. In larger concentrations it prevents any fractionation procedure. Strong acid, Filter-Cel (several grades of this material are made by Johns-Manville Corporation) colloidal copper hydroxide, and acetone are the best reagents so far found for removing it, but each solution has presented a new problem. No preparation has been crystallized until the carbohydrate and glucosamine content have been reduced to less than 1 per cent."

An effective treatment of swine gastric mucosa for the isolation of pepsinogen is described as follows:[610]

[606] J. A. Hall and W. E. Baier, *Ind. Eng. Chem.*, **6**, 203 (1934).

[607] D. S. Bentley, *Food Industries*, **19**, 1359 (1947).

[608] J. H. Northrop, *Crystalline Enzymes*. Columbia Univ. Press, New York, 1939. Also J. H. Northrop, M. Kunitz, and R. M. Herriot, *Crystalline Enzymes*. Columbia Univ. Press, New York, 1948.

[609] M. Kunitz and J. H. Northrop, *J. Gen. Physiol.*, **19**, 991 (1936).

[610] R. M. Herriott, *J. Gen. Physiol.*, **21**, 501 (1938).

"3400 gm. of twice minced, prepared, frozen swine gastric fundus mucosae is mixed with saturated ammonium sulfate solution in sodium bicarbonate solution. To this, 100 gm. of Filter-Cel and 50 gm. Hyflo per liter is added.   The mixture is stirred 15 minutes, and then filtered on a 30 cm. Büchner funnel with Whatman No. 3 paper covered with a thin cake of Hyflo.   Subsequent operations are also made with additions of diatomaceous filter aid."

6. Emulsions

It is frequently necessary to remove solid particles and impurities from emulsions.   For this purpose a filter medium should be selected which will remove the solid particles without disturbing the stability of the emulsion system.   Metal screens or filter cloths may suffice.   If the impurities are of fine size, it may be necessary to use paper or fibrous materials such as mineral wool.   Many particles in emulsions are peculiarly subject to deformation under pressure.[611]   Repeated filtrations through a coarser medium are better than attempting a single filtration with too fine a medium.

Another problem frequently arising in the laboratory is the removal of a small amount of highly dispersed or even emulsified liquid from another liquid.   Traces of volatile oils, for instance, may contaminate and give odor or other undesired characteristics to an aqueous extract or organic materials.   Emulsified oils may be removed most effectively by a combined adsorption and filtration operation.   Many filter media, particularly those of organic nature, have some capacity for the sorption and removal of particles in the dispersed phase, particularly at the start of a filtration. This action cannot be depended upon for any prolonged period and is always subject to the objection that it is difficult to tell when the sorptive capacity is exhausted or falling off seriously.   The addition of gelatinous precipitates, such as aluminum or ferric hydroxides, to liquids is effective in removing oils, etc.   Fuller's earth, decolorizing clays, carbons, or other adsorbents may be used similarly.[612]   An activated diatomaceous product, Sorbo-Cel, is effective for removing either mineral or vegetable oils from dilute, fine suspensions.

Glass fiber filters have been suggested for some emulsion problems.[613] It is pointed out that glass surfaces are normally hydrophilic, but may be rendered permanently hydrophobic by application of silicone materials, thus making glass fiber filters versatile for different emulsion requirements. Sometimes it is preferable first to wet the porous medium slightly with the liquid to be removed, which would be in the dispersed phase.   The sur-

---

[611] E. Hatschek, *Kolloid-Z.*, **7**, 81 (1910).

[612] E. Manegold, *Emulsionen*. Strassenbau, Chemie und Technikverlags, Heidelberg, 1952.

[613] C. A. Smucker and W. C. Marlow, Jr., *Ind. Eng. Chem.*, **46**, 176 (1954).

faces so wetted tend to collect more of the same liquid by preferential adsorption.

Troublesome emulsions may sometimes be handled by complete removal of one liquid by appropriate filtration, or the emulsion may be broken by passing through a filter member, permitting ready separation of the liquids in the filtrate by sedimentation, mechanical means, or centrifuging. Filter media of fine particle size, e.g., diatomaceous earth, are most effective with some emulsions. Studies in the filtration of emulsions such as oil refinery wastes lead to the recommendation of a precoat filter with filter aid.[614] The use of surfactants in extraction and demulsification techniques in handling emulsions was studied for plant extracts.[615] An anionic surfactant, Ultrawet K,[616] is reported as most satisfactory when used in combination with sodium sulfate. The use of surfactants in breaking petroleum oil–water emulsions was reported earlier.[617]

7. Washing and Purifying Operations

Filtering apparatus and techniques are often convenient for the segregation of solids so that they may be washed free from impurities or dissolved in a solvent. The procedures of qualitative analysis involve numerous precipitations, collections on filters, and subsequent solution of the precipitate. For qualitative purposes it is sufficient to wash the solids free enough of adherent soluble matter in the mother liquor so as to avoid complications in the next tests to be made. In quantitative work the requirements are more rigid; the solids must be washed scrupulously, sometimes be completely dissolved, and all traces removed from the filter.

The principles and empirical rules for washing precipitates are familiar to every chemist. The subject was subjected to mathematical treatment by Ostwald in a classical analysis of this operation.[618] It is also possible to consider the washing of solids, such as organic substances with ether, washing of precipitates, etc., as examples of infinite series.[619] The mechanics of washing solids and residues is still incompletely understood despite consideration of the fundamental[620] and practical aspects.[621] Pro-

[614] E. Q. Camp and C. Phillips, *Oil and Gas J.*, **48**, 214 (1950).

[615] C. L. Dunn and R. H. Earle, Jr., *Anal. Chem.*, **26**, 1099 (1954).

[616] Atlantic Refining Co., Phila., Pa.

[617] A. S. C. Lawrence and W. Killner, *J. Inst. Petroleum Tech.*, **34**, 821 (1948).

[618] W. Ostwald, *Die wissenschaftlichen Grundlagen der analytischen Chemie*, Engelmann, Leipzig, 1894. English translation, *The Scientific Foundations of Analytical Chemistry*, Macmillan, New York, 1908.

[619] J. W. Mellor, *Mathematics for Students of Chemistry and Physics with Special Reference to Practical Work*. Longmans, Green, London, 1919, pp. 269–270.

[620] E. Hatschek, *J. Soc. Chem. Ind.*, **39**, 226T (1920).

[621] F. H. Rhodes, *Ind. Eng. Chem.*, **26**, 1331 (1934).

cedures and precautions for washing precipitates, however, have now become fairly well standardized and may be referred to in various texts and handbooks of analytical chemistry. Most of the more important recent investigations have been made from the standpoint of chemical engineering[622,623] wherein one of the major factors is economic considerations. Of these, time is usually the most important from the laboratory standpoint. In essence, it may be considered that the real mechanism of first importance in washing filter residues is similar to the displacement of liquid from a section of a circular capillary tube. At first, the undiluted filtrate must be displaced and then the concentration of solubles in the residue decreases inversely as the square of the ratio of the volume of filtrate to the volume of filter residue voids. It is thus assumed that diffusion effects are usually less than displacement action. A study by Atkinson[624] in which one liquid is displaced from a bed of porous solids by another liquid supports the viewpoint expressed above. The practical application of this study is mostly for the separation of oils from fuller's earth.

When a series of precipitates is to be washed with several reagents and when it is desired to collect the washings in separate receivers, a multiple filtration assembly developed for potash determinations by the Lindo-Gladding method is of interest.[625] In the set-up described the filtrates may be collected in any one of three receivers by manipulations of stopcocks.

In *preparative chemistry* washing is necessary in order to obtain pure compounds. As a general principle the filter should be completely drained of liquid before adding fresh liquid for washing. Suction filters are advantageous because the solids can be sucked and pressed dry. It is often advisable to cover the material with a *rubber dam*. If the solid has been collected in a Büchner funnel, the latter is covered with the rubber dam, which may be fastened by a rubber band applied at the outside of the funnel close to the rim. The rubber dam soon is sucked tight to the top of the filter cake and to the inside walls, protecting the cake. Mechanical pressure, *e.g.*, by means of a stopper or a spatula, may be applied in order to squeeze out liquid retained by the cake. Washing in pressure filters is accomplished by replacing the liquid feed with clean wash liquid. It is generally necessary not to permit the pressure to be released at any time during a pressure filtration or wash period, when a vertical filter element is employed; otherwise, the solids may drop from the filter. In treating some solids it is advantageous to stir the solids during filtering and washing

[622] H. E. Crosier, "Washing of Liquids from Porous Media and Conduits," Ph.D. Thesis, Univ. of Michigan, Ann Arbor, 1949.

[623] H. E. Crosier and L. E. Brownell, *Ind. Eng. Chem.*, **44**, 631 (1952).

[624] D. I. W. Atkinson, *J. Imp. Coll. Chem. Eng. Soc.*, **4**, 78 (1948).

[625] C. V. Marshall, *Chemist-Analyst*, **41**, 68 (1952).

so that the formation of channels is avoided. In other instances it is well to wash in the filter intermittently, allowing the wash liquid to remain in contact with the solid particles for a considerable period to dissolve the impurities. It may be preferable or necessary to remove the solids completely from the filter and stir or agitate vigorously with fresh wash liquid, and then to refilter the solids.

From a physical standpoint the washing of solids resembles filtration, and the principles expressed in the theory of filtration may be applied to washing operations. An important difference is that in washing the liquid passes through a substantially constant thickness of residue. Also, in washing there is greater variability in the residue. In filtration any temporary unevenness in cake formation is automatically corrected for by the tendency of the solids to be deposited at once at the point of least resistance to flow. In washing there is no such tendency, and if a comparatively large percentage of the solids is removed by dissolving, the residue may become unduly porous with resultant channeling and ineffective removal of solubles.

As an accessory operation to separating solids on filters and washing, *drying* may be accomplished by replacing the original liquid with a more volatile *cosolvent*, as replacing water with acetone. Air or warm gases may be sucked through solids on a filter and the solids may thus be partially or completely dried.

Surface-active agents may be used in some wash liquids for washing precipitates. The washing action is thus accelerated and the liquid content of the final residue is reduced. Aerosol[626] agents for aqueous systems are available for neutral washes in grades OT, MA, or AY, whereas grades H or OS are recommended for strongly acid or alkaline wash liquors. An aid to prevent the troublesome creeping of some precipitates during washing is the Anti-Creep preparation of Schleicher and Schuell. For washing minute quantities of precipitates wash bottles of polyethylene are helpful, since slight hand pressure on the bottles permits controlled delivery of small amounts of liquid.

8. Highly Viscous Materials

Highly viscous materials are generally difficult to filter and are frequently almost impossible to handle with the usual laboratory facilities.[627] Unless the nature of the solids counterindicates a pressure filtration, the highest pressure convenient with available facilities should be employed. Some types of high-pressure laboratory filters which have been used in handling

---

[626] American Cyanamid Co., New York.
[627] "The Filtration of Viscous Liquids," *Chem. Age* (*London*), **25**, 380 (1931).

viscous materials are shown in Figures 31 and 32.   Unless otherwise objectionable, it is always advantageous to filter viscous liquids at the highest permissible temperature.

Some resins, waxes, high-polymer compounds, plastics, gumlike mixtures, etc., which are semirigid or solid at room temperature, may be heated above their melting points or liquefying temperatures and filtered like other liquids.   It is necessary, of course, to make sure that materials of these types do not resolidify on the filtrate side of the filter septum.   This difficulty may be avoided by using the devices for hot filtration described in Section III.6, by heating with other means, or by insulating all exposed parts of the filtering apparatus.   An example of the exacting requirements for the filtration of viscous materials is in the extraction and clarification of pectinous fruit juices.[628]

The filtration of viscose and similar solutions is a somewhat specialized field.   A review of the problems involved in the filtration of rayon was given by Meyer.[629]   Samuelson[630] pointed out some of the difficulties in viscose filtration.   In another viscose study[631] it was concluded that the plugging of the filter medium is due in part to the deterioration of xanthate aggregates because of shearing stresses.   The plugging is related quantitatively to the structure and concentration of the dispersed cellulosic particles.[632]   Another viewpoint is that technical viscose contains a sol phase of dissolved xanthate and a gel phase of highly polymerized cellulose particles.   In filtration a portion of the gel phase is retained by the filter medium and this plugs its pores.[633]   A general critique of viscose filtration by Gonsalves[634] summarizes the state of knowledge up to 1950.   An attempt at the mathematical treatment of viscose filtration based on the conventional equations led to the conclusion that it is impossible to define completely the quality of viscose by constants obtained from filtration alone. A combination of filtration data and stress–strain properties of the xanthate gel is proposed for quality characterization.

In a later investigation[635] it was concluded that a single constant is not satisfactory for defining the clogging effect.   An equation based on the slope of a portion of a clogging effect curve was derived.   It is claimed that it is thus possible to segregate the filtering characteristics of viscose into

[628] J. C. Bell and E. H. Wiegand, *Oregon Agr. Expt. Sta. Circ.*, No. 63 (July, 1925).

[629] A. Meyer, *Zellwolle u. Kunstseide*, **2**, 99 (1944).

[630] O. Samuelson, *Svensk Papperstidn.*, **48**, 517 (1945).

[631] T. Bergek and T. Ouchterlony, *Svensk Papperstidn.*, **49**, 470 (1946).

[632] H. L. Vosters, *Svensk Papperstidn.*, **53**, 29 (1950).

[633] T. Kleinert and V. Mossmer, *Oesterr. Chem. Ztg.*, **51**, 29 (1950).

[634] V. E. Gonsalves, *Rec. trav. chim.*, **69**, 873 (1950).

[635] H. L. Vosters, *Svensk Papperstidn.*, **53**, 59 (1950).

a part relating to the filter clogging and another to the rheological properties of the viscose.

A laboratory testing procedure, which filters the viscose through two sintered glass filters, is followed in Japan. Results give substantially straight-line curves when plotted as the volume of filtrate at any instant versus the log of the integral volume from the start of the filtration.[636] Another study, using a high-pressure filtering apparatus with a 15% cellulose acetate solution in acetone–water, arrives at a similar expression.[637] It is concluded that the differences in filtration behavior of different viscoses are due mainly to nonuniformities in contents of fiber fragments, fiber gels, and insoluble salts. A further similar study was carried out on viscoses made from hardwood sulfate pulp and softwood sulfite pulp.[638] Small quantities of solutions containing hydrolyzed cellulosic solids are said to be much more readily filtered in paper thimbles supported in a filter. A plug of glass wool supporting the thimble permits the application of moderate suction.[639] Diatomaceous filter aids have been reported to be helpful in the filtration of viscose spinning solutions,[640] whereas the use of fibrous materials such as finely divided wood pulp, ramie, etc., has been recommended for filtering cellulose dopes.[641]

The simple expedient of "diluting" a viscous mixture to lower the viscosity is an effective means for improving filtration when the purpose is to obtain the solids and when the diluent does not cause undesirable precipitation or dissolution, as referred to in Section VI.1. If additional liquid is not objectionable in the filtrate or the diluent can be removed by evaporation or distillation, this expedient is also satisfactory when the liquid is desired. In some cases the filtrate may be concentrated to the original viscosity by evaporation or distillation.

9. Filtrations Involving Adsorbents

Solid adsorbents, including carbons, fuller's earth, hydrated aluminum oxides, magnesium oxide, activated clays, silica gel, hydrous metal oxides, etc., are used to decolorize, deodorize, and otherwise purify many organic liquids and solids in solution.[642] The use of adsorbents is discussed in

[636] H. Okada and T. Yamoji, *J. Japan. Tech. Assoc. Pulp Paper Ind.*, **5**, 318 (1951).

[637] L. A. Cox and W. K. Mohney, *Ind. Eng. Chem.*, **45**, 1798 (1953).

[638] G. M. Vyas, *J. Sci. Ind. Research (India)*, **B12**, 262 (1953).

[639] R. H. Pierson, *Anal. Chem.*, **25**, 1939 (1953).

[640] A. Marschall, *Kunstseide u. Zellwolle*, **24**, 188 (1942); *Ver. deut. Chemiker, Beih.*, **55**, 49 (1942).

[641] C. I. Haney, U. S. Pat. 2,330,211 (Sept. 28, 1943).

[642] V. R. Deitz, *Bibliography of Solid Adsorbents, 1900–1942*. U. S. Cane Sugar Refineries, Bone Char Manufacturers, and National Bureau of Standards, Washington, D. C., 1944. Also New edition, 1943 to 1953, *Natl. Bur. Standards Circ.*, No. 566 (1956).

Volume V of this series, and is considered here only to emphasize some filtering procedures involved.

Liquids or solutions may be filtered through columns of theadsor bent in glass or metal tubes, cylinders, or other types of vessels which may be jacketed and heated if necessary. Adsorbents for this type of treatment are preferably in granular form. Liquids of low viscosity or those containing only small amounts of impurities to be adsorbed filter rather readily through columns of adsorbent, even if the particle size is small. Aqueous materials and higher viscosity liquids may filter more slowly.

Finely divided adsorbents added directly to liquids, with agitation or digestion, are highly effective for decolorizing and purifying by adsorption, because of the great surface area of the adsorbent. The contact of adsorbent with liquid in this way is economical in the use of adsorbent and is usually more rapid than percolation through granules. For laboratory purposes the contact use of powders is generally preferred over the use of granules. The adsorbent must be separated from the liquid after the treatment. Filtration is a common means of effecting the separation. Adsorbents, depending upon the type and the liquid, may be readily or difficultly filtered out after contact. Finely divided clays and some carbons are particularly hard to remove completely. Proper selection of filter type and filter medium usually solves this problem. The value of decolorizing and adsorbent carbons for the clarification of organic solutions in the laboratory has now become rather well recognized.[643]

Filter aids are helpful and sometimes necessary for the removal of adsorbents.[644] The filter aid may be added to the liquid along with the adsorbent and both filtered out together. Thus, the use of diatomaceous silica has been reported advantageous in the removal of Norite and Super Filtrol adsorbents from vitamin-containing preparations from *Mycobacterium tuberculosis* cultures.[645] The filtering-out carbons are widely employed in the preparation of fruit pectins and are filtered out after contact.[646] Powdered fuller's earth adsorbents are produced in this country by Minerals and Chemicals Corp. of America, Attapulgus Division, Philadelphia, Pennsylvania and Floridin Co., Tallahassee, Florida. Filtrol is the most common type of activated clay in the United States. In Germany Tonsil and Terrana correspond.

A laboratory study on filtration through clay and diatomaceous earth in

[643] G. R. Robertson, *Laboratory Practice of Organic Chemistry*. Rev. ed., Macmillan, New York, 1947.

[644] A. B. Cummins, L. E. Weymouth, and L. L. Johnson, *Oil & Soap*, **21**, 215 (1944).

[645] R. C. Mills, G. M. Briggs, T. A. Luckey, and C. A. Elvehjem, *Proc. Soc. Exptl. Biol. Med.*, **56**, 240 (1944).

[646] W. A. Rooker, *Fruit Pectin, Its Commercial Manufacture and Use*. Avi, New York, 1928.

the determination of Parathion extracted from residues of vegetables and fruits provides the following procedure:[647]

"A single plug of cotton is placed in the bottom of a 150 ml. separatory funnel, and 10 gm. or more of Attapulgus clay adsorbent (2 parts of Attapulgus clay and 1 part of Hyflo Super-Cel, well mixed) are added; 50 ml. of benzene are added and the mixture is stirred until completely wetted and free of air bubbles; the benzene is drawn by suction almost to the surface of the adsorbent. The benzene extract is then poured off."

The passage of a solution through Tswett columns and chromatographic adsorption towers is a special form of filtration. The selection of material for the adsorption column must be made on the basis of the action of the adsorbent, but, within limits, the particle size of the adsorbent or adsorbents, the height of the columns, etc., may be selected to obtain reasonable filter rates. The use of inert filter aids, particularly diatomaceous silica, in combination with adsorbents, offers many advantages. For details on adsorption techniques and chromatographic analyses see Volume V of this series.

VII. TECHNIQUES OF FILTRATION TESTING

1. Objectives and Measurement of Filterability

The apparatus and methods employed for laboratory filtration testing as distinguished from ordinary laboratory filtrations are sufficiently specialized to warrant description. Controlled testing in filtration is needed for such purposes as the following:

(A) To obtain information and reliable quantitative data for the filtration of specific materials. Such information is: (1) essential in establishing the quality or purity of the filtered liquid, which can only be determined by tests as required on the filtrate, and which in turn are correlated with the filtration test results; and (2) to establish filter performance so that larger scale or even full production plant equipment may be "scaled-up." Thus, properly conducted laboratory filtration testing may be employed to establish the preferred process to be adopted for production as well as for the type and size of equipment to be employed.

(B) For the evaluation of filter media, filter aids, etc., the suitability of paper, textiles, rigid septa, and other filter media for specific filtrations must be established by actual laboratory testing. The quality and action of filter aids may also be determined in the laboratory so that the type of filter aid, the proper amount to use, the method of addition, and other factors may be determined prior to plant usage. Laboratory filtration testing techniques are a vital factor in routine production control of the manufacture of diatomaceous and other filter aids.

[647] P. R. Averell and M. V. Morris, *Ind. Eng. Chem., Anal. Ed.*, **20**, 753 (1948).

"Filterability" is a term with somewhat different meanings but it usually means, in a practical sense, the comparative ease or difficulty in filtering. This implies not only the filter rate, but also the readiness of obtaining the necessary quality and clarity of filtrates.   The measurement of filterability, therefore, affords a means of understanding better the filtering characteristics of materials and is essential for studies in process work, wherein variables must be controlled to insure adequate filter performance as well as to control the characteristics of filtrates as they may be treated subsequent to filtration.

As an example, filterability of solutions of cellulose derivatives is of prime importance in the treatment of such materials.   A laboratory test method to measure the filterability of cellulose acetate solution employs a filter apparatus in which cotton linters sheathing is the filter medium.[648] It was concluded that the filtration behavior of the polymer is affected mainly by nonuniformities in the solution, such as fiber fragments, fiber gels, gels, insoluble salts, and dirt, and that the filterability of cellulose acetate is determined further by the type of pulp employed, its pretreatment, and acetylation conditions.   In another field, it has been pointed out that among the factors which affect the filterability of serums and proteins are pH and concentration of neutral salts.[649]

Methods for determining the filterability of sugar solutions have been the subject of much concern for many years in raw sugar manufacture and in subsequent refining.   The Elliott filterability test as originally proposed[650] and as later modified[651] has been used internationally to indicate the filtering behavior and subsequent refining qualities of raw sugar and sugar products.   This simple suction leaf test has been considered satisfactory when simplicity and ease of performance are more important than precision.   However, a pressure filtration test, patterned after the Johns-Manville "bomb" filter as described hereinafter (Sect. VII.2B) is used for sugar filterability testing when greater accuracy is required.[652-654]   Honnig[655] later detailed a laboratory study on methods and procedures as de-

[648] L. A. Cox and W. K. Mohney, *Ind. Eng. Chem.*, **45**, 1798 (1953).

[649] W. Elford, P. Grabar, and W. Fischer, *Biochem. J.*, **30**, 84 (1936); **30**, 92 (1936).

[650] A. A. Blowski, *Facts About Sugar*, **20**, 758 (1925).

[651] C. A. Browne and F. W. Zerban, *Physical and Chemical Methods of Sugar Analysis*. 3rd ed., Wiley, New York, 1941, pp. 1050–1053.

[652] R. W. Harman, *Intern. Sugar J.*, **37**, 471 (1935).

[653] A. L. Holven, M. McCalip, and L. Lang, "Tests for the Evaluation of the Refining Qualities of Raw Cane Sugar," *Report from the Referee on Subcommittee on Subject No. 10*, U. S. National Committee, International Commission for Uniform Methods of Sugar Analysis, July 7, 1949.

[654] H. I. Knowles, International Commission for Uniform Methods of Sugar Analysis, *Report of the Proceedings of the 10th Session*, Brussels, 1949, Subject 10, pp. 24–30.

[655] P. Honnig, paper presented at the 11th Annual Meeting of the Sugar Industry Technicians, New York, 1951.

veloped in Java for the evaluation and the expression of the relative filterabilities of various sugar solutions.

A theory on the filterability of fluids has resulted in an ingenious means for measuring and recording this property.[656-659] The apparatus described automatically measures and records the rate of increase in resistance to flow of a liquid through a microscreen or sand bed with respect to the volume filtered under various conditions. The chief disadvantage of the method is that it fails to take account of the clarity of the filtrate. This apparatus, while developed for water filtration, appears to be applicable—with some changes—to organic laboratory filterability determinations.

2. Methods and Procedures

A. PRELIMINARY TESTS

The selection of filtering equipment for processing plants and manufacturing operations and the working out of details for filtration processes come within the fields of chemical and process engineering. However, the basic information for the design of plant filters and the determination of operating procedures must usually originate in the laboratory. This initially involves "beaker or bench tests" in which the *character* of the material to be handled is studied in view of the requirements of the filtration. Qualitative or semiquantitative information can frequently be obtained with ordinary laboratory apparatus. A quick filtration with a funnel and filter paper or with a simple suction filter indicates whether the material filters rapidly or slowly and what the filtrate looks like. The nature and amount of solids may be determined. The effects of heat or other permissible treatments are established. Preliminary tests with funnels, suction filters, filter sticks, and the like indicate the types of filter media, filtering equipment, and procedures to be followed. Whether or not the use of a filter aid is necessary or advantageous may thus be determined. The probable properties of the cake and the clarity of the filtrate should also be indicated by these tests.

A convenient method for comparing the filtering properties of a series of solutions involves a filter "stick" (see Sect. III.4.E). The stick is arranged to discharge into a calibrated receiver so that the solutions may be directly compared by timing the collection of given volumes of filtrate. This test method is particularly adaptable to the use of a precoat since the stick

[656] P. L. Boucher, "Straining of Water and Effluents," Ph. D. Thesis, Faculty of Engineering, Univ. of London, 1944.

[657] P. L. Boucher and N. A. F. Rountree, U. S. Pat. 2,572,436 (Oct. 23, 1951).

[658] P. L. Boucher, *J. Inst. Civil Engrs. London*, **27**, 415 (1946).

[659] D. H. Matheson, *Water and Sewage Works*, **101**, 517 (1954).

needs only to be dipped into a slurry of filter aid for a few seconds before being immersed in the test solution.   Special techniques such as those mentioned in Section VI may be worked out to advantage on the "beaker and Büchner" scale.   Not only is this conservative with material but it also saves considerable time.   Procedures that show definite promise on the small scale may then be tried out with larger or more precise equipment.

B.   LABORATORY TEST FILTERS

Small experimental pressure filters have proved to be of greatest value in controlled laboratory filtration testing.   Such a filter is shown in Figure 60.

Fig. 60. Two-unit pressure leaf filter.   (Courtesy Johns-Manville Corp.)

This filter has a vertical filter leaf and an attachment for precoating. It is provided with accessory equipment for the measurement and control of all variables important in establishing the filtering behavior of the material under test.   A description of a four-unit filter of this type and its method of operation is given in the original journal reference[660] and in the first edition of this book (Sect. VI, page 570).   Such a unit may be used for the evaluation of filter aids by adopting a standard test liquor and varying the percentage or type of filter aid.   A multiple unit is generally used so that the test sample may be directly compared with a standard sample, both being run with standard liquor prepared in the same batch.

[660] A. B. Cummins and L. E. Weymouth, *Ind. Eng. Chem.*, **34**, 392 (1942).
[661] E. G. Gillett and R. F. Black, *Intern. Sugar J.*, **56**, 307 (1954).

A slightly modified type of bomb filter has been described by Gillett and Black.[661]   Their device has two compartments—one for precoat liquor and another for filtering liquor.   The filter leaf is movable and may be transferred from one chamber to the other without opening the bomb.   Their paper describes a complete test assembly.   Precision is said to be ±2% while scale-up data on sugar are usually within 5% of the realized performance.

Three different sizes of pressure leaf test filters are available from Dorr-Oliver, Inc.: the A cell with a filtration area of 56 sq. in., the B cell, 144

Fig. 61. Oliver "C" cell.   (Courtesy Dorr-Oliver, Inc.)

sq. in., and the C cell, 24 sq. in.   The C cell is shown in Figure 61.   A number of the units mentioned in Section III.5 are also applicable. Sperry[662] used a test filter with two horizontal filtering surfaces: in one, the filtration was in a downward direction; in the other, in the upward direction.   Thus, any settling effects should cancel out.   A unique device for filtering at constant rate was described by Rietema.[663]   Slurry was fed to the filter from a cylinder which contained a screw-actuated piston for expelling the fluid at constant rate.

C. RESEARCH AND TESTING ASSEMBLIES

In addition to the filter itself, a satisfactory filtration test assembly must include auxiliary facilities to provide the required precision and accuracy in the control of experimental variables.   Provision should also be made for properly observing and recording test data.   These operations may be

[662] D. R. Sperry, *Chem. Met. Eng.*, **15**, 198 (1916).
[663] K. Rietema, *Chem. Eng. Sci.*, **2**, 88 (1953).

carried out manually but the advantages of automatic control and recording are obvious.   An early device for recording filtrate volume versus time was described by Sperry.[662]   A pen which was attached to a float in the receiver traced the liquid rise on a drum rotated by a clock mechanism. Pressure program controllers are available from instrument companies. Strain gages and other types of transducers may be adapted to the measurement and recording of pressure and filtrate volume.

A laboratory filtration apparatus with complete instrumentation has been described by Grace.[664,665]   The essentials of this set-up are: (a) agitated stainless-steel pressure vessel for montejus filtration at pressures up to 500 p.s.i., (b) separate vessel for holding liquid for washing experiments, (c) various types of interchangeable filter elements, and (d) instrumentation for the control, measurement, and recording of time, pressure, and filtrate volume.

A filtration test assembly[663] used in a study of stabilizing effects in compressible cakes features multiple manometer attachments for the measurement of liquid pressure at different points in the filter cake.   The apparatus also has a unique arrangement for filtering at constant rate.

The compression-permeability cell (see Fig. 62) is a practical device for characterizing a material over a wide range of pressure conditions.   A cake is formed inside a precision cylinder where a piston is used to apply mechanical stress.   The permeability is determined under various conditions of pressure, thus allowing the specific filtration resistance to be calculated under these conditions.   The original idea is credited to Ruth[666] but it remained for Grace[664,667] to develop the method further and correlate the data with actual filtration results (see Sect. II).   A similar apparatus was described by Haruni and Storrow.[668]

Details for three experimental filtration units, especially adapted for university instruction, are given in the text by Zimmerman and Lavine.[669] These descriptions are particularly useful since they include sample calculations and other information on the mathematical expression of filtration data.   There are many cases in which vacuum filtration assemblies have been used for purposes similar to those for pressure filters.   A recent example is described by Jones.[670]   Ingmanson et al.[671,672] described a set-up

[664] H. P. Grace, *Chem. Eng. Progress*, **49**, 367 (1953).

[665] H. P. Grace, private communication.

[666] B. F. Ruth, *Ind. Eng. Chem.*, **38**, 564 (1946).

[667] H. P. Grace, *Chem. Eng. Progress*, **49**, 303 (1953).

[668] M. M. Haruni and J. A. Storrow, *Ind. Eng. Chem.*, **44**, 2751 (1952).

[669] O. T. Zimmerman and I. Lavine, *Chemical Engineering Laboratory Equipment.* Ind. Res. Service, Dover, N. H., 1943.

[670] E. L. Jones, *J. Roy. Tech. Coll. Glasgow*, **5**, 148 (1950).

[671] W. L. Ingmanson, *Tappi*, **35**, 439 (1952).

[672] W. L. Ingmanson and R. P. Whitney, *Tappi*, **37**, 523 (1954).

for filtration and permeability testing. His apparatus is constructed primarily of plastic tubing and brass and is suitable for constant-pressure work. This is a good example of the use of filtration test apparatus, the techniques of filtration testing, and the application of filtration theory to one branch of organic chemistry, paper making.

Fig. 62. Compression-permeability test cell. (Courtesy Johns-Manville Corp.)

D. LIQUID PERMEABILITY TESTING

Liquid permeability testing is important in that permeability data may be used to calculate filtration resistance (see Sect. II.2). Since permeability determinations are more easily carried out than filtration tests, it is worthwhile to consider this as a method for predicting filtration behavior. Permeability measurements have long been used in other fields,[673] but the

[673] M. Muskat, *The Flow of Homogeneous Fluids through Porous Media.* McGraw-Hill, New York, 1937, Chap. 2.

correlation of such data with filtration results is relatively recent. Ruth[666] compared filtration and permeability data on calcium carbonate and found them to agree within 15%. A study of the correlation was made by Hoffing and Lockhart[674] who worked with mixtures of sized quartz and filter aid. An average deviation of only 3.6% was reported for the correlation. Other authors have since confirmed the correlation.[663,667,668,671,672]

The following is a brief description of the liquid permeability method and apparatus used in the writers' laboratory. The original idea, usually attributed to Carman,[675] and later modified by other authors,[674] has been adapted to suit the needs of general laboratory liquid permeability testing. Figure 63 shows the apparatus and accessory equipment employed.

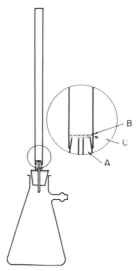

Fig. 63. Liquid permeability apparatus: (A) No. 00 rubber stopper; (B) 100 x 100 wire cloth; (C) 60 x 60 wire cloth.

A 25 ml. section of an ordinary 50 ml. buret is used. Two circles of wire cloth, one 100 x 100 and the other 60 x 60, form the septum and are supported by a one-hole No. 00 rubber stopper. With the cell arranged to discharge into a filter flask, vacuum is applied and a thin precoat is formed from a slurry of material of greater permeability and different color than the material to be tested. Without allowing the cake to blow dry, the reciprocal rate of water passage (sec./ml.) is measured. A cake is then built up from a slurry of specified concentration and the reciprocal rate is again measured. The first rate is subtracted from the second to obtain the reciprocal flow rate of the fluid through the cake. A pressure correction corresponding to the head of liquid above the cake is applied to the value read from the manometer. Cake height (a function of volume) may be read directly from the graduations on the buret. Viscosity may be measured or, in the case of water or other pure liquid, taken from a handbook. Equation (6) (p. 624) is used to calculate

[674] E. H. Hoffing and F. J. Lockhart, *Chem. Eng. Progress*, **47**, 3 (1951).
[675] P. C. Carman, *Ind. Eng. Chem.*, **31**, 1047 (1939).

permeability, the reciprocal of which is cake resistance. The following factors have been found to be essential in obtaining consistent results:

(*a*) The slurry concentration must be held constant in comparing the permeability of solids, since permeability (or cake resistance) varies with prefilt concentration.[676]

(*b*) A bubbler should be used to agitate the slurry during cake formation. This is especially necessary when materials of low permeability are being tested.

(*c*) All of the slurry added to the tube should not be allowed to deposit but rather the last portion should be withdrawn while simultaneously adding clear water. This eliminates possible error arising from sedimentation of solids in the tube.

(*d*) If water is used, it should be prefiltered or otherwise treated to remove dissolved air. With materials of low permeability, a very large error can result from having air bubbles form inside the cake.

(*e*) The reciprocal rate of water through the precoat should not exceed 20% of the total reciprocal rate.

E.   METHODS FOR DETERMINING DEGREE OF CLARIFICATION

One of the more difficult problems of filtration testing is to measure the improvement in filtrate properties that results from the filtration. Usually the property of most interest in a filtered liquid is the presence or absence of suspended particles. Thus, when the main purpose of the filtration is to obtain a clear liquid, the problem is to express accurately the degree of clarification. Such terms as cloudy, turbid, dull, trace of turbidity, bright, clear, brilliant, sparkling, etc., are used to indicate varying degrees of clarification or the lack of it. Obviously, such qualitative expressions have different meanings and are of value only as general descriptive terms. If filtered liquids are compared with other filtrates of known history or with prepared turbidity standards, the comparison becomes somewhat more definite. Thus, if a given sample is defined as more clear than one comparison liquid but less clear than a second standard liquid, there is some basis for evaluating the result of the filtration. Such comparisons, however, are at best semiquantitative and depend upon the judgment and experience of the observer. For some purposes this is entirely adequate but for more exact requirements may be quite unsatisfactory. Liquids of relatively high turbidity may be evaluated by examination of transmitted light. For more highly clarified liquids, it is necessary to study the light that is scattered or reflected at some angle outside the path of the transmitted beam.

Clarity comparisons may be made with a set of prepared standard samples of graduated degrees of turbidity which are developed for the particular type of material involved. The standards may be prepared from

[676] P. M. Heertjes and H. v. d. Haas, *Rec. trav. chim.*, **68**, 361 (1949).

filtrates of the liquid under study or may be artificially prepared.   Some
methods for the determination of turbidity in water call for standards prepared from silica or fuller's earth.[677-679]   The development of physical
standards of turbidity has been under investigation by the American Society of Brewing Chemists for the past decade.   Realizing the importance

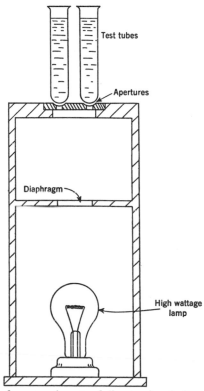

Fig. 64. Simple comparison tyndallmeter for clarity observation.

of such standards, the National Bureau of Standards is currently collaborat-
ing in this study.[680]   As a result of this long-range study, suspensions of
formazin have proved most satisfactory not only for visual comparison but
also for use in photoelectric instruments.[681]   In the selection of such standards, stability and reproducibility are the two most important factors.

[677] G. C. Whipple and D. D. Jackson, *Technol. Quart.*, **12**, 283 (1899); **13**, 274 (1900).
[678] P. V. Wells, *U. S. Natl. Bur. Standards Sci. Paper No. 367*, **15**, 693 (1920); *J. Am.
Water Works Assoc.*, **9**, 488 (1922); *Chem. Revs.*, **3**, 331 (1927).
[679] *Standard Methods for the Examination of Water and Sewage*.   10th ed., Am. Pub.
Health Assoc., New York, 1955.
[680] *Proc. Am. Soc. Brewing Chemists*, **1952**, 172.
[681] *Proc. Am. Soc. Brewing Chemists*, **1954**, 160.

Visual comparison in transparent containers is the simplest method of evaluating turbidity.   The type of container and method of illuminating and viewing are normally prescribed for reproducibility.   Instruments offer more precise means for clarity measurements and may be divided into two major classes.   One class, usually referred to as turbidimeters, measure the attenuation of the transmitted beam.   This type of instrument is most

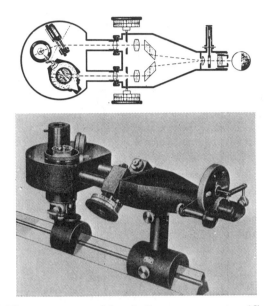

Fig. 65. Pulfrich Photometer as used for clarity measurements.   (Courtesy Carl Zeiss, Jena.)

effective for liquids with sufficient turbidity to reduce the intensity of the transmitted light by at least 5%.   The other major class, referred to as nephelometers and tyndallmeters, measures turbidity in terms of the intensity of the light scattered or reflected outside the path of the transmitted beam.   Instruments in this class are best suited for the more highly clarified liquids.

Instruments in either of these two major classes may be either of the visual type or the photoelectric type and may be simple or highly complicated, particularly for quantitative measurement.[682,683]   Of the visual tur-

[682] A. Weissberger, ed., *Physical Methods of Organic Chemistry*, 2nd ed., Interscience, New York-London, 1949, Chap. XXII.   T. R. P. Gibb, Jr., *Optical Methods of Chemical Analysis*, McGraw-Hill, New York, 1942, pp 160–181.

[683] J. H. Yoe and H. Kleinmann, *Photometric Chemical Analysis.*   Vol. II, Wiley, New York, 1929.

bidimeters, the Jackson candle turbidimeter[684] is one of the oldest and is still in use today, particularly in calibration of physical standards for visual turbidity measurements. The Burgess-Parr turbidimeter[685] may also be used for fairly turbid liquids. A wide range of photoelectric turbidimeters is available. In this group there are a large number of colorimeters and abridged spectrophotometers which may be adapted for measurement of the more turbid liquids. The Klett-Summerson,[686] the Lumetron,[687] and the Fisher electrophotometer[688] are typical examples. Another instru-

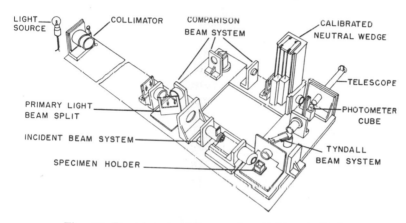

Fig. 66. Precision tyndallmeter for highly clarified liquids. (Courtesy Johns-Manville Corp.)

ment used as a photoelectric turbidimeter is the Beckman DU spectrophotometer.[689] The design of this equipment provides both greater sensitivity and a source of monochromatic illumination. Also, the optics permit measurements of *absolute turbidity*[690] values in liquids where absorption due to color is not present.

In the nephelometer and tyndallmeter class of instruments, one of the simplest of the visual group is illustrated in Figure 64. It can easily be made in the laboratory and permits critical comparison of two samples in test tubes. In a dark room such a simple apparatus can be of much value.

---

[684] M. O. Leighton, *U. S. Geol. Survey, Water Supply and Irrig. Paper*, No. 151, Washington, D. C., 1905.

[685] S. W. Parr and W. D. Staley, *Ind. Eng. Chem., Anal. Ed.*, **3**, 66 (1931).

[686] Klett Mfg. Co., New York.

[687] Photovolt Corp., New York.

[688] Fisher Scientific Co., Pittsburgh, Pa.

[689] H. H. Cary and A. O. Beckman, *J. Opt. Soc. Am.*, **31**, 682 (1941).

[690] A. Weissberger, ed., *Physical Methods of Organic Chemistry* (Vol., I, *Technique of Organic Chemistry*). 2nd ed., Interscience, New York-London, 1949, Chapter XXII, p. 1466.

The Pulfrich Photometer[691] (as supplied for turbidity studies) is a visual instrument capable of quantitative measurement of light scattering even in very highly clarified liquids. It also has the unusual distinction of being equipped with a permanent reference turbidity standard made of optical glass. This instrument is shown in Figure 65. Typical of the photoelectric nephelometers are the Coleman photo-nephelometer Model 7[692] and the Fisher Nefluoro-Photometer.[693]

Fig. 67. Portable photoelectric tyndallmeter. (Courtesy Johns-Manville Corp.)

One of the first instruments capable of measuring turbidity in a colored liquid was designed by Mecklenburg and Valentiner.[694] Provision was made for evaluating light scattering at measured depths within the sample. By extrapolation the amount of light scattered at zero depth was determined, which gave a measure of turbidity free from effect of color absorption. A much more sensitive instrument[695,696] was later developed in the

[691] Carl Zeiss, Jena, supplied by Ercona Corp., New York.

[692] Coleman Instruments, Inc., Maywood, Ill.

[693] Fisher Scientific Co., Pittsburgh, Pa.

[694] W. Mecklenburg and S. Valentiner, Z. Instrumentenk., 34, 209 (1914); Kolloid-Z., 14, 172 (1914).

[695] A. B. Cummins, M. S. Badollet, and M. C. Miller, Facts About Sugar, 32, 186 (1937); U. S. Pat. 2,045,124 (June 23, 1936).

[696] A. B. Cummins and L. E. Weymouth, Ind. Eng. Chem., 34, 392 (1942).

Johns-Manville Corporation laboratories for quantitative measurements of turbidity free from color effect in strongly colored liquids of high degree of clarity.   This instrument is illustrated in Figure 66.   Using data obtained from this instrument, it was possible to calibrate a portable photoelectric tyndallmeter[697] (illustrated in Fig. 67) so that it could be used in filtration studies in the field to obtain relative turbidity values which, for all practical purposes, were color corrected.

Methods for expressing clarity measurements in terms of the amounts, sizes, and shapes of dispersed particles require procedures for correlating the measurements of tyndallmetric instruments with corrections for indices of refraction, color, etc.   Thus, to characterize the clarity of a solution

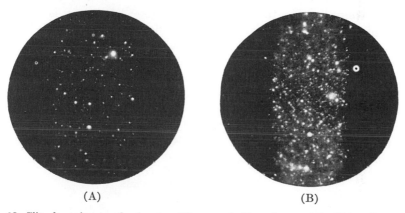

(A)   (B)

Fig. 68. Slit-ultramicrographs showing differences in filtered materials: (A) well-clarified liquid; (B) same liquid, not so well clarified.   (Courtesy Johns-Manville Corp.)

completely, it would be necessary to determine its scattering and absorbing properties for the entire visible spectrum and at adjacent areas thereto and also at all scattering angles.   While too involved for description here, it should be noted that many fundamental studies along these lines have been made, particularly in the last seven years.   This has been due primarily to the development of specialized instruments typical of which are the Brice-Phoenix Photometer[698] and the Aminco light scattering microphotometer.[699]

The ultramicroscope has also been employed in the authors' laboratory to show small differences in the clarities of filtered liquids.   Figure 68 illustrates the differences that show up when samples are observed visually

[697] L. E. Weymouth and M. C. Miller, *Sugar*, **40**, 44 (1945).   M. C. Miller, U. S. Pat. 2,436,262 (Feb. 17, 1948).

[698] B. A. Brice, M. Halwer, and R. Speiser, *J. Opt. Soc. Am.*, **40**, 768 (1950).

[699] G. Oster, *Anal. Chem.*, **25**, 1165 (1953).

or when recorded photographically. For high accuracy and for critical comparisons, considerable care is required in controlling light intensities, selection of film for uniformity, and standardization of all other steps in the procedure.

VIII. LARGER SCALE LABORATORY FILTRATIONS

Some reference to larger scale laboratory filtration apparatus is called for in a treatise on organic chemistry techniques. The unique service of this size of equipment is that it bridges the important gap between the bench and larger scale operations. Thus, an approach is made to the field of chemical and process engineering, but no consideration is given here to plant equipment. The function of the filtration laboratory is limited to tests which may be made therein, thus indicating further work in semi-works or plant. The use of larger scale laboratory filtration apparatus in organic chemistry is generally for one of two purposes: (1) to prepare organic compounds in larger quantities as needed, and (2) to obtain technical information that cannot be derived from tests with smaller apparatus. These two different requirements are considered separately. Data are given in Tables IX and X on some typical small filters and accessory pumps suitable for laboratory use, since a compilation of this type is not generally available.

1. Preparation of Materials

There are requirements at times in research work and preparative organic chemistry for the filtration of substantial quantities of materials. Further, many organic chemicals, pharmaceuticals, and biological preparations which have high value and which require great care in handling must be prepared under substantially laboratory conditions. For such operations, larger scale laboratory filtration equipment is an essential requirement.

Larger laboratory filters may be of the gravity, suction, or pressure types. Some are large-scale modifications of the types referred to in Section III, while others are small models of industrial filters. In recent years a number of filter companies have marketed small test models of their industrial filters, and this has been of great help in securing units of suitable size for laboratory use. Descriptions of industrial filters are not included here but are described in most modern texts on general chemical engineering and in a number of works on filtration. A listing of the more important of these is included in the general references found at the end of this chapter. This is done because some consideration of commercial filters must be made for the intelligent selection of large-scale laboratory filters. The essential features of the most economical and efficient filters may thus be adopted.

TABLE IX

SOME AVAILABLE FILTERS SUITABLE FOR LARGE-SCALE LABORATORY USE[a]

Type	Manufacturer	Model	Filter medium	Filter area, sq. ft.	Materials of construction[b]
Rotary drum[c]	Dorr-Oliver, Inc., New York, N. Y.	1' diam × 1' face	Fiber or metal cloth	3	A, B, CI, SS
Rotary precoat	Dorr-Oliver, Inc., New York, N. Y.	1' × 2" 1' × 1'	Fiber or metal cloth	0.5 3	A, B, CI, SS A, B, CI, SS
Rotary drum[c]	Eimco Corp., Salt Lake City, Utah	18" × 12"	Fiber or metal cloth	4	CI, SS, B, L, M, S
Rotary disc[c]	Eimco Corp., Salt Lake City, Utah	18" × 1 18" × 2	Fiber or metal cloth	2 4	CI, SS, B, L, M, S CI, SS, B, L, M, S
Sweetland, Leaf	Dorr-Oliver, Inc., New York, N. Y.	Lab.	Fiber or metal cloth	1, 1.5, 3	CI
Kelly, Leaf[d]	Dorr-Oliver, Inc., New York, N. Y.	Lab.	Fiber or metal cloth	3	CI
Plate and frame[c]	T. Shriver & Co., Harrison, N. J.	—	Cloth	→4[e]	WV
" " " "	British Filters, Ltd., Maidenhead, England	PB.4D[e]	Cloth or paper	→1.46	B, SS
" " " "	D. R. Sperry & Co., Batavia, Ill.	Lab.[e]	Cloth or paper	→6	WV
Disc[c]	Ertel Eng. Corp., Kingston, N. Y.	EWB[e]	Asbestos	3–6	SS, NPB
"	Ertel Eng. Corp., Kingston, N. Y.	E-1	Asbestos	0.5	NPB, SS
Horizontal disc[c]	Sparkler Mfg. Co., Chicago, Ill.	P-18-4[e]	Fiber or metal cloth	→6	WV
Tri-Plastic, Leaf	Hercules Filter Corp., Hawthorne, N. J.	Test	Fiber or metal cloth	0.5	L, PC, PE
Surfamax, Leaf	Micro Metallic Corp., Glen Cove, N. Y.	V[e]	Porous SS	2	SS
	U. S. Stoneware, Akron, Ohio	JS[f]	Porous SS	1	SS
Large ceramic filters for gravity, vacuum, and pressure use	General Ceramics & Steatite Corp., Keasbey, N. J.	Various models	Cloth or paper	0.5–6	P, CS
	Hathernware Ltd., England				
Tubular[c]	Croll-Reynolds Eng. Co. Inc., New York, N. Y.	Titeflex economy	Wound wire, wire mesh, or porous stone	1, 3, 5	WV

[a] 0.5–6 sq. ft. filter area.

[b] A—aluminum, B—bronze, CI—cast iron, SS—stainless steel, L—Lucite, PC—polyvinyl chloride, PE—polyester resins, WV—wide variety, L—lead, M—Monel, S—steel, P—porcelain, CS—chemical stoneware, NPB—nickel-plated bronze.

[c] Available as portable unit with pump.

[d] Steam jacketed for high-temperature work.

[e] Other models available in this size range.

[f] Withstands pressures up to 10,000 p.s.i.

TABLE X

Some Available Pumps Suitable for Large-Scale Laboratory Filtration[a]

Manufacturer	Type	Model	Materials of construction[b]	Capacity at 10 p.s.i., g.p.m.	Max. pressure, p.s.i.	Special characteristics
Eastern Industries, Inc., New Haven, Conn.	Centrifugal	B-1 D-11 D-A	M, SS, H, CI, B B	2.5 5.0 0-10	17 18 34	Can be furnished for temperatures up to 500°F. (D-11) Air operated
Jabsco Pump Co, Burbank, Cal.	Centrifugal	1/4"[c] 1/2"	B, SS, CI, HR	2.2 5	21 26	Neoprene impeller Neoprene impeller
Hypro Engineering, Inc., Minneapolis, Minn.	Flexrotor centrifugal Flexroller centrifugal	1/2"	B-case SS-shaft Pr-impeller	5 4	50 100	
Vanton Pump Corp, New York, N. Y.	Eccentric rotor	6 30[c]	WV WV	0.8 4.7	15 40	Metal parts isolated from fluid being pumped
Eco Eng. Co., Newark, N. J.	Eccentric rotor	PP-1M	B, SS T rotor	4.0	150	Can be run at speeds up to 3450 r.p.m. Not recommended for abrasive service
Eastern Industries, New Haven, Conn.	Rotary vane	VW-1[c]	SS	2.0	60	Not recommended for abrasive slurries
Ertel Eng. Corp., Kingston, N. Y.	Gear	ESP-3[c]	SS	3.6	100	Built-in by-pass valve, plastic gears
Eastern Industries, New Haven, Conn.	Gear	GW-1[c]	B, SS	0.6	200	Not recommended for abrasive slurries
Geo. D. Roper Corp., Rockford, Ill.	Gear	K, 1 1/2"[c]	CI, B	1.5	150	Not recommended for abrasive service
Viking Pump Co, Cedar Falls, Ia.	Gear	EFH[c]	CI, B	3.5	50	Not recommended for abrasive service
Dorr-Oliver, Inc., New York, N. Y.	ODS, diaphragm	1 1/2	R-lined	0-5	100	Air operated, gentle to slurries

T. Shriver & Co., Harrison, N. J.	Diaphragm	00	WV	1.5	100	Excellent for abrasive slurries
Lapp Insulator Co., Inc., Leroy, N. Y.	Liquid-actuated diaphragm	CPS-3-1½ᶜ	WV	1	175	Excellent for abrasive slurries
Milton Roy Co., Phila., Pa.	Piston	ACᶜ	WV	0.5	460	
Proportioneers, Inc., Providence, R. I.	Piston	2XDE	WV	1.1	200	
John Bean Food Machinery & Chem. Co., Lansing, Mich.	Royalette, piston	4ᶜ	WV, C-cylinder	4	400	Excellent for abrasive slurries
Robbins & Myers, Inc., Springfield, O.	Moyno	B2-2	SS-rotor, BK-stator	4.5	80	Very gentle to slurries
Sigmamotor, Inc., Middleport, N. Y.	Sigmamotor	T-6	—	0.5	25	Liquid does not touch pump, but is propelled through rubber tubing
		T-4		3	25	

ᵃ Capacity, 0.5–5.0 g.p.m. at 10 p.s.i.
ᵇ B—bronze, SS—stainless steel, CI—cast iron, HR—hard rubber, BK—bakelite, L—Lucite, P—polyethylene, C—ceramic, T—Teflon, M—Monel, H—Hastelloy, WV—wide variety.
ᶜ Other models available in this capacity range.

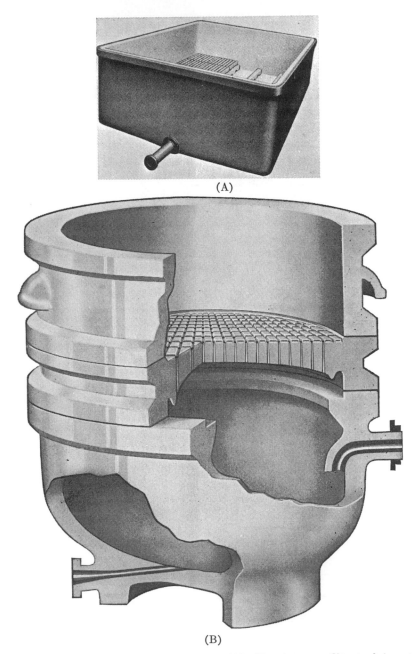

(A)

(B)

Fig. 69. Large laboratory stoneware filters: (A) white stoneware filter tank (courtesy Hathernware, Ltd., Loughborough, England); (B) three-piece vacuum filter (courtesy U. S Stoneware, Akron, Ohio).

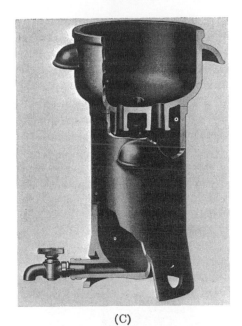

(C)

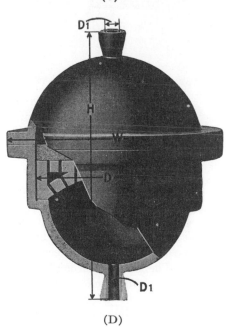

(D)

Fig. 69 (*continued*).   (C) Bag filter (courtesy General Ceramics Co., Keasbey, N.J);
(D) pressure filter (courtesy General Ceramics Co., Keasbey, N. J.).

False-bottom filters, for batch preparations and occasional use, are among the most useful appliances for large-scale laboratory preparations. Simplicity in operation, low cost, and ready accessibility for operation and observation account for the popularity of these filters. Large trays, tanks, and similar equipment of the required size may be constructed and fitted at the bottom with a supporting screen and filter cloth. Similarly, a *drainage box* or "*cage*" *filter* consists of a structure lined on the bottom and sides for filtration. Such filters may be constructed for gravity, vacuum, or pressure operation. Collected solids may be removed manually or by dumping or flushing through bottom openings arranged for this purpose. *Ceramic ware filters* of this type (see Fig. 69) are to be recommended for general large-scale laboratory preparative work. The vacuum type is most widely used. These filters are frequently operated at moderate vacuum, or may be used for a gravity filtration with a suction wash. The use of ceramic filters in modern small-scale production of chemicals has become quite general.

Fig. 70. Small vacuum plate filter. (Courtesy Dorr-Oliver, Inc.)

Filters of the *suction leaf* type are well adapted to the collection of solids, particularly when extreme care in washing is necessary and when open tank operation is permissible. The suction leaf is also useful in clarifying solutions. If the solids to be removed tend to plug the filter, a precoat and filter aid admix may easily be used. Figure 70 shows a useful vacuum plate filter. This unit has a filtration area of 0.5 sq. ft. and is widely used as a freeness tester on wood pulp, etc. It is generally fitted with a more shallow pan for general filtration test work.[700]

[700] G. O. Hillier, *The ABC of Oliver Filtration.* Dorr-Oliver, Inc., New York, 1943.

A *miniature rotary vacuum filter* designed for laboratory use or when only small amounts of material are available, is shown in Figure 71. The filter has been used to great advantage in the Johns-Manville Filtration Laboratory. The total filtering surface is only 13.4 sq. in. When used as a precoat filter, a thick cake of diatomaceous earth is built up on the drum before introducing the liquid to be filtered. Then as the filtered solids build up, the advancing scraper knife shaves off a very thin section of filter aid, together with the collected solids, thus providing a fresh surface of filter aid for further cake deposition.

Fig. 71. Small, continuous, rotary, vacuum filter for bench use. (*A*) Close-up. (*B*) Set up for use. (Courtesy Johns-Manville Corp.)

Pressure filters most often used for large-scale laboratory work fall into two categories: (*1*) chamber or plate-and-frame type, and (*2*) leaf filters. Each type has certain advantages and is widely used. *Plate-and-frame filters* are adaptable for the collection of solids, liquids, or both. They may be used for clarification, washing, bleaching, steam extraction, drying of solids, etc., and are therefore used for a large number of laboratory filtering operations. Delicate or volatile materials may be filtered without exposure to the atmosphere. Plate-and-frame filters have numerous advantages for use in pharmacy.[701] The trade publications of D. R. Sperry, Batavia, Illinois, and T. Shriver and Co., Harrison, New Jersey, and others give much information on the use of these filters in the laboratory. For organic liquids of low viscosity, plate-and-frame filters must be constructed with leakage channels or have special gaskets at all joint surfaces.

There are many different types of plate-and-frame filters. Details cannot be given here but are included in most standard chemical engineering texts and in some reviews.[702,703] The structure of a typical plate-and-

[701] J. F. Couch and J. E. Kersey, *Am. J. Pharm.*, **89**, 71 (1917).

[702] E. A. Alliott, *J. Soc. Chem. Ind.*, **39**, 261T (1920); *J. Ind. Eng. Chem.*, **13**, 976 (1921).

[703] P. Kriegel, *Ind. Eng. Chem.*, **30**, 1211 (1938).

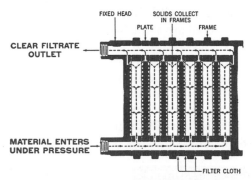

Fig. 72. Sectional view of typical plate and frame filter press, closed delivery type.
(Courtesy T. Shriver and Co., Inc.)

Fig. 73. Small disc filter-pump unit.   (Courtesy Ertel Engineering Corp.)

frame filter is indicated in Figure 72, which shows a section view of a closed-delivery filter press.   Figure 73 shows a small portable laboratory filter press and pump combination.   Similar units are available from a number of manufacturers.   Filter presses with plates in a horizontal position have excellent cake stability for washing, drying, or treatment with solvents.[704] Intermittent operation is possible without disturbing the collected solids,

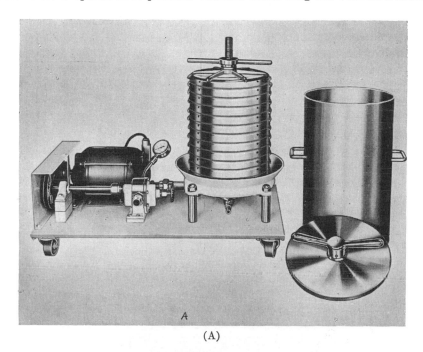

(A)

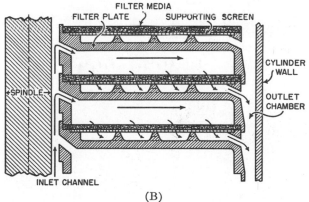

(B)

Fig. 74. Horizontal plate filter: (A) filter-pump unit; (B) cross section. (Courtesy Ertel Engineering Corp.)

[704] "Horizontal Plate Diatomaceous Earth Filter," *Ind. Eng. Chem., News Ed.,* **16,** 496 (1938).

which is particularly advantageous when using filter aids. Figure 74 shows a filter of this type.

Pressure filters with *leaf*, *disc*, *cylindrical*, and other types of filter ele-

Fig. 75. Vertical leaf filter with transparent housing. (Courtesy Hercules Filter Co.)

Fig. 76. Sweetland laboratory filter. (Courtesy Dorr-Oliver, Inc.)

ments have numerous advantages for large-scale laboratory use, and are available from most manufacturers of these types of commercial filters. These filters are convenient for the collection of solids as well as for the clarification of liquids. Many are adaptable for the use of different types

Fig. 77. Portable filter-pump assembly with tubular filter element. (Courtesy Croll-Reynolds Engineering Co., Inc.)

of filter media. Enclosed pressure filters are satisfactory for the handling of flammable liquids and toxic materials. A simple leaf-type pressure filter may be constructed and assembled in the laboratory shop at low cost. Figure 75 shows a pressure filter with vertical leaves and a transparent plastic housing. This filter has an area of 0.5 sq. ft. and is equipped with a built-in washing assembly. The unit is available with a stainless-steel housing for use at higher pressures.

Figure 76 illustrates a laboratory size *Sweetland* pressure filter, which may be fitted with two to six vertical leaves. This small, compact filter has the liquid feed in the trunnion support through a manifold to distributing inlets in the bottom of the filter housing. A filter which uses tubular elements 2 in. in diameter is shown in Figure 77. Wound wire, wire mesh covered, or stone filtering elements are available.

2. Obtaining Technical or Operating Data

When the filtration process has been investigated with small-scale tests, the next step is to carry out controlled experiments with the general type of larger scale laboratory equipment as illustrated or described. Data thus obtained should make possible the selection of equipment for the full-scale process. A scale-up of 100:1 or even more is generally considered reasonable, provided a safety factor of about 20% is added. These tests should also establish operating conditions of temperature, pressure, agitation, etc. As a further step, the economic aspects of the filtration may frequently be developed with satisfactory accuracy. In planning a larger filtering operation, the filter is but one part of the assembly. Provision must be made for the preparation of materials, measurement and control of all of the variables in the filtration operation, and proper sampling of product for examination and evaluation. It is entirely beyond the scope of this paper even to outline the experimental techniques and equipment which have been used or suggested for this work. The works on chemical engineering and filtration given in the list of general references contain helpful information.

In the study of filtration problems, the method of conducting the tests cannot be prescribed in general terms, but will vary depending upon the objectives, *i.e.*, whether the main purpose is to obtain data for better understanding of filtration practice,[705,706] for selection of commercial equipment,[707] for predicting plant operation and the design of filters,[708] or for studying filtration variables from a theoretical angle.[709,710] Since some types of pilot filters are expensive and often require a large amount of accessory

[705] H. B. Faber, *Chem. Met. Eng.*, **22**, 17 (1920); *J. Soc. Chem. Ind.*, **39**, 21T (1920).

[706] D. R. Sperry, *Ind. Eng. Chem.*, **18**, 276 (1926).

[707] P. C. Carman, *Trans. Inst. Chem. Engrs. London*, **12**, 229 (1934); *Chem. Industries*, **37**, 457 (1935).

[708] E. L. McMillen and H. A. Webber, *Trans. Am. Inst. Chem. Engrs.*, **34**, 3 (1938); *Ind. Eng. Chem.*, **30**, 708 (1938).

[709] H. P. Grace, *Chem. Eng. Progress*, **49**, 367 (1953).

[710] K. Rietema, *Chem. Eng. Sci.*, **2**, 88 (1953).

equipment, most large filter manufacturers lend or rent assembled units for test purposes.   Some companies also have a rental-purchase plan which makes a credit allowance for all or a part of the money paid in rent in the event that the rented filter or a larger one is purchased.   Several of the larger filter companies maintain filtration laboratories and evaluate slurries and, on request, make recommendations.   A listing[711] of some companies that provide "packaged" filtration units includes some that are well suited to laboratory test work as referred to here.

Figure 78 shows the essentials of a layout for large-scale laboratory filtration testing.   The set-up may be operated manually or the filtration data may be electronically measured and recorded.[709]   Equipment is also

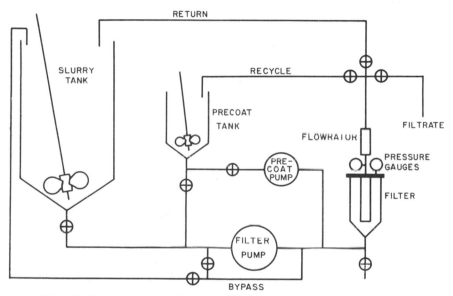

Fig. 78. Diagram for useful large-scale laboratory filtration test assembly.

available for controlling the filtration rate.   For best results the slurry tank, lines, and filter should be insulated so that heated or cooled slurries may be filtered at constant temperature.   Almost any type of pressure filter may be used with this set-up, provided that the filter is suited to the type of slurry being filtered, i.e., a plate-and-frame filter is usually unsatisfactory for water filtration because of the small size of the inlet and outlet ports as compared with the filtration area.   The assembly may be more or less permanent for laboratory use or may be completely or partially portable for use in various plant locations.   This may be essential for some

[711] R. Stephenson and G. W. Preckshot, J. Chem. Ed., 41, 435 (1951).

filtrations, as it is frequently necessary to make the tests with fresh materials or at some particular point in process.

In operation with filter aids a precoat of 0.08–0.15 lb. per sq. ft. of filter area is applied with the filter pump from a slurry of clear liquid and filter aid. A good rule-of-thumb is to make the precoat slurry volume about one and one-quarter times the combined volume of the filter and auxiliary equipment. The precoat liquid is recycled until the filtrate is clear and all of the precoat is deposited. The slurry tank valve is then opened and the precoat valve shut. The filtrate is generally returned to the slurry tank until it clears, at which time the output is directed to a receiver. In very careful work, however, the partially clarified filtrate would not be returned to the slurry tank because of the error in slurry concentration thus introduced. The flow rate is controlled with the by-pass valve at the pump. If filter aid admix is used, a concentrated filter aid slurry is made up and metered from the precoat tank by means of a filter aid feed pump. An alternate procedure, in the case of batch operation, is to add all of the filter aid admix at once to the batch of slurry contained in the slurry tank.

General References

A. REVIEWS

Underwood, A. J. V., "A Critical Review of Published Experiments on Filtration," *Trans. Inst. Chem. Engrs. London*, **4**, 19–41 (1926).

Carman, P. C., "Fundamental Principles of Industrial Filtration, A Critical Review of Present Knowledge," *Trans. Inst. Chem. Engrs. London*, **16**, 168–188 (1938).

Brieghel-Müller, A., "Die Entwicklung und der jetzige Stand der Theorie der Filtration von Suspensionen," *Kolloid-Z.*, **92**, 285–299 (1940).

"Filtration in the Chemical Process Industries," *Chem. & Met. Eng.*, **51**, 117–124 (1944).

Heertjes, P. M., "Industrial Filtration," *Research (London)*, **3**, 254–259 (1950).

Miller, S. A., "Recent Advances in Filtration Theory," *Chem. Eng. Progr.*, **47**, 497–501 (1951).

Miller, S. A., "Filtration," *Ind. Eng. Chem.*, **39**, 5–8 (1947); **40**, 25–27 (1948); **41**, 38–41 (1949); **42**, 52–55 (1950); **43**, 85–89 (1951); **44**, 63–68 (1952); **45**, 68–73 (1953); **46**, 100–105 (1954); **47**, 546–551 (1955).

Streatfield, E. L., "Filtration. Fundamentals, Equipment, Filter Aids and Media, and Applications," *Intern. Chem. Eng.*, **33** (No. 2), 71–76 (1952).

"Filtration. Theory: Experimental Data and Design; Equipment and Applications; Filter Aids and Media," *Chem. & Process Eng.*, **34** (No. 2), 44–7 (1953).

"Filtration: Fundamentals, Equipment, Filter Aids and Media, Applications," *Chem. & Process Eng.*, **35**, 143–146 (1954).

B. THEORY: ANNOTATED

Hatschek, E., "The Mechanism of Filtration," *J. Soc. Chem. Ind.*, **27**, 538–544 (1908). One of the first attempts to analyze the various factors which are important in filtration. The approach is qualitative but remains one of the most important contributions leading to the development of filtration theory.

Almy, C., Jr., and Lewis, W. K., "Factors Determining the Capacity of a Filter Press," *J. Ind. Eng. Chem.*, **4**, 528–532 (1912). An effort to show a numerical relationship between the flow of liquid through a filter cake, the pressure, and the thickness of cake. The expressions derived are empirical, but it is shown that the relationships above are not usually simple.

Sperry, D. R., "The Principles of Filtration," *Chem. & Met. Eng.*, **15**, 198–203 (1916); **17**, 161–166 (1917). These two papers constitute a classical treatment of filtration from the standpoint of physical phenomena. The attempt is made to present a "fundamental law of filtration," which is today considered to be, in general, too complicated and too empirical for wide application. However, an important advance in filtration theory.

Hatschek, E., "The Principles of Technical Filtration," *J. Soc. Chem. Ind.*, **39**, 226T–228T (1920). Qualitative considerations only.

Walker, W. H., Lewis, W. K., and McAdams, W. H., "Filtration," in *Principles of Chemical Engineering*. 1st ed., McGraw-Hill, New York, 1923, Chap. XI, pp. 336–374. Equations are proposed for the filtration of incompressible and compressible sludges together with comment on the interpretation of the equations. This constitutes a summary and generalization of much work done previously at Massachusetts Institute of Technology to develop a satisfactory theory of filtration. The equations are largely empirical, but represent a step forward in filtration theory.

Hinchley, J. W., Ure, S. G. M., and Clarke, B. W., "Studies in Filtration," *Trans. Inst. Chem. Engrs.*, **3**, 24–38 (1925). Experiments in the filtration of inorganic precipitates and expression of results by method of Lewis or Sperry equations.

Underwood, A. J. V., "A Critical Review of Published Experiments on Filtration," *Trans. Inst. Chem. Engrs.*, **4**, 19–41 (1926). An exhaustive review of theoretical filtration equations as developed up to this date.

Kozeny, J., "Über Kapillare Leitung des Wassers im Boden," *Sitzber. Akad. Wiss. Wien, Math.-naturw. Klasse, Abt. IIa*, **136**, 271 (1927); *Wasserkraft u. Wasserwirt.*, **22**, 67, 86 (1927). Classical study on fluid flow through granular beds, in which the bed permeability is defined in terms of particles and bed properties—specific surface, bed porosity, etc. Kozeny himself did not consider the application of his theory to filtration as such, but the similarity between Kozeny's equation and the differential rate equation for filtration was recognized by others. Thus, Kozeny's work may be considered the basis for the modern trend in the theory of filtration.

Underwood, A. J. V., "The Mathematical Theory of Filtration," *Ind. Chemist*, **4**, 463–466 (1928). Review of filtration equations.

Van Gilse, J. P. M., Van Ginneken, P. J. H., and Waterman, H. I., "Studies in Filtration I–IV," *J. Soc. Chem. Ind.*, **49**, 444T–446T, 483T–490T (1930); **50**, 41T–

44T, 95T–100T (1931). Laboratory filtration test results are given to support an equation:

$$(1/A)/(dV/d\theta) = P/(C + KP)\delta$$

The term $r_1 = (C + KP)\delta$ indicates that the resistance is directly proportional to the quantity of solid matter on the filtering medium per unit of surface.

Underwood, A. J. V., "Filtration Equations for Compressible Sludges," *J. Soc. Chem. Ind.*, **47**, 325T–329T (1928). Modification and amplification of equations for incompressible sludges to cover compressible sludges. The assumption of the "scouring" effect in filtration is questioned.

Ruth, B. F., Montillon, G. H., and Montonna, R. E., "Studies in Filtration. I. Critical Analysis of Filtration Theory," *Ind. Eng. Chem.*, **25**, 76–82 (1933). Points out inadequacies of filtration equations as of 1933; the idea of specific resistance is questioned; emphasizes need for further study in this field.

Ruth, B. F., Montillon, G. H., and Montonna, R. E., "Studies in Filtration. II. Fundamental Axiom of Constant-Pressure Filtration," *Ind. Eng. Chem.*, **25**, 153–161 (1933). Experimental work on the mathematical relation between filtrate volume and the time of filtration. A simple equation is proposed as the fundamental axiom of constant-pressure filtration.

Ruth, B. F., "Studies in Filtration. III. Derivation of Filtration Equations," *Ind. Eng. Chem.*, **27**, 708–723 (1935). A summary article giving the mathematical derivation of equations for constant-rate and constant-pressure filtrations as developed by the Ruth school. Experimental basis is given for the equations to be supplied in subsequent papers.

Ruth, B. F., "Studies in Filtration. IV. Nature of Fluid Flow Through Filter Septa and Its Importance in the Filtration Equation," *Ind. Eng. Chem.*, **27**, 806–816 (1935). Poiseuille's law governs liquid flow through filter septa under most conditions. Experimental evidence is presented to show that flow is viscous throughout the entire filtration cycle, and thus supports the Ruth filtration equations.

Ruth, B. F., "Correlating Filtration Theory with Industrial Practice," *Ind. Eng. Chem.*, **38**, 564–571 (1946). Concludes that the specific filtration resistance of finely divided solids is generally greater than that which would be predicted from the Kozeny equation. The concept of a "dead" void volume is proposed to explain this discrepancy. It is pointed out that electrokinetic phenomena may be important in filtration behavior.

Walker, W. H., Lewis, W. K., McAdams, W. H., and Gilliland, E. R., "Filtration," *Principles of Chemical Engineering*. 3rd ed., McGraw-Hill, New York, 1937, Chapter XI, pp. 323–364. The theory of filtration as covered on pages 342–364, is an amplification and modernization of the work of the M.I.T. school. The treatment is from the standpoint of a text for chemical engineering students and emphasizes the practical use and interpretation of filtration equations.

Hermans, P. H. and Bredée, H. L., "Mathematical Treatment of Constant-Pressure Filtration," *J. Soc. Chem. Ind.*, **55**, 1T–4T (1936); "Zur Kenntnis der Filtrationsgesetze," *Rec. trav. chim.*, **54**, 680–700 (1935). Rather complete and satisfactory review of filtration theory and derivation of equations.

Brieghel-Müller, A., "Die Entwicklung und der jetzige Stand der Theorie der Filtration von Suspensionen," *Kolloid-Z.*, **92**, 285–299 (1940).

Brieghel-Müller, A., "Über Filtrationsuntersuchungen, I," *Kolloid-Z.*, **93**, 297–318 (1940). A detailed review of filtration theory, with laboratory controlled experiments to support theories.

Brieghel-Müller, A., *Über Filtrations-Untersuchungen*, Arnold Busck Nyt Nordisk Forlag, Copenhagen, 1940. A separate publication covering the above two articles from *Kolloid-Zeitschrift*.

Sperry, D. R., "Analysis of Filtration Data," *Ind. Eng. Chem.*, **36**, 323–328 (1944). Test procedures for making filtration analyses of slurries are given. Filtration terms are defined and simple derivations of the basic filtration formulas are included.

Carman, P. C., "A Study of the Mechanism of Filtration. Part I," *J. Soc. Chem. Ind.*, **52**, 280T–282T (1933). Consideration of filter cake structure and mathematical analysis of pressure differences therein which cause deformation of the solid particles. Formulas are derived on the assumption that the pore area or specific resistance is a function of the pressure.

Carman, P. C., "A Study of the Mechanism of Filtration. II. Experimental," *J. Soc. Chem. Ind.*, **53**, 159T–166T (1934). Experiments in filtration of finely divided particles to support theory presented in Part I.

Carman, P. C., "A Study of the Mechanism of Filtration. III," *J. Soc. Chem. Ind.*, **53**, 301T–309T (1934). Further development of Carman's equations for filtration to cover compressible cakes. Experimental values are given for viscosities and specific resistances.

Carman, P. C., "Filtration as a Unit Operation," *Trans. Inst. Chem. Engrs. London*, **12**, 229–241 (1934). Review of filtration theory with practical applications in operation of filters.

Carman, P. C., "Determination of the Specific Surface of Powders. I." *J. Soc. Chem. Ind.*, **57**, 225T–234T (1938). Experimental work and theory to show the relationship between the surface of particles in a granular bed and the permeability of the bed. Evidence is presented to support Kozeny's permeability equation.

Carman, P. C., "The Action of Filter Aids," *Ind. Eng. Chem.*, **30**, 1163–1167 (1938); **31**, 1047–1050 (1939). (*1*) A filter aid must be correctly proportioned in the filter cake. The specific permeabilities of slurries containing various proportions of filter aid and at different pressures were determined. The function of a filter aid is to provide a rigid filter cake structure of high porosity, *i.e.*, its action is mainly mechanical. (*2*) Further tests with diatomaceous filter aid and quartz particles which show that the increase in permeability effected by the filter aid is due to the porosity of the cake.

Carman, P. C., "Fundamental Principles of Industrial Filtration. A Critical Review of Present Knowledge," *Trans. Inst. Chem. Engrs. London*, **16**, 168–188 (1938). An excellent review of the principles and theories of filtration. Has a complete bibliography covering structure of granular beds, d'Arcy's law for porous media, membranes, nonlaminar flow in granular beds, and principles of filtration.

Carman, P. C., "Fluid Flow Through Granular Beds," *Trans. Inst. Chem. Engrs. London*, **15**, 150–166 (1937). Critique of the laws of the flow of fluids through porous media.   Considers d'Arcy's law and its derivatives and Kozeny's equation.

Walas, S. M., "Resistance to Filtration," *Trans. Am. Inst. Chem. Engrs.*, **42**, 783–793 (1946).   Modification of Kozeny's equation for moderately compressible filter cakes.   Conclusions are that particle size, density, and porosity as a function of pressure define the filtration behavior of a slurry.   Largely based on Walas' Ph.D. Thesis, Univ. of Michigan, 1941.

Belkin, A. G., *Khimicheskaya Prom.*, **1946**, No. 7–8, 10–14.   Derivation of Belkin's equation in which the specific resistance is expressed as a relation between the volume porosity and the rate of compression of the pores.

Brownell, L. E., and Gudz, G. B., "Blower Requirements of Rotary-Drum Vacuum Filters," *Chem. Eng.*, **56**, 112–115 (1949).   A good example of how filter design problems are simplified by integrated equations and curves, based on laminar flow. Equations are given to correct for turbulence and pressure.

Friedel, F. A., "Zur Theorie der Filtration von Flüssigkeiten," *Chem.-Ing.-Tech.*, **21**, 382–383 (1949).   Qualitative theory, based on principles of colloid science. Considers surface attractions.   Nonmathematical.

Bellas, H. W., "Theory of Filtration," in article "Filtration," by D. F. Irvin, in J. H. Perry, ed., *Chemical Engineers' Handbook*. 3rd ed., McGraw-Hill, New York, 1950, p. 965.   Brief review of filtration theory with special emphasis on the practical significance of filtration equations.

Heertjes, P. M., "Industrial Filtration," *Research*, **3**, 254–9 (1950).   Good review of filtration theory and equations.   Attempt is made to correlate the work of previous investigators.

Mondria, H., "Continuous Filtration.   Influence of Some Variables on Filtration Rate and Cake Quality," *Applied Sci. Research*, **A2**, 165–183 (1950).   Theoretical material on the rates of filtration and cake washing as related to rotational speed of a rotary drum filter.

Brownell, L. E., "Filtration," in *Encyclopedia of Chemical Technology*. R. E. Kirk and D. F. Othmer, eds., Vol. VI, Interscience Encyclopedia, New York, 1951, pp. 506–530.   Short review of filtration theory and equations.   Emphasizes theory of washing.

Hoffing, E. H., and Lockhart, F. J., "Resistance to Filtration," *Chem. Eng. Progress*, **47**, 3–10 (1951).   Theory and experimental data to establish that theoretical equations for permeability should be applicable to filtration.   Tests are with noncompressible particles only and are of limited value.   Largely an extension of work done by Carman, *Ind. Eng. Chem.*, **30**, 1163–1167 (1938); **31**, 1047–1050 (1939).

Miessner, H., and Göthel, H., "Filterapparate," in *Chemischer Apparatebau und Verfahrenstechnik*, E. Wicke and E. Römer, eds., comprising Vol. 1 of F. Ullmann, *Encyklopädie der technischen Chemie*, W. Foerst, ed., 3rd ed., Urban & Schwarzenberg, Munich-Berlin, 1951, pp. 481–510.   Good summary of qualitative filtration theory, mostly from the physicochemical viewpoint, rather than the mathematical.

Miller, S. A., "Recent advances in filtration theory," *Chem. Eng. Progress*, **47**, 497–502 (1951).   General review of filtration theory, past and present.   Follows mostly the approach of Ruth.

Miller, S. A., and Fuhrmeister, C., Jr., "Latest Filtration Theory and Practice," *Chem. Eng.*, **58**, 303–304 (1951). General, and in nature of a review.

Mondria, H., "Continuous Filtration. Calculation of Cake Impurity and Liquid Yield," *Chem. Eng. Sci.*, **1**, 20–35 (1951). Mathematical formulas and detailed experimental data to establish the effects of process variables in filtration of petroleum oil–butane–benzene mixtures in dewaxing.

Rietema, K., "Overzicht von Filtratietheorieën," *De Ingenieur*, **63e** (4), Ch. 1–7 (Jan. 26, 1951). A review. No general laws for blocking filtration are possible, since blocking and cake filtrations both occur simultaneously. Kozeny's equation is analyzed and applied. There is some discussion of how filtration experiments should be made and what can be derived from such experiments.

Wilson, B. W., "Principles of Filtration," *Plating*, **38**, 831–835 (1951). May be considered a review of qualitative theory based on simple concepts as shown by a simple model filter. Mechanisms for separations in various types of filtration are suggested. Mechanical blocking, collision and adhesion, and electrical attraction are discussed.

Gardy, M., *La Filtration*. Presses Documentaires, Paris, 1952, 35 pp. General review of modern filtration theory.

Heertjes, P. M., "Technische Filtratie," *Chem. Weekblad*, **48e**, 573–578 (1952). General review of modern theory, with examples illustrating limitations. Considers particularly cake structure and compactibility.

Heinrich, K., "Die Filtration und ihre Gesetze," *Zucker*, **5**, 465–473 (1952). A general review of filtration theory including qualitative concepts as well as the filtration equations. Applications to sugar liquors suggested.

Ponomarev, V. D. and Ni, L. P., "Theory of Filtration," *Zhur. Priklod. Khim.*, **25**, 730–739 (1952); *J. Applied Chem. U. S. S. R.*, **25**, 807–815 (1952). Mostly a résumé and amplification of earlier work by S. G. Belkin. The approach is mathematical and theoretical, with some experimental and computed data to support the theory.

Rietema, K., "A Study on the Compressibility of Filter Cakes," Thesis, Technological Univ. of Delft, 1952. A complete report with experimental data for the paper presented by Rietema in 1953 (q.v.).

Grace, H. P., "Resistance and Compressibility of Filter Cakes. Part I. Under Conditions of Uniform Compressive Pressure." *Chem. Eng. Progress*, **49**, 303–318 (1953). An important detailed study of the resistance factor and the changes occurring in the structure of filter cakes. A compression-permeability technique is described. Largely an evaluation of the Kozeny-Carman theory.

Grace, H. P., "Resistance and Compressibility of Filter Cakes. Part II. Under Conditions of Pressure Filtration," *Chem. Eng. Progress*, **49**, 367–377 (1953). Correlation of filtration data with compression-permeability data. Kozeny's porosity relationship is found to be invalid in the case of compressible solids.

Grace, H. P., "Resistance and Compressibility of Filter Cakes. Part III. Under Conditions of Centrifugal Filtration," *Chem. Eng. Progress*, **49**, 427–436 (1953). Theory applied to centrifugal filtrations.

Ingmanson, W. L., "The Concept of Filtration Resistance of Compressible Materials," *Chem. Eng. Progress*, **49**, 577–584 (1953). Relations are shown in constant-pressure filtrations between the Kozeny constant, bed surface, specific volume, compacting pressures, and frictional pressure drop. Equations are derived for calculating specific surfaces and volumes from filtration (dynamic) data and for calculating filtration resistance from permeability (static) data.

Rietema, K., "Stabilizing Effects in Compressible Filter Cakes," *Chem. Eng. Sci.*, **2**, 88–94 (1953). Mostly a study of polyvinyl particles. The method of measuring cake porosities at different thicknesses by dry measuring electrical resistances is important. It is concluded that layers of filter cakes are not compressed gradually, but only after a critical cake thickness is attained.

Tiller, F. M., "The Role of Porosity in Filtration, Numerical Methods for Constant-Rate and Constant-Pressure Filtration Based on Kozeny's Law," *Chem. Eng. Progress*, **49**, 467–479 (1953). A study on Kozeny's law relating rate of flow to porosity. As fluid flows through the solid the liquid pressure drops and solid pressure rises in relation to the per cent voids, the applied pressure, and the pressure on the liquid and the solids. This function is applied to the Kozeny equation and mathematical concepts, involving both constant-rate and constant-pressure filtrations, are derived.

Finzi-Contini, B., "Modelli Elettrolitici e Campi di Filtrazioni," *Chimica e ind. Italy*, **36**, 448–452 (1954). A theoretical and mathematical consideration of the applicability of electrolytic field studies to filtration. Studies were made with Nutzsche-type filters and two units with nonuniform flow.

Freshwater, D. C., "Filtration," *Perfumery Essent. Oil Record*, **45**, 96–101 (1954). Simplified consideration of underlying principles.

Ingmanson, W. L., and Whitney, R. P., "The Filtration Resistance of Pulp Slurries," *Tappi*, **37**, 523–534 (1954). A theoretical study in evaluating filtration resistance as a property of paper-making fibers. The resistance is resolved into components, principally specific surface and effective specific volume. This constitutes a direct application of the general filtration theories to a practical art.

Okamura, S., and Shirato, M., "Ruth's Coefficient of Constant-Pressure Filtration," *Chem. Eng. Japan*, **18**, 59–63 (1954). The coefficient of Ruth's equation is shown to be independent of filtrate volume for certain limits of slurry concentration, but is a function of this concentration when the value is below 0.17.

Orlicek, A. F., Schmidt, A., and Schmidt, H. (The Optimum Capacity of Filter Presses and Other Discontinuous Filter Machines), *Chem.-Ztg.*, **78**, 266–270 (1954). Theory and practice are correlated in showing that the optimum capacity may be derived for both constant-pressure and constant-rate operations. This occurs when the filtering time bears a definite ratio to the time for breaking down the press to remove the cake.

Tiller, F. M., "The Role of Porosity in Filtration. Part II. Analytical Equations for Constant Rate Filtration," *Chem. Eng. Progress*, **51**, 282–290 (1955). Equations are derived for compressible solids showing the relationships between pressure and time in constant-rate filtrations. An approximate formula for the Kozeny equation is shown to be valid for pressures up to 100 p.s.i.

C. ORGANIC HANDBOOKS AND TEXTS

Gattermann, L., *Die Praxis des organischen Chemikers*, H. Wieland, ed. 34th ed., de Gruyter, Berlin, 1952. Also, *Laboratory Methods of Organic Chemistry*, translation from 24th German ed., Macmillan, London, 1941.

Klosa, J., *Grundriss der präparativen organischen Chemie*. P. E. Blank, Gera, 1951, Abt. 8.

Mann, F. G., and Saunders, B. C., *Practical Organic Chemistry*. 3rd ed., Longmans, London, 1952.

Abderhalden, E., *Handbuch der biochemischen Arbeitsmethoden*. Vol. I, Urban & Schwarzenberg, Berlin-Vienna, 1910–1919, pp. 94–112.

Cohen, J. B., *Practical Organic Chemistry*. 3rd ed., Macmillan, London, 1924.

Houben, J., and Weyl, T., *Die Methoden der organischen Chemie, ein Handbuch für die Arbeiten im Laboratorium*. 3rd ed., Vol. I, Thieme, Leipzig, 1925, pp. 407–416, 417–419, 427–453.

Vanino, L., *Handbuch der präparativen Chemie*. 3rd ed., Enke, Stuttgart, 1925–1937.

Lassar-Cohn, *Arbeitsmethoden für organisch-chemische Laboratorien*, 5th ed., Vol. I, Voss, Leipzig, 1923, pp. 136–144, 156–170. Also translation from 5th ed. by R. E. Oesper, *Organic Laboratory Methods*, Williams & Wilkins, Baltimore, 1928, pp. 211–230.

Norris, J. F., *Experimental Organic Chemistry*. 3rd ed., McGraw-Hill, New York, 1933.

Morton, A. A., "Filtration," in *Laboratory Technique in Organic Chemistry*. McGraw-Hill, New York, 1938, pp. 166–180.

Weygand, C., *Organisch-chemische Experimentier-Kunst*. Part 1, Barth, Leipzig, 1938.

Meyer, H., *Analyse und Konstitutionsermittlung organischer Verbindungen*. 6th ed., Springer, Vienna, 1938.

Lang, K., and Lehnartz, E., eds., *Hoppe-Seyler-Thierfelder, Handbuch der physiologisch und pathologisch-chemischen Analyse*. 10th ed., Vol. I, Springer, Berlin, 1953.

D. LABORATORY FILTRATION

Dodd, R. E., and Robinson, P. L., *Experimental Inorganic Chemistry, A Guide to Laboratory Practice*, Elsevier, Amsterdam, 1954.

Fieser, L. L., *Experiments in Organic Chemistry*. 3rd ed., Heath, New York, 1955.

Prausnitz, P. H., *Glas- und keramische Filter im Laboratorium für Filtration Gasverteilung, Dialyse, Extraktion*. Akadem. Verlagsgesellschaft, Leipzig, 1933.

Strain, H. H., *Chromatographic Adsorption Analysis*. Interscience, New York-London, 1945.

Müller, F., in W. C. Boettger, ed., *Physikalische Methoden der analytischen Chemie*, Akadem. Verlagsgesellschaft, Leipzig, 1933–1939. Reproduced by Edwards Bros., Ann Arbor, Mich.

Jander, G. and Wendt, H., eds., *Lehrbuch der analytischen und präparativen anorganischen Chemie*. Hirzel, Stuttgart, 1952.

Villanova, A. C., "A Filtração em Quimica Analitica," *Rev. quim. farm.*, **15**, 287–323 (1950).

E. INDUSTRIAL FILTRATION

Irvin, D. F., and Bellas, H. W., "Filtration" in J. H. Perry, ed., *Chemical Engineers' Handbook*. 3rd ed., McGraw-Hill, New York, 1950, pp. 964–992.

Meissner, H., and Göthel, H., "Filterapparate," in F. Ullmann, ed., *Encyklopädie der technischen Chemie*. Urban & Schwarzenberg, Munich-Berlin, 1951, (*Chemischer Apparatebau und Verfahrenstechnik*, Vol. I), pp. 481–510).

Kufferath, A., *Filtration und Filter*. 2nd ed., Dr. G. Bodenbender, Chemisch-technischer Verlag, Berlin, 1952.

Waeser, B., *Chemisch-technische Arbeitsgänge und Apparaturen*. 3rd ed., Chemisch-technischen Verlag, Dr. G. Bodenbender, 1950–1951.

Dickey, G. D., and Bryden, C. L., *Theory and Practice of Filtration*. Reinhold, New York, 1946.

Berl, E., and Lunge, G., *Chemisch-technische Untersuchungsmethoden*. 8th ed., Hirschwaldsche Buchhandlung, Berlin, 1931.

Siegel, W., "Filtration," in A. Eucken, and M. Jacob, eds., *Der Chemie-Ingenieur*, Vol. I, Part 2, Akadem. Verlagsgesellschaft, Leipzig, 1933, pp. 191–307.

Berl, E., *Chemische Ingenieur-Technik*. 3 Vols., Springer, Berlin, 1935.

Badger, W. L., and McCabe, W. L., *Elements of Chemical Engineering*. 2nd ed., McGraw-Hill, New York, 1936.

Walker, W. H., and others, *Principles of Chemical Engineering*. 3rd ed., McGraw-Hill, New York, 1937.

Zimmerman, O. T., and Lavine, I., *Chemical Engineering Laboratory Equipment—Design, Construction, Operation*. Industrial Research Service, Dover, N. H., 1943.

Brownell, L. E., "Filtration," in *Encyclopedia of Chemical Technology*. R. E. Kirk and D. F. Othmer, eds., Vol. VI, Interscience Encyclopedia, New York, 1951, pp. 506–530.

Lauer, B. E., and Heckman, P. F., *Chemical Engineering Techniques*. Reinhold, New York, 1952.

Waeser, B., "Die Technik des Filtrierens und Klärens," *Deut. Farben Z.*, **6**, 393–398 (1952); "Filterprobleme im Betrieb," *Erdöl u. Kohle*, **7**, 297–300 (1954).

Von der Heide, R., "Die Klarfiltration," *Chem.-Ztg.*, **77**, 145–148, 181–184, 208–211 (1953).

F. FILTER MEDIA

Grüne, A., *Filtrierpapiere und Filtrieren*. Schleicher & Schuell, Einbeck/Hans, 1951.

Smith, E. G., "Fabric Filter Media," *Chem. Eng. Progress*, **47**, 545–549 (1951).

Deadmore, D. L., "Sintered Alumina for Filter Purposes," *Ceramic Age*, **56**, 15–17, 23–24 (1951).

Viode, M. J., *Les metaux poreux filtrants*. Presses Documentaires, Paris, 1951.

West, C. J., "Filter paper; A Reading List," *Paper Trade J.*, **71**, 34, 36, 38, 40 (1920).

Rudolph, H., "Der Filterstein," *Chem. Fabrik*, **5**, 137 (1932); *Chem.-Ztg.*, **104**, 235 (1936).

Prior, R. O., and Walker, R. G., "Character of Woven Filter Media," *Chem. & Met. Eng.*, **45**, 250–252 (1938).

Van Antwerpen, F. J., "Filter Media," *Ind. Eng. Chem.*, **32**, 1580–1584 (1940).

Daumas, M., "Tissus filtrants anciens et nouveaux," *Chimie & Industrie*, **52**, 10–15 (1944).

G. FILTER AIDS

Eastick, J. J., "Filtration and Aids to Filtration as Applied to the Sugar Industry," in Buehler ed., *Filters and Filter Presses for the Separation of Liquids and Solids.* Rodger, London, 1914.

Olin, H. L., and associates, "The Properties and Functions of Filter Aids and the Adsorptive Properties of Filter Aids," *Trans. Am. Inst. Chem. Engrs.* **18**, 379–390 (1926); **20**, 251–272 (1927).

Hendey, N. I., "Diatomite: Its Analysis and Use in Pharmacy," *Chemist and Druggist*, **113**, 123–126 (1930).

Carman, P. C., "The Action of Filter Aids," *Ind. Eng. Chem.*, **30**, 1163–1167 (1938); **31**, 1047–1050 (1939).

Cogger, R. N., and Merker, H. M. "Evaluating Filter Aids," *Ind. Eng. Chem.*, **33**, 1233–1237 (1941).

Cummins, A. B., "Clarifying Efficiency of Diatomaceous Filter Aids," *Ind. Eng. Chem*., **34**, 403–411 (1942).

Meyer, K. S., "Some Practical Aspects of Industrial Filtration. Results Obtained with Different Filter Aids," *Ind. Chemist*, **25**, 5–8 (1949).

Stewart, E. D., Brenner, M. W., and Mayer, M. J., "Filter Aids, their Properties, Use and Conservation," *Amer. Brewer*, **85**, 29–33 (1952).

Kramer, W., "Neuere Methoden der Feinfiltration," *Dechema Monographien*, **19**, 79–92 (1953).

Deitz, V. R., *Bibliography of Solid Adsorbents; An Annotated Bibliographical Survey of Scientific Literature on Bone Char, Activated Carbons, and Other Technical Solid Adsorbents, 1900–1942.* U. S. Cane Sugar Refiners and Bone Char Manufacturers and Natl. Bur. Standards, Washington, 1944. Also New Edition, same title, 1943 to 1953, *Natl. Bur. Standards Circ.*, No. 566, pp. 1528 (1956).

H. BACTERIOLOGICAL FILTERS

Meyeringh, H., "Über Bakterien-filtration mit Zsigmondy-Bachmann Filtern," *Z. Hyg. Infektionskrankh.*," **97**, 116–136 (1922).

Rosenthal, W., "Filtration und Ultrafiltration zur Darstellung von Bakterienprodukt und von ultravisiblen Virus," in R. Kraus, and P. Uhlenhuth, eds., *Handbuch der mikro-biologischem Technik*, Vol. III, Urban & Schwarzenberg, Berlin, 1924, p. 1969 *et seq.*

Mudd, S., "Filters and Filtration," in T. M. Rivers, ed., *Filterable Viruses.* Williams & Wilkins, Baltimore, 1928, pp. 55–94.

Knöll, H., "Über Bakterienfiltration," *Z. ergebn. Hyg. Bakteriol. Immunitätsforsch. u. exptl. Therap.*, **24**, 266–364 (1941).

Knöll, H., "Ein Beitrag Zur Prüfung von Bakterienfiltern," *Z. Hyg. Infektionskrankh.*, **121**, (H.3) 298 –311 (1940).

I. MICROFILTRATION

Cheronis, N. D., *Micro and Semimicro Methods*, A. Weissberger, ed. (Vol. VI, *Technique of Organic Chemistry*). Interscience, New Yor.·-London, 1954.

Pregl, F., *Quantitätiv organische Mikroanalyse*. 6th ed., rev. by H. Roth. Springer, Vienna, 1949.

Lieb, H., and Schoeniger, W., *Präparativ Mikromethoden in der organischen Chemie*. Vol. I, Part 1, in F. Hecht, and M. K. Zacherl, eds., *Handbuch der mikrochemischen Methoden*. Springer, Vienna, 1954.

Weygand, C., *Quantitätiv analytische Mikromethoden der organischen Chemie*. 3rd ed., Akadem. Verlagsgesellschaft, Berlin, 1931.

Emich, F., and Feigl, F., *Microchemical Laboratory Manual*. Translated by F. Schneider, Wiley, New York, 1932.

Benedetti-Pichler, A. A., *Microtechnique of Inorganic Analysis*. Wiley, New York, 1942.

Wyatt, G. H., "Microfiltration: A Review," *Analyst*, **71**, 122–129 (1946).

J. ULTRAFILTRATION

Literaturverzeichnis über Veröffentlichungen auf dem Gebiet der Ultrafiltration, zusammengestellt bis Ende 1953. Membranfilter Gesellschaft Sartorius-Werke, A. G. & Co., Göttingen, 1954.

Bechhold, H., "Ultrafiltration," in E. Abderhalden, ed., *Handbuch der biologischen Arbeitsmethoden*. Vol. III, Part B, Number 2, Urban & Schwarzenberg, Berlin, 1922, p. 333.

Zsigmondy, R., *Kolloidchemie*. 5th ed., Spamer, Leipzig, 1925.

Bechhold, H., "Ultrafiltration and Electro-ultrafiltration," in Alexander ed., *Colloid Chemistry, Theoretical and Applied*. Vol. I, Chemical Catalog Co., New York, 1926, pp. 820–837.

Bechhold, H., *Die Kolloide in Biologie und Medizin*, 5th ed., Steinkopff, Dresden-Leipzig, 1929. Also, 3rd ed., translation by Bullowa, *Colloids in Biology and Medicine*, Van Nostrand, New York, 1919.

Jander, G., and Zakowski, J., *Membranfilter, Cella- und Ultrafeinfilter, Kolloidforschung in Einzeldarstellungen*. Vol. IX, Akadem. Verlagsgesellschaft, Leipzig, 1929.

Alexander, A. E., and Johnson, P., *Colloid Science*. Oxford Univ. Press, London, 1949.

Rheinboldt, H., in J. Houben and T. Weyl, eds., *Die Methoden der organischen Chemie*. Vol. I, Voss, Leipzig, 1921, pp. 451–453.

Amat, M., (Ultrafiltration), *Rev. real acad. cienc. exact. fiss. y nat.*, Madrid, **35**, 251–285 (1941).

Bugher, J. C., "Characteristics of Collodion Membranes for Ultrafiltration," *J. Gen. Physiol.*, **36**, 431–448 (1953).

CHAPTER VI

SOLVENT REMOVAL, EVAPORATION, AND DRYING

GEOFFREY BROUGHTON, *University of Rochester, Rochester, New York*

I. INTRODUCTION

The freeing of an organic material from a solvent or solvent mixture is frequently the last step in its preparation or isolation and, according to the degree of freedom attained, is usually known as evaporation in the case of solids in solution, or distillation if the material being isolated is itself a liquid. If the water or other liquid is present in relatively small amount, its removal, leaving the pure, dry chemical, whether it be a gas, liquid, or solid, is known as drying. Other methods of concentration, such as freezing out or mechanical separation of the solvent, are also sometimes resorted to in the laboratory. Some methods are applicable whether or not the solvent and compound form a homogeneous phase; others are limited to nonhomogeneous mixtures.

Drying in ordinary laboratory practice differs from distillation in that no attempt is made to recover the component which it is desired to remove. However, in some commercial operations, in which the drying removes an organic solvent such as ether or alcohol, cost considerations may make it desirable to arrange for its recovery. Since this lies outside the field of normal laboratory usage, no attempt will be made to describe such installations.[1]

The organic chemist over the course of the last century has developed, often empirically, many techniques for the removal of water or other solvents from compounds. These methods differ widely in effectiveness and, at first sight, even in principle. Confusion has perhaps been caused from the theoretical point of view by a failure to distinguish between processes for the removal of the liquid by mechanical means of separation and processes in which the liquid is removed by vaporization. Indeed, it is not uncommon for a material to be concentrated by a combination of mechanical and vaporization methods, e.g., the preliminary drying of cellulose fibers may be done by mechanical expression of the water, while the last 25–50% of the initial water content will require removal by vaporization. However, certain fundamental principles underlie the techniques used, and whether a gas, solid, or liquid is being concentrated or dried, the methods can be classified in such a way that a few basic theories can be used as guides to greater efficiency in laboratory drying or concentration procedures.

To review briefly the operations that must be dealt with in actual practice, it is useful to group the systems under study into two broad classes. The water and chemical may be miscible completely, forming a continuous phase—often the case encountered in the drying of liquids and gases or the evaporation of solutions—or the components may be only partly miscible or immiscible, forming a two-phase system. In either case, evaporation or drying is understood to be the operation of removing a liquid component, usually water, from the mixture. When the mixture is of the single-phase type, mechanical means of separation cannot be applied, and it is necessary to use methods which require vaporization of the solvent or employment of a hygroscopic absorbent. When a two-phase system is under purification, a mechanical method of separation may be applicable although, in any specific case, particular properties of the mixture may make it impractical. Whenever possible, mechanical separation is undoubtedly the simplest method of concentration, and it is sometimes possible to apply it by changing the physical conditions of the material in such a way that separation into two phases occurs, the water phase then being isolated mechanically. The drying of gases by refrigeration illustrates this principle.

---

[1] For information on large-scale installations where solvent recovery is practiced see, e.g., J. H. Perry, *Chemical Engineers' Handbook.* 3rd ed., McGraw-Hill, New York, 1950, pp. 875–877.

When mechanical separation cannot be carried out, transfer of water from one phase to another, which is intrinsically a more complex operation, is necessary.   Thus, in the drying of solids by air or of liquids by a hygroscopic material, water has to make its way across a boundary between two phases.   This involves diffusion, and a thorough understanding of such diffusion processes is of value.   To a discussion of this, the next section will be devoted.

II. THEORY OF EVAPORATION AND DRYING PROCESSES

1. Equilibria

Vaporization.   Consider a beaker partially filled with liquid allowed to stand at room temperature.   Given sufficient time, even a liquid of high boiling point will disappear completely, indicating that molecules of the liquid continuously must be leaving the surface.   According to kinetic theory, the molecules in the liquid are to be pictured in a state of constant irregular motion.   Some will have velocities higher, and some lower, than the mean velocity of all the molecules, which is regarded as characteristic of any given absolute temperature.   Below the boiling point of the liquid, the mean velocity of the molecules obviously is insufficient to carry them through the surface-boundary layer and permit them to escape, although there will always be a few molecules with velocities greater than the mean escaping through the surface, thus accounting for the slow evaporation in the open beaker.   The escape of the molecules of higher energy will result in a lowering of the temperature of the bulk of the liquid, but conduction through the beaker walls from the surroundings will tend to maintain the temperature constant.   This again results in vaporization of more liquid as more molecules gain sufficient energy to pass through the boundary layer.

The rate of evaporation can be controlled experimentally in a number of ways.   If the top of the beaker is closed, the air space reaches saturation and, ultimately, as many molecules return to the liquid in any given time interval as leave it.   On the other hand, if the beaker is evacuated, the molecules leaving the liquid are removed continuously with no opportunity to return to the liquid layer.   In the first case, evaporation ceases; in the second, its rate is accelerated.   The rate is also affected greatly if the heat input to the beaker is controlled, rather than allowed, as in the foregoing examples, to remain at a value sufficient to maintain the liquid temperature constant.   Imagine the beaker to be thermally insulated so that no heat can be transferred from the surroundings.   As the molecules with higher energy cross the boundary layer, the liquid temperature falls, with a consequent slowing in evaporation rate.   Conversely, if a steady supply of heat is transmitted to the beaker, more molecules acquire the minimum energy required to cross the boundary and consequently the rate of evaporation increases. It follows that for vaporization of a liquid to proceed continuously, two requirements must always be met: (1) the heat necessary for vaporization of the liquid must be supplied; and (2) the liquid molecules, as they escape through the boundary layer, must constantly be removed. These are the basic principles of all vaporization processes, whether evaporation or drying. In order to allow calculations on a quantitative basis and to follow them in more detail, it is convenient to define and discuss certain properties of liquids.

Vapor Pressure. Returning to our first illustration, if the beaker were completely sealed and evacuated, the pressure exerted upon the walls of the vessel by the molecules of the liquid would be constant at any one temperature; this is known as its vapor pressure. Naturally, it increases with temperature and, at the boiling point of the liquid, becomes equal to 760 millimeters. Table I shows the boiling points of a number of the solvents commonly used in organic chemistry. Figure 1 shows the dependence of their vapor pressures upon temperature. A comprehensive compilation of vapor pressure data for over 1200 organic and 300 inorganic compounds has been made by Stull,[2] while Jordan[3] is also a useful reference for such data.

TABLE I

HEATS OF VAPORIZATION AND BOILING POINTS (760 MM.) OF SOME COMMON ORGANIC SOLVENTS

Solvent	Boiling point, °C.	Latent heat of vaporization, g. cal./g.
Ethyl ether	34.54	83.8
Acetone	56.13	124.4
Chloroform	61.15	59.0
Methyl alcohol	64.65	262.8
Carbon tetrachloride	76.75	46.4
Ethyl alcohol	78.32	204.3
Benzene	80.12	94.1
Cyclohexane	80.8	85.6
n-Heptane	98.35	76.3
Water	100.00	539.4
Pyridine	115.3	107.4
Acetic acid	118.2	96.7

[2] D. R. Stull, *Ind. Eng. Chem.*, **39**, 517–550 (1947).

[3] E. T. Jordan, *Vapor Pressure of Organic Compounds*. Interscience, New York-London. 1954

For many liquids a plot of the logarithm of the vapor pressure against the reciprocal of the absolute temperature gives a straight line,[4] or:

$$\log p = A/T + B \qquad (1)$$

In the absence of experimental data it is sometimes convenient to be able to calculate the vapor pressure–temperature curve of a liquid.   Duhring's rule is useful
for this purpose and may be stated as follows: "If the temperatures at which two

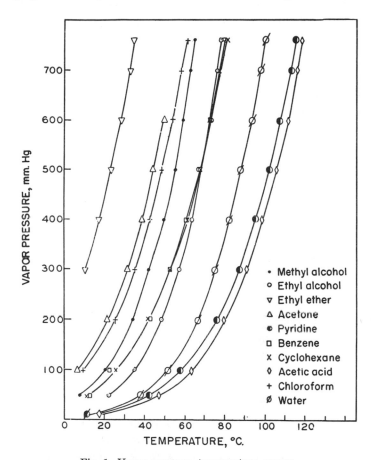

Fig. 1. Vapor pressure–temperature curves.

chemically similar liquids exert the same vapor pressures are plotted against each
other, a straight line results."   Hence, if only two points on the vapor pressure
curve of a liquid are known, its complete curve can be drawn with considerable
accuracy if a suitable reference liquid with known vapor pressure–temperature curve

[4] R. L. Copson and P. K. Frolich, *Ind. Eng. Chem.*, **21**, 1116 (1929).

is available.   The curves of Figure 1 may be used for this purpose.   Thus, suppose that a liquid is known to have vapor pressures of 53.8 mm. Hg and 223.0 mm. Hg at 50° and 90°C., respectively.   Reference to Figure 1 shows that pyridine has these vapor pressures at 45° and 79°C.

A plot of these values can be made; and, knowing that the boiling point of pyridine is 115°, the boiling point of the unknown can be predicted as 133°C.   Actually it is 134°C. (ethylbenzene), indicating reasonably good agreement.

Logarithmic plots of the vapor pressures of liquids against a reference liquid at corresponding temperature values also give straight lines over wide temperature ranges and their use has been advocated by Othmer.[5]

Another useful method of expressing vapor pressure–temperature relations is the Cox chart.[6–8]   In this a single reference liquid, such as water or mercury, is selected and its vapor pressure–temperature data are plotted as a straight line with a slope of about unity.   This is done by plotting the logarithm of the vapor pressure as the ordinate and marking off the abscissa scale with the proper temperatures.   Corresponding vapor pressure–temperature data for other materials also form straight lines when plotted in this way on the same chart and homologous compounds yield lines which intersect at a common point.   Hence, knowledge of the boiling point at atmospheric pressure of a liquid is often sufficient to establish its complete vapor pressure–temperature curve.

Vapor Pressure and Latent Heat of Vaporization.   The heat required to change unit mass of a liquid to vapor at constant temperature is the latent heat of vaporization.   The molal latent heat, ML, is related to the vapor pressure, p, by the Clausius-Clapeyron equation:

$$(d \ln p)/dT = ML/RT^2 \tag{2}$$

where T is the absolute temperature and R the gas constant.   Over small temperature intervals, the integrated form:

$$\ln \frac{p_1}{p_2} = \frac{ML}{R} \frac{T_1 - T_2}{T_1 T_2} \tag{3}$$

is useful in calculating heats of vaporization from vapor pressure–temperature data.

Heats of vaporization of some common organic solvents at their boiling points are given in Table I.   The much greater heat of vaporization of polar compounds, due to the greater attractive intermolecular forces, is obvious.

Raoult's Law.   In vaporization processes, the equilibria of pure sol-

[5] D. F. Othmer, *Ind. Eng. Chem.*, **32**, 841 (1940).

[6] E. R. Cox, *Ind. Eng. Chem.*, **15**, 592 (1923).

[7] G. Calingaert and D. S. Davis, *Ind. Eng. Chem.*, **17**, 1287 (1925).

[8] R. R. Dreisbach, *P–V–T Relationships of Organic Compounds*.   Handbook Publishers, Sandusky, Ohio, 1952.

vents are not always in question; unfortunately, it is sometimes necessary to deal with mixtures, which are usually much more complex in their behavior.   Returning again to our beaker partially filled with liquid, suppose that instead of a pure liquid, the beaker is filled with a mechanical mixture of two materials of low mutual solubility, such as water and petroleum ether.   There will be no interaction between the two varieties of molecules and each will behave as if the other were not present; hence the pressure in the evacuated vessel would be equal to the sum of the vapor pressures of the two components:

$$P_{tot} = p_1 + p_2 \tag{4}$$

This is the basic principle of steam distillation.   A limiting case of great importance in drying occurs when one of the nonmiscible materials is nonvolatile, *e.g.*, cellulose and water.   The vapor pressure of the mixture is that of the liquid, water, and is completely unaffected by the presence of the solid.

The situation is more complex when the beaker contains two mutually soluble materials, *e.g.*, benzene and toluene.   Because of the attraction of the molecules of one for the other, and vice versa, the escaping tendency of each liquid will be reduced and consequently their partial pressures lowered.   Since the vapor pressure of the mixture is the sum of the partial pressures of the components, it also will be lowered.   Consideration will indicate that, for materials of similar nature, the partial vapor pressure of either component should be proportional to its mole fraction or:

$$p_m = mp \tag{5}$$

where p_m is the partial pressure of one component, p the vapor pressure of the pure material at the same temperature, and m the mole fraction of the component.   The total pressure will of course be:

$$P_{tot} = {}_1p_m + {}_2p_m = m_1p_1 + m_2p_2 \tag{6}$$

If one component of the mixture is nonvolatile, *e.g.*, sucrose in a sucrose–water mixture, the vapor pressure of the mixture will simplify to m_1p_1.

Raoult's law, while useful, can be regarded only as a limiting law for dilute or ideal solutions.   It fails, often with a very large error, for concentrated solutions and is, of course, not valid for electrolytes where dissociation occurs.   Nevertheless, the law indicates that the relative vapor pressure, p_m/p, for a mixture should be practically independent of temperature, and it is useful for mixtures of compounds with similar chemical properties.   For mixtures of materials of widely differing chemical nature, recourse must be had to experimental determination of their vapor pressures.

Dühring's rule can again be utilized to minimize the number of experimental points required to construct the vapor pressure–temperature curve.

Humidity and the Drying Gas. Returning once more to the beaker and liquid, the concentration of the volatile liquid molecules in the gas above the liquid surface will affect the rate of evaporation, and it is convenient to consider the ways of specifying and determining this content in the air space. The following discussion will be restricted to water, since this is the case most commonly met and of greatest importance.

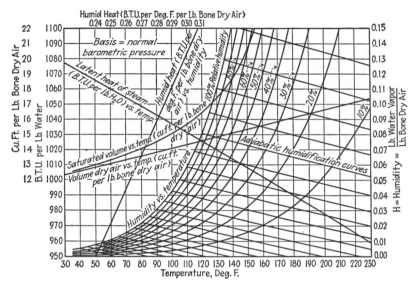

Fig. 2. Psychrometric charts.[9]

The *absolute humidity*, H, of the gas is defined as the number of pounds of water carried by one pound of dry air. For any given temperature, there will be a value of H beyond which water will deposit; this will occur when the partial vapor pressure, p, of the water vapor becomes equal to the vapor pressure of water, P_s, at the same temperature. It is convenient to define the degree of saturation of the air in terms of the per cent relative humidity $100p/P_s$. If air partially saturated with water vapor is cooled, it will ultimately reach a temperature at which the partial vapor pressure, p, of the water becomes equal to the vapor pressure of water and moisture will be deposited if further cooling is carried out. This temperature is known as the *dew point*.

Other important properties of the gas when used in a drying operation may be conveniently defined at this point, namely, *humid heat*–the number of B.t.u. necessary to raise the temperature of one pound of dry air with its accompanying water vapor 1°F. This is greater, the higher the moisture content of the air. *Humid volume* is the volume, in cubic feet, of one pound of dry air with its accompanying water vapor. Figure 2[9] shows the interrelationship of these quantities for air and water, together with the variation of the latent heat of water with temperature and the adiabatic humidification curves. These last are of great utility in many drying operations and deserve careful consideration.[10]

Suppose air at temperature t_1 flows over the surface of water of temperature T contained in a well-insulated container so that the system is adiabatic. Some of the water will be evaporated, the humidity of the air changing in the process from H_1 to H_2 and its temperature dropping to t_2. Writing an over-all heat balance:

$$(H_2 - H_1) \quad (r_2) \; + \; (H_2 - H_1) \quad (t_2 - T) \; = \; S_1 \quad (t_1 - t_2) \quad (7)$$

| (water evaporated) | (latent heat of evaporation) | (water evaporated) | (temperature rise of water) | | (humid heat) | (temp. drop of air) |

However, if sufficient surface is allowed for complete equilibrium to be attained and make-up water is supplied at the same temperature, T, the air will become saturated at a temperature t_3 and:

$$(H_s - H_1) (t_s - T + r_s) = S_1(t_1 - t_s) \qquad (8)$$

or if $t_s = T$, this simplifies to:

$$(H_s - H)/(t_s - t) = - S_1/r_s \qquad (9)$$

which allows plots of H versus t to be made on the humidity chart for a number of values of H_s and t_s. In Figure 2 they are made for values of t_s at 5° intervals. Even if final equilibrium is not reached, these can be used as path curves with very little error. Thus, for example, if air at 130°F. and humidity 0.028 lb. water per pound dry air comes into contact with a water surface at 95°F., no heat transfer into or out of the system being allowed, the water content of the air will increase progressively along the adiabatic humidification curve connecting the point 95°F. on the saturation curve with the point of coordinates, 130°F. and $H = 0.0280$, while its temperature drops to 95°F. If contact is not long enough for the air to reach its saturation temperature of 95°F., but it leaves the insulated system at 110°F., its moisture content will be 0.0328 lb. water per pound dry air.

Wet- and Dry-Bulb Temperatures. So far only the case of adiabatic evaporation with make-up water of constant temperature has been con-

---

[9] W. H. Walker, W. K. Lewis, W. H. McAdams, and E. R. Gilliland, *Principles of Chemical Engineering*. 3rd ed., McGraw-Hill, New York, 1937.

[10] See, *e.g.*, R. Hendry and A. W. Scott, *J. Inst. Fuel*, **23**, 286 (1950), for a thorough discussion.

sidered.   Suppose that a drop of water is exposed to air not fully saturated
with moisture.   A dynamic equilibrium will be set up (Fig. 3).   Water
molecules will diffuse through a very thin, stagnant air layer surrounding
the droplet and be swept away by the air stream.   The rate at which this
occurs, $dw/d\theta$ is given by:

$$-dw/d\theta = kA(P - p) \tag{10}$$

where k is the diffusion constant, A the area of the drop, P the vapor pressure of water at its temperature, T, and p the partial pressure of the water
in the air of temperature t.   Clearly, k will depend upon a number of
factors, in particular the thickness of the thin, stagnant air layer, in turn

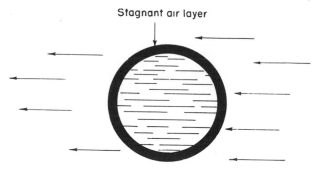

Fig. 3. Water droplet in equilibrium with air.

governed by the air velocity.   While transfer of moisture from drop to air
is taking place, transfer of heat from the air to water drop (if $T < t$) is also
occurring.   Ultimately, a dynamic equilibrium must be reached where
the temperature of the water drop cannot increase further, all subsequent
heat received from its surroundings being used to provide the heat of vaporization for the water evaporating into the air stream.   If h is the coefficient of heat transfer through the stagnant gas film on the drop surface, the heat transferred, q, will be given by:

$$dq/d\theta = hA(t - T) \tag{11}$$

When equilibrium is reached at a water temperature, t_w, known as the
wet-bulb temperature:

$$dq/d\theta = r_w(dw/d\theta) = kAr_w(P_w - p) = hA(t - t_w) \tag{12}$$

$$P_w - p = (h/kr_w)\,(t - t_w) \tag{13}$$

where r_w is the latent heat of evaporation of the water at t_w.

Thus, if it is desired to know the moisture content of air by passing
it over two thermometers, the bulb of one dry, the bulb of the other wet

by a cloth or wick thoroughly soaked with water, the difference in the readings of the wet- and dry-bulb thermometers gives $(t - t_w)$. In the equation:

$$p = P_w - (h/kr_w)\ (t - t_w) \tag{14}$$

all quantities are now known except h/kr_w; and over the ranges commonly met with water and air, this is practically 0.5, if temperatures are given in degrees centigrade and pressures in millimeters mercury. P_w and p are obviously intimately related to H_w and H, and it can be shown that:

$$H_w - H = (h/k'r_w)\ (t - t_w)$$

or:

$$(H_w - H)/(t - t_w) = h/k'r_w \tag{15}$$

an equation very similar in form to that of the adiabatic saturation curve (Eq. 9). Indeed, it is found experimentally that the adiabatic saturation temperature and wet-bulb temperature are identical, h/k' being equal to s, allowing the curves of Figure 2 to be used to obtain the humidity, if the wet- and dry-bulb temperatures are known. This is true only for water; for many organic solvents and air the wet-bulb temperature is greater than the adiabatic saturation temperature.[11,12]

The use of the wet- and dry bulb thermometers can be illustrated with the following example:

A given stream of air has wet- and dry-bulb temperatures of 60° and 85°F., respectively, and it is desired to know its humidity. The humidity is obtained by following the cooling line starting at 60°F., the wet-bulb temperature, down to 85° F., where reference to the scale on the right-hand side of the chart shows the humidity to be 0.5053 lb. per pound dry air.

In the determination of wet-bulb temperature, it is important that radiation effects should not be large since these are not allowed for in equation (12). Air velocity over the wick should be great enough so that heat transfer by radiation is a negligible factor. For ordinary laboratory practice, this is attained with the sling psychrometer, in which the two thermometers are whirled by hand to attain the necessary velocity. When a sling psychrometer cannot be used, an air sample can be drawn over the thermometer bulbs, taking care to avoid radiation effects and to obtain a velocity of at least 15 ft. per second.

The moisture content of air or other gases can also be determined less

[11] W. H. Walker, W. K. Lewis, W. H. McAdams, and E. R. Gilliland, *Principles of Chemical Engineering.* McGraw-Hill, New York, 1937, pp. 590–594

[12] T. K. Sherwood, *Chem. Canada,* **2,** No. 6. 19 (1950).

conveniently by chemical means or by cooling the air to a temperature, the dew point, at which moisture just begins to deposit from the gas.[13] Knowing the dew point or saturation temperature, the humidity can be read off directly from Figure 2. Thus, air with dry-bulb and wet-bulb temperature of 60° and 85°F., respectively, would have a dew point of 40°F. This is the basis of some humidity meters now on the market. Hair hygrometers are used only for rough measurements of humidity, probably because of the hysteresis effect which they normally exhibit.[14]

2. Drying as a Diffusional Operation

The most common type of drying consists in the removal of water from sheet or lump materials by vaporization of the moisture into air. Figure 4 shows diagrammatically the passage such water must take. For the sake of simplicity, the material is represented as being contained in a tube

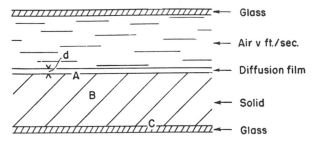

Fig. 4. Path of water in drying of sheet or lump materials in air.

through which air passes at v ft. per second. Water molecules will travel through the air film at the surface and escape into the moving air stream. In this way, the surface of the material being dried will be lowered in moisture content and a concentration difference will be set up across the slab, moisture tending to travel from B to A. Two things can now happen, either moisture will travel from B to A as rapidly as it can vaporize through the surface film or it will not travel sufficiently rapidly to maintain the moisture content at A. In the first case, diffusion through the air film at the surface controls drying rate; in the second, moisture movement through the material itself is the governing factor. In the first case, the drying rate will be constant, dependent only upon the thickness, d, of the air film and the humidity difference across the film, being entirely independent of the moisture content of the bulk of the material. In the second case, moisture does not move to the surface as rapidly as it vaporizes from the surface and

[13] R. C. Amero, J. W. Moore, and R. G. Capell, *Chem. Eng. Progress*, **43,** 349 (1947).
[14] N. J. Abbott, *Text. Res. J.*, **24,** 59 (1954).

the drying rate is controlled by the travel of water through the material itself.   This, in turn, is a function of the moisture content of the material being dried, its nature, porosity, etc.   This results in curves of the type shown in Figure 5.

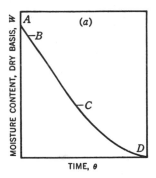

(a) Moisture content vs. time.

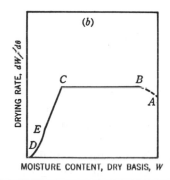
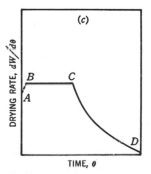

(b) Drying rate vs. moisture content.   (c) Drying rate vs. time.

Fig. 5. Periods of drying.[14a]

The moisture content of a solid being dried drops continuously with time (see Fig. 5)[14a] and may or may not show the constant-rate period BC, during which moisture evaporates from the solid surface in substantially the same way as from a free water surface under identical drying conditions.   At C, corresponding to the critical moisture content, W_c, the surface starts to dry out and the falling-rate period of drying begins.   This rate will be governed by the internal liquid flow.[15]   This may be by:

[14a] W. R. Marshall, Jr., "Drying," in *Encyclopedia of Chemical Technology*, R. E. Kirk and E. F. Othmer, eds.   Vol. V, The Interscience Encyclopedia, Inc., New York, 1950, p. 237.

[15] O. A. Hougen, H. J. McCauley, and W. R. Marshall, *Trans. Am. Inst. Chem. Eng.*, **36**, 182 (1940).

(*a*) diffusion in homogeneous solids, (*b*) capillary flow in porous and granular solids, (*c*) thermal diffusion caused by temperature gradients, (*d*) vaporization followed by condensation, (*e*) special shrinkage and pressure gradients, or (*f*) gravitational forces.   Such phenomena are complicated and it is difficult to disentangle the various effects that occur.[16]   According to Oliver and Newitt,[17] granular solids in which capillary forces are most responsible for moisture movement show curves of the type shown in Figure 6.   In this there are two falling-rate periods, the critical points becoming less clearly marked as the particle size decreases.   The zone of unsaturated surface drying follows immediately after the critical point where the surface fails to be completely wetted and dry portions of the solid protrude

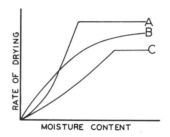

Fig. 6. Typical drying rate curves.[17]

into the air film.   Because the effective wetted area is frequently a linear function of the solid's water content, the curve A is linear in this region until the second critical point is reached.   At this point the surface becomes dry and in this zone water vapor reaches the surface by molecular diffusion through the bed.   Hence, it is sometimes called the zone of internal liquid diffusion controlling.   Particle size can greatly influence the critical moisture content, W_c, as shown for a series of crushed, graded silicas in Table II, presumably because of the larger water adsorption by particles of greater surface area.   Critical moisture content also increases with increase in rate of drying and with thickness of the solid layer being dried; hence experimental determinations are nearly always necessary.[18]

Curves B and C are characteristic of solids in which moisture movement is mainly by vapor diffusion.   Wood, soap, and clays behave similarly to curve C.   Their critical moisture content may be so great, *e.g.*, 300% for gelatin, that the constant-rate period of drying may be unobserved in some cases.   Solids in which the moisture movement may be either by capillary action or partially by vaporization should show drying rate curves

[16] M. Coleman, *Research*, **6,** 384 (1953).

[17] T. R. Oliver and D. M. Newitt, *Trans. Inst. Chem. Eng.*, **27,** 9–18 (1949).

[18] D. B. Broughton, *Ind. Eng. Chem.*, **37,** 1184 (1945).

TABLE II
INFLUENCE OF PARTICLE SIZE ON CRITICAL MOISTURE CONTENT[19]

Particle diameter, μ	W_c, %
800	2
400	4
125	6
45	9
15	16
5	31

similar to A or B, according to the conditions holding when drying occurs.

Consideration will indicate that, when the drying rate is a constant and diffusion of moisture from the interior is not the controlling factor, the surface behaves as though it were free water and we have a case similar to the evaporation of the water drop discussed above. The stock being dried will reach the wet-bulb temperature, just as did the water spherule, provided that no heat reaches it except from the air. The same equation holds for mass transfer:

$$dw/d\theta = k'A(H_w - H) \tag{16}$$

where $dw/d\theta$ is the rate of diffusion in lb./hr., k' is the film coefficient of diffusion in lb./(hr. $\times$ ft.^{2} $\times$ atmospheric humidity difference), H_w is the humidity of the air at the air–water interface in lb. water/lb. dry air, and H is the humidity of the air in lb. water/lb. dry air. For heat transfer similarly:

$$dq/d\theta = hA(t - t_w) \tag{17}$$

where $dq/d\theta$ is the heat transferred in B.t.u./hr., h is the mean film coefficient of heat transfer in B.t.u./(hr. $\times$ ft.^{2} $\times$ °F.), t is the temperature of air in °F., and t_w is the wet-bulb temperature of the air in °F. It follows that:

$$dw/d\theta = (h/r_w)\, A\, (t - t_w) \tag{18}$$

Either equation (17) or (18) can be used to calculate the drying rate, provided that the process occurs under substantially adiabatic conditions. It is generally preferable to utilize equation (17) because heat transfer coefficients are generally more reliable; also, the assumption that the surface of the drying solid is at the wet-bulb temperature introduces a more serious error into mass transfer calculations than into those for heat transfer.

If the surface C (Fig. 4) is heated or the material is subjected to radiant

[19] D. M. Newitt and M. Coleman, *Trans. Inst. Chem. Eng.*, **30**, 28 (1952).

heat, these simple equations will no longer hold because the process ceases to be adiabatic. A new heat balance must be written and considerations of absorption of the infrared radiation by the drying solid may be important.[20,21] Clearly, once the temperature and humidity of the air have been chosen, the drying rate is controlled by the magnitude of the film coefficients which depend principally upon the thickness, d, of the air film at A. With high air velocity the stagnant air layer will be cut down in thickness, with resulting increase in film coefficients k' and h. Again the angle of approach of the air stream will affect the diffusion coefficients, perpendicular leading to higher values than parallel impingement.[22] That the diffusion coefficients are considerably changed and hence the drying rates greatly increased at high air velocities is indicated by the following equations:[23]

$$k' = 0.0512G^{0.75} \tag{19}$$

$$h = 0.0170G^{0.76} \tag{20}$$

where G is mass velocity of the air parallel to the surface in lb./(hr. $\times$ ft.^{2}).

If heat is transferred from sources other than the drying air or by radiation, the rate of drying can be increased, but the stock surface will no longer be at the wet-bulb temperature and calculations become more difficult.

Calculations for the falling-rate period, where as already explained moisture which travels through the solid itself is the controlling factor, are more difficult and complete prediction of drying rates from theoretical considerations is generally impossible.[24] Fortunately, for coarsely granular or fibrous materials, in which categories many organic chemicals belong, the falling rate $(dw/d\theta)_f$ can be expressed with moderate accuracy by the equation:

$$(dw/d\theta)_f = -K(w - w_e) \tag{21}$$

where K is a function of the constant rate of drying $(dw/d\theta)_c$:

$$K = (dw/d\theta)_c/(w_c - w_e) \tag{22}$$

Here w_e is the moisture content in equilibrium with the external conditions. Substituting from equation (18) the proper value for $(dw/d\theta)_c$:

[20] J. H. Perry, *Chemical Engineers' Handbook*. 3rd ed., McGraw-Hill, New York, 1950, p. 803.

[21] G. Broughton, *Paper Trade J.*, **131**, No. 16, 18–19 (1950).

[22] M. C. Molstad, P. Farevaag, and J. A. Farrell, *Ind. Eng. Chem.*, **30**, 1131 (1938).

[23] C. B. Shepherd, C. Hadlock, and R. C. Brewer, *Ind. Eng. Chem.*, **30**, 388 (1938).

[24] See, however, W. H. Walker, W. K. Lewis, W. H. McAdams, and E. R. Gilliland, *Principles of Chemical Engineering*. McGraw-Hill, New York, 1937, p. 647 *et seq.*

$$\left(\frac{dw}{d\theta}\right)_f = -\frac{hA(t - t_w)(w - w_e)}{r_w(w_c - w_e)} \tag{23}$$

Or expressed on a weight instead of an area basis:

$$\left(\frac{dw}{d\theta}\right)_f = -\frac{h(t - t_w)(w - w_e)}{\rho L r_w(w_c - w_e)} \tag{24}$$

where ρ is the density of the dry solid in lb./ft.^{3}, and L is the thickness of solid being dried in feet, assumed constant.   It will be noted that the drying time varies directly as the thickness.   By integration of equations (18) and (23), the total drying time (θ_c) can be obtained as the sum of the constant-rate and falling-rate periods:

$$\theta_t = \frac{(w_0 - w_c)r_w}{hA(t - t_w)} + \frac{r_w(w_c - w_e)}{hA(t - t_w)} \ln \frac{w_c - w_e}{w_t - w_e} \tag{25}$$

$$= \frac{1}{K} \frac{w_0 - w_c}{w_c - w_e} + \ln \frac{w_c - w_e}{w_t - w_e} \tag{26}$$

where w_t is the average moisture content at time θ_t in lb./lb. dry solid.

For systems such as soap, gelatin, glue, wood, starches, clays, and other hydrophilic solids where liquid diffusion is the controlling factor, Sherwood[25] has shown that if D is the liquid diffusivity in ft.^{2}/hour, and L is the solid thickness in feet, equation (27) holds:

$$dw/d\theta = -\pi^2 D/4L^2 (w - w_e) \tag{27}$$

Integration gives the drying time, θ_f, for the falling-rate period, liquid diffusion controlling:

$$\theta_f = \frac{4L^2}{D\pi^2} \ln \frac{w_c - w_e}{w_t - w_e} \tag{28}$$

Equilibrium Water Content.   If drying is continued, whether it occurs at a constant or falling rate, or normally first at a constant rate followed by a falling-rate period, a point is reached at which the material loses no more water and is at equilibrium with the air.   It then contains w_e lb. water/lb. dry solid, the equilibrium water content.   For some materials, this water content may be almost zero, but others show a pronounced hygroscopicity and maintain a considerable moisture content.   It is usual to plot the percentage of water in the material against the relative humidity of the air with which it is in equilibrium, since it is found that the equilibrium moisture is comparatively unaffected by temperature but

[25] T. K. Sherwood, *Ind. Eng. Chem.*, 21, 12 (1929).

very sensitive to relative humidity. Figure 7 shows some curves for a few typical materials. Such curves can readily be obtained by suspending specimens in small closed vessels in which the relative humidity is controlled by saturated salt solutions and weighing them at intervals until equilibrium is reached[26] or by a simple manometric method.[27]

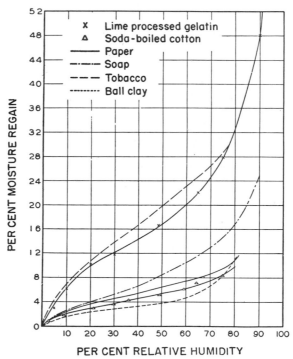

Fig. 7. Variations of equilibrium water content with relative humidity.

III. DRYING OF GASES

Four methods are available for the drying of gases: compression, refrigeration, adsorption, and passage over or through hygroscopic reagents. The last two are the most convenient for use in the laboratory, although the second finds occasional application.

1. Compression

When a gas is compressed, its saturated humidity decreases rapidly with total pressure if the temperature is kept constant. Moreover, the de-

[26] W. A. Wink, *Ind. Eng. Chem., Anal. Ed.*, **18**, 251 (1946).
[27] J. F. Vincent and K. E. Bristol, *Ind. Eng. Chem., Anal. Ed.*, **17**, 465 (1945).

crease is greatest at low pressures and becomes progressively smaller at higher pressures. In spite of this, the necessary equipment makes the process unwieldy and unsuitable for the organic laboratory, and, if very dry gases are a requisite, pressures of 150–200 atmospheres may be required. In addition, at high pressures certain gases form solid hydrates,[28] which may plug equipment.

2. Refrigeration

The vapor pressure of ice drops rapidly with temperature, as shown in Table III, and hence the saturated humidity of gases also decreases rapidly with temperature. Thus, at 0°F. the humidity of saturated air is only

TABLE III
VAPOR PRESSURES OF ICE

Temperature, 0°C.	Vapor pressure, mm. Hg.
	4.58
−10	1.95
−20	0.78
−30	0.29
−50	0.030
−70	0.0019
−80	0.0004
−100	0.0001

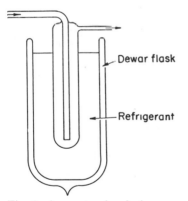

Fig. 8. Apparatus for drying gases by refrigeration.

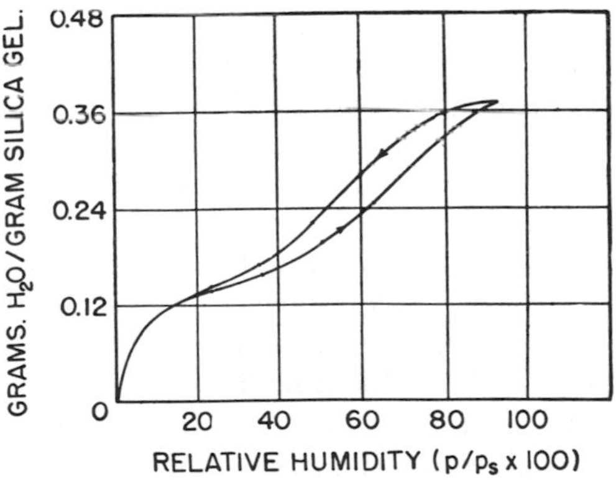

Fig. 9. Affinity of silica gel for water.

about 5% of that at 70°F., 0.000781 lb. per pound dry air compared to 0.01578 lb. per pound dry air. At −20°F., it is less than 2% of the value

[28] W. I. Wilcox, D. B. Carson, and D. L. Katz, *Ind. Eng. Chem.*, **33**, 662 (1941).

at 70°F. Similar results are observed with other gases. For cooling by refrigeration in the laboratory, a simple arrangement such as that shown in Figure 8 is usually sufficient. Suitable cryostats are discussed in Part II, Chapter II, Sect. V.2. The main difficulty in refrigeration drying is caused by the formation of ice on the cooling surface, which impedes heat transfer and periodically must be melted. It should be noted that the air does not necessarily leave the tube with a water content corresponding to its dry-bulb temperature; it is then drier than saturated because its dew point approaches the surface temperature of the tube.

3. Adsorption

In general, the lowest attainable dew point of air dried by condensing out the moisture is 2.5° above the temperature of the coolant. For low humidities, of the order of 0.003 milligram per liter of gas, the use of chemical drying agents or adsorbents is generally more practical. Some porous solids, such as silica gel, show considerable affinity for water, although forming no definite chemical compounds or hydrates. Thus, with air, dew points of −50°F. with silica gel and of −60°F. with alumina can be reached without trouble and such sorbents are widely used industrially.[29] Materials of this type show a definite equilibrium moisture content with any relative humidity of the gas, although a hysteresis loop may be present. Such an adsorption curve is shown in Figure 9. More exact data for silica gel are shown in Figure 10.[30] It may be seen that 20–30% of the gel's own weight of water can be taken up. Most materials of this class can be reactivated for use by being heated to a higher temperature in a stream of air. Indeed, silica gel and alumina are still efficient after several thousand recycles. Activated alumina, essentially granular, porous, amorphous aluminum trioxide, under favorable conditions can take up 10% of moisture before its drying efficiency falls and it is necessary to regenerate it by heating to about 250° C. Alumina should not be used to dry chlorine, sulfur dioxide, or other gases of acidic nature, which gradually deactivate it. Activated bauxites, containing about 67% by weight of alumina, resemble it in character and are also used industrially.

In practice, the adsorbent material is placed in drying tubes or towers through which the gas is passed. For ordinary laboratory use, reactivation is not usually worth while, since the common adsorbents alumina and silica gel are relatively inexpensive. Efficiency of adsorption is good, being somewhere between that of phosphorus pentoxide and that of sulfuric acid (see Table IV); and it remains good until the "break point"

[29] F. M. Waterhouse, *Chem. Eng.*, **61**, No. 6, 237 (1954)

[30] S. S. Hubard, *Ind. Eng. Chem.*, **46**, 356–358 (1954).

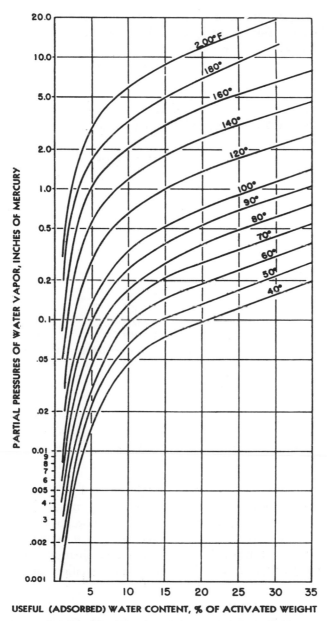

Fig. 10. Useful (adsorbed) water capacity of regular density (0.70 to 0.75) silica-gel as a function of partial pressures at various temperatures.[30]

(defined as the per cent concentration of water in the dry gel when the adsorption efficiency falls to 99%) is reached. At the break point, the back pressure of the water vapor over the adsorbent begins to rise rapidly and it is necessary to regenerate or to replace the reagent.

TABLE IV

EQUILIBRIUM WATER VAPOR CONTENT OF GASES DRIED OVER COMMON REAGENTS AT 25°C.

Reagent	Mg./liter gas	% by volume	Dew point, °F.	Ref.
Filter at −194°C	1.6×10^{-23}	—	—	(31)
P_2O_5	2×10^{-5}	—	—	(31)
$Mg(ClO_4)_2$ (anhyd.)	5×10^{-4}	—	—	(31)
$Mg(ClO_4)_2 \cdot 3H_2O$ (30% water)	0.002	0.0002	−102	(32)
MgO	0.008	0.0007	−90	(31)
BaO	0.00065	—	−111	(33)
$Ba(ClO_4)_2$ (anhyd.)	0.82	0.094	−10	(33)
H_2SO_4 (95%)	0.003	0.0003	−100	(31)
H_2SO_4 (80%)	0.20	0.021	−38	(34)
Alumina	0.003	0.0003	−100	(31)
Silica gel (dry)	0.003	0.0003	−100	(31)
CaO	0.003	0.0003	−100	(35)
$CaCl_2$ (granulated)	0.14–0.245	0.0149–0.0264	−44 to −34	(31)
$CaCl_2$ (fused)	0.36	0.0395	−25.4	(31)
$CaSO_4$ (anhyd.)	0.005	0.0005	−95	(31)
$CaBr_2$	0.20	0.021	−38	(31)
$ZnBr_2$	1.1	0.124	−4	(31)
$ZnCl_2$ (sticks)	0.8	0.092	−10	(31)
$CuSO_4$	1.4	0.165	2	(31)
KOH (fused)	0.014	0.0015	−80	(31)
NaOH (fused)	0.16	0.0170	−42	(31)

Silica gel and alumina have considerable adsorptive power for many organic materials as well as water and must, therefore, be used with caution for drying organic gases. On some adsorbents, e.g., alumina, explosions have been observed when first hydrogen and then oxygen are passed through freshly activated adsorbent[36] and such reactions must be guarded against.

[31] International Critical Tables. Vol. III, McGraw-Hill, New York, 1938, p. 385.
[32] H. H. Willard and G. F. Smith, J. Am. Chem. Soc., 44, 2255–2259 (1922).
[33] M. B. Ranken, Modern Refrig., 16, 225–228, 261 (1953).
[34] S. C. Chang and N. B. Hutcheon, Can. J. Tech., 31, 175 (1953).
[35] J. H. Bower, J. Res. Natl. Bur. Standards, 12, 246 (1934).
[36] D. J. C. Bailey, Chem. & Industry, 1954, 492.

4. Use of Hygroscopic Materials

The most usual laboratory method for drying gases is by contact with solid or liquid materials which have a marked affinity for water (Table IV).   Some reagents combine with water to form definite hydrates and a comparison of their equilibrium relationships at normal temperature suggests their relative efficiency, although, in practice, actual equilibrium may not always be attained.   In addition to drying power, drying rate is of importance, particularly in large-scale installations.   It is dependent upon the thickness of the layer, rate of flow, etc.[37-40]   For most desiccants contact times should be of the order of 5 seconds or more for good results. Table V suggests suitable drying agents for a number of gases.   For any given gas, a little reflection usually suggests a suitable reagent for use. Obviously, sulfuric acid would not be used for amines nor fused caustic potash for gases with an acidic character.

TABLE V

SUITABLE DRYING AGENTS FOR SOME COMMON GASES

Drying agent	Gases
Lime.....................	NH_3, amines
Calcium chloride.........	H_2, HCl, CO_2, CO, SO_2, N_2, CH_4, O_2, paraffins, ethers, olefins, alkyl chlorides
Phosphorus pentoxide......	H_2, O_2, CO_2, CO, SO_2, N_2, CH_4, C_2H_4, paraffins
Sulfuric acid..............	H_2, N_2, CO_2, Cl_2, CO, CH_4, paraffins
Fused potassium hydroxide..	NH_3, amines

When chemical reaction with the gas to be dried does not occur, phosphorus pentoxide is always the best drying agent and, because of ready availability, is, next to granulated calcium chloride, probably the most frequently used material.   Because phosphorus pentoxide, after some use, forms a smooth surface film of metaphosphoric acid, which prevents further drying action by the unchanged pentoxide underneath, it is essential to break it up from time to time or, better, to sift the pentoxide initially over glass wool so that the active surface of the reagent is greatly increased.

Metallic oxides, although they have high efficiency, must be fresh since their surfaces quickly become coated with inactive material, particularly the carbonate if carbon dioxide is present in the gas stream.   Barium oxide is of great value when dehydration must be carried out at high tem-

[37] O. A. Hougen and W. R. Marshall, Jr., *Chem. Eng. Progress*, **43,** 197 (1947).

[38] W. L. Ross and E. R. McLaughlin, *Refrigerating Eng.*, **59,** 167–173 (1951).

[39] L. E. Eagleton and H. Bliss, *Chem. Eng. Progress*, **49,** 543 (1953).

[40] R. C. Amero, J. W. Moore, and R. G. Capell, *Chem. Eng. Progress*, **43,** 349 (1947).

peratures because its efficiency is practically equal to that of phosphorus pentoxide and its dehydrating action is effective at temperatures up to 600° C. Moreover, it has a high capacity, is cheap, and is easily handled. It cannot be regenerated by heating, is strongly alkaline, and allowance must be made in design of containers for its expansion as it absorbs water. Calcium oxide has a high capacity but suffers from the same defects as barium oxide, without its absorptive power at high temperatures. Magnesium oxide has relatively low absorptive capacity.

Calcium sulfate dehydrates gases by formation of its hemihydrate, $CaSO_4 \cdot {}^1/_2 H_2O$, and because of its inert nature can be used with most organic gases. Although its efficiency is high, its capacity is somewhat

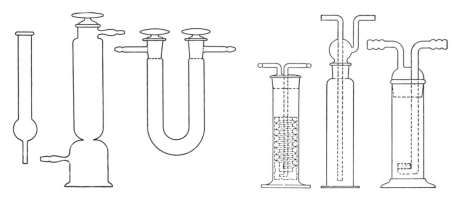

Figs. 11 and 12. Laboratory apparatus for drying gases.

low,[41] it is sensitive to overheating, and it cannot be regenerated through as many cycles as alumina or silica gel. This latter fact is unimportant in laboratory usage for which its low cost and inertness make it valuable. Magnesium perchlorate is among the best desiccants in drying efficiency but should not be used for drying organic or acid materials because of the danger of explosion. It is difficult to regenerate, a temperature of 200°C. and high vacuum being required, but it is chemically neutral and contracts rather than expands as it absorbs water.

In order to avoid channeling solid reagents are packed in vertical columns so that the gas passes evenly through the lumps or granules (Fig. 11). Fused potassium or sodium hydroxides are best supported mechanically in some manner by an inert material so that, as water is absorbed, a dense mass is not formed, through which it would be difficult to force the gas.

With liquid reagents, there are two problems: (1) to insure perfect

[41] S. H. Jury and W. Licht, Jr., *Ind. Eng. Chem.* **44**, 591–594 (1952).

contact with the gas, and (*2*) to avoid entrainment or mechanical carry-over of the absorbent as spray in the gas.[42]   These are achieved to varying degrees in the designs shown in Figure 12, the sintered-glass plate of the wash bottle shown in Figure 12 being particularly efficient in securing maximum contact of gas with reagent.[43]   In order to insure attainment of equilibrium, a number of drying towers or bottles in series are frequently used.

The degree of dryness attained after any given procedure is probably best determined by measurement of the dew point[44-46] or by the electrical conductance of a film of hygroscopic electrolyte exposed to the gas.[47] Chemical methods, such as absorption in phosphorus pentoxide, are much more tiresome and probably not as accurate when gases with water contents of the order of 0.01 mg./liter are involved.   Hurst and Roman[48] have described a method using Karl Fischer reagent good to 20 micrograms water per liter for gases such as air, oxygen, nitrogen, and hydrocarbons.

IV.   DRYING OF LIQUIDS

1. Methods Involving Vaporization of Water

Distillation.   When water and the liquid under consideration form no constant-boiling mixture and their boiling points are separated widely enough, simple distillation at, above, or below atmospheric pressure can be resorted to although sufficient water often remains in the liquid to render treatment with a hygroscopic material after distillation advisable.   Apparatus and techniques for distillation are discussed in Volume IV of this series.

The principle of steam distillation can sometimes be applied to the drying of liquids (or solids).   Thus, if a wet hydrocarbon solution of an organic substance (benzene and toluene are very suitable) is distilled, the first portion of the distillate consists of hydrocarbon and water.   When all the water has been removed, the pure hydrocarbon distils, leaving the pure dry organic material.   This procedure is also the basis of the well-known Dean and Stark method for the estimation of moisture in many organic materials.[49,50]

[42] F. H. Rhodes and D. R. Rakestraw, *Ind. Eng. Chem., Anal. Ed.*, **3**, 143 (1931).

[43] P. H. Prausnitz, *Anal. Chem.*, **4**, 430 (1932).

[44] R. M. Ilfeld, *Anal. Chem.*, **23**, 1086 (1951).

[45] S. H. Jury and W. Licht, Jr., *Anal. Chem.*, **22**, 1536 (1950).

[46] R. C. Amero, J. W. Moore, and R. G. Capell, *Chem. Eng. Progress*, **43**, 349 (1947).

[47] E. R. Weaver, *Anal. Chem.*, **23**, 1076 (1951).

[48] A. Hurst and W. Roman, *Analyst*, **76**, 10 (1951).

[49] E. W. Dean and D. D. Stark, *J. Ind. Eng. Chem.*, **12**, 486 (1920).

[50] W. R. Fetzer, *Anal. Chem.*, **23**, 1062 (1951).

Azeotropic Distillation. While some liquid mixtures obey Raoult's law (Sect. II.1), water forms constant-boiling mixtures with many liquids, *i.e.*, the mixtures deviate from Raoult's law giving boiling-point composition curves at constant pressure of the type shown schematically in Figure 13. Thus, if a 50% mixture (by weight) of ethanol and water is distilled, the mixture of minimum boiling point boils at a lower temperature than any other mixture of the two components and distils first at constant temperature, 78.15°C., without any variation of composition, leaving behind the

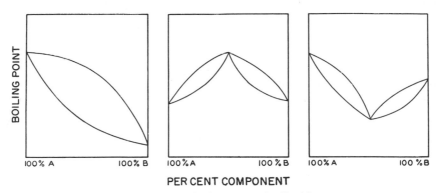

Fig. 13. Distillation curves for liquids.

excess of water. This constant-boiling mixture is composed of 95.59% ethyl alcohol and 4.41% water. Thus, by repeated fractional distillation the constant-boiling mixture and one of the components, in this case water, can be isolated. Dry ethanol can be obtained by fractionation at atmospheric pressure only from those mixtures which contain less than 4.4% water. However, by adding a third substance which itself forms a constant-boiling mixture with water and ethanol, it is possible to remove all the water, leaving a mixture of the added material and ethanol. The added liquid forms a binary or ternary azeotrope with a boiling point sufficiently widely separated to allow easy isolation of the ethanol by distillation. Benzene can be used in the case of the drying of ethanol. A sufficient amount is added to allow removal of all the water in the form of the ternary azeotrope (b.p. 68.24°C.). Finally, pure ethyl alcohol (b.p. 78.5°C.) distils.

Lecat[51] studied such azeotropic mixtures extensively, and a recent survey was made by Horsley.[52]

While of great commercial utility, azeotropic means of drying are not

[51] M. Lecat, *Tables Azéotropiques Vol. I. Azéotropes binaires orthobares.* 2nd ed., M. Lecat, Uccle-Bruxelles, 29, Auguste Danse, 1949.

[52] L. H. Horsley, *Anal. Chem.*, **19**, 508 (1947); **21**, 831 (1949).

used extensively in the organic laboratory since the best liquid to add to new compounds as a ternary component is not usually known and extensive experimentation may be required to find a suitable material.   The actual techniques and apparatus suitable for azeotropic drying are, of course, the same as those used in distillation (see *Distillation*, pp. 316–387, Volume IV of this series).   Pressures above or below atmospheric are advantageous in some cases.

2. Removal of Water by Means Other Than Vaporization

Freezing.   If water is immiscible with the liquid to be dried, it can be separated by decantation or by use of a separating funnel, but, even when

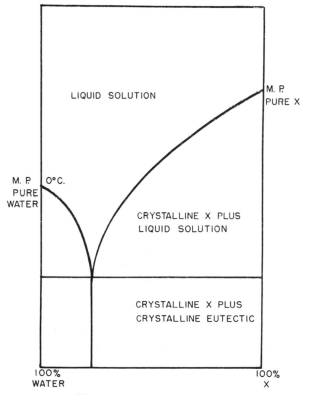

Fig. 14. Freezing-point curve.

miscible, it can be at least partially removed by freezing, followed by mechanical separation, filtering out the ice crystals formed. Again, aqueous ethanol may be used as an example. If a 20% mixture (by weight) is frozen, pure ice separates at $-10.0°C$. and the ethanol can be concentrated in this way. Ultimately a eutectic is reached and no further concentration can be effected, but the method is particularly useful for the preliminary concentration of weak aqueous solutions of liquids. Consideration of the illustrative freezing point curve of Figure 14 indicates that final dehydration of a liquid cannot be accomplished by this method, if water and the liquid are at all miscible.[53] However, if the liquid has a convenient freezing point, it can itself be crystallized as the final stage of its purification. The techniques of freezing for the removal of traces of impurities are fully described in Chapter III, pp. 496 ff.

Extraction by Brines. Countercurrent extraction of water by a strong solution of a suitable salt is also useful for dehydration of liquids, such as methyl ethyl ketone, which are only partially miscible with water or brine solutions. The strong brine abstracts water from the organic liquid, and eventually an equilibrium which can be predicted is reached.[54] However, this method is of greater industrial than laboratory utility. Chapter II of this volume may be consulted for a discussion of experimental techniques.

Use of Hygroscopic Materials. The same solid hygroscopic materials useful for the drying of gases are applicable in the case of liquids and the same principles apply. In addition to the materials already mentioned, potassium carbonate, anhydrous magnesium, calcium, copper, and sodium sulfates, and barium oxide are often useful. The anhydrous sulfates can be used for drying most liquids, although copper sulfate should not be used for amines. Copper and magnesium sulfates have both good intensities and good capacities in their drying action. Calcium sulfate possesses high intensity and low capacity, while the reverse is true for sodium sulfate. Any hygroscopic agent used must be chemically inert and insoluble in the liquid which it is desired to dry and, in equilibrium with the moisture abstracted, must have a very low water partial pressure.

Usually the solid, *e.g.*, calcium chloride or phosphorus pentoxide, is added to the liquid in a tightly corked or stoppered flask, allowed to stand for several hours, and occasionally shaken. As low a temperature as possible should be used since this reduces the solubility of water in the organic liquid and also the vapor pressure. In general, the lower the solubility of water in the liquid the easier it is to dry it. The solid withdraws water from the liquid and goes into solution, forming a layer immiscible with the liquid. A little of the liquid tends to dissolve in the new aqueous layer, but losses due to this are usually very small. Maximum possible dehydration occurs

[53] R. S Tipson, Chapter III, pp. 446 ff.
[54] H. P. Meissner, C. A. Stokes, C. M. Hunter, and G. M. Morrow, III, *Ind. Eng. Chem.*, **36**, 917 (1944).

when excess of the solid component is present in addition to the two liquid phases.   If much water is present it is preferable to add the drying agent in portions, removing each addition before the next portion is added.   In this way the highest hydrate of the desiccant is formed first and less is required, thus cutting down loss of liquid due to entrainment by the desiccant and also the quantity of desiccant required.   Entrainment and loss of liquid can be minimized by washing the desiccant with a pure dry solvent after pouring off the liquid, by dilution with a solvent, or by using a fused, nonporous form of the dessiccant.   When the liquid cannot be simply poured off, centrifuging or filtration to remove the drying agent can be applied.   Filtration is best carried out not through filter paper, but by use of a plug of dry cotton or glass wool.   In some cases, particularly when the boiling point of the liquid is low, distillation is conducted without prior removal of the desiccant, although the vapor pressure of the water over the hygroscopic agent (and hence the amount carried over) is greater at high temperatures than at room temperature.   For large quantities of liquids column drying[55] is sometimes convenient.   The cylindrical container, down which the liquid percolates, is filled with alumina, bauxite, quicklime, or some other desiccant.

An approximate evaluation of the degree of dryness of a liquid after treatment with a drying agent can be made if Raoult's law is assumed. Suppose that amyl alcohol, molecular weight 88, is being dried with an excess of calcium sulfate.   The hydrate formed is $CaSO_4 \cdot 1/2 H_2O$, which has a vapor pressure of 0.004 mm. Hg at 25°C.   If Raoult's law holds, the mole fraction of water in the amyl alcohol at equilibrium at this temperature is $0.004/23.7 = 0.00017$.   This is equivalent to 0.0035% by weight.   Actually, since Raoult's law does not hold, the water content is somewhat less than this figure.   Table VI shows the vapor pressures of the hydrates formed by a number of common dehydrating agents so that rough estimates of drying efficiency can be carried out.

TABLE VI

VAPOR PRESSURES OF HYDRATES OF SOME COMMON DRYING AGENTS AT 25°C.

Hydrate	Vapor pressure, mm. Hg	Hydrate	Vapor pressure, mm. Hg
$BaO \cdot H_2O$	10^{-16}	$KOH \cdot H_2O$	1.5
$CaSO_4 \cdot 1/4 H_2O$	0.004	$ZnCl_2 \cdot 1^1/_2 H_2O$	2.3
$CaCl_2 \cdot H_2O$	0.04	$CuSO_4 \cdot H_2O$	0.8
$NaOH \cdot H_2O$	0.7	$MgSO_4 \cdot H_2O$	1
$CaO \cdot H_2O$	0.8	H_2SO_4, 95%	0.001
$K_2CO_3 \cdot 1^1/_2 H_2O$	1.1	$Na_2SO_4 \cdot 10H_2O$	22.3

[55] Oesper, R. E., translation of Lassar-Cohn's *Organic Laboratory Methods*.   Williams & Wilkins, Baltimore, 1928, p. 395.

Meissner and Stokes[56] have presented a method for predicting the maximum degree of dehydration obtainable with any given liquid and dehydrating agent.

Chemical reaction with water rather than hydrate formation can also be used for drying purposes and has the advantage that it is usually more irreversible under the conditions employed. Hydrocarbons, for example, are best dried with sodium wire or with liquid sodium–potassium alloy (16K:10Na), the latter having the advantage that, by shaking, the surface can be renewed constantly. Sodium wire becomes encrusted with a difficultly permeable layer of the hydroxide, which slows down reaction.

During distillation, unless special precautions are taken, traces of the drying agent may be entrained and the possible occurrence of this should be kept in mind. Thus, when a liquid is dried over a strong alkali such as barium oxide, it might appear, under critical conditions, to behave somewhat differently from the same liquid dried over calcium chloride. Most alcohols, ethers, and ketones are exceedingly hygroscopic when thoroughly dry and precautions (phosphorus pentoxide tube) should be taken to protect them against reabsorption of moisture.

Table VII suggests suitable drying agents for a number of classes of organic compounds.

TABLE VII

SUITABLE DRYING AGENTS FOR SOME COMMON CLASSES OF ORGANIC LIQUIDS

Drying agent	Suitable for drying	Unsuitable for drying
Phosphorus pentoxide	Alkyl halides, hydrocarbons, halogenated hydrocarbons, CS_2	Bases, ketones, aldehydes or other materials where polymerization may be caused
Sulfuric acid	Alkyl halides, saturated hydrocarbons, halogenated hydrocarbons	Bases, ketones, alcohols, aldehydes, phenols, etc.
Calcium chloride	Ethers, esters, alkyl halides, aryl halides, etc.	Alcohols, amines, phenols, aldehydes, amides, fatty acids
Potassium hydroxide	Bases	Ketones, aldehydes, esters, acids
Potassium carbonate	Bases, some halides, ketones	Fatty acids, esters
Sodium sulfate	Most materials	
Magnesium sulfate	Most materials	
Anhydrous copper sulfate	Ethers, alcohols, etc.	Amines
Sodium	Ethers, saturated hydrocarbons	Alcohols, amines, esters
Calcium sulfate	Most materials	

Small quantities of water in supposedly dry liquids can sometimes be detected by adding calcium carbide or anhydrous cobaltous chloride or bromide, evolution of acetylene or appearance of a pink color being posi-

56 H. P. Meissner and C. A. Stokes, *Ind. Eng. Chem.*, **36**, 816 (1944).

tive indications. Cobaltous bromide can detect 17 to 20 p.p.m. of moisture in a liquid hydrocarbon.[57] Potassium permanganate has also been suggested as a water detector.[58] Perhaps the most generally applicable quantitative method for water estimation in small quantities is by Karl Fischer reagent titration, which under suitable conditions is sensitive to about 0.2 mg. of water.[57-61] Interfering materials are carbonyl compounds, mercaptans, peroxides, thio acids, and hydrazines. Infrared spectrometry—unfortunately not applicable to liquids which absorb appreciably at the 2.67 μ water band, thus precluding the analysis of most compounds containing hydrogen—is even more sensitive, being good where applicable, e.g., carbon tetrachloride, to 1 p.p.m. in the range 0 to 10 p.p.m.[62] For some liquids water can be very accurately estimated by measurement of its effect on the critical solution temperature or cloud point of the liquid with a third component,[63,64] e.g., 1% water raises the critical solution temperature of ethyl alcohol-dicyclohexyl from 23.4° to 41.4°C.

Stringer[65] has devised the humidoscope for the detection of traces of water in oils. A metal tube is divided into upper and lower chambers by a pipe clay diaphragm. The upper chamber contains dry air. The air in the lower chamber is dried by a desiccant connected to the instrument until an oil manometer connected to both chambers gives a zero reading, indicating zero relative humidity. The bottom chamber of the tube is then placed over a receptacle filled with the oil under test. Moisture diffuses into the lower chamber and pressure measurements allow calculation of the absolute moisture content of the oil.

V. ISOLATION OF SOLIDS

The organic chemist finds himself confronted with many different types of drying problems, ranging from drying a few grams of a stable crystalline compound to handling many pounds of a labile, easily oxidizable, gelatinous, and hygroscopic material. No one technique is universally applicable: indeed, for the simplest cases no more than a sheet of filter paper and some warm air is required; for the more troublesome cases, more elaborate

[57] R. C. Amero, J. W. Moore, and R. G. Capell, Chem. Eng. Progress, 43, 349 (1947).

[58] M. B. Jacobs and L. Scheflan, Chemical Analysis of Industrial Solvents. Interscience, New York-London, 1953, pp. 46–53.

[59] J. Mitchell, Jr., Anal. Chem., 23, 1069 (1951).

[60] W. S. Hanna and A. B. Johnson, Anal. Chem., 22, 555 (1950).

[61] A. R. Martin and A. C. Lloyd, J. Am. Oil Chem. Soc., 20, 595–597 (1953).

[62] A. F. Benning, A. A. Ebert, and C. F. Irwin, Anal. Chem., 19, 867 (1947).

[63] G. R. Robertson, Ind. Eng. Chem., Anal. Ed., 15, 451 (1943).

[64] W. Seaman, A. R. Norton, and J. J. Hugonet, Ind. Eng. Chem., Anal. Ed., 15, 322 (1943).

[65] J. E. C. Stringer, Nature, 169, 412 (1952).

techniques, *e.g.*, freeze drying, are required. Some methods of drying, *e.g.*, spray drying, are inherently unsuitable for small quantities of material and must be ruled out in such cases. Others are suitable only for small quantities. In Table VIII are indicated a few of the factors which may govern the choice of drying or evaporation methods.

TABLE VIII

EVAPORATION AND DRYING METHODS

SOLUTIONS

Small volume, stable to heat and/or oxidation	Evaporating dish	pp. 818–820
Small volume, unstable to heat and/or oxidation	Vacuum evaporator	pp. 819, 821
Large volume, foaming no factor	Flash evaporator	p. 821
Large volume, foaming	Hot-air evaporator	p. 820
Large volume, unstable, or solubility of product very important	Spray drying	pp. 821–822

SOLIDS

Small quantity, stable, crystalline, nonhygroscopic	Drying on water or toluene bath. Air drying on paper or porous plate	p. 838
Large quantity, stable, crystalline	Drying on water or toluene bath. Oven drying	pp. 825–828
Small quantity, stable, hygroscopic	Desiccator (possibly with infrared)	pp. 823–825
Large quantity, stable, hygroscopic	Oven drying	pp. 825–828
Small quantity. Unstable to heat and/or oxidation	Vacuum desiccator, freeze drying, solvent extraction	pp. 829–837 p. 838
Large quantity. Unstable to heat and/or oxidation	Freeze drying, vacuum drying, solvent extraction	pp. 831–837 pp. 829–831 p. 838

1. Methods Involving Vaporization of Water

Evaporation. When large quantities of water or other solvents are to be removed, the process is usually known as evaporation. In the simplest method, the solution or suspension is placed in an evaporating dish, which may be heated directly over an open flame or on a steam bath. An inverted funnel may be placed above the dish as a protection against dust. Consideration of the basic principles involved (Sect. II.2) indicates that rapid evaporation is favored by large surface area and an air stream directed across the liquid–air interface, thus securing a high mass-transfer coefficient by rapid removal of the solvent vapors and diminution of the film thickness. It is convenient to blow clean air through the funnel mentioned above.   If a surface crust forms as evaporation proceeds, it should be broken up to allow free egress of the vapor.

During evaporation, creep of the liquid or crystals may occur.   To avoid this in some degree, the dish may be placed in a larger dish, and the use of a tall, narrow beaker less than one-third full is sometimes helpful. For aqueous solutions, the rim of the crystallizing vessel may be coated with a thin smear of petroleum jelly or a suitable silicone compound.   On occasion, it is also helpful to place the dish below a source of heat and allow evaporation to proceed as a result of heat striking the surface.   In this connection, infrared radiation is sometimes useful.   With suitable equipment, such as that shown in Figure 15, evaporation can be made to occur from the surface layer without boiling and with less chance of losses due to bumping.[66]

Fig. 15. Infrared evaporation unit. Courtesy Quartz Products Corporation.

Simple laboratory evaporators which can be used for the vacuum concentration of solutions, such as those obtained in chromatographic separations,[67,68,68a] have been described.   Frothing or bumping is minimized by a device allowing rapid rotation of the evaporating flask (Fig. 16).

[66] F. Heinrich and P. Petzold, *Chem.-Ztg.*, **60**, 145 (1936); **61**, 568 (1937).
[67] S. M. Partridge, *J. Sci. Instruments*, **28**, 28 (1951).
[68] P. Nemerof and K. Reinhardt, *Anal. Chem.*, **25**, 364 (1953).
[68a] L. C. Craig, D. C. Gregory, and W. Hausmann, *Anal. Chem.*, **22**, 1462 (1950)

When foaming may be a factor making evaporation under reduced pressure difficult, an evaporator utilizing hot air passing over a thin film of liquid may be convenient.[69,70]   Materials such as urine can be concentrated in an apparatus of this type without their temperature rising above 35°C.   Concentration takes place by convective surface evaporation and requires as large a surface as possible for exchange between liquid and gas. Other continuous evaporators have been described.[71]

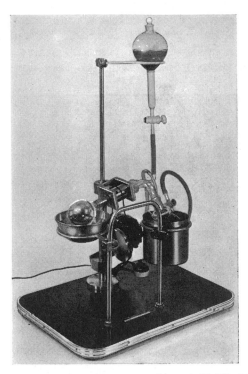

Fig. 16. Constant rotating evaporator.   Courtesy E. Machlett & Son.

When high temperatures during evaporation must be avoided at all costs, *e.g.*, in the concentration of some protein solutions, the solution to be evaporated is placed in a bag made of uncoated cellophane tubing and the bag is allowed to stand in a current of air.[72]   Water diffuses through the membrane and evaporates into the air stream; in some cases cooling may be so great that the solution freezes.

[69] E. A. Bell. *Chemistry & Industry*, **1953**, 741.
[70] N. W. Vere-Jones, *New Zealand J. Sci. Technol.*, **B31,** No. 3, 1–4 (1949).
[71] K. S. Kemmerer, *Ind. Eng. Chem., Anal. Ed.*, **17,** 466 (1945).

When recovery of the solvent is desired, distillation can be resorted to, and for large quantities of material, the falling-film evaporator may be advantageous.   Laboratory flash evaporators operating at 75–100 mm. Hg pressure are available.[73]   In these the time of contact at the evaporation temperature is very short and the evaporation is itself low due to the vacuum maintained.   Decomposition of heat-sensitive materials is thus kept at a low level.

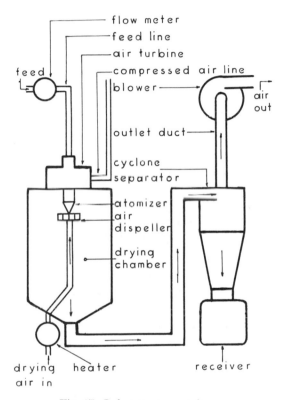

Fig. 17. Laboratory spray dryer.

Lindsay[74] has recently published an excellent review of evaporation procedures on the industrial scale.

Spray Drying, which is becoming very important industrially, may be regarded as a special form of evaporation.   A hot solution of the material to be isolated is forced under pressure into a large chamber, producing a

[72] P. A. Kober, *J. Am. Chem. Soc.,* **39,** 944 (1917).

[73] W. H. Bartholomew, *Anal. Chem.,* **21,** 527 (1949).

[74] E. Lindsay, *Chem. Eng.,* **60,** No. 4, 227 (1953).

fine mist of solution droplets, which rapidly evaporate in a current of hot gas. In this way the solid falls in the form of fine particles to the bottom of the chamber. The method is somewhat inconvenient for the laboratory although Woodcock and Tessiner have described the construction of a small laboratory spray drier.[75] Laboratory spray driers, capable of evaporating 2 to 15 pounds of water per hour, are available (Fig. 17), but are somewhat expensive for the ordinary laboratory. Furthermore, they give particles in the 5 to 50 μ size range as compared to 50 to 125 μ for most commercial driers.

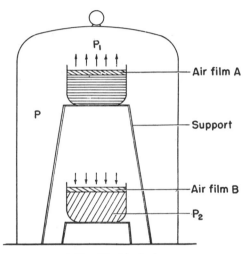

Fig. 18. Air drying.

Spray drying is particularly suited for heat-sensitive materials such as foods since the drying time is so short—of the order of 3 seconds—that deterioration in quality cannot occur. Thus, it is possible to spray dry ferrous salts at 500°F. without oxidation.[76] With proper control of drop formation by suitable atomization, spherical particles of any desired size, readily soluble, are obtained. Commercially they are used to dry pharmaceuticals, rubber latex, clay slips, foods, soaps, and detergents, but on a small scale the drying process is somewhat clumsy and difficult to control. For a discussion of spray drying and its theory the reader is referred to Marshall and Seltzer[77] and to Seltzer and Settelmeyer.[78]

Air Drying. As the last stage in many organic preparations, the drying

[75] A. H. Woodcock and H. Tessier, *Can. J. Research,* **A21,** 75 (1953).

[76] K. Bullock and J. W. Lightbown, *Quart. J. Pharmacol.,* **16,** 213–221 (1943).

[77] W. R. Marshall, Jr., and E. Seltzer, *Chem. Eng. Progress,* **46,** 501, 575 (1950).

[78] E. Seltzer and J. T. Settelmeyer, *Advances Food Research,* **2,** 399 (1949)

of the solid receives less attention perhaps than it should, and a consideration of the processes occurring would result in increased efficiency and economy of time.   As pointed out in Section II.2, drying is a diffusional operation, its velocity during the constant-rate period being dependent upon the diffusion coefficient (itself dependent on air velocity) and the difference in the partial pressures of the water vapor over the solid and in the drying air.   The filter cake from the last stage of an organic preparation may be 50% water, much of which can be removed by absorption on a good absorbing paper or porous tile.   The residual solvent in some cases may be removed by simple exposure to air at room temperature; in other cases heating may be required.   The drawback to the latter is that the solid may evaporate, oxidize, decompose, or even liquefy below its true melting point due to the solvent present.

Perhaps most used in the organic laboratory for completing the final stages of drying is the ordinary desiccator, in which the water vapor concentration in the drying air is kept low by means of a suitable hygroscopic agent placed in a container at the bottom of the dish.   The material to be dried is placed in another container, and drying is effected by the process shown diagrammatically in Figure 18.   Water molecules of partial pressure P_1 must travel through the air film A over the material to be dried and diffuse through the desiccator to pass through the stagnant air film B over the desiccant.   If P is the partial pressure of the water vapor in the air and P_2 that over the desiccant, then for drying to occur:

$$P_1 > P > P_2 \tag{29}$$

The greater the difference between P_1 and P_2, the more rapid the drying action.   Reference to Table IV indicates that best action should be obtained with phosphorus pentoxide.   This material, sulfuric acid, and calcium chloride are most frequently used.   Sulfuric acid is very useful since it absorbs water and all organic solvents except hydrocarbons and their halogen derivatives.   If desired, the sulfuric acid can be made to act as its own indicator for too great dilution by dissolving in it 18% barium sulfate.   This is precipitated as $Ba(HSO_4)_2$, giving a cloudy appearance as water is absorbed.   However, sulfuric acid oxidizes acetone vapors with formation of sulfur dioxide.   To absorb this a small dish of caustic soda or soda lime may be kept on the plate of the desiccator, the sulfuric acid being at the bottom.   Indeed, a desiccator equipped with sulfuric acid and dishes containing caustic soda and paraffin wax shavings is equipped for the absorption of almost all solvents and has general utility, although in vacuum desiccator operation it should be remembered that below 5 mm. sulfuric acid becomes appreciably volatile.   Paraffin wax flakes absorb hydrocarbons, ether, and some halogenated solvents.   They should be replaced as they become semifluid.

Under some circumstances, absorbent cotton, previously thoroughly dried in a steam oven, can be used as an absorbent for water.

With only stagnant air in the desiccator, not only are the diffusion coefficients through the air films A and B at their minimum values, but travel of the water molecules between A and B is dependent entirely upon diffusion and convection currents.   In practice, the latter are found to be very effective, moist air being lighter than dry air and tending to rise.   The time required to reach equilibrium is less than would be predicted if only diffusion were occurring.[79]   Thus, as shown in Table IX,[80] in an ordinary desiccator equilibrium between the desiccant and the air is reached in a period of from 7.5 to 15 minutes.

In the ordinary desiccator, because the air is stagnant, the rate of drying cannot be altered by increasing the diffusion coefficient, k' (Sect. II.2), since the coefficient is independent of most factors other than air velocity over the surface film.   However, many stirring devices have been developed for use in closed desiccators or similar closed containers.   Magnetic

TABLE IX

ABSORPTION OF MOISTURE IN A 3000 ML. DESICCATOR OVER BARIUM OXIDE, ANHYDROUS CALCIUM CHLORIDE, AND CALCIUM SULFATE

R.H., %	Desiccant	Water vapor blank	Residual water vapor after			Absorption efficiency		
			0.5 min.	10 min.	25 min.	0.5 min.	10 min.	25 min.
43	Barium oxide	12.2	7.3	0.0	—	42.5	100	—
40	Calcium chloride	10 8	4.1	0.4	0.4	62.0	96.0	96.0
62	Calcium sulfate	17.5	12.3	0.1	—	29.7	99.0	—

stirrers,[81] shakers with flexible connecting shafts, induction stirrers,[82] or circulating pumps[83] have proved useful.   Liquid seals, using oil or mercury, are also sometimes useful in arranging suitable agitation.[84]   Proper mixing accelerates drying both by reduction of the diffusion coefficient and by acceleration of the air currents so that the water reaches the desiccating agent surface more rapidly.   As the sample becomes more nearly dry the effect of stirring, as might be expected since diffusion of water vapor

[79] G. Broughton and J. P. Mather, *Am. Dyestuff Reporter*, **27**, 438 (1938).
[80] G. F. Smith, D. N. Bernhart, and V. R. Wiederkehr, *Anal. Chim. Acta*, **6**, 42 (1952).
[81] F. J. Zink, *Ind. Eng. Chem., Anal. Ed.*, **7**, 442–443 (1935).
[82] W. G. Dauben, J. C. Reid, and P. E. Yankwich, *Anal. Chem.*, **19**, 828–832 (1947).
[83] V. H. Blackman and B. D. Bolas, *Ann. Botany*, **40**, 275–276 (1926).
[84] J. T. Donnelly, C. H. Foot, H. Nielson, and J. Reilly, *J. Soc. Chem. Ind.*, **47**, 1–4T, 139–142T, 142–143T, 189–192T (1928).

through the surface layer is no longer controlling, becomes less marked. Clearly, drying is also accelerated if the area of the wet solid is large, if there is a wide path and minimum distance between solid and desiccant, and if P_1 can be increased; the last is most readily done by raising the temperature of the solid to be dried.   This has led to the form of apparatus shown in Figure 19, the Abderhalden drying pistol, in which the solid to be dried is maintained at a suitably elevated temperature by an oven or in the vapor of a boiling liquid, while the hygroscopic solid which absorbs

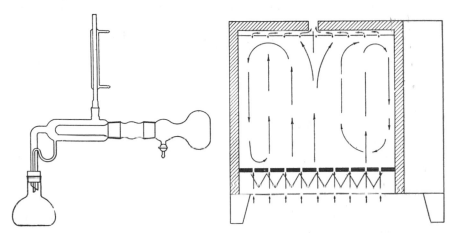

Fig. 19. Apparatus for drying by raising temperature of solid to be dried.

Fig. 20. Oven for drying.

the water driven off is kept at room temperature.[85]   Other modifications also have been described.[86,87]   Mitchell[88] has made a thorough study of the effect of the different variables on the drying of sugar solutions in desiccators.

Many organic materials are sufficiently insusceptible to heat to allow oven drying, by steam or air oven (see Sect. II.1).   The method is widely used also for determination of water in solids, although the process may be more complex than is sometimes thought.[89]   Figure 20 shows a type of oven in common use.   Again, the principles discussed in Section II apply; the important factors influencing drying rate are the state of division of the substance, the amount of water present, the pressure, time, and tem-

[85] E. Abderhalden, *Handbuch der biologischen Arbeitsmethoden*.   Urban & Schwarzenberg, Berlin, 1921, Section 1, Part 3, p. 433.

[86] J. D. Reinheimer, *J. Chem. Ed.*, **30**, 139 (1953).

[87] R. T. Schenck and T. S. Ma, *Mikrochemie ver. Mikrochim. Acta*, **40**, 236–244 (1953).

[88] T. J. Mitchell, *Chemistry & Industry*, **1950**, 815.

[89] C. O. Willits, *Anal. Chem.*, **23**, 1058 (1951).

perature of heating, and the humidity of the air in the oven. Air velocity is very important. Many crystalline organic materials show a prolonged constant-rate drying period with a critical moisture content of about 10%. A schematic curve is shown in Figure 21; the determination of such curves is best made by the use of small laboratory dryers such as described by Hart and Dunlap.[90] A small laboratory dryer for obtaining curves with infrared drying has also been described.[91]

Many laboratory dryers are unequipped with any means of circulating air except a small ventilator placed near the bottom of the oven. Air

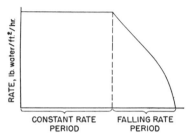

Fig. 21. Drying-rate curve.

is drawn in through this by convection and passes out at the top of the oven through a small vent. Adjustment of the entrance panels allows the most suitable air volume to be obtained. Such ovens show poor uniformity in temperature, with local hot and cold areas and a slow come-up time. Tray dryers are more satisfactory in which some positive means of circulating air are provided.[92] Stagnant air pockets of high humidity in the oven are eliminated and the hot, humid air is removed constantly by fresh, drier air. In addition, if suitable baffles are installed, the air can be forced over the material so that air velocity is increased and, as predicted by equations (17) and (18), the diffusion coefficients are raised correspondingly (Fig. 22). Drying is usually about four times as fast in mechanical convection ovens as in the simple gravity type.

In most laboratory ovens the material being dried does not stay at the wet-bulb temperature of the circulating air during the constant-rate period, as would be expected from theory, but remains considerably above it because of radiation and conduction from the walls. Indeed, special provision is made in some ovens for the charge to receive heat from sources other than the air. The use of an oven, in which heating elements are

[90] E. E. Hart and H. L. Dunlap, *J. Chem. Ed.*, **30**, 364 (1953).

[91] G. Broughton and L. I. Gilman, *J. Chem. Ed.*, **29**, 34 (1952).

[92] C. F. M. Fryd and P. R. Kiff, *Analyst*, **76**, 25 (1951).

placed under the trays, so that a series of graded temperatures is available at one time, has been suggested by Heywood and Odell[93] for drying organic preparations.   By increasing the wattage and, hence the temperature, from the bottom to the top shelf, natural convection was insured and it was found that an air change occurred every 15 seconds without the use of a blower.   Thus, it was possible to dry simultaneously preparations at 40°, 60°, and 85°C. by placing them on the appropriate shelves in the oven.

When charging the trays for oven drying, the substance should obviously be spread out evenly, and, if the bottom of the oven is heated directly, the material should be placed several inches above this or half-way up the oven.   Some substances, *e.g.*, dye pastes, seem to dry down to a

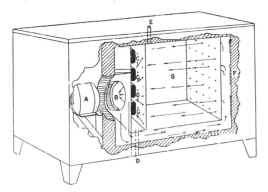

Fig. 22. Forced-circulation type of oven:
(A) motor, (B) fan, (C) heaters, (D) air inlet,
(E) air exit, (F) insulation, and (G) drying area.

coherent mass, and it is advisable to break these up from time to time during the drying operation.   In small-scale laboratory drying the material of the container greatly affects the drying rate, as does its size and shape.[94] The drying rate is considerably greater for aluminum than for glass, silica, or porcelain dishes.   Deep dishes cause a pronounced drop in drying rate, presumably because ready egress of the water vapor is prevented.   Mitchell found that the rates of evaporation measured for water in a laboratory oven were very much lower than those calculated from theory for evaporation into still air.   This may be because evaporation is influenced by edge effects, which protect a portion of the area from the currents of air.   In agreement with Thomas and Ferguson,[95] evaporation or drying from full circular dishes was found to be proportional to the 3/2 power of their radius.

[93] B. J. Heywood and D. P. Odell, *Chemistry & Industry*, **1952**, 777–778.
[94] T. J. Mitchell, *Chemistry & Industry*, **1950**, 751.
[95] N. Thomas and A. Ferguson, *Phil. Mag.*, **34**, 308 (1917).

Heat-sensitive materials can also be dried satisfactorily in many instances by drying in high-velocity dry air at relatively low temperatures. This is of particular value with materials which may be simultaneously heat-sensitive and decompose under vacuum. The discussion of wet- and dry-bulb temperatures (Sect. II.1) indicated that the material being dried remains at the wet-bulb temperature of the drying air if drying is adiabatic. Hence, the maximum temperature which the stock can reach is

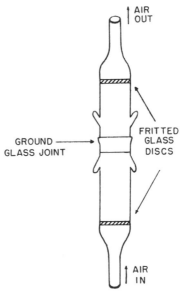

Fig. 23. Drier and solvent evaporator apparatus.[96]

limited by the air conditions, which can be controlled as desired. A suitable apparatus for the drying of small amounts of organic solids is sketched in Figure 23.[96] This consists of two Pyrex Büchner-type funnels, with fritted glass discs, to each of which is sealed a ground-glass joint provided with glass hooks. The sample is placed in the filter having the outer joint, and the apparatus is closed and secured with rubber bands over the glass hooks. Dry air (or inert gas if necessary) is passed upward through the solid, which usually dries in from 5 to 15 minutes.

The drying of microquantities of material requires special techniques (see, for example, Schneider[97] and Cheronis and Entrikin[98]). Infrared

[96] I. R. Hunter, *Anal. Chem.*, **20**, 186 (1948).

[97] F. Schneider, *Qualitative Organic Microanalysis*. Wiley, New York, 1946, pp. 72–76.

[98] N. D. Cheronis and G. B. Entrikin, *Semimicro Qualitative Organic Analysis*. Crowell, New York, 1947.

rays are also useful on occasion for rapid drying when the material is insensitive. Frequently seen is the set-up shown in Figure 24 where A is a simple infrared lamp readily available at any drugstore.

The removal of the last traces of a liquid is often particularly difficult in the case of high polymers and preparations such as proteins. Prolonged evacuation at regular or higher temperatures is generally resorted to but frequently the diffusion and removal of the volatile component may

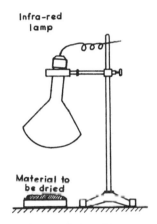

Fig. 24. Infrared lamp.

be accelerated by the addition of a third liquid of lower molecular weight which can diffuse rapidly into or out of the polymer, sometimes with consequent swelling and shrinkage. Figure 25 shows some results of Priest[99] illustrating the increased rate of removal of dioxane from polyacrylic acid when the polymer was rehumidified between drying cycles. Lewis and Mayo[100] have suggested a procedure for the rapid removal of liquids from high polymers by freezing a solution of the polymer in a suitable solvent, e.g., benzene, and removing this solvent by sublimation.

A review article by Mactaggart[101] describes the most usual forms of dryers now in industrial use and Perry[102] can also be consulted on this subject.

Vacuum Drying. Consideration of the principles discussed earlier indicates that evacuation of the desiccator should speed up drying; this is

[99] W. J. Priest, in *Investigation of Rates and Mechanisms of Reactions* (*Technique of Organic Chemistry*, Vol. VIII). Interscience, New York-London, 1953, p. 446.

[100] F. M. Lewis and F. R. Mayo, *Ind. Eng. Chem., Anal. Ed.*, **17**, 134 (1945).

[101] E. F. Mactaggart, *Trans. Inst. Chem. Eng.*, **27**, 23 (1949).

[102] J. H. Perry, *Chemical Engineers' Handbook*. 3rd ed., McGraw-Hill, New York, 1950, pp. 815–870.

found to be the case (see, for example, Mitchell[103]), and has led to wide-spread use of the ordinary vacuum desiccator. While P_1 and P_2, the vapor pressures of the mixture and desiccant, respectively, are not changed by evacuation, travel of the water molecules between the material and the drying agent is accelerated and the drying time may be cut to one-third. For drying large batches of materials, the "dumbbell desiccator" of Pingert[104] is useful.

Vacuum drying ovens also have important advantages for certain materials. Diffusion through the surface film is a minor factor, the water boiling at relatively low temperature when the pressure is low, and, if

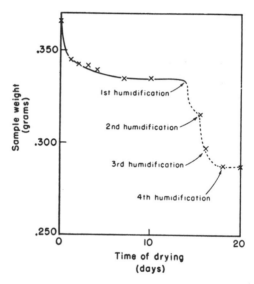

Fig. 25. Increased rate of removal of dioxane from polyacrylic acid after rehumidifying the polymer between drying cycles.[99]

heat is supplied at a rapid enough rate, the drying rate can be great. Thus, for materials susceptible to heat or oxidation, drying *in vacuo* is indicated. Provided that the heat supply is constant, a curve similar to that of Figure 21 is again obtained, a constant-rate drying period being observed until free water is removed. This is followed by a falling-rate period, during which the temperature rises to approximately that of the heating medium. The critical moisture content is not necessarily identical with that found for drying at atmospheric pressure.[105] Because of the

[103] T. J. Mitchell, *Chemistry & Industry*, 1950, 815.

[104] F. P. Pingert, *Ind. Eng. Chem., Anal. Ed.*, 15, 175 (1943).

[105] R. C. Ernst, J. W. Ridgeway, and F. M. Tiller, *Ind. Eng. Chem.*, 30, 1122 (1938).

absence of any rapidly moving air stream, an advantage of this system of drying is that there is little dust loss.

Small laboratory vacuum dryers, operating at 20 to 30 mm. Hg vacuum, are available and are particularly useful for larger laboratory batches of pharmaceuticals, dyestuffs, easily oxidizable chemicals, etc., which are difficult to handle in ordinary drying ovens.   The trays should not be filled to more than about 1 inch in depth, the drying time being roughly proportional to the square of the depth of loading.   The time is also a

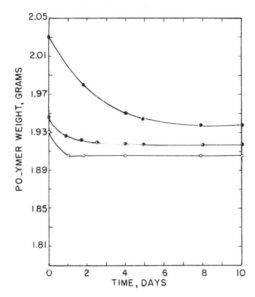

Fig. 26. Effect of temperature on rate of solvent removal from porous polymer.[100]

function of temperature as shown in Figure 26,[100] where t is the time in days required by a sample of polystyrene to reach constant weight when benzene is removed at $T°K$. and 1 mm. Hg pressure.   Kemp and Straitiff[106] described a vacuum drying apparatus particularly suitable for unstable polymeric materials, in which purified nitrogen is used to flush out the liquid vapors, while Goddard[107] described large-scale vacuum dehydration.

Freeze Drying.   A new field in drying, known as freeze drying, was opened up by modern high-vacuum technology.[108]   In this method, the water after preliminary freezing is removed by sublimation of the ice

[106] A. R. Kemp and W. G. Straitiff, *Ind. Eng. Chem., Anal. Ed.*, **17**, 387 (1945).

[107] D. R. Goddard, *J. Sci. Instruments Suppl.*, No. 1, pp. 43–46 (1951).

[108] E. W. Flosdorf *et al.*, *J. Immunol.*, **50**, 21 (1945); *J. Chem. Ed.*, **22**, 470 (1945).
E. W. Flosdorf, *Freeze-Drying; Drying by Sublimation*, Reinhold, New York, 1950.

formed at low temperature and high vacuum. Whereas the vacuum ovens described above operate at 10–30 mm. Hg, the new high-vacuum drying units operate at pressures of the order of 100–300 μ (0.1 to 0.3 mm. Hg). The water vaporized is usually collected by being condensed as ice on a refrigerated surface or absorbed in a desiccant such as lithium chloride solution. Permanent gases are removed and the vacuum is maintained by oil-sealed rotary pumps or diffusion pumps. The heat of sublimation must be supplied at a controlled rate by conduction through the walls of the container or by infrared radiation[109] in such a way that the solid never melts and the temperature does not fall until the vapor pressure of ice is negligible. In practice few materials are dried at temperatures lower than $-30°F$., because of the very low vapor pressure of ice below this temperature.

At the present time freeze drying is used principally for labile biologicals and other heat-sensitive materials. Laboratory freeze drying has been reviewed by Harris[110] while Chambers[111] and others[112] have discussed the characteristics and performance of commercial freeze drying plants. In ordinary drying where the water remains liquid any solutes, e.g., dissolved salts in protein preparations, tend to migrate toward the surface layers where the high concentrations may damage the finished product. In freeze drying the solutes are "locked" into position by the initial freezing and no migration can occur during the subsequent drying. So-called case hardening is absent. Furthermore, bubbling and foaming are impossible in a prefrozen mass, thus eliminating any possibility of surface denaturation, which with susceptible materials is sometimes observed during ordinary drying. Again, because the mass is frozen no shrinkage occurs during drying and the highly porous, friable solid produced is readily redispersible in water. Hence, the material retains its lyophilic properties and the process of freeze drying is sometimes called "lyophilization." Once dried in this manner many lyophilized materials lose their last moisture faster than normally.[113]

Figure 27 depicts a simple apparatus[114] useful for drying materials by subliming out the water as ice. Four flasks are one-quarter filled with the solution or material to be dried. Each is then chilled in dry ice while held at an angle and rotated so that an even layer is obtained on the walls. The flasks are then attached at B, and vacuum is applied at A. If desired

[109] W. H. Zamzow and W. R. Marshall, Jr., *Chem Eng. Progress*, **48**, 21 (1952).

[110] R. J. C. Harris, *Vacuum*, **1**, 11 (1951).

[111] H. H. Chambers, *Trans. Inst. Chem. Eng.*, **27**, 19 (1949).

[112] L. G. Beckatt, *J. Sci. Instruments Suppl.*, No. 1, pp. 66–68 (1951).

[113] B. Makower and E. Nielsen, *Anal. Chem.*, **20**, 856 (1948).

[114] D. H. Campbell and D. Pressman, *Science*, **99**, 285 (1944).

the flask at the base can be used as a drip trap. Self-freezing is slower than shell freezing and is only practical for amounts of over 2 ml.; in this the flasks with their charge are attached to the ports and first degassed to avoid frothing and loss of material through the pumping tube. The vacuum is slowly built up over 20 to 30 minutes and, when degassing is complete, allowed to reach its final value. Freezing by evaporation then

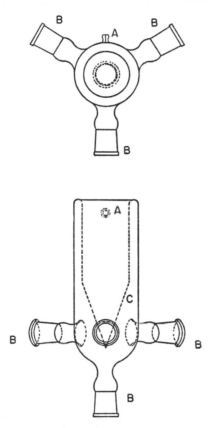

Fig. 27. Apparatus for drying by sublimation of ice.[114]

takes place within a few minutes. The condenser cone is filled with a dry ice–Cellosolve mixture and ice collects on the tapered surface, C. The temperature of the material in the flasks remains below freezing until almost all the water has been removed; one may then warm the flasks in cold water or with a current of air. If there is a tendency to spatter, a gauze screen should be placed in the neck of each flask. Complete desiccation may take from 2 to 24 hours, Figure 28 showing a characteristic curve for an organic dyestuff,[115] the sample thickness being 3.8 mm. and the vacuum 80 μ Hg. A constant-drying rate for the first 50 minutes, followed by a falling-rate period, is observed. If heat transfer to the flask contents should be too rapid so that they start to melt, this can often be prevented by wrapping the vessel with cloth or paper. If, on the other hand, it is too slow, perhaps because the solid has pulled away from the container wall, cautious use of infrared radiation speeds up the process.

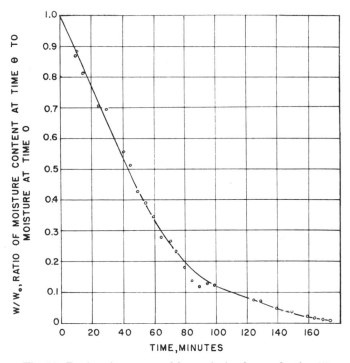

Fig. 28. Drying-time curve of freeze drying by conduction.[115]

Somewhat larger equipment may be of the manifold or chamber type. The former allows several different types of products or containers to be handled at the same time and drying to be plainly observed. Prefreezing, which obviates foaming, is also easily carried out. The chamber-type freeze dryer, on the other hand, allows larger quantities of material to be handled conveniently. In this case, to obviate foaming where self-freezing is adopted, a method developed by Greaves[116] can be used. In this the tubes containing the material to be dried are rotated by a centrifuge and

[115] W. H. Zamzow and W. R. Marshall, Jr., *Chem. Eng. Progress*, **48**, 27 (1952).
[116] R. J. N. Greaves, *Nature*, **153**, 485 (1944).

motor mounted in the evacuated glass bell.   The material is thus shell-
or wedge-frozen to give a large drying area.

In small units up to a batch capacity of 3500 ml., conduction of heat
from the outside of the container may be sufficient to provide heat for ice
sublimation but for larger units, and even for smaller units, some form of
heat with thermostatic control is desirable.   Electrically heated shelves
or radiant heating[109] may be used.   The water vapor produced may be
removed by absorption on a solid desiccant, by condensation on a surface
cooled with dry ice, or by freon-refrigerated plates.   Where available dry
ice provides highest capacity at lowest equipment capital cost, freon

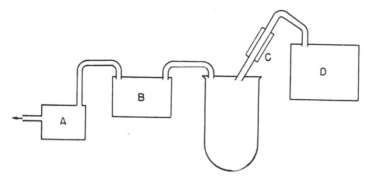

Fig. 29. Simple commercial system for drying by sublimation of ice.

refrigeration is low in operating but high in first cost, while chemical
desiccants are convenient to use and intermediate in operating cost.

Figure 29 illustrates schematically a simple commercial system.   Preliminary evacuation is carried out with a rotary, oil-sealed pump (A),
the diffusion pump (B) taking over to reach the low vacuum operating in
the condenser or "cold trap" (C) and the dehydration unit (D) itself.
The dehydration unit may be built like a drying oven, being equipped
with shelves and heaters at the top and bottom of the cabinet.   The cold
trap may be cooled with acetone and dry ice.   The water molecules leaving
D are trapped in C, and a degree of dehydration equivalent to the vapor
pressure of water at the temperature of the cold trap, e.g., 0.0004 mm.
Hg at −80°C., is ultimately reached.   Figure 30 shows a typical drying
curve in a large-scale dryer for calcium penicillin.   Still larger scale operations are described by Kekwick[117] and Schwarz and Penn.[118]

The freeze drying process, like ordinary drying, appears from Figure 30
to occur in two stages.[115,116,119]   In the first, which occurs at constant-

[117] R. A. Kekwick, *Chem Proc. Eng.*, **35**, 14 (1954).
[118] H. W. Schwarz and F. E. Penn, *Ind. Eng. Chem.*, **40**, 938 (1948).
[119] C. J. Brandish, C. M. Brain, and A. S. McFarlane, *Nature*, **159**, 29 (1947).

drying rate, a boundary between upper partially dry product and lower frozen product steadily recedes until it reaches the supporting tray surface. A number of isolated ice crystals then remain distributed throughout the mass. The removal of these constitutes the second stage, which proceeds at a much diminished rate of vaporization and may be hastened by infra-red radiation[109] or by raising the tray temperature. Figure 31 shows a diagram of the conditions during the constant-rate period of freeze drying. Heat must flow through the frozen solid and because the thermal conductivity of ice and most organic solids is low the rate of heat transfer, $dq/d\theta$, is low. It can be written:

$$\frac{dq}{d\theta} = \frac{A(t_1 - t_s)}{1/h_1 + D/k_w + k/k_m} \tag{30}$$

where A is the area through which heat transfer occurs, t_1 is the temperature of the heating medium, t_s is the temperature of the surface from which

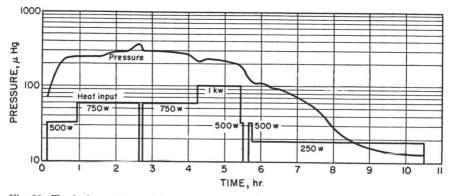

Fig. 30. Typical curve for calcium penecillin solution in tray $13.5 \times 14 \times 1$ in. Average thickness of cake 11 mm. Courtesy National Research Corp.

sublimation is occurring, h_1 is the film heat transfer coefficient of the heating fluid, D is the thickness of the separating wall, k_w is the thermal conductivity of the separating wall, d is the thickness of the ice–solid layer, and k_m is the thermal conductivity of the ice-solid layer.

Furthermore, if there is not perfect contact between the ice-solid layer and the wall an additional thermal resistance, R_{ws}, must be introduced. This may well be a major factor in the equation:

$$\frac{dq}{d\theta} = \frac{A(t_1 - t_s)}{1/h_1 + D/k_w + R_{ws} + d/k_m} \tag{31}$$

In most cases, since there is little or no resistance to mass transfer or passage of vapor through the dry solid, this gives the rate of sublimation or drying. It seems probable that $1/h_1$ and D/k_w are quite small and that the factors controlling freeze drying are thickness of the frozen solid, thermal conductivity of the ice–solid mixture, and degree of contact of the frozen solid to the heated wall. If the latter is poor, radiation may predominate as the mechanism of heat transfer from the outside to the frozen solid. In any event, equation (31) may be simplified to:

$$dw/d\theta = dq/d\theta\, r_w = UA\, \Delta t/r_w \qquad (32)$$

where U is the over-all heat transfer coefficient in B.t.u./(hr.) (ft.²) (°F.), t is the temperature difference (°F.) between the heating medium

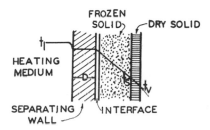

Fig. 31. Conditions during the constant-rate period of freeze drying.

and the ice temperature, and r_w is the latent heat of sublimation at the temperature of sublimation, B.t.u./lb. The magnitude of U varies widely with conditions but a value of 1.0 B.t.u./(hr.) (ft.²) (°F.) has been reported as typical for the constant-rate drying period.[120]

Dielectric or High-Frequency Drying. The only method of drying which allows the material, even when wet, to be heated as rapidly at its center as at its surface is dielectric drying (Fig. 32). In this the heat of evaporation of the water is supplied by placing the material in a strong electrostatic field produced by frequencies between 2 and 100 megacycles per second. The material to be heated is made part of a tuned circuit. During one portion of the electrical cycle the upper plate is charged negatively and the lower plate positively; during the second portion this situation is reversed. This rapid reversal of field generates heat, both ohmic and dielectric, in the wet material between the electrodes and this heating is uniform throughout the material. This means that in an intense

[120] J. H. Perry. *Chemical Engineers' Handbook.* 3rd ed., McGraw-Hill, New York, 1950, p. 856.

enough field water can be evaporated in the interior of the material and the mechanism of drying previously discussed for air drying is no longer applicable.[121] A thermometer placed in the interior of a wood block in such a field can read 150°F. and the drying rate can be eighteen times greater than with air at the same temperature. For good results the material must be porous, allowing ready escape of the water vapor; gelatin heated quickly dielectrically boils up into a froth since there is no ready egress for the water vapor.

Dielectric drying like spray drying requires expensive equipment and hence is not likely to be used extensively in the laboratory. However, it has specialized industrial uses such as in the plywood and rayon industries

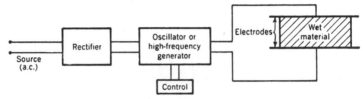

Fig. 32. Simplified diagram of dielectric drier.

but these are strictly limited because of the high cost of drying by this means.

2. Removal of Water by Means Other Than Vaporization

Solvent Extraction. This laboratory technique has been used for many years, but, unlike many laboratory techniques, has not received extensive commercial application. The solid can be washed with a liquid, in which it is itself insoluble but in which water is soluble, thus removing most of the latter. Absolute alcohol is used frequently for this purpose. A modification of this method, in which the water is actually vaporized, consists of the distillation of a moist solid with a liquid such as xylene or chloroform. The water is vaporized with the first of the liquid to be distilled, forming in some cases a constant-boiling mixture (Sect. IV.1). The solid can be filtered off from the organic liquid remaining, after all the water has been removed.

Absorption. This is also an old laboratory technique. Moist preparations can be spread on a porous, absorbent solid such as filter paper, porous unglazed tile, or a plaster of Paris block, the water soaking up into the solid. Usually, the tile or other material is placed in a desiccator over a desiccant to complete drying. Some solid is always lost by adherence to the absorbent and cannot be removed completely by scraping.

[121] R. L. Stephens, *Trans. Inst. Chem. Eng.*, **27**, 37 (1949).

Compression. The operation of pressing as a means of removing water may be regarded as a special form of filtration and for that reason will be mentioned only briefly. Upon occasion, the mixture which is to be dehydrated may be placed in a muslin (or other suitable fabric) bag and pressure applied. Excess liquid is readily removed, but the remaining liquid is expressed only slowly, several thousand pounds pressure being required to obtain substantially dry material. An investigation of fibrous materials was made by Gurnham and Masson.[122] When practical this is the cheapest method of liquid removal. On a large scale continuous presses are available for dewatering. Material of high moisture content drops between two large revolving discs, the faces of which come progressively closer together until maximum pressure is reached at minimum clearance. The disc faces then again separate to the discharge point. The expelled water passes through the material to perforated screens and discharges at the bottom of the press.

Centrifuging. While a centrifuge cannot completely dry a solid, it removes much of the water and such treatment is often useful in the laboratory (see Chapter IV). Most laboratory centrifuges are of the basket type, the crystals or other solid material to be dried being retained in the centrifuge bowl while the liquid flows out through perforations in the bowl, or of the test tube type, in which a cup or test tube holds the material and the solid sediments to the bottom. The former type permits considerable drying to be done, it only being necessary to remove the last traces of water.

Freezing. This technique, mentioned previously for liquids (Sect. IV.2) can also be used for dehydration of solid solutions.[123]

General References

G. G. Brown *et al.*, *Unit Operations*. Wiley, New York, 1950.

O. A. Hougen and F. W. Dodge, *The Drying of Gases*. Edwards, Ann Arbor, 1947.

W. R. Marshall, Jr., "Drying," in *Encyclopedia of Chemical Technology*, Vol. V, The Interscience Encyclopedia, Inc., New York, 1950.

"Symposium on Drying and Air Conditioning," *Ind. Eng. Chem.*, **30**, 1119 (1938).

W. H. Walker, W. K. Lewis, W. H. McAdams, and E. R. Gilliland, *Principles of Chemical Engineering*. 3rd ed., McGraw-Hill, New York, 1937.

[122] C. F. Gurnham and J. J. Masson, *Ind. Eng. Chem.*, **38**, 1309 (1946).

[123] F. Haurowitz, *Z. physiol. Chem.*, **186**, 141 (1930).

A

Absorption, in drying of solids, 824, 838–839
Acetal, as crystallization solvent, 559
Acetamide, as crystallization solvent, 558
Acetic acid, as crystallization solvent, 555, 558
Acetic anhydride, as crystallization solvent, 558
Acetone, as crystallization solvent, 555, 559
Acetonitrile, as crystallization solvent, 561
Acetyl bromide, as crystallization solvent, 558
Acetyl chloride, as crystallization solvent, 558
Acids, effect on microfilters, 674
  filtration of, 647, 682, 683, 684, 693, 711
  inorganic, as crystallization solvents, 553–554
  organic, as crystallization solvents, 557
  systems for separation by extraction, 307
Adapters, for filtering crucibles, 652
  Swinny hypodermic, 721
Adduct formation, in crystallization, 459–467. See also *Complexes, formation.*
Adiabatic saturation temperature, 794, 795, 797
Adsorbents. See also *Filter aids.*
  Attapulgus clay, 747–748
  and filtrations, 746–748
  fuller's earth, 747
  Norite, 747
  powders, 747
  Super Filtrol, 747
  Terrana, 747
  Tonsil, 747
  in treatment of emulsions, 741–742
Adsorption, in barrier separations, 46–47, 49, 52, 57, 62
  chromatographic, use of filter aids, 706
  in drying of gases, 806–808

in extraction of solids, 215–216
  in zone electrophoresis, 125
Adsorption columns, as filters, 747–748
Adsorption effects, in crystallization, 434–437
  in filtration, 624, 735
Adsorption theory of semipermeability, 76
Aerosol-OT, as filtration aid, 728
Aerosols, filtration, 688
  in wash liquids, 744
Agar, in zone electrophoresis, 136–137
Agitation, effect on crystallization, 482, 521, 524, 526
Air filters, 688
Air-lift, in extractors, 229–230, 231, 235, 315
Air velocity and drying rate, 802, 825–828
Alcohols, as crystallization solvents, 555–557
  separation, zone electrophoresis, 144
Aldehydes, as crystallization solvents, 559
Alkalies, concentrated, as crystallization solvents, 554
  filtration of, 649, 682, 683, 711
Alkaloids, systems for separation by extraction, 309
Allyl alcohol, as crystallization solvent, 556
Aloxite filters, 693, 710
Alsop laboratory filter, 736–737
Alternate withdrawal methods in extraction, 182–184, 189
Alumina, as drying agent, 806, 808
  as filter medium, 651, 693, 710
Aluminum bromide, as crystallization solvent, 555
Alundum, for filtration, 653, 693, 710
Amberplex membranes in electrodialysis, 100–101
Aminco microphotometer, 761
Amino acids, partition chromatography 213, 214

Cumulative Indexes, Volumes I–IX

AUTHOR INDEX

*Listings for Volumes I, II, and III refer to the Second Editions of these volumes.

867

*Listings for Volumes I, II, and III refer to the Second Editions of these volumes.

* Listings for Volumes I, II, and III refer to the Second Editions of these volumes.

SUBJECT INDEX

* Listings for Volumes I, II, and III refer to the Second Editions of these volumes.

* Listings for Volumes I, II, and III refer to the Second Editions of these volumes.

*Listings for Volumes I, II, and III refer to the Second Editions of these volumes.

*Listings for Volumes I, II, and III refer to the Second Editions of these volumes.